DIE DESIGN AND DIEMAKING PRACTICE

DIE DESIGN AND DIEMAKING PRACTICE

A treatise for die designers and diemakers containing illustrated descriptions of a large variety of selected dies for all kinds of power press operations, with practical information and data on approved designing practice and die construction

Edited by

FRANKLIN D. JONES

Third Edition — Seventh Printing

INDUSTRIAL PRESS INC., 200 Madison Avenue, New York 10016

Library of Congress Catalog Card Number: 51-9432

PRINTED IN THE UNITED STATES OF AMERICA

CONTENTS

DIE DESIGN AND DIEMAKING PRACTICE

CHAPTER I

DIES FOR CUTTING BLANKS FROM FLAT STOCK

THE numerous designs and types of dies used on power presses for the production of sheet-metal work, may be divided into two very general classes. In the first class are all dies which simply cut or punch flat blanks or pieces of the required outline from the stock, and in the second class are all dies which change the form of the material from its original flat condition by drawing, forming or bending it. This second main division, however, often includes features which are common to the first; that is, some dies are a combination of cutting and shaping dies, in that the blank to be shaped or formed is first cut out to the required outline from the stock and then shaped to the desired form. When dies combine the features of different types, proper classification often is perplexing.

Dies of the "blanking" class are used for cutting blanks usually from flat sheets or strips of stock; such blanks may or may not be drawn, formed or bent, either by other parts combined with the blanking members, or by means of separate dies. If the chief or only function of the die is to cut blanks, it is a blanking die; if the blanking operation is followed by a more important operation in the same die such as drawing, then the term "drawing die" would be applied, the blanking part being considered a secondary feature of the design.

As dies are now used very extensively, there are a tremendous number in use and the designs, even for dies of a given class, vary widely and range from simple inexpensive dies to those which are quite complicated and costly. In this book, very simple designs will be used first to illustrate the different types of dies and these will be followed by many of the more unusual designs all selected from actual practice.

Difference Between "Punch" and "Die" as Defined by Common Usage.—As this treatise will be read by many who have had little or no experience in die design, the distinction between the terms "punch" and "die" will be explained at the outset to avoid confusion, since these terms are used in connection with practically every design to be described.

The term "die" is often applied to an entire press tool including both upper and lower members, while the names "punch" and "die" are used to designate parts or sections of a complete die. These main sections should properly be classified with reference to shape, rather than by location, notwithstanding the fact that the punch is usually but not invariably the upper member. When the name "die" is applied to part of a press tool, it refers ordinarily to the member that has an opening or cavity to receive a punch, for blanking, drawing, or forming whatever stock or part is confined between the punch and die members.

A "punch" is that part of a press tool which enters into an opening or cavity formed in the die section. The punch usually is the upper member, being attached to the press slide or ram, but it may be the lower member, as in the case of press tools of inverted design. Whenever the function of the upper and lower members is identical, as, for example, in embossing the sides of coins or medals, the upper die section would ordinarily be called the punch merely because the punch member of most dies occupies the upper position; nevertheless, it is form rather than location which, in general, is the distinguishing feature between the punch and its mating die.

One member of a press tool may combine the functions of both a punch and die, as, for example, in a compound die where the lower member enters an upper one for punching or blanking, thus serving as a punch, and also has a central opening for receiving an upper punch which may, for example, pierce a central hole. In the latter case the lower member serves as a die.

Plain Blanking Dies.—Plain blanking dies are the simplest of all types of dies and are used to cut out plain, flat pieces of stock. This type of die consists of a die-block *D* (see Fig. 1), which has an opening that conforms to the shape of the part to be cut or blanked out; a punch *P*, which accurately fits the opening in the die-block and, by a shearing action, does the cutting as it descends into the die-block opening; and a stripper plate *S*, which strips the stock off of the punch as the latter ascends. The opening in the stripper plate conforms to the

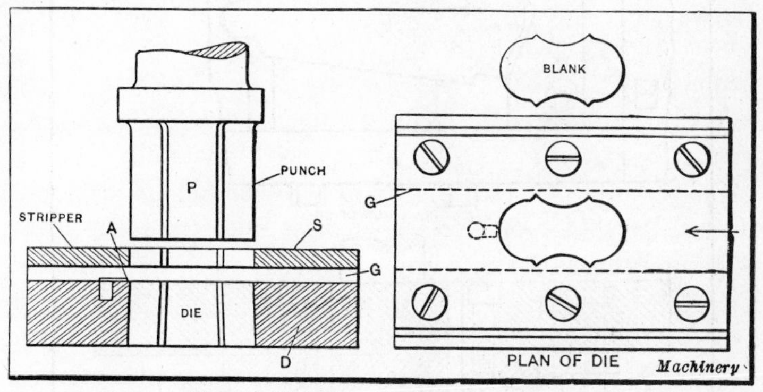

Fig. 1. Plain Blanking Punch and Die

shape of the punch and is either slightly larger to provide a little clearance, or close fitting to steady the punch. Between the stripper plate and die-block there is a guide *G*, which serves to keep the stock in alignment with the die opening as it is fed along. This guide (which may be formed by planing a channel on the under side of the stripper) is made so that the space between the die and stripper will be somewhat greater than the thickness of the stock used; in fact, this space must be sufficient to allow the stock to move along easily even when the surface is made somewhat irregular by the operation of the punch. In a simple die of this kind, the spacing of the holes punched in the stock is commonly controlled by some form of stop-pin *A*, which engages the edge of each successive opening; for instance, after a blank is cut out, the operator feeds the stock along until the opening thus made comes against the stop, thus locating the stock for cutting out the next blank.

Two Passes Through Die to Economize in Stock.—The die shown in Fig. 2 is for cutting the flat blanks used for making the arms of an automobile steering wheel. The blank is cut to the irregular outline *X*, and it is approximately 7½

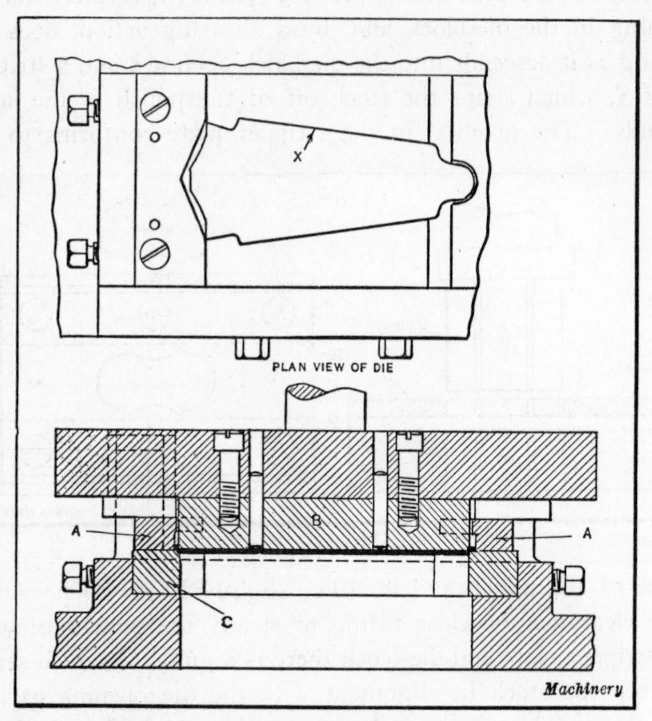

Fig. 2. Die Used to Produce the Blank from Which the Steering Spider Arms are Formed

inches long by 3¼ inches wide at the maximum point. As the part is tapered, sufficient space is left between the blanks to permit of reversing the stock after one pass through the die, and cutting blanks from the stock left between the openings in the first pass. A large saving in stock has been effected by this method. The stock is guided through the die by blocks *A* and is blanked as punch *B* enters die *C* on the downward stroke of the press ram. Each blank falls through the die-block to a receptacle beneath the bed of the press. Die *C* is made in four sections.

Gang or Multiple Dies.—When large numbers of blanks are required, multiple or gang dies are sometimes used. These dies have a number of duplicate punches with similar openings in the die-block and cut as many blanks as there are punches, at each stroke of the press. Fig. 3 illustrates a simple form of gang or multiple die which might be called a multiple blanking die. As will be seen, there are, in this case, three blanking punches. At the first stroke of the press, the stock is blanked out as at *A*; then, by feeding it a distance *x* for each

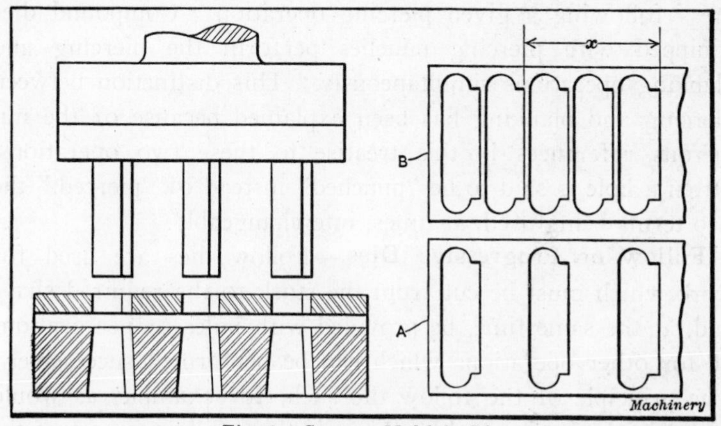

Fig. 3. Gang or Multiple Die

stroke, the blank will be cut as at *B*. As will be noted, the punches in this case are located twice the center-to-center distance between the openings cut in the stock, instead of being close together. This is done because it would not be practicable to have the openings in the die-block as close as they should be in order to blank out the stock economically, since there would not be metal enough between the die openings to insure sufficient strength. The term "gang die" is often applied to a follow die; this usage is generally conceded to be incorrect, however, as the word "gang," as used in mechanics, ordinarily means a combination of similar tools so arranged as to act simultaneously for producing duplicate parts.

Blanking and Piercing.—The terms "blanking" and "piercing" are frequently applied to punches and dies and there is a distinction between these terms which should be understood. If a part cut from sheet stock in a die requires small holes or openings of any kind, these are first cut by what are commonly known as piercing punches. The removal of the complete part from the strip of stock is done by the blanking operation. It will be seen, therefore, that many dies combine the piercing and blanking operations. In the case of a progressive or follow die the piercing, as for example, of a hole in a washer, would be done before the blanking which is performed farther along and during the second stroke of the press following a given piercing operation. Compound dies equipped with piercing punches perform the piercing and blanking operations simultaneously. This distinction between piercing and blanking has been explained because of the numerous references in this treatise to these two operations. Often a hole is said to be "punched" instead of "pierced," the two terms being used, at times, interchangeably.

Follow or Progressive Dies.—Follow dies are used for work which must be cut from the stock to the required shape and, at the same time, be provided with holes or perforations or for other operations which can be performed successively. The principle of the follow die such, for example, as would be used for piercing and blanking, is that while one part of the die punches the hole in the stock, another part blanks out the work at a place where, at a former stroke, a hole or opening was punched, so that a completed article results from each stroke of the press; in reality, however, two separate operations have been performed, the operation being a progressive one in which the holes are first pierced after which the stock moves along until the pierced section is in line with the blanking punch. A simple form of follow die designed for cutting washers is shown in Fig. 4. This die is practically a blanking die having two punches. The blanking punch is located at *B* and the piercing punch at *C*. As the stock is fed along in the direction indicated by the arrow (see plan view of die) the hole in the washer is first made by the piercing punch; then, on the next stroke of the press, the stock is fed a distance x so that the pierced hole is directly under the blanking punch, which cuts out the completed washer. The action of the two punches relative to the stock is indicated at *A* which illustrates a small section of the stock. As both punches operate at the same time, obviously, a completed washer is cut out at each stroke of the press. If the washers were required in large quantities, the die would be designed to cut out two or more washers at each stroke of the press.

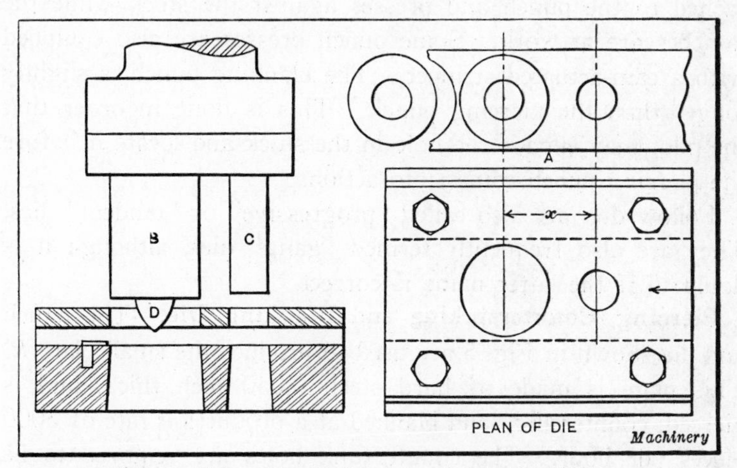

Fig. 4. Follow Die for Piercing and Blanking Washer

Many dies of this type have a pilot *D* on the end of the blanking punch which engages the pierced hole after the stock has been approximately located by a stop-pin, or otherwise. In this way, the stock is located so that the outside is cut concentric with the hole, within a small limit of variation. When the blanking punch is without a pilot, the accuracy of the work is dependent upon the accuracy with which the stock is fed through the die. For instance, if an operator should fail to push the stock against the stop-pin, the cut made by the blanking punch would not be correctly located relative to the pierced hole. Hence, pilots are commonly used, although they have one objectionable feature: If the punch should descend when the pierced hole was not under the pilot, a broken punch might result, unless a spring-supported pilot, which could recede, were employed. Even when a pilot is used, extremely accurate work cannot be produced in a follow die because there must be a slight clearance between the pilot and the pierced hole and this causes more or less error; moreover, when using a die of the design shown, the stock is distorted or wrinkled to some extent by the action of the punches because the stock lies loosely between the stripper and the die. To avoid this trouble, some blanking dies have a spring-supported stripper which is attached to the punch and presses against the stock while the punches are at work. Some punch presses are also equipped with a cam-actuated stripper. The blanking punch is slightly longer than the piercing punch. This is done in order that the pilot may engage the hole in the stock and locate it before the piercing punch comes into action.

Follow dies are also called "progressive" or "tandem" dies. They are also frequently termed "gang" dies, although it is doubtful if the latter name is correct.

Piercing, Countersinking and Blanking Die.—The punch and die shown in Fig. 5 are used to produce the small plate *R*. This plate is made of hard steel, 0.040 inch thick, and is pierced, countersunk, and blanked at a production rate of 3000 pieces per hour. The countersunk holes are required to be accurately positioned, and all the dimensions, some of which are shown in the illustration, have to be held within close limits. The die is of the pillar type and can be quickly set up on the press. The cast-iron die-shoe *A* has a slot milled in its upper surface into which the die-block *B* is fitted. The die-block is made from tool steel and contains four bushings, two for the piercing punches *C*, Fig. 6, and two for the countersinking punches *D*. It also contains a rectangular opening for the blanking punch *E*.

Stripper *F* is made of machine steel, and is held in place by four fillister-head screws and three dowels which extend through the die-block into the die-shoe. The strips *G* that guide the stock are 1/8 inch thick. The holes in the stripper

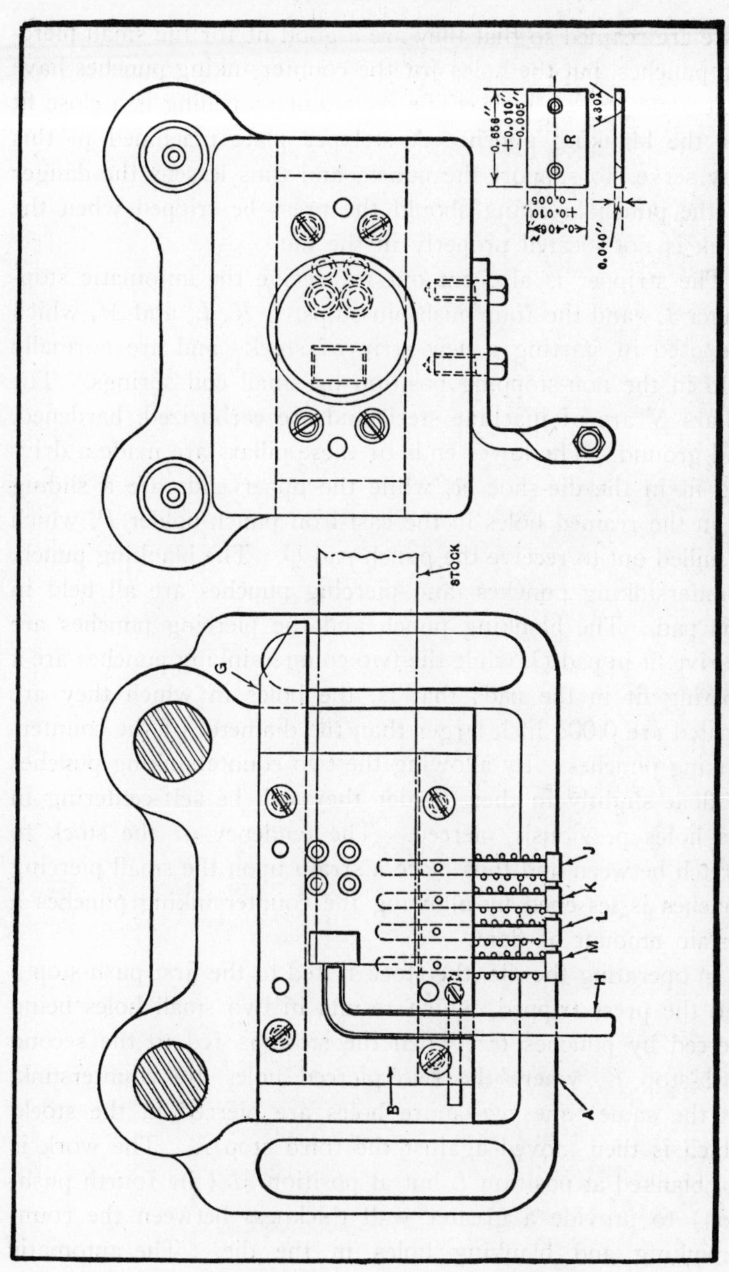

Fig. 5. Plan Views of Piercing, Countersinking and Blanking Die and Punch

plate are reamed so that they are a good fit for the small piercing punches, but the holes for the countersinking punches have a clearance of 1/64 inch. The rectangular opening is a close fit for the blanking punch. A stripper plate machined in this way serves to support the punch, and thus lessens the danger of the punch breaking should the press be tripped when the stock is not located properly in the die.

The stripper is also cut out to receive the automatic stop-finger *H*, and the four push-pin stops, *J*, *K*, *L*, and *M*, which are used in starting a new strip of stock and are normally held in the non-stopping position by small coil springs. The pillars *N* are of machine steel, and are carburized, hardened, and ground. The lower ends of these pillars are made a driving fit in the die-shoe *A*, while the upper ends are a sliding fit in the reamed holes in the cast-iron punch-holder *P*, which is milled out to receive the punch pad *Q*. The blanking punch, countersinking punches, and piercing punches are all held in this pad. The blanking punch and the piercing punches are a drive fit in pad *Q*, while the two countersinking punches are a floating fit in the pad; that is, the holes in which they are located are 0.005 inch larger than the diameter of the countersinking punches. By allowing the two countersinking punches to float slightly in their holder they will be self-centering in the holes previously pierced. The tendency of the stock to stretch between and thus place a strain upon the small piercing punches is lessened by allowing the countersinking punches a certain amount of float.

In operating the die, the stock is fed to the first push-stop *J* and the press tripped, which results in two small holes being pierced by punches *C*. Then the stock is fed to the second push-stop *K*, where the two pierced holes are countersunk. At the same time two more holes are pierced in the stock, which is then moved against the third stop *L*. The work is not blanked at position *L* but at position *M* (the fourth push-stop) to provide a greater wall thickness between the countersinking and blanking holes in the die. The automatic stop-finger *H* then comes into use and locates the stock from

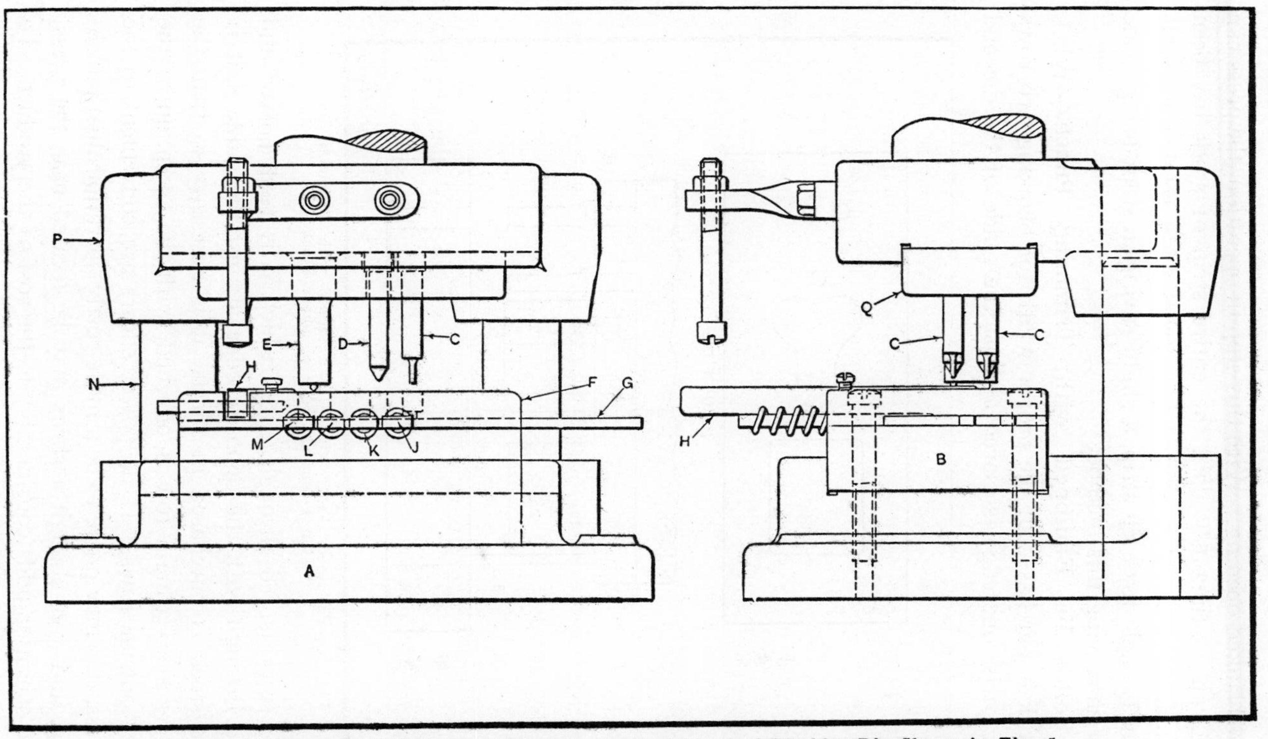

Fig. 6. Front and End Views of Piercing, Countersinking and Blanking Die Shown in Fig. 5

the blanked opening. With this stop in operation, the press can be run continuously until the entire strip of stock has been blanked. The stock used is 1½ inches wide, so that a double run is made for each strip, a slight saving in stock being made by employing this method.

Follow-die Equipped with Trimming Punch.—When stock is purchased of the proper width for blanking two rows of parts, one edge is placed against the guide of the die and

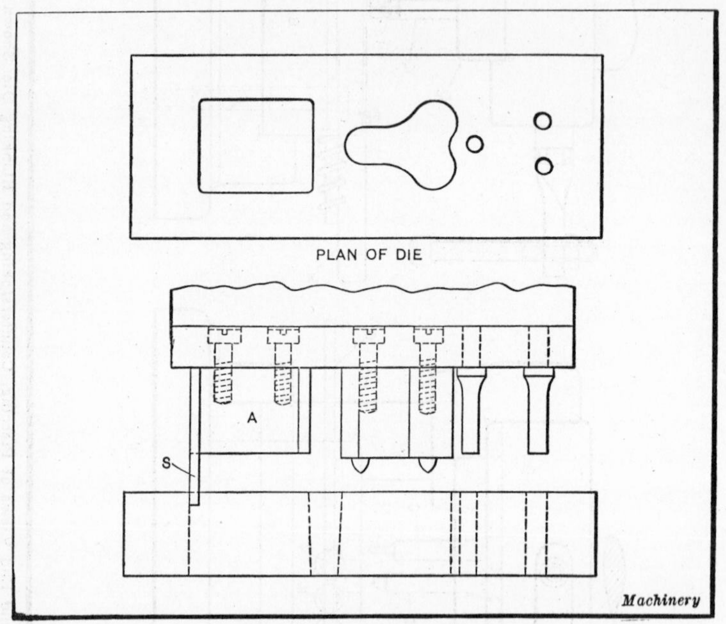

Fig. 7. Follow or Progressive Die Equipped with Trimming Punch for Trimming Edge of Sheet Stock

the stock is fed through, after which it is turned over and fed through with the opposite edge against the guide, but if the stock is purchased in sheets, it is necessary to trim the edges every time a row is punched, with the exception of the two outside rows. If no power shears are convenient to the press, this may prove to be a more costly operation than punching, and even though a shear may be located near the press, the operation adds considerably to the cost of the product. To avoid this trouble and expense, a trimming punch *A* is sometimes added, as illustrated in Fig. 7, which shows a die of the follow type. The purpose of this punch is to remove the scrap between the openings in the sheet and also to trim the edge of the sheet straight so that it may be used for guiding the stock when blanking out the next row. When a trimming punch is employed, a stop of the type shown at *S* in the illustration is used. The end of the scrap strikes this stop, thus locating the stock; when the punch descends, the scrap formed by the blanking operation is cut away, thus trimming the edge straight. When making dies of this class, it is necessary to have the blanking punch longer than the others in order that the locating or pilot-pins on the end can engage the holes in the stock before the other punches begin to cut. It is also advisable to place the stop so that the stock will go a little farther (say, 0.010 inch) than its correct location; then, when the pilot-pins engage the pierced holes they will draw the stock back to the proper position, whereas, if the diemaker attempted to set the stop so as to locate the stock exactly, any dirt or other foreign substance between the end of the scrap and the stop would cause trouble.

Self-contained Feeding Device on Follow-die for Blanking Washers.—A progressive type of piercing and blanking die with an automatic feeding device is shown diagrammatically in Fig. 8. This type of die can be operated in a single-action press. The illustration is intended to show the action of the feeding device, and does not represent the actual construction of the die. While this style of die is primarily intended for use in the manufacture of washers, it can also be adapted to the manufacture of various kinds of small blanks, rings, cups, etc.

The feeding device is very simple, and may be made as sturdy and strong as the work requires. It can be used on follow-dies designed to pierce and blank two, four, six, or eight washers simultaneously, or for dies designed to blank only one piece at a time, as in the case shown. Either strip or coil stock can be used. In equipping a die with this automatic feeding device, it is necessary to cut or mill a slot at an angle in the blanking end of the die, as indicated at *A*. On the down stroke of the press ram the feed-finger *B* on the punch engages the bottom of this slot, thus causing the finger to pivot about pin *C* in a clockwise direction.

The pivoting movement imparted to the feed-finger causes the front face of this member to come in contact with the bridge section *D* of the blank stock, so that the stock is fed forward until the pierced hole *F* in the strip stock is under the pilot *G* of the blanking punch. As the punch continues its downward movement, hole *F* is brought into alignment with the blanking punch *J* by pilot *G*. The view at the right-hand

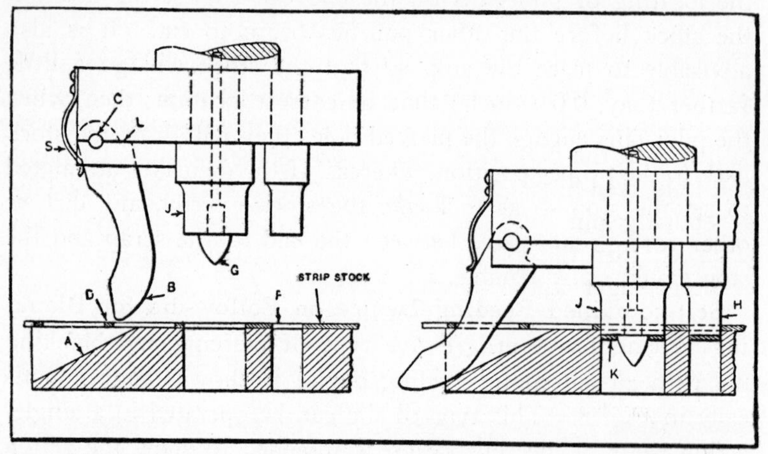

Fig. 8. Diagrams Illustrating the Action of an Automatic Feeding Device for a Follow-die

side of the illustration shows the punch at the end of the downward stroke, at which time piercing punch *H* has pierced the central hole of another washer, and blanking punch *J* has blanked the washer *K* that was pierced on the preceding down stroke of the punch. It will be noted that the feed-finger is cut away at the front so that it will clear the bridge *D* as soon as it has advanced the stock far enough to permit pilot *G* to engage the pierced hole *F*.

The location of the feeding finger and its shape and length, as well as the angle and position of the bottom of the slot *A* in the die, must be carefully determined in order to provide the required feeding movement and insure the proper functioning of the feeding device. As the illustration is intended only to show the principle on which the feeding device operates, the actual design of the die parts may require some modification, to obtain the best results.

It will be noticed that the top of the feeding finger has a shoulder at *L*. The pivoting movement of the feeding finger in a counter-clockwise direction on the upward stroke of the ram is produced by a spring *S*. The shoulder at *L* limits the movement in this direction, so that when the punch is at the highest point of its travel, the feeding finger will be in the position shown in the view at the left-hand side of the illustration. In starting the press, one end of the strip or coil stock is placed under the piercing punch, and the center hole of the first washer is punched. The stock is then moved forward until the center hole is located under the blanking punch, in line with the pilot *G*. Continue adjusting the stock by hand and hold feed-finger *B* out of engagement with the stock (by a retaining pin or otherwise) until two washers have been blanked; then the press is ready for continuous operation as feeding finger automatically advances stock at each stroke.

Piercing and Blanking Die for Spacing Collar.—The progressive type of piercing and blanking die shown in Fig. 9 is designed to produce spacing collars used in automobile construction. The material from which the washers are blanked is designated as "half hard" cold-rolled steel. It is 3/16 inch thick and is obtained in strips 2 inches wide by 36 inches long. The operations are piercing the 1.085-inch hole and blanking the 1.625-inch diameter indicated in the detailed view.

The strip stock is fed under the stripper plate *A* until its edge strikes finger-stop *B*, which is previously pushed in by the left hand of the operator. The press is then tripped, allowing punch *C* to pierce the 1.085-inch hole, after which the stock is again pushed forward until it strikes pin *D*. On the second stroke, pilot *E* enters the 1.085-inch hole, thus centering the stock while punch *F* blanks the 1.625-inch diameter.

The punch and die are aligned by means of pins *G*, which are driven into the die bed and made a good sliding fit in holes machined in the cast bosses of the punch-holder. Hole *J* in the punch-holder is provided to permit the pilot *E* to be pushed out, when the face of punch *F* is to be ground. Referring to the side elevation in the lower right-hand corner of the illustration, it will be noted that the cutting end of piercing-punch *C* is given shear. The amount of shear is about two-thirds the thickness of the strip stock.

After the die had been in operation a short time, it was noticed that the blanking punch did not stand up well. In order to remedy this fault die *K* was also given shear as shown at *L* in the lower right-hand corner. As will be noted, the shear on the die consists of four grooves spaced 45 degrees apart and about 1/8 inch deep. These grooves were ground into the die on a surface grinder with a wheel dressed to a radius of 7/8 inch. The two grooves at *M* were made less deep than the others to avoid grinding into the piercing hole *N* of the die. The sharp corners at *P* were rounded by stoning the edges so as to prevent the die from tearing the metal.

Follow-die for Eight-Spoke Wheel.—In Fig. 10 is shown the plan view of a follow-die designed to pierce and blank the eight-spoked wheel shown at *A*, Fig. 11. This die, however, proved unsatisfactory in use, due to the weakness of sections *B*, Fig. 10, which correspond to the spokes of the wheel. In order to overcome this difficulty, the follow-die shown at *E*, Fig. 12, was designed. The spokes are formed by this die in two piercing operations instead of one, as in the case of the die shown in Fig. 10. From view *E*, Fig. 12, it will be seen that the latter die is constructed so that alternate spaces are pierced by each of the multiple piercing punches.

In laying out the die, a plate *G*, shown in Fig. 11, was first cut from 1/8-inch sheet stock. A circle with a radius equal to the diameter of the wheel plus the bridge between the blanks was next scribed on the plate. This circle was then divided into eight equal parts. A 0.125-inch hole was next drilled at each of the division points and also at the center of the circle.

drill four similar gr[illegible] each piercing die center. The three h[illegible]s drilled located the corners of the o[illegible]ng dies. For example, the holes [illegible] were drilled by using plate *G* a[illegible]nner: First the shank of a C[illegible]h the central

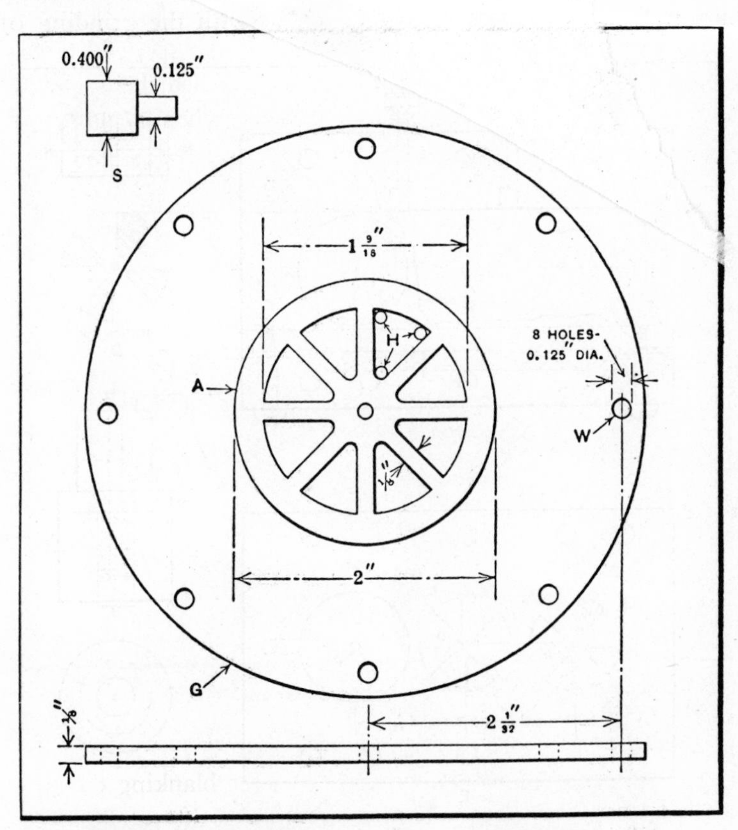

Fig. 11. Lay-out Plate Used in Making the Spoked Wheel Die

hole of plate *G* and into hole *O* of the die; next the shank of another drill was inserted in hole *W* of plate *G*, Fig. 11, and pushed into hole *P*, Fig. 12, of the die, which was located previously by means of plate *G*; next the three holes corresponding to holes *H* were drilled through the die, using plate *G* as a drill jig. By properly indexing plate *G* and repeating the drilling operations, it was a simple matter to locate the corners of each opening accurately. After all the holes were drilled, the metal was worked out between the three holes in plate G in order that the plate could be used as a gage for filing out the die.

In the upper left-hand corner of Fig. 11 is shown a solid button *S* which was used in connection with the grinding of

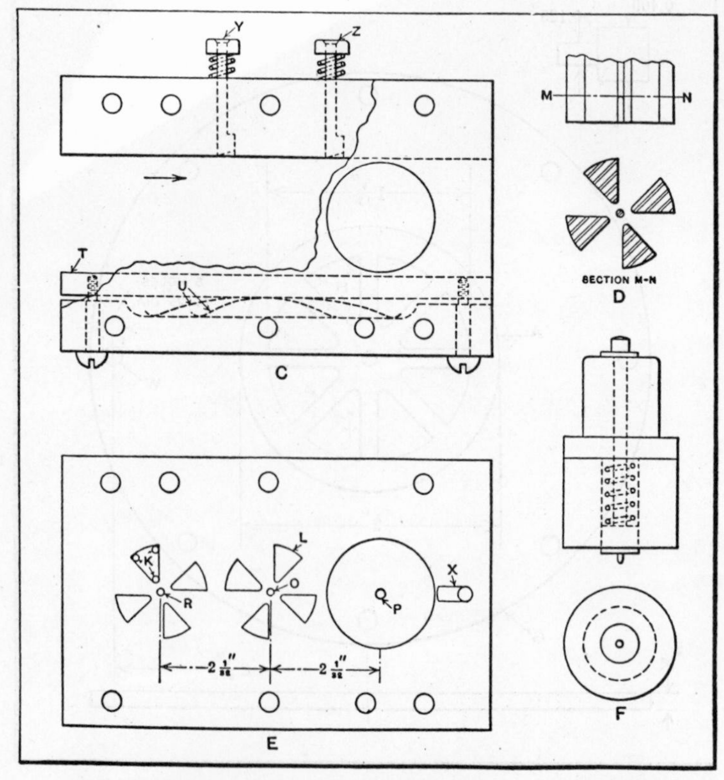

Fig. 12. Stripper, Follow-die, and Punches of Improved Design

the blanking die. This button has the same diameter as that of a commonly used jig button and also a 1/8-inch pilot made to fit the punch holes *R* and *O* in the die, Fig. 12. Two of these buttons were made and used in the following manner: The pilot of one button was placed in hole *R* and the pilot of the other in hole *O*; a regular locating button was then attached to a piece fitted into the previously rough-bored blanking die hole; then by the use of the straightedge and a micrometer, the 0.400-inch diameter locating button was brought into accurate alignment with the two buttons in holes *R* and *O* respectively, so that the jig button could be used for indicating the work with the machine spindle when grinding the blanking die.

At *D* is shown a sectional view of one of the piercing punches, and at *F* the blanking punch, while *C* is a view of the stripper plate used with the die. This plate is provided with a guide strip *T* actuated by flat springs *U*, which keeps the strip stock pressed against the opposite side of the stripper block, thus compensating for variations in the width of stock. The stops *Y* and *Z* are used only when starting the stock, *Y* being used to locate the work for the first piercing operation and *Z* for the second operation. After the stock is properly started, stop *X*, shown in view *E*, locates the work in the proper position for each succeeding stroke of the punch.

Follow-die Equipped with Work-stacking Attachment.—Switch plates like the one shown at *A*, Fig. 13, are used on the walls and floors of houses to cover electric switches. The brass stock from which this type of plate is made is 0.017 inch thick. As shown, there are four pierced holes in the plate and the outer edges are bent down to give the work a beveled appearance. The work is shown drawn to a larger scale than the die. The two larger holes in plate *A* are for the switch buttons, while the two small holes receive the fastening screws. The plates are given a brush finish, and the corners are required to be stamped sharp on the outside. The various parts of a follow-die used to pierce, stamp, and trim the plates from the strip stock are shown in the sectional view, Fig. 14.

The method of production before this die was made consisted of first cutting the metal up and piercing the holes to the proper size and in their correct positions. The plates were next stacked in boxes which were trucked to the stamping room, where they were fed, one at a time, under a drop-hammer, which stamped them to the desired shape. After this operation the plates were again stacked and trucked back to the press room where they were fed by hand, one at a time, into a trimming die. It is important that the faces of the plates should not become dented or nicked, as this would prolong the buffing operation, and if the dent is too deep to be removed by buffing, the plate must be scrapped. It will be seen, therefore,

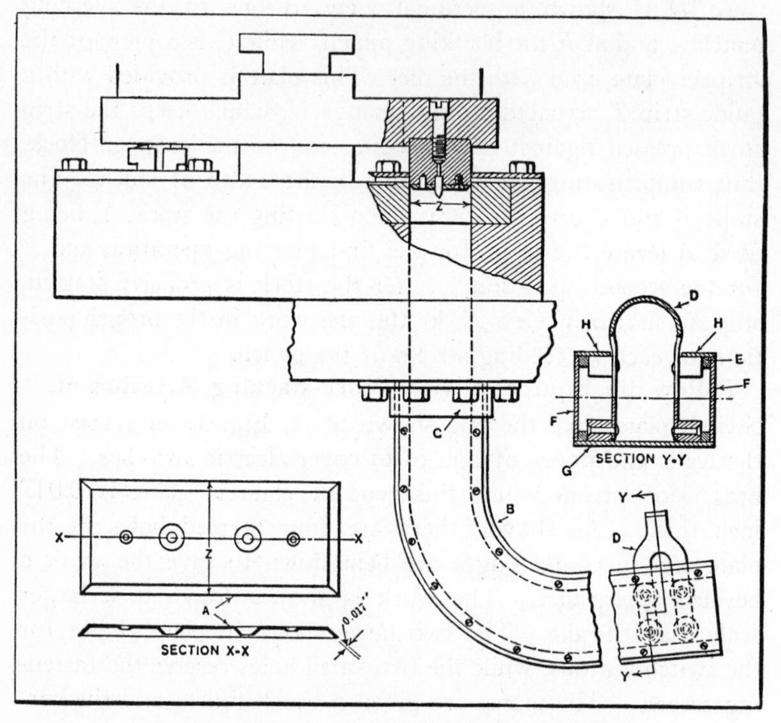

Fig. 13. Follow-die Equipped with Stacking Device

that it was necessary to catch the plates as they came from the trimming die, and stack them again, in order to prevent them from becoming dented.

The follow-die shown was so designed that one operator could attend to all operations on the plates except buffing. In order to accomplish this, a catching and stacking device was necessary and this is shown at *B* in Fig. 13, attached to the die. The stamping operation forces some of the metal below the top surface of the strip stock, thus forming a projection on the under side. It is therefore necessary to arrange for lifting the stamped portion out of the die and providing clearance for the stamped portion when the metal is lowered again in the succeeding position.

The operation is as follows: The metal is started at the left and fed under plate *A*, Fig. 14, until the entering end is flush with the right-hand edge of the plate. The roll feed is then engaged and the press started. As the ram descends, stripper *B*, which supports the piercing punch *C* and receives its tension from springs *D* (only one of which is shown), engages the metal between it and the spring pad *E*, which, in turn, receives its tension from springs *F*. The stock is then carried down into contact with the top of the die *G*, where it is pierced by punch *C*. The scrap passes out through a hole in the die-block. As the ram ascends, stripper *B* strips the metal from the piercing punch *C*, and spring pad *E* lifts the metal up high enough so that it will clear the forming die *H*.

For clearness the smaller punch which pierces the screw hole is not shown, but it should be borne in mind that all four piercing punches are in line and held in the same manner as punch *C*; Fig. 14 shows only a cross-section taken through one of the punches.

The strip is again fed forward, and on the next stroke the metal is engaged between the forming pad *J* and the forming punch *K*. When in this position, the stock is located by the forming pegs at the center of pad *J*, which act as pilots. All four forming pegs are held in plate *M* in the same manner. The forming pad *J* is supported by three springs *N* so that the metal, when it is drawn over the beveled edge of the die *H*, will have no tendency to wrinkle or pull. The stock is also kept from wrinkling by the spring pad *P*, which holds the surrounding stock between its lower face and the die *H*. This pad is held in place by screws *Q* and receives its tension from springs *R*.

At first, much difficulty was experienced in fôrming sharp corners on the outside of the plate, but this was overcome by making the punch as shown in the enlarged section at *S*. The ridge around the edge of the punch was ground from 0.004 to 0.005 inch higher than the major face of the punch, and about 0.040 to 0.050 inch in width. This ridge forces the metal out so that it fills in the space in the die (and sometimes throws a slight "fin," which is removed in the buffing operation), making a sharp corner where otherwise there would be a round corner having a radius equal to the thickness of the metal. As the ram ascends, the springs *N* force the pad *J* up, which, in turn, lifts the formed plate up so that it can be fed across the die *H* without catching on the corners of the die recess. The pad *J* bottoms on the steel plate *M*, which receives considerable pressure when the punch is at the end of the downward stroke.

The metal is again fed forward, so that at the third stroke of the press the holes pierced in the first position are in line with pilots *T*. The plate is trimmed as the punch *V* enters the die *U*. The punch *V* has a formed plate *W* of soft steel fastened to it which fits the work. This form is removed when the punch is being ground. As the distance between the centers of the piercing and forming dies is equal to two blanks plus the bridging, it was necessary to cut a clearance at *X* to receive the impression made in the stock by punch *K*. As the ram ascends, the metal is stripped from the punch by the stripper plate *Y*, which is beveled at its front end to eliminate any tendency for the metal to catch or stick when being fed forward.

The plate, when trimmed, passes down through the die bed into the chute *B*, Fig. 13, which is fastened to the bolster plate by four angle-irons *C*. The stacking is started by placing friction spring *D* up as far as it will go in chute *B* and filling the remaining space between it and the die with plates. Then when a plate is trimmed, it is forced through the die, and presses the friction spring *D* down a distance approximately equal to the thickness of the plate. The chute is bent to an angle of slightly less than 90 degrees, and after the plates are stacked beyond this bend, the friction spring may be removed,

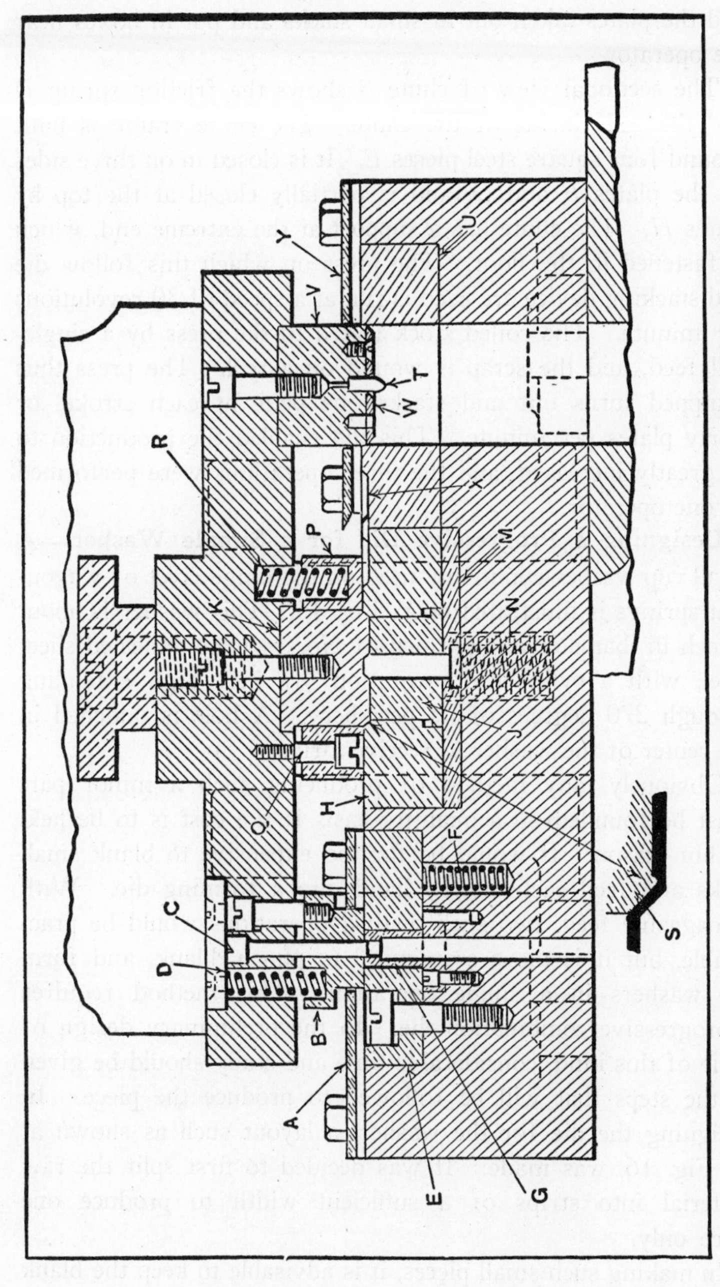

Fig. 14. Sectional View of the Follow-die for Piercing, Forming and Trimming Switch Plates

and the plates taken out in small stacks and put in boxes near the operator.

The sectional view of chute *B* shows the friction spring *D* and the rolls inside of the chute. The chute frame is built around four square steel pieces *E*. It is closed in on three sides by the plates *F* and *G*, and is partially closed at the top by plates *H*. The chute has a support at the extreme end, which is fastened to the floor. The press on which this follow die and stacking device are used is run at a speed of 30 revolutions per minute. The coiled stock is fed to the press by a single-roll feed, and the scrap is wound on a reel. The press thus equipped turns out and stacks one plate at each stroke, or thirty plates per minute. This die enabled the production to be greatly increased, and the three operations were performed by one operator.

Designing a Progressive Die for a Simple Washer.—A small cup washer commonly used on the hinge rivet of wagon-seat springs is illustrated at *X*, Fig. 15. This washer is about 1 inch in diameter and formed of No. 14 gage annealed sheet steel, with a cylindrical projection 3/16 inch high extending through 270 degrees of its periphery. A hole is punched in the center of the washer to receive a rivet.

Obviously, any method of producing such a minor part must be founded on a quantity basis if the cost is to be held within reason. It would be far too expensive to blank small disks and feed each one by hand into a forming die. With a magazine feed, two such distinct operations would be practicable, but it is more economical to punch, blank, and form the washers in a single operation. This method requires a progressive combination die. In the preliminary design of a die of this kind, considerable time and study should be given to the steps that will be followed to produce the piece. In designing the die for the washer, a layout such as shown at *X*, Fig. 16, was made. It was decided to first split the raw material into strips of a sufficient width to produce one piece only.

In making such small pieces, it is advisable to keep the blank attached to the strip as long as possible. If this can be done until the final operation is about to be performed, it will avoid the necessity of the operator paying much attention to the location of the pieces of work as they pass through the various stages. In the present example, it was decided to hold the different pieces together by means of a neck *A* until just before the final step.

It was also decided that in starting a new strip through the die, the first step would consist of blanking away the material around one side of the piece from point *B* to point *C* and that with each successive advance of the bar, the blanking punch

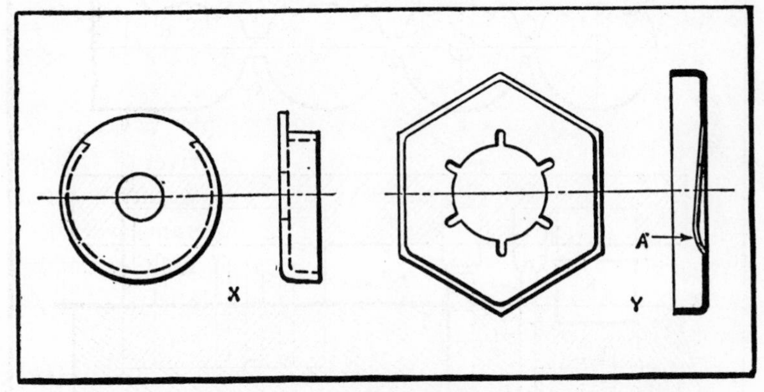

Fig. 15. Two Special Washers Produced in Large Quantities in Punch Presses

would cut away the stock from point *B* to point *D* along one edge and from point *C* to point *E* along the other edge. In this way, two pieces are blanked for one-half of their periphery at each stroke of the ram. The second stroke consisted of punching the central hole, and the third stroke, of blanking out neck *A*, and forming the part to the shape illustrated at *X*, Fig. 15.

Construction of the Progressive Die.—The die, built as outlined, is shown at *Y*, Fig. 16. It will be seen that all four punches are held in one block *F* which is attached to the ram. The blanking punch is shown at *G*, the piercing punch at *H*, the cutting-off punch at *J*, and the forming punch at *K*. Die-block *L* supports the stock in the blanking step, the stock being held down on this block by a stripper plate (not shown). The trimmings, of which there are a good many, fall down a slight incline on both sides of the die-block, so that the operator is relieved of removing them. When trimmings must be removed by an operator, he is often compelled to place his hands in a hazardous position, and, besides, dies are frequently broken through his neglect in removing the trimmings. The successful operation of a die often lies in eliminating the human factor as much as possible.

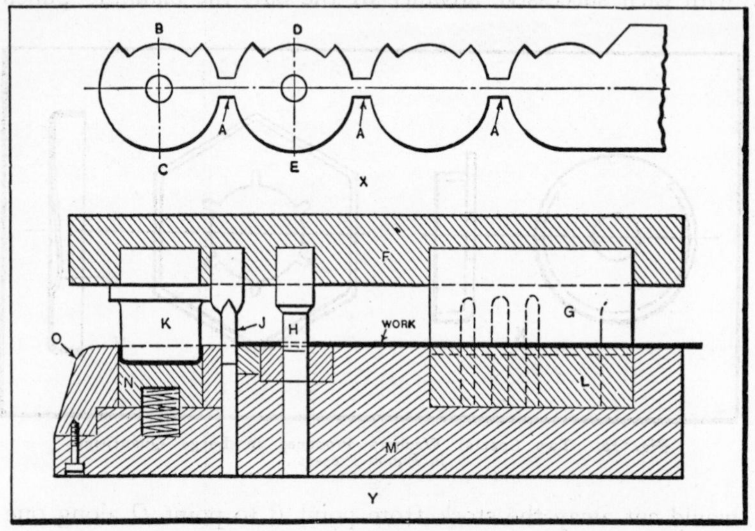

Fig. 16. Progressive Die for Producing Washer X, Fig. 15, Complete from Strip Stock

Die-shoe *M* has a groove in it, in which the stock is fed through the die manually, although an automatic feed could be utilized. The advantage of a manual feed is that if a piece should become stuck in the forming operation, further feeding of the stock can immediately be stopped until the ejector has removed the part. However, the advantage of an automatic feed is that every stroke of the machine is used, and so production is greatly increased.

In this die, a stop is provided at each step to locate the work properly. As punch *H* produces the hole in the center of the blank in the second step, the slug falls through a hole in the die and the die-block. In the next step, punch *J* severs the blank from the bar by blanking out the small neck previously mentioned, which also falls through the die-block. Finally, punch *K* forms the piece to the desired shape by forcing the blank into die *N*, which is free to slide vertically in a recess machined in shoe *O*. A coil spring beneath die *N* backs it up during the forming stroke and raises it at the end of the operation to eject the work. With the next advance of the stock, the work is pushed off die *N*. The downward travel of this die is limited by the depth to which the washer is formed.

Progressive Die for a Hexagonal Lock-washer.—Another example of parts produced rapidly in a power press is the hexagonal lock-washer shown at *Y*, Fig. 15. This washer is made of No. 16 to 18 gage sheet steel, containing from 0.15 to 0.25 per cent carbon. The central part of the washer around the opening is formed into a spiral to conform to the thread, and the washer is made with a hexagonal flange so that it can be turned readily with a standard wrench. When it is drawn down on a bolt as the nut is tightened, lip *A* grips the bolt thread so firmly as to prevent removal of the nut except with the aid of a wrench. These washers are made in different sizes.

The sequence of steps followed in producing the washers may be studied from the lay-out of the stock strip shown at *X*, Fig. 17, which illustrates the different steps up to and including the forming. At *Y* are shown a plan view of the die that is employed and a sectional view of the punch and die. In starting a new piece of stock through this die, the stock is inserted until it comes in contact with stop *A*. Then, at the descent of the punch ram, punch B shears away the stock to form three sides of a hexagon. Stop *A* is next pulled back and the stock advanced to the second stop *C*. At the second stroke of the die, punch *B* trims two more sides of the first washer and two sides of the next one. The stock is now advanced to the third stop *D*, for punching the hole and the small slots around the hole with punch *E*, which enters die *F*.

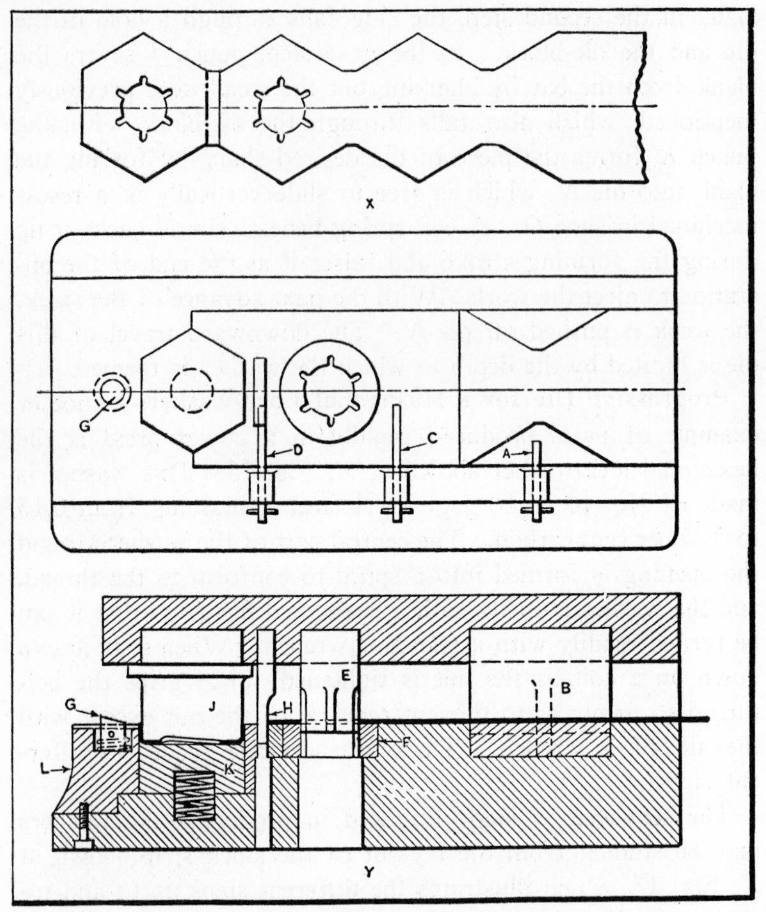

Fig. 17. Punch and Die Equipment Employed in Making a Hexagonal Lock-washer

Finally, the stock is advanced to the fourth stop *G*, in which position the washer is severed from the strip by punch *H* and formed to shape by means of punch *J* and die *K*.

Stop *G* is beveled on top, and is surrounded by a spring that tends to hold it in an elevated position. With this construction, the stop can be depressed to allow an ejected piece to be forced over it when the bar of stock is advanced for finishing a successive piece. As soon as the finished part is pushed over the stop, the latter springs up into place to locate the stock for forming the next washer. Stops *A*, *C*, and *D* are withdrawn after the first strip of stock is fed past them, because stop *G* functions to locate the stock for all subsequent washers after the first one of a strip reaches it. Stop *D* must never be in the position shown during a stroke, or punch *H* will strike it. On the side of die-shoe *L* adjacent to the punch *H*, there is a small shear blade which assists in cutting the washer from the strip. In this example, the forming die *K* is also movable in the shoe, and is equipped with a spring which raises the die to hold the work firmly against the punch during the forming stroke and to eject the formed blank at the end of the operation.

Designers have a tendency to make dies of the type here described too light to withstand the work required of them. The small size of the work often leads to the conclusion that the die may be very light, with the result that it soon becomes worn or broken. This type of die is operated at a high speed in order to keep down production costs, and therefore even a few minutes loss of time in repairing a die means a considerable loss in the number of parts produced. The working elements should be given liberal bearing surfaces, and the different sections as great an area of metal as is consistent with the space available, so as to reduce repairs to the minimum.

The metal from which the die is made has a considerable bearing on its life. For small intricate parts, carbon tool steel is always preferable, and in many cases the parts should be heat-treated to increase their life. The punch-blocks, die-blocks, and die-shoes of the examples here given are made of machine steel, while the punches and dies are made of carbon steel, hardened and ground. In larger dies, iron and steel castings are often suitable for certain parts, but when iron castings are used, a mixture containing about 10 per cent steel scrap and enough carbon to permit easy machining is preferable.

Compound Dies.—Compound dies differ from plain blanking and follow dies in that the simple punch and die elements are not separated but are combined so that both the upper and the lower members contain what corresponds to a punch and die, as well as suitable stripper plates or ejectors. The faces of the punches, dies, and stripper plates are normally held at about the same level and the strippers are spring supported so as to recede when the stock is being cut. A compound die produces more accurate work than the types previously referred to for the reason that all operations, such as piercing one or more holes and cutting the outer edge, are carried out simultaneously at one stroke, while the stock is firmly held

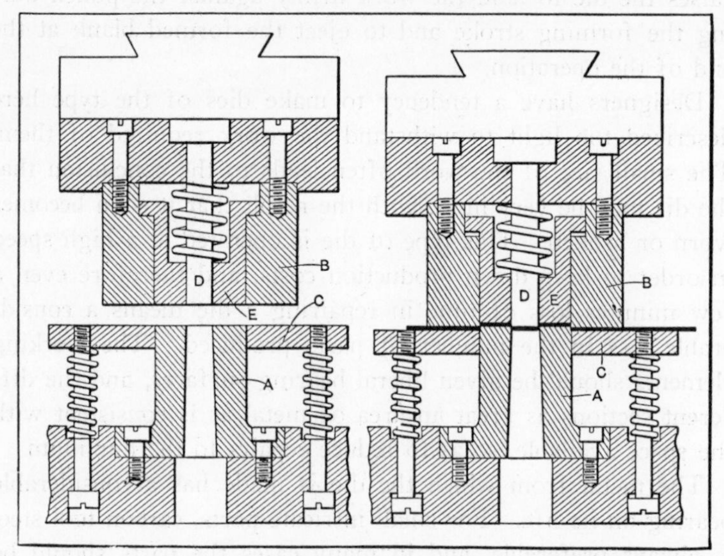

Fig. 18. Compound Die which Pierces and Blanks Simultaneously

between the spring supported stripper plates and opposing die-faces. A compound die is shown in Fig. 18. The operation of this die is as follows: The upper die descends and depresses stripper plate *C*. As the downward movement continues, the blank is cut from the stock by members *A* and *B* and, at the same time, a central hole is pierced by punch *D*, as indicated by the right-hand view. The blank is forced out of the upper die *B* by ejector *E* as the ram ascends, and the stripper plate *C* also pushes the stock up off of the die-block *A*. The scrap punched from the hole falls through the opening in die-block *A*, which has clearance to provide a free passage-way. The blank is returned to the strip of stock, from which it can easily be removed.

Inasmuch as the piercing and blanking operations are performed at the same time, very accurate work can be obtained in a die of the compound type. Such delicate parts as armed wheels or gear punchings for clocks, meters, etc., are examples of the work that can be done in this form of die. Such parts are made complete, including the arm spaces, center hole, and holes in the arms or rim if desired, with one stroke of the press. The stock from the arm spaces and other holes is forced down through the die while the blank is returned to the strip from which it was punched. The punchings obtained in a compound die are flat, accurate as to size, shape, and position of holes, and can be made very rapidly. One method of using a die of the compound type is to fit the punch into the socket of the slide of the press, and, after aligning, to clamp the die-block to the bolster plate. This method is fairly satisfactory for simple punches and dies, but, with more complicated designs, the aligning is more difficult and it is also more important that it should be as perfect as possible.

To secure accurate alignment, many dies, especially for accurate work, are equipped with some form of guide for the punch. The "die-sets" which have been placed on the market consist of a punch holder, base, and pillars or guides for accurately holding the upper and lower members in alignment and as a complete unit which may readily be applied to a press. Die-sets of this general type are manufactured in different standard sizes. They are so arranged that the user merely equips the die-set with whatever punches and dies or die openings, are required for a given operation.

The "sub-press" described later is another type of self-contained die which has a guide for the punch.

Compound Washer Die.—The compound die illustrated in Fig. 19 is designed to pierce and blank a special washer used on the shaft of a generator which comprises part of the electrical equipment of an automobile. The operation of the die

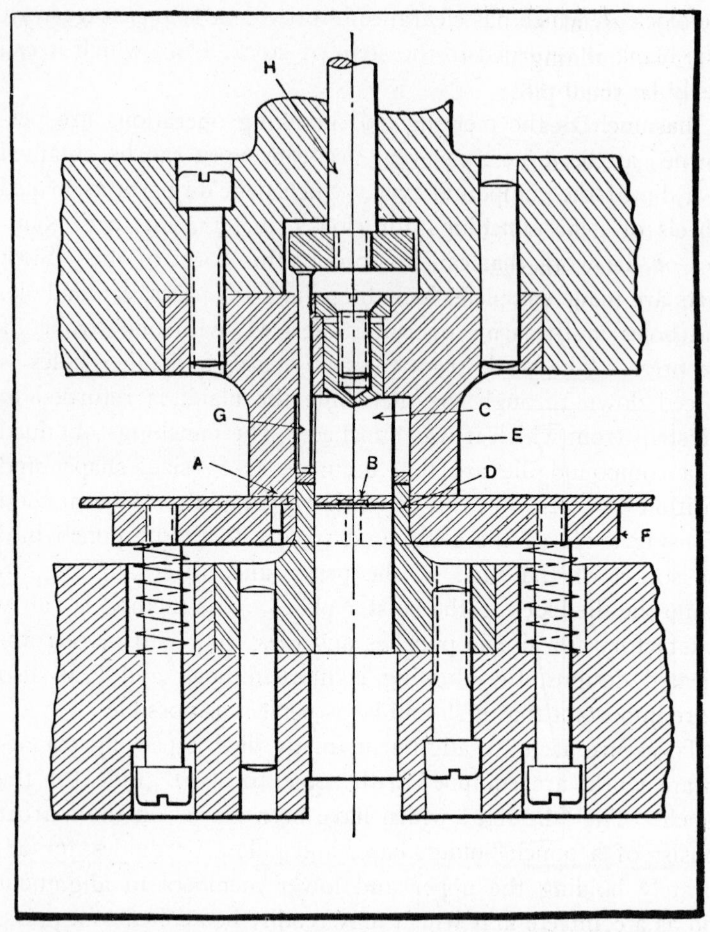

Fig. 19. Compound Die for Piercing and Blanking Special Washers

is similar to that of any ordinary compound die. The piercing punch *C* pierces the 25/32-inch hole, and punch *D* blanks the 1 1/8-inch outside diameter. Stripper *F* strips the stock from the punch on the upward stroke, and the three knock-out pins, one of which is shown at *G*, eject the blank from the die *E* through the action of knock-out rod *H*. The punch and die members are kept in alignment by two pillars located at the back of the die-bed. This type of die, when furnished with locating pins as described, provides an effective means of producing special washers when the quantity required does not warrant building a more expensive die of the multiple type, or when small pieces of scrap stock are used.

Shaving Dies.—Dies of this class are sometimes used for finishing the edges of comparatively thick blanks which have been cut out in a regular blanking die. A blanking die used for cutting heavy stock must have a certain amount of clearance between the punch and the die opening, the amount depending upon the thickness and kind of material. As the result of this clearance (which lessens the danger of breaking

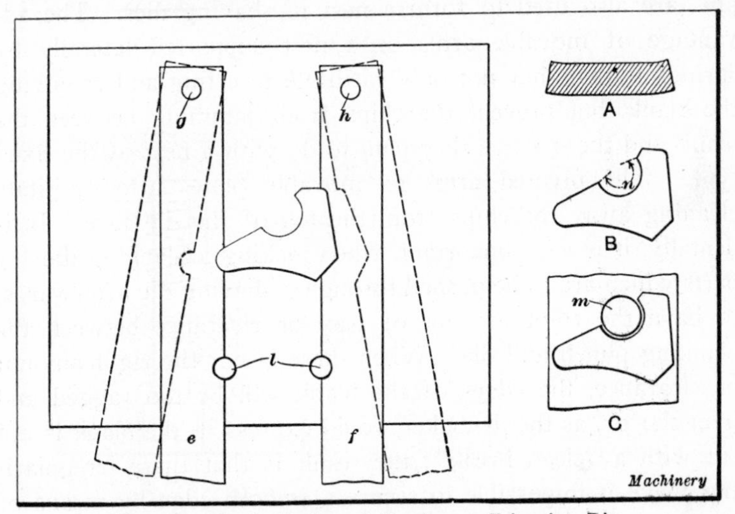

Fig. 20. Simple Design of Shaving or Trimming Die

the punch and reduces the pressure required for the punching operation), the edges of thick blanks are somewhat rough and also tapering, as shown at *A*, Fig. 20. To secure smooth square edges, shaving dies are used in some cases. The plan view to the left illustrates a simple form of shaving die designed for finishing the blank, shown at *B*. This die has an opening which conforms to the shape required for the finished blank and it is equipped with two arms *e* and *f* which are pivoted at *g* and *h*, respectively. These arms are notched to receive and locate the rough blank directly over the die opening. In the operation of the die, the arms are swung outward as indicated by the dotted lines, and are then closed in on the blank and against the locating pins *l*. The press is then tripped and the punch (which fits the hole in the die) descends and pushes the blank through the die, thus shaving and finishing the rough edges.

Shaving dies do not always have pivoted arms to locate or form a "nest" for the blank, but are sometimes provided with movable plates which are held in position by springs and have beveled edges so that they are forced outward slightly each time a blank is pushed downward through the die. Spring pins are also used to form a nest in shaving dies. The advantage of movable arms or a nest supported laterally by springs is that they not only facilitate inserting and removing the blank, but prevent the chips from jamming between the blank and the nest, as they tend to do with a nest of the fixed type. The pivoted arms or movable plates also facilitate cleaning away the chips from the top of the die face. Incidentally, it is very important, when making a blanking die for parts which are to be pushed through a shaving die afterwards, to have the right amount of play or clearance between the blanking punch and die. When there is not the right amount of clearance, the edges of the blank will be too ragged and irregular or, as the diemaker would express it, the blank is not cut with a "clean break"; the result is that these irregularities make it impossible to secure a smooth edge by means of the shaving die.

When Only Part of Blank Edge Requires Shaving.—Sometimes the entire edge or contour of a blank does not need to be finished but it is necessary to have part of the surface smooth. In such a case, the effect of shaving may be obtained in the blanking die, and without a separate shaving operation, by piercing a hole adjacent to the edge where a good finish is required. The principle of this method is illustrated at *C*, Fig. 20. Assuming that it is only necessary to have the curved edge *n* (see sketch B) smooth, hole *m* should be pierced in the stock adjacent to edge *n*, prior to the blanking operation, by means of a piercing punch. The result is that, when the part is blanked, edge *n* is subjected to a shaving action, owing to the thin strip of metal at this point. The amount of metal left for shaving should be equal to about 10 per cent of the stock thickness for mild steel.

Die for Obtaining Smooth Edges by Removing Adjoining Metal Before Blanking.—The die shown in Fig. 21 is for piercing and blanking the pawl illustrated at *A*. As the V-shaped projection *B* on one end of this pawl and the straight surface *C* had to have a smooth finish, the effect of a shaving operation on these surfaces was required. This operation is

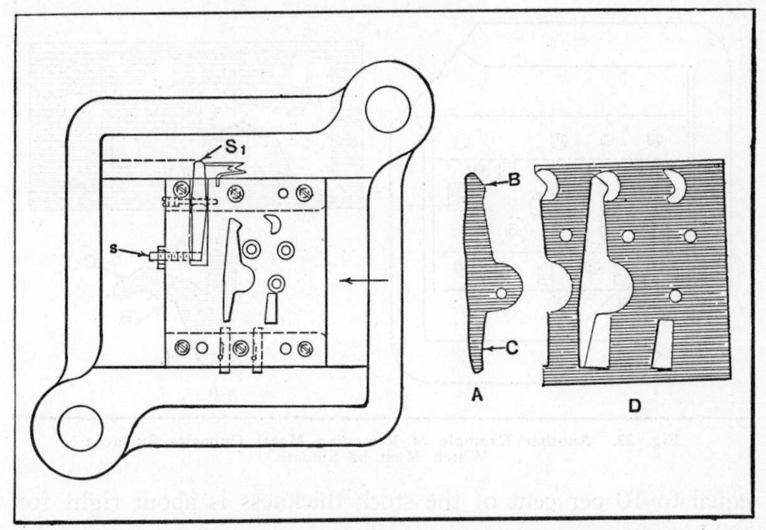

Fig. 21. Metal Adjacent to Surfaces *B* and *C* is Removed Prior to Blanking to Obtain a Shaving Effect and Smooth Edges

not performed in a shaving die after blanking, as would be necessary if the entire contour of the part had to be finished, but it is done in the blanking die by removing a certain amount of metal adjacent to these surfaces, during the piercing operation as shown by the sample of scrap at *D*. The result is that when the pawl is blanked, the edges opposite these openings are subjected to a shaving action which leaves a smooth surface that is entirely free from the roughness found on the other edges where the stock is sheared from the solid. The narrow shavings, which are removed from the surfaces to be finished, remain attached to the scrap in this particular instance, as the illustration shows. It will be seen that when this method of securing a finished edge is employed, the stock must be accurately located, as the removal of a shaving that is too thick would roughen the edge. In the die illustrated, the stock is located by the two pilot-pins on the punch, one entering the hole in part *A*, and the other a hole pierced in the scrap portion, simply to give a two-point location, thus insuring accuracy. In practice it has been found that a shaving

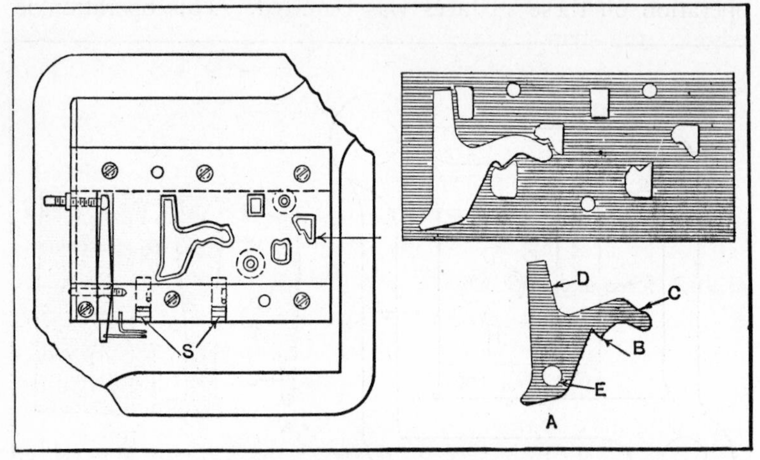

Fig. 22. Another Example of Removing Metal Opposite Surfaces Which Must be Smooth

equal to 10 per cent of the stock thickness is about right for mild steel.

This die is equipped with an automatic stop S_1 which is operated by a projecting screw on the punch in the usual way. The hole in this stop for the pivot on which it swivels is tapered toward the center from both sides, thus giving it a movement horizontally as well as vertically. With the stop mounted in this way, slight adjustments, to compensate for any error there might be in the location of the stop with reference to the pilots in the punch, can easily be made when the die is being tried out, by simply turning the screw *s* until the stop is properly positioned. The function of the stop is, of course, to locate the stock approximately, and its flexibility prevents the pilots from being subjected to excessive strains. The horizontal adjustment has an additional advantage in that the stop does not have to be located so accurately when this adjustment is provided.

Another punch and die of the piercing, shaving, and blanking type is shown in Fig. 22. In this case the work *A* had to be finished in three places, *B*, *C* and *D*, as shown by the perforations on the scrap portion. The stock is pierced for shaving by three punches. A fourth punch forms hole *E* in part *A* and a fifth punch pierces an extra hole near the opposite edge of the strip. This hole is merely for locating purposes, there being two pilots which give a two-point location. This die is also equipped with an automatic stop similar to the one previously described, and it has small hand stops *S*.

Disappearing Nests for Shaving Punches.—When shaving a sheet-metal punching, the work is generally located by pilot-pins or by nest plates. As the former method is usually preferable, holes are occasionally punched merely to permit the use of pilot-pins in subsequent operations. When pilot-pins cannot be used, and the ends or sides to be shaved must also serve as locating surfaces, the disappearing nests described in the following may be used to advantage.

In the illustration (Fig. 23), the work or punching *A* (a plan and side view of which are shown by heavy dot-and-dash lines) is required to have holes *B* and *C* accurately located from the ends *D* and *E* to within 0.0005 inch. Therefore, the ends were shaved and the holes pierced at the same stroke of the press. The work is located endwise by the disappearing or swinging nests *F* and *G*, which are pivoted on pins *H* and *I* to brackets *J* and *K*, respectively. Before shaving punches *L* and *M* come in contact with the ends of the work, they first hit swinging nests *F* and *G*, thus depressing the latter and bringing them out of contact with the work. On the upward or return stroke, springs *N* and *O* bring the nests back to their normal positions. The work is located sidewise by pilot-pins *U*, *P*, *Q*, and *R*. Holes *S* and *T* provide clearance for the pilot-pins that are shown at *U* and *Q*.

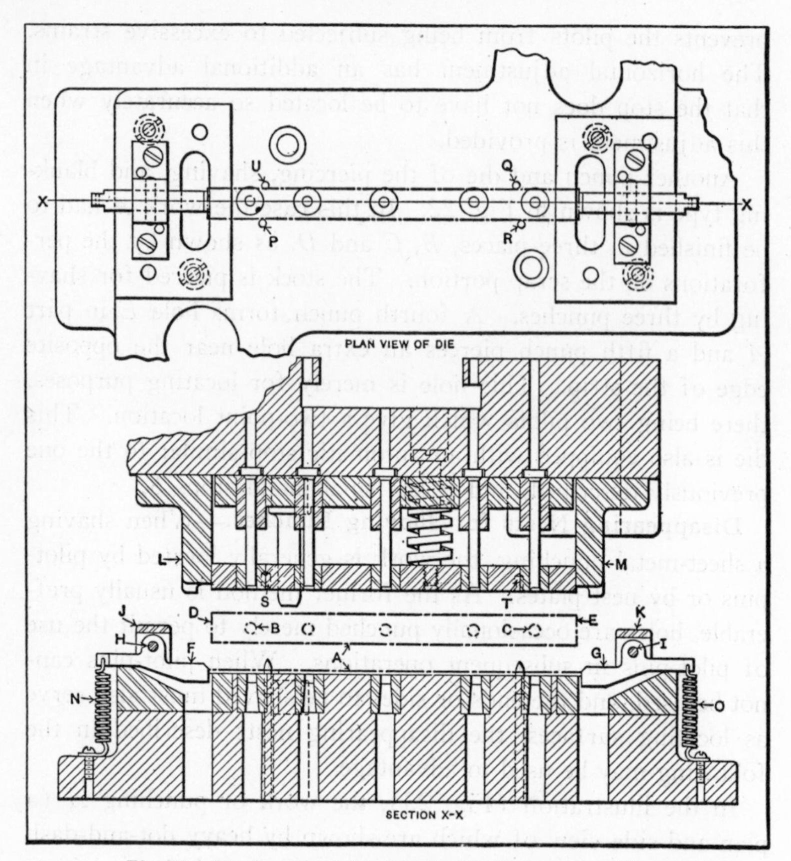

Fig. 23. Shaving Punch Equipped with Disappearing Nests

Burnishing Dies.—When an exceptionally good finish or polish is required, blanks which have been trimmed in a shaving die are pushed through what is known as a burnishing die. Such a die has an opening which tapers slightly inward toward the bottom, and it is finished very smooth, so that, when the blank is forced through by the punch, the metal around the edges is compressed and polished. Naturally, the degree of finish on the blanks will depend largely upon the finish of the burnishing surface of the die.

Die-Cut Spur Gears.—The punch press offers one of the most economical methods of manufacturing certain classes of small spur gears. Most manufacturers of adding machines, typewriters, cash registers, etc., make the gears entering into the construction of their product by this method. Gears may be produced on the punch press at a fraction of the cost involved by other methods.

The main initial cost in equipping a press for producing gears is the expense of the dies. However, a well designed and properly constructed set of dies will produce over 100,000 gears, provided the material from which the gears are punched is not hard enough to cause the dies to wear rapidly. The labor cost of operating punch presses is very small. In considering the adaptability of a product to this manufacturing method, there are three points to be analyzed: (1) The material from which the gears are to be produced; (2) size and design of work; and (3) accuracy required.

Adaptability of Gears to Punch Press Manufacture.—The most suitable materials from which gears may be punched are good grades of punching steel, which generally run soft, medium, or hard. Soft steel, as a rule, is likely to tear in punching, with the result that the gears have rougher edges than when produced from medium or hard steel. On the other hand, if the material is too hard, there is difficulty in maintaining the cutting edges of the punch and die. However, the material to be punched may be annealed before stamping and rehardened after the operation. A cast-iron gear cannot be successfully machined by means of dies, and neither can brass nor aluminum castings, although both brass and aluminum flat or strip stock can be blanked satisfactorily.

It is impossible to give hard and fast rules regarding the maximum size of gears that can be produced; this must be decided mainly from experience. If the maximum thickness of metal ranges from 5/16 to 3/8 inch (the exact thickness depending on the over-all diameter of the gear) satisfactory results may be obtained. It is possible to obtain smooth and uniform teeth with metal of a thickness up to this maximum range.

The pitch of the teeth does not have to be considered to any great extent; however, it is best not to attempt to blank gears, say, 3/8 inch thick, having fine-pitch teeth, because the load on the punch and die would be likely to strip the teeth. The size of the hole in a gear also determines the possibility of producing the work in a die. It would not be advisable to attempt to produce a gear of say, 24 pitch, 1 inch diameter, 1/4 inch in thickness, having a 5/8-inch hole at the center, because experience shows that the pressure applied when blanking

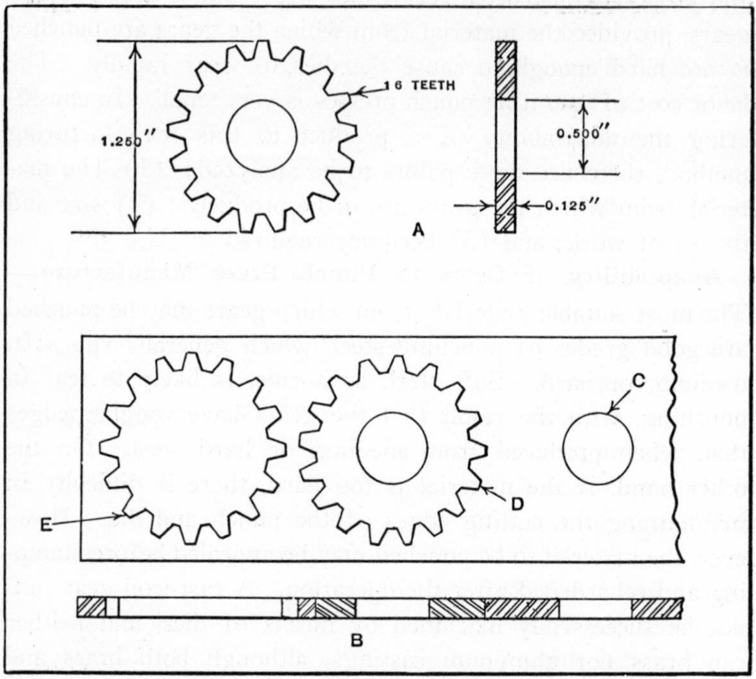

Fig. 24. (A) Gear for which Dies were Designed; (B) Appearance of the Stock as it is Fed Through the Blanking Die

would twist the gear out of shape, and would cause the cutting edges of the punch and die to become rounded.

As it is possible to maintain accurate limits on die work, not much trouble is encountered in manufacturing gears to the required accuracy by this method. The greatest difficulty in maintaining accuracy arises from the material that is used. There is generally a difference in the hardness of the stock, and this affects the size of the blank to a certain extent. However, the variation is small, and in most cases the size will be within the required limits of accuracy. If the important dimensions of a gear are held to a tolerance of 0.0005 inch, the gear can be successfully produced. It is, of course, necessary to regrind the faces of the punch and die occasionally in order to produce the work within the required limits. The average tolerance specified on punched gears is about 0.001 inch.

After it has been determined that a gear may be satisfactorily produced by the punch press, it must be estimated whether the quantity to be manufactured will be sufficiently large to warrant the expense of making a set of dies. Obviously, it would not be advisable to construct dies for a comparatively small quantity of gears, because the cost per part would probably be prohibitive. The approximate cost per piece of producing gears on a punch press may be determined by dividing the cost of the die by the estimated number of parts which can be produced by it, and adding the labor and overhead costs.

For example, if a gear such as shown at *A*, Fig. 24, is to be produced in 100,000 lots, and the set of dies costs $1000, the tool cost per piece is one cent. In addition to the labor cost, an allowance must also be made for the cost of regrinding the punch and die faces as they become dull. If the die is properly designed and made, the cost of repairs will not be worth considering.

Examples of Die-cut Gears.—In manufacturing gears on a punch press the common procedure is to employ a progressive blanking die to blank the gear and pierce a hole through its center, and then use a shaving die to smooth the contour of the teeth and the hole to the required accuracy. Various styles of gears can be produced by means of dies, the most common form being a flat gear having a hole at the center but no projecting hub. Fig. 25 shows a number of typical examples.

At *A* is shown a flat gear having a hub fastened to it by means of three rivets. This hub is fitted into the gear blank after the blank has been finished. At *B* is shown a similar example with the exception that the hub is integral. In this case the hub is first produced on a screw machine, after which blanking and shaving dies are used to form the teeth and the hole. In some instances when a small-diameter hub is desired, it is possible to form the work from flat stock as shown at *C*. Gears of this kind are blanked, drawn, and swaged prior to the shaving operations. It is often necessary to assemble gears together, and at *D* is shown an example of this kind, the two gears having their hubs produced on screw machines. These gears are riveted together in a manner similar to that employed

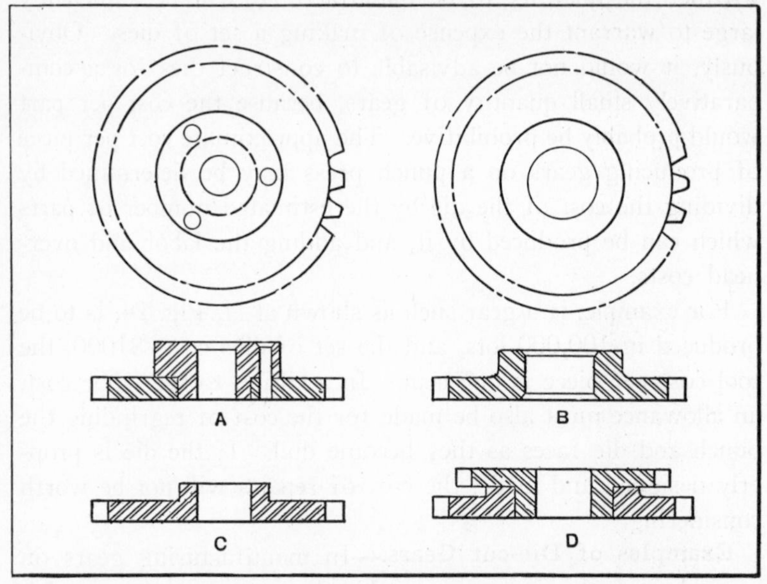

Fig. 25. Typical Examples of Gears that may be Manufactured by the Use of Punches and Dies

in attaching the hub to the gear in the example shown at *A*. In addition to these examples, other forms of gears, such as sectors, racks, etc., may be successfully produced by means of dies.

Progressive Blanking Die for Gears.—In order to illustrate the method followed in designing a blanking die for punching gears, it will be assumed that the gear shown at *A*, Fig. 24, is to be produced from a medium-grade punching steel 0.125 inch thick. It will be further assumed that the required accuracy necessitates shaving 0.012 inch of stock from both the hole and the contour of the teeth.

The first step is to determine the width of stock required, and then make a lay-out, such as shown at *B*, which indicates the various operations performed by the progressive die. It will be seen that the center hole *C* of the gear is pierced first, a sufficient amount of stock being allowed for the shaving later. Teeth *D* are then blanked, after the stock has been moved sufficiently to the left to bring the center of the punched hole in alignment with the center of the punch used in blanking the teeth. The appearance of the stock after the gear has been removed is shown at *E*.

It is necessary to allow a width of stock between each blanked hole and the edges of the strip, about equal to the thickness of the blank. A similar amount of stock should be allowed between the blanked holes. In this instance, the strip must be 1½ inches wide to provide the proper amount of stock between the blanked holes and the edges of the strip, and the center-to-center distance between the blanked holes must be 1⅜ inches. The latter dimension makes it possible to determine the length in which the strips should be supplied in order to avoid unnecessary scrap loss.

In making a progressive blanking die, particular care should be taken to obtain proper alignment between the punch and die members, because the life of the tools greatly depends upon this. Fig. 26 shows the progressive blanking die designed for producing the gear. The stock is fed through the die in the direction indicated by the arrow in the plan view shown in the lower part of the illustration.

Before blanking the first gear, the strip is fed until the end reaches the point indicated by the dotted line *A*. The ram of the press is then brought down and the center hole of the gear pierced. The strip is then advanced until the front end reaches position *B*, when the press is again brought into action and the gear blanked out. From the sectional view it will be seen that the hole of the gear is pierced by a punch *C* attached to the same holder as the blanking punch *D*. The blanked gear

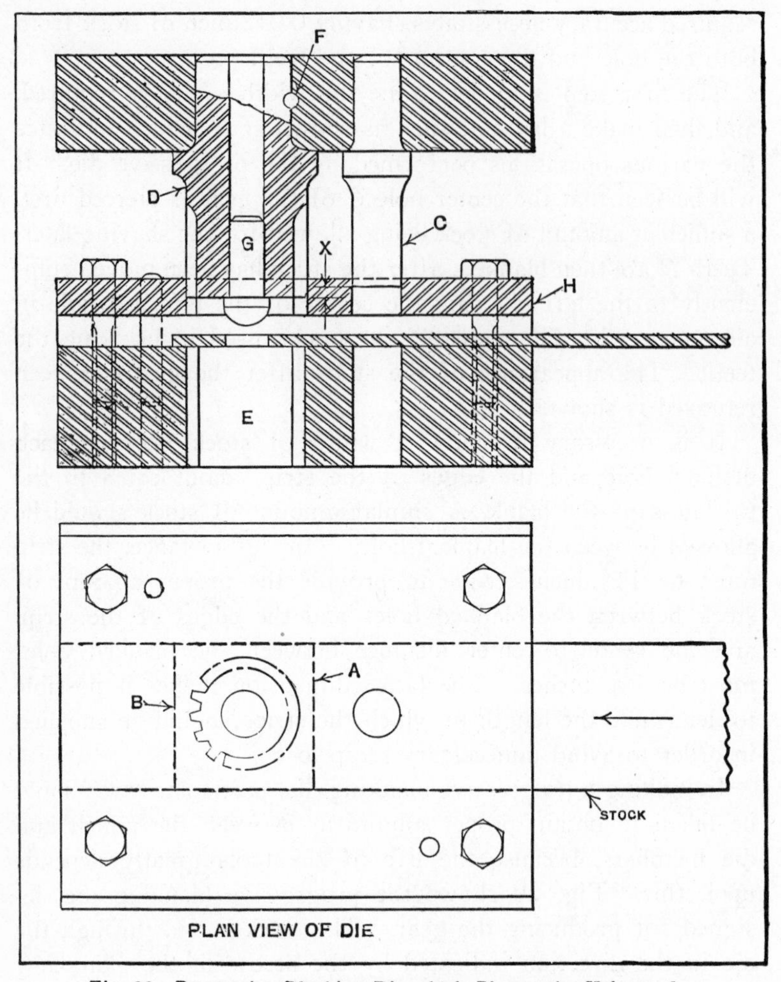

Fig. 26. Progressive Blanking Die which Pierces the Hole at the Center of the Gear and Blanks the Teeth

falls through the opening in die-block *E*. Punch *D* has teeth machined on its lower end for producing the teeth on the work. This punch is held from turning in the punch-holder by pin *F*.

In operation, the blanking punch passes through the stock before the piercing punch comes into contact with it. This will be obvious by referring to dimension *X* which is equal to the thickness of the stock. The strip is stopped at the right positions by means of a finger-stop, which is not shown because, in most cases, it is a standard equipment of punch presses. As there may be slight inaccuracies in the operation of this finger-stop, it is common practice to provide the blanking punch with a pilot *G* which fits into the hole previously pierced in the stock, and aligns this hole properly for the blanking step in case the strip has shifted out of place.

In making a die of this kind, the diemaker should be extremely careful to align all parts correctly, and so machine the teeth in both the punch and the die that these members will fit one another properly. These parts should be made from a good grade of tool steel, and the die should be of sufficient size to prevent spreading or cracking when it is being hardened. There is danger of this happening if sufficient stock is not left around the die opening. In the die illustrated, 1½ inches of stock is allowed all around the opening, and this is considered good practice for work of this size and shape. It would be possible to use a sectional die with each section taking in a certain number of teeth, but there is more danger of spreading and other troubles with a die of this kind than when the die is constructed from a solid piece of steel. The method illustrated of securing the punches to the holder is probably the best, although in some shops a large flange is provided on the punch instead of a shank, and the punch is attached to the holder by screws. Such a change in design need not alter the construction of the other parts of this die.

Amount of Stock Allowed for Shaving.—If a part produced in a punch press is carefully examined, it will be found that its edges are comparatively rough, due to the cutting action of the punch and die. In most cases the punch cuts the metal through about one-third of its thickness and the die cuts it the same amount. The remaining one-third at the middle is torn or sheared off. The result of this action may be clearly seen by examining the edges of a punched part through a magnifying glass. As a rule, the metal near the edge of the part on the side nearest the die is smoother than near the edge on the side next to the punch. In order to mesh properly, it is necessary for the gears to have smooth tooth faces. If they were used as they came from the blanking die, they would only bear at points close to the edges and would wear rapidly, resulting in considerable backlash and other inaccuracies.

The purpose of the shaving operation is to smooth the tooth faces, tops and roots, and the hole. It is generally found most satisfactory to perform this operation in two steps, but this depends upon the accuracy required, and in many cases only one shave is needed. The amount of metal removed by a shaving

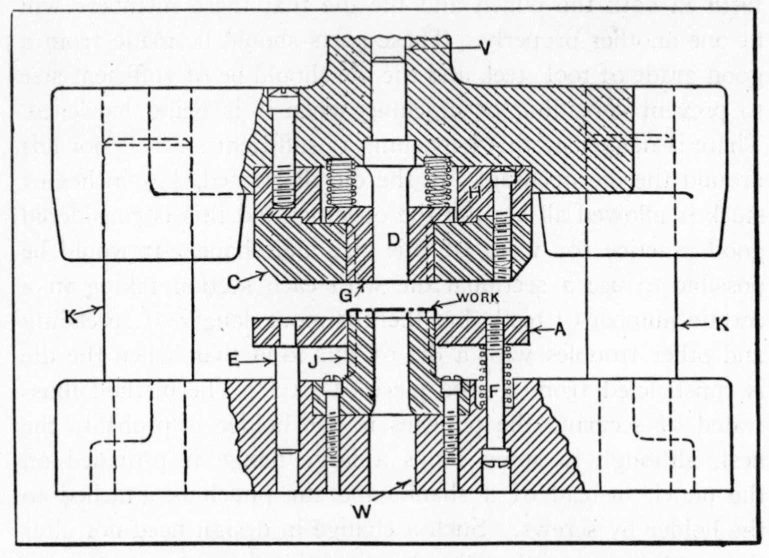

Fig. 27. Compound Die Employed for Shaving the Contour of the Gear Teeth and the Hole at the Center

die should be proportionate to the thickness of the blank. With a medium-steel gear, $\frac{3}{16}$ inch thick, which is shaved in one operation, the amount of stock removed should be about 8 per cent of the gear thickness, or 0.015 inch. If there are to be two shavings, it is necessary to allow 10 per cent of the thickness, taking off two-thirds of this amount in the first shave and one-third in the second.

The shaving operation must be performed on all materials, but the amount of stock removed varies with the kind of material. With soft steel, a smaller amount need be removed than with hard steel, and in shaving brass gears it is generally necessary to allow the same amount as for hard steel gears. The correct amount of stock to be removed is an important matter, as it is quite possible to remove too much on the first shave and produce surfaces practically as rough as the original blanked edge. Likewise, the deepest ridges will not be eliminated if sufficient stock is not removed. In many cases, gears properly shaved are smoother than those produced by milling, and have very good wearing surfaces.

A compound die designed to shave both the contour of the teeth and the hole of the gear illustrated in Fig. 24 is shown in Fig. 27. The work rests on stripper *A* as shown, being located by means of three "nests" (not shown). Two of these nests locate the gear by means of one tooth, while the third has two teeth. Besides providing a good means of locating the work, the nests hold it rigidly in position. The thickness of the nests should be somewhat less than that of the work; in this die, they are 0.100 inch thick, whereas the work has a thickness of 0.125 inch.

Operation of the Shaving Die.—The upper die *C* shaves the work on the downward stroke of the press ram. When this die reaches the nests it carries them and the stripper downward until the botton of the stroke is reached. The hole in the work is shaved by punch *D* at the same time that the contour is machined by the die. The stripper is provided with three guide pins *E* which prevent it from buckling under the pressure exerted by the ram. The raised position of the stripper is controlled by means of three fillister-head machine screws *F*, the stripper being actuated on the upward stroke of the ram by coil springs around these screws.

Work sticking in die *C* on the upward stroke is removed from this member by an ejector *G* which fits the center of the die and is forced downward relative to the die by means of coil springs. On the downward stroke of the ram the ejector remains stationary against the work. Die *C* is assembled on a sub-plate by means of a tongue and several fillister-head machine screws. This sub-plate, in turn, is fastened to the punch-holder by screws, after being properly aligned by means of a counterbored hole and dowel-pins. Punch *J* is also located on the die-bed by means of dowel-pins and a counterbored hole, and is fastened by machine screws. The punch-holder is held in alignment with the die-bed by guide pins *K*.

A die of this type is not difficult to make and the alignment of the parts is comparatively simple, because all parts are round and easily assembled. All working parts should be made of a good grade of tool steel and hardened. As die *C* and punch *D* become worn, they may be reground across the face, about 3/8 inch of stock being allowed for regrinding. The die used in the second shaving operation is of the same design as the one just described, but the dimensions of die *C* and punch *D* are such that a different amount of stock is removed from the work. The locating nests are also made to slightly different dimensions so as to accommodate the gear as it comes from the first shaving operation.

Die for Piercing and Cutting Off Sections of Band Iron.— A die for cutting off, piercing, and notching flat band iron, 1/8 inch thick and 7/8 inch wide, is shown in Fig. 28. The stock is required to be cut off to various lengths, with rounded ends and pierced holes which must be a given distance from the ends. In addition, some of the bars must be notched. In starting a strip of band iron *A*, it must be operated on once by punch *E*, which rounds the end, as shown at *X*, and pierces the hole *G*. For this operation, the strip is fed in just far enough to permit the punch *E* to round the end. After this has been done, the strip is fed through to the full length *F* against the stop *C*. Punch *E* then cuts through the bar of stock, leaving both ends rounded, and at the same time, the two small holes *G* and *H* are pierced in the usual manner. The stock is fed under a stripper plate at *I*, and the scrap pieces pass out through an opening in the die.

On most of the work this is all that is required, but as quite a number of bars must also be notched, the punch *E* is made with a tongue-shaped projection at *J* which notches the work when it is put in place under the stripper plate at *K*,

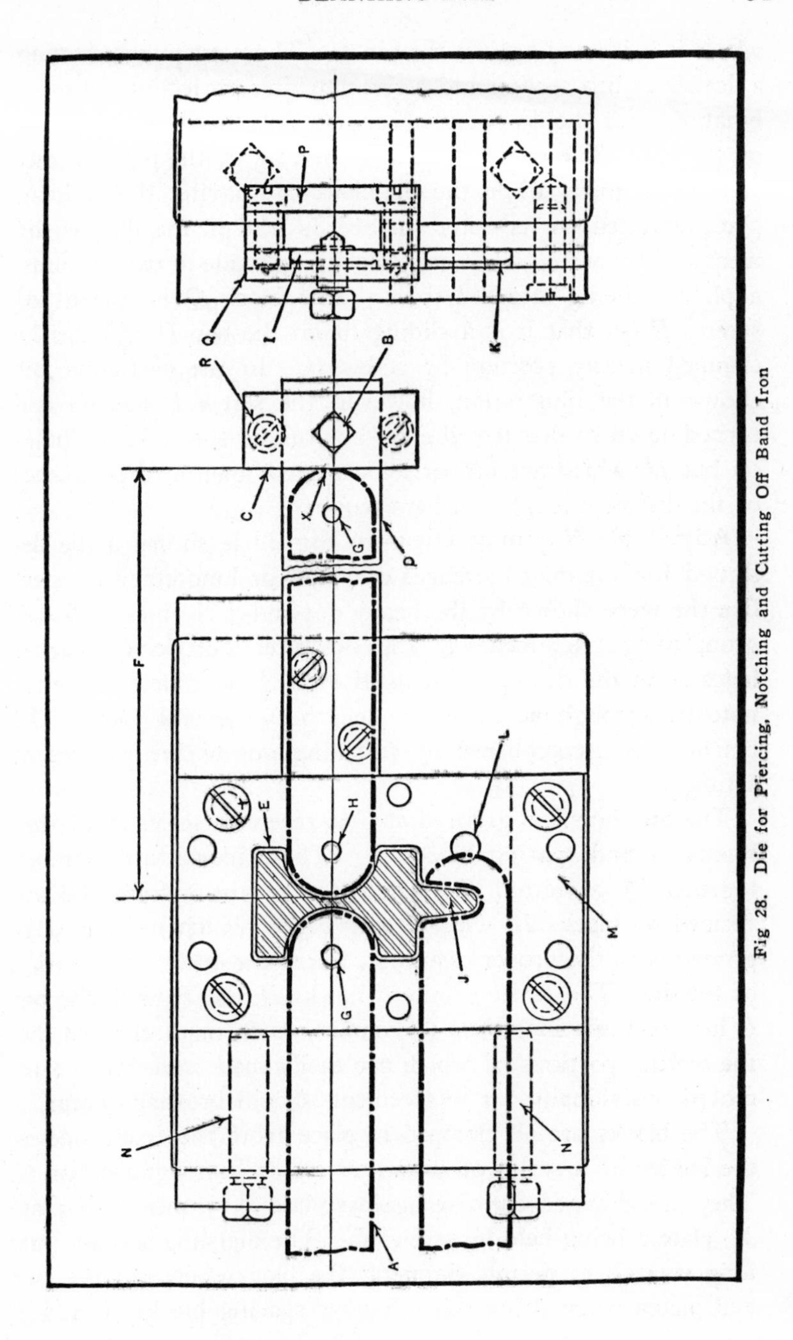

Fig 28. Die for Piercing, Notching and Cutting Off Band Iron

where it is located against the pin *L*. Thus one punch, having a double radius section and a slot-notching projection, in combination with the die die member, does all the work necessary on the bar. The punch is held to the ram of the press in any suitable manner, while the die-block *M*, having the stripper plate mounted on its outer surface, is held in the die bed by means of screws *N*. The gage-block *C* is made in two sections, a plate *P* being attached to a sliding block *Q* by means of screws *R*, so that it is a sliding fit on the bar *D* and can be clamped in any position by screw *B*. In the particular die shown in the illustration, however, the screw *B* has its end turned down so that it will enter any one of the series of holes on bar *D*, which are properly located for gaging the distance of the different lengths of bars required.

Adjustable Notching Die.—In Fig 29 is shown a die designed for notching the edges of plates or long strips of steel like the piece shown by the heavy dot-and-dash lines at *S*. A group of twelve punches *D*, Fig. 30, enter the twelve shearing holes *A* in the die. The strip of steel *S* may have one edge notched throughout its entire length of several feet. The notching is accomplished by punching out twelve notches at a time.

The die-shoe *B* is grooved at *C* to receive a series of cutting blocks *D* and spacing blocks *E*. These blocks are clamped together by a tie-rod *F*. The sides of the cutting die are formed by blocks *D*, while a long bar *G* which has one edge ground with the proper clearance, forms the other cutting edge of the die. The entire group of blocks *D* and *E*, with the bar *G* held securely in groove *C*, combine to form a sectional die, the cutting portions of which are easily made and may be removed individually for replacement, should breakage occur.

The blocks are all clamped in place from the front side of the holder by a series of screws *H* which bear against bar *G*. They are clamped endwise against plate *J* by means of plate *M*, plate *J* being held by screws *L*. The die-shoe is made just long enough to permit clamping the blocks between the two end plates when using the filling or spacing blocks *N* and *P*

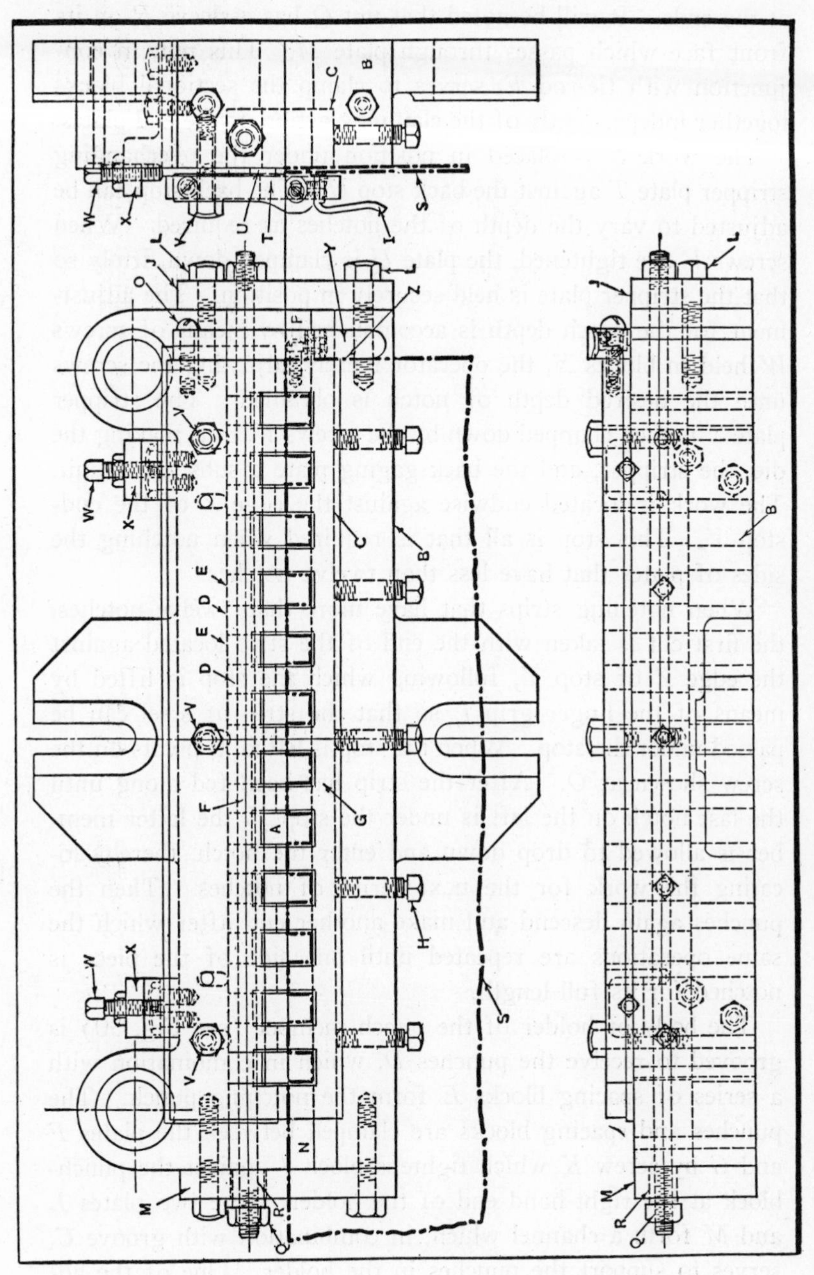

Fig. 29. Lower Member of Adjustable Notching Die

at the ends. It will be noted that nut *Q* has a sleeve *R* on its front face which passes through plate *M*. This nut, in conjunction with tie-rod *F*, serves to clamp the sectional blocks together independently of the clamping action of the end plates.

The work *S* is placed in position under the overhanging stripper plate *T* against the back stop *U*. The back stop can be adjusted to vary the depth of the notches as required. When screws *V* are tightened, the plate *U* is clamped down firmly so that the stripper plate is held securely in position. The adjustment for the notch depth is accomplished by means of screws *W* held in blocks *X*, the operator merely adjusting the screws until the desired depth of notch is obtained. The stripper plate *T* is then clamped down by the screws *V*, thus making the die, the stripper, and the back gaging plate a substantial unit. The work is located endwise against the edge *Z* of the end-stop *Y*. This stop is all that is required when notching the sides of plates that have less than twelve notches.

When notching strips that have more than twelve notches, the first cut is taken with the end of the strip located against the edge *Z* of stop *Y*, following which the stop is lifted by means of the finger grip *I*, so that the strip of steel can be passed under the stop. When the stop is lifted, it pivots on the screw shown at *O*. After the strip has been fed along until the last notch on the left is under the stop *Y*, the latter member is allowed to drop down and enter the notch, thereby locating the work for the next series of notches. Then the punches again descend and make another cut, after which the same operations are repeated until one side of the piece is notched for its full length.

The body or holder of the punch member (see Fig. 30) is grooved to receive the punches *D*, which in combination with a series of spacing blocks *E* form the notching punch. The punches and spacing blocks are clamped between the plates *F* and *G* by screw *K* which tightens block *J* against the punch-block at the right-hand end of the holder. The two plates *L* and *M* form a channel which, in combination with groove *C*, serves to support the punches in the holder. One of the ad-

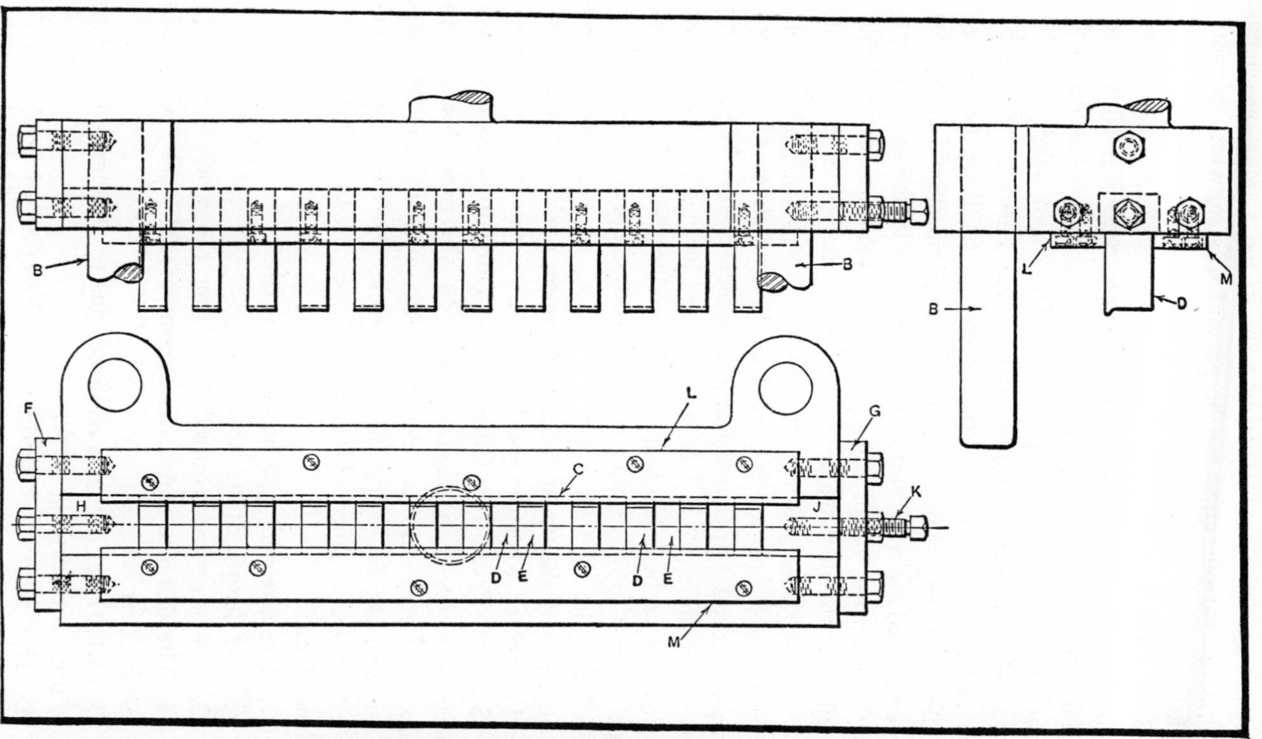

Fig. 30. Punch Used with Adjustable Notching Die Shown in Fig. 29

vantages gained by constructing a die in the manner described is that the various units can be ground to size, which permits replacements to be easily made.

Shut Height of Press.—The term "shut height" as applied to power presses, indicates the die space when the slide is at the bottom of its stroke and the slide connection has been adjusted upward as far as possible. The "shut height" is the distance from the lower face of the slide, either to the top of the bed or to the top of the bolster plate, there being two methods of determining it; hence, this term should always be accompanied by a definition explaining its meaning. According to one press manufacturer, the safest plan is to define "shut height" as the distance from the top of the bolster to the bottom of the slide, with the stroke down and the adjustment up, because most dies are mounted on bolster plates of standard thickness, and a misunderstanding which results in providing too much die space is less serious than having insufficient die space. It is believed that the expression "shut height" was applied first to dies rather than to presses, the shut height of a die being the distance from the bottom of the lower section to the top of the upper section or punch, excluding the shank, and measured when the punch is in the lowest working position.

Size of Press for Given Job.—Difficulties have always been experienced in selecting the right size press for a given job. No very definite rules have been available for this purpose, and the following information may prove helpful. According to the Toledo Machine & Tool Co., the selection may depend on:

1. The size and type of die required.
2. The length of stroke necessary.
3. The pressure required for doing the work.
4. The distance above the bottom of the stroke where this pressure first occurs.
5. Additional pressure required, due to attachments, such as are used for drawing work.
6. The method of feeding, the direction of feed, and the size of sheet, blank, or article.

The third item in this list can be determined as explained in the following: The pressure required for doing the work, if the work is punching or shearing, depends on the kind of material, its shearing strength, and the area sheared.

Punching and Shearing Pressures.—Table 1 gives the approximate pressure, in pounds, required for punching and shearing different thicknesses of steel and brass plate. In punching, if pressures for other diameters than one inch are required, multiply the pressure for one inch by the required

Table 1. Pressure, in Pounds, Required for Punching and Shearing

Thickness, No. of Gage, U. S. Std. Plate, or Inches	Punching			Shearing		
	For 1-inch Diameter Hole without Shear on Dies			For 1-inch Length without Shear on Dies		
	Mild Steel	High-Carbon Steel	Brass	Mild Steel	High-Carbon Steel	Brass
20	5,890	8,835	4,123	1,875	2,812	1,312
18	7,854	11,781	5,498	2,500	3,750	1,750
16	9,817	14,726	6,872	3,125	4,687	2,187
13	14,765	22,148	10,335	4,700	7,050	3,290
11	19,635	29,452	13,744	6,250	9,375	4,375
3/16	29,452	44,178	20,616	9,375	14,062	6,562
1/4	39,270	58,905	27,489	12,500	18,750	8,750
5/16	49,087	73,631	34,361	15,625	23,437	10,937
3/8	58,905	88,357	41,233	18,750	28,125	13,125
7/16	68,722	103,080	48,104	21,875	32,812	15,312
1/2	78,540	117,810	54,978	25,000	37,500	17,500
5/8	98,175	147,262	68,722	31,250	46,875	21,875
3/4	117,810	176,715	82,467	37,500	56,250	26,250
7/8	137,445	206,167	96,211	43,750	65,625	30,625
1	157,080	235,620	109,956	50,000	75,000	35,000

diameter. The figures are based on the following values: Shearing strength per square inch of mild steel = 50,000 pounds; shearing strength per square inch of high-carbon steel = 75,000 pounds; shearing strength per square inch of brass = 35,000 pounds.

Crankshaft Capacity.—When the pressure occurs at or near the bottom of the stroke, with a comparatively short stroke, the tonnage given in Table 2 is safe for a given size of crankshaft, as all parts of a standard press are generally designed to withstand the listed pressure at the bottom of the stroke. At this point the crankshaft is under a bending load, similar to a beam. The tonnage figures do not apply to end wheel presses with an overhanging crankpin. The crankshafts referred to are forged from billets of about 0.45 carbon steel having a high elastic limit. The crankshaft diameters given are the frame bearing sizes of standard presses.

When the pressure occurs at quite a distance above the bottom of the stroke or when a comparatively long stroke is re-

Table 2. Capacity of Crankshafts at the Bottom of the Stroke

Crank-shaft Diameter, Inches	Tons		Crank-shaft Diameter, Inches	Tons	
	Single-crank Press	Double-crank Press		Single-crank Press	Double-crank Press
1⅜	6		6½	150	150
1½	7.5		7	180	180
1⅝	9		7½	215	215
1¾	10.5		8	255	255
1⅞	12		9	345	345
2	14		10	440	450
2⅛	16		11	545	650
2¼	18		12	665	900
2½	22	22	13	790	1150
2¾	26.5	26.5	14	920	1400
3	31.5	31.5	15	1060	1700
3¼	37	37	16	....	2000
3½	43	43	16½	1300	....
4	56	56	17	....	2300
4½	71	71	18	1560	2700
5	88	88	20	1950	....
5½	106	106	22	2380	....
6	126	126	24	2860	....

quired, as in toggle drawing presses, thereby increasing the effective crank arm, the load on the crankpin produces a torsional load on the crankshaft. This load on the crankpin is limited by the gearing and the amount of torsion that the crankshaft will safely withstand.

On some single-crank presses with a very long stroke, on double-crank presses of great width or with a long stroke, and on all large single- and double-crank presses, "twin gearing," or a gear on each end of the crankshaft, is employed.

This arrangement increases the gearing strength and torsional capacity of the crankshaft, and in the case of wide double-crank presses, reduces the torsional deflection of the crankshaft. Under these conditions, the load at the bottom of the stroke would still be limited by the figures given in Table 2. In all cases where twin gearing is used, the press would be operated by a friction clutch.

When there is any doubt as to whether a given press will have sufficient capacity for the work it is proposed to do, it is advisable to communicate with the press manufacturer, giving him all the data available.

Calculating Punching and Shearing Pressures.—Pressures for punching and shearing depend not only upon the physical properties of the material but they may be affected decidedly by a clearance between the punch and die; consequently, the rules or formulas commonly used for estimating pressures give only approximate results and in many cases there is considerable difference between the calculated pressure and the actual pressure.

A common method of calculating pressure is to multiply the area of the sheared surface by the ultimate shearing stress of the material. To illustrate, if a 1-inch hole is to be punched into stock ⅛ inch thick, and if the shearing stress for the material is about 40,000 pounds per square inch, then, on the basis of shearing stress,

$$\text{Approx. Pressure} = 1 \times 3.146 \times 0.125 \times 40{,}000 = 15{,}700 \text{ pounds}$$

Such a simple calculation may show that the pressure required for a given job is or is not within the rated capacity of an available press. The proper relationship between press capacity and maximum pressure for a given job is important. If the press is too small, excessive stresses or even breakage may result. On the other hand, if the press is too large, it may prove inefficient and require considerably more power than is needed for the work. The ideal condition calls for the smallest press that will operate the die efficiently, especially when large quantities of parts are being produced.

For mild steel up to 0.08 per cent carbon content, allow an ultimate stress of 50,000 pounds per square inch of sheared area, assuming that there is no rake on the shear edges or vertical stagger of the punches. For example, assume that a rectangular hole 2 by 3 inches is to be punched in a plate of mild steel ½ inch thick and of 0.08 per cent carbon content. The area to be sheared equals the sum of the lengths of the four sides of the rectangular hole multiplied by the thickness of the stock. Thus the sheared area in this case is $10 \times 1/2 =$ 5 square inches, and the load at a shearing stress of 50,000 pounds per square inch $= 50{,}000 \times 5$, or 250,000 pounds.

For every 0.01 per cent of carbon content above 0.08 per cent, add 550 pounds per square inch to the ultimate shearing stress, previously given as 50,000 pounds per square inch. For example, let

$C =$ carbon content, in hundredths of 1 per cent; and

$S =$ ultimate shearing stress, in pounds per square inch.

Then, $S = 550 \times (C - 8) + 50{,}000$

Thus, for a steel of 0.18 per cent carbon content, the ultimate shearing stress would equal

$550 \times (18 - 8) + 50{,}000 = 55{,}500$ pounds per square inch.

For hot-punching at a temperature of 1060 degrees F., the load is only 40 per cent of that required to punch the same material when cold.

The pressure calculated as described will in most cases exceed the actual pressure, especially if the die has shear and the proper amount of clearance. Incidentally, shear may be applied either to the punch or to the die. In some cases, the maximum load required for blanking several holes or openings may be reduced by varying the lengths of the punches so that they come into action progressively, as explained later.

Blanking Pressure for Thin Stock.—In blanking or shearing thin stock having a thickness of, say 0.025 inch or less, the shearing stress for calculating the pressure should be taken at about one-half the full value. Thus, for thin stock of the usual mild steel material having a shear stress of 50,000 pounds per square inch, 25,000 should be substituted for

50,000 in the rule when calculating the pressure actually required for blanking the stock. This gives the formula:

$$B = 25{,}000 \times P \times t$$

in which B = blanking pressure;
P = perimeter, or length of cut; and
t = stock thickness.

Applying this formula, the approximate blanking pressures for cuts 1 inch in length in mild steel stock having thicknesses ranging from 0.0080 to 0.0250 inch are given in the accompanying table:

Stock Thickness, Inch	Blanking Pressure per Inch Cut, Pounds
0.0250	625
0.0205	512.5
0.0180	450
0.0155	387.5
0.0125	312.5
0.0110	275
0.0100	250
0.0090	225
0.0080	200

For aluminum and brass stock, in which the shear stress is 35,000 pounds per square inch, pressures should be reduced accordingly; that is, 17,500 should be substituted for 25,000 in the formula given. These pressures are never very high, and consequently, such factors as the degree of penetration, bolster load and center of blanking pressure assume less importance in blanking thin stock. Thus, if the dies are made with ample shear, very light presses can be used for blanking thin stock such as is referred to here.

Determining Punching or Shearing Pressure by Actual Test.—The simple type of press shown by the diagram, Fig. 31, may be used for determining the pressure for punching or shearing a given material. This press may also be used for finding the amount of clearance between the punch and die when the pressure is minimum.

The helical spring C should be stiff enough to force the punch through the metal when the spring is compressed by handwheel B and before the spring is compressed solid. The amount of spring deflection is utilized in determining the pressure. The spring, for purposes of calibration, is removed from the press, placed upright, and a piece of steel or cast iron, picked at random, placed on top of the spring. A diagram such as illustrated in Fig. 32 should then be constructed by laying out a line of length *a* to represent the free length of the spring and marking off on this line a length *b* corresponding to the height of the spring when compressed by the weight *Q* that was selected. The diagram should be constructed at

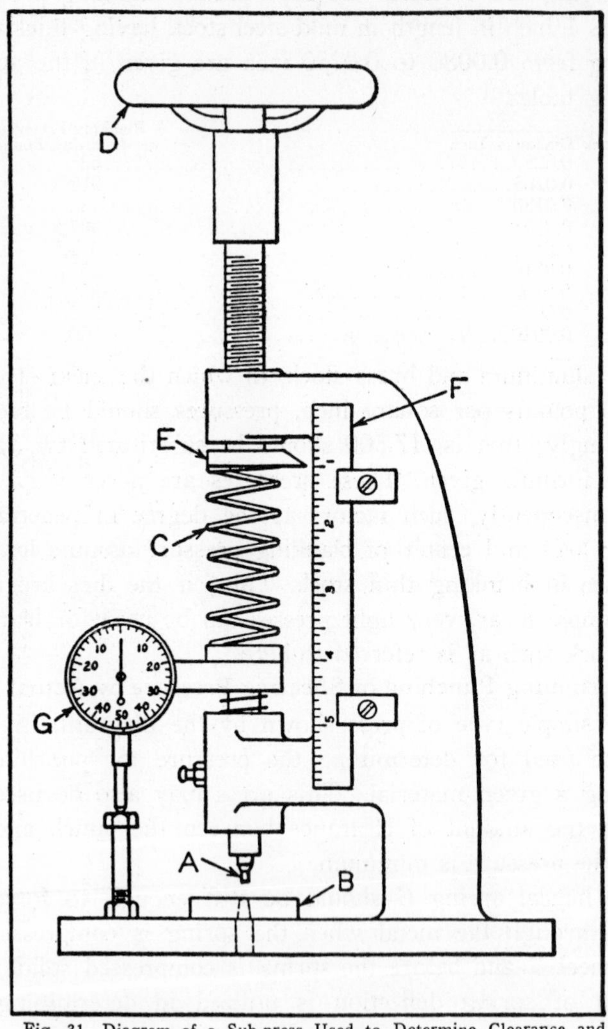

Fig. 31. Diagram of a Sub-press Used to Determine Clearance and Shearing Pressure in Designing Blanking Die for Any Material

least four times actual size in order to insure that the readings will be sufficiently accurate.

A perpendicular is next erected to line b representing weight Q. The length c of this line should be determined by assuming each $\frac{1}{64}$ inch to represent 1 pound of weight Q. Therefore, if weight Q amounts to 76 pounds, the line c would be $1\frac{3}{16}$ inches long. After length c has been determined, line fg may be projected through the end of line c, so as to obtain angle X. From this diagram it will now be possible to determine the weight S that will cause the spring to deflect any

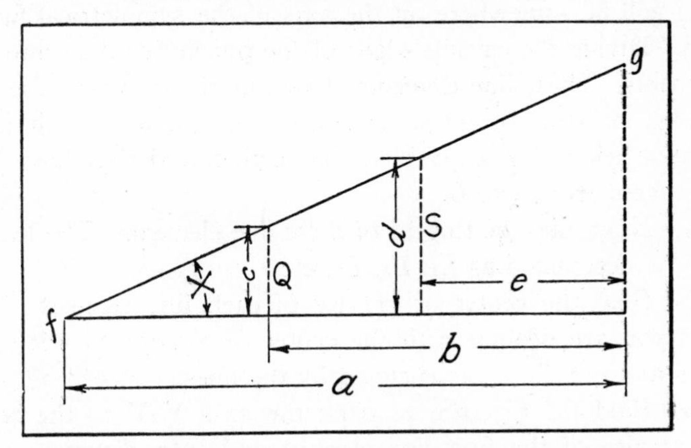

Fig. 32. Method of Determining Pressure Applied in Deflecting Spring C, Fig. 31, Any Specific Amount

specific amount e. This is ascertained by merely measuring the height of the perpendicular line d. This operation may be expressed mathematically as follows:

$$d = (a - e) \tan X$$

$$\text{Tan } X = \frac{d}{a - e}$$

To find the weight S required to deflect the spring to height e, simply multiply length d by 64.

In this manner is derived the most important factor (weight S) involved in determining the shearing pressure required for blanking various materials.

Finding Center of Pressure of a Blanking Die.—To prevent excessive strain and wear on aligning pins and ram guides, the center of pressure of a blanking die should be in line with the center of the ram. This pressure center may be accurately located by the method given here. The procedure is as follows:

1. Draw an outline of the actual cutting edges, as indicated in Fig. 33.
2. Draw axes *X–X* and *Y–Y* at right angles in a convenient position. If the figure is symmetrical about a line, let this line be one of the axes. The center of pressure in this case will be somewhere on the axis of the symmetrical figure.
3. Divide the cutting edges of the punch (or die) into line elements. These line elements shown by the diagram, Fig. 33, consist of straight lines, a semi-circle, and a ½-inch circle located below the larger blanking section, and they have been numbered from 1 to 6.
4. Next, find the lengths of these line elements. The lengths will be designated as L_1, L_2, L_3, etc.
5. Find the center of gravity of each line element. Note that you are dealing with the center of gravity as related to lines and not the areas enclosed by the lines.
6. Find the distance x_1 from the axis *Y–Y* to the center of gravity of the first line element and then distance x_2 for the second line, and so on.
7. Find the distance y_1 from the axis *X–X* to the center of gravity of the first line element, the distance y_2 to the second element, and so on.
8. Calculate the distance (which we shall designate as *A*) from axis *Y–Y* to the center of pressure *C*.

$$A = \frac{L_1x_1 + L_2x_2 + L_3x_3 + L_4x_4 + L_5x_5 + L_6x_6}{L_1 + L_2 + L_3 + L_4 + L_5 + L_6}$$

9. Calculate the distance (which we shall designate as *B*) from axis *X–X* to the center of pressure *C*.

$$B = \frac{L_1y_1 + L_2y_2 + L_3y_3 + L_4y_4 + L_5y_5 + L_6y_6}{L_1 + L_2 + L_3 + L_4 + L_5 + L_6}$$

Before using these formulas, we must determine the lengths L_1, L_2, L_3, etc., of the lines, and also the distances x_1, x_2, x_3, etc., and y_1, y_2, y_3, etc.

The dimensions given on the diagram show that length L_1 of line $1 = 2\frac{1}{2} + 1\frac{1}{2} = 4$ inches. The length L_2 of line 2 equals one-half the circumference of a circle having a radius

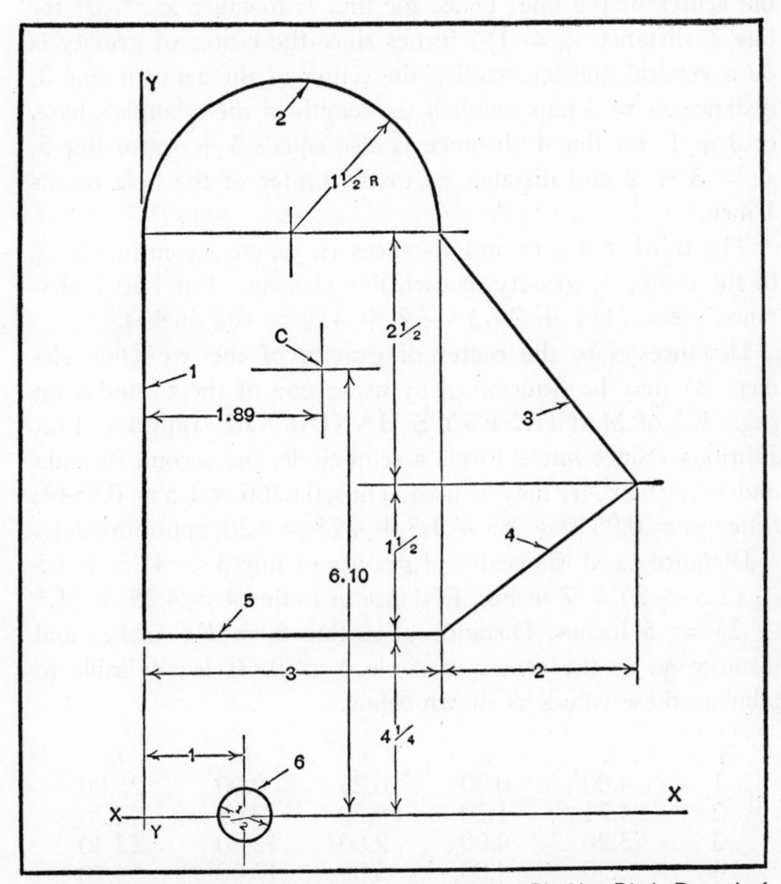

Fig. 33. Diagram Illustrating how Center of Pressure of a Blanking Die is Determined

of $1\frac{1}{2}$ inches or 4.71 inches, approximately. The length L_3 of line 3 equals about 3.2 inches which is the length of the hypotenuse of a right triangle having a 2-inch base and an altitude of $2\frac{1}{2}$ inches. Line 4 is the hypotenuse of another right triangle and its length is 2.5 inches. The length of line 5 is 3 inches as the diagram shows, and the circumference of the ½ inch hole is 1.57 inches.

The next step is to determine the distances x_1, x_2, etc., from axis Y–Y to the center of gravity of each line element. In the case of straight lines, the center of gravity is, of course, at the center of the line; hence for line 1, distance $x_1 = 0$; for line 2, distance $x_2 = 1\frac{1}{2}$ inches since the center of gravity is on a vertical line intersecting the center of the arc; for line 3, distance $x_3 = 3$ plus one-half the length of the triangle's base, or $3 + 1$; for line 4, distance x_4 also equals $3 + 1$; for line 5, $x_5 = 3 \div 2$ and distance x_6 to the center of the hole equals 1 inch.

The third step is to find distances y_1, y_2, etc., from line X–X to the center of gravity of each line element. For line 1, distance $y_1 = (1\frac{1}{2} + 2\frac{1}{2}) \div 2 + 4\frac{1}{4} = 6\frac{1}{4}$ inches.

Distance y_2 to the center of gravity of the arc (line element 2) may be determined by using one of the formulas on page 305 of MACHINERY'S HANDBOOK, 13th and 14th Editions. Since line 2 forms a semi-circle, the second formula under *Circular Arc* may be used. Thus, $0.6366 \times 1.5 = 0.9549$; hence $y_2 = 0.9549 + 2.5 + 1.5 + 4.25 = 9.20$, approximately.

Distance y_3 to the center of gravity of line $3 = 4.25 + 1.5 + (2.5 \div 2) = 7$ inches. Distance y_4 to line $4 = 4.25 + (1.5 \div 2) = 5$ inches. Distance y_5 to line $5 = 4\frac{1}{4}$ inches and distance y_6 to the center of circle $6 = 0$. It is advisable to tabulate these values as shown below.

Line No.	L	x	y	Lx	Ly
1	4.00	0.00	6.25	0.00	25.00
2	4.71	1.50	9.20	7.05	43.20
3	3.20	4.00	7.00	12.80	22.40
4	2.50	4.00	5.00	10.00	12.50
5	3.00	1.50	4.25	4.50	12.75
6	1.57	1.00	0.00	1.57	00.00
	18.98			35.92	115.85

Tabulation of these figures facilitates making a check of all measurements and calculations.

These values are then substituted in the preceding formulas from which,

$$A = \frac{35.92}{18.98} = 1.89 \text{ inches}; \; B = \frac{115.85}{18.98} = 6.10 \text{ inches}$$

The center of pressure C is therefore located as indicated in the illustration, Fig. 33,

CHAPTER II

METHODS OF DETERMINING BLANK DIAMETERS

BEFORE making the blanking part of a drawing die, it is necessary to determine how large the flat blank must be in order to produce a shell or cup of the required form. Until the blank diameter is known, obviously that part of the die which cuts out the blank cannot be made. If the stock did not stretch while being drawn or was not "ironed out" and made thinner, the diameter of the blank could be determined quite accurately by calculating the area of the finished article and then making the blank the corresponding area. In some cases, there is not much ironing and stretching, as, for example, when the part is drawn or formed to shape in one operation, and then the area method of calculating the blank diameter gives quite accurate results, but if the metal is to be made thinner as it is drawn to shape, the blank should, of course, be proportionately smaller in diameter. The kind of metal to be drawn, that is, whether steel, brass, copper, aluminum, etc., and whether it is hard or soft, also affects the size of the blank to some extent.

Owing to the uncertainty of obtaining the right blank diameter by calculation, a common method of procedure, especially when constructing drawing dies for parts requiring more than one or two drawing operations, is to make the drawing part of the die first. The actual blank diameter can then be determined by repeated trials, after which the blanking part of the die may be finished. One method is to get a trial blank as near to size as can be estimated. The outline of this blank is then scribed on a flat sheet, after which the blank is cut to the outline and drawn. If the finished shell shows that the blank is not of the right diameter, a new trial blank is cut, either larger or smaller than the size indicated by the line previously scribed, this line serving as a guide. If a model or sample shell is available, the blank diameter can also be determined by the weight method which is simple and will be described first.

The Weight Method of Determining Blank Diameters.—If a sample shell is at hand, the blank size can be determined with fair accuracy by first weighing the sample; a blank of the same material is then made to whatever size is required to equal the weight of the sample. One method is to cut the blank larger than the required size and then trim it down until its weight equals the weight of a sample shell. To avoid unnecessary trimming the blank size required for a given weight may be estimated. In making this estimate the sample is first weighed, after which the surface area of a piece of sheet metal of the required thickness and of the same weight as the sample is found by reference to a table giving the weights per square inch for sheet metal of various thicknesses. For instance, let it be assumed that the sample shell weighs ½ pound and is produced from 20-gage steel. As 20-gage steel weighs 1.25 pounds per square foot, the area of the required shell is evidently equal to $(144 \times 0.5) \div 1.25 = 57.6$ square inches. Reference to tables such as the one on page 55 of MACHINERY'S HANDBOOK shows that the area of a circle 8⅝ inches in diameter is 58.4 square inches and we will therefore assume that a blank 8⅝ inches in diameter will be about the right size.

The Spinning Method.—The spinning method of determining the blank diameter can be used on round work only. In this case a wooden form or chuck of the required shape is turned up in the lathe, and blanks of different sizes are spun over this form by hand. A skilled metal spinner will usually be able to determine the correct blank diameter after two or three trials.

The Area Method of Estimating Blank Diameters.—Although the area method is only approximate, it is the only practicable way, assuming that no sample shell is at hand for determining the blank size by the weight method; hence rules or formulas for determining the diameter of a flat blank required for forming a shell of given shape, are based upon the area of the drawn shell, the blank area being made equal to the area of the drawn part. For example, if the area of the finished shell equals say 15 square inches, reference to a table of diameters and corresponding areas (such as will be found in MACHINERY'S HANDBOOK) will show that the blank diameter in this particular case should be about 4⅜ inches. Any stretching or thinning of the stock in drawing affects the accuracy of this method of determining the blank diameter, but as it is impracticable to determine beforehand just how much stretching will occur, the blank diameter, as found by the area method,

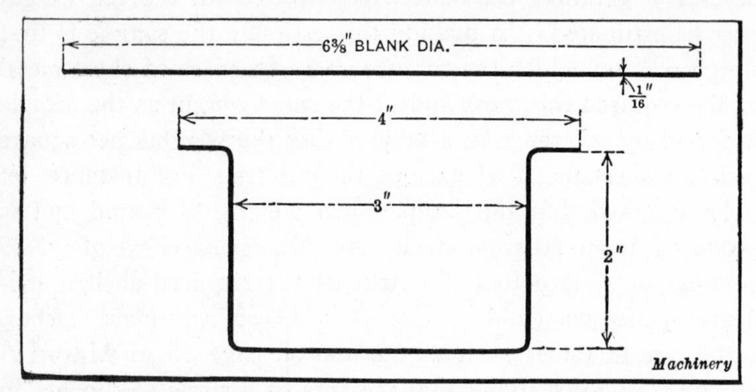

Fig. 1. Flanged Cup and Flat Circular Blank of Corresponding Area

is only approximate. The slight error, however, is on the safe side.

Example Illustrating Principle of Area Method.—To illustrate the area method, suppose the diameter of the blank for the flanged cup shown in Fig. 1 is required. The area of the bottom, which is 3 inches in diameter, equals 7.06 square inches. The area of the side equals $2 \times 3\frac{1}{16} \times 3.1416 = 19.24$ square inches. The area of the flange equals the area of a 4-inch circle minus the area of a 3-inch circle, or $12.56 - 7.06 = 5.5$ square inches. The total area equals $7.06 + 19.24 + 5.5 = 31.80$. The diameter of a circle having an area of $31.80 = 6\frac{3}{8}$ inches, nearly. When drawing a trial blank, it is the practice of some diemakers to cut the blanks somewhat smaller than the estimated size and then increase the diameter as may be required. When beginning with blanks that are oversize, the shell is liable to break owing to the excessive stress on the metal. Some metals stretch more than others and the pressure of the blank-holder as well as the radius or shape of the drawing punch and die, and the amount that the metal is ironed out, all enter into the problem and affect the result. Incidentally, the pressure of the blank-holder should be just enough to prevent formation of wrinkles as the stock is drawn radially inward, and this pressure should be as uniform as possible around all sides.

General Rules Based Upon Area Method.—To determine the blank diameter for a plain cylindrical shell without allowance for rounding at the corners, multiply the shell diameter by its height; then multiply the product by four, and add the result to the square of the shell diameter; the square root of this final sum equals the blank diameter. If a cylindrical shell has a flat flange, multiply the shell diameter by its height, as before; then multiply the product by four and add the result to the square of the flange diameter; the square root of this sum equals the blank diameter.

Formulas for Blank Diameters.—The diameters of blanks for plain cylindrical shells can be calculated by the following formula which corresponds to the rule previously given. This formula gives a close approximation for thin stock and is one that has been extensively used:

$$D = \sqrt{d^2 + 4\,dh} \qquad (1)$$

in which $D =$ diameter of flat blank; $d =$ diameter of finished shell; $h =$ height of finished shell. The blank diameters given in the accompanying table are based on this formula and are for sharp-cornered shells. The application of the formula is illustrated by the following example:

If the diameter of a finished shell is to be 1.5 inch, and the height, 2 inches, the trial diameter of the blank would be found as follows:

$$D = \sqrt{1.5^2 + 4 \times 1.5 \times 2} = \sqrt{14.25} = 3.78 \text{ inches.}$$

Approximate Diameters of Blanks for Cylindrical Shells

Diameter	Height of Shells																						
	¼	½	¾	1	1¼	1½	1¾	2	2¼	2½	2¾	3	3¼	3½	3¾	4	4¼	4½	4¾	5	5¼	5½	5¾	6
¼	0.56	0.75	0.90	1.03	1.14	1.25	1.35	1.44	1.52	1.60	1.68	1.75	1.82	1.89	1.95	2.01	2.08	2.14	2.19	2.25	2.30	2.36	2.41	2.46
½	0.87	1.12	1.32	1.50	1.66	1.80	1.94	2.06	2.18	2.29	2.40	2.50	2.60	2.69	2.78	2.87	2.96	3.04	3.12	3.21	3.29	3.36	3.44	3.50
¾	1.14	1.44	1.68	1.89	2.08	2.25	2.41	2.56	2.70	2.84	2.97	3.09	3.21	3.33	3.44	3.54	3.65	3.75	3.85	3.95	4.04	4.13	4.22	4.31
1	1.41	1.73	2.00	2.24	2.45	2.65	2.83	3.00	3.16	3.32	3.46	3.61	3.74	3.87	4.00	4.12	4.24	4.36	4.47	4.58	4.69	4.80	4.90	5.00
1¼	1.68	2.01	2.30	2.56	2.79	3.01	3.21	3.40	3.58	3.75	3.91	4.07	4.22	4.37	4.51	4.64	4.77	4.91	5.03	5.15	5.27	5.39	5.50	5.62
1½	1.94	2.29	2.60	2.87	3.12	3.36	3.57	3.78	3.97	4.15	4.33	4.50	4.66	4.82	4.98	5.12	5.27	5.41	5.55	5.68	5.81	5.94	6.06	6.18
1¾	2.19	2.56	2.88	3.17	3.44	3.68	3.91	4.13	4.34	4.53	4.72	4.91	5.08	5.26	5.41	5.58	5.73	5.88	6.03	6.17	6.31	6.45	6.58	6.71
2	2.45	2.83	3.16	3.46	3.74	4.00	4.24	4.47	4.69	4.90	5.10	5.29	5.48	5.66	5.83	6.00	6.16	6.32	6.48	6.63	6.78	6.93	7.07	7.21
2¼	2.70	3.09	3.44	3.75	4.04	4.31	4.56	4.80	5.03	5.25	5.46	5.66	5.86	6.05	6.23	6.41	6.58	6.75	6.91	7.07	7.23	7.39	7.54	7.69
2½	2.96	3.36	3.71	4.03	4.33	4.61	4.87	5.12	5.36	5.59	5.81	6.02	6.22	6.42	6.61	6.80	6.98	7.16	7.33	7.50	7.66	7.82	7.98	8.14
2¾	3.21	3.61	3.98	4.31	4.62	4.91	5.18	5.44	5.68	5.92	6.15	6.37	6.58	6.79	6.99	7.18	7.37	7.55	7.73	7.91	8.08	8.25	8.41	8.58
3	3.46	3.87	4.24	4.58	4.90	5.20	5.48	5.74	6.00	6.25	6.48	6.71	6.93	7.14	7.35	7.55	7.75	7.94	8.12	8.31	8.49	8.66	8.83	9.00
3¼	3.71	4.13	4.51	4.85	5.18	5.48	5.77	6.04	6.31	6.56	6.80	7.04	7.27	7.49	7.70	7.91	8.11	8.31	8.50	8.69	8.88	9.06	9.24	9.41
3½	3.97	4.39	4.77	5.12	5.45	5.77	6.06	6.34	6.61	6.87	7.12	7.36	7.60	7.83	8.05	8.26	8.47	8.67	8.87	9.07	9.26	9.45	9.63	9.81
3¾	4.22	4.64	5.03	5.39	5.73	6.05	6.35	6.64	6.91	7.18	7.44	7.69	7.92	8.16	8.38	8.61	8.82	9.03	9.24	9.44	9.63	9.83	10.02	10.20
4	4.47	4.90	5.29	5.66	6.00	6.32	6.63	6.93	7.21	7.48	7.75	8.00	8.25	8.49	8.72	8.94	9.17	9.38	9.59	9.80	10.00	10.20	10.39	10.58
4¼	4.72	5.15	5.55	5.92	6.27	6.60	6.91	7.22	7.50	7.78	8.05	8.31	8.56	8.81	9.04	9.28	9.50	9.72	9.94	10.15	10.36	10.56	10.76	10.96
4½	4.98	5.41	5.81	6.19	6.54	6.87	7.19	7.50	7.79	8.08	8.35	8.62	8.87	9.12	9.37	9.60	9.84	10.06	10.28	10.50	10.71	10.92	11.12	11.32
4¾	5.22	5.66	6.07	6.45	6.80	7.15	7.47	7.78	8.08	8.37	8.65	8.92	9.18	9.44	9.69	9.93	10.16	10.40	10.62	10.84	11.06	11.27	11.48	11.69
5	5.48	5.92	6.32	6.71	7.07	7.42	7.75	8.06	8.37	8.66	8.94	9.22	9.49	9.75	10.00	10.25	10.49	10.72	10.95	11.18	11.40	11.62	11.83	12.04
5¼	5.73	6.17	6.58	6.97	7.33	7.68	8.02	8.34	8.65	8.95	9.24	9.52	9.79	10.05	10.31	10.56	10.81	11.05	11.28	11.51	11.74	11.96	12.18	12.39
5½	5.98	6.42	6.84	7.23	7.60	7.95	8.29	8.62	8.93	9.23	9.53	9.81	10.08	10.36	10.62	10.87	11.12	11.37	11.61	11.84	12.07	12.30	12.52	12.74
5¾	6.23	6.68	7.09	7.49	7.86	8.22	8.56	8.89	9.21	9.52	9.81	10.10	10.38	10.66	10.92	11.18	11.44	11.69	11.93	12.17	12.40	12.63	12.85	13.08
6	6.48	6.93	7.35	7.75	8.12	8.49	8.83	9.17	9.49	9.80	10.10	10.39	10.68	10.95	11.23	11.49	11.75	12.00	12.25	12.49	12.73	12.96	13.19	13.42

For a round-cornered cup, the following formula, in which r equals the corner radius, will give fairly accurate diameters, provided the radius does not exceed, say, ¼ the shell height:

$$D = \sqrt{d^2 + 4\,dh} - r. \qquad (2)$$

Method When Stock Thickness Is Reduced.—These formulas are based on the assumption that the thickness of the drawn shell is the same as the original thickness of the stock, and that the blank is so proportioned that its area will equal the area of the drawn shell. This method of calculating the blank diameter is quite accurate for thin material, when there is only a slight reduction in the thickness of the metal incident to drawing; but when heavy stock is drawn and the thickness of the finished shell is much less than the original thickness of the stock, the blank diameter obtained from Formulas (1) and (2) will be too large, because when the stock is drawn thinner, there is an increase in area. When an appreciable reduction in thickness is to be made, the blank diameter can be obtained by first determining the "mean height" of the drawn shell by the following formula. This formula is only approximately correct, but will give results sufficiently accurate for most work:

$$M = \frac{ht}{T} \qquad (3)$$

in which M = approximate mean height of drawn shell; h = height of drawn shell; t = thickness of shell; T = thickness of metal before drawing. After determining the mean height, the blank diameter for the required shell diameter is obtained from the table previously referred to, the mean height being used instead of the actual height.

Example.—Suppose a shell 2 inches in diameter and 3¾ inches high is to be drawn, and that the original thickness of the stock is 0.050 inch, and thickness of drawn shell, 0.040 inch. To what diameter should the blank be cut? Using Formula (3) to obtain the mean height:

$$M = \frac{ht}{T} = \frac{3.75 \times 0.040}{0.050} = 3 \text{ inches.}$$

According to the table, the blank diameter for a shell 2 inches in diameter and 3 inches high is 5.29 inches, the mean height being used when referring to the table, as previously mentioned. This formula is accurate enough for all practical purposes, unless the reduction in the thickness of the metal is greater than about one-fifth the original thickness. When there is considerable reduction, a blank calculated by this formula produces a shell that is too long. This, however, is an error in the right direction, as the edges of drawn shells are ordinarily trimmed. If the shell has a rounded corner, the radius of the corner should be deducted from the figures given in the table. For example, if the shell referred to in the foregoing example had a corner of 1/4-inch radius, the blank diameter would equal $5.29 - 0.25 = 5.04$ inches.

Formula Based Upon Cubic Contents of Drawn Shell.—Another formula which is sometimes used for obtaining blank diameters for shells, when there is a reduction in the thickness of the stock, is as follows:

$$D = \sqrt{a^2 + \left(a^2 - b^2\right)\frac{h}{t}}. \qquad (4)$$

In this formula D = blank diameter; a = outside diameter; b = inside diameter; t = thickness of shell at bottom; h = depth of shell. This formula is based on the cubic contents of the drawn shell. It is assumed that the shells are cylindrical, and no allowance is made for a rounded corner at the bottom, or for trimming the shell after drawing. To allow for trimming, add the required amount to depth h. When a shell is of irregular cross-section, if its weight is known, the blank diameter can be determined by the following formula:

$$D = 1.1284 \sqrt{\frac{W}{wt}} \qquad (5)$$

in which D = blank diameter in inches; W = weight of shell; w = weight of metal per cubic inch; t = thickness of the shell.

Formulas for Various Shapes.—The tables "Blank Diameter Formulas for Drawn Shells," contain the formulas for

Blank Diameter Formulas for Drawn Shells—1

Shape of Body	Diameter of Blank D =
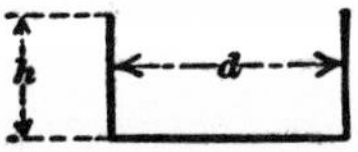	$\sqrt{d^2 + 4dh}$
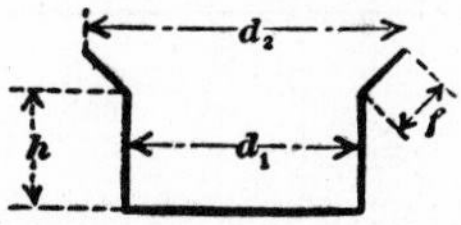	$\sqrt{d_1^2 + 4d_1h + 2f(d_1 + d_2)}$
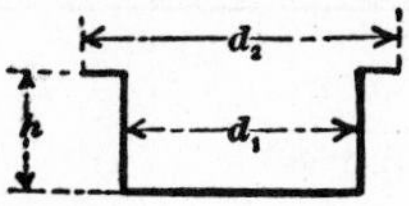	$\sqrt{d_2^2 + 4d_1h}$
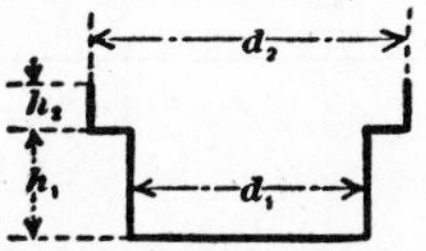	$\sqrt{d_2^2 + 4(d_1h_1 + d_2h_2)}$
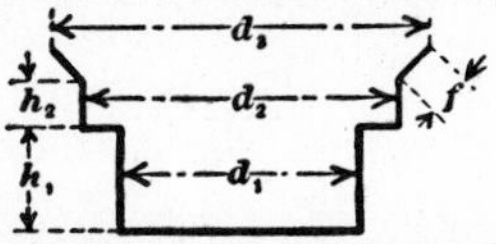	$\sqrt{d_2^2 + 4(d_1h_1 + d_2h_2) + 2f(d_2 + d_3)}$
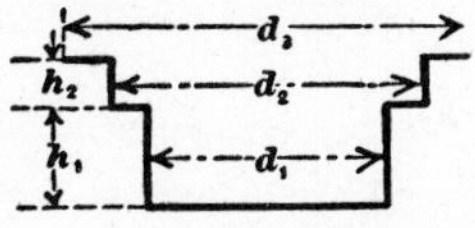	$\sqrt{d_3^2 + 4(d_1h_1 + d_2h_2)}$
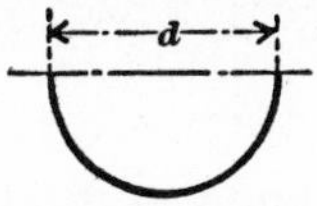	$\sqrt{2d^2} = 1.414d$
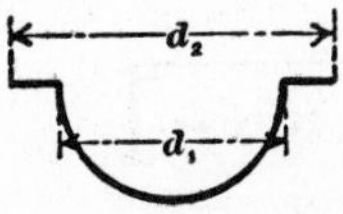	$\sqrt{d_1^2 + d_2^2}$
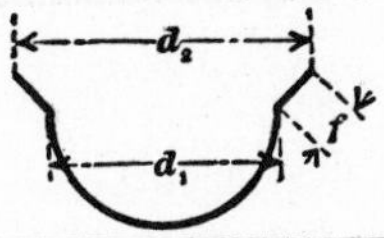	$1.414\sqrt{d_1^2 + f(d_2 + d_1)}$

Blank Diameter Formulas for Drawn Shells—2

Shape of Body	Diameter of Blank D =
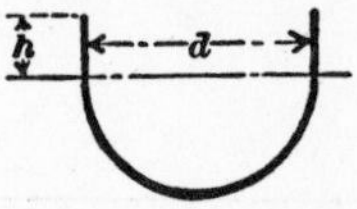	$1.414\sqrt{d^2 + 2\,dh}$
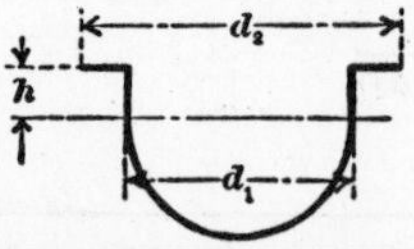	$\sqrt{d_1^2 + d_2^2 + 4\,d_1h}$
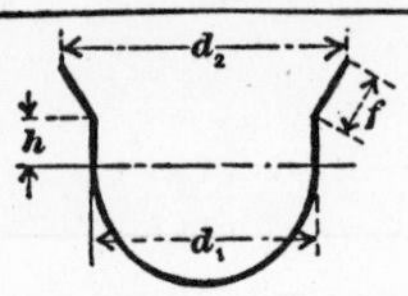	$1.414\sqrt{d_1^2 + 2\,d_1h + f\,(d_1 + d_2)}$
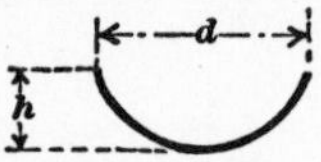	$\sqrt{d^2 + 4\,h^2}$
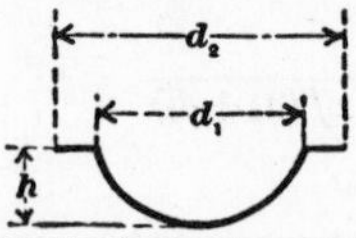	$\sqrt{d_2^2 + 4\,h^2}$
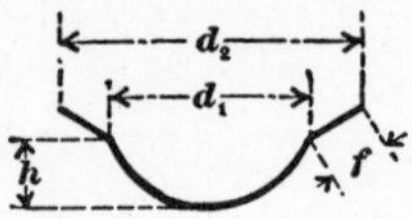	$\sqrt{d_1^2 + 4\,h^2 + 2\,f\,(d_1 + d_2)}$
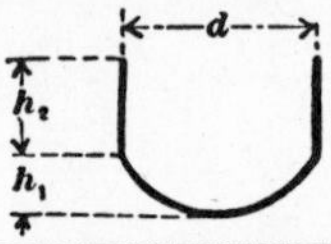	$\sqrt{d^2 + 4\,(h_1^2 + dh_2)}$
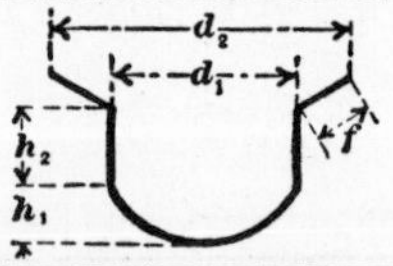	$\sqrt{d_1^2 + 4\left[h_1^2 + d_1h_2 + \frac{f}{2}\,(d_1 + d_2)\right]}$
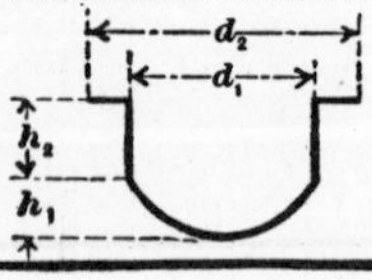	$\sqrt{d_2^2 + 4\,(h_1^2 + d_1h_2)}$

Blank Diameter Formulas for Drawn Shells—3

Shape of Body	Diameter of Blank $D =$
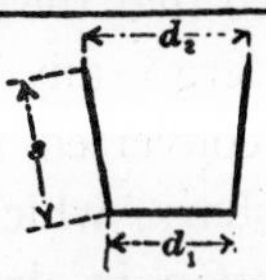	$\sqrt{d_1^2 + 2s(d_1 + d_2)}$
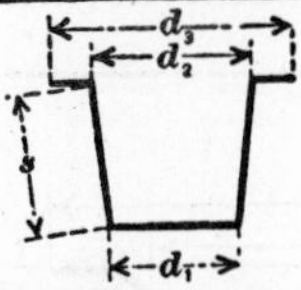	$\sqrt{d_1^2 + 2s(d_1 + d_2) + d_3^2 - d_2^2}$
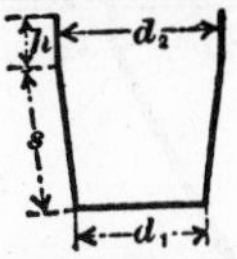	$\sqrt{d_1^2 + 2[s(d_1 + d_2) + 2d_2h]}$
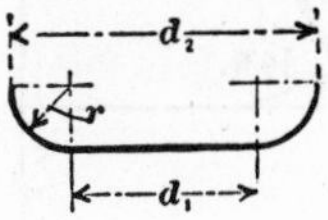	$\sqrt{d_1^2 + 6.28rd_1 + 8r^2}$; or $\sqrt{d_2^2 + 2.28rd_2 - 0.56r^2}$
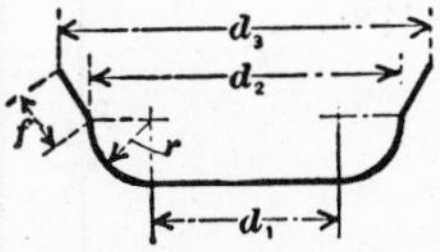	$\sqrt{d_1^2 + 6.28rd_1 + 8r^2 + 2f(d_2 + d_3)}$; or $\sqrt{d_2^2 + 2.28rd_2 + 2f(d_2 + d_3) - 0.56r^2}$
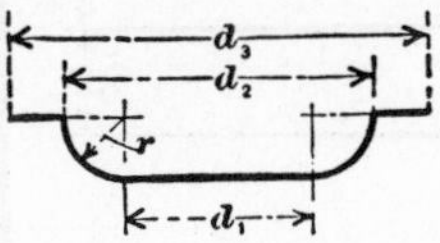	$\sqrt{d_1^2 + 6.28rd_1 + 8r^2 + d_3^2 - d_2^2}$; or $\sqrt{d_3^2 + 2.28rd_2 - 0.56r^2}$
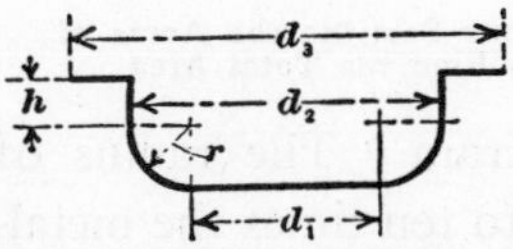	$\sqrt{d_1^2 + 6.28rd_1 + 8r^2 + 4d_2h + d_3^2 - d_2^2}$; or $\sqrt{d_3^2 + 4d_2(0.57r + h) - 0.56r^2}$
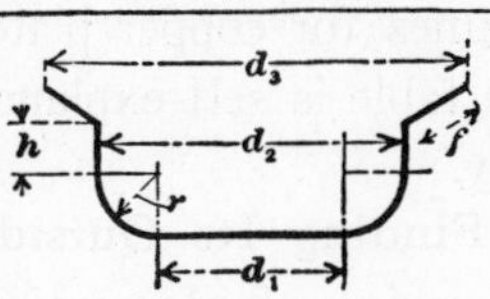	$\sqrt{d_1^2 + 6.28rd_1 + 8r^2 + 4d_2h + 2f(d_2 + d_3)}$; or $\sqrt{d_2^2 + 4d_2\left(0.57r + h + \frac{f}{2}\right) + 2d_3f - 0.56r^2}$

many common shapes. These formulas are based upon the long-established rule that the area of the blank equals approximately the area of the shell. It is also assumed that the metal, which is comparatively thin, does not undergo any great change of thickness while the flat blank is converted into a shell. All corners at the bottom are shown sharp, which is a condition that is practically impossible to obtain in drawing

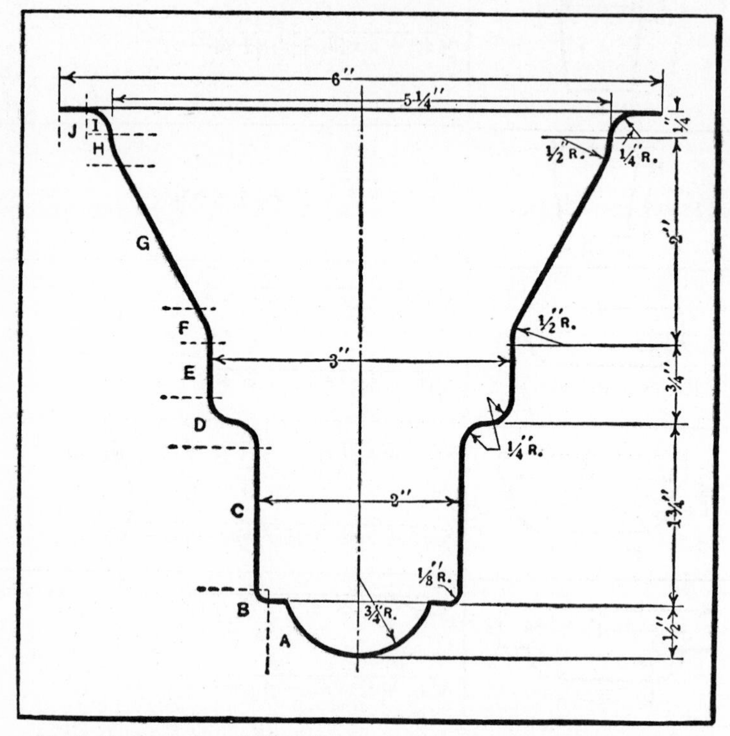

Fig. 2. Cross-section of Shell Composed of Various Sections the Areas of Which are Determined Separately in Order to Find the Total Area

dies, as the metal will not stand the strain. The radius of these corners should not be less than six to ten times the metal-thickness for tin plate and four to five times for copper plate, according to the quality. Otherwise, the table is self-explanatory and no further comment is necessary.

Dividing a Shell into Sections for Finding Its Outside Area.—Round shells are formed of a series of elementary bodies such as disks, hollow cylinders, etc., and the areas of these sections may be found by the rules of geometry. It is evident that the area of the outside surface of a shell is equal to the sum of the outside areas of its various elementary parts or sections. Elementary sections of shells, together with formulas for finding the areas of their outside surfaces are given in Figs. 1 to 15, inclusive, of the accompanying table "Areas of Drawn Shells." The actual calculations can be greatly simplified by the use of the tables in MACHINERY'S HANDBOOK, which give the circumferences and areas of circles. In actual use, all dimensions should be taken to the outside of the shell, although for the sake of simplicity, the section of each shell will be considered as a line of no width.

Example Illustrating Sectional Method.—In order to illustrate the use of this method, assume that it is required to find the diameter of a blank for a shell having the cross-section illustrated in Fig. 2. The shell is first divided into the elementary sections *A*, *B*, *C*, *D*, etc., indicated by the dotted lines on the left side of the cross-section. The necessary dimensions of section *A*, which conforms to that shown in Fig. 3 of the table, "Areas of Drawn Shells," are d_1, which equals 1¾ inches, and *h*, which equals ½ inch. According to the formula, $\text{area} = 3.1416 \times \left(\frac{1.75^2}{4} + 0.5^2\right) = 3.1907$ square inches. In like manner, the areas of sections *B*, *C*, *D*, *E*, *I*, and *J* may be readily calculated, by using the formula applicable to each individual section. To find the areas of sections *F*, *G*, and *H*, it is first necessary to determine several dimensions.

In Fig. 3, in which line *LM* is an enlarged detail of the line governing sections *F*, *G*, and *H*, line *AD* is drawn through the centers from which the curved sides of sections *H* and *F*, Fig. 2, are struck. Next *AB*, Fig. 3, is drawn perpendicular to *BK* and extended to meet line *CD* which is drawn parallel to *BK* through center *D*. Then

$$(AD)^2 = (DE)^2 + (AE)^2 = 4 + 0.0156 = 4.0156$$
$$(DC)^2 = (AD)^2 - (AC)^2 = 4.0156 - 1 = 3.0156$$
$$BK = DC = 1.737 \text{ inches. Also}$$

Areas of Drawn Shells—I

Segment of Shell	General Rule	Formula
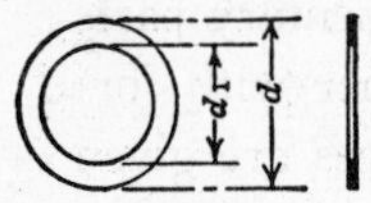 Fig. 1	Area equals area of circle of diameter d, minus area of circle of diameter d_1.	$\text{Area} = \dfrac{\pi(d^2 - d_1^2)}{4}$
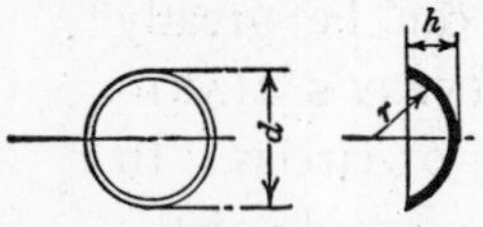 Fig. 2	Area equals numerical value of circumference of circle of diameter $2rh$ or sum of areas of two circles of diameters d and $2h$.	$\text{Area} = 2\pi rh$ or $\text{Area} = \pi\left(\dfrac{d^2}{4} + h^2\right)$
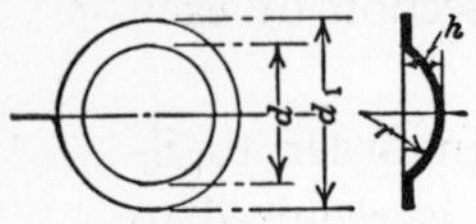 Fig. 3	Area equals sum of areas of two circles of diameters d_1 and $2h$.	$\text{Area} = \pi\left(\dfrac{d_1^2}{4} + h^2\right)$ $h = r - \sqrt{r^2 - \dfrac{d^2}{4}}$
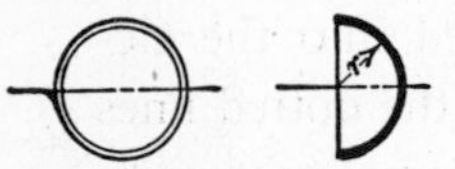 Fig. 4	Area equals twice area of circle of diameter $2r$.	$\text{Area} = 2\pi r^2$
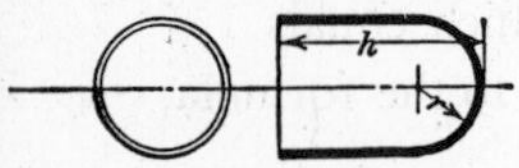 Fig. 5	Area equals numerical value of circumference of circle of diameter $2rh$.	$\text{Area} = 2\pi rh$
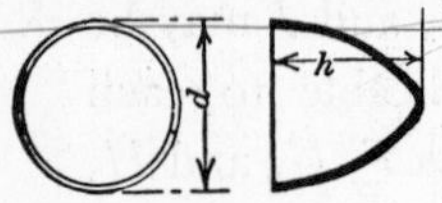 Fig. 6	Shape of shell does not permit of a simple rule.	$\text{Area} = 2.222\, d\sqrt{h^2 + \dfrac{d^2}{4}}$
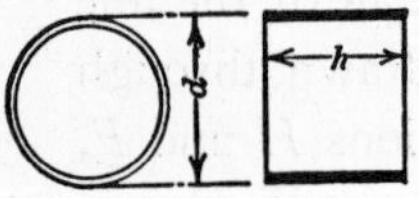 Fig. 7	Area equals numerical value of circumference of circle of diameter dh.	$\text{Area} = \pi dh$
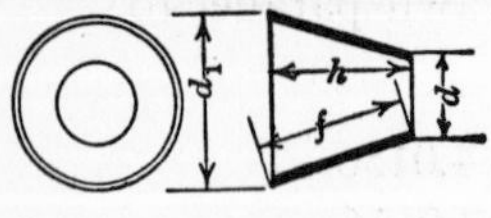 Fig. 8	Area is numerically equal to circumference of circle of diameter $f\left(\dfrac{d + d_1}{2}\right)$.	$\text{Area} = \pi f\left(\dfrac{d + d_1}{2}\right)$ $f = \sqrt{h^2 + \left(\dfrac{d_1 - d}{2}\right)^2}$

Blank diameter equals square root of area multiplied by 1.128

Areas of Drawn Shells—2

Segment of Shell	General Rule	Formula
Fig. 9	Area equals numerical value of circumference of circle of diameter $2rh$.	$\text{Area} = 2\pi rh$
Fig. 10	Area equals product of circumferences of two circles of diameters r and $\frac{d}{2}$, plus twice area of circle of diameter $2r$.	$\text{Area} = 2\pi r^2 + \frac{\pi^2 rd}{2}$
Fig. 11	Area equals product of circumferences of two circles with diameters of r and $\frac{d}{2}$ minus twice area of circle of diameter $2r$.	$\text{Area} = \frac{\pi^2 rd}{2} - 2\pi r^2$
Fig. 12	Area equals numerical value of circumference of circle having a diameter of $(ds + 2rh)$.	$\text{Area} = \pi(ds + 2rh)$
Fig. 13	Area equals numerical value of circumference of circle having a diameter of $(ds - 2rh)$.	$\text{Area} = \pi(ds - 2rh)$
Fig. 14	Area equals product of circumferences of two circles of diameters d and r, respectively.	$\text{Area} = \pi^2 rd$
Fig. 15	Area found by rule given for Fig. 14.	$\text{Area} = \pi^2 rd$

Blank diameter equals square root of area multiplied by 1.128

$$\text{Tan } b = \frac{AE}{DE} = 0.0625 \text{ inch and } b = 3 \text{ degrees } 35 \text{ minutes}$$

$$\text{Tan } a = \frac{AC}{DC} = 0.5757 \text{ inch and } a = 29 \text{ degrees } 56 \text{ minutes}$$

Then $d = a + b = 33$ degrees 31 minutes

$$h = DK \sin d = 0.276 \text{ inch}$$

$$KO = KD \cos d = 0.4169 \text{ inch}$$

and $x = LD - KO = 0.0831$ inch

The length of arc KL is found by the use of the following formula:

$$KL = MB = \frac{\pi r d}{180}$$

in which d is taken in degrees. Thus

$$KL = \frac{3.1416 \times 0.5 \times 33.517}{180} = 0.2925 \text{ inch}$$

Section G in Fig. 2 conforms to the shape of the shell in Fig. 8 of the table, and it will be evident that f in the latter illustration is the same as BK in Fig. 3, which was found to be 1.737 inches. Also, using the reference letters in Fig. 8 of the table in connection with Fig. 3.

$$\frac{d + d_1}{2} = \frac{(3 + 2x) + (5.25 - 2x)}{2} = 4.125 \text{ inches; and}$$

$$\pi f \times \frac{d + d_1}{2} = 3.1416 \times 1.737 \times 4.125 = 22.5095 \text{ square inches.}$$

Summary of Calculations.—The necessary dimensions for calculating the areas of sections F, G, and H (Fig. 2) having been obtained, it is now possible by using the formulas for the different sections, to determine all of the areas, which may then be tabulated as follows: (The figure numbers represent those in the table.)

Area of section A (Fig. 3) = 3.1907 square inches
B (Fig. 10) = 1.1777
C (Fig. 7) = 8.6394

Area of section D (Fig. 15) =	6.1685 square inches
E (Fig. 7) =	4.7124
F (Fig. 13) =	2.8086
G (Fig. 8) =	22.5095
H (Fig. 12) =	4.7721
I (Fig. 11) =	6.7011
J (Fig. 1) =	2.3071
Total area of shell =	62.9871 square inches

The diameter corresponding to a given area may be obtained either by referring to the tables of the circumferences and areas of circles or by multiplying the square root of the area by 1.128; thus $1.128\sqrt{62.9871} = 8.95$ inches, approximately, which is the required blank diameter of the shell illustrated in Fig. 2. Any other round shell may be treated in a similar manner.

Determining Shell Area by Graphical Method.—Many drawn shells are of such form that it is not practicable to determine the area by mathematical methods. There is, however, a fairly accurate graphical method of determining the area and the corresponding blank diameter. The shell shown in Fig. 4 will serve as an example to illustrate this method.

A sectional view of the work showing its form after the final drawing operation, is first laid out accurately to scale. This view is then divided into sections, as indicated, in order to determine the surface area. It will be noted that the first section at the top of the part is hemispherical, and the next cylindrical, the latter being 1 inch in diameter and 1 inch long. The areas of these sections are found by exact formulas (see the formulas given opposite Figs. 4 and 7 in the table "Areas of Drawn Shells") and the results written down at A and B, respectively. The next division C has an irregular curved surface which is divided into sections by 1/8-inch divisions set off on line LM. Dotted lines are drawn through these division points perpendicular to the vertical axis of the part, as indicated. Midway between these divisions, full lines are drawn across the figure at right angles to the axis. The diameters, as measured on each full line from the opposite inner surfaces, are then written in the left-hand column headed "Diameter." The diameter of each section is next multiplied by $\pi \times 1/8$ to obtain the area of each individual section. These areas are written between the dotted lines in the column headed "Area" and their total set down at *C*. In order to simplify the illustration, the columns headed "Diameter" and "Area" are not shown filled out.

The remaining four divisions below the irregular, curved

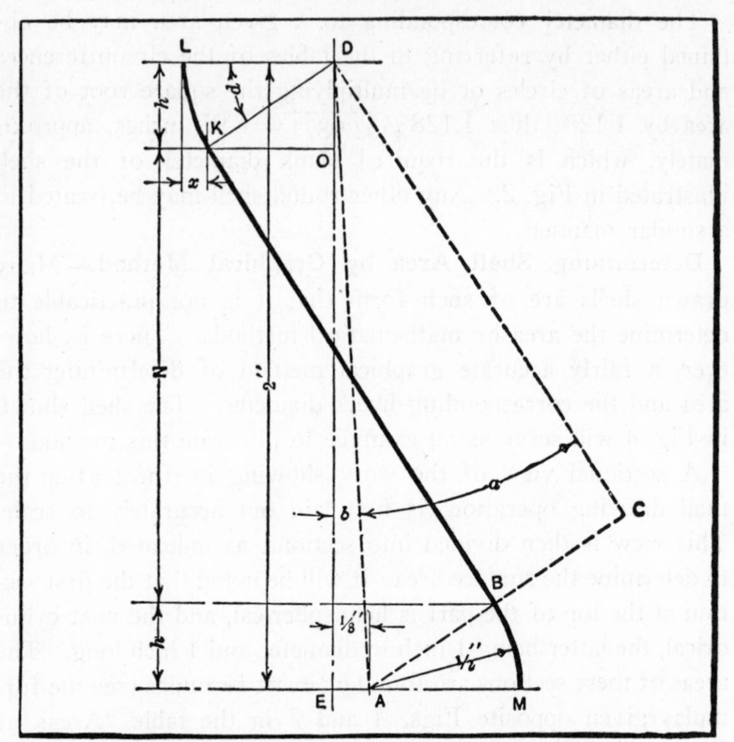

Fig. 3. Lay-out for Determining Certain Dimensions Required in Calculating the Areas of Segments *F*, *G*, and *H*, Fig. 2

section consist of a cylindrical surface; the flat part of the base; and the cylindrical part below the flat surface, to which is added 1/8 inch to allow for trimming. The area of each of these sections is calculated by formulas and written in the proper positions *D*, *E*, *F*, and *G*. The sum of the areas of the individual sections represents the area of the blank. Having the blank area, we obtain the blank diameter by the formula $D = 1.128\sqrt{A}$, where D and A are the blank diameter and area, respectively.

It is apparent that both sides of the blank have the same area before drawing but that they do not have the same area after the drawing operation has been performed. It would seem, therefore, that the mean diameters of the various sections, instead of their inside diameters, would be taken as a basis for calculating the blank area. However, it was found

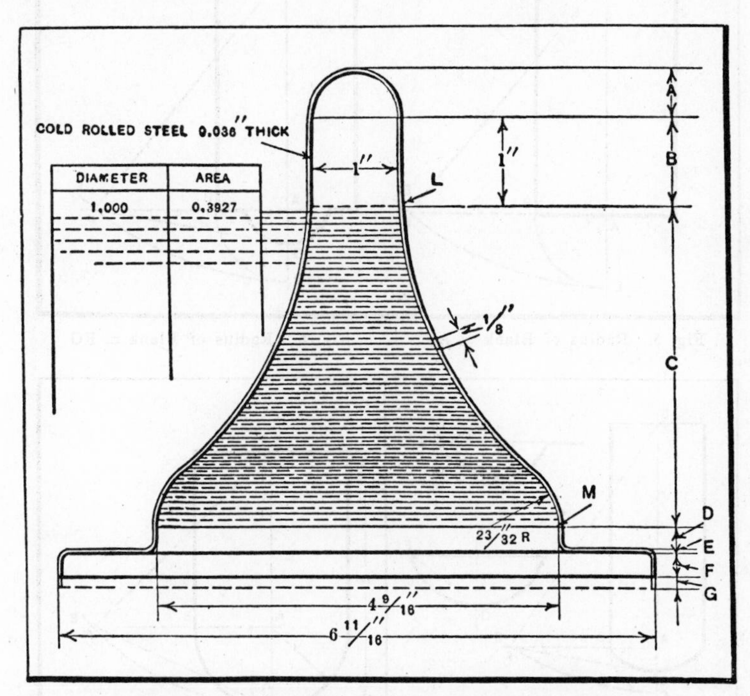

Fig. 4. Graphical Method of Determining Blank Area

that a blank having an area equal to that of the inner surface of the object to be drawn, proved satisfactory for cold-rolled steel 5/32 inch and less in thickness. For hot-rolled steel, experience showed that the blank area should be 5 per cent greater than for cold-rolled steel.

Direct Method of Determining Blank Diameters Graphically.—Graphical methods of finding the diameters of blanks for shells of various shapes will now be presented. Taking the common shell shown in Fig. 5 as the first example, the procedure is as follows: With line *AB* as a radius and *A* as a center, draw arc *BC*. Then draw arc *CE*, with *D* as a center. This arc intersects line *AB* extended, at point *F*. The radius of the blank required to produce this shell is *AF*.

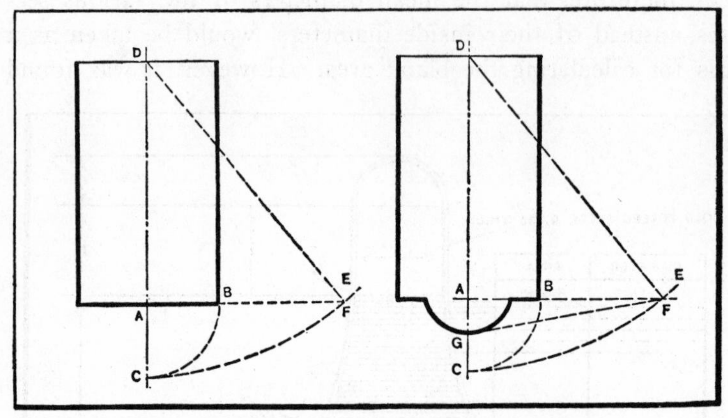

Fig. 5. Radius of Blank = AF **Fig. 6. Radius of Blank = FG**

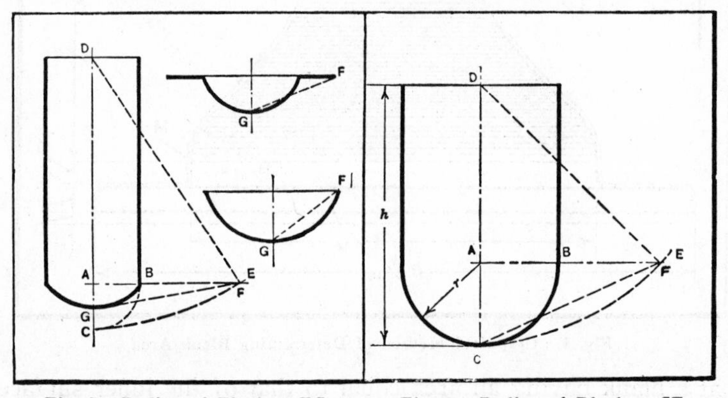

Fig. 7. Radius of Blank = FG **Fig. 8. Radius of Blank = CF**

To find the radius of a blank for the shell in Fig. 6 the procedure is as follows: With radius *AB* draw arc *BC*. Then with radius *DC* draw arc *CE*, cutting line *AB* extended, at point *F*. The radius of this blank is *FG*. Fig. 7 gives examples of other similar problems.

The construction for finding the blank diameter of the shell in Fig. 8 is as follows: With D as a center, draw arc CE, cutting line AB extended, at point F. Then chord CF is the radius of the blank.

Shells with Elliptical Cross-section.—Fig. 9 shows a shell of an elliptical cross-section. The construction necessary for determining the blank diameter by the graphical method is first to extend AB to C, making $BC = AJ$. Then draw a semicircle ADC with the center at H, and draw BE of any length perpendicular to BK, and BF of such a length that $\frac{BF}{BE} = \frac{19}{16}$

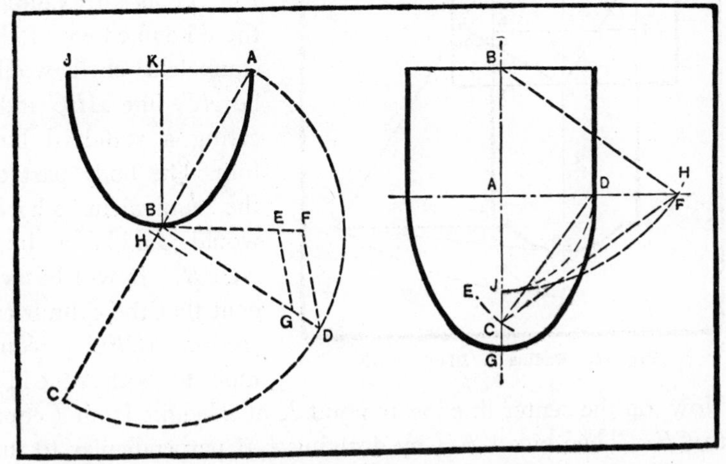

Fig. 9. Radius of Blank = BG Fig. 10. Radius of Blank = CF

Next draw FD and EG parallel. Then BG is the radius of the blank.

If a shell has an elliptical bottom and a cylindrical body, like that illustrated in Fig. 10, proceed as follows to find the blank radius: Draw arc EC with D as a center and a radius equal to the radius of blank which would be required for the bottom alone; this is found as described in connection with the foregoing example. Then with A as a center draw arc DJ, and with B as a center, draw arc JH cutting line AD extended, at point F. Length FC is the radius of the blank required for the entire shell.

Cylindrical Shell Having Two Diameters.—For shells with more than one cylindrical body diameter and various bottom sections, it is first necessary to find a shell of a shape like one previously considered, having an area equivalent to that of the shell for which the blank radius is being determined. Then by finding the radius of the blank for the equivalent shell, the radius of the required blank can be found.

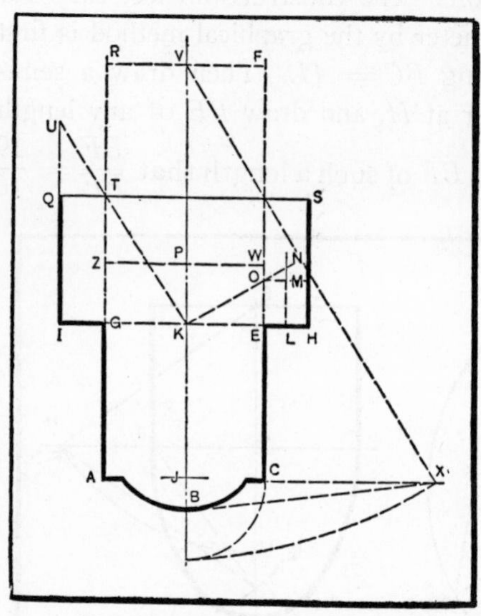

Fig. 11. Radius of Blank = BX

Taking the shell in Fig. 11 as an example, the diameter of the equivalent shell would be *AC*, line *ABC* indicating a standard bottom. The body part of the equivalent shell would follow lines *ACFR*. It will be evident that the cylindrical section *ACEG* is common to both shells. Now, on the center line locate point *K* at a height from *J* equal to *CE*. Then bisect *EH* by drawing *LM* perpendicular to this line, and lay out *EO* on line *CF* equal to *EH*. Then draw KO, which, extended, cuts *LM* at *N*. Line *LN* is the height of the cylinder of diameter *AC* having an area equal to that of *IH*. Next so locate *P* on the center line that *KP* equals *LN*.

For the cylinder *HIQS*, extend *IQ* and locate *T* on the equivalent shell section so that *GT* equals *IQ*. Then draw *KT* continuing to the extension of line *IQ* and intersecting it at *U*. Line *IU* is the height of a cylinder of diameter *AC* which has an area equal to the cylinder of *HIQS*. Therefore, locate *V* on the center line a distance above *P* equal to *IU*, and draw *FR* perpendicular to *FC* through point *V*. Then shell *ABCFR* will have the same area as the original shell, and consequently will require the same blank diameter. The radius of this blank is equal to BX, as will be apparent by referring to Fig. 6.

Finding Length of Cylinder Equal in Area to a Larger Cylinder.—Fig. 12 shows a cylinder of diameter d and height h. To find the height H of a cylinder of diameter D, which will have the same area as the given cylinder, first locate point B where line AC cuts the center line, and draw BK through intersection J, extending the line until it cuts CF extended. Finally draw KN parallel to AC, which will produce length H. As BGJ and BCK are similar triangles,

$$\pi HD = \pi hd$$

Therefore, the two cylindrical shells have the same area.

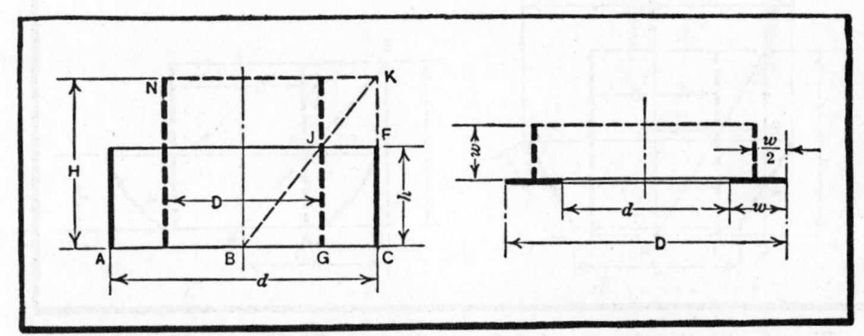

Fig. 12. Finding Length of Cylinder Equal in Area to Larger Cylinder

Fig. 13. Finding Size of Cylinder Equal in Area to Flat Ring

Finding Size of Cylinder Equal in Area to Area of Flat Ring.—Fig. 13 shows the method of finding the dimensions of a cylinder having the same area as a ring. The area A of this ring may be found by the following formulas:

$$A = \frac{\pi}{4} \times (D^2 - d^2) = \pi w\,(d + w)$$

The second of these two formulas obviously may also be used for finding the area of the dotted cylinder. In finding the area of a complicated shell, this flat ring would be converted into another cylindrical part having a diameter equal to that of the equivalent shell, by means of the method used for the case illustrated in Fig. 12. Now, referring back to

Fig. 11, cylinder *WFRZ* has the same area as cylinder *HIQS*, and cylinder *EGZW* has the same area as ring *IEGH,* as previously indicated.

Finding Length of Cylinder Equal in Area to Conical Segment.—The construction of a cylinder of a given diameter *D*, Fig. 14, equivalent to the conical segment shown, will now be given. Intersection *A* of line *BC* is at the middle of the side *f*, this side being bisected by line *BC*. The latter must be equal in length to *f* and drawn parallel to the center line. Then draw *BK* and *CE* perpendicular to the center line, intersecting the cylinder of diameter *D* at points *F* and *G*, respectively. Finally, draw *EF* and extend this line and *CB* until

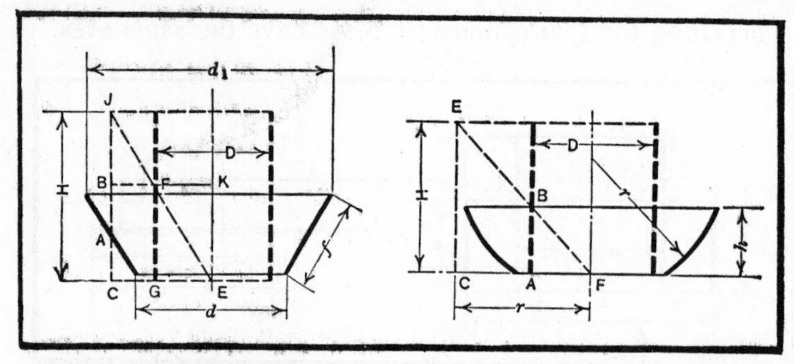

Fig. 14. Finding Length of Cylinder Equal in Area to Conical Segment

Fig. 15. Finding Length of Cylinder Equal in Area to Spherical Segment

they intersect at *J*. Line *CJ* is the height *H* of the cylinder of diameter *D* which has an area equal to that shown by the full lines. Proof:

$$FG = BC = f$$

$$CE = \frac{d_1 + d}{4} \text{ and } \frac{H}{f} = \frac{d_1 + d}{2D}$$

$$HD = \frac{f(d_1 + d)}{2} \text{ and } \pi HD = \pi f \times \frac{d_1 + d}{2}$$

Finding Length of Cylinder Equal in Area to Spherical Segment.—In Fig. 15 *A* and *B* are the points where the bottom and top edges of the given segment cut the required cylinder of diameter *D*. First draw *CE* parallel to the center line and at a distance from it equal to r. Then draw FB and extend until it meets CE. Then the line CE is the height H of the cylinder of diameter D having an area equal to that of the given segment. Proof:

$$\frac{H}{h} = \frac{2r}{D}$$

$$DH = 2rh \text{ and } \pi DH = 2\pi rh$$

To find graphically the length of a cylindrical segment having the same area as the segment in Fig. 16, first draw line

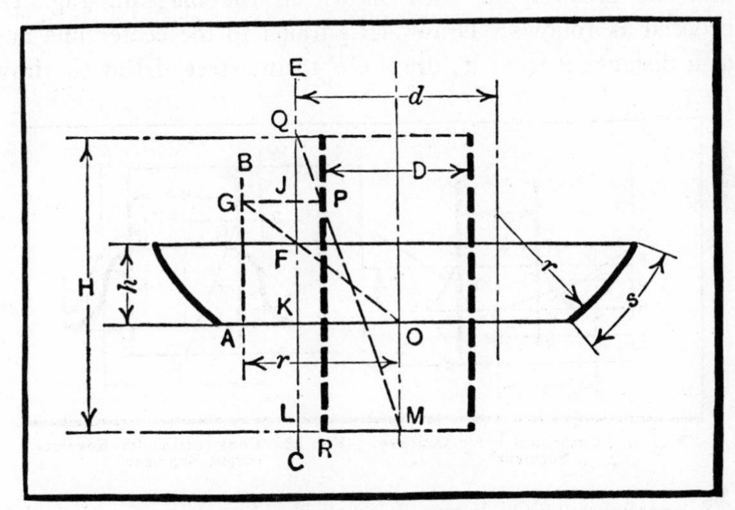

Fig. 16. Construction when Centers of Arcs of Segment are on Different Center-lines

AB parallel to the center line and at a distance r from it. Then through point F, where CE intersects the upper edge of the segment, draw OF and extend it until it intersects AB at G. Next draw GP parallel to AO, intersecting CE at J; locate the bottom edge of the dotted segment so that KL equals s; and then draw MP and extend it until it intersects CE at Q. Then LQ is the height H of the cylindrical segment equal in area to the segment indicated by the full lines. Proof:

$$r : \frac{d}{2} = AG : KF \text{ and } JK = AG = \frac{2rh}{d}$$

As $KL = s$,

$$PR = JL = \frac{2rh}{d} + s \qquad PR : \frac{D}{2} = QL : \frac{d}{2}$$

Then $$PR = \frac{HD}{d} = \frac{2rh}{d} + s \quad \pi HD = \pi(2rh + ds)$$

This proves that the area of the given segment is equal to that of the cylindrical segment of diameter D and height H.

Size of Cylinder Equal to Area of Concave Segment.—To find the area of the shell shown in the diagram Fig. 17, proceed as follows: Draw AB parallel to the center line and at a distance r from it; draw OF to intersect AB at G; draw

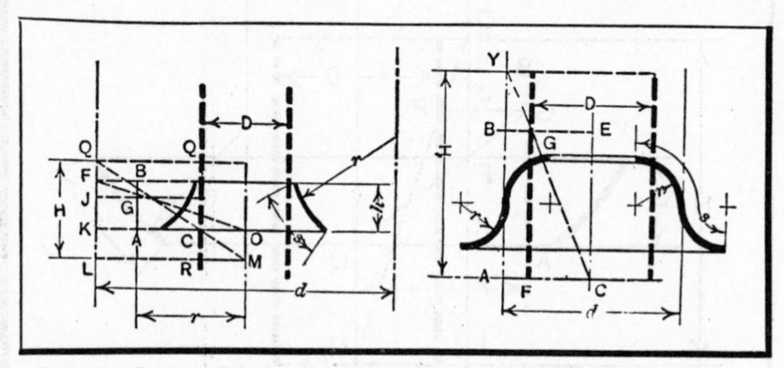

Fig. 17. Construction for Concave Segment **Fig. 18.** Construction for Reverse-curve Segment

GJ parallel to CO; locate L so that JL equals s; draw LM parallel to CO; cutting the center line and cylinder of diameter D at R; and finally draw MC, extending it to intersect FL extended, at Q. Line LQ is the height H of the cylindrical segment of diameter D equal in area to the segment shown by the heavy solid lines. Proof:

$$r : \frac{d}{2} = AG : FK \text{ and } JK = AG = \frac{2rh}{d}$$

$$JL = s \text{ and } CR = s - \frac{2rh}{d}$$

$$LQ : CR = \frac{d}{2} : \frac{D}{2} \text{ and } LQ = H = \frac{d}{D} \times \left(s - \frac{2rh}{d}\right)$$

$$\pi HD = \pi(ds - 2rh)$$

Size of Cylinder Equivalent to Area of Reverse-curve Segment.—For the segment in Fig. 18, lay out on line XY a distance AB equal to s, which, in turn, equals πr. Then draw AC and BE perpendicular to the center line and cutting the cylinder of diameter D at F and G, respectively; next draw CG, extending it to its intersection with XY. Then AY is the height H of the cylindrical segment of diameter D, the area of which equals that of the reverse-curve segment. This is proved as follows:

$$FG = AB = s = \pi r \text{ and } FG : AY = \frac{D}{2} : \frac{d}{2}$$

$$H = AY = \frac{\pi rd}{D} \text{ and } HD = \pi rd$$

Then

$$\pi HD = \pi^2 rd$$

Example Showing Application of Graphical Methods.—Fig. 19 shows a graphical method of finding the radius of blank for the shell indicated by the heavy full line. This cross-section includes most of the segments dealt with, and is an example intended to make clear the use of the constructions employed in the foregoing for finding the blank radius of a complete shell. The equivalent shell will have the bottom XYZ and a diameter d. The various heights of segments of diameter d which are equal in area to segments B, C, D, E, etc., are then found by the foregoing methods and summed up on the line KT which is drawn outside the figure to avoid confusion. The sum of all the heights of cylinders of diameter d having areas equal to the various segments from B to J, inclusive, equals KT. From T a line TU is drawn parallel to ZX. The blank radius of the equivalent shell $UWXYZ$ can then be readily found. This radius is AY.

Diameters of Blanks for Zinc Shells.—The ordinary formulas for determining blank diameters, which are based upon the shell area, do not allow for the "draw," or stretch, of the metal that takes place during the stamping operation.

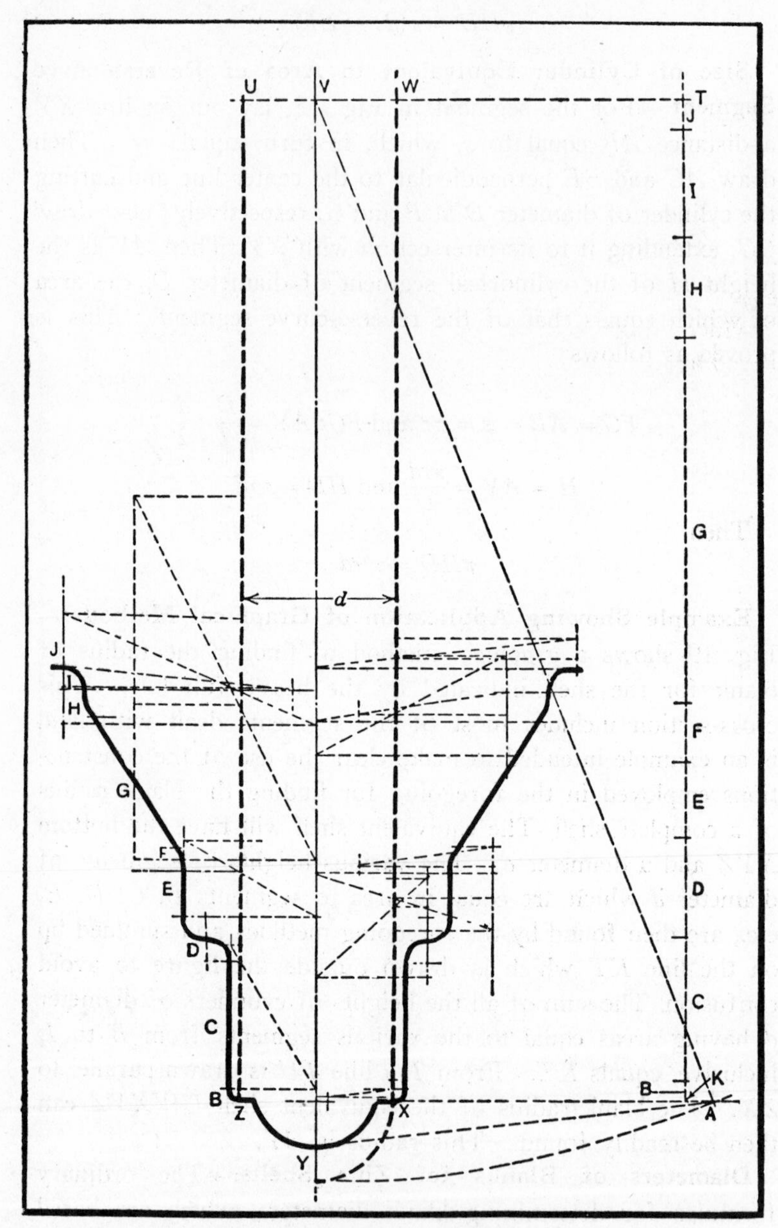

Fig. 19. Example Showing Application of Graphical Method of Finding a Cylinder of Equal Surface Area and Then the Required Blank Size

This draw is in proportion to the depth of the shell and is different for different metals. To determine the blank diameter for a zinc shell of known depth and diameter, made in one drawing operation, the chart shown in Fig. 20 will be found accurate. This chart is made with each division representing $\frac{1}{64}$ inch. The abscissas represent the depth of the

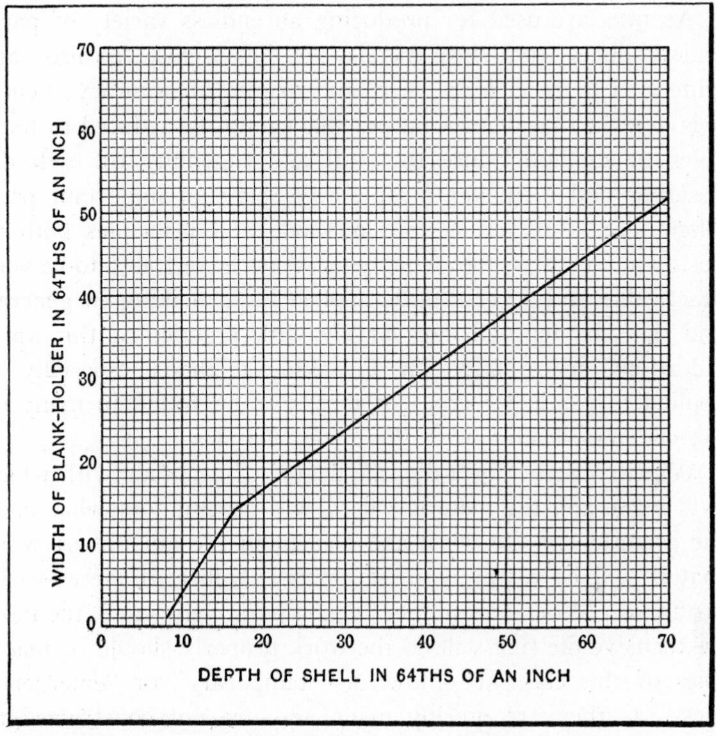

Fig. 20. Chart for Determining Blank Diameters for Zinc Shells

shell, and the ordinates, the width of the blank-holder. For example, suppose that it is desired to find the blank diameter of a shell 2 inches in diameter and $1\frac{3}{16}$ inch deep. Now $1\frac{3}{16}$ inch is $\frac{52}{64}$, so following the vertical line from 52 to the curve and reading the horizontal line that it intersects at that point, the width of the blank-holder is found to be $\frac{39}{64}$ inch. $\frac{39}{64} \times 2 = 1\ \frac{7}{32}$, which, added to the diameter 2 inches, gives a blank diameter of $3\ \frac{7}{32}$ inches.

CHAPTER III

LAYING OUT BLANKING DIES AND GENERAL DIEMAKING PRACTICE

As DIES are used for producing an endless variety of parts and products from sheet metals, the dies themselves also vary widely as to type, form, size, and degree of accuracy; hence, it is evident that diemaking practice cannot be reduced to fixed rules or methods since the skill and ingenuity of both die designer and diemaker must always play an important part. There are, however, certain methods and principles both in design and construction which diemakers have found to be both practicable and successful as applied to diemaking in general, and this chapter will deal largely with practice of this kind. Additional information on diemaking methods, especially as applied to particular types of dies, will be found in many of the chapters dealing with these special types.

When constructing a die, the degree of accuracy with which it is made and the materials used will depend somewhat upon the accuracy of the work and also upon the amount of work that it will be required to do or the number of pieces to be produced. When this number is comparatively small, the most inexpensive die that will do the work properly should be made. Dies of this class are known as "temporary" or "emergency dies," as they are quickly made and are not constructed to withstand long and continuous usage. When, however, a die is to be used incessantly for a long period, or, perhaps, until it is worn out through use, first-class materials and workmanship are required. Of the many different kinds of dies in use, the blanking die is the most common type. The reason for this is that almost all work that requires the use of various other kinds of dies either has its beginning with the blanking die, or is cut from the flat stock after it is completed by other dies which may or may not be combined with the blanking die. In making a blanking die, there are a few essential points to be taken into consideration, among which are the following:

1. Use good tool steel of a sufficient length, width, and thickness to enable the die to withstand the work for which it is intended.

2. In laying out the die, care should be taken that as little of the stock as possible is left over, as waste, in cutting out the blanks.

3. Be sure not only that the die has the proper amount of clearance but also that the clearance is filed or machined *straight*, so as to enable the blanks to drop through readily.

4. In working out the die, machine out as much as possible to avoid excessive filing.

Laying Out Blanking Dies.—A most important point for the diemaker to bear in mind in making blanking dies for odd shapes is to lay them out so that the minimum amount of metal will be converted into scrap. In fact, hardly too much stress can be laid upon this one point alone, as it is an easy matter to waste a considerable percentage of the stock by layouts which may appear to be fairly economical. In the following, the object will be to point out by actual examples how stock can be saved which may be converted into scrap, if the diemaker is not constantly watching out for possible economies.

Beginning with a simple illustration, it sometimes happens that by laying out the dies so that the blanks are cut from the strip at an angle instead of at right angles to the edge of the stock, a considerable economy of metal can be effected. As will be seen by referring to Fig. 1, the angular location permits the use of narrower stock and materially reduces the amount of scrap metal. By comparing the upper and lower views, the saving in metal by diagonal blanking is apparent, as it is not only possible to use a much narrower strip of stock, but more blanks can also be obtained from a given length, as will be understood by noting the difference between the dimensions *a* and *b*. When thousands of blanks are to be produced, the saving in metal that is effected is considerable. The most economical lay-out can often be determined easily and quickly by cutting out a few paper templets and arranging them in various ways until the best method of blanking is ascertained.

When the shape of the blanks is such that there would, unavoidably, be a considerable amount of metal between the punched holes, the stock can, at times, be cut to a better advantage by so locating the stop- or gage-pin that sufficient metal is left between the holes to permit the strip being turned around and again passed through the press. If a large number

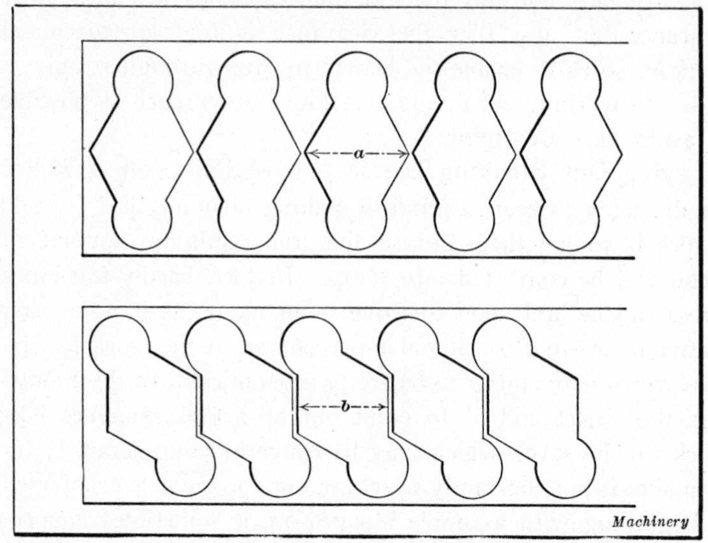

Fig. 1. Illustration of the Saving of Metal Effected by Cutting the Blanks Diagonally from the Stock

of blanks are to be made a double die would be preferable.

An example of stock which is passed through the die twice is shown in Fig. 2. The upper view shows the stock after the first passage and the lower view the scrap after the second passage. The lay-out of the blanking die for this operation is shown in Fig. 3. Each blank is pierced with three small holes as the plan view of the die indicates. Besides cutting and piercing the blank when the stock is run through the first time, the three small holes for the blanks to be cut out during the second passage are also pierced, as the upper view, Fig. 2, shows. This is done for the reason that when the metal is run through the second time, the pierced holes serve as a guide in locating the stock and prevent the cutting of "half blanks" by "running in," or, in other words, the liability of cutting imperfect blanks by punching into that part of the metal from

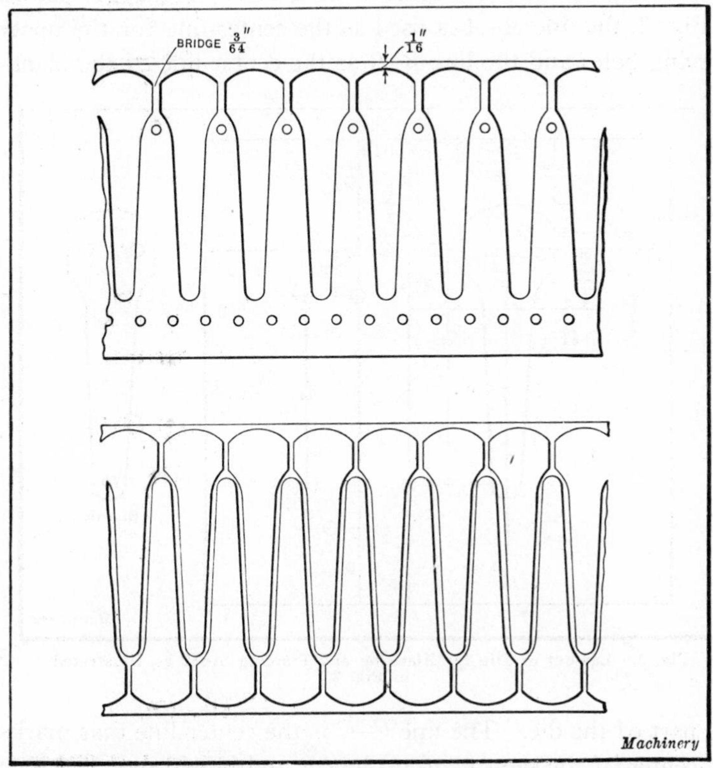

Fig. 2. (Upper View) Stock after One Passage Through Blanking and Piercing Die. (Lower View) Stock after the Second Passage Through the Die

which blanks have already been cut. This guiding action is effected by three pilot pins in the blanking punch which engage the three pieced holes made when the strip was run through the first time. The pilot pins engaging with the pierced holes cause the second lot of blanks to be cut centrally with the holes, and also to be accurately centered between the portions of stock from which the blanks have already been cut. When this die is in use, the metal is run through in the usual way from right to left until half of the required amount of blanks is cut, after which the piercing punches for the holes are taken out and the metal is run through again and the other half of the required amount of blanks is cut.

In laying out this die, which is done after the manner shown in Fig. 3, the line *A–A* is used as the center-line for the upper piercing holes and the line *B–B* as the center-line of the blank-

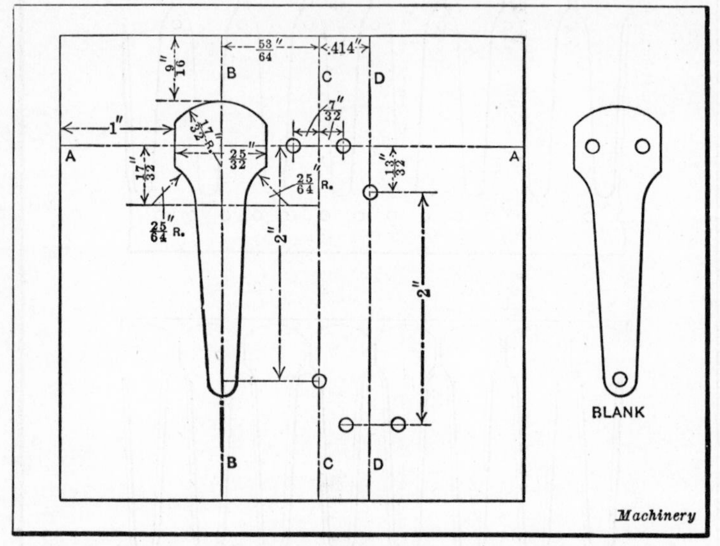

Fig. 3. Lay-out of Die for Blanking and Piercing Stock as Illustrated in Fig. 2

ing part of the die. The line C–C is the center-line that marks the center of the next blank to be cut and is laid out 53/64 inch from the line *B–B*. This dimension is fixed by the fact that the widest part of the blank is 25/32 inch, and the bridge between the blanks is 3/64 inch, the sum of which equals the distance from center to center of adjacent blanks. The line *D–D* is the center-line for the blank which is cut when the metal is run through the second time, and is made at 0.414 inches or one-half of 53/64 from the line *C–C*, inasmuch as the blanks cut at the second passage of the stock are midway between those cut the first time the stock goes through the die.

At *A* in Fig. 4 is shown a double die for blanking and piercing brass stock, producing the shape shown in the sketch at the left; it is laid out so as to save as much of the metal as is practically possible without added expense so far as the operation of blanking and piercing is concerned. By referring to sketches *B* and *C*, it can be seen that the strip of metal from which the blanks are cut is run through a second time for reasons that will be given. One reason is that wider metal can be used by doing this, which in itself is a saving so

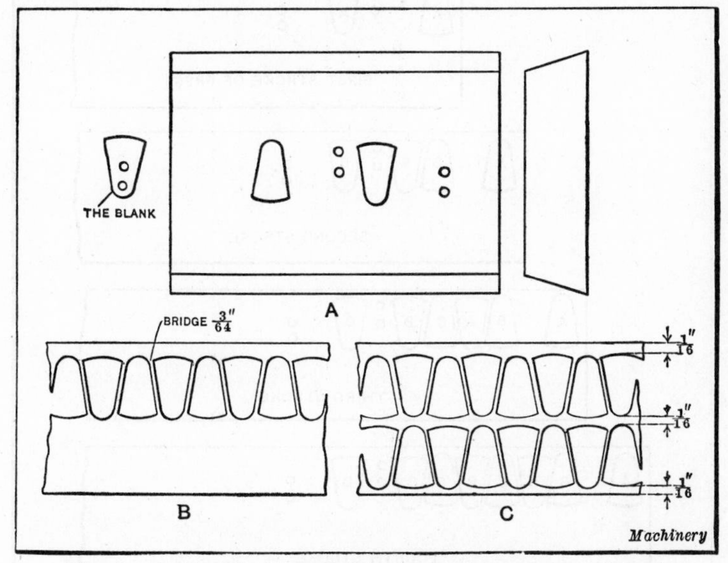

Fig. 4. Double Blanking and Piercing Die—Appearance of Stock after Passage Through the Die

far as the cost of metal is concerned. Wide brass can be bought at a lower price per pound than narrow brass. The other reason is that a strip of metal 1/16 inch wide and as long as the entire length of the strip is saved on every strip that is run through. If narrow metal were used, there would be waste of 1/8 inch of metal (*i.e.*, 1/16 inch on each side) of every strip run through, and on two strips from which no more blanks could be cut than from the wider strip shown at *C*, there would be waste of 1/4 inch of metal. On the other hand, by using wide metal and running it through the die twice, the waste would be only 3/16 inch, as indicated at *C*.

To fully understand the manner in which the metal is gradually worked up after each stroke of the press, short sections are shown in Fig. 5. At the first stroke four holes are pierced and two plain blanks *A*, having no holes, are cut out. At the second stroke there are also four holes pierced and the two

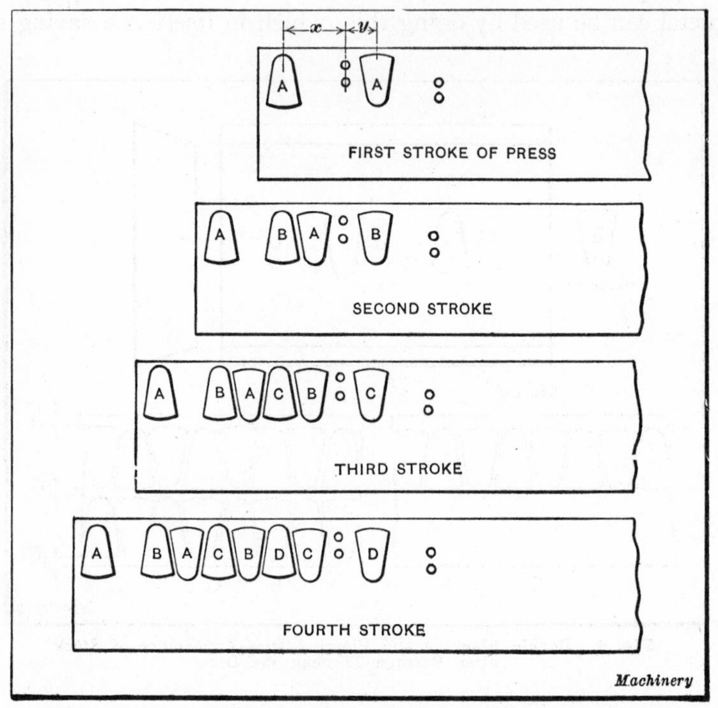

Fig. 5. Diagram Illustrating Progressive Action of Double Die Shown in Fig. 4

blanks *B*, for which the holes were pierced at the previous stroke, are cut. At the third and fourth strokes the holes begin to match in with each other, as shown, so that when the metal is run through it will look like the strip shown at *B*, Fig. 4. It should be borne in mind that four holes are pierced and two blanks are cut at each stroke of the press; also that the metal is fed after each stroke a distance x equal to the distance from the center of the leading blanking punch to the center of the first set of piercing punches, as indicated in the strip marked "first stroke." In this particular case the feeding movement x equals $^{25}/_{32}$ inch, and the die is so laid out that the distance y equals one-half the feeding movement or $^{25}/_{64}$ inch.

Relation Between Form of Stamping and Direction of Stock Grain.—The relation between the grain of the stock and the shape or form of the stamping must be considered in certain instances in laying out dies. For example, if a stamping has lugs which must be bent either to provide means of fastening or for some other reason, the flat blank should be cut from the strip of stock so that the bend will be *across* or at right angles to the grain and not parallel to it, to prevent breakage during bending. The direction of the grain must also be considered in making certain bent springs from flat stock, and especially for any parts which require bending and are made from comparatively hard material. When the grain of the stock must be considered for the reasons mentioned, it may not always be possible to lay out the die strictly with reference to reducing the waste stock to a minimum, since the direction of grain in some cases is of greater importance. By the "grain" is meant the way in which the metal was drawn when passing through the rolls. If it is required to make bends at right angles to each other or approximately so, the blanks should be punched out diagonally across the grain.

Laying Out Dies for Washers.—To lay out a single washer die is a very easy matter, but to lay out a die for cutting two or more washers at one time, so as to cut the greatest amount of blanks from the least amount of stock, is not understood as it should be. In laying out a washer die for blanking two or more washers at one time, one of the main points to be remembered is that all the holes from which the blanking and piercing are done must be laid out in an exact relation to each other, so as to eliminate the possibility of "running in," *i.e.*, cutting imperfect or half blanks by cutting into that part of the metal from which blanks have already been cut. The required amount of blanks must also be considered, for it sometimes happens that the amount wanted does not warrant the making of a die that will cut more than one at a time.

Fig. 6 shows how a die is laid out for blanking and piercing two washers at one time, so as to utilize as much of the metal as possible. As shown, the ¾-inch holes marked *C* and *D* are the blanking part of the die, while the ¼-inch holes *A* and *B* are for the piercing punches. The distance between the

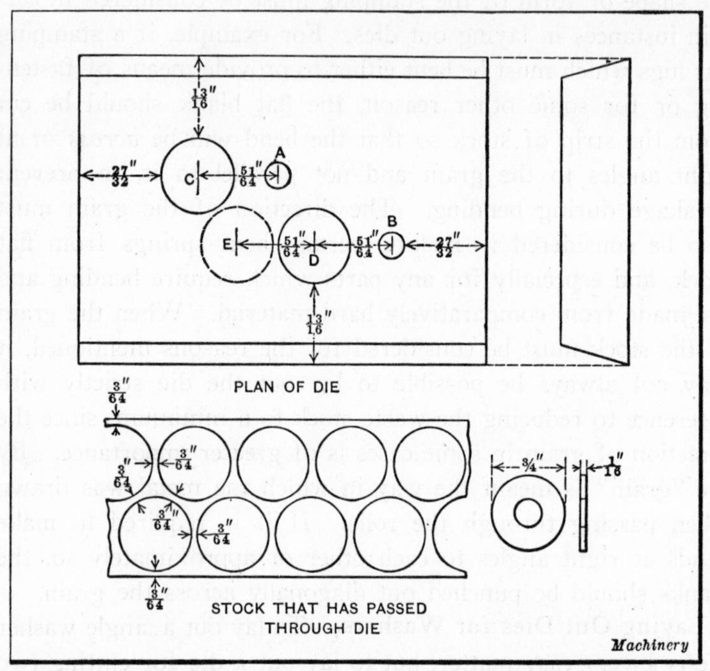

Fig. 6. Die for Piercing and Blanking Two Washers Simultaneously

center of *C* and *A* is 51/64 inch, as is also the distance between *D* and *B*. By referring to that part of the illustration which shows a section of the stock after it had been run through the die, it will be seen that there is a narrow margin of 3/64 inch of metal, known as "the bridge," between the holes. In laying out the die this margin must be taken into consideration, when determining the center-to-center distance; thus, diameter of washer to be cut plus bridge equals distance from center of piercing punch to center of blanking punch. For example, $\frac{3}{4} + \frac{3}{64} = \frac{51}{64}$. The dotted circle on the plan view of the die shows that the die is laid out so that one washer is skipped in running the metal through at the start. The holes are located in this way in order to make the die a substantial and strong one. It can very readily be seen that if the circle *E* were the blanking part instead of *D*, the die would be a frail one, and would not be strong enough for the work for which it is intended. Another important point in laying out a die of this kind is to lay it out central, or so that when it is keyed in position ready for use in the center of the die-bed, it

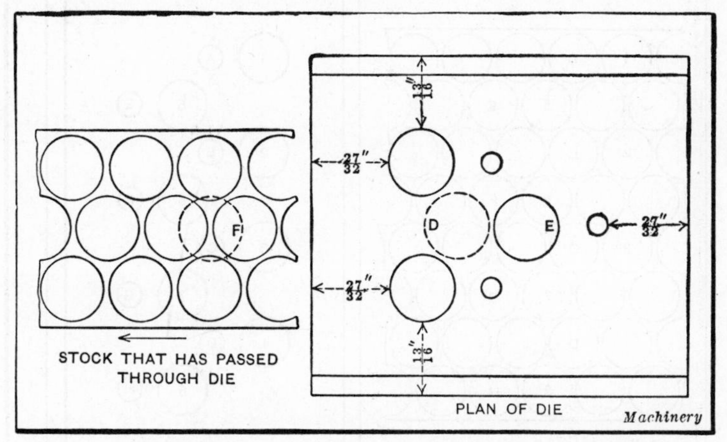

Fig. 7. Die for Piercing and Blanking Three Washers Simultaneously

will not have to be shifted to the right or left side in order to make it line up with the punch. Incidentally, the punch plate, which holds the blanking and piercing punches in position, should also be laid out central.

Fig. 7 shows the lay-out for blanking and piercing three washers at one time. A section of the stock after it has been run through this die is shown to the left in the illustration. As will be seen, the holes match in very close together and very little stock is left in the form of scrap; moreover, the holes are "staggered" instead of being in a straight line across the width of the strip. This is done in order to save metal;

the dotted circle *F* is merely drawn to show that wider metal would have to be used if the holes were in a straight line.

The plan of a die for blanking and piercing eight washers at one time is shown to the right in Fig. 8. The holes which are numbered are for blanking and those which are lettered are for piercing the holes in the washers. This die is laid out similarly to the one shown in Fig. 7, with the exception that there is provision for eight blanks instead of for three. A section of stock after it has been run through this die is shown

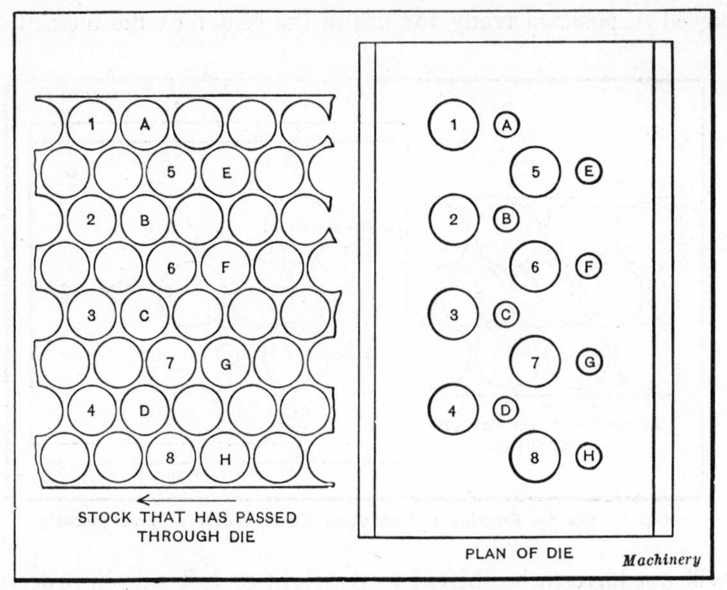

Fig. 8. Die for Piercing and Blanking Eight Washers Simultaneously

to the left. To give a better idea as to how the blanks are punched out in the manner shown, the sixteen holes in the metal from which blanks have been cut are numbered and lettered the same as the die. The metal is fed through in the usual way, which is from right to left, and the holes are, of course, pierced before the blanks are cut. By referring again to Fig. 8, the lay-out for cutting two, three, four, five, six and seven blanks can be determined. The parts numbered and letters 1—*A* and 5—*E* are the lay-out for two blanks; for three blanks, 1–*A*, 2–*B*, and 5–*E*; for four blanks, 1–*A*, 2–*B*, 5–*E*, and 6–*F*; for five blanks, 1–*A*, 2–*B*, 3–*C*, 5–*E*, and 6–*F*; for six blanks, 1–*A*, 2–*B*, 3–*C*, 5–*E*, 6–*F*, and 7–*G*; for seven blanks, 1–*A*, 2–*B*, 3–*C*, 4–*D*, 5–*E*, 6–*F*, and 7–*G*. It should be remembered that all holes in dies of this kind are lapped or ground to size after hardening; they should be perfectly round and have 1 degree clearance. In some shops the holes are left straight for ¼ inch, and then tapered off 2 degrees.

Saving Stock by Changing Design of Blanked Part.—A follow-die designed for manufacturing box-opener keys is shown in Fig. 9. The original design of these keys is shown at *A*, but it was realized that by changing the design slightly, considerable stock could be saved. Accordingly, the key was redesigned as shown at *B*, which enabled a simpler die to be constructed. The construction of the die as as follows: A machine-steel punch-holder carries the machine-steel punch-plate *C* in which the shearing punch *D* and the machine-steel punch-holder *E* are riveted. The shearing punch is shaped to the contour indicated at *J*, which represents the shape of the stock cut off from the end when first fed into the die, and this punch is hardened only on the front cutting edge. The tool-steel piercing punch is secured in the holder *E* by a set-screw, so that it can be easily removed for regrinding. The die-block or shoe *F* is made of machine steel and supports the hardened tool-steel die *G*, which is fastened by screws and dowel-pins to it. The stripper plate *H* is a machine-steel member, and serves not only as a stripper, but also as a backing plate for the shearing punch *D*.

The stock is fed into the die until it abuts against the stripper plate at *I*. The shearing punch *D* then descends, cutting out the piece *J*, and at the same time the piercing punch produces the hole *K* in the strip. On the next downward stroke of the ram a second piece is blanked out without a hole, and it is not until the third stroke that a completed piece, as shown at *B*, is punched out. By providing a suitable stop for the stock, even these two pieces of stock could be saved, so that there would be no waste except the punching from holes *K*. The

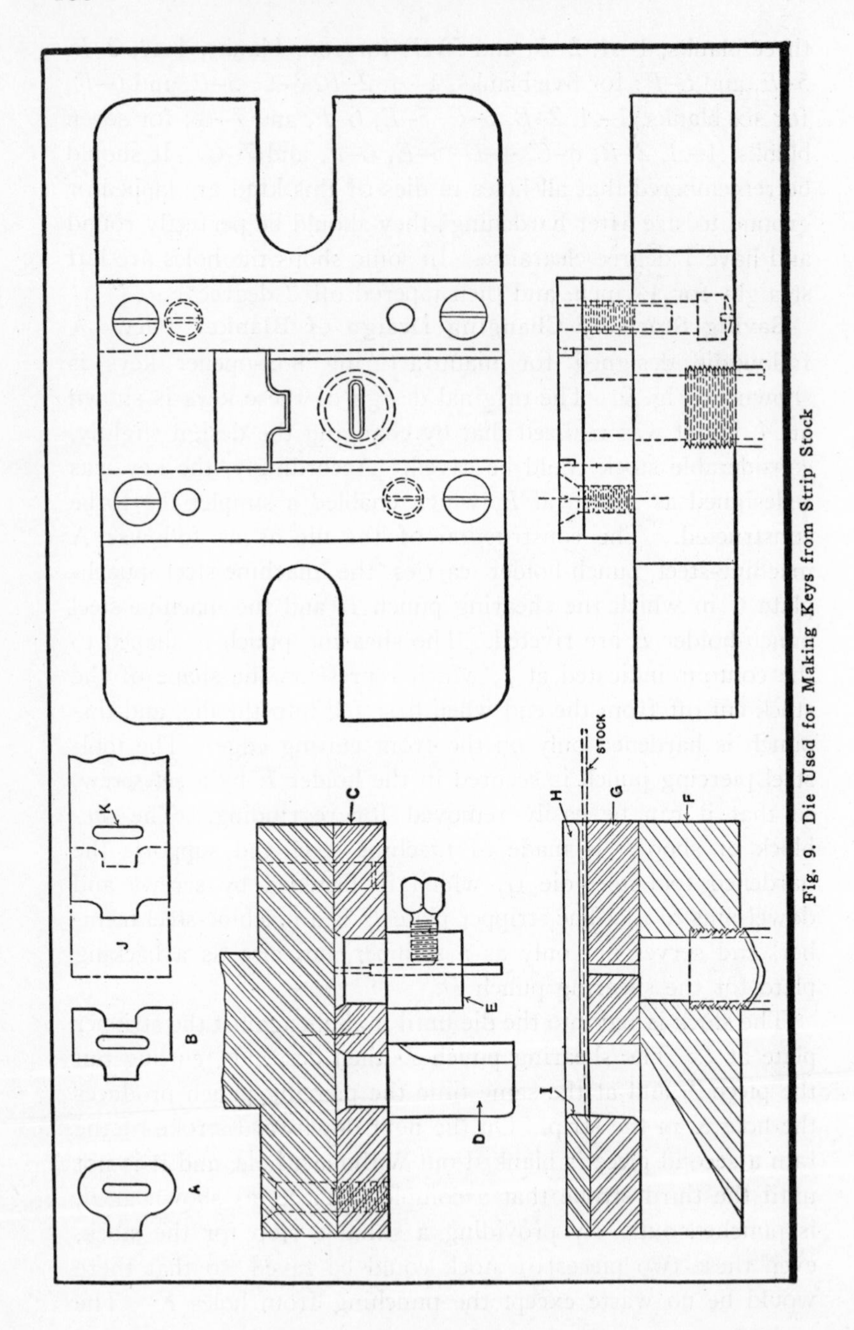

Fig. 9. Die Used for Making Keys from Strip Stock

keys are pushed through the die and slide down the inclined surface of the die-block and into a suitable receptacle. The scrap from the hole passes through a tube screwed into the under side of the die-block. The press used operated at 200 revolutions per minute.

Another Example of Stock Saving by Change in Method of Blanking.—The piece shown at *A* in Fig. 10 was at first produced on a follow-die designed to pierce and blank the piece from the strip stock. The strip stock in this case was a little wider than the work. The whole die was composed of one block of steel and was rather expensive to make. The new die was designed to cut the pieces from strip stock the same width as the finished piece. This reduced the amount of scrap or waste, and eliminated one of the objectionable features of the follow-die. The construction of the new die will be understood from the following:

The die-shoe *B* is grooved or slotted to receive the die *C*. This die is held in place by means of the three screws *D* and the two dies *E* and *F*, which are of the bushing type. The dies *E* and *F* are set into the die-shoe, and thus serve as dowel-pins as well as dies. The notched openings in die *C* were made with a milling cutter, and the necessary clearances filed by hand. The die after being hardened was rounded off at *G* by grinding, to give the teeth produced on the part a slight curl that is completed in another operation.

The strip stock is a loose fit in the slot milled in the stripper plate *H*, and the thrust imposed on the notching and shearing cutters is taken up by the stripper plate. The spring stops *J* and *K* are set in slots in the stripper plate. The machine-steel punch-holder *L* is provided with a punch-plate *M* in which the punches *O* and *P* are held. To prevent the punches from pulling out of plate *M*, the ends are headed over in the usual manner. The piercing punches *Q* are made of drill rod and are fitted and riveted into punch-holders *R*, which also have shoulders that prevent them from being pulled out of plate *M*. A shear blade *S*, attached to the end of the punch-holder, as shown, cuts off the pierced and notched pieces.

In operation, the stock, which comes in 10-foot lengths, is fed into the die by hand until it comes up against the stop *J*. The press is then tripped, and on the down stroke of the ram, the two punches seen at *Q* pierce two holes, and the punch *O* notches the side of the stock. On the same stroke, punch *P*

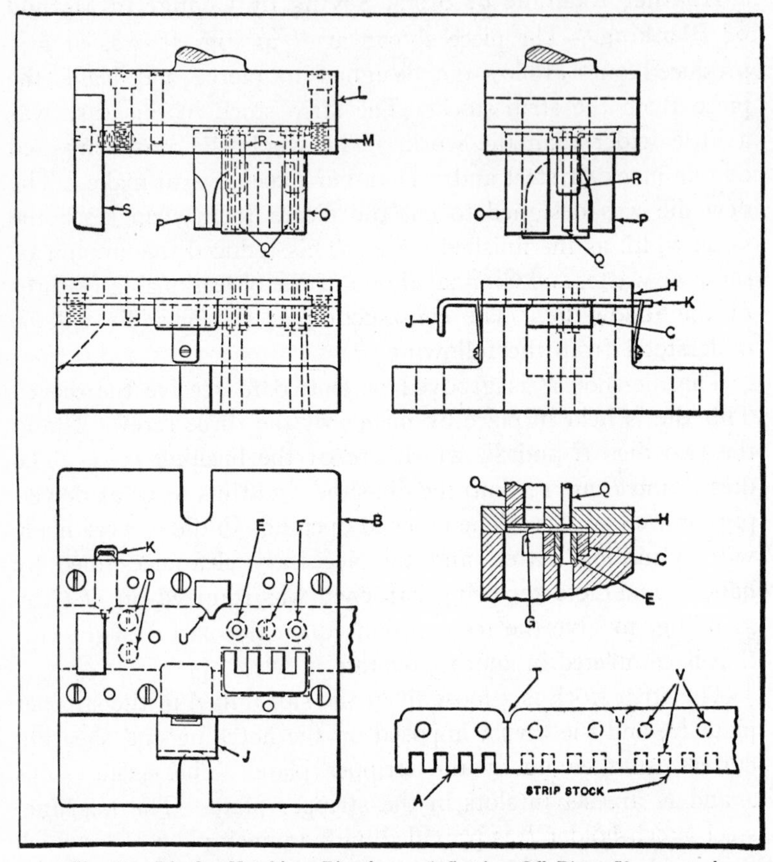

Fig. 10. Die for Notching, Piercing and Cutting Off Piece Shown at *A*

entering die opening *U*, notches or rounds the end of the stock. Upon the completion of the first stroke, the operator pulls back stop *J*, so that the stock can be fed up to stop *K*. The second set of notches and holes is then punched. Stop *J* now acts as a friction shoe, pressing the stock up against one side of the slot in the stripper.

Stop *J* is of the snap type, so that by pushing on the stock, the latter can be fed along to the third position, where stop *K* will snap into notch T previously produced by punch *P*. Here the third set of notches and holes is punched in the stock, as indicated by the dotted lines *V* in the view at the lower right-hand corner of the illustration, and the first complete piece *A* is sheared off. After the stock is started in the die, the press is run continuously at a speed of 90 revolutions per minute. The scrap or punchings cut out by punches *O*, *P*, and *Q*, pass down through the die to a scrap box, while the sheared off pieces slide down the chute at the back of the press.

Templets for Blanking Dies.—When making a blanking die it is common practice to begin by making a templet that conforms to the shape of the blank which the die is to produce. This templet is then used as a gage when finishing the hole in the die. Sheet steel is commonly used for templets. The thickness depends somewhat upon the size of the templet, but for comparatively small work, steel about 3/32 inch thick will suffice. The outline of the templet should be laid out very carefully, and finished to conform exactly to the required shape and size of the hole to be cut in the die blank. It is absolutely necessary, if accurate work is to be produced by punches and dies, that the templet be accurate. This is one of the first points which the diemaker should be sure of before beginning to make the punch die. At times it requires a considerable degree of skill to make a templet that will answer for the work in hand.

The templet shown at *A* in Fig. 11 will be used as an example. After blanking and bending the small projection at the top of the piece to be made, it was to be closed around a groove in the end of the rod, as shown at *B*. After closing, the outside of the blank was supposed to be circular. The die was made to a templet and it was found less difficult to make the die than the templet. In this instance, it was necessary to make two pieces of the desired shape exactly alike, one of which was closed on the grooved rod and tested. The points that were not right were located on the one that had not been closed up.

Then others were laid out from it, due allowance being made for the imperfections of the first. When making the templet, two pieces of stock were placed together, and one half was worked to the laying out lines, as shown at *C*. After the other half had been blocked out somewhere near the line, the pieces were reversed and each half that had been blocked out was filed to conform to the finished half. In this way the ends were made duplicates. When one templet was forced down or closed on the rod and was found correct, the other answered for the templet to be used in laying out the die, and as a gage when finishing the hole in the die.

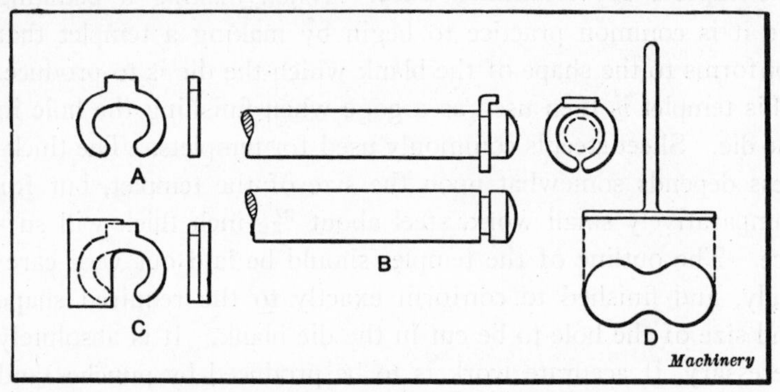

Fig. 11. Example of Blanking Die Templets

In order that templets may be easily handled, it is customary to attach some form of handle to them, which is sometimes done by drilling and tapping a hole in the templet, and cutting a short thread on a piece of wire which is screwed into the tapped hole. Another common method is to attach a piece of wire by means of a drop of solder, as shown at *D*.

Laying Out Die from Templet.—The templet or master blank for a blanking die may be used for laying out the die by transferring the outline of the templet directly to the die-face. The top surface of the die blank should be brightened with a piece of emery cloth, and the surface prepared for laying out by either applying a coppering solution or by heating the die blank evenly all over until a dark blue color is obtained, and then immersing it in oil. The surface will then be either coppered or blued, depending upon the method employed, and on such surfaces all lines made by a sharp scriber will be bright, and made plainly visible by the contrast with the darker background. The templet, or master blank, can now be used for laying out the die. It is first clamped on the face of the die blank; then, by following the outline of the templet with a sharp scriber, its shape is transferred to the face of the blank. Before locating the templet, however, the most economical way of cutting the blanks from the stock must be determined; that is, the way to obtain the greatest number of blanks from a given weight of stock, as explained in connection with the laying out of blanking dies.

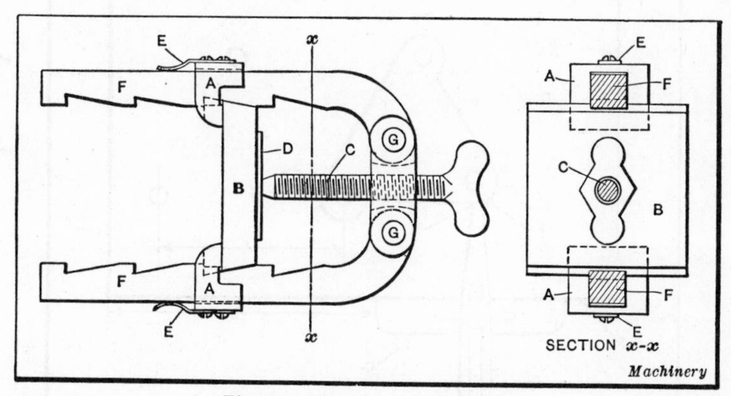

Fig. 12. Diemakers' Crab Clamp

A type of clamp which is very convenient for clamping the templet to the die-face, as well as for other die work, is shown in Fig. 12. With this clamp there is no time wasted in screwing the clamp screw *C* up and down when pieces of different thicknesses are placed between the arms *F*, because the jaws, *A* are made so that they can slide up and down on the arms *F*, which are provided with steps or notches so that the jaws can rest at various places on them as shown. The springs *E* act as frictions, and prevent the jaws from dropping when not resting on the steps. The arms *F* are free to swing on pins *G*, thus making it possible to accommodate various widths of the die blanks.

Adjustable Templet Holder.—The tool shown in Fig. 13 was designed to simplify the laying out of blanking dies of the progressive type when a templet is available. The device consists of two pieces of cold-rolled steel *C* and *G* having slots that permit them to be clamped together with a screw and nut. The member *C* serves as a guide that can be held against the edge of the work, while the member G serves as a holder to which the templet *E* may be temporarily secured by a little solder at *S*. For example, the blank die *D* is to be properly

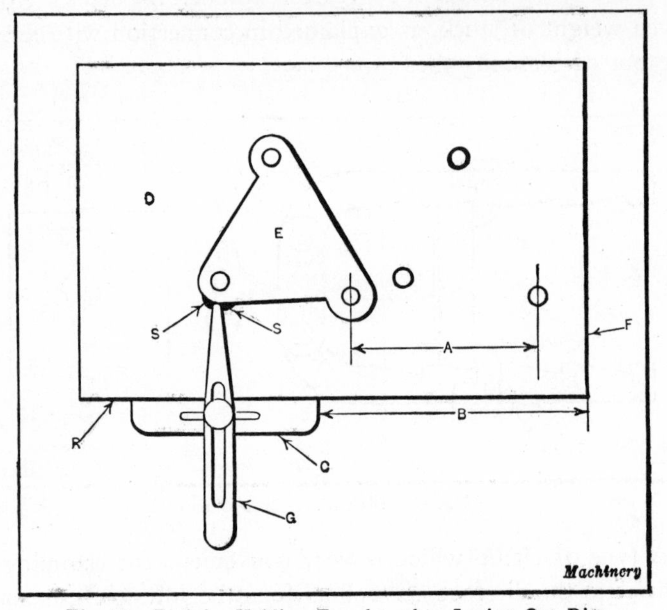

Fig. 13. Tool for Holding Templet when Laying Out Dies

laid out for blanking and piercing pieces like the one shown at *E*. In this instance, the sample piece *E* is employed as a templet in laying out the die. After the piercing holes are drilled, it is necessary to move the templet *E* along a distance *A* to the correct position for scribing the outline of the blanking opening. This is easily accomplished by measuring from the edge *F* of the die to the end of member *C*, as indicated by dimension *B*. The measurements can be made with a combination square or a depth gage. With the tool shown, the templet E can be moved along the die without changing its position relative to the edge R.

Machining Opening in Blanking Die.—After the die has been laid out accurately the next step is to machine the hole for the blanking punch. The way in which this is done will, of course, depend somewhat upon the shape of the blank which is to be produced. As the hole through the die which we have selected as an example (which is shown in Fig. 14) has circular ends, the lathe can be used to advantage for machining these ends. When dies have circular ends or arcs, the machining of the opening can also be facilitated by drilling, the sizes of the drills being selected with reference to the radii of the

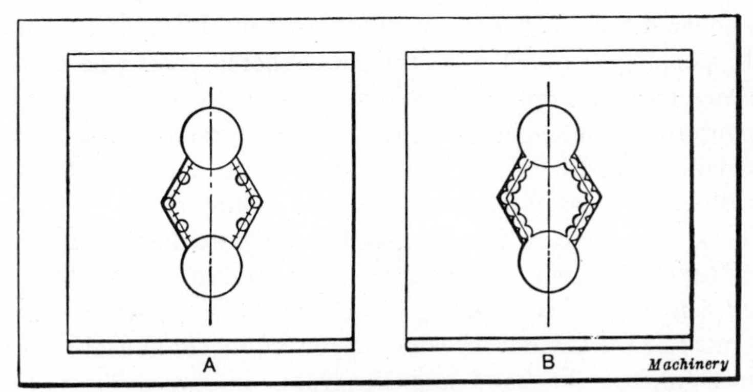

Fig. 14. Example Illustrating One Method of Removing Core of Blanking Die

circular sections. For instance, if the core of the die illustrated in Fig. 14 were to be removed entirely by drilling, a large drill should be used for the circular ends and a smaller size for drilling the rows of holes about the central core. Of course, boring out the ends in the lathe would be a more accurate method than drilling. When drilling a row of holes for the purpose of removing a core (which is a very common method) if each alternate hole is first drilled, as indicated at A, and then the remaining ones, the holes can be spaced closer and drilled with less difficulty, and there will be no bridges between adjacent holes to hold the core in place.

As a blanking die must have clearance, in order that the

blanks, when sheared from the stock, may fall through the die, it is common practice, when drilling, to insert a thin strip beneath the blank and on the side farthest from the hole being drilled, so that the hole is inclined from the vertical equal to the clearance angle. The holes can also be drilled at right angles to the face of the die and then be reamed out with a taper reamer, but the former method is more practicable.

After drilling, most of the surplus metal can be removed with a sharp chisel, but if the die is large it can be machined on the planer or shaper by strapping it to an angle-plate which is inclined to the vertical sufficiently to give the die the proper amount of clearance, or by clamping it between two 1½ degree parallels. Of course, this work may be done more easily on a regular die-slotting machine or die shaper, if one is available. If chipping is resorted to, the chisel should always be driven away from the top of the die as there is danger, when chipping from the other direction, of the metal breaking away outside of the lines. At times it may be advantageous to drill a single hole large enough to insert a milling cutter, and then work out the core on a vertical milling machine. A taper cutter can be used for giving the die clearance. A much more efficient way to cut openings in blanking dies, whenever warranted by the amount of work is by using modern metal-sawing machines of the band and jig types, or special die-milling machines.

Finishing a Blanking Die by Filing.—After the opening in a blanking die has been machined to approximately the required shape and size, the exact shape and size is ordinarily obtained by filing. This may be done by hand or in a filing machine. When the die is to be filed by hand it is fastened in a vise with its top or face toward the back of the vise. The hole is then filed until it fits the master blank or templet. The templet should be frequently tried in the hole, the bearing points being marked with a pencil, and then removed with the file; this operation is repeated until the hole fits the templet perfectly and is large enough to allow it to just pass through. When testing the hole, the surface of the templet should be kept parallel with the top of the die. As the work is nearing completion, it may be necessary to remove it from the vise each time the templet is inserted, to enable one to see the minute openings. A piece of white paper held on the opposite side of the blank will, however, suffice for the earlier stages of the work. When filing, it is sometimes advisable to protect ends which may have been finished previously by the method illustrated in Fig. 15. Piece *A* prevents the edges of hole *P* in the die from coming into contact with the edge of the file when the die is filed out. Piece *B* simply serves the purpose of permitting the die to be held parallel in the vise.

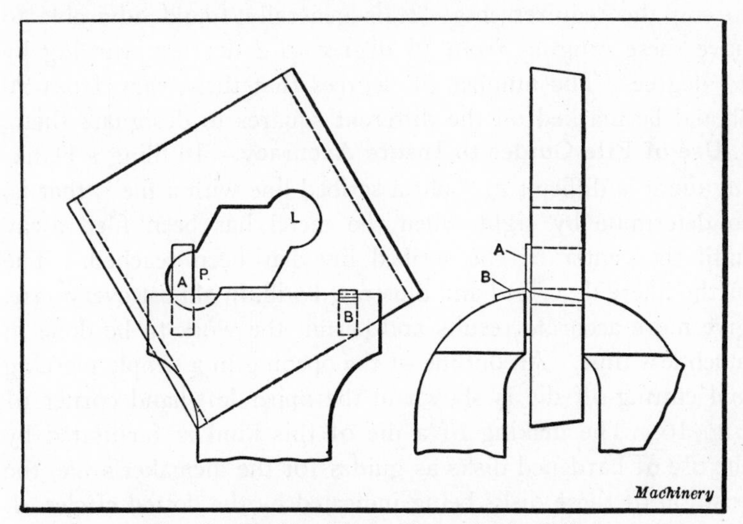

Fig. 15. Blanking Die in Vise ready for Filing

When finishing the hole in the die, the clearance should be filed as straight as possible, so that the blanks, when cut, can easily fall through the opening. To file a narrow surface straight is difficult and requires considerable practice, and while one becomes proficient in work of this kind only through practice, still a hint as to the proper method of procedure may be useful. When the file begins its stroke, the downward pressure exerted by the left hand holding the outer end should be maximum, while a minimum pressure is given by the right hand; as the file advances, the pressure from the left hand decreases, while that from the other increases. After considerable practice, one is enabled, unconsciously, to regulate the pressure on each end of the file so that any "rocking" motion of the file is prevented. If the surface being filed becomes rounded this can usually be remedied by using a sharp scraper which will cut the metal quite rapidly. In filing out the die, it is convenient to have a set of small "squares" which vary from ninety degrees, an amount equal to the angle required on the die for clearance. These may be made from 1/16-inch sheet steel with the base 1/2 inch wide by 2 inches long, and the beam 1/8 inch wide by 1 1/2 inch long, or they can be made to suit the requirements. It is generally found advisable to have these ranging from 1/2 degree to 2 degrees, varying by 1/2 degree. The number of degrees that these vary from 90 should be marked on the different squares to designate them.

Use of File Guides to Insure Accuracy.—In filing a blanking die it is difficult to "split a scribed line with a file"; that is, to determine by sight when the metal has been filed away until the center of the scribed line has been reached. The method here described and illustrated will, in almost every case, give more accurate results and permit the work to be done in much less time. An outline of the opening in a simple piercing and cutting-off die is shown in the upper left-hand corner of Fig. 16. The making of a die of this kind is facilitated by the use of hardened disks as guides for the diemaker's file, the position of these disks being indicated by the dotted circles *A*. Hardened parallels, the positions of which are indicated by the dotted lines *B*, are also used as guides when filing the straight portions of the die-opening. The disks should ordinarily be made from stock 1/8 or 3/16 inch in thickness. As the profile of the punch used with this die is exactly the same as the profile of the work, the radius *R* of the die should be slightly smaller than the radius of the work. For work requiring ordinary accuracy, or for work having limits of plus or minus 0.002 inch, the disks may be turned and bored on a lathe, and then hardened. When extreme accuracy is required, they should be hardened and ground all over and located by the use of gage-blocks or a height gage. The disks employed in making dies can be used over and over, so that it is not usually necessary to charge up the cost of making them to any one job. A set of parallels and disks consisting of four 2-inch and four 4-inch parallels, and a few disks of the more commonly used sizes will cover a surprisingly large range of work. Disks which are not of a standard size should be stamped with the

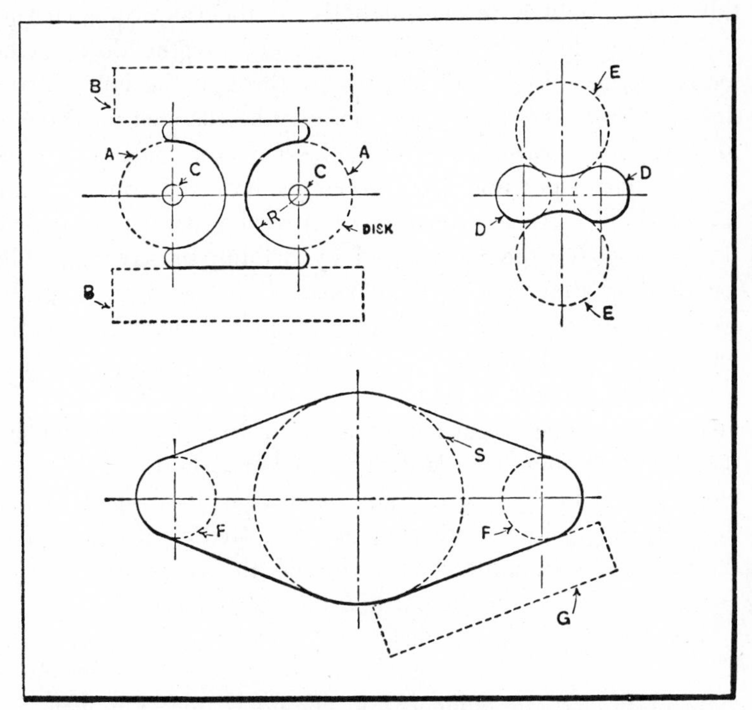

Fig. 16. Use of Hardened Disks and Parallels to Guide File when Filing Die Opening

tool or die number on which they are used, to facilitate identification.

Since the forms or outlines of practically all dies consist of combinations of true geometric figures, it is evident that there are but few cases in which disks and parallels cannot be used to advantage. The disks and parallels, or "masters," as they are sometimes called, are intended to be used as guides for the workman's file, and thus prevent the opening in the die from being filed beyond the limiting profile line. It is true that a file in the hands of a careless workman will be quickly dulled by continually striking the hard edges of the disks, but the number of unskilled workmen to be found in tool-rooms is, or should be, very small.

Regarding the setting of the disks *A*, the two piercing holes *C* should first be laid out, drilled, and reamed. The disks in this case should have central holes of the same diameter as the piercing holes in the die. This permits the disks to be located by pushing small plug gages through the holes in the disks and into the die. The disks may be clamped or soldered in place, great care being taken, if they are soldered, to see that the heat does not change their position. Parallels *B* are then located in their proper relation to the disks, after which the core of the die is removed by drilling or sawing. The locating or attaching of the "masters" before removing the core will prevent drilling or sawing into the metal beyond the outline of the die profile.

In making a die having a profile such as indicated in the view at the upper right-hand corner of Fig. 16, it is evident that holes *D* should be laid out and bored first, after which plugs placed in these holes may be used in locating hardened disks in the positions indicated by the dotted circles *E*. After the disks have been attached to the die, the plugs are removed from holes *D* and the die opening filed to shape.

The method of using disks and parallels in making a die having an opening or profile such as indicated in the lower view in Fig. 16, is evident, and should require but little explanation. The positions and relative sizes of the disks required in making this die are indicated by the dotted circles *F* and *S*, while the position of one of the parallels is indicated by the dotted lines at *G*.

The contour or outline of the die shown in Fig. 17 is such that all the disks or "masters" required cannot be placed on or attached to the die at one time. After the four holes *H* and the two holes *J* have been bored, four small holes *K* should be drilled in the die, if this is permissible. The drilling of these small holes will facilitate the placing of parallels such as indicated by the dotted lines at *L*. After the sides of the die opening determined by these parallels have been finished, the parallels are removed, and disks having the correct radius *R* are attached to the die, being located by holes *K*.

The position of one of the disks located in this manner is indicated by the dotted circle at *M*. If it is not permissible

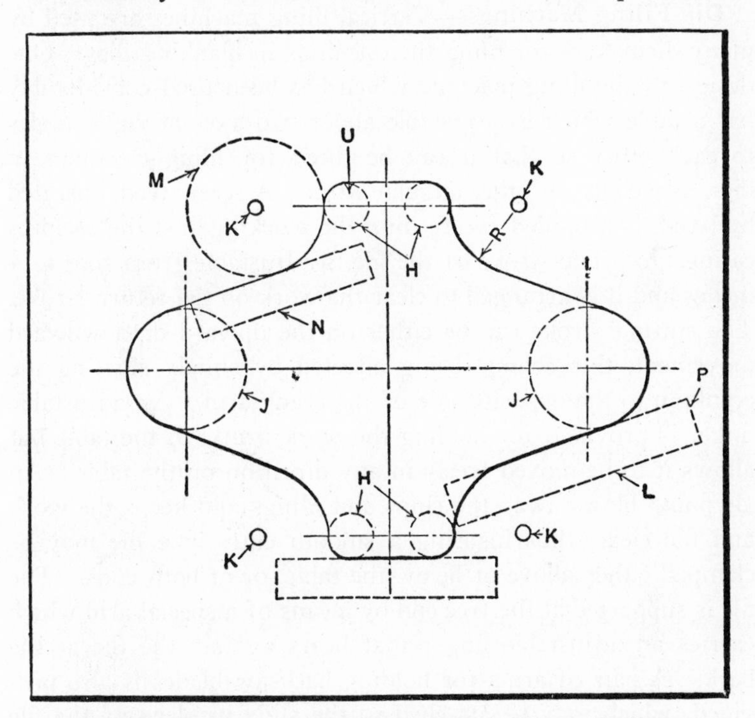

Fig. 17. Method of Drilling Small Holes in Die to Facilitate Location of Disks

to drill holes *K* in the die, the disks may be located against parallels clamped to the die. The correct position of a parallel used for this purpose is indicated by the dotted lines at *N*. With a parallel in this position, the disk can be properly located by bringing its edge into contact with both the parallel and a plug inserted in hole *H*. After attaching the disk to the die, the plug and parallel are removed, and the profile of the die filed to shape in the manner previously described.

The "masters" are exceptionally useful when making shaving and burnishing dies having perpendicular walls or no clearance angle. For dies of this kind disks should be placed both on the face and on the back of the die blank. Care must, of course, be taken to see that the face of the die is parallel with the back of the die, and a height gage or other accurate gaging methods must be employed in setting the "masters."

Die-Filing Machines.—Vertical filing machines are used by many diemakers for filing the openings in blanking dies. One design of die-filing machine which has been used considerably has a table which is adjustable about two axes at right angles to each other so that it can be tilted for filing clearance in dies, as well as for other angular work. A screw feed, operated by hand, is provided for feeding the work against the reciprocating file. The stroke of the file is adjustable from zero to 4 inches and it is arranged to clear the work on the return stroke. The cutting stroke can be either on the upward or downward movement, this change being effected by simply shifting the crankpin to the opposite side of the crank-arm. An adjustable finger is provided for holding the work firmly to the table but allows it to be moved freely in any direction on the table. An air pump blows away the chips and filings and keeps the work and file clear, thus insuring a smooth cut. The file may be clamped either above or below the table, or at both ends. The file is supported at the free end by means of a special arm which carries an adjustable finger that bears against the file at the back. A pair of arms for holding hacksaw blades is also provided, which may be attached to the slide in place of the file arms. Saws are sometimes employed for cutting out the core of the die. One advantage of the die-filing machine, as compared with hand filing, is that straight or flat surfaces can be filed without difficulty because the file is mechanically guided and moves in a straight line, whereas, when filing by hand, it is difficult to do the work accurately.

Fitting the Punch to the Die.—It is customary to make the die and harden it, and then make the punch and fit it to the die. After squaring the end of the punch that is to enter the die, the surface is colored with blue vitriol solution, or by heating it until a distinct brown or blue color is visible, after which the desired shape is marked on the face by scribing. It is often considered advisable to lay out the shape by means of the templet or master blank, but if the templet is not of the same shape on its two edges, or if the shape is irregular and not symmetrical, it will be necessary to place the opposite side against the punch from that placed against the die; therefore, it is the practice, in many cases, to mark the punch from the die instead of using the templet. If the face of the die is given shear, the punch should be marked before the die-face is changed. When laying out several punches from a die which has a number of openings, it is necessary to lay out the punch from the die.

Before transferring the outline of an intricately shaped die to the punch, it is good practice to coat the face of the blanking punch with solder; then machine the solder so that it is level. Coating the punch with solder enables one to obtain a much better outline than would be possible when scribing on the hard steel, and the very narrow and intricate parts can be laid out more easily. If 1/16 inch of solder is evenly placed on the punch, it allows the die to cut a perfect impression in the solder, which is a great help in milling the punch, as the milling cutter can be brought down until it just scrapes the solder. and the cut taken. At the completion of the milling operation the solder is removed.

The surplus stock on the punch is removed by filing, chipping, milling or planing, until it is but a trifle larger than the opening in the die. Usually the punch is machined to within say 1/64 inch of the finished size. The soft punch is then forced into the die to a depth of about 1/64 inch by means of a screw press, after which the punch is filed to about 0.003 or 0.004 inch of the outline produced by the die. This shaving and filing process is repeated until the punch enters the die the required distance. It is then filed or scraped until the desired fit is obtained. When shearing the punch through the die, be sure that it stands perfectly square with the top face of the die. Care should also be taken to see that the die does not remove too much stock. If the die removes a nice curling chip from the punch it is not removing too much stock, but if the chip cracks and breaks as it is severed, it is obvious that it is removing too much stock, and before going any further the punch should be removed and reduced in size, at the point or points where the die was removing too much stock. It is advisable always to use oil on the punch when shearing it through the die.

There are instances in which it is advisable to make punches somewhat differently from the method described. When the nature of the stock to be punched is such as to cause it to cling to the punch, making the operation of stripping difficult, to the extent that any stripper plate put on the die would be bent, or the end of the punch pulled off during the operation, the punch may be made straight for a distance that allows of grinding several times; then the portion immediately above this may be given a taper. This tapered portion of the punch is intended to enter the stock, *but not the die.* Its action is to increase the size of the opening somewhat, thus making the operation of stripping possible without endangering the stripper or punch.

Punches for piercing and blanking copper should be polished quite smooth, as copper clings tightly and is difficult to strip from the punch. If the punch is left rough, the force necessary to strip the blank from the punch may bend it out of shape or break the punch.

Method of Fitting Irregular Shaped Punch Into Die.—A good method of fitting an irregular shaped punch to a die is as follows: A lighted wax taper is held close to the face of the punch so that it is covered with a film of black soot. After the entire face of the punch has been covered with soot in this way the punch is struck into the die. It will be found that the soot will not spread—a difficulty which is often experienced when preparations containing oil are used—and that the punch shows a clear white line where it comes into contact with the die. As a result the punch may be machined to an accurate fit.

The same method may be employed in fitting a force to a die used for stamping up irregular shaped brass shells, where it is required to have the force bear all over the inside of the work in order to harden and toughen the metal. The first step is to stamp up the shell after the force has been fairly well fitted to the die by the aid of narrow brass strips of metal that are of the same thickness as the shell. The inside of the shell is next covered with soot from a lighted wax taper in the manner previously described, after which the shell is again placed in the die and given a second blow. When the shell

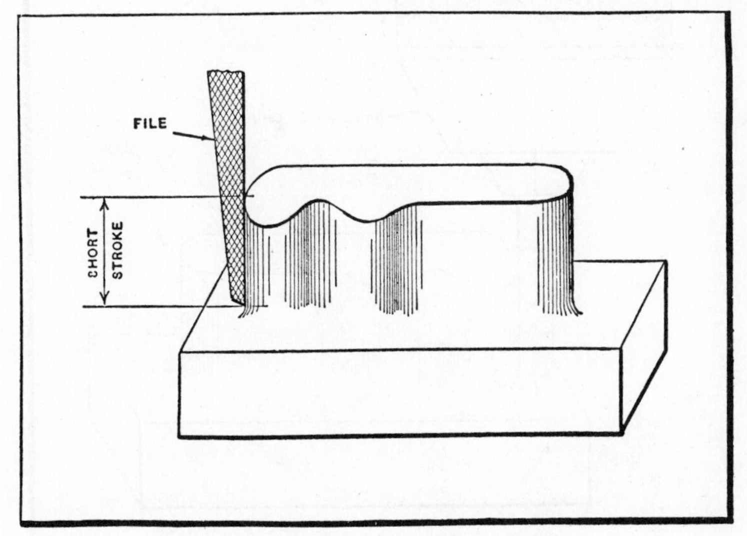

Fig. 18. Method of Hand-filing a Punch

has been removed it will be found that the soot has been deposited on the high spots of the force, which should be machined down to enable it to find an even bearing surface on the entire inside of the shell.

Finishing Punch by Rotary Filing.—After the punch has been sheared and fitted into the die by hand filing (the distance fitted generally being 7/8 inch, although it is sometimes as much as 1 1/2 inches), the punch is next hand-filed under size for "break clearance." As much as 0.010 inch is sometimes filed off, depending on the thickness of the stock to be blanked.

After the punch is hardened, it is often found that the proper amount of clearance has not been provided for, so that it is necessary to stone it down thus making the operation slow, difficult, and extremely expensive.

A punch of common design is shown in Fig. 18. In finishing a punch of this kind, the hand-filing is done with the extreme end of the file, a very short stroke being used. The filing of a flat and square surface by this method is difficult,

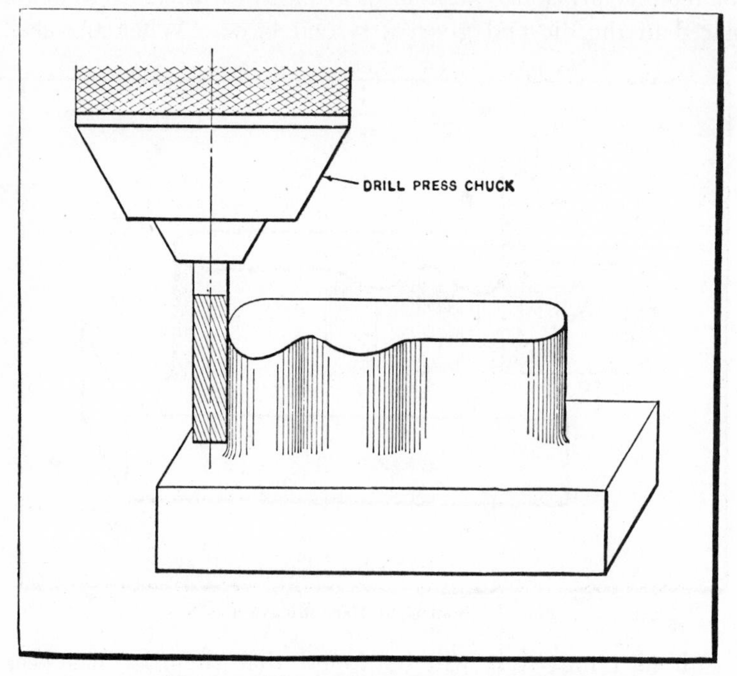

Fig. 19. Filing a Punch with a Rotary File

slow, and costly. Furthermore, the filing of the break clearance, in places where measuring instruments cannot be employed, is but guesswork and most diemakers leave more stock than is required, so that much stoning is necessary.

This painstaking and expensive method can be eliminated by the use of rotary files. Fig. 19 illustrates the method of using rotary files. The file is held in a high-speed drill press chuck, and the punch is brought to bear against it with a gentle pressure. The action is practically the same as in end-milling. The rotary file can also be used for filing dies, templets, gages, etc., and wherever hand-filing can be easily and economically superseded. It will be noticed that the outline traced on the face of the punch is always visible.

In Fig. 20 is shown a clearance rotary file. The shank of the file is smaller in diameter than the body by the same amount as the break clearance on the punch. After the punch has been

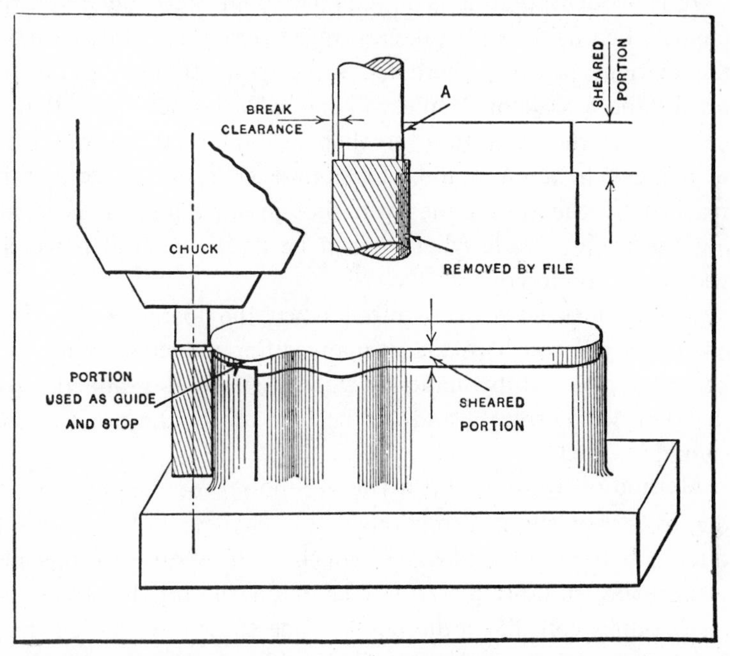

Fig. 20. Using Sheared Part of Punch as a Guide for Rotary File

rough end-milled, a regular rotary file is used to file to within 0.003 or 0.004 inch of the line, and the punch is sheared in about 1/8 inch. Then a clearance rotary file is held in the chuck so the shank will contact with the work as the file mills away the stock, and act as a guide against the sheared part of the punch at *A*. As the work is pushed against the file, the stock is cut away until the shank touches the sheared portion, at which time the desired clearance has been obtained, the shank acting as a guide and stop. At the end of this operation, there is a shoulder left at the sheared portion of the punch due to the reduced diameter of the file shank, but this may be quickly removed with a straight rotary file. In hand-filing operations of this kind, the depth of clearance must often be guessed at because of the impossibility of employing measuring instruments, but with this file, measurements of that kind are unnecessary. Another advantage is that the outline of the punch or die is always within plain view during an operation.

It is evident that it is impossible to file too much off the punch when using a "break clearance" rotary file; furthermore, the amount is everywhere the same as it should be for the break, and a well made file will mill away much more than a hand file in the same time, so that the time required for fitting is reduced to a minimum. Of course sharp fillets cannot be reached by the round file even though its diameter is small, but the saving made where it can be used makes it a worth-while tool to employ.

Rotary files such as required when the methods described are employed can be made in many different ways. They can, of course, be cut by hand or milled. A good grade of steel that will keep straight and not become too brittle nor too soft should be used.

Method of Stoning Out a Die.—Stoning or lapping out a die, to correct slight distortions due to changes in hardening, is often a tedious job and can be much more easily accomplished when using suitably placed guides or guards for the stone. As an example, consider a die like the one shown in Fig. 21, having a square hole to be stoned out. First the outside of the die is ground as nearly parallel with two of the sides of the square hole in the die as possible. Then a block *A*, made of soft steel, having two sides beveled at the same angle as the die, is set parallel with surface *B* and at the correct height. During the lapping operation this block *A* will furnish a good guide for the stone or lap.

Metal Sawing Machines which are used for Diemaking.—While standard types of machine tools are used for many of the operations connected with diemaking, there are certain special types which often can be used to advantage. Machines of the metal-sawing type represent one notable development. These machines are made in two general classes. One class or type operates with a reciprocating action and the other is a continuous cutting band-saw design. These machines are used for sawing out the openings in dies. A hole is first drilled to provide space for the saw, and then the saw is guided along the outline of the opening which may, in this manner, be formed quite close to the size required, there being some stock left for finishing.

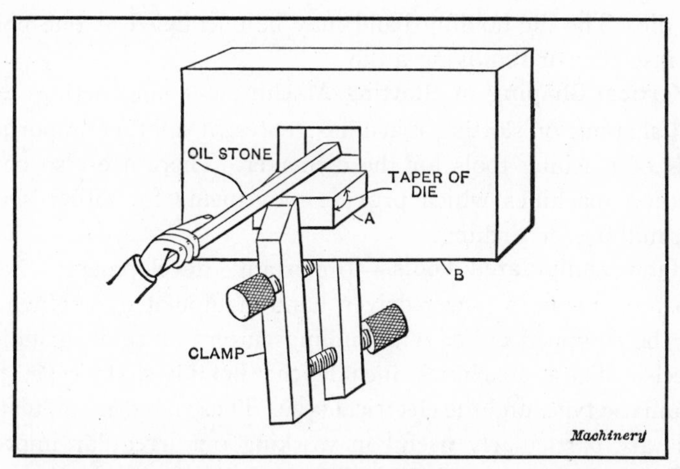

Fig. 21. Diagram Illustrating Method of Stoning out a Blanking Die

When the reciprocating type of machine is used, the saw blade is inserted through the hole drilled in the blank and is then held by clamps attached to the reciprocating member. If a band-saw type of machine is used, it is necessary to break the saw blade and braze the ends together after inserting the saw through the drilled hole. If the proper equipment is at hand this brazing may be done quickly, about three minutes being required for one narrow-blade band-saw which has been designed expressly for die and similar tool work. The continuous cutting action of a band-saw machine makes it possible to work very closely to the required outline of the die opening.

At least one machine of the reciprocating type may be used either for sawing or for filing.

Filing Machine of Continuous Type.—One design of filing machine adapted to die and similar work is of the continuous filing or band type. This machine is designed along the general lines of a band saw and the files, which are attached to a flat steel band, provide a continuous filing or cutting action. As the filing movement is always in the working or cutting direction, there being no reversal, the life of the files is greatly increased. This machine may be equipped with files of whatever cross-sectional shape conforms closest to the outline of the die. The file-holding band may be uncoupled at one point for inserting or removing a die.

Vertical Shaping or Slotting Machines.—Quick-acting vertical shaping or slotting machines represent another important class of machine tools for the diemaker. There are also combination machines which provide movements for either shaping, milling, or drilling.

Hand-manipulated Tools.—Important developments have also been made in power-driven hand-manipulated tools which may be equipped either with milling cutters or small grinding wheels. These machines include the flexible-shaft type, the pneumatic type, and the electrical type. These hand-manipulated tools are particularly useful in working out irregular impressions for forming or similar classes of dies.

One of the commercial air-driven types of grinders adapted for finishing die impressions and for similar work weighs 13½ pounds and has a spindle speed of 28,000 revolutions per minute. Another air-driven grinder weighs only 12 ounces and has a spindle speed of about 40,000 revolutions per minute. The object of these extremely high speeds is to operate the small grinding wheels required for finishing many die cavities, at efficient surface speeds. A hand-manipulated grinder of this type is particularly useful in making any die which has a cavity or impression for forming metal stampings. It is also adapted for finishing both die-casting and drop-forging dies and for various miscellaneous classes of work of a similar nature.

Machines for Die-sinking.—The operation of forming impressions or cavities in dies by milling is commonly referred to as "die-sinking." A simple or plain type of "die-sinker" is similar, in its general arrangement, to a vertical-spindle milling machine and in milling out an impression, cutters are used which will assist, as far as possible, in obtaining whatever shape is required for the die-cavity. One type of machine is largely manipulated by hand, and, in finishing the cavity, it is often necessary to do more or less chipping, filing, scraping, and "typing" by hand. Many die-cavities have circular or spherical impressions or sections. The term "cherrying" relates to the milling of these circular or spherical impressions in dies, as, for example, when a milling cutter is sunk to one-half its depth in milling out a circular recess. Many devices and attachments have been devised to eliminate chipping and the difficult hand work. For example, die-sinking machines have been equipped with a cherrying head or attachment to facilitate milling circular impressions in dies.

Die-sinking Machine Classed as Universal Type.—A die-sinking machine known as a universal type, is so designed that both cherrying and straight die-sinking operations can be performed without special attachments or special cutters. The principal feature of this type is an oscillating head by means of which an ordinary die-sinking cutter can be moved through a circular path, so that both roughing and finishing cherrying operations can be performed. A binder provides for locking the entire oscillating head solidly to the column when the machine is to be used for ordinary die-sinking cuts in which the table elevating and transverse movements are employed. The oscillating head is equipped with power feed and it may also be moved by hand, through a handwheel on the front of the head. This machine will perform many types of cherrying cuts that are impossible on a plain machine. For instance, by combining the rotary table feed and the oscillating cutter movement, it is possible to sink a spherical cut in the surface of a die. The oscillating movement without the rotary motion produces a cylindrical cavity.

As explained later, some types of machines for milling cavities in dies reproduce the shape of a model or master form.

Cutter Shapes for Die-sinking.—In using a die-sinking machine of either the plain or universal types previously described, the shape of the milled cavity may be obtained partly from the shape of the cutter, although, in most cases, the shape is due chiefly to proper manipulation of the machine by the operator, excepting cases where the form is obtained by a cherrying operation, as previously described. A ball or round-end cutter is one common form. The cylindrical cutter having a square end similar to an end-mill is another common shape. A third form that is often required is tapering and has a ball end or round point. With these three simple shapes, a great variety of cavities can be formed by proper manipulation of the machine.

Duplicating Type of Machine.—Some machines for milling dies are so designed that a master form or model of the required form is reproduced in the die. One design is equipped with a vertical milling spindle, a vertical tracer spindle, and a table capable of moving horizontally in any direction. These horizontal movements of the table, in conjunction with vertical movements of the cutter-spindle and tracer spindle, make it possible to reproduce or duplicate various classes of dies, molds, patterns, etc. The duplicator consists of a regular high-speed vertical-spindle milling machine equipped with a duplicator table and tracer head. The work is held upon the duplicator table. At the operator's right, there is an auxiliary table for holding the master or model to be reproduced. This table may be adjusted longitudinally and laterally, and it is equipped with micrometers for setting the model in accurate relation to the work.

The vertical movements of the cutter-spindle and tracer spindle, which operate in unison, are controlled either by a hand-lever or handwheel manipulated by the workman's left hand. The right hand manipulates a hand-lever for moving the duplicator table in whatever direction may be required. These combined movements make it possible to mill various classes of dies, plastic molds, glass molds, etc. The reproduction in this case is full size, there being no enlargement or reduction from the original model. The duplicator table, which is mounted on ball-bearing slides, may be clamped in position either when setting up work or for roughing out cavities by feeding with the regular milling machine table screws. These roughing cuts can be taken with standard end-mills; but for finishing operations, single-flute cutters are recommended. These cutters may have square, rounded, pointed, or other shapes, and they are easily resharpened or reground to whatever shape may be required.

Pantograph Type of Machine.—This type of machine is so designed that the required shape or contour can be reproduced from an *enlarged* model. For example, if a part must be milled to a certain shape or contour, an enlarged master templet is made to the same contour. The operator guides the tracing point around the master templet and the cutter reproduces the templet shape on a reduced scale. The master templet, which may be of brass or steel, frequently is from three to five times larger than the work, so that any slight errors which may exist in the templet are reduced proportionally on the milled part. The reduction is obtained by a pantograph mechanism. A pantograph is a combination of links which are so connected and proportioned as to length that any motion of one point in a plane parallel to that of the link mechanism will cause another point to follow a similar path either on an enlarged or a reduced scale. Such a mechanism may be used as a reducing motion. For instance, most engraving machines have a pantograph mechanism interposed between the tool and a tracing point which is guided along lines or grooves of a model or pattern. As the tracing point moves, the cutting tool follows a similar path, but to a reduced scale, and cuts the required pattern or design on the work. A pantograph mechanism, as applied to a profiling machine, may be designed to give reductions between the templet and work ranging from no reduction or 1 to 1 down to 6 to 1. The pantograph is provided with scales or graduations showing the adjustment required for obtaining any reduction within the minimum and maximum range. Machines of this kind are used in making blanking dies, templets, or for milling various other irregular contours.

Machine of Three-dimension Pantograph Type.—Machines are available for milling practically any shape required, by reproducing the shape of a model or pattern. These machines of the "three-dimension" type are used in milling forming dies, molds for plastics or glass, molds for die-castings, dies for silverware, or other forming operations. The pattern or model to be reproduced is larger than the work, to insure accurate reproduction of all of the finer details. As a tracer point is moved over the surface of the model, the cutter follows a similar path but on a reduced scale, as determined by the adjustment of the pantograph mechanism. The pantograph bars may be graduated for reductions ranging from 2 to 1 to 8 to 1, or more. As a general rule, reductions of 2, 3 and 4 ordinarily are employed. When this machine is in use, both cutter-spindle and tracer spindle remain vertical to the work and to the model or pattern. In other words, any vertical movement of the tracer, as it is traversed across the model, is imparted to the cutter-spindle in a reduced ratio as determined by the pantograph adjustment.

Machine for Irregular Form Milling which Automatically Reproduces the Master or Model.—The Keller machine may be operated either manually or with automatic control of the tracer and cutter. Machines of this general type are used for milling various sunken or raised forms on molds, dies, etc., and for milling certain machine parts. The master form or templet to be reproduced is the same size as the work and is attached to a vertical work-holder above the work itself. When the operation is simply that of contour milling, the cutter is set to the required depth and remains at this depth while the tracer and master templet control the horizontal and vertical movements of the machine. For these contouring operations, a thin sheet-metal templet ordinarily is used.

A second type of tracer control is used for three-dimensional work such as milling sunken or raised forms. Tracer control in this case is automatic. The tracer continuously seeks contact with the surface of a solid master model, as the automatic longitudinal and transverse feeding movements cause the cutter to cover the entire surface, thus finally reproducing the complete shape of the model. This method is employed for milling various classes of molds, forming dies, forging dies and die-casting dies, as well as other kinds of work. Another type of tracer control regulates the horizontal and vertical movements, as in contour milling, by following around the edge of a master while, at the same time, controlling whatever depth variations may be required. This control may be utilized for such work as cutting a small groove or bead which extends irregularly over a surface of varying depth.

Cutters Used.—Several different forms of cutters have been designed especially for use on Keller machines. For example, the end of the cutter may be square, partially rounded, or fully rounded to a ball shape. For ordinary profiling, a mill having a right-hand cut and left-hand spiral flutes is recommended. In milling molds or dies requiring a slight taper or draft around the sides, a cutter having a taper of 5 to 7 degrees may be used. For very fine delicate engraving work, where fine details must be duplicated accurately, a sharp pointed type of cutter is used. For some classes of work, special cutters are required.

Tracer Points.—Tracer points may be cylindrical or tapering. If cylindrical, the ends may be square, partly rounded, or fully rounded to a ball form to suit the type of cutter. These tracer points are also made to various sizes or diameters in order to adapt them to different classes of work. For example, a tracer of a certain size or shape might make proper contact with one model but not with another of different form.

Clearance Between Blanking Punch and Die.—Usually there is some clearance between a punch and die, the punch being somewhat smaller than the hole in the die. The purpose of this clearance is to assist the shearing action, reduce the pressure required, and produce smoother edges on the blanked part. It may not always be possible to determine the ideal amount of clearance, except by actual experiment, because it depends upon the thickness of the stock and its physical properties, and may also be affected by the relation between the size of the punch and the stock thickness, especially for relatively small piercing punches. (For additional information concerning the effect of clearance upon the action of a blanking die see Chapter X, which deals in part with clearance as related to the action of metal in shearing.)

Various approximate rules are employed by diemakers for determining clearance and some of these differ widely, partly because of different conditions, as well as on account of differences of opinion. These variations in practice probably are also due, in some cases, to the fact that *clearance* may be regarded by some designers as the space between the punch and die on one side, whereas others use the term to indicate total clearance or twice the clearance per side.

How Diemakers Define Clearance.—In order to obtain definite information in regard to the prevailing practice in designating clearance, data was secured from fourteen firms specializing in die work. Seven of these firms define clearance as the space between the punch and die on any side, or one-half the difference between the punch and die sizes. The remaining seven firms consider clearance as the total difference between the punch and die sizes.

Some of the firms in the first group pointed out that the advantage of designating clearance as the space on each side is particularly evident in the case of numerous dies of irregular form or dies of angular shape. In other words, while the practice of designating clearance as the difference between the punch and die diameters may be satisfactory in the case of round dies, it leads to confusion when the dies are of special unsymmetrical forms. One firm also refers to the advantage of measuring clearance on one side only by using a thickness gage, especially when the shape of the die opening is irregular. It is evident from the foregoing that the term "clearance" should not be used in specifications without indicating clearly just what it means. According to the practice of one prominent manufacturer of dies, the term "cutting clearance" is used to indicate the space between the punch and die on each side, and the term "die clearance" refers to the angular clearance provided below the cutting edge so that the parts will clear as they fall through the die.

Determining the Amount of Clearance.—The proper amount of clearance between a punch and die will result in a clean fracture of the metal and, consequently, less wear on the dies. In order to obtain a clean fracture, soft stock requires more clearance than hard stock. Even a small difference in the amount of clearance may have a decided effect upon the character of the fracture; hence in determining clearance, rules, at best, serve only as a general guide. If the term *clearance* is understood to mean the space between the punch and die on one side, the clearance according to a rule that has been widely used, equals 0.04 to 0.06 times the stock thickness for mild steel and brass. If clearance means the total difference between the punch and die sizes, then clearance equals 0.08 to 0.12 times the stock thickness.

Hand-operated Press for Testing Clearance.—The proper amount of clearance that should be provided between a punch and die for blanking any material can be determined with the aid of an inexpensive sub-press, such as illustrated diagrammatically in Fig. 31, Chapter I. First a simple punch, 0.125 inch in diameter, and a corresponding die should be made for use in this press, as indicated at *A* and *B*.

Experiments should be made in blanking the material with various degrees of clearance between the punch and die. Starting with a snug fit, the clearance should be increased by lapping the die until burrs commence to show around the pierced hole. Readings should be taken with each 0.0001 inch increase in the diameter of the die hole, of the amount of reduction in the length of spring *C* at the instant that blanking occurs. This can be conveniently done by noting the position of pointer *E* along scale F. The diameter of the die corresponding with the smallest amount of spring deflection during a blanking operation provides the proper amount of clearance for the material blanked.

Clearances for Magnesium Alloys.—In blanking and punching magnesium alloys the clearance should be held to a minimum; in fact, for sheets under 0.065 inch in thickness, the punch should be sheared into the die whenever possible. For sheets thicker than 0.065 inch, the clearance on the side should not exceed 0.03 to 0.05 times the stock thickness. Most blanking and punching operations on magnesium sheets are done cold; however, sheets thicker than 0.065 inch may be blanked at an elevated temperature. The amount of clearance depends upon thickness of the stock, area of the blank, hardness and ductility of the material, and its resistance to shear.

Clearance for Blanking Aluminum.—Tests conducted in the research department of the Aluminum Company of America indicate that dies for aluminum should have more clearance than is generally considered correct. These tests were made on fifteen different grades and tempers of aluminum and the object was to determine the maximum and minimum clearances for a given stock thickness, which produces the smoothest sheared surfaces. The smallest clearances for the different materials tested were found to range from 0.078 × stock thickness to 0.145 × stock thickness, and the maximum clearances were found to range from 0.119 × stock thickness to 0.194 × stock thickness. The results indicated that the larger clearances are satisfactory for thick sheets, but for sheets under 1/8 inch in thickness the clearance should equal the average value. An average of 0.14 × stock thickness can be used in nearly all cases with quite satisfactory results regardless of the kind and temper of the aluminum or aluminum alloy used. The indications are that smooth surfaces on the edges of blanks will eliminate many of the difficulties caused by edge cracking and burrs that occur during later operations.

Angular Clearance for Dies.—The amount of angular clearance ordinarily given a blanking die varies from one to two degrees, although dies that are to be used for producing a comparatively small number of blanks are sometimes given a clearance angle of four or five degrees to facilitate making the die quickly. Many small dies have a clearance of one-quarter to one-half degrees. There are two methods of giving clearance to dies: In one case the clearance extends to the top face of the die as indicated at *A* in Fig. 22; in the other, there is a space about ⅛ inch below the cutting edge which is left practically straight, there being a very small amount of clearance. A die of this type is illustrated at *B*. For very soft metal, such as soft, thin brass, the first method is employed, but for harder material, such as hard brass, steel, etc., it is better to have a very shallow clearance for a short distance

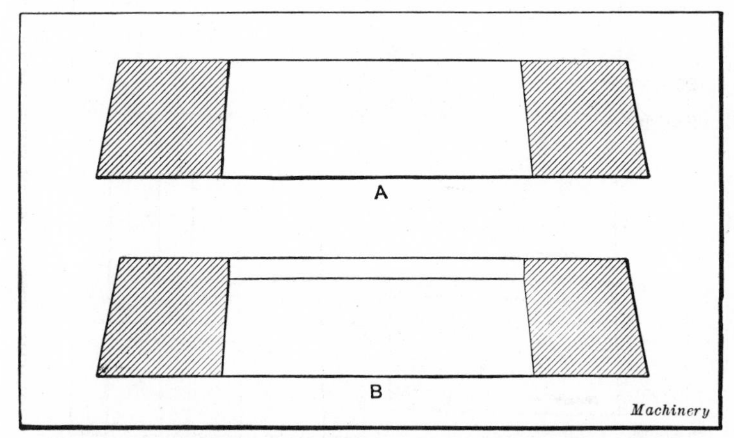

Fig. 22. Sectional Views of Blanking Die Illustrating Two Methods of Giving Clearance to the Cutting Edge

below the cutting edge. When a die is made in this way, thousands of blanks can be cut with little variation in their size, as grinding the die-face will not enlarge the hole to any appreciable extent.

For aluminum, the angular clearance should be at least one degree on both the punch and die. Punches and dies for this metal should be carefully cleaned occasionally to remove the fine particles of aluminum that adhere to the edges of the tools and the surfaces of the tools should be kept bright and polished. As aluminum is a soft metal, it clings tightly to the punch, and unless the surface is smooth, difficulty in stripping off the work is likely to be met with. The use of a good lubricant has an important effect on the appearance of finished articles. For deep-drawing tools a cheap grade of vaseline or lard oil is recommended, but for blanking, stamping, and shallow-drawing tools a thinner lubricant, such as paraffin, is preferable.

Shear of Punches and Dies.—When the cutting face of a die is inclined each way from the center, as at *A*, Fig 23, or is made hollow, as at *B*, it is said to have *shear*. The cutting

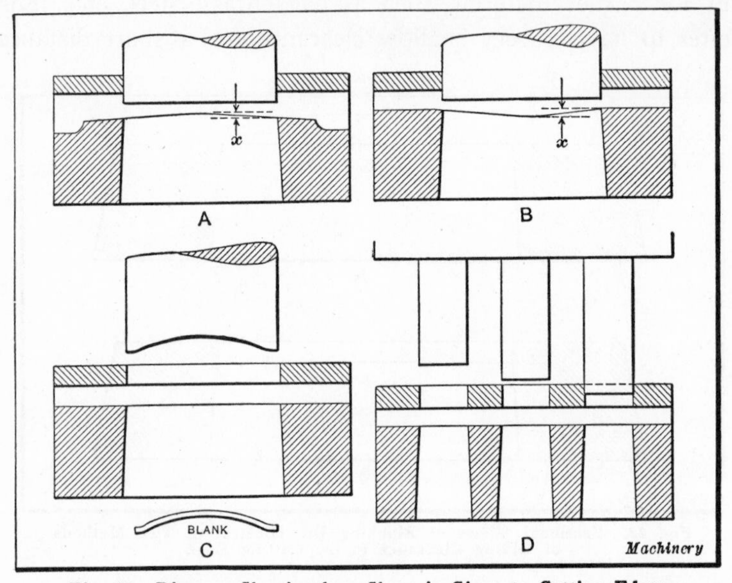

Fig. 23. Diagram Showing how Shear is Given to Cutting Edges

faces of dies are given shear for the same reason that the teeth of some milling cutters are made helical or spiral, in that the shear makes it possible to cut the blank from the sheet with less expenditure of power and therefore reduces the strain on the punch and die. Whether a die should be given shear or not depends upon the thickness of the stock to be cut and, in some cases, upon the power of the press available. When comparatively thick material is to be blanked out, shear on the die face reduces the power required, as previously mentioned. A die is also given shear, at times, when the stock is not very thick but for the reason that it is necessary to use a small press.

If shear is required it is customary to give shear to the face of the die but there are instances when it is advisable to leave the face of the die flat and give shear to the punch instead. In general, the shear is given to the punch when the stock around the hole is the desired product and the material removed by the punch is the scrap. The face of the die is sheared when the blank or that part which is cut out by the punch is the product. The amount of shear which a die should have to give the best results depends not only upon the thickness of the stock but also upon the length of the blank to be cut and the power of the press.

The Amount of Shear.—Ordinarily the amount of shear *x* Fig. 23 should equal about twice the thickness of thin light stock, but for heavy material the shear should equal the stock thickness. The exact method of obtaining the shearing effect depends somewhat upon the shape of the die. An oblong or rectangular-shaped die may be given shear as illustrated at either *A* or *B*. The method shown at *B* is generally considered preferable. The die-face is ground so that the cutting edges slope towards the center, which should be rounded and not sharp, because a sharp corner tends to crack the metal at this point. A space about 1/4 or 1/2 inch wide, depending upon the size of the die, is left flat at the ends. When a die is sheared as at *B*, the punch will begin cutting at both ends instead of at the center, and if the hole in the die is long in proportion to the width, this tends to give better support to the punch because both ends enter the die at the beginning of the cut; moreover, the stock is held more securely during the blanking operation. Some dies are given shear by simply grinding them concave on the face of the grinding wheel. This concave or circular form is inferior to that shown at *B*, because there is less shearing effect toward the center of the die. The cutting edge of a round blanking die is generally given shear by grinding a series of three or four waves on the top surface, thus leaving a corresponding number of raised portions where the cutting action begins as the punch comes into contact with the stock.

Forming End of Punch to Produce Work of Required Shape.—When the face of the punch is left flat and shear is given to the die, the blanks cut out by the punch will be approximately flat and the remaining stock or scrap will be bent and distorted somewhat, whereas, if the shear is given to the punch and the die is left flat, the order will be reversed; that is, the part cut by the punch will be bent and the rest of the stock will come out flat. This effect which the shear has upon the shape of the stock is utilized in some instances in order to cut out a blank and bend or form it in one operation. The principle is illustrated by the diagram at *C*, Fig. 23. The end of the punch is made to conform to the required shape of the blank; when the punch descends and cuts out the blank the latter is pressed in against the concave end and is bent to shape, thus eliminating a second operation. This method is only practicable for producing blanks of simple form.

The blank C in Fig. 24 can be formed to the convex shape shown, by simply rounding the end of the punch to a radius slightly in excess of that desired on the blank. The punch in the lower left-hand corner is used to produce the part shown at *D*. This piece is termed a "pin catch," and millions of them have been made by tools similar to the one shown.

The die is made the same as any ordinary blanking die, of a size and shape that will produce the developed blank. After the punch has been sheared into the die, the end is milled to the shape shown, which must be determined by experiment. After the shape has been established, a gage or templet is made from a piece of sheet steel which can be used as a guide when sharpening the punch. When the tool is in operation, the point *A* enters the stock first, and as it descends, the stock is curled away from the inclined edge. When the flat portion *B* reaches the stock, the upper rounded portion of the catch has been completely formed, so that the piece *D* is completed when the flat portion is blanked out by end *B*.

Another type of die, used largely in the jewelry industry, is shown in the lower right-hand corner of the illustration. This design is referred to as a "pinch-off" tool or die, and as the name implies, it pinches off the stock after drawing the blank. This tool is used in the production of shallow cup-shaped blanks which are made from thin, soft metal such as brass, silver, or rolled-gold plate. As an example of the use of this type of die, assume that a cup ½ inch in diameter, with a wall $\frac{1}{16}$ inch

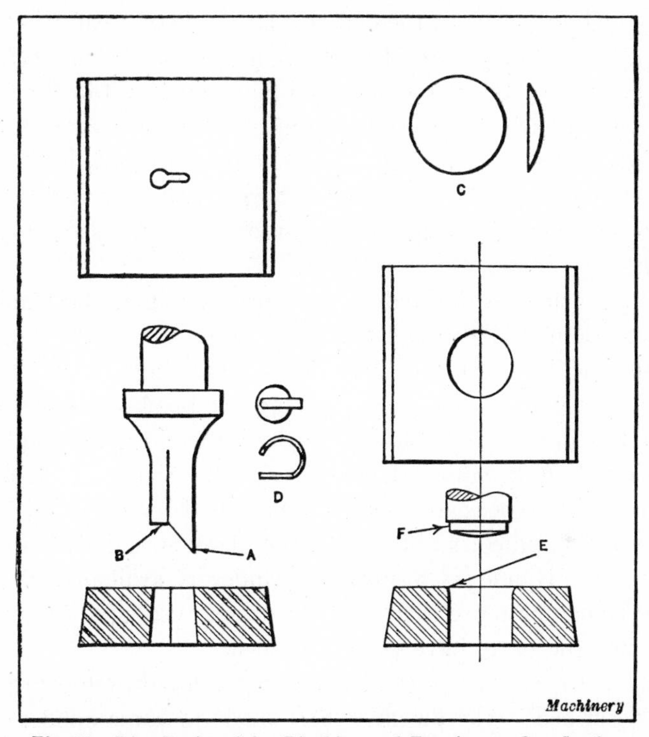

Fig. 24. Dies Designed for Blanking and Forming at One Stroke

high, having its base slightly rounded is to be made from stock 0.010 inch thick. A hole slightly less than ½ inch in diameter is first bored in the die, and the upper edge of the hole is rounded to a radius of about $\frac{1}{64}$ inch, as shown at *E*. The die is then hardened and lapped to a mirror finish, care being taken to keep the hole straight, after which the radius *E* is stoned to remove all tool marks.

The punch is next turned and filed to a snug fit in the die, and a radius is formed on its end to produce the required radius in the bottom of the blank. The end of the punch is then turned down as shown at *F*. The length of the step thus formed is made equal to the height of the cup measured on the inside, while the diameter is less than the large diameter of the punch by an amount slightly less than twice the thickness of the stock. The step portion should be smooth and tapered slightly toward the end so that the blanks can be easily stripped from the punch. In making a cup of the size specified, the diameter of the step end would be about 0.478 inch. This causes the punch to have an ironing effect on the stock which prevents it from wrinkling. The shoulder formed at the end of the step should be square and sharp, because it is this part of the punch that pinches off the stock as it enters the top of the die.

The punch is so located in the press ram that the blank is pushed completely through the die. When the punch is withdrawn, the walls of the blank spring out slightly and catch on the sharp edge of the die, causing the blank to be stripped from the punch. The lower face of the die is ground off occasionally to keep the edge of the opening sharp. In making a die of this type, care must be taken to keep the hole from being bell-mouthed, as otherwise the blank would stick to the punch. Of course, if a suitable grinder is available, dies of this type can be more easily and accurately produced by grinding after the parts have been hardened.

Blanks of irregular outline are also produced by tools of the type described. The punch is first made to correspond to the shape of the outside of the blank required, but without a step on the end. The punch is then hardened and faced off flat, after which it is used to broach the opening in the die. After the die has been broached, the punch is annealed and a step formed on its end by milling wherever possible and chipping or filing the points that cannot be milled. The radius at the edge of the die opening is first filed, and then stoned smooth after the die is hardened.

Varying Punch Lengths in Multiple Punching.—The sketch *D* (Fig. 23) illustrates the stepped method of making a multiple or gang punch, which is sometimes resorted to in order to secure the effect of shear. When several holes are to be punched at each stroke of the press, the work can be distributed by varying the length of each successive punch an amount, for steel, equal to about one-third the thickness of the stock; then as the punch descends, the holes will be punched progressively instead of simultaneously, and, as the longest punch will have done all or nearly all of its work before the next one comes into action, the full power of the press is available for each punching operation. The difference between the lengths of successive punches is often made equal to the stock thickness, but this difference should equal the amount of penetration required to fracture the blank, as this will result in smoother action. In blanking or piercing steel, the blank is practically severed in most cases when the punch has passed about one-third the way through the sheet, but the amount varies more or less depending upon the ductility of the metal. In any case, it is preferable to have a following punch engage the stock before the preceding one is relieved of *all* pressure, because the punching of successive holes is then done by a more continuous application of power and a jerky action, which might result otherwise, is avoided.

Locating Punches in Follow-dies.—In making follow- or tandem-dies, considerable trouble is often experienced in getting the small punches to line up properly with the holes in the die. This is especially true when the punch-holders are made of cast iron, as the sand-holes and soft places cause the drill to run out of square, which frequently makes the method of spotting holes through the die impossible. Another method of doing this work consists of placing a jig button on the punch-holder in exactly the same position as the hole in the die with which it is to mate. The punch-holder is then set in a lathe and the button is made to run dead true. The button is next taken off and the hole is drilled or bored to the required size for the shank of the punch. This method requires very careful measurements to be made which, of course, involves a considerable amount of time.

The method to be outlined does not require any measurements to be made. The first step is to make the guide *A*, Fig. 25. Satisfactory results can be obtained with guides made of cast iron, although it would be better to make them of steel, hardened and ground. The important point is to get

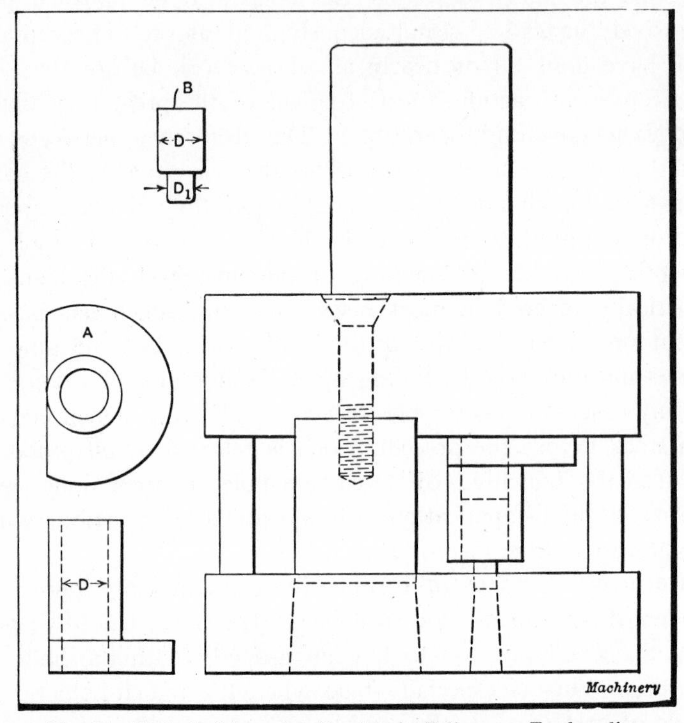

Fig. 25. Method of Locating Punches in Follow- or Tandem-dies

the guide hole square with the bottom of the flange; the height of the guide should be 1/8 inch less than the height from the surface of the punch-holder to the end of the punch, and the wall around the hole should preferably be 1/8 inch thick. The flange is made about 1 1/2 inch in diameter by 1/4 inch thick and is cut away on one side to enable a hole to be made close to a large punch.

The hole in the guide is the same size as the shank of the

punch which is to be carried by the punch-holder. The next part to be made is shown at *B*; it consists of a small piece of cold-rolled steel about 3/4 inch long. The large diameter *D* is turned so that it will push into the guide without shake, and the small diameter D_1 so it can be entered into the hole in the die with a light tap. The small end is made about 1/4 inch long and the large end 1/2 inch in length.

In setting up a job, the small end of the piece *B* is fitted into the die and the large end into the hole in the guide, as shown in the illustration. The large blanking punch is next fastened in the holder and then lowered into the die. Two parallel strips (see illustration) are then placed between the die and punch-holder, which are of sufficient height to keep the holder from striking the guide. The guide is then drawn up against the punch-holder to which the flange is secured with two parallel clamps. The die is now removed and the pilot taken from the guide; the holder can then be turned up and spotted through the guide with a drill of the proper size to fit the hole. The hole is drilled to the required depth and of a diameter 1/64 inch smaller than the required size, the final finish being obtained with a rose reamer. If the reamer is a proper fit in the hole in the guide, the hole in the holder will be square with the surface and line up exactly with the hole in the die. This operation must be repeated for each hole that is required, and after the method has been used in a shop for some time, the necessary guides and plugs for any size of punch will have accumulated, thus saving a considerable amount of time and labor in making punch-holders.

Locating Punches in Punch-holder.—A simple method of locating round, piercing punches in the punch-holder, which has proved very satisfactory, is illustrated in Fig. 26. The holes for the punches can be located, drilled and reamed very quickly, and if reasonable care is taken in setting, the work will be sufficiently accurate for ordinary conditions. This method is used when punches are secured in the punch-holder by set-screws.

Referring to the illustration, *A* is the punch-holder and *B* is a holder made of cast iron, carefully machined top and bottom, and bored to fit the shank of the punch-holder, which is fastened in it by the set-screw *C*, the punch-holder resting on parallels. *D* is a locating button hardened and ground, having a ½-inch hole in the upper part and a ¼-inch hole in the lower part. The ½-inch hole should be ground straight and true and with its axis at right angles to the bottom of the button. *H* is a pilot made of tool steel hardened and ground, with a Morse

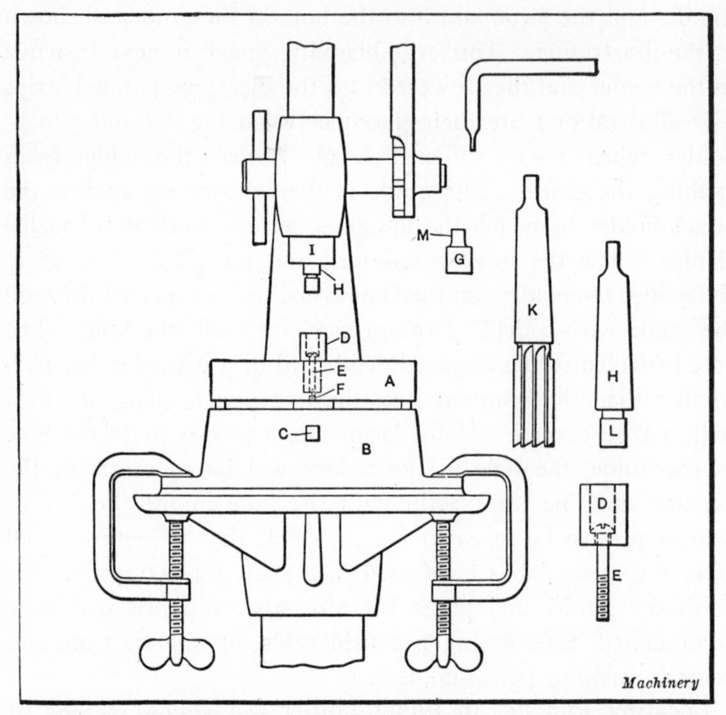

Fig. 26. Simple Method of Locating Piercing Punches in Punch-holder

taper shank to fit the spindle of the drill press and has a portion *L* which is made a good sliding fit in button *D*. (See enlarged detail.) *G* is a plug made to fit snugly in the button *D* and has a portion *M*, which is the same size as the body of the punch; it is also made to fit snugly in the templet. These plugs are made in a large variety of standard sizes and form a permanent part of the outfit. The reamer or end-mill *K* is made with a

Morse taper shank and is ground so that it will ream a hole which shall be a drive fit for the shank of the punch.

To lay out the holes in the punch-holder for the punches, proceed in the following manner: Lay out the various holes from the templet which was used in laying out the die, and drill holes 1/32 inch smaller in diameter than the shank of the punch, to the depth that the punch is to be set in the punch-holder. Then the small hole shown at *F* is drilled and tapped for a button-head machine screw. The first punch-holder is now reamed with the reamer *K* and the punch is driven in place. The button *D* is then held in place with a screw *E* over the next hole in the punch-holder, the plug *G* placed in the button *D*, and with the templet in place on the first punch, the button *D* is located for the second hole and securely held in place by the screw *E*. The pilot *H* is now placed in the spindle *I* of the drill press and the punch-holder located on the table, so that pilot *H* enters the button *D*. The holder is then held in place by the C-clamps shown, the button *D* removed by means of the bent screw-driver *J*, which is made from 1/4-inch round steel, the pilot *H* removed, and the reamer *K* placed in the spindle of the drill press, when the hole can be reamed to size; the same procedure is followed for all the punches. In using this method it is necessary to see that the spindle of the drill press is carefully adjusted and that the table lines up properly with it. This same method could also be used on the milling machine.

Aligning a Punch With a Die.—In making dies, a method known as "staking" is sometimes employed to change the position of the punch slightly in the punch-holder so that it will be in accurate alignment with the die. The "staking" operation is often accomplished by making prick-punch marks in the punch-holder close to one side of the punch. The compressing of the metal in this manner forces the punch over a little. When the shape of a die is changed slightly by the hardening process, the punches can often be "staked" over so that they will be brought into alignment again. It is difficult to align punches properly by this method when they are spaced close together. It has been found, however, that punches that have been aligned by "staking" often give trouble, so this method must be regarded as a makeshift and should not be commended except in unusual cases.

A better method of obtaining accurate alignment when two or more round punches are to be located in line with the holes in the die, is to harden and grind the dies before making the punch-holder. In this case, the finished die is fastened to the unbored punch-holders by means of accurately fitted temporary dowel-pins. The punch-holder with the die attached to it is then clamped to the faceplate of the lathe. After the hole in the die has been aligned with the spindle of the lathe by the use of an indicator, the die is removed and the hole bored in the punch-holder. The same procedure is followed until the holes for all the punches have been bored. For irregular shaped punches, it is customary to shave the punch into the die. to transfer the shape of the die to the punch end.

Position of Punch Relative to Forming and Bending Dies.—When setting up a press for forming operations the blank as formed by the tools is used to locate the punch in the die before securing the die to the press. If the tools are being tried out for the first time and no sample has been made, they may be set with strips of metal cut from the stock to be formed. When setting the die for a piece in which the bends are not parallel but off at an angle, it is usually impracticable to set them with a previous blank, because, when the punch is brought down, the tendency is to push both die and blank away. The more practical method is to locate it approximately with the blank and slightly tighten the screws in the press bed; then with two strips of metal the same size as the blank, gage the exact distance, after which the die can be secured to the press. Do not assume that a die is certain to be satisfactory when the samples have been produced by bringing down the press slowly by hand, as there is sometimes more or less variation in what the tools will do when operated by hand and when operated by power.

Aligning Stock Guide Opening in Stripper Plate.—The proper alignment of the stock guide opening in the stripper plate of a progressive die is important. If the stock guide is not properly aligned, the stock will be pulled over by the pilots. Fig. 27 shows a simple method of obtaining accurate alignment. With this method a strip *A* having an offset is used. The thin end of this strip is located against the pilot *B*, and the heavy end is placed against the corresponding perforating punch *C*. A pair of small parallel clamps *D* may be used to hold the strip *A* in position.

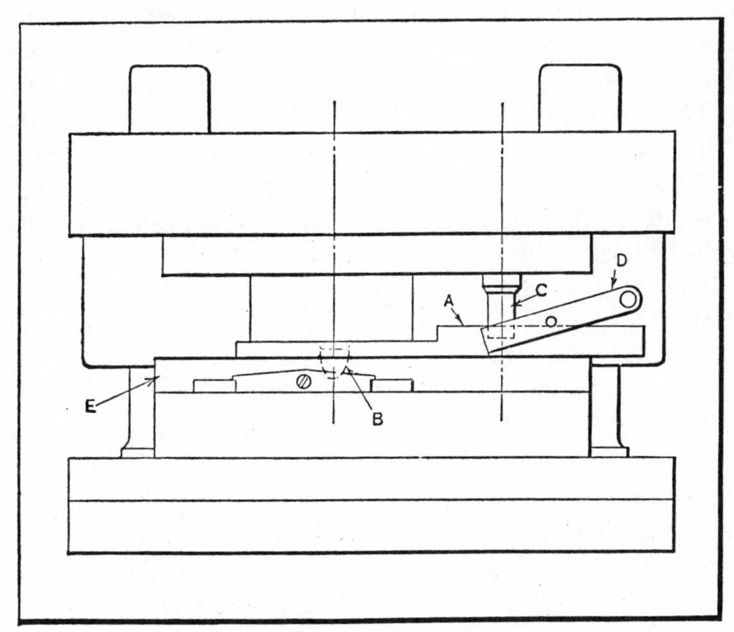

Fig. 27. Diagram Showing Method of Aligning Stock Opening in Stripper Plate

After clamping the strip in place, the die is closed, as shown in the illustration, and a line scratched on the stripper plate *E*, using the edge of strip *A* as a guide. This line makes it a very simple matter to set up the work properly for machining the opening for the stock. The accurate location of the stock guide slot by this method will save many broken pilots and eliminate much repair work. When this method is employed the die does not need to be finished on any of its sides to facilitate laying out the work as it is commonly done. On work that does not require great accuracy, it is simply necessary to lay a templet on the die and drill the required holes.

The offset strip *A* is also of value in testing the alignment of dies which do not function properly. For this work, a line is first scribed on the stripper plate, as previously described. The stripper plate is then mounted on an angle plate where it is aligned in a horizontal position, using the scribed line as a guide. The parallelism of the stock opening with respect to the scribed line is tested by running an indicator along the edge of the stock opening. If it is found necessary to remachine the stock opening in a shaper or milling machine, the scribed line is simply transferred to the opposite side of the plate by means of a surface gage while the stripper is mounted on the angle-plate. The vise of the machine can then be swung to whatever angle is required to machine the opening parallel with the scribed line.

Gage Plates.—In making gage plates for locating large blanks of irregular shape, they should be made to fit the blank only at the point where accuracy is essential, and not to conform exactly to the irregular shape of the blank.

Gage plates should never be secured with two screws and one dowel-pin. It is far more practical in most cases to use one screw and two dowel-pins. A good method of holding gage plates before their exact position is determined is to clamp them to the die with fillister screws having washers under their heads, and to drill the holes in the gage plate about 1/16 inch larger than the diameter of the screws, so that the gage plate may be shifted around. Always drill the screw holes for the gage plates through the die so that in case a new gage plate is required the holes will be spotted from the die. Whenever the gage plate comes close to the working portion of the die, cut the punch back far enough so that the body of the punch will come within 1/8 inch or 1/4 inch of the gage plate.

Correcting Mistakes Made in Dies.—Should the workman, through misunderstanding or carelessness, make the opening in a die too large at any point, he should not attempt to peen the stock cold, as is sometimes done, for while it is possible to do this and then finish the surface in such a manner that it will scarcely be noticeable, the stock directly below where the peening took place will almost surely crack during the life of the die. Should the mistake referred to occur, heat the die to a forging heat, when the stock may be set in without injury to the steel. When setting in, a blacksmith's fulling tool may be used; this is placed on the face of the die and struck with a sledge. If there is objection to disfiguring the top surface of the die, this method cannot, of course, be used. It is never good practice to bend, set in, or otherwise alter the form of steel when cold, if it is to be hardened, as such attempts nearly always end in a manner entirely unsatisfactory.

Reworking Worn Dies.—When a die becomes worn so that the opening is too large, or the top edge of the walls of the opening are worn so that the die is "bell-mouthed," it may be heated to a forging heat, set in with a fulling tool, or a punch of the desired shape, after which it is reheated to a low red and annealed. After annealing it is reworked to size. This reworking, if care and judgment is used, gives excellent results, and effects a considerable saving, as otherwise it would be necessary to make new dies, while the die may be reworked at a fraction of the expense of a new one.

When making a sectional die, it is possible, in case the opening is a trifle too large, to work a little stock off the faces that come together, provided the outer edges have not been planed to fit the holder; also, if it is allowable, these surfaces may be cut away the desired amount, and a strip of stock of the proper thickness placed between the die and holder. Considering the liability of a mistake taking place when a beginner is doing work of this kind, it is generally advisable to leave the fitting of the die to the holder until the opening has been worked to size.

Punch Troubles and Remedies.—The punch should always be polished in a lengthwise direction as this also aids in stripping the work. Small perforating punches which have annular marks left on them from turning or polishing are much more liable to fracture than those having marks which run parallel with the punch, especially when perforating heavy stock. This is due to the fact that the metal presses into the minute lines or grooves, thus increasing considerably the force required for stripping. As is generally known, most punches when used on heavy metal are broken while stripping the stock and not while perforating it; therefore, the stripping should be made as easy as possible. The stripping can be facilitated by making the punch slightly tapering towards the top, although this is not practicable for small punches, because the strength of the punch would be reduced too much. When the face of a punch which is used on heavy metal tends to chip off, it is caused either by the punch being too hard or the diameter of the die hole being too near to the diameter of the punch. If the stripper plate is not parallel with the die, this will also cause broken punches. Even though the error in alignment is small, the constant bending action that the punches must undergo every time the stock is stripped tends to shorten their life. Sometimes the stripping is much harder on one end of the die than on the other, because more holes are perforated at one end. In such a case, special care should be taken to see that the stripper plate starts the stock from the punches evenly and uniformly. The making of small perforating punches requires attention to minute details in order to secure the best results. For instance, a punch should not be made with sharp corners but rather with rounded corners. It should never be undercut, because even if it is scored very slightly this will establish a breaking point.

When a die has a number of large and very small punches, it is often advisable to make the large ones long enough to perforate the stock and just enter the die before the small ones touch the metal, especially if the stock is heavy, because the jar resulting from the action of the large punches may shift the stock slightly which would tend to break the smaller punches, provided they entered the stock at the same time. This method of varying the lengths of punches has often been used to advantage in dies having a large number of punches, and has made it possible to use a certain press which otherwise would have lacked the necessary capacity, inasmuch as the pressure required for punching is distributed somewhat. When locating punches in the holder, one of the principal points to consider is that the stripping strain should be as equally divided in relation to the punch-holder shank as possible; the surface of the holder which bears against the slide of the press should also be of such a size that the face of the slide will not be injured. Punches often shear themselves because a depression has been worn in the face of the slide and for that reason the holder is not properly supported. Inaccuracies in laying out pilot holes in punches and the use of eccentric pilots in order to make them register properly have also been the cause of much spoiled work. The trouble is that when the punch is sharpened, this necessitates the removal of the pilot which often is not replaced in the same position, and, consequently, it does not engage properly with the pierced holes in the stock.

It sometimes happens that the blanking punch or certain perforating punches are of such a shape that they tend to incline to one side and cause shearing when passing through the metal, thus injuring the edge of both punch and die. This is caused by the shearing thrust not being equal on all sides. For instance, the shearing strain from two long sides sometimes crowds the punch over toward the shorter side. To prevent this trouble the face of the punch should be ground to a slight angle so that it enters the shorter side first; then this side will be backed up by the die to take the thrust when cutting the remaining part of the blank.

Preventing Punchings from Sticking in Die.—Small holes in plain piercing dies often have a tendency to become clogged up by the slugs or punchings. This clogging of the die may in some cases cause the punches to be broken. The shape of the hole through which the slugs pass has a great deal to do with this difficulty. Many diemakers enlarge the lower part of the hole in the die-block or in the shoe, as shown at *A* and *B* in Fig. 28, allowing a clearance of about 1/16 inch for the slugs to fall through. This practice, however, of making cylindrical clearance spaces, does not always prove satisfactory, especially in the case of light metal.

There are instances in which trouble has been encountered even when the hole in the die-shoe is made 1/4 inch larger than the piercing punch. If there is considerable oil on the stock, the slugs stick together and have a tendency to slide. By moving around in the enlarged portion of the hole in the piercing die, the slugs become wedged into a compact mass which obstructs the hole. The result is a broken punch, and sometimes the toolmaker has considerable difficulty in removing the slugs from the hole. If trouble of this kind is experienced with small punches, it is advisable to make the piercing holes as shown at *C* or *D*. Taper-reaming the holes, as shown at

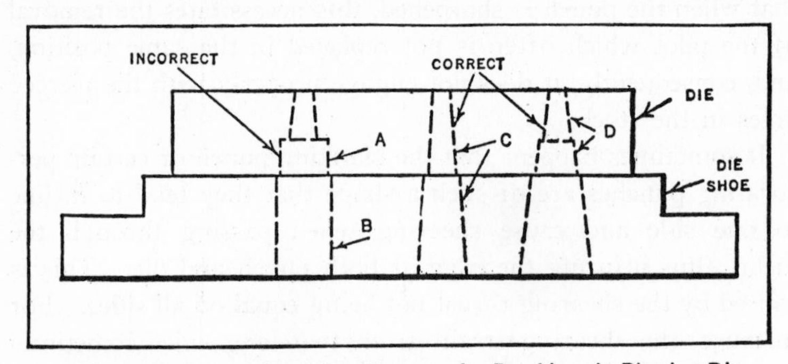

Fig. 28. Methods of Providing Clearance for Punchings in Piercing Die

C and *D*, for the full length of the die and the die-shoe will prevent the slugs from being wedged in the die or die-shoe.

Temporary Blanking Die Construction.—In pressed-steel work, the blanking tool, if made in the usual way, is a considerable factor in the cost of the finished part. This is especially true when the order does not call for enough of the parts themselves to absorb any considerable tool charge. The problem then becomes largely a matter of building the tools the cheapest.

The use of so-called "temporary" dies has effected a great saving in many instances in the cost of producing sheet-metal parts. The discarding of expensive blanking and piercing dies during the process of developing and perfecting a new model is unnecessary when temporary dies are used, as dies of the latter type can be employed until the stamp of approval has been placed on the product by the purchasers. The expense of making alterations in the product during its period of development is generally less if separate dies are used for the blanking and piercing operations, as was done in the case of the temporary dies described in this article. This practice allows alteration of the shape of the part without affecting the punch and die for piercing, and the piercing die can be altered without affecting the design of the blanking die.

Construction of Blanking Die.—The blanking die shown in Fig. 29 is used for blanking the piece shown at *A*, Fig. 30. This piece is made from 0.050-inch flat steel. Referring to Fig. 29, the die proper *B* is made from 0.3125-inch tool steel, and the stripper plate *C* is made somewhat thicker than is the usual practice (0.1875 inch in this case) for the purpose of guiding the punch *D*, which is ground flat on its top surface. A plain stock stop-pin *E* is shown just under the sight-hole at *F*. The spacer guides *G* allow sufficient clearance to permit the stock to be raised up over the stop-pin when feeding the stock to the next position. By this method of construction a self-contained punch and die is obtained, thus saving the expense of the sub-press design, as well as the cost involved in assembling the punch and die.

It is also an improvement over the old-style of temporary punch and die which did not have the punches guided in the stripper plate and which required the punch to be fastened to the ram and the die to the bolster after alignment of the members. The tool here described, produced very satisfactory work. If properly made and if the requirements of production justify the expense, a die of this type can be mounted on a standard sub-press.

Construction of Combination Piercing Dies.—Considerable saving in the cost of constructing piercing dies can be obtained by grouping the parts in suitable combinations, provided a large production is not required. In Fig. 30 pieces *B*, *C*, *D*, and *E* are flat parts such as are used in cash registers, adding machines, typewriters, etc. These parts are blanked out in a die similar to that shown in Fig. 29 and the holes are pierced in a separate operation in the combination die shown in Fig. 31, the locating nests being removed or replaced to suit the part being perforated.

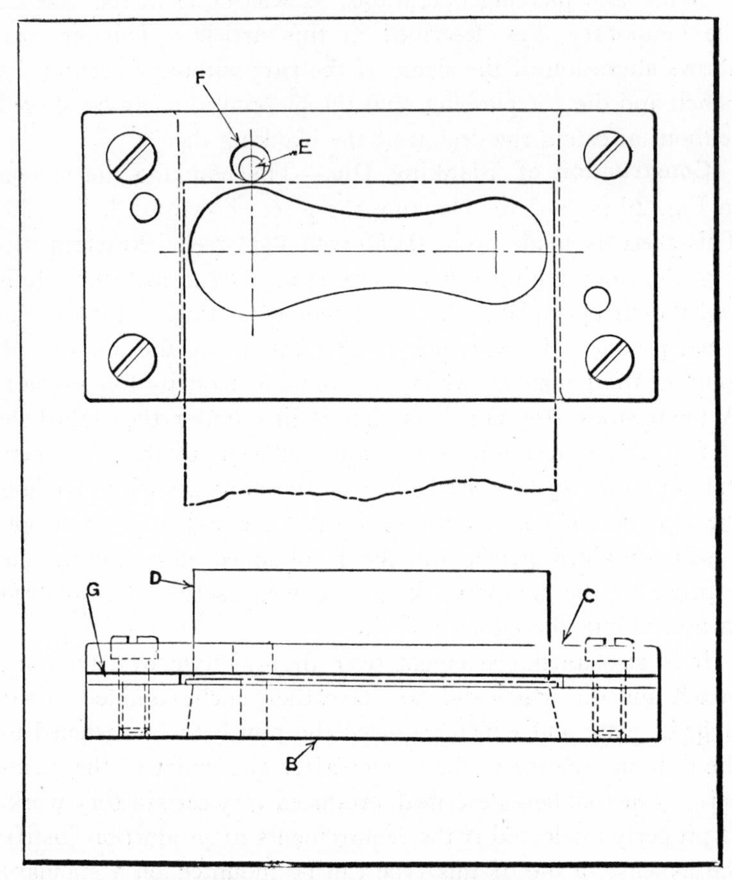

Fig. 29. Temporary Blanking Die

In designing a die of this kind a careful study of the parts is made, and the parts are grouped or located on the die in such a way that holes of the same size on different parts can be pierced with the same punch. The nest plates for the die shown in Fig. 31 were designed, as far as practicable, to accommodate more than one piece. In laying out this die, the 0.3125-inch holes of parts *C* and *D*, Fig. 30, were matched so that the same punch could be used for both parts. A study of the other parts and the relative sizes of holes showed that

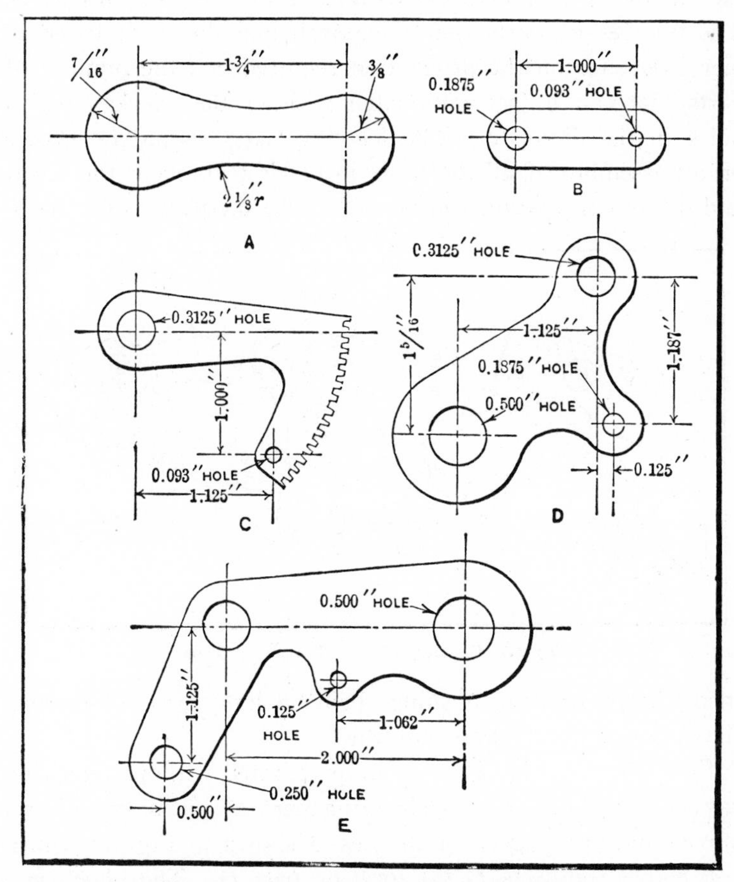

Fig. 30. Parts Produced with Temporary Dies

the 0.093-inch hole in part *B* checked with the smaller hole in part *C* and that part *B* also required the punching of a hole 0.1875 inch in diameter which was the same size as the smaller hole in part *D*, so that in locating the latter part it was swung around the center of the 0.3125-inch hole until the 0.1875-inch hole was placed 1 inch from the 0.093-inch hole in part *C*, thus providing for both holes in part *B* without adding any more punches.

The remaining part *E* has only a 0.500-inch hole which is common to any of the other parts. This part is located with the 0.500-inch hole matched with the same size hole in part *D*. The number of parts that the punch and die is designed to pierce depends on the production required and the number of parts that can be accommodated without the overlapping of holes in the die-plate. The locating nests should be shown on an assembly of all the nests in order to prevent the screw and dowel holes from overlapping. The die-plate is not hard-

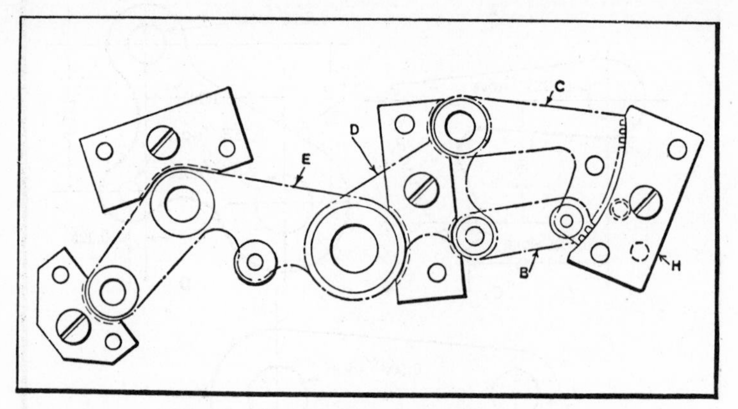

Fig. 31. Piercing Dies of Temporary Type

ened, the perforating bushings being a light press fit therein allowing for their ready removal.

Part *C* or *E*, Fig. 31, may be perforated without removing any of the nests. For perforating part *B*, the nest *H* is removed and exchanged for the nest *J* shown in Fig. 32, which also shows the nests *K* for locating part *D*. The punch was mounted in a large-sized sub-press in order to allow space for additional parts.

Experimental Die Made from Cold-rolled Steel.—Fig. 33 shows a form of die which possesses extraordinary value for experimental purposes, and for use during the preliminary process of establishing an industry and perfecting any appliance or device that is eventually intended for the market. If this type of die is used for all preliminary developments until stability of design is assured, many thousands of dollars may be saved by the manufacturing concerns in this country, as it is a well-known fact that in the development of various kinds of machines, many costly dies constantly go into the scrap pile by reason of slight changes and improvements which are a necessary part of the evolution of such machines. The cost of making the die shown is not more than 15 to 20 per cent of

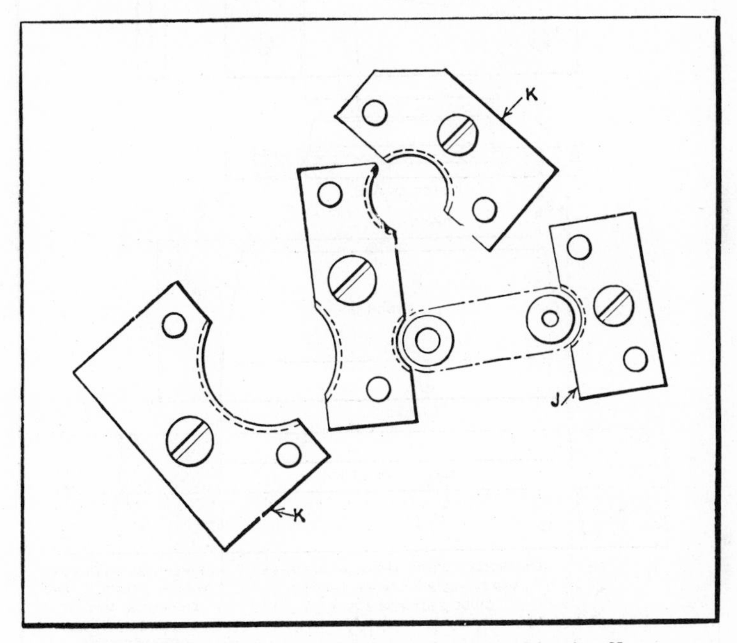

Fig. 32. Diagram showing Method of Attaching Locating Nests

the cost of an ordinary die with guide posts, yet it will do equally as good work where not more than five thousand blanks are to be made from one die. Also work that would require two or three operations with the ordinary form of die can be accomplished in one operation with this type. Cold-rolled stock may be used for the punch, stripper, and die, and an ordinary filing machine can be used to good advantage in making these dies. This die can be used in any kind of press. It is not bolted down, and ordinary strip stock can be fed through

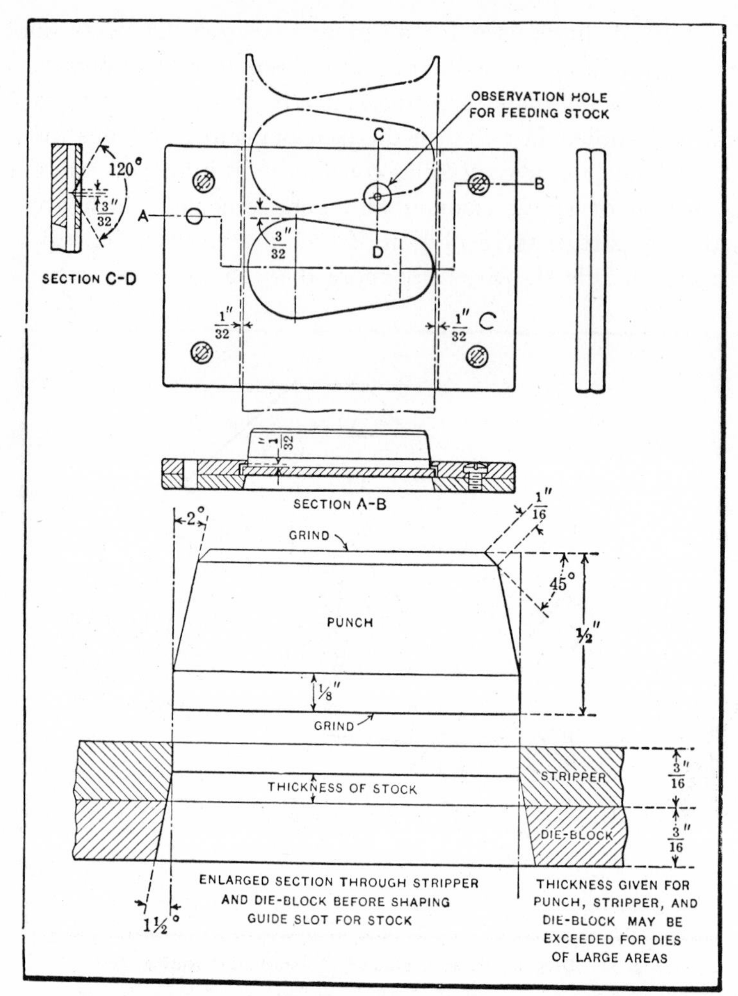

Fig. 33. Experimental Blanking Die made from Cold-rolled Steel

to the stop-pin or sight-hole in the usual way, with the difference that as soon as the punch is driven through the stock into the die, the punch, die, and stock are pulled out together from under the dummy driving punch, the blank and the punch, which is only one-half inch thick, being dropped through into the operator's hand. The stock is then fed through and the operation repeated. The die and punch are both casehardened about twenty or twenty-five thousandths inch deep. This does not materially alter the shape of either punch or die, yet they are hard enough for punching out stock up to one-eighth inch thick.

A blueprint similar to that reproduced in Fig. 33 is given the diemaker for making this type of die. The instructions given in the following paragraph are placed beneath the drawing. These instructions are typewritten on thin transparent paper and placed over the tracing when making the blueprint. In some cases the punch is first finished to the shape of the blank, relieved to within one-eighth inch of the face, which is left parallel, then casehardened, and used to shear through the die. The strip channel is then cut or the stock-pin inserted as the case requires. The die is then casehardened.

Instructions for Making Experimental Dies.—In making an experimental die, designed as shown in Fig. 33 the following procedure is recommended:

1. Make templet from 1/16-inch stock. Work to figures; do not scale drawing.

2. Assemble stripper and die-block, using 1/8-inch dowels and 10-32 screws.

3. Stamp symbol and tool number on both stripper and die-block.

4. Transfer contour from templet to stripper.

5. Drill and file die opening square through stripper and die-block, fitting opening to templet.

6. File 1 1/2-degree taper in die-block and stripper as follows: Commencing from bottom of die-block, file so that taper extends part way up into stripper measured from parting between stripper and die-block to a distance equal to thickness of stock to be used.

7. File punch square to fit stripper plate opening, fitting opening from bottom up through tapered die-block opening.

8. Remove stripper.

9. Increase diameter of dowel holes to 3/16 inch in die-block *only*.

10. Carburize and harden die-block; straighten after hardening, but do not grind.

11. File 2 degrees taper on punch upward, commencing 1/8 inch from bottom of punch.

12. File 1/16-inch chamfer around top of punch to distinguish it from bottom, and stamp symbol and tool number on top.

13. Carburize punch.

14. Fit punch to die-block, if necessary, to take care of possible distortion in die-block during hardening.

15. Harden punch; stone after hardening in case of distortion to suit die-block opening.

16. Grind punch top and bottom.

17. Align stripper and die-block.

18. Transfer 3/16-inch dowel holes from die-block into stripper.

19. Shape clearance slot in stripper to suit stock—amount of clearance shown on drawing.

Points on Making Compound Dies.—Compound dies are made without clearance, and the blanks are ejected by the knockout as soon as the punch leaves the die. Piercing holes in the punch, however, should be taper-reamed and larger at the top, so that the piercings will pass up through the punch easily. The throwing out of the piercings from a compound die is aided by setting the die in an inclined press. If a double compound die is required to produce two blanks on one stroke of the press, care should be taken to see that the knockouts are ground to the same height, and also that the blanking punches are perfectly level, so that both blanks will be flattened alike. The spring or rubber pad which operates the knockout in the compound die should not be adjusted tighter than needed to insure the blanks being removed. The knockout should just bring the blank to the surface of the die.

Points on Sub-press Die Construction.—In constructing sub-press dies it is important to have a good stand or frame, because upon its construction depends in no small measure the proper working of the die. If the standards are well made, they can be used indefinitely for different dies, owing to the adjustment provided for wear. It is a disputed point whether the plunger should be babbitted before or after the punch and die are fitted. Some prefer to make the punch and die first, enter the punch into the die attached to the plunger, and pour the babbitt, but it is generally conceded that the better way is to babbitt the plunger first; in fact, most manufacturers at the present time buy them already fitted up from one of the several companies manufacturing them for the trade. One advantage in having the plunger babbitted first is that it can be run continuously for a day or so to secure a good bearing, the cap-nut being set up occasionally. In this "working out," the plunger is sure to "creep" or change its position slightly; this is probably caused by the babbitt not flowing evenly and, obviously, it is much better for this change to take place before the alignment of the punch and die. In recessing the cylinder or frame to receive the base, the proper way is to place the plunger on the centers of the lathe with the cylinder attached and recess and face out on the bottom, using the plunger for a mandrel. With this method (which is applicable when the plunger is babbitted first) one has the assurance that the plunger is exactly central and in a vertical position with the base.

In milling the three grooves in the plunger, it is well to space them unevenly, as it will then be impossible to insert it in any but its proper position. In locating the holes in the back-plate and shedder, a round master plate is usually used, thus insuring greater accuracy. This master plate can also be used for duplicating the die, if, at any time, this should be necessary. In boring the holes in the master plate, they should be made a trifle larger than the largest hole in the work, which gives clearance for the boring tool to pass through. When boring the back-plate, it should be set perfectly central with the master plate and then be fastened with a drop of soft solder on opposite sides. Having done this, a taper pin is inserted in the center of the faceplate of the bench lathe, and turned up on the end that projects, to the size of the holes in the master plate. One of the holes in the master plate is then wrung onto the pin, after which the master plate is clamped to the faceplate and one of the holes bored. The work is then located for boring the remaining holes by shifting the master plate in the usual manner. The holes should be left small, so as to correct the error from hardening, by grinding.

When grinding, the work is placed upon the master plate in the same manner and position as when boring. The grinding is done by means of a steel lap several thousandths inch smaller than the hole, the enlarged end of which is charged with diamond dust. In separating the die from the master plate, the best way to remove the solder is to turn it off with a lathe tool before the work is removed from the faceplate.

When making the die, great care must be exercised, as the die is straight and the templet must be worked through without any clearance; this allows an even sliding fit for the shedder. In case it is impossible to avoid a little clearance, it can sometimes be corrected in the lapping operation, after hardening.

The idea of making the bore of the barrel of the sub-press taper is not simply to keep the babbitt from dropping down, as a shoulder would answer for that; but the main reason is that if the piston becomes loose from wear at any time, the babbitt, which has been left high on top, can be forced downward by using a ring and a powerful press, thus taking up the wear. The retaining ring or cap on the top of the barrel is not powerful enough to do this, as it is only intended to keep the babbitt from coming out.

In fitting a punch and die into a sub-press, a good method is as follows: The master punch is fitted into the piston, and a die blank, the top of which is tinned with solder, is fitted into the base; the punch is then brought down and an impression of the outline made in the solder. The die blank is then removed and drilled out as close to the lines of the impression as it is safe to do, after which the die is slowly and carefully worked out and finished, using the master punch as a guide.

General Procedure in Sub-press Diemaking.—Although many watch parts are punched in drop- and double-action presses, sub-presses are used when very accurate work is required. These sub-presses are of the regular type, except that the bases of many sub-presses used for watch work are made longer than usual and need no clamps to hold them to the bolster of the punch press.

Before starting to make a die, it is first essential to see that the sub-press is in good condition. In one plant where considerable sub-press work is done, the presses are "run in" by a machine built especially for that purpose. But this test is not considered good enough for fine watch work, so the plunger is taken out and the babbitt scraped and pressed in again until a good bearing is procured. Usually the babbitt is tightened until the plunger can be driven down by five or six blows of a lead hammer. The upper part of the press is then put on lathe centers, bored out, and faced true with the plunger; this must be done carefully, or there will be difficulty in aligning the punch and the die later on.

Making Master Punches and Plates.—A model of the part to be punched is given to the workman, who makes a master punch to conform with it. The method is as follows: A center hole is drilled and reamed in the model, and when possible, two other holes are drilled and reamed for relocating. The model is then soldered to the master-punch blank, the center hole being located in the center of the blank punch, and then the locating holes of the model are transferred to the punch. This punch is milled almost to the model, about 0.002 inch being left for lapping; if there are square or odd-shaped corners, the punch must be milled until the model is touched by the milling cutter. The model is then removed and the punch is hardened and drawn to a light straw. Then the punch is aligned by lapping the bottom until the center hole runs true with the diameter of the base. After the model is relocated on it by means of pins or dowels, as shown at *A* in Fig. 34, the punch is lapped cylindrically by a diamond lap held in the bench lathe, as shown at *B*. The punch is held against a drill pad, or flat center, in the tailstock of the lathe and the lap is revolved at the highest speed possible. The punch is then moved around the lap, using a light pressure, until the model is touched evenly.

To make the lap, a piece of drill rod slightly smaller than the smallest curve of the punch is ground true and straight, for a distance of about 3/8 inch. The rod is ground instead of being turned, because diamond powder "charges in" better in a ground surface; grinding also makes a smoother cutting lap. Diamond powder is then rolled in.

For constructing a compound die with piercing punches, a master plate, Fig. 35, is usually made, and this is kept for future reference. A blank plate is clamped to the faceplate of a lathe and a recess is turned to fit the base of the master punch; a center hole of some standard size is also bored through the plate; and this size must be maintained on all the

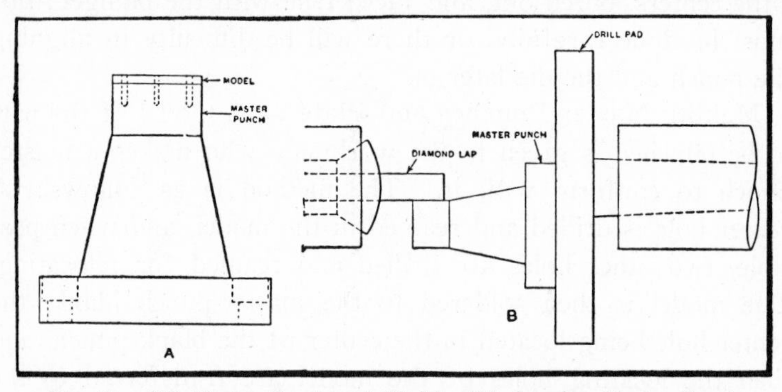

Fig. 34. (A) Master Punch and Model; (B) Lapping Master Punch

holes in the plate. The master punch is then set in the recess, screws and dowels holding it in position, and the plate is moved on the faceplate until the holes in the model on the master punch run true. A very good indicator must be used, as this is one of the most important operations. When a hole is trued, the master punch is taken out and a hole is bored through the plate, corresponding to the hole in the model. When all the holes in the model have been transferred to the master plate, the plate is removed and located "on center" by a pin that fits the center hole of the plate. A larger recess is then turned for the die-holder. All punches and die-holders should be made to standard sizes for a given size of press so that they will be interchangeable.

Making Die-holder and Die.—The die-holder is left soft. After it is made to fit the recess in the master plate, all the holes in the master plate are transferred to it. Both straight and back taper holes are used, and both are backed up by a hardened plate in the plunger. If straight punches are used, they must have button heads to prevent their being drawn out of the holder. The die blank is then made to fit the holder, which has a taper shoulder of 20 degrees, as illustrated at *A*

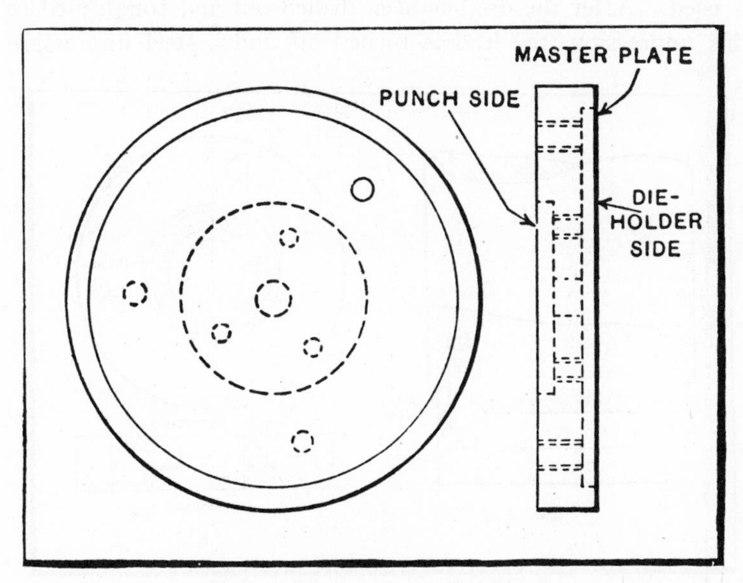

Fig. 35. Master Plate for Die Work

in Fig. 36. The sub-press plunger is now recessed to fit the die-holder, and the holder and die are screwed to the plunger.

Sub-press Base.—The sub-press bases are extra long, as previously mentioned. Two dowel holes of different sizes are drilled part way through the bottom, using a jig, and the dowels are then located in the lathe faceplate to hold the blank base nearly central. Two bolts hold the base to the faceplate. The base is now recessed for the master punch and the stripper plate; it is also turned to fit the upper part of the sub-press. The advantage of using dowels for locating the base to the faceplate is that if the base has to be relocated on the faceplate, it is not necessary to use an indicator, the two dowels making location certain. The master punch is now located in the base in such a position that the maximum number of pieces can be punched from a given length of stock.

Transferring Impression to Die and Shaving.—The blank die is next covered with solder and faced off true, to get what is called a "lead impression"; this is generally done in the screw press, but if the master punch is delicate a lead hammer is used. After the die has been drilled out and rough-filed to this impression, the lead is turned off and a steel impression

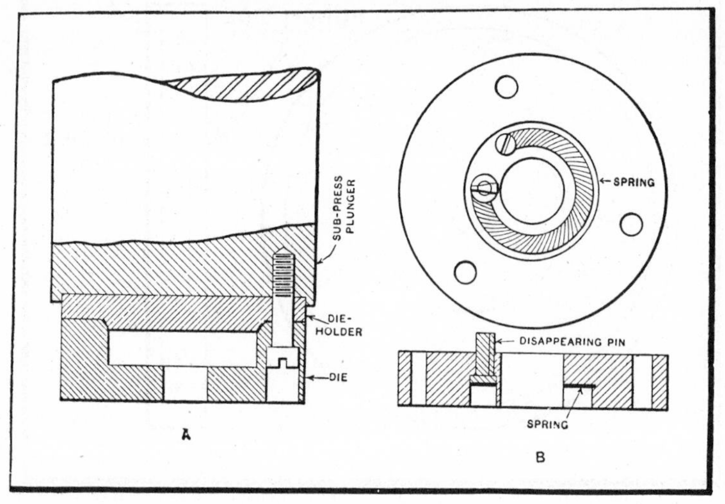

Fig. 36. (A) Die-holder and Die; (B) Stripper and Guide Pin

is taken, which need not be more than a few thousandths of an inch deep. The die is then filed to within about 0.002 inch of the correct size, the excess stock being shaved off. The amount to leave for shaving is a matter of judgment rather than measurement; if too much stock is left, the die will tear and rough up and a poor job will result. The shaving is done by pounding the plunger with a lead hammer, as the screw press tears the work; only about 0.015 inch can be shaved at one time. The plunger is then drawn out and the burr, or shaving, is carefully removed. This operation is repeated until the punch has been forced through the die.

If a very smooth die is required, as in trimming, or compound blanking and swaging work, the die is not shaved by the master punch; but when ready to be shaved, it is hardened. A brass blank is then soldered over the hole and worked out to the design of the die. This blank is shaved by the master punch to the correct shape, and the die is lapped to this shape in a filing machine. For this work a diamond lap, which is a soft file blank charged with diamond powder, is used; No. 1 powder is used for roughing and No. 2 for finishing. After the die has been lapped to the brass impression, it will be found that the master punch will not enter the die, as the brass blank shrinks after shaving. The brass impression is then removed and the die is lapped again until the master punch enters the die about 1/32 inch, which means that the die is slightly bell-mouthed. This amount is later ground off, leaving a perfectly straight die, a little smaller than the master punch; it is necessary for the die to be smaller than the punch, as the die blanks expand after coming out of the die.

Working Punches.—It has been found that, on an average, one die will last as long as eight or ten working punches; hence it is necessary to make a set of punches. The punch blanks are covered with solder, faced off true, and a lead impression is taken from the die. This impression is rough-milled in a bench lathe, using a table rest. Saws and form cutters are used on the saw arbor in the head of the lathe. In this operation, the top of the punch must be set level with the center line of the lathe, or the work will "hog in." The punch is held against the saw, free hand. This is a quick way of milling punches. It gives a radius cut, but all that is wanted is to make a steel impression. The solder is turned or ground off, and a steel impression about 1/16 inch deep is taken. As this is a heavy cut it makes the punch too small. If the punch were milled to this size, there would be nothing to shave, so the edge of the punch is peened slightly or upset and the punch is shaved down again almost to the previous depth.

The punch is now ready for milling, which, again, is a matter of judgment, for if just enough is left for shaving, a smooth punch will result. The punches are set up in the master plate and the holes are transferred in the same way as in making the die-holder, except that the opposite side of the master plate is used. After this, the punches are hardened and drawn to a purple; the dies should be drawn to a light straw. The punches are aligned by lapping the bottom on a cast-iron lap, using fine emery, until they cut tissue paper evenly. This is done by sharpening both punch and die and bringing them together in a sub-press with tissue paper between; then, with a light blow of the lead hammer, the tissue is marked. The side of the punch that cuts the paper first is the side that must be drawn toward the center. If the paper is cut evenly, the punch is in line.

Shedder, Stripper Plate, and Guide Pin.—A brass punching is made and this punching is soldered to the shedder blank, and the shedder blank is milled until the cutter touches the punching. The holes in the master plate must be transferred through the shedder. This is done by putting the master plate on a lathe, the die-holder being placed in the recess of the master plate and the die (with the shedder inserted) on the holder; then the holes are bored as in the holder. The shedder is then hardened, replaced and ground out, using diamond laps if the holes are small.

A stripper plate *B*, Fig. 36, is next made to strip the stock from the lower punch, but it must not fit the punch closely; there should be a space of 0.004 or 0.005 inch between the punch and the stripper.

A disappearing guide pin seems the best for most work. Sometimes a track slightly wider than the punch is milled through the stripper plate, but this necessitates the use of stock that is perfectly straight and of a certain width, whereas watch stock is rolled for thickness in the works, and is likely to come from the rolls slightly curved. The disappearing pin permits the use of stock of any width; the strip does not have to be held at exactly right angles, but it must be held close to the guide pin.

In the foregoing a general outline of the method of making

dies for fine watch work is given. A more detailed description is necessary to give a clear idea of the several varieties of watch dies.

Blanking and Burnishing Dies.—Dies for steel parts blank, pierce and burnish the edges in one operation. The die is made as already described, except that the cutting edge is stoned round and polished to a high finish. The radius of the round edge must be determined by experiment; it is best to start with a small corner and work up until the edge of the blank shows perfect burnishing. The inside of the die must be very smooth and the radius of the cornering must blend in without sharp corners. The punches must fit perfectly in the die, or a ragged edge will result on the punching. This method of burnishing, or drawing, the edges of steel work is used in optical work on gold-filled flat stock, in which the pure gold must be drawn from one side, over the edge of the composition, to meet the gold on the opposite side, and withstand the acid test.

Brass and nickel parts are usually blanked and trimmed, the trimming being done in a die about 0.005 inch smaller than the blank. The die is placed in the plunger of the sub-press, the punch being in the base with the stripper and nest to locate the blank. A gash is milled through the back of the sub-press into the plunger, so that punchings may pass through the die and out back of the press. In very high-grade work, a burnishing die must be used after trimming. This die is made slightly tapered and lapped very smooth. The top is large enough to start a blank without cutting, and the small end is finished to size.

Dies for Balance Ring and Balance Capsule.—Brass balance rings are punched from flat stock; they are drawn to cup shape and the bottoms are punched out in one operation. This work, however, is not done in a sub-press, a double-action punching and drawing die being used, as shown at *A* in Fig. 37.

Balance capsules are punched from what is called "low brass"; that is, brass that melts at a higher heat than the bal-

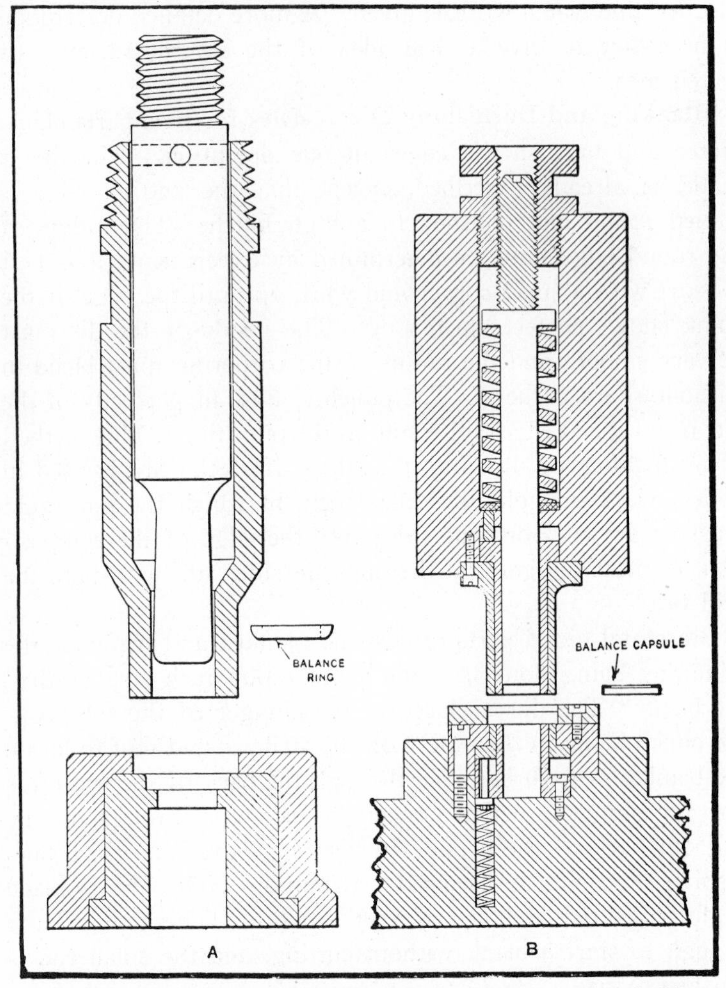

Fig. 37. (A) Double-action Balance-ring Die; (B) Balance Capsule Die

ance-ring, which is a "high brass." These capsules are used to hold the steel center and brass rim of the balance together while brazing, as the brass rim fuses to the steel before the capsule melts. The sub-presses of the capsule dies are not babbitted. The cast-iron shell is bored out perfectly straight and lapped smooth, using a lead lap and emery. The plunger is made from machine steel, casehardened and ground to fit the press; there are no guide slots nor ribs, as in babbitted presses, as the punches are round. Presses made in this way withstand the swaging operation better than the babbitted press. This press is called the double compound die because it blanks, draws, swages and pierces in one operation. The base contains the blanking die (see sectional view *B*, Fig. 37), lower punch and lower shedder; the plunger holds the blanking punch (which is also the drawing die), swaging shedder and center punch. These dies have an automatic roll feed, but to make sure that every piece is ejected, a blast of compressed air is placed so as to strike the capsule as it is ejected from the lower punch, blowing it into a wire basket.

Watch-hand Dies.—The dies for second hands are of the compound type; that is, they blank and pierce the center hole in one operation, using an automatic finger feed. The die is made in two pieces, which are ground together as one, one-half the hand being produced in each piece. In making a die of this kind, the first operation after fitting the sub-press is to make a holder for the split die. This is made with a one-degree taper, and about 0.400 inch deep. Two die-blocks are made to fit this holder, and then one-half is cut away, making one block split exactly in the center. The holder is now indicated in the lathe with the split blocks in place, and a center hole is drilled and reamed to the size wanted in the hub of the second hand, leaving enough to lap after hardening. If the hand is of the design known as a "ball second," this hole in the die is also drilled and reamed. The dies are then hardened and drawn. The two parts are blocked or lapped flat on the parts that join. The center hole is lapped to size, using a drill rod or brass lap and flour of emery as an abrasive. The two die-blocks are next held together by wire and soldered. A pin, or arbor, is ground true in the lathe and the die is wrung on and ground on the outside to fit the holder. To grind the arms, or center web, and the tail of the hand, a bench lathe is used, with an angle iron having micrometer adjustment in the head of the lathe. The screw is removed from the slide-rest and a cam movement substituted. The diamond form laps are about one inch in diameter. If the second hand is to be a "spade second," a form lap must be used to grind the form of the spade.

The punches are made in large quantities, as their life is short, owing to their delicate size and shape. They are made as already described, except that all the milling is done in the bench lathe. The radius cut of the saw, or cutter, leaves enough of the punch straight to make further milling unnecessary. A depth of 0.025 inch is sufficient, this being reduced after hardening to 0.015 inch. High-carbon steel makes better punches than any other steel, as it can be drawn to a purple, which is the proper color, and still be tough.

Three operations are necessary for making the hour and the minute hands—blanking, swaging and piercing. The blanking dies are made in two pieces, held together with screws and dowels, and used in sub-presses. Swaging is done in a drop-press, as a uniform blow is necessary; the piercing is done in small, open-front sub-presses. The fancy hands are first blanked and the intricate shapes are punched out in separate operations, after which the hands are swaged in drop-presses.

Dies for Metal Dials.—Metal dials are made in many shapes other than round. They are blanked and pierced and the figures and dial foot recesses are swaged in one operation. The die is like most compound dies, except that the force, or swage (which is the dial in relief), is on the upper shedder. Therefore, after a blank has been punched, the plunger must be carried down until the shedder "hits the bottom." Careful adjustment must be made to swage the figures to the correct depth. The recesses for the dial-foot pins are on the opposite side of the dial from the figures, and are swaged by pins projecting above the surface of the lower punch, backed up by a hardened steel plate under the punch. These swaging pins are very near the rim of the punch, making it difficult to harden the punch without cracking. This difficulty is overcome by drilling the hole part way through from the bottom, leaving about 1/4 inch solid, and piping it out after hardening.

The method may be of interest. The punch is aligned by lapping the bottom until the center hole runs true. Then the punch is placed in the master plate and located on the lathe faceplate, as previously described. A pipe is then made, the outside diameter of which is from 0.01 to 0.015 inch smaller than the hole wanted. The hole in the pipe must be large enough to leave only a thin wall of about 0.015 inch. This pipe is mounted in a traverse spindle grinder (care being taken to get the spindle on the dead center of the lathe) and used as a diamond lap, cutting on the end. The speed of the spindle should be about 20,000 revolutions per minute. Loose No. 1 diamond powder is used freely, being placed in the cut; the lap charges itself. After cutting out the center, the hole is brought to size with an ordinary diamond lap.

The swaging plates, which stamp the figures on the dials, are about 0.055 inch thick, when finished, and are held to the upper shedder by a button stud made from "Hecla" vanadium steel. These plates are first decarbonized and the figures raised by swaging in the screw press. A steel block ½ inch thick is engraved to correspond with the dial, and hardened. The swage blank is placed in the center of the dial block and pressed until the figures are raised perfectly. A punch with flat teeth is used to swage the plate, as small sections are thus driven down at one time, the punch being turned around slightly after each blow of the press.

Swaging Dies.—Swaging dies are made by a force or master punch, and are used where rounded shapes and steps are necessary, as in regulators, pallets, etc. Swaging-die blanks are surfaced off and lapped on a ground-glass lap, using powdered oilstone and oil. This gives a dead smooth gray finish, without scratches, which is absolutely necessary, as all imperfections are carried down by the force and cannot be polished out. The force is pressed into the die blank to slightly more than the required depth, and ground off after hardening. The impression is polished with a peg-wood stick and No. 4 diamond powder. Blanks of the part wanted are placed over the impression and struck by a drop-press, leaving a flash, which is trimmed off in the trimming die that also burnishes the edges. The round corners of the trimmer also help to locate the work.

Wheel Dies.—Dies for punching the escape wheel and other wheels are compound, but they do not punch the teeth or the center hole. The teeth are cut on a slotted arbor that holds the wheels by the inside of the rim. The center hole is drilled and bored by holding the wheel by the pitch diameter of the teeth in special machines. The most important parts of wheel die work, and the most difficult to make, are the segment

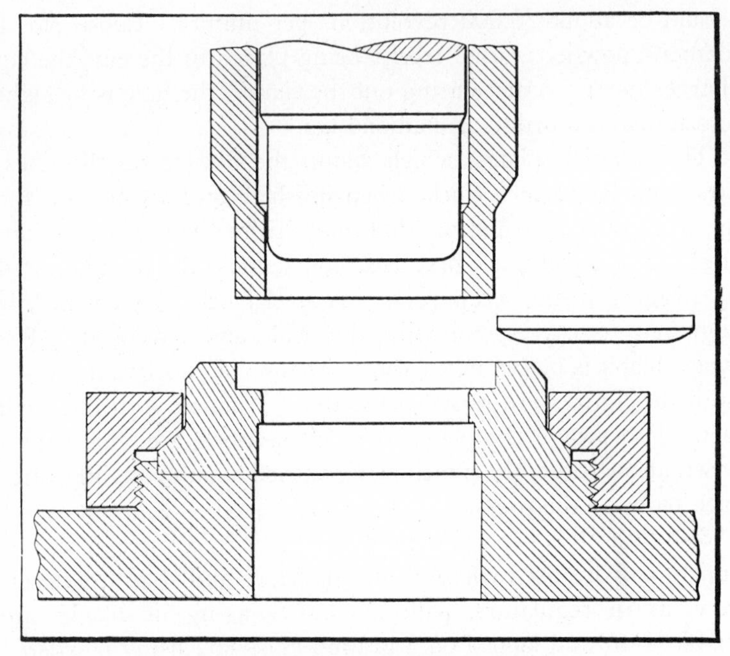

Fig. 38. Blanking and Drawing Die for Watch Case

punches. These punches are ground by holding them in a block that has been planed to give correct angles, a surface grinder being used.

Dies for Watch Cases.—The first operation on the rim of a case is to punch and draw a cup-shaped blank in a double-action press, using a die like that shown in Fig. 38. This die is of the same design as the balance-ring die, except that the blanks do not cling to the center punch, but pass on through the die. As the blank passes the sharp shoulder of the lower die, it expands slightly, which prevents it from returning with the punch. It will be noted that the die is held in the recess of a cast-iron plate by a large hexagonal nut; this method is used on all dies of this kind.

After the work passes through a punching and curling die, Fig. 39, it is ready for spinning; the punching and curling are done in one operation.

Watch-case backs are blanked and drawn in a die like that shown in Fig. 38. These blanks are then passed through a

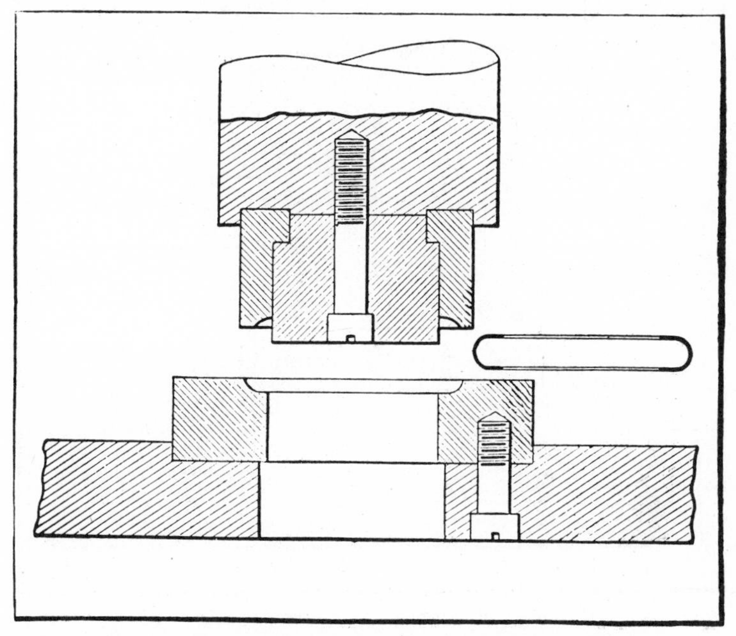

Fig. 39. Punching and Curling Die for Watch-case Rim

curling die, Fig. 40, which curls the blank to the form shown; this die is used in a sub-press. After the curling operation, the back is swaged, as shown in Fig. 41, which leaves the work ready to thread. This operation, as in the case of the rim, is done in a bench lathe with a threading attachment. The bezel is the same as the back, except that the bottom is punched out after swaging. A die that swages the reflector of the bezel is shown in Fig. 42.

Making Coining and Embossing Dies.—The processes of making coining and embossing dies are similar in some respects. In the coining die, the letters and figures are generally cut directly in the surface of the steel. Since the upper and lower designs are generally different, both members of the die must be engraved; that is, one die cannot be made from the other, as may often be done in the case of embossing dies.

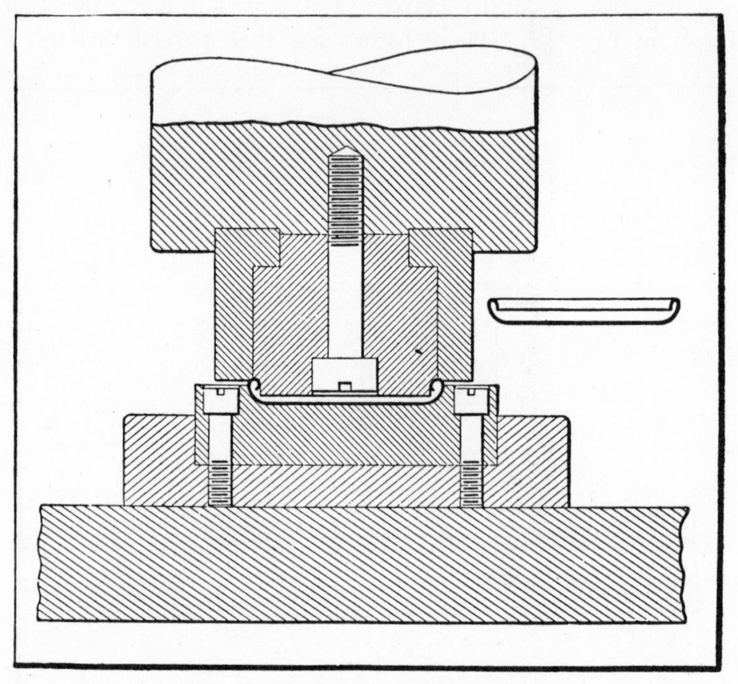

Fig. 40. Curling Die for Watch Case

Embossing dies are generally made by the hob method in the case of comparatively small dies, and by die-sinking in the case of large dies. The latter method is also used on small dies, and not infrequently we find a combination of the two methods employed. The hob is comparatively easy to make, because the design stands out in bold relief. It is made of tool steel, the face of the steel being first blued and the design traced thereon, after which the stock is cut away, leaving an outline of the design. The raised surface is then worked over with chisels, files, and gravers until the design is complete. In this case the design is the exact counterpart of that which will appear in the finished work. The hob is then hardened.

The die-block is first recessed on a die-sinking machine or in some other manner until the recess conforms approximately to the desired outline. The hob is then placed in the recess and driven down by means of a drop-hammer or heavy sledge until the design in the block is shaped to suit. Then the die is polished and hardened.

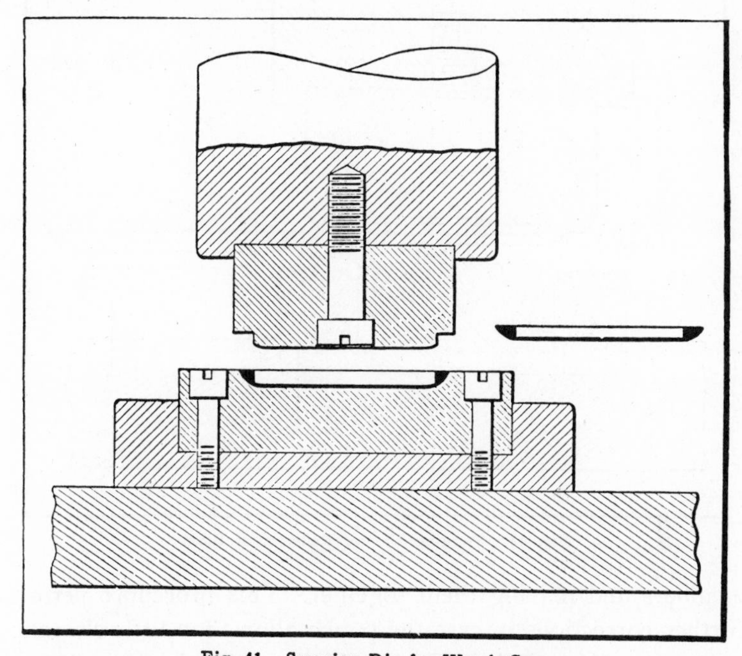

Fig. 41. Swaging Die for Watch Case

The next operation consists of making the upper part of the die or the punch. When the metal to be embossed is comparatively thin, the punch may be made direct from the lower die. To do this, a piece of tool steel is pointed to approximate the design of the die, heated to a bright red, and driven into the die recess until the design has been transferred to the punch end, after which the punch is removed and allowed to cool. Polishing then completes the punch. After the scale has been removed and the design polished, the punch design will be slightly smaller than the die design. This is the condition desired. Before hardening the punch, however, it is well to test the die by placing a sheet of soft metal between the two

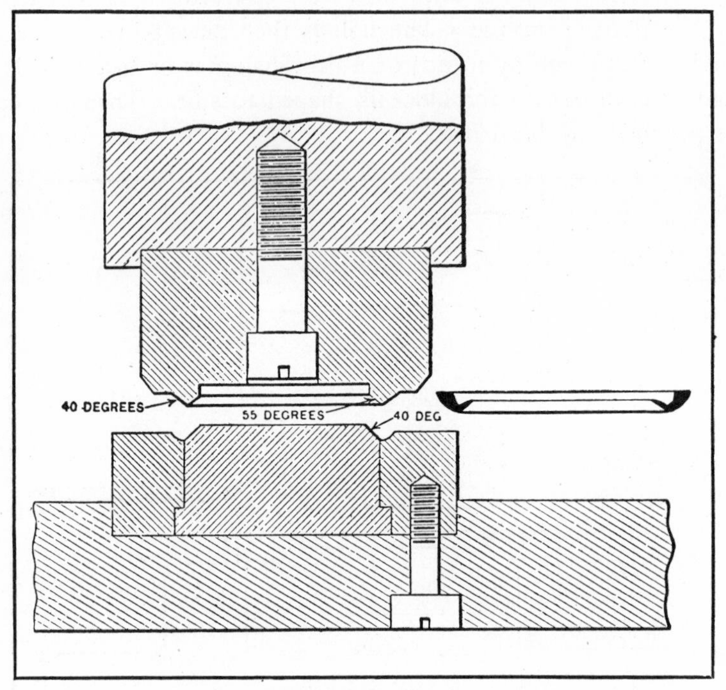

Fig. 42. Swaging Die for Reflector of Bezel

members and driving them together. This procedure permits further corrections in case the punch allows too little clearance at some points. Reheating should be avoided, since the repeated scaling may cause the punch to become too small.

CHAPTER III A

MATERIALS USED IN DIEMAKING

In modern diemaking practice, a large variety of materials is available for use. These include many different kinds of steels, castings of both ferrous and non-ferrous metals, and even non-metallic materials. Since dies are used not only for an endless variety of parts and products but for classes of work differing greatly as to size, quantity and accuracy, the die designer or diemaker in selecting materials must take into account a number of important factors. These factors usually are related either directly or indirectly to the cost of producing dies that will prove satisfactory, and also to the toughness, hardness, and durability of the material and, in the case of steel dies to the distortion or warpage in connection with heat-treatment. The following practical questions are typical of those which frequently arise in selecting die materials.

In producing certain parts is it necessary to use steel, or will some less expensive material be sufficiently durable for drawing or forming a given quantity of parts? If steel is necessary, will a plain carbon grade do the work or will a more expensive alloy steel such as a "non-deforming" type be cheaper in the long run? If sheet metal parts must be formed, possibly in an automobile or aircraft plant, is it feasible to use a relatively low-cost die material that can be cast to the required form, thus further reducing expense by eliminating machining largely or entirely and, at the same time, produce a die that is sufficiently durable for the job at hand? Will a plastic of some kind or perhaps some other non-metallic material be sufficiently durable for a given job and greatly reduce die costs? Does the job warrant the extreme durability obtained by using cemented carbide as a die material? If the die is for temporary use or perhaps for experimental purposes, will it be satisfactory if made of cast iron or possibly of casehardened machine steel?

The nature of the operation, the size of the part and form of the die required are other factors having a bearing upon material selection. For dies of simple form, a water-hardening steel may be suitable, whereas for more intricate die designs, one of the oil-hardening steels generally would be preferable. Practice among diemakers in the selection of die materials does not conform to any generally accepted standard, partly because there are differences of opinion and also because satisfactory results often are obtained in using steels differing more or less in composition, for dies requiring the same general qualities. The steel compositions which follow are intended as a general guide in selecting die steels.

Carbon die steel.—This steel may contain 0.90–1.15 carbon, 0.20–0.45 manganese, 0.16 silicon. 0.025 phosphorus, and 0.025 sulphur.

Carbon die-block steel.—0.55–0.65 carbon, 0.50–0.70 manganese, 0.15–0.30 silicon, 0.04 phosphorus, 0.04 sulphur.

Alloy die-block steel.—0.50–0.65 carbon, 0.40–0.80 manganese, 1.25–1.75 nickel, 0.60–1.10 chromium. The steel with a higher nickel content may also have 0.25 molybdenum and 0.12 vanadium.

Non-deforming Die Steels.—When tool steels are hardened there is always some change in dimensions or form but some steels are classed as "non-deforming" because the dimensional changes are relatively small. Non-deforming steels may either be oil-hardening or air-hardening. The latter are said to hold the original dimensions somewhat better than the oil-hardening type. Steels of the non-deforming class are used in preference to water-hardening steels not only to minimize distortion but to reduce or eliminate the danger of cracking, especially when heat-treating dies of intricate design which are costly to produce. Steels in the non-deforming group are deep-hardening in comparison with water-hardening steels.

Manganese Oil-Hardening Steel.—Non-deforming steels are hypereutectoid, which means that they contain over 0.85 carbon. The carbon range is usually 0.85–0.95; manganese, 1.00–1.60; chromium, 0.40–0.60; tungsten, 0.40–0.60; silicon, 0.20–0.35; and in some cases about 0.25 vanadium may be added.

Tungsten Oil-Hardening Steel.—This steel contains about 1.20 carbon, 1.75 tungsten, and 0.25 manganese. The composition otherwise is similar to that of the manganese oil-hardening steels.

High-Alloy Oil-Hardening Steels.—This class of non-deforming steel contains about 2.15 carbon, 12.00 chromium, and a manganese content of about 0.35. Vanadium, tungsten, and nickel are other elements which may be added to this class of steel.

Manganese Air-Hardening Steel.—A typical composition contains 0.90 carbon, 2.5 managanese, 1.5 chromium, 1.00 molybdenum, and 0.30 silicon.

Chromium Air-Hardening Steel.—This steel usually contains about 1.00 carbon, 5.00 chromium, 1.00 molybdenum, 0.50 manganese, 0.25 silicon, and in some cases 0.50 vanadium is added.

High-Alloy Air-Hardening Steels.—These steels, like the high-alloy oil-hardening type, have about 12.00 chromium. The carbon content varies from 1.00 to 2.15; manganese, 0.35; silicon, 0.35; molybdenum, 0.80; and in some cases, 0.50 vanadium.

Die Steel with High Wear Resistance and Minimum Distortion.—This die steel was developed to meet the need for a steel that would combine the properties of high wear resistance and minimum distortion with relatively low cost. This steel is a modification of a 1 per cent carbon, 5 per cent chromium, air-hardening steel, made by the addition of 0.20 per cent vanadium to insure a wide heat-treating range and to provide protection against excessive grain growth, and 1 per cent molybdenum to induce high hardness and retention of hardness after drawing.

The effect of molybdenum on the hardness of 1 per cent carbon, 5 per cent chromium steel is shown by comparing one steel (designated *C*) with a steel containing no molybdenum (*A*) and one containing a low molybdenum content (*B*). These three steels have the following compositions:

	A Per Cent	B Per Cent	C Per Cent
Carbon	1.03	1.00	0.97
Chromium	4.89	4.94	5.05
Vanadium	...	0.20	0.18
Molybdenum	...	0.48	1.07

After air-hardening, the hardness ranges of these steels were as shown in Table 1. After drawing, the hardness range of the three steels at different drawing temperatures was found to be as shown in Table 2.

Table 1. Comparative Hardness of Three Types of Steel after Air-Hardening

Hardening Temperature, Degrees F.	Rockwell C Hardness		
	A	B	C
1700	39	46	64.5
1750	49	51	65.0
1800	54	64	65.0
1850	54	64	63.0

Table 2. Comparative Hardness of Three Types of Steel after Drawing

Drawing Temperature, Degrees F.	Rockwell C Hardness		
	A	B	C
As quenched	54	64	65
300	50	62	62
400	50	60	60
500	50	60	60
900	49	56	58
950	49	54	59
1000	..	..	58

With this steel, full air-hardening can be obtained at the comparatively low temperature of 1700 degrees F. in small sections, say up to 1 inch thick, while higher temperatures—up to 1800 degrees F.—are required for larger sections. It will be seen from Table 2 that this steel retains its hardness to a remarkable degree at high drawing temperatures.

Two solid radiator grill dies will be taken as an example of resistance to distortion in heat-treatment. These dies were pack-hardened and air-quenched from 1800 degrees F., and afterward drawn at 400 degrees F., for three hours. The final hardness was 61 Rockwell C. Before hardening, the dimensions of the embossing die were 8.545 by 10.607 inches, and those of the perforating die, 8.880 by 10.548 inches. After hardening, the dimensions of the former were 8.547 by 10.609 inches, and those of the latter, 8.886 by 10.553 inches. The maximum change in any direction is very small, considering the size and nature of the dies.

Die Steels to Use for Mica.—Natural mica—a mineral varying in color and composition—is obtained in sheets. It has a shearing strength of 18,000 to 38,000 pounds per square inch. Both natural and manufactured mica are highly abrasive, and tend to flake, crumble, and powder when worked. These tendencies should be carefully considered in designing dies for punching mica. If this is done, runs of a half million strokes between grinds can be maintained, while some dies have made runs of as high as a million strokes.

The tool steel employed for punches and dies used on mica is the most important factor in producing trouble-free, high-production, low-maintenance dies. Tool steels having low wearing properties and high abrasive resistance, such as water-hardening carbon steel, oil- and air-hardening die steels, high-carbon, high-chromium, and high-speed steels, were tried with varying success. An oil-hardening tool steel with a chemical composition of 0.90 per cent carbon, 0.30 per cent silicon, 0.30 per cent manganese, 1.6 per cent chromium, 0.45 per cent tungsten, and 0.10 per cent vanadium, and with a hardness of 62 to 63 Rockwell C, has proved to be satisfactory.

The cutting edges and faces of the punch and die should have a quality of finish (ground and well-polished) that will offer maximum resistance to abrasive wear. The higher the polish or smoothness, the greater the resistance to abrasive action. In resharpening the punch and die, care should be exercised to see that all scores are removed.

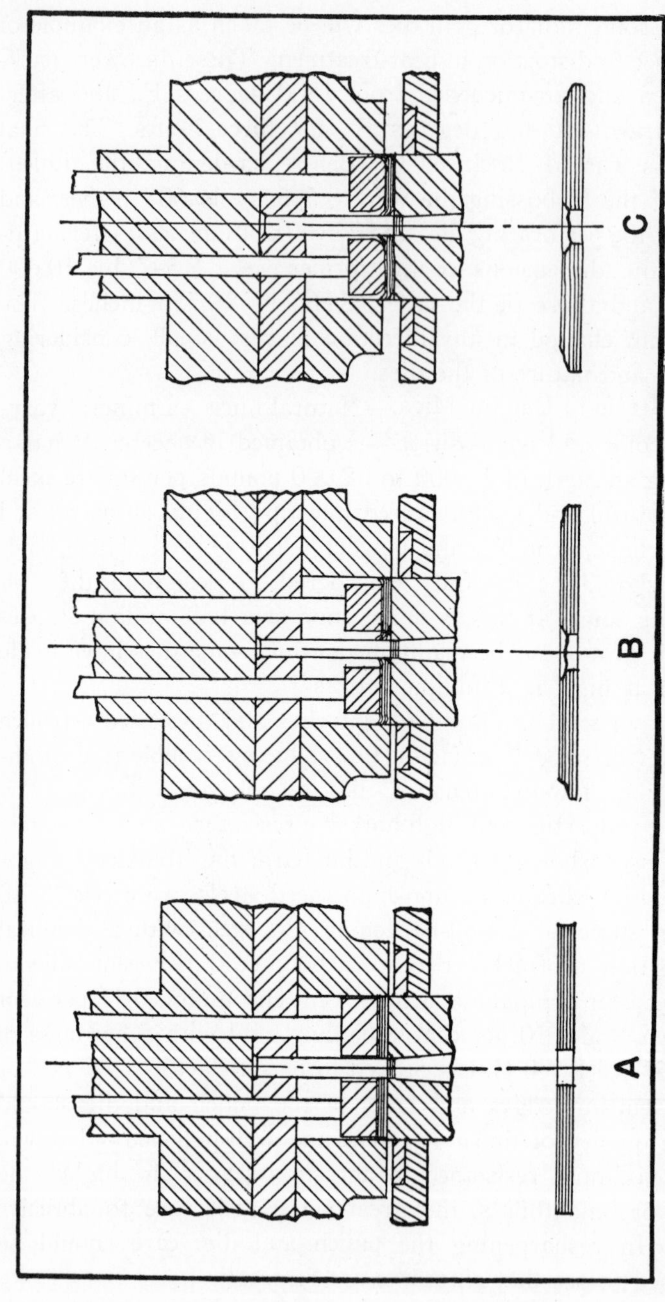

Fig. 1. Effect of Stripper Clearance and Stripper Hardness on Mica Punchings; (A) Stripper with Clearance of 5 Per Cent of Material Thickness on a Side; (B) Effect of Increased Clearance; (C) Result of Using a Soft Stripper

To prevent flaking of the mica punching along the cut edges while being removed from a compound die, the die stripper should have a maximum clearance of approximately 5 per cent of the material thickness on a side. The stripper should be made of a good grade of oil- or air-hardening tool steel, and should be hardened, ground, and well polished. It should have sharp edges. The effect of strippers made in this manner is illustrated at *A,* in Fig. 1. The edges of the punching will be true and square, due to the small amount of clearance and the sharp edges of the stripper supporting the punching very close to the cut edges, thereby preventing flaking during its removal from the die.

The effect of increased clearance between the stripper and die is shown at *B*. Inadequate support of the punching close to the cut edges allows flaking during its removal and the top edges of the punching tend to break away. Furthermore, the flakes produced set up an excessive abrasive action between the punch, die, and stripper, reducing the normal die life. They also work up into the cavity between the punch-plate and the stripper, and eventually fill this cavity, with resultant damage to the die.

The same undesirable results are obtained, as indicated at *C,* when a soft stripper is used. In this case, the abrasive action rounds off the edges of the stripper, regardless of the amount of clearance, again allowing excessive flaking of the punching.

In the case of progressive dies, used for manufactured mica only and run in presses equipped with roll feeds, spring type strippers are always utilized. Such strippers hold the material firmly to the face of the die during the entire cutting and stripping cycle. The same relationship of clearance between punch and stripper, and degree of hardness, applies to these spring type strippers as to strippers for compound dies.

Small spring type strippers are made of hardened tool steel. However, because of the warpage and distortion encountered in the hardening of large pieces of tool steel, it is often advantageous to make spring type strippers from machine steel and to utilize hardened tool-steel inserts around the punches, as shown at *A* in Fig. 2. This illustration also shows material guides.

Pilots should be made of a good grade of water- or oil-hardening tool steel and should be hardened, ground, and well polished. They should be replaced when definite signs of abrasive wear are seen. Better results are obtained from pilots having a vertically polished surface instead of a rotary polished surface. Material guides should also be made of a good grade

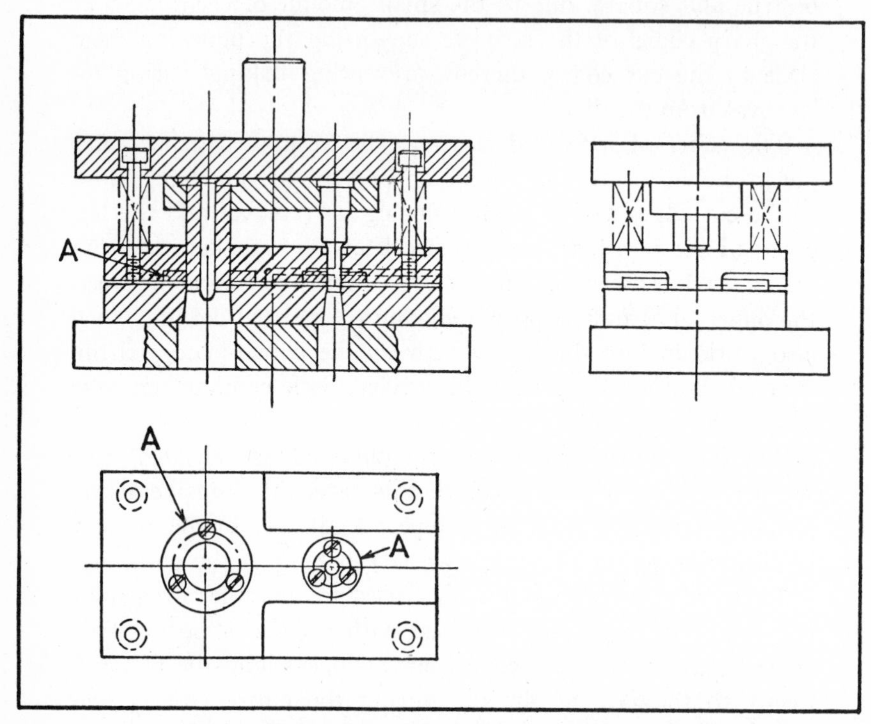

Fig. 2. Mica Stamping Die with Hardened Inserts *A* Around the Punches

of water- or oil-hardening tool steel, and should be hardened, and the work sides ground. Strippers, stripper inserts, pilots, and guides should be of as high a Rockwell C hardness as is practicable for the particular type or brand of tool steel used.

The clearance between the punch and die should be approximately 4 per cent of the material thickness on a side, this practice having given very satisfactory results. Increased clearance gives a tearing rather than a shearing action and produces a combined residue of fine mica flakes and granules. These will wedge between the sides of the punch and die and cause excessive wear.

A clearance angle is required within the die in all cases where the blank is pushed through the die, as in progressive dies, or where slugs are pushed through, as in both progressive and compound dies. A straight portion or land, 1/16 inch in depth from the cutting edge of the die, and below the land a clearance angle of 1/2 degree on a side works out very satisfactorily. With this design, slugs and blanks clear the die readily, and maximum die life is insured before the opening in the die has become increased enough in size, through abrasion and successive resharpenings, to result in ragged-edged punchings. No clearance angle is provided in the die-blocks of compound dies, since the punching is not pushed through.

Sectional dies are preferable to solid ones on high-production operations, provided the size and contour of the punching is suitable for such dies. The die sections can be ground accurately and fitted to the contour of the punch, leaving the cutting edges and faces readily accessible for polishing and allowing a precision fit to be made between the punch and die.

The small clearance allowable between the punch and die makes it imperative that die sets be utilized. Standard rear-post sets are satisfactory for low to medium production runs, but it is recommended that the more accurate center-post or four-post sets be used for intricate work or high-production operations.

No lubricant of any kind should be used in punching mica. A low-pressure air blast can be utilized for removing the flakes and powder from the dies. In such cases, an adequate exhaust is needed to carry off the mica particles.

Cemented Carbide Dies.—Cemented carbides, because of their hardness and wear resistance are frequently used for dies. For some classes of work, carbide is the only suitable material for dies. In other cases, carbide is used in preference to steel because it is much more durable. According to some production records, the life of a carbide die usually is at least twenty times greater than that of a steel die, whereas the difference in cost, while considerably higher for carbide, is relatively unimportant whenever the amount of production is large enough to warrant the higher initial cost. There is also the advantage of much higher production per grind, as well as greater uniformity of product and a superior finish. Carbide dies are extensively used for drawing wire, bars or rods and tubing. Carbide is also used for various classes of punching, blanking, drawing and forming dies.

The carbide die usually consists of a steel body with rings or inserts for those sections which are subject to wear when the die is in use. (See Figs. 3 and 4.) The design of a car-

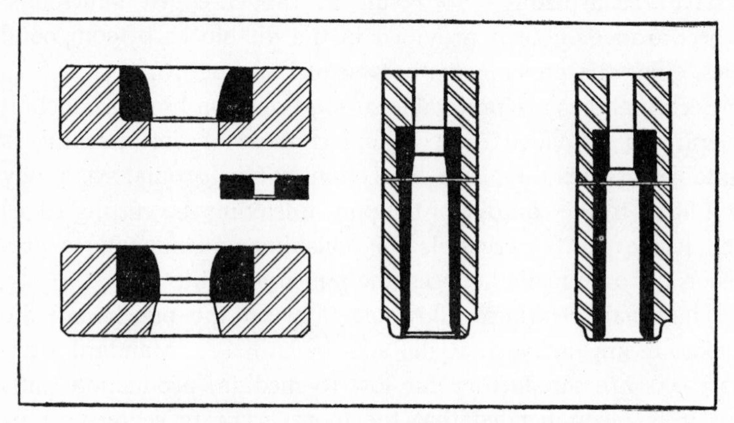

Fig. 3. Dies with Carbide Inserts

bide die does not differ basically from that of an all-steel die, except that the guide pins and die-bolster are made heavier to insure accurate alignment and prevent deflection; also, tolerances on the finished carbide sections are closer. It is these factors, plus the principles employed in segmenting and finishing the carbide sections and in attaching them to the punch-holder and bolster-plate, that determine the success or failure of the application.

A progressive die made of carbide costs, on an average, four times as much as an ordinary steel die, but its life is

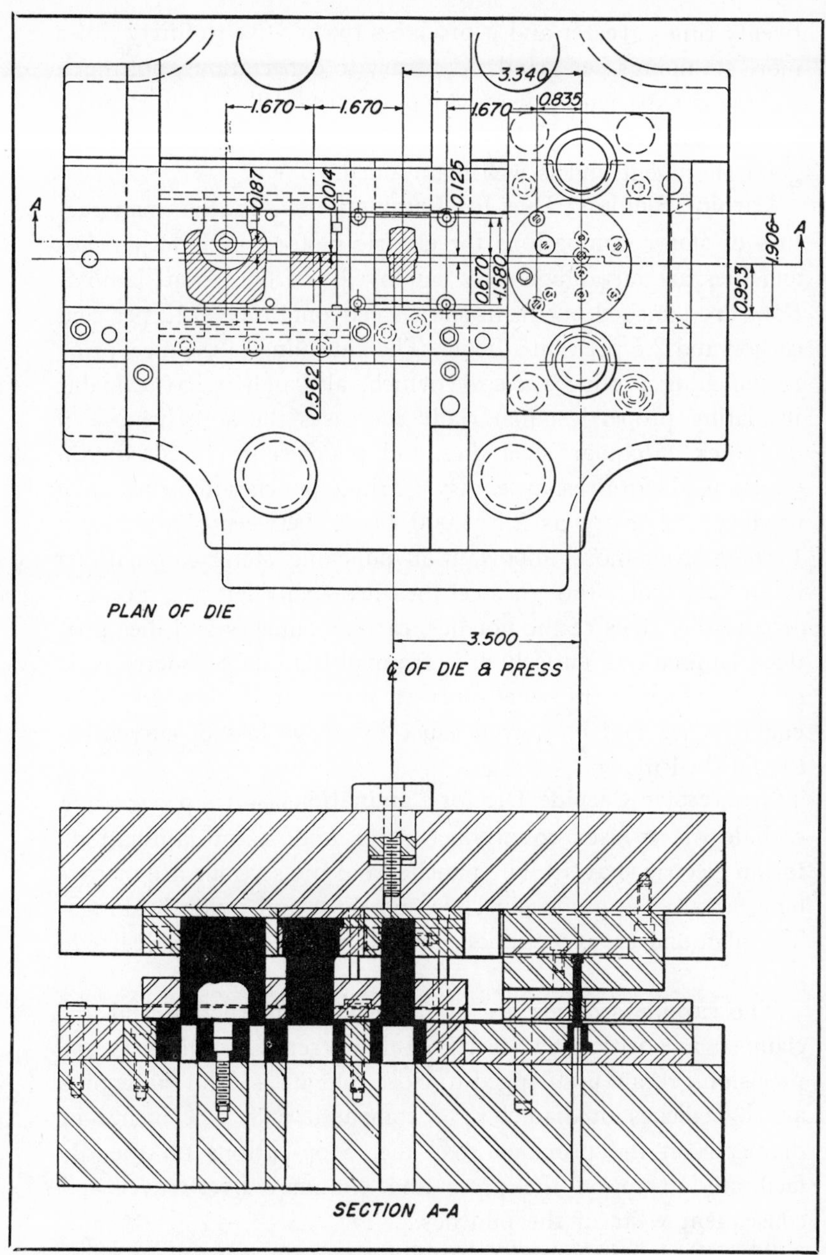

Fig. 4. Progressive Die Equipped with Carbide Inserts as Shown by the Solid Black Sections

twenty times greater and it produces twenty-five to thirty times more stampings per grind. Contrary to expectations, not much trouble is experienced from chipping, provided the die is properly designed and used on a press or dieing machine that is in good alignment and is well maintained.

Carbide Blanking Dies for Laminations.—In the manufacture of stator laminations for electric motors, carbide punches and dies are advantageously employed. In one plant, laminations are punched out from sheet steel containing 0.12 per cent carbon and 2.5 per cent silicon. The annealing of the steel prior to punching produces a scale which, although it has valuable insulating properties, materially increases the abrasiveness of the stock. Regular steel dies and punches produced 46,000 punchings before resharpening. Carbide punches and dies have produced as many as 2,304,000 pieces between sharpenings. Perhaps even more important in punching stator laminations is the fact that although steel dies invariably left a large burr around the edges of the notches, carbide punches and dies produce laminations entirely free from objectionable burrs. It is said that such burrs, when present, make the laminations difficult to stack and may even cause excessive loss of current in the finished motor.

Progressive Carbide Die for Laminations.—A progressive carbide die is used to produce rotor and stator laminations for an electric shaver. The punches and die sections are of carbide, as are the guide pins, pick-up pins, and guide bushings. The plan and cross-sectional views (Fig. 4) show the carbide inserts.

The carbide sections are of segmental construction and are clamped in position by steel hold-down screws. All parts are precision-ground and lapped to close tolerances. The guide pins are 1½ inches in diameter, as compared with 1⅛ inches in diameter on the previous steel die. Stop-buttons on the die facilitate set-up on the press and eliminate over-travel and consequent wear of the punches.

This die has produced thirty-five times the number of parts that can be stamped on a steel die between grinds.

Carbide Die for Transformer Lamination.—This die, which is a push-through type, blanks an L-shaped transformer lamination from strip stock that is automatically unrolled and fed into the die. The material is 3 per cent silicon steel, 0.025 inch thick. The carbide parts of this die also are made in sections to secure adequate strength, insure greater accuracy, and permit replacement of damaged die parts in case of an accident. (Small pieces can be more accurately pre-formed than larger pieces and fewer internal stresses are set up in sintering them.)

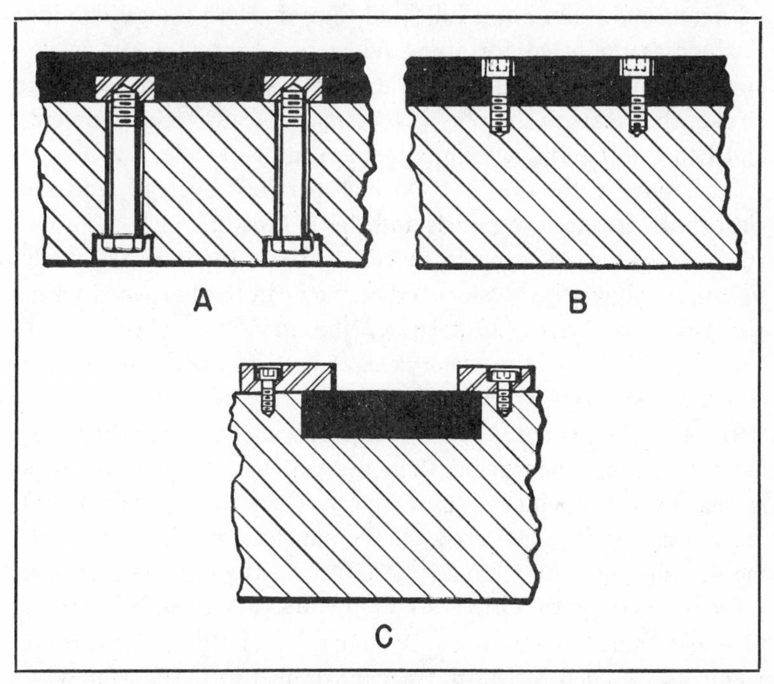

Fig. 5. Methods of Fastening Carbide Sections to the Bolster-plate Include (A) Cap-screws Passing through the Bolster-plate and into Brazed-in Steel Inserts in the Carbide; (B) Cap-screws passing through the Carbide Sections and into the Bolster; and (C) Steel Hold-down Clamps

There are two methods of fastening such sections. First, they may be keyed to one another, and second, they may be held in position either by cap-screws passing through the carbide and into the bolster; by cap-screws passing through the punch-holder or bolster-plate and into the carbide; or by steel hold-down clamps, as shown in Fig. 5.

The bolster of this lamination die is 1½ times heavier than a comparable unit for an all-steel die, and is scraped to provide flat surfaces and hence rigid support for the inserts. Three steel guide pins (2 inches in diameter as compared with 1½ inches in diameter for a steel die) are fitted into the die-bolster and three drawn-in steel bushings are used in the punch-holder. Drive fits are not employed because they often result in some distortion during assembly.

The bushings are designed with an oil well to hold the lubricant and maintain a full fluid film of oil on the guide pins. Carbide is not used for the guide pins. Since the die is designed for use on a high-speed automatic press having a 1-inch stroke, the wear on the pins is too small to cause misalignment, and hence not enough to justify the use of carbide.

The relief in the die is 0.003 inch per inch over all, and the clearance between the punch and die is 0.00125 inch per side. Another feature of note is that all carbide sections are made to project above the bolster so that they can be sharpened without being removed. Otherwise, the grinding wheel would become loaded with the softer steel or cast iron from the bolster and make sharpening impossible.

In operation, this die has averaged about twenty-eight times more stampings per grind than a steel die. It or other dies in use have not chipped excessively, even though occasional mispunchings have occurred. If the punch is in alignment with the die, mispunchings have little effect on the carbide sections.

Carbide Die with Thirty-six Segments.—A carbide die used to punch stator laminations is composed of thirty-six carbide segments, ¾ inch in length, which are held in the bolster with a conventional bowl ring. Carbide guide pins and bushings are used to guide the stripper and to act as stabilizers for the punches. Ball-bearing guide pins are employed; the punch-holder and bolster are larger than usually found in dies of this size; and the clearances and relief are the same as for the transformer lamination die.

Used in an automatic inclinable press equipped with micro-switches to insure that the blank is properly seated, this die has produced one run of 592,000 laminations without being reground. Other carbide dies include shaving dies for removing 0.006 inch from the inside bore of a stator blank, blanking dies for stamping E- and I-shaped transformer laminations, and a progressive die for punching and forming transformer wedges. Carbide is applied only in the last or forming stage of the last-mentioned die, a practice feasible when only one stage is subjected to severe wear.

Where single-stage or progressive dies are used, this is not because compound dies are impractical, but rather because the large pieces of carbide required for their construction are difficult to pre-form and fasten to the bolster without inducing strain; therefore, such dies are inherently weaker than progressive units. For this reason, and because of the added complexity of the compound die, carbide dies of the progressive type are recommended for ordinary shaving, punching, or forming operations.

Cemented Carbide Deep-Drawing Dies.—Carbon steel, stainless steel, and non-ferrous metals are being deep-drawn in carbide dies that frequently have a life of from twenty to one hundred times that of comparable steel dies. The experience of one large producer of high-pressure gas cylinders will indicate the advantages obtained through the use of carbide drawing dies. This company estimates that more than 4,000,000 distinct deep-drawing operations are performed in its plant each year. At present 95 per cent of all the sheet-metal drawing—covering a wide range of thicknesses in a variety of metals—is being performed with carbide dies. Neither the operation of the presses nor the lubricant had to be changed when shifting from steel to carbide dies. Some alterations were made in the die size, but no change was necessary in the basic die design.

It is said that the use of carbide dies on a large scale has reduced scrap by 50 per cent in this plant. It has also increased the number of pieces passing inspection by 30 per cent, and it has materially improved the product by eliminating surface defects in the finished drawn parts. Conventional steel dies needed repolishing after an average of 2500 draws. Carbide dies do not require such attention until after performing about 10,000 comparable operations.

Grinding of Carbide Dies.—A 100-grit vitrified diamond wheel having 100 concentration should be used for rough-grinding of carbide dies, and a 180- to 220-grit wheel with the same concentration for finish-grinding. In mounting a new diamond wheel, extreme care should be taken to make certain that the wheel runs true. The wheel should be tested with a dial indicator on all surfaces, and once tightened on its mount, should not be removed. Such wheels can be dressed efficiently by using a silicon-carbide wheel. The silicon-carbide wheel is not power-driven, but is rotated only by means of the diamond wheel, which revolves against it.

In dressing a rounded contour on a diamond wheel, a common practice is to use a radius dresser which is mounted on a high-speed grinder equipped with a silicon-carbide wheel that revolves in a direction opposite to that of the diamond wheel. In surface-grinding carbide with a diamond wheel, common practice is to use a depth of cut of approximately 0.0002 inch and a cross feed of about 0.0005 inch. From 0.001 to 0.002 inch of stock should be left on the piece after grinding. This amount of stock is generally necessary to obtain a good surface finish in the subsequent lapping operation.

Polishing Carbide Dies.—It is an established fact that carbide dies work best, and give the longest life, when they are lapped and polished to a good surface finish. This is a relatively easy task if proper methods and materials are employed. In polishing the round draw ring, best results were attained with a surface speed of 1400 to 1600 feet per minute. A brass pin, mounted in a hand grinder and coated with diamond powder suspended in olive oil, quickly removes grinding or boring marks from the surface of the carbide.

A wooden lap, mounted on a pin held in a hand grinder and coated with No. 5 diamond powder and olive oil, will produce a satin finish. This should be followed by an operation in which a felt polishing wheel is substituted for the wooden wheel. Medical cotton, wrapped around a piece of wood, will produce the same results. In lapping small holes, cotton twisted on a small wooden pin is usually satisfactory. A very small amount of No. 5 diamond paste is used in this operation. If an extremely high polish is desired, the same procedure should be repeated, substituting No. 6 diamond paste for No. 5 in the second lapping operation.

Materials for Producing Low-cost Dies.—In the manufacture of aircraft and various other products there have been important developments in making dies of materials other than steel or cast iron, which meet practical requirements and yet make it possible to greatly reduce the die costs. This is particularly true where sheets, such as aluminum and magnesium, must be formed or drawn but in quantities that are not large enough to require as durable and expensive a material as steel, for example. These low-cost dies may be made of non-ferrous alloys such as Kirksite and Cerrobend and non-metallic materials may also be used such as Masonite, plastics, Bakelite, densified wood, and rubber. These dies are utilized for drawing or forming in the usual manner and also in conjunction with the stretch-forming process. Such dies are not only used for production runs within the durability limits of the materials mentioned, but in experimental shops or where frequent design changes would make it impracticable to use expensive dies. The low-cost dies referred to are extensively used for medium and large size forming and drawing operations. They may be produced at relatively low cost, chiefly because the material used simplifies the job of die making when compared with steel or cast iron. More specific information on this point is given in the following sections dealing with different materials.

Kirksite Dies.—This is a zinc-base alloy, in both cast and rolled forms, that is especially useful in the aircraft or other industries for making low-cost sheet metal forming dies. Even large forming or cutting dies may be made readily. Forming dies are cast to shape and little or no machining or hand work is required. Kirksite can be remelted repeatedly. It is not intended to replace steel or cast-iron dies but is for use when the total production or manufacturing conditions justify a low-cost die construction. Melting point, 717 degrees F., tensile strength, 37,800 pounds per square inch sand cast, and 62,000 rolled. Rolled Kirksite is applied to blanking or trimming dies.

This alloy has been used extensively in making dies not only for aluminum alloys but also Inconel stampings and stainless steels. Kirksite dies have been used in conjunction with various types of mechanical presses, hydro-presses, and drop hammers. In its rolled form, Kirksite is used for blanking dies usually in conjunction with a steel punch.

Dies for forming are cast to shape. The pattern used in making the mold should be accurate as to dimensions and have a smooth surface. When the die is cast, it will be a duplicate of the pattern reduced 0.14 inch per foot in all dimensions as the result of shrinkage. Either plaster or wood patterns may be used. The former can be produced more quickly and are less liable to warp. The economy in using Kirksite is due chiefly to the elimination of machine and hand work in forming the die. The metal can be remelted and re-cast indefinitely if proper care is taken to control the temperature and prevent contamination. While Kirksite hardness is lower than that of many alloys, it resists wear very well because of its natural oiliness or self-lubricating property. It will not scratch sheet metal nor gall or "load up" as do steel and iron dies under certain conditions. In using Kirksite for steel or Inconel stampings, it is not necessary to polish the die because a smooth surface is obtained after a few stampings have been produced. This smoothness is due to the fact that the sheets are harder than the Kirksite. In forming aluminum alloys, however, the die should be polished with a fine abrasive disk driven by a flexible shaft grinder. Another method is to use the die for making several steel stampings of the proper gage, thus smoothing the die surfaces.

Use of Kirksite Dies in Bus Building.—In a plant producing buses, the bodies are built completely from aluminum and the frame is also constructed entirely from that metal, except for several tubular steel cross-members. The use of aluminum sheets for the contoured body sections has been greatly facilitated by the adoption of manufacturing methods originally developed in the aircraft industry. The technique involves the use of Kirksite dies on pneumatic hammers, and forms of the same material on stretch presses. Some of the Kirksite forms weigh as much as 50 tons.

Over 200 different aluminum parts are produced by this technique for one type of bus, and 175 additional parts for another type of bus which also uses a considerable number of parts identical to those made for the first type. A self-contained aluminum sheet production department has been established. The plaster molds are built up, the Kirksite and lead dies and forms are cast and finished, and the drawing and stretching operations are performed.

Kirksite for making the dies and the stretch forms is melted in two electric-controlled, oil-fired 10,000-pound furnaces of a tilting type. There is a third furnace of the same construction, which is used for melting lead. Lead punches are generally used with the Kirksite dies, except in cases where steel sheets are to be formed or where sharp definition is required. Lead, being softer, conforms readily to the shape of the die in operations on pneumatic hammers. There is, therefore, no need of spotting a lead punch to its die.

Punches for Use with Kirksite Dies.—The punches which are used in conjunction with Kirksite dies may be made of antimonial lead, Kirksite, or thermoplastics. The common practice has been to cast only the die or the punch from a pattern and then produce the mating member from this casting. If the die cavity is used to form the punch, the punch material must be sufficiently ductile when under pressure in the press to fill up any excess space between it and the die caused by the shrinkage of the punch during solidification. Antimonial lead is sufficiently ductile and yet durable enough for fairly long runs on light gage metal. The addition of antimony to lead increases hardness and fluidity and decreases ductility, shrinkage, melting point, and density. A maximum of ductility as measured by percentage of elongation is obtained with 6 per cent antimony and this would be suitable for a drop hammer die but in a forming press which does not deliver such a sudden blow, a higher percentage of antimony and a harder punch could be used safely.

Use of Plastics for Press Tools.—In one aircraft manufacturing plant it is estimated that tooling costs have been reduced about 50 per cent on many forming operations by the use of plastic tools. Drawing dies, spinning chucks, blocks for stretch-forming, and tube-bending mandrels are some of the tools successfully made from plastic. "Catavar," a thermosetting plastic is used in this plant. It is cast to the desired tool shape in plaster molds. Surface finish of the cast plastic tool depends upon the condition of the mold. Generally the tool can be used in the "as cast" condition, without further processing. If the plaster mold is rough, however, the casting can be sanded to a smooth surface finish.

Plastic material can usually be employed for any forming tool where the plastic is confined by the metal being formed. It is not, however, applicable to heated dies required for forming magnesium, since the plastic will expand and crack when subjected to high temperatures. Also, it is not satisfactory for applications where shock loads are encountered, as, for example, in dies employed on drop-hammers.

Plastic drawing dies have proved unusually satisfactory. Parts deep-drawn in such dies have shown no appreciable reduction in metal thickness due to stretching. Less resistance is offered to the flow of the metal than is the case with steel dies, and a good surface finish is produced on the drawn part. Plastic dies that have served their purpose can be used as filler in the manufacture of new dies.

Plastic Punches.—Plastic punches, in conjunction with Kirksite dies, have been used extensively in plants of the Lockheed Aircraft Corporation for drop hammer and hydraulic press drawing punches. Experience has shown that plastic punches will form metal parts in Kirksite dies more consistently than the lead punches formerly in exclusive use. Because plastic punches are more pliable than lead punches, they give more readily and force the metal being formed closely into the die impressions, in this way somewhat duplicating the effects obtained by using rubber pads in forming operations. Workpieces can, therefore, be drawn or formed to closer dimensional tolerances, particularly as far as beads and similar details are concerned.

Another important advantage derived from plastic punches is the greatly reduced cost of preparing them for use. As in the case of lead punches, it is the practice to pour the molten plastic into a finished Kirksite die. When this step has been completed and the material has solidified, the plastic punch is ready for immediate use.

Although the plastic compresses, it readily returns to its original shape, and this accounts for its good metal-forming qualities. This elasticity enables plastic punches to retain their original shape even down to small details, whereas surfaces of small radius on lead punches are generally beaten back to larger radii and reduced heights. It is the practice to place rubber strips in dies to compensate for such deformation of lead punches and to insure that the sheet metal will be forced to the bottom of the die impressions. The use of rubber for this purpose causes still further deformation of punch details, with the result that a new lead punch is often necessary for restriking formed work.

Plastic punches are only one-tenth as heavy as lead ones, and they can, therefore, be handled far more easily. Still another advantage is derived from the fact that when a plastic punch is brought into sharp contact with the work and die in drop-hammer operations, only a dull thud is emitted, instead of the sharp ringing sound usually produced when both the punch and die are made of metal. This reduced noise also tends to alleviate operator fatigue.

Excellent results have been obtained by casting plastic punches from Nos. 8 and 9 Plastalloy and Tenite II. Research has proved that either of these plastics may be used for most punches required for forming aluminum and its alloys.

Preparation of a Kirksite die for casting a plastic punch is much the same as for casting a lead punch, except that it is unnecessary to pre-heat the die or to spray it with whiting.

The final operation in producing a plastic punch is to heat the die to a temperature slightly above the melting point of the plastic with the punch removed from the die. Then the punch is located on the die and pressure is applied by means of ordinary clamps, such as are employed by cabinet-makers. This causes the surface next to the die to be slightly remelted, so that the punch fills in areas of the die from which it may have shrunk in the initial cast. A water spray quench is next applied to cool the punch and die as rapidly as possible. This operation, which is called "searing," compensates for all shrinkage and insures the fit between the punch and die. In the event that the face of a punch becomes marred or deformed during use, a similar searing operation will reproduce the face just as accurately as when the punch was new, thus eliminating the necessity of recasting the punch.

Since the top surface of the cooled plastic punch is not ordinarily smooth, it is the custom to machine this surface with the punch resting on the die, so that the top surface of the punch will be finished parallel to the bottom of the die. This machining operation is done either on a planer or a radial drilling machine equipped with a fly cutter.

When plastic punches were first placed in use, considerable difficulty was experienced when the punches were taken from outdoor storage areas and placed into immediate use. Experience has shown that Plastalloy punches should not be worked at temperatures lower than 70 degrees F., because they become brittle at lower temperatures and will fracture from hammer blows. On the other hand, Tenite II seems to be unaffected by temperatures considerably lower than 70 degrees F.; as a matter of fact, the tensile strength appears to increase with decreased temperatures. Tenite also has a higher melting point, and therefore can be used at higher temperatures.

Neither of the thermoplastic materials from which Lockheed punches are made should be ground or sanded, because of the heat generated by tools used in such operations. On the other hand, they may be drilled, tapped, planed, or cut with machines or hand-operated woodworking tools.

Dies Made from Cerrobend.—Cerrobend is another alloy which may be utilized in producing low-cost dies. It is especially useful in aircraft, experimental or other shops where design changes are necessary either during construction or after completion of an experimental model and it is impractical to use standard tooling because less expensive tools meet the requirements. Repair bases often have the same problem of fabricating one or only a few parts under conditions of limited facilities and time.

Cerrobend—an alloy containing 26.7 per cent lead, 13.3 per cent tin, 10 per cent cadmium, and 50 per cent bismuth—has proved the answer to many of the problems involved in making parts in small quantities. This alloy possesses physical properties that make it a suitable material from which to produce hand-forming, hydraulic press, and drawing dies; backing blocks; punches and pressure plates; power-brake joggle dies; and numerous other tools. Generally, these tools can be made from Cerrobend in less time than it would take to make the patterns for standard tools.

Since the melting temperature of this alloy is only 160 degrees F., which is 52 degrees cooler than boiling water, it can be safely and easily handled in the molten state. A tank of suitable size, in which hot water can be maintained for keeping a working quantity of the molten alloy, is the main part of the necessary apparatus. The only other equipment required is a tank or trough of cold water for quenching the castings. Cooling by water greatly reduces the normal cooling time and improves the granular structure of the casting. This is a unique process, inasmuch as the presence of even a small amount of moisture around most molten metals may cause serious explosions. Cerrobend is always handled at a temperature below 200 degrees F., which eliminates all possibilities of steam explosion. Since most of the tooling is of a temporary nature and the alloy is 100 per cent salvageable, only a small working stock is needed. In many cases, the tools are remelted into stock Cerrobend as soon as the aircraft parts for which they were made are completed.

While the tensile strength of Cerrobend is rated at about 6000 pounds per square inch and its Brinell hardness is 9.2, its elongation under extreme conditions has been as high as 200 per cent of the original length of the specimen.

Cerrobend was originally manufactured for use in tube-bending processes. Tubes are filled with the molten metal and quenched in cold water to form a practically solid bar, which can be bent to any desired radius or contour. Because the material expands slightly after cooling, it gives a tight fit within the tube, producing the solid bar effect. The expansion of from 0.003 to 0.006 inch per inch, while not enough to damage good tubing, is sufficient to reveal defects, such as cracks or faulty seams, which might otherwise go unnoticed until failure in service.

When tooling is required to duplicate a sheet-metal part, the part itself can be used as a pattern and a Cerrobend punch and die cast simultaneously on each side. This method insures an accurate fit of a punch to its mating die. Forming dies made in this manner are now being used to take the place of many expensive conventional type drop-hammer and hydraulic press dies.

For duplicating parts already on planes, plaster casts are made of the parts and used as a pattern or mold. In some cases, the Cerrobend castings are made right on the airplane. Tools for a part that is not available can be quickly made from Cerrobend, since modeling clay, plaster-of-paris, sheet metal, or soft wood can be used for the pattern. Because of its low melting temperature, Cerrobend can be cast directly against any of these pattern materials with excellent results.

The completion of both large and small dies can be hastened by using a sheet-metal box mold around the pattern and circulating cold water around the mold. Since the surface of the pattern will be duplicated upon the die, only a negligible amount of cleaning up of the die is necessary. Casting the punch within the die itself insures a true fit. Metal thickness allowance and insulation of the die from the heat of the molten punch are easily taken care of by coating the inside of the die with clay or casting plaster. For general use, a mixture of dry clay and clear lacquer, applied with an ordinary paint spray gun, has proved very satisfactory.

Drawing dies with punches and pressure plates made of Cerrobend can also be produced by the method described. In using one of these die sets, the pressure plates are held to the die with C-clamps, so that as the punch is forced into the die by a press ram or other suitable means, the material is actually stretch-formed or deep-drawn around the punch in the same manner that parts are formed on double-acting hydraulic press or punch press dies. Jobs that would necessitate lengthy hand-forming operations can be completed by this method in a comparatively short time.

Cerrobend punches and dies give remarkable results, even under the severe blows of drop-hammers or the heavy pressures of hydraulic presses. Wheel wells, odd-shaped air ducts, air scoops, hemispherical tank sections, and contoured skin segments of steel, as well as of aluminum, are a few of the types of parts that are successfully made by Cerrobend dies for drop-hammer and hydraulic press operations.

The size of dies that can be made from Cerrobend is limited only by the facilities for pouring, cooling, and handling. Many hydraulic press blocks are made entirely from this material, while others made of Masonite have Cerrobend inlays for beads, joggles, lightening holes, etc. Backing blocks for hand-forming operations on surfaces that are not both smooth and flat are made with Cerrobend in a fraction of the time required by previous methods. Backing blocks to match compound contours or difficult angles or joggles which would require considerable time of the patternmaker if made in the conventional manner can be produced in a few minutes by casting Cerrobend directly against the form block.

Cast-iron Dies.—There are some classes of dies for which common cast iron is suitable. This is especially true when the plant in question operates its own pattern shop and foundry. Dies of this class are suited for the simpler bending and forming operations, where the work is more in the nature of direct bending or compressing rather than a drawing action which may cause abrasion of the wearing surfaces.

The principal advantage of cast-iron dies is the economy and speed with which they can be made. In some cases, where a high degree of accuracy is not required, the die need not be machined. For such a die, the pattern may be sent to the foundry one morning, and the die made ready for service the next. It might be possible, of course, to do this in some cases with a steel die, but the cost of machining, as well as the cost of the material would be far in excess of that of the cast-iron die. Such dies are of particular advantage on experimental work, where the exact size or form must be determined by trial. This plan is sometimes used for drawing dies, in determining the size of the blank and the depth of draw that can be made at one operation, after which the permanent set of hardened dies is made up. A cast-iron drawing die will last for a considerable time if the pressure between the drawing surfaces is not excessive.

Fig. 6 shows examples of cast-iron dies. Those shown, with one exception, are used in forming the blades for multi-blade fans. At *A* is shown a die for forming the break in the angular fan blade shown at *B*. The blanks are first sheared to width and length, and then notched at the ends to allow for flanging the ends at right angles to the blade. This die was finished on the bearing surfaces, and the stop or locating strip *J* was fastened to one side of the die for locating the blank.

The blade shown at *F* is curved to a 3-inch radius and the ends are flanged back at right angles in one operation, by the die shown at *E*, which consists of member *K*, the punch *L*, and the end-flanging blocks *M*. This die was cast from a wooden pattern, and placed directly in service without any machining whatever. At *G* is shown the same die with a spring-operated stripper added, for forcing the blade from the die.

At *D* is shown an "ogee" blade which is formed in the die *C*. This die is also used in the rough-cast condition without machining the forming surfaces. The principal wear on such a die is on the inner surfaces of the blocks *N* over which the

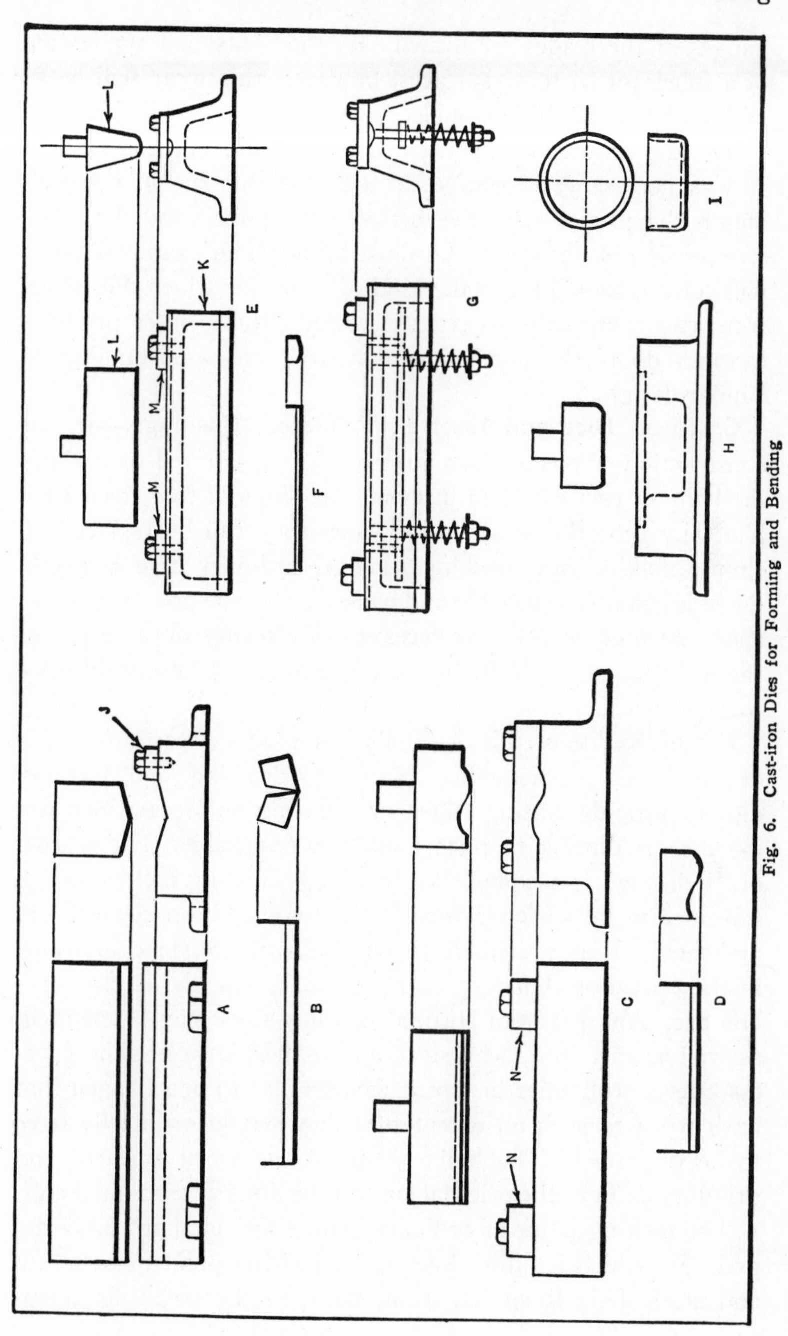

Fig. 6. Cast-iron Dies for Forming and Bending

flanges of the blades are drawn. By the occasional application of a lubricant to these surfaces, however, this wear will be so slight as to cause little trouble.

The die shown at *H* is used in forming the cup shown at *I*. It was necessary, of course, to machine this die in order to obtain the proper clearance between the punch and die. The stripper is not shown in the illustration. The examples given will convey some idea of the kind of work for which dies made from cast iron have proved successful. Many other products can, no doubt, be handled equally well on cast-iron dies of similar design.

Cast-iron Dies and Inserted Tool-steel Bushings.—In the construction of some dies a saving may be effected by making the body of cast iron and inserting bushings of tool steel; then if at any time the dies become worn they can be replaced by simply making new bushings, and if ordinary care is taken, the holes will be concentric and consequently the proper distance apart, so there will be no necessity of altering the location of the punches, as might be the case if a die made of a solid piece was hardened.

Use of Stellite on Dies.—Stellite is used on certain classes of dies such as trimming, blanking, drawing and forming dies to provide cutting edges or drawing surfaces which are much more durable than steel and also renewable. The process of "stelliting" is accomplished by simply flowing melted stellite rod on a metal surface which has previously been cleaned and preheated. It is preferable to use the oxy-acetylene blowpipe in the operation, but it is also possible to use the electric carbon arc. Any grade of straight or alloy steel may be stellited, as well as cast iron, semi-steel, and malleable iron. The process effects economies in that it enables dies to be salvaged that have worn to such an extent that they would ordinarily have to be discarded. The building up of the worn surfaces and grinding them to the original size can be done at a nominal cost.

The melting point of ordinary stellite rod is about 2335 degrees F., which is quite close to the melting point of cast iron and steel. This is an important point in the stelliting operation, as both the stellite and the base metal are brought to a state of fusion by the oxy-acetylene flame. The similar melting points insure a strong and properly alloyed bond between the stellite and the base metal. To stellite a surface successfully, it is necessary to avoid blow-holes on or beneath the stellite coating and checks or surface cracks caused by uneven cooling. Thorough preheating and annealing of the base metal is essential to the successful application of the process, because even though the melting points of steel and stellite, and the coefficients of linear expansion, are approximately the same, stellite changes from the liquid to the solid state more quickly than steel when both are cooled in air. Therefore, unless the steel is preheated evenly, kept up to heat during the operation, and cooled slowly, internal strains will be set up that are great enough to check the stellited surface. Preheating also facilitates the stelliting operation and the quick removal of scale.

Meehanite Dies for Drawing and Forming.—Meehanite is used in producing various forming and drawing dies. These dies, which are applicable both to cold and hot forming, are cast to form and have great strength and endurance. They are free from galling, scuffing, and scoring. When the dies are in use they cold work to a high polish and high degree of surface hardness.

Meehanite dies may be flame-hardened or heat-treated for "extra" properties. For example, complex punches or dies with a variety of embossings and offsets may be cast in one piece and after complete machining and finishing the working edges may be flame-hardened. Such a die will provide an excellent tool for a good production rate on such stampings as automobile gasoline tanks, refrigerator panels, stove and washing machine parts. Runs of 500,000 stampings on 22-gage material and up to 200,000 on 14-gage material have not been uncommon.

The limitations of Meehanite depend upon the service conditions demanded. It is not recommended for drop forging dies except when a limited number of forgings are required and where the design of the forgings assures safety. For hot forming dies such as shovel blanks and various other agricultural implements and for hammer bed dies, Meehanite may be used to advantage. In cases where stampings are to be manufactured from heavier gage steels with severe drop and sharp corners, the dies should be heat-treated. Heat-treating cycles are simple—generally consisting of an oil quench from 1600 degrees F., followed by a draw. Little or no distortion should follow if the hardening operation is carried out properly.

Use of Rubber for Forming of Light Metals.—For certain forming and drawing operations, a press may be used that is equipped with a pad of rubber, the function of which is similar to that of a punch. The die which is used in conjunction with this rubber pad is formed to suit the work, and the rubber, because of its flexibility, is capable of conforming to the shape of the die when subjected to sufficient pressure. This method is frequently used in forming, drawing, blanking, and flanging sheets of aluminum and magnesium. A rubber pad is held within a steel or cast iron container which prevents lateral expansion of the rubber during a forming or drawing operation. This container should not only be strong enough to withstand the bursting pressure but deep enough to provide for the maximum displacement of the rubber incident to the drawing or forming operation. When the pad is fully compressed, there should be sufficient room for the platen to enter. In many cases, the thickness of the pad is about two-thirds the depth of the container. The platen should fit into the container closely to prevent any extrusion of the rubber between the sides of the platen and the container or "pressure box," as it is sometimes called.

When a sheet of metal such as aluminum or magnesium is placed between the rubber pad and the die (or group of dies for multiple forming, drawing, or blanking) and sufficient pressure is applied, the metal is forced (within the limitations of this process) to duplicate approximately at least, the shape of the die or form block. While the pressure varies for different classes of work, a range between 300 and 500 pounds per square inch is fairly common. The principle of the process

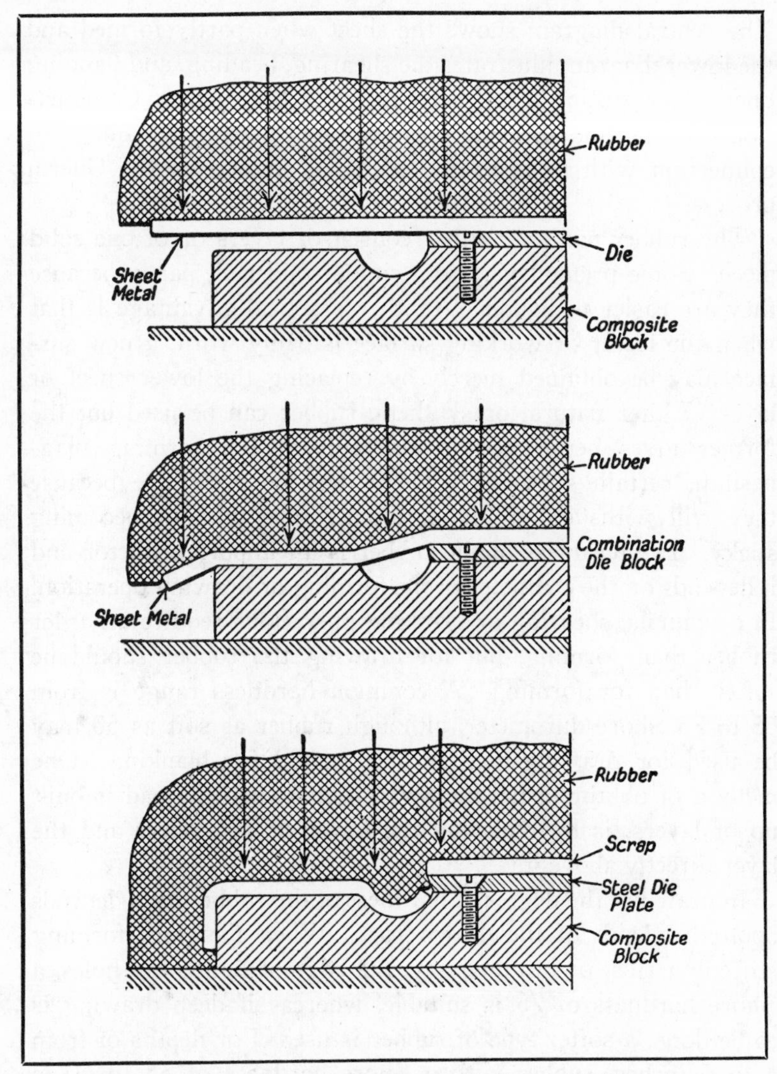

Fig. 7. Successive Stages in Forming the Beading on the Edge of a Lightening Hole

is illustrated by the diagrams, Fig. 7, which show successive stages in shearing or blanking a hole for lightening the part, forming a bead around its edge, and also an outer flange. (The container in which the rubber pad is housed is not shown.)

The central diagram shows the sheet when partly formed and the lower diagram illustrates the shearing, beading, and flanging operation resulting from the pressure of the rubber. Combination forming and shearing dies are often used to advantage in connection with this process, which is known as the Guerin process.

The rubber pad may either consist of layers or of one solid piece. Some prefer layers to a single solid pad, partly because they are easier to handle. Another practical advantage is that when the lower or working surface is badly worn, a new surface may be obtained merely by replacing the lower sheet or layer. Either natural or synthetic rubber can be used but the former gives better results although in hot forming magnesium, certain synthetic rubbers may be preferable because they will withstand a higher temperature without becoming sticky. The hardness of the rubber is an important factor and it depends on the character of the forming or drawing operation. For example, shearing or blanking operations require a harder rubber than forming, but for drawing the rubber should be softer than for forming. A common hardness range is from 65 to 75 Shore durometer, although rubber as soft as 50 may be used for drawing and as hard as 80 for blanking. One method of obtaining hardness variations when the pad is built up of layers, is by replacing the lower or face sheet and the layer directly above it.

In drawing, the degree of hardness of the rubber used depends upon the depth of the drawn part. When flanging, forming stiffening ribs, or beading, say, the edge of lightening holes, a Shore hardness of 75 is suitable, whereas if deep drawing is to be done, a softer type of rubber is used. For depths of from 4 to 6 inches, rubber with a Shore hardness of 55 to 60 is suitable.

In flanging operations, if the rubber is too soft, it becomes excessively deformed and tends to flow behind the metal, thus preventing the flange from being properly formed as illustrated by the left diagram Fig. 8. When, however, the rubber is of suitable hardness, its deformation is less at a given pressure, and the flanging is completed before the rubber flows behind the metal to prevent it, as illustrated by the right-hand diagram.

It is common practice to produce a number of parts at one stroke of the press. This is done by placing a group of dies either on the platen or on an auxiliary removable table supported by the platen. A single sheet of stock may then be placed over the group of dies, especially if the latter can be arranged so as to avoid excessive waste of stock. Another method is to use a separate blank for each die and position each blank by locating pins on the die. The use of two or more removable

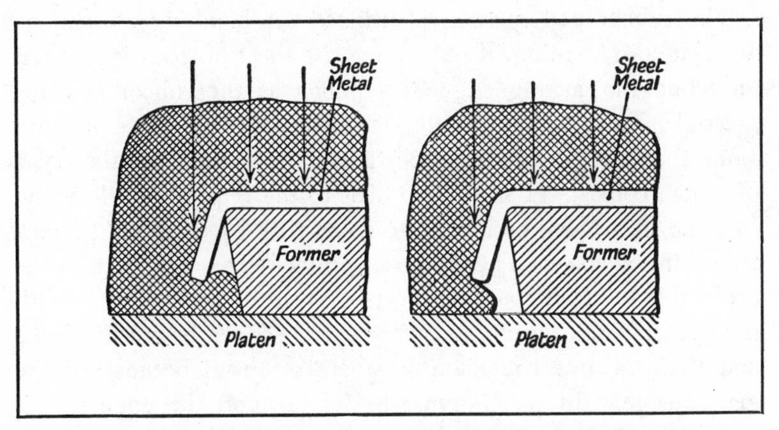

Fig. 8. If the Rubber is too Soft it Flows Behind and Obstructs the Sheet being formed as Shown at the Left. When Hard Rubber is Used, This Difficulty is Not Experienced (see Right-Hand View)

tables permits loading or unloading one auxiliary table while another is on the press, thus increasing the efficiency of the process. In all drawing operations it is advisable to use a lubricant between the rubber and the metal being drawn or formed. Powdered French chalk or graphite have given satisfactory results.

When the rubber is compressed as the press ram descends, one might assume that the surface of the work would be subjected to a uniform unit pressure over the entire area. There is, however, more or less variation and, consequently, in many cases a part may not be formed as fully as required. To overcome this difficulty, auxiliary rubber pads are sometimes placed upon the flat blank to obtain greater pressure wherever this may be needed.

The form blocks may be made from some material, such as Masonite, Kirksite, hard wood or a plastic that will withstand the pressure. The materials mentioned may also be formed readily to the required shape; hence the dies may be produced at low cost and they are sufficiently durable for a great many different applications. The Guerin process is especially adapted to forming or drawing shallow parts and impressions especially for producing parts in small- or medium-sized lots.

The rubber pad method is utilized for blanking as well as drawing and forming. In blanking, the sheet of stock is sheared off along the cutting edge of a punch as the rubber is compressed. This punch usually is made of steel plate ground along the cutting edge with a little negative rake. Another type of punch consists of steel strip bent to the required outline and inserted in a block of Masonite so as to project about 1/8 inch above the surface. There are several reasons why it may be preferable to cut a stack of sheets by routing or sawing. With the rubber blanking method, only one sheet can be cut at a time and there is also considerable waste of metal because of the generous margin which must be left around the edge of the punch. Then, too, the rubber pad tends to stress the metal around the edge of the blank.

The hydraulic press is especially adapted to the use of rubber in conjunction with press tools because this type of press with its modern control system permits speed variations, gradual "inching," and also any dwell that may be required at the end of the power stroke. Toggle type presses have also been employed but the ordinary crank type are not as a rule recommended, especially if conditions are such that the accumulated energy of the flywheel is liable to build up enough pressure in the restrained rubber to stall the press and possibly cause damage.

A common cause of failure in working any metal is that not enough time is given to allow the metal to flow uniformly—a condition particularly necessary when magnesium-aluminum alloys are being worked. If the metal to be formed is homogeneous and free from internal strain, it can be drawn at a moderately high speed. Physical variations, however, exist, and it is necessary to "persuade" the metal and not force it to flow.

Additional information on the use of rubber in conjunction with press tools will be found in Chapter XIX A.

Forming Magnesium Alloys by Guerin Process.—In forming operations on magnesium alloys, the metal is heated to obtain greater elasticity and elongation unless the operation is a very simple one that does not require much drawing or forming. The Guerin process has been used extensively for shallow forming or drawing operations on magnesium alloys. The usual practice is to heat the dies either by placing them upon a heated platen or by inserting the heating elements within the die—especially the more complicated forms. A common method of heating forming dies is by means of automatically controlled gas-fired burners. Electrical heating elements are also employed. In most cases, it is essential to control the heating units thermostatically. This may be done by providing a thermocouple for each burner and an automatic pyrometer for regulating the fuel supply. Small thin sheets are ordinarily heated by simply placing the cold blank upon the heated die. In forming comparatively thick or heavy material, time is saved by preheating the sheet. If the temperature for forming varies from about 250 to 350 degrees F., natural rubber of 70 durometer hardness may be used but for higher temperatures up to 450 degrees F., natural rubber would become sticky and synthetic rubber should be used. Synthetic rubbers have been developed that will withstand temperatures up to 450 degrees F. without becoming sticky. Incidentally, powdered or flake mica has been used to prevent the rubber from adhering to the heated blanks and tools; ordinary wax paper has also been used for this purpose. Aluminum alloy, Kirksite, and magnesium alloy are recommended for die materials, because they have approximately the same thermal expansion coefficient as the material being formed. When steel dies are used, expansion differences between the die and the formed part must be considered.

Steel Punches and Dies for Drawing and Forming Magnesium.—The steel punches and dies used for blanking, drawing, and forming magnesium are similar to those employed for other metals such as steel, brass, and aluminum excepting that means must be provided for heating them. Hardened tool steel is generally used for a blanking die. The punch used with this die is not hardened so that it can be formed by shearing it into the die in order to obtain a very slight clearance only.

For drawing dies, tool steel should be used for the draw rings and pressure pads of high production dies. When the greater durability of tool steel is not required, less expensive mild steel is generally used. Several different materials may be used for the punch. These include steel, cast iron, magnesium, and aluminum.

Magnesium alloys are exceptionally well adapted to drawing at elevated temperatures. A slow, uniform operation, such as that obtainable with hydraulic presses, is recommended. Since the majority of drawing operations require considerable time, the usual practice is to heat the draw-ring and blank-holder to keep the material at its proper temperature during the drawing operation.

Draws deeper than those ordinarily made with aluminum alloys are quite common. They are successful because the variation in temperature in different parts of the piece being formed can be used to advantage. For example, the punch is ordinarily not heated, in which case it chills the sides of the part being drawn and increases the tensile strength at the point where failures ordinarily occuring in drawing.

Only mild forming of magnesium alloys in the hard condition is possible at room temperature. Sheets in the annealed condition and extrusions in the "as extruded" condition can be formed, but not severely. Most forming of the hard materials at elevated temperatures is limited to 300 to 400 degrees F. to minimize annealing. In the annealed condition, temperatures as high as 700 degrees F. may be used. Most magnesium parts in shapes commonly made of aluminum alloy can be formed at some elevated temperature, but this temperature is frequently so high as to make it impossible to obtain parts of high strength, because high strength is not obtainable by heat-treating after annealing.

Most of the common methods used for converting any metal sheet and extrusions into useful shapes are applicable to magnesium. Deep drawing, shallow drawing, pressing, stretch forming, spinning and similar processes are in regular commercial use. Press drawing is done on both hydraulic and mechanical presses although hydraulic presses usually are preferred because of better control of drawing speed. Because of its crystalline structure, the working of magnesium at elevated temperatures puts more planes of slip into play and many intricate parts can be drawn in one operation without intermediate annealing steps and with only one set of dies being necessary. Hot working likewise results in parts made to exact size with no "spring back" when the finished piece is removed from the die. An entering radius on the draw ring of 5 to 7 times the sheet thickness gives maximum drawability. The male die or punch is usually heated by means of gas burners or electric strip heaters inside the punch. The draw ring is also heated. Care should be taken when using a gas flame that it impinges only on the surface to be heated and not on the magnesium sheet. The magnesium sheet is usually preheated in an oven prior to forming. Shallow parts, flanges, and similar shapes not requiring deep drawing action can be rubber formed by the Guerin process of rubber forming.

The drop hammer has been successfully used as a means of forming magnesium sheet. Zinc alloys are satisfactory for drop hammer dies when the temperatures do not exceed 500°F. Lead-antimony alloy, which can be cheaply converted into a punch by casting in the zinc alloy die, is satisfactory for working temperatures up to 400°F. As in deep drawing, both drop hammer and die should be heated. A ring burner may be used in the die.

Magnesium possesses a very high elongation at elevated temperatures which makes the metal ideally suited to stretch forming. Punches for hot stretch forming are conveniently made of zinc alloy if temperatures do not go too far above 400°F. The punch can be heated by means of gas burners and the sheet preheated in an oven and kept hot during forming by means of contact with the punch.

Bending Magnesium.—Magnesium sheet and extrusions can be bent with the same type of tools customarily used for other metals. Bending rolls are used on sheet for such operations as the production of cylindrical tanks. Pipe bending machines of standard design are suitable for bending magnesium tubing. Press brakes and folding leaf type brakes are being used for magnesium sheet. The bending of other extrusions such as bars, rods, and shapes is accomplished by the same methods used for aluminum and other metals. When heating of the stock is necessary for making bends, the heat can be applied in any convenient manner. On small production runs simply passing a torch over the work may be adequate. On long runs, and where the equipment permits, the electric strip heaters can be attached to bending brakes. 500 to 650°F. is the desirable working temperature for annealed magnesium sheet and extrusions. Sheet in the hard rolled condition should not be heated over 400°F., otherwise annealing will result. A contact pyrometer should be used to check the temperature of the material. In case such an instrument is not available, the crude but effective temperature indications known to many metal workers can be substituted. Typical of these are; a smear of laundry soap on the metal turns dark brown at about 400° F.; a mark made with the blue carpenter's chalk will lose its color at approximately 600°F.

Densified Wood for Forming and Drawing Aluminum.—Densified wood or "compreg" when employed for dies is known as "Hi-Den". It is made from selected layers of birchwood that are impregnated with Bakelite phenolic resin and compressed to approximately 50 per cent of their original thickness. The composite material is cured by subjecting it to high pressures and elevated temperatures. This treatment transforms the wood into a tough, hard, water-resistant material having high dimensional stability. Cross ply construction is employed to provide uniform strength characteristics in all directions.

Dies made from Hi-Den can be quickly and easily constructed or altered, and their high strength provides long life. The low coefficient of friction of the smooth dies minimizes scratching of the metal being formed, and produces an even distribution of metal in the drawn parts. A minimum production of about 200 parts is generally required to warrant the use of densified wood tooling.

Physical properties of this grade of Hi-Den are: Specific gravity, 1.30; tensile strength, 15,000 pounds per square inch; modulus of rupture, 20,000 pounds per square inch; Izod impact, 3 foot-pounds per inch of notch.

The material is purchased in flat sheets. Conventional woodworking equipment can be employed to machine the material to the desired shape. Wood-working planers or jointers, however, should not be used on this material, as it will cause breakage of the blades.

A good surface finish is obtained in holes or on threads with carbon steel drills or taps. A fly cutter, mounted in the spindle of a drill press, can be used to counterbore densified wood. Hand scraping tools, buffing wheels, or sanding machines produce good surface finish. A tolerance of $\pm$ 0.005 inch is generally specified on such dies.

Excellent metal flow is obtained between the smooth densified wood surfaces, providing a very good surface finish on the drawn parts. Sharp corners can be produced with a minimum of tearing. There is a smooth sliding action, without slippage, between the gripping surfaces of the punch and die, so that very little thinning out of the metal takes place. No gripping bead is required, as is common practice in conventional deep-drawing dies.

"Compreg" dies can be easily adapted to suit changes in the design of a product by building them up or machining them as required. Densified wood has been successfully applied to tools other than drawing dies, punches, and pressure pads. Included in such applications are form blocks for stretch-forming aluminum, spinning chucks, bending brake dies, tube bending blocks, inspection fixtures, and drilling, sawing, and spot-welding jigs.

CHAPTER IV

PUNCH AND DIE DETAILS

IN THE design of punches and dies, it is important to consider carefully such details as methods of holding both punches and dies in position; the means of locating the stock in the proper position for blanking or other operations; the arrangement for stripping the stock from blanking, piercing, forming or drawing punches; and devices for ejecting the work. Details of the kind mentioned are found on practically all classes of dies and the same principles of design are frequently applied to dies of different types. This chapter and the one which follows will deal with these details, particularly as they apply to die construction in general. Details of the same general classes and others which are more or less special in design, will be found in various chapters dealing with dies of particular types.

Methods of Holding Punches.—Punches are attached to their holders in quite a variety of ways. The method may depend upon the size and shape of the punch and whether it is to be used singly or in combination with other punches. The service for which the punch is intended is another point that should be considered; that is, whether the material to be punched is light or heavy and also whether the die is for producing comparatively few parts or is intended for continuous service. When punching heavy material, the punch must be firmly secured against vertical thrust in either an upward or downward direction, because when the punch ascends and is stripped from the stock, it is subjected to a heavy downward pull. If the die is a type intended for a small amount of work, a cheap and quick method of making both the punch and the die would ordinarily be employed. The personal ideas of the designer or toolmaker also affect the construction of punches and dies, and even those who have had wide enough experience to qualify as experts often disagree on important and fundamental points. Therefore, owing to the different factors which govern punch and die design, the practice is variable and far from being standardized.

A number of different methods of attaching punches, which are commonly employed in diemaking practice, are referred to in the following. When only a single punch is required, it is

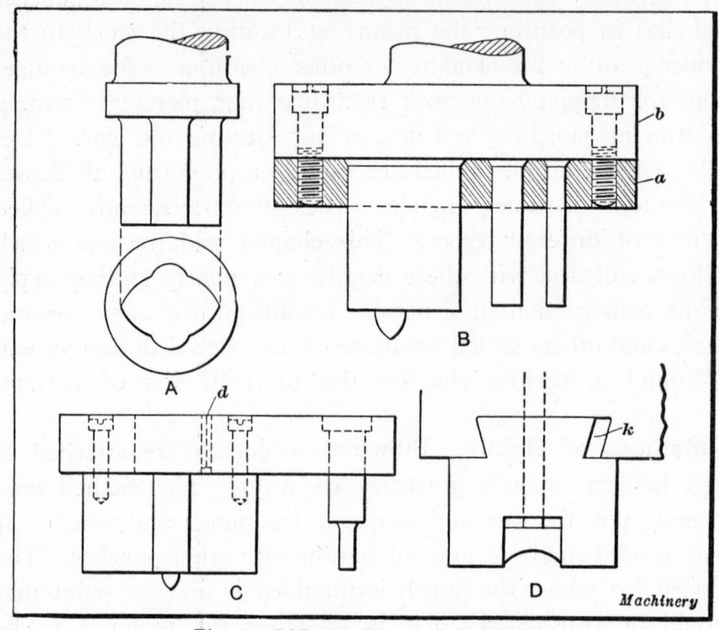

Fig. 1. Different Types of Punches

ordinarily made in one solid piece, as illustrated at *A*, Fig. 1, the punch being integral with the round shank which enters and is clamped in the ram or slide of the press. Usually it is necessary to fasten several punches to a holder and then the construction is different. The method illustrated at *B* is common, especially when the shapes of the punches are not intricate or very irregular. As the diagram shows, each punch passes through a punch plate *a* and bears against the punch-holder *b*. The upper end is riveted over to prevent the punch from pulling out when being stripped from the stock, and the punch plate is held to the holder by machine screws, as shown. Evidently, a round piercing punch can easily be attached in this way, but if the shape is very irregular, the work of machining the opening in the punch plate is much more difficult. Furthermore, if thick material is to be punched, there is danger of pulling out the punches when stripping the stock, especially if they are not well riveted at the top; therefore, some diemakers only hold punches in this way when the openings in the punch plate are readily machined and the punch is intended for medium or light service. Another disadvantage connected with the construction illustrated at *B* is that if the punch is not tightly fitted to punch plate *a*, it tends to loosen. For instance, if the press operator should make a miscut or a "half-cut," the punch which is not sufficiently rigid springs to one side and either shears off or loosens the riveted end, thus causing trouble. This method, however, has been used extensively and with satisfactory results.

Another way of holding punches is illustrated at *C*. The large blanking punch at the left is provided with a round shank which is driven tightly into the punch plate. The punch is prevented from turning by a dowel-pin driven in at *d*, and, in addition, machine screws are used to prevent the punch from pulling out of the plate when stripping the stock. This method of holding a blanking punch, especially if the shape is quite irregular, is preferred by some diemakers, because it is only necessary to machine a round hole through the punch plate instead of an irregular opening such as is required when the punch passes through the punch plate. In some cases, two dowel-pins, placed as far apart as possible, would be used instead of one dowel at the side of the shank. If the punch were intended for quite heavy material, it might be advisable to rivet over the end of the shank, although riveting makes it more difficult to remove the punch, if this should be necessary.

The diagram *D*, Fig. 1, illustrates how punches are sometimes held in a dovetailed groove in the holder. The slightly tapering key *k*, which is driven in at one side, holds the punch securely in place. The slides of some presses have a dovetailed slot across the lower end so that punches may be attached to them directly by a dovetailed fitting. This method is especially desirable for large punches or those subjected to heavy duty.

Still another arrangement, which is a modification of the one illustrated at *C*, Fig. 1, is shown at *A*, Fig. 2. The blanking punch is provided with a shank and is riveted over at the top, but, instead of using dowel-pins to secure it in position, a slot or groove is planed part way through the punch-holder as the illustration shows. The sides of the blanking punch are made to fit tightly into this groove or channel, thus giving it a rigid

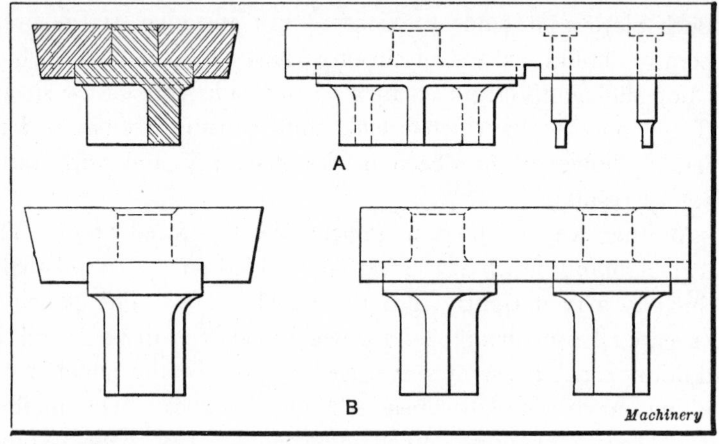

Fig. 2. Illustrating Method of Attaching Blanking Punch to Punch Plate

support. This same method, as applied to the holding of two blanking punches in the punch-holder, is illustrated at *B*. These two punches are used in connection with a double-blanking die for cutting two blanks at one stroke of the press. In this case, the slot is milled along the entire length of the punch-holder and the punches are driven in and securely held in position in the same manner as indicated at *A*. The advantage of attaching an irregular blanking punch to a punch-holder in this way, as compared with the method illustrated at *C*, Fig. 1, is that it does away with all screws or dowel-pins and gives a rigid construction.

The method of attaching a punch illustrated at *A*, Fig. 3, is similar to the method shown at *C*, Fig. 1, except that the blanking punch is held to the punch-holder by a shank against which a set-screw is tightened. The shank is spotted to receive the end of the set-screw, and this spot is slightly offset so that the punch will be drawn upward against the collar when the set-screw is tightened. As will be noted, the group of small piercing punches to the right is attached by a separate punch plate which is screwed to the holder, as shown by the lower plan view.

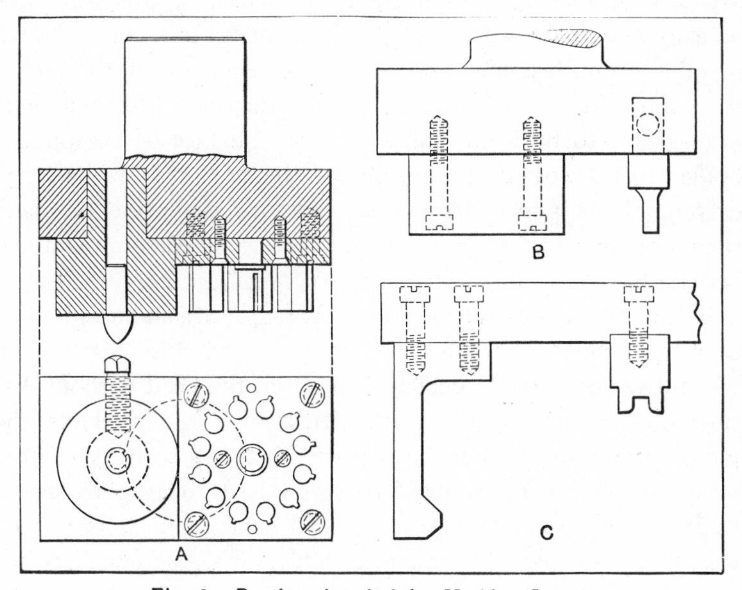

Fig. 3. Punches Attached by Machine Screws

Some punches are simply attached to the holder by machine screws, dowel-pins being used to keep them in position. An example is shown at *B*, Fig. 3. This is a cheap construction and is usually employed when the die is only intended for temporary use. Obviously, the punch should not be held in this way if it is to be used on heavy stock, owing to the excessive downward thrust or pull when stripping the stock. For many operations, such as bending, curling, or cutting light blanks, the downward pull is light and screws may be used. Sketch *C*, Fig. 3, shows part of a bending punch which is held together by screws. Large punches for blanking, bending, drawing, or curling are often bolted directly to the press slide.

Types of Piercing Punches and Methods of Holding.— Piercing punches are made in several different forms and attached to the punch-holder in different ways, as indicated by the diagrams in Fig. 4. The form of punch used, in any case, depends to some extent upon the purpose for which the die is intended. The set-screw method of holding the punch, illustrated at *A*, is not to be recommended but is sometimes used in cheaper grades of dies. Punches of this kind are occasionally made with taper shanks in order to secure a better fit on the punch-holder and lessen the tendency of the punch to become loose. The punch *B* is sometimes used where it is desirable to have the punch seat on the face of the punch-holder instead of at the bottom of the hole into which it is driven. This punch, of course, is more expensive to make than one not having a collar but the construction is much better.

The methods illustrated at *C*, *D*, *E*, and *F* are employed when a large number of punches are to be located close together or when it is necessary to detach them from the head without disturbing the alignment. With either of these methods the punch passes through a punch plate which, in turn, is secured to the punch-holder by machine screws. Referring to sketch *C*, it will be seen that the upper end of the punch is riveted over and abuts against the punch-holder, whereas punch *D* has a head which rests in a counterbored seat in the plate. The form shown at *D* is considered by many diemakers to be an ideal method of making and attaching a small punch of this kind, because it has a firm support against the upward thrust when punching and is also securely held while the stock is being stripped. This method of holding is especially adapted for punching heavy material. Punch *E* has a shoulder the same as punch *B* but the upper end is secured by riveting, as the illustration shows. Obviously, this form cannot be subjected to as heavy a strain or downward pull as would be possible with punch *D*; moreover, it is objectionable because the riveted end must be cut away if for any reason it is necessary to remove the punch. Sketch *F* illustrates a method of guiding and steadying a slender punch which is sometimes employed. The punch is made of straight drill rod and the upper end is riveted over, while the lower end is made a close working fit in the stripper plate attached to the die. Instead of making the punch straight throughout its length, it is good practice to use drill rod of standard size and then turn down the lower end for a

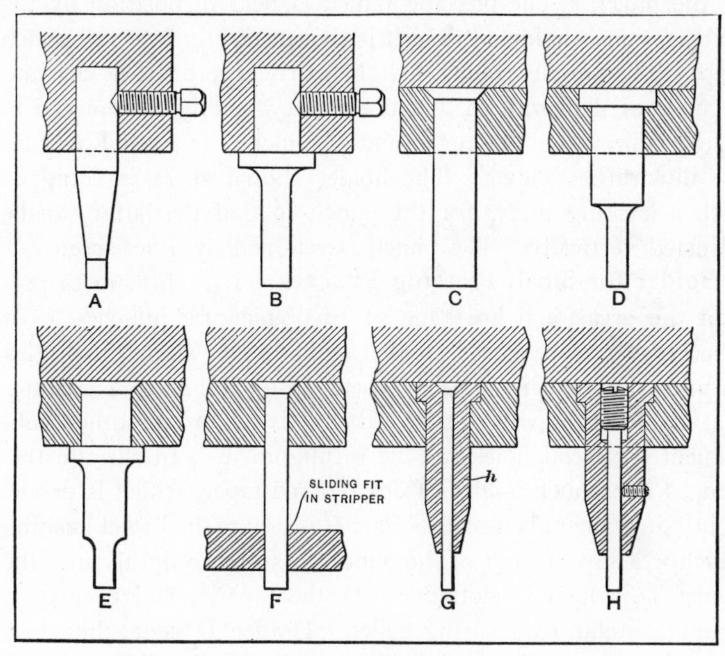

Fig. 4. Various Methods of Holding Piercing Punches

length of about ¼ inch and to the diameter of the hole to be pierced. This allows the body part of the punch to be well entered into the stripper plate, in which it should be a close fit, before the piercing operation begins, so that the punch is rigidly supported when at work. The body of the punch should be a driving fit into the punch plate and be riveted over at the upper end and filed flush. When made in this way, the punch will be rigid, even though it is used for piercing small holes, and if it is well supported in the stripper plate, a much smaller punch can be employed than would be possible otherwise. When piercing heavy stock, it is well to insert a hardened steel disk in the punch-holder just above each piercing punch. This disk prevents the end of the punch from forming a depression which would allow the punch to slide up and down at each stroke.

The piercing punches shown at *G* and *H* are called "quill" punches and are used where a large amount of stock is to be pierced or when the stock is thick in proportion to the diameter of the punch. The piercing punch is held in position by the quill or punch-holder *h*, which is driven tightly into the punch plate. The piercing punch is lightly driven into the holder and is made of drill rod, so that it can very readily be replaced in case it is broken. The upper end of punch *G* is riveted over, as the illustration shows. The holder shown at *H* is equipped with a backing screw for the punch so that the latter can be adjusted vertically. The punch is retained by a set-screw.

Holder for Small Piercing Punches.—It is difficult to prevent the occasional breakage of small piercing punches, even when they are supported rigidly. The holder shown in Fig. 5 permits the punch to be replaced easily in such a manner that its location will not be disturbed. Thus all other subsequently pierced holes will be in alignment. In the illustration, *A* is a punch-holder of any desired taper, which is driven tightly into the punch-plate. Part *B* is a hardened steel bushing which is a slip fit in *A*. The punch *C* is driven lightly into the holder *D*, which is slotted across the tapered end to give it spring, similar to a spring collet. Holder *D* is machined so that it will be a slip or sliding fit in *B*. Punch *C* is made of drill-rod so that it can easily be replaced in case it is broken, although breakage seldom occurs when a holder of this type is used. The upper end of the punch is riveted over, as shown, and retained by a set-screw *E*. When the set-screw *E* is tightened, the holder *D* is forced down against the angular surface *F*, thus gripping the punch *C* firmly.

Standard Punch Sizes.—In designing punches and dies requiring the use of round punches, it is preferable, whenever possible, to use tool steel rod made to Stub's steel wire gage sizes, so that the punches may be made directly from commercial stock. The Stub's steel wire gage sizes will be found in MACHINERY'S HANDBOOK. The largest size, No. 1, has a diameter of 0.227 inch, and punch sizes which are larger than this should be made to fractional dimensions.

Pilots or Guide Pins for Punches.—The pilots or guide pins which are placed on the ends of some punches (as at *B*

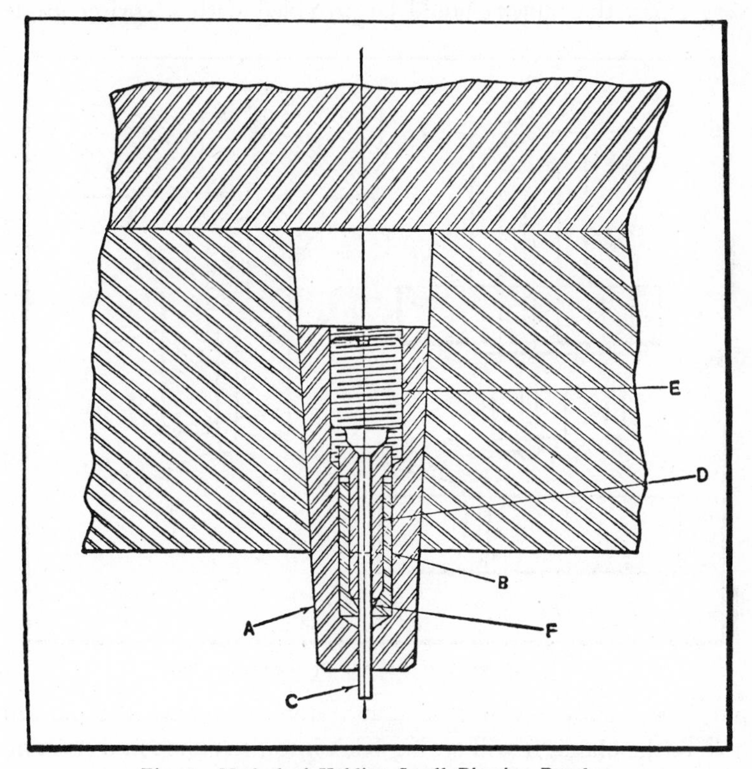

Fig. 5. Method of Holding Small Piercing Punches

Fig. 6) for aligning the stock before blanking, by entering holes that have been pierced previously (by punch *C* in this die), should be made slightly smaller than the hole in the blank and should be straight for the thickness of the stock, and then rounded off similar to the point of an acorn. The heads of all guide pins should be turned true with the shank. Care should be taken to see that the guide pins are also exactly in line with the pierced holes. If they are not in line they have a tendency to shift the metal strip, so that after a few blanks have been punched, the strip will not be in alignment with the die. Precaution should be taken to see that the stock does not cramp between the guide pins and the stop, or betwen the guide pins and the back gage, because if this is neglected it will generally cause trouble. When the pierced holes are very small the punch should be provided with a spring guide

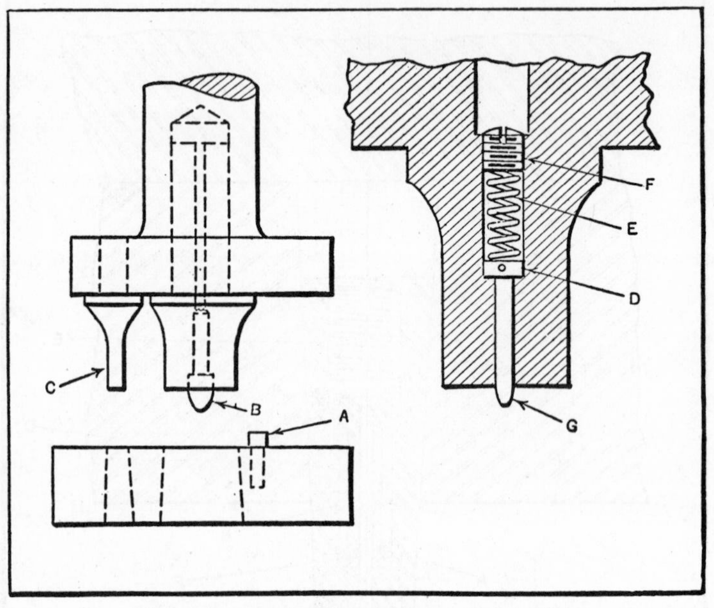

Fig. 6. Progressive Die and Spring-backed Pilot

pin (see sectional view) so that if the pin misses the pierced hole in the blank, it will spring back into the punch and nothing is spoiled except the blank. The pilot *G* is made a sliding fit in the punch, and has a collar *D* held in place by a pin that acts as a stop. The spring *E*, which is held in place by the screw *F*, keeps the pilot in position under normal operating conditions, but allows it to recede into the body of the punch when it strikes the solid stock, so that neither the pilot nor the punch is damaged. The value of the spring-backed pilot depends upon the type of die and nature of the work.

Types of Die-beds or Bolsters.—Dies are usually held in position on the bed of a punch-press by means of a die-bed or bolster, although the large dies are often attached directly to the press bed. The subject of die-beds or bolsters is one of considerable importance, and is deserving of greater attention than it often receives, because many of the troubles encountered in the use of press tools are due to these parts being badly designed or poorly constructed. Many a fine die has been ruined because it has not been properly secured in the die-bed and consequently has shifted while in operation; or because the holes in the die-bed through which the blanks or punchings are supposed to pass have not been made large enough to allow them to pass through freely. As a consequence the blanks get jammed in the die-bed and pile up into the die itself and are compressed by the pounding of the punch, until the punch or die breaks from the strain. The principal functions of a die-bed are: first, that of supplying an adequate support for the die, and a holder to hold the die in its proper position to be engaged by the punch; and, second, to furnish a means of attachment to the press. Therefore the principal points to be considered in the design and construction of a die-bed are first, the method of securing the die, and second, the method of securing the die-bed to the press. Due consideration, of course, should also be given to proportion and strength.

Die-bed of Common Design.—A die-bed of the type generally found in the jobbing shop is shown in Fig. 7. The dovetail method of holding the die, with set-screws E to lock it in proper position, is employed. It is fitted with a flange on each end with slots B to receive the clamping bolts which pass through the slots into the press bolster. In the center is a rectangular cored hole to let the punchings pass through. This type of die-bed is cheap and convenient for use where several dies are to be used in one die-bed. The dies can be easily slid into place and fastened by means of the set-screws, and are easily removed when another die is to be used. The angle α of the dovetail should be from 75 to 80 degrees. This die-bed has the following disadvantages: first that the die is held into it by set-screws which always have a tendency to jar loose in punch press work, and, second, the cored hole *C*, being necessarily made large to accommodate various shapes of blanks, weakens the die-bed and lessens the support to each of the dies. It is always better, if possible, to have a separate die-bed for each die.

Die Held in Tapering Dovetail.—In Fig. 8 is shown a die-bed for use on an inclined press. In this bolster the dovetail method of holding the die is used, but without the use of set-screws. The dovetailed opening to receive the die is slightly tapered and the die is driven into place with a copper mallet, and is then made doubly secure by the insertion of a dowel *G* which is driven through the die into the die-bed. The method

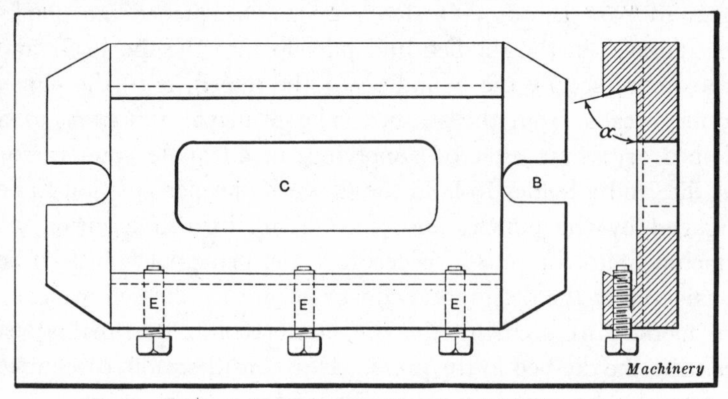

Fig. 7. Form of Die-bed commonly Used in Jobbing Shops

of clamping this die-bed to the press bolster is different from that shown in Fig. 7, in that the bolt slot in one flange runs at right angles to that in the opposite flange. By having the slots in this position, the die-bed may be attached or removed without the necessity of taking out the bolts, thus not only saving a great deal of time and trouble in setting the tools, but also preventing the bolt holes from being filled with scrap or dirt and the bolts from getting lost. This is an excellent die-bed for blanking and piercing work. Another common method of holding a die without the use of set-screws is to make the dovetail slot tapering and somewhat wider than the die, so that a taper key can be driven in lengthwise.

Die-bed for Holding Dies of Different Sizes.—An improved type of die-bed for general utility is shown in Fig. 9. In this bed the dovetail method of holding the die is used. In the illustration it will be noticed that there are four parallel pieces or gibs *E* placed along the sides of the die. The object of this construction is to provide for dies of various sizes. When a larger die is to be used one or more of these gibs may be taken out. This bolster, in addition to four bolt slots, has a

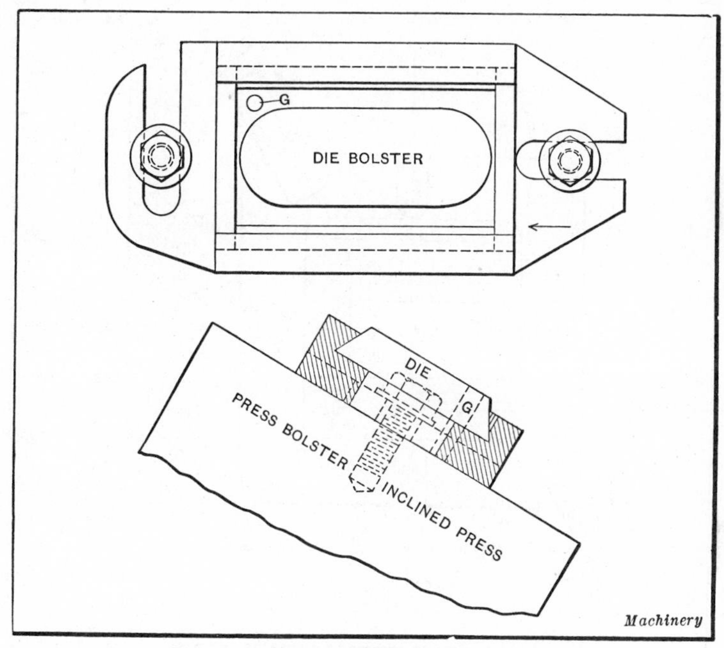

Fig. 8. Die-bed Adapted to Inclined Press

flange *B* all around it so that it may be clamped in any position. The set-screws *H* which hold the die in place should be provided with a lock-nut as shown at *I* to lessen the chances of jarring loose. The great advantage of having a flange all around the bolster will be apparent when it becomes necessary to swing the die-bed around enough to bring the bolt slots out of line with the tapped holes in the press bolster. In a case of this kind a die-bed with a flange all around it may be clamped by means of clamps as shown at *D*, using the tapped holes *G* located at different places in the press bolster.

Die-bed Designed for End Thrust.—In Fig. 10 is shown another die-bed of the dovetail and side set-screw variety, but with the additional feature of end-thrust set-screws. This end-thrust arrangement is a novel feature. In order to obtain this additional means of holding the die securely, two square grooves *B* are cut in each end of the die-bed at right angles to

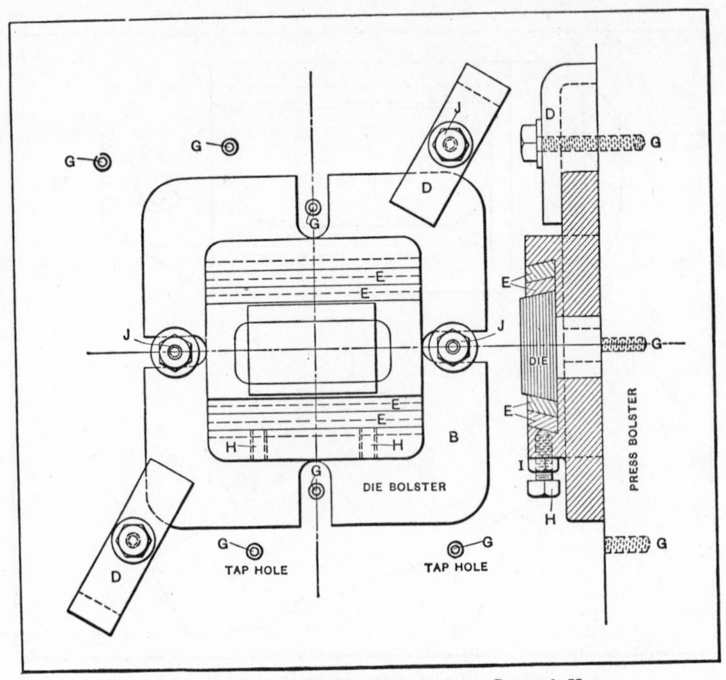

Fig. 9. Form of Die-bed Adapted to General Use

the opening for the die. Into these grooves a plate *C* is fitted in which there is a set-screw in such a position as to come into contact with the end of the die. With one of these plates at each end, and the set-screws screwed tightly against the ends of the die, there is less likelihood of its shifting while in operation. When short dies for simple blanking or piercing are used, the end-thrust plates may be inserted in the inner grooves as shown in the illustration, whereas if it is desired to use a long die such as is used for progressive work where there is one or more piercing operations before the work reaches the blanking punch, the plates with the set-screws may be placed in the grooves further from the center, and thus allow for the increased length of die. When the set-screws are used in these outer grooves, the heads of the screws will come directly over the slots in the flanges where the clamping bolt should be placed; for this reason the bed should be provided with two extra slotted flanges, as shown in the illustration, to be used when necessary.

Die-bed for Sectional Dies.—A die-bed for sectional forming or blanking dies or for split dies is shown in Fig. 11.

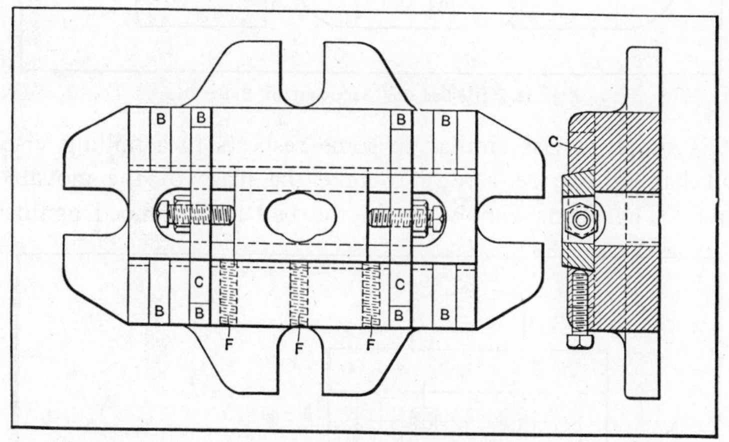

Fig. 10. Die-bed of the Dovetailed Type, Equipped with Side Set-screws and End-thrust Screws

This die-bed is provided with a square receptacle to receive the dies, and with two set-screws on each side to hold the dies in place. The square forming die shown is made in four sections *B* which are held tightly against each other by means of the set-screws *C*, and are held from working up by screws through the bottom of the die-bed—one in each section of the die. A square recess is cast in the die-bed so that when machining the die-bed it is only necessary to plane off the bottom and top of the flanges, mill the bottom of the recess, and drill and tap for the set-screws. The sides of the recess need not be finished by machining because the dies have no bearing on them.

Die-bed for Bending or Forming Dies.—A very simple type of die-bed for bending and forming dies is shown in Fig. 12.

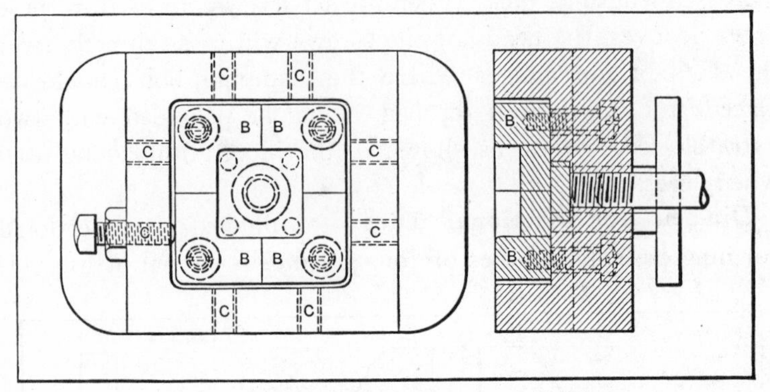

Fig. 11. Die-bed for Sectional or Split Dies

It is simply a vise similar in some respects to a milling vise, but having two set-screws to take the place of the movable jaw. The die is simply set in the bed and clamped against

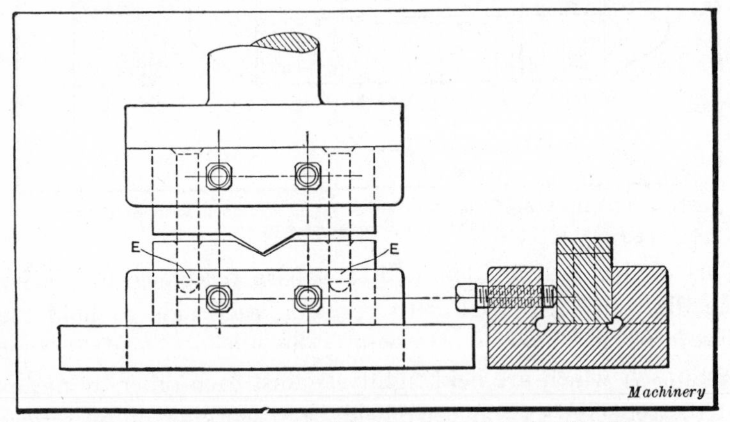

Fig. 12. Simple Form of Die-holder Adapted to Bending Dies

the solid jaw by means of the set-screws. This type of bolster is intended for use only on dies that do not require a "push up," or "knockout," and when the bending or forming operations are done on a solid surface. In order to obtain the best results from this die-bed, the complete outfit of punch-holder, punch, and die of the type shown in the sketch should be used. The punch and die are kept in alignment when in operation by the two guide pins *E* which are secured in the punch and which enter the die at every stroke of the press, making it practically impossible for the tools to shift while in operation. If it be desired to change the tools it is not necessary to disturb the punch-holder or die-bed. They may be left in the press, and, by simply loosening the set-screws in the die-bed and punch-holder, the punch and die, held together by the guide pins, may

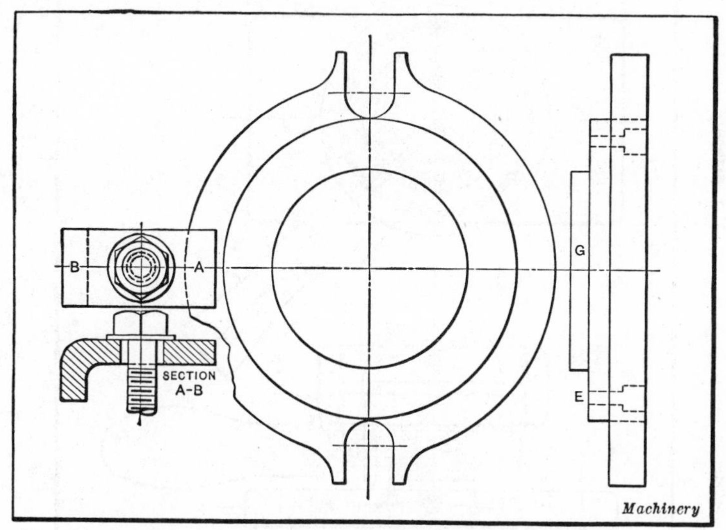

Fig. 13. Die-bed or Bolster for Combination Dies Designed for Round Drawing Operations

be taken out and set aside and another set slipped into their places.

Circular Form of Die-bed.—A bolster for combination dies for round drawing work is shown in Fig. 13. This bolster requires but little explanation. It is circular in shape with two steps or extensions, two bolt slots, and a flange all around it to allow it to be clamped at any convenient place. When the combination dies are turned in the lathe, the bottom die is counterbored to be a driving fit on the extension *G*, and is held down by screws that pass through the bed at *E* into the die.

Materials for Die-beds.—Die-beds are commonly made of cast iron, cast steel, or machine steel. Many large concerns have all their die-beds made from semi-steel castings, or of machine steel for certain classes of heavy work, instead of from cast iron. This is done because a cast-iron die-bed that is used day after day for holding dies for cutting heavy metal will not stand up during long and hard usage as it should. Past experience has proved that gray iron die-beds in time become out of square; then, again, they sometimes crack.

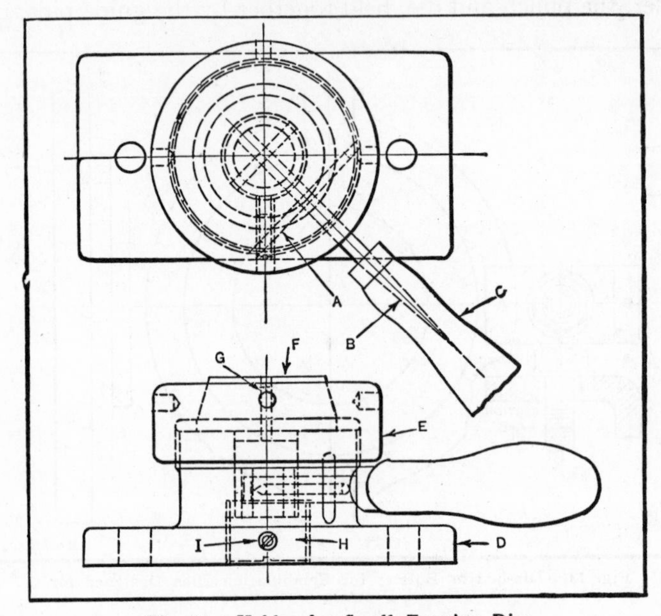

Fig. 14. Holder for Small Forming Dies

With the semi-steel, or the soft steel die-bed, this does not happen. It has been found that semi-steel and machine steel die-beds pay for themselves many times over.

Screw Cap Holder for Small Dies.—A screw cap die-bed or holder which has been used with very good results for holding forming dies for very small metal parts is shown in Fig. 14. It consists of a base *D* which is threaded at the top to receive the nut *E*. Nut *E* holds the die-block *F* securely in position. The adjusting nut *H*, which is locked by the set-screw *I*, is used to back up the knock-out plug *G*. An ordinary file handle *C* is fastened to the lever *B*, which is mounted on a fulcrum pin *A*. This handle is used to operate the knock-out plug *G*.

Indexing Mechanism for Die-holder.—The mechanism shown in Fig. 15 is designed to provide a safe and positive means of indexing the die-holder of a three-station upsetting die used on a large punch press. The die is hand-actuated and of the circular progressive type. In operation, the workman simply inserts the blanks (not shown in the illustration) in the rotating die-holder *A*, and trips the press. The die is then indexed one space, another blank inserted, and the press tripped again; thus the press can be kept in continual operation. The ram is equipped with two punches. The first punch performs the work, and the second punch simply serves to push the completed part through the die, which is left open at the bottom to permit the parts to drop into a tote box. It will be evident from the preceding description that a piece is loaded into the locating die-holder, another piece upset and a third piece ejected, each time the press is tripped.

As the work is of irregular shape and is required to be held to very close limits, it is obviously necessary that the die-holder be indexed accurately and locked firmly in each position. If this is not done, the punch will not be properly aligned with the die, and either the punch or the die will be damaged or broken. Obviously it is also necessary to provide a safety device which will prevent the punch from being tripped at any time except when the die-holder is properly indexed and locked in place.

In the illustration, the safety device is shown in the position occupied when the die-plate *A* is being rotated to the succeeding station. It will be noted that the part *C* is held out or away from the die-holder *A* by the cam *B* which is attached to the die-holder. The nose of part *C* is spherical, and is kept in contact with cam *B* by means of spring *D*, so that the moment the end of cam *B* passes the spherical end of part *C*, the latter is forced in toward the die-holder, thus lifting the

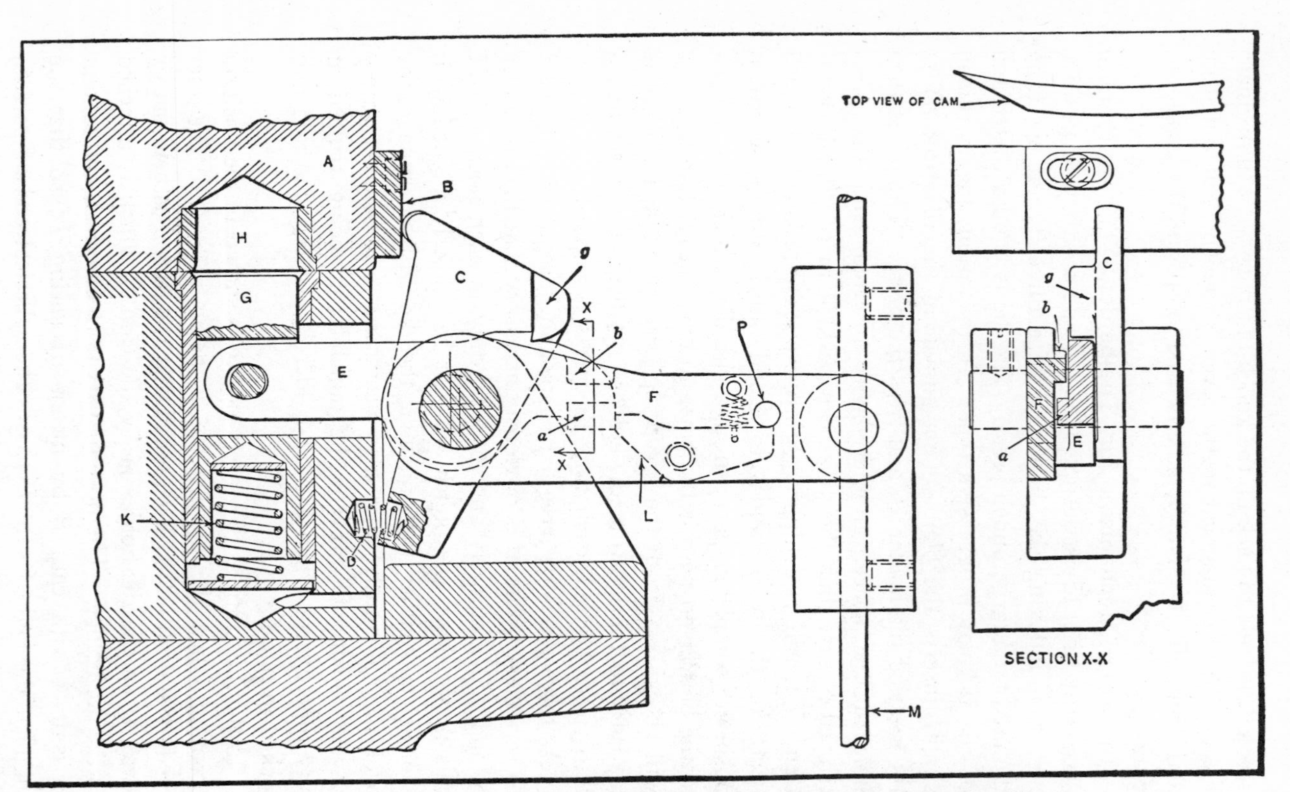

Fig. 15. Mechanism for Indexing the Die-holder of a Three-station Upsetting Die

trigger portion *g* of part *C* out of engagement with the projecting corner of part *E*.

Part *E* has a projecting tongue *a* (see sectional view), which permits tongue *b* on part *F* to descend a limited distance. Now if part *C* is held away from the die-holder by cam *B*, the end *g* of part *C* will be held down, thus effectually locking part *E* so that its outer end cannot be moved downward. As the trip-rod *M* may be pulled down by means of a foot-pedal for about 1½ inches before actually tripping the press, it will be evident that as long as part *C* is held in the outward position by cam *B*, trip-rod *M* cannot descend far enough to trip the press, being prevented from so doing by contact of tongue *b* with tongue *a*. Cam *B* can be adjusted to permit the spherical end of part *C* to travel inward toward the die-holder *A* at exactly the proper moment, or a fraction of a second before plug *G* is brought in position opposite hole *H*.

As the end of part *C* drops or rides off the end of cam *B*, spring *D* forces the end of part *C* toward the die-holder. This action lifts the latch *g*, thus permitting spring *K* to force plug *G* upward into the indexing hole *H*. The press is then tripped, and as lever *F* descends, the dog *L* will ride over the nose of part *E*. When lever *F* has moved down a certain distance, the nose of dog *L* snaps down under the tongue *a*, due to the fact that the fulcrum of levers *E* and *F* are at different points. The opposite end of dog *L* is prevented from rising by a pin *P*, when a spring (not shown) on the end of the trip-rod *M* returns the latter member to its first position. This movement elevates lever *F*, thus raising the nose of part *E* and compressing spring *K*, as well as withdrawing the indexing plug *G* from the hole *H*. At the same time the spherical end of part *C* rides up on the beveled end of cam *B* and pushes *g* downward, so that the entire mechanism is locked in the original position shown in the illustration.

A little experimenting was necessary at first to determine the size of spring *K* which would maintain the proper balance with the trip-rod spring of the machine, but having solved this problem satisfactorily the mechanism gave excellent results.

Stripping Stock from Punch.—When punches are operated on sheet stock, the latter will be carried upward when the punch ascends, unless there is some device to prevent this. The simplest arrangement for stripping the stock from the punch and one that is applied to most blanking dies, consists of a plate which is attached to the die and has an opening for the punch to pass through. Beneath this stripper plate there is a passage-way or opening through which the stock is fed. Obviously, the space between the die face and stripper plate must be greater than the thickness of the stock to permit the latter to be fed along easily. As the result of this play between the stripper plate and die the stock is distorted to some extent by the action of the punch. This distortion, in many cases, does not cause trouble, especially when the die simply cuts out plain blanks, but when a follow die is used and flat accurate blanks are required, or when the operation is that of piercing a number of holes in sheets or flat plates, it is often necessary to hold the stock firmly against the die while the punches pass through it, in order to prevent any wrinkling or buckling.

Stripper Attached to Punch.—One method of preventing the stock from being wrinkled or distorted by the action of the punch is illustrated in Fig. 16. The stripper plate *M* is fastened to the punch-holder instead of to the die, and it is backed up by a stiff coil spring at each corner. On the downward stroke of the press, the stripper plate presses the stock firmly against the die, holding it level while the punches perform their work. The stripper is so located that the punches do not come quite flush with its lower face, so that the stock is subjected to pressure before the punches come into action. As the stock is fed through the die it is guided by the small pins *N* at each end of the die. The stripper should not fit the punches closely because if the operator should make a miscut or if a piece of scrap punching should get under the stripper, it would cause it to tilt and probably break the small punches. With a die of this type the difficulty connected with wrinkled work is overcome. On the other hand, when a follow die is made with a fixed stripper of the usual form, the work is distorted somewhat, so that the location of pierced holes relative to the outer edges of the blanks is not always sufficiently accurate. As the die illustrated was made without guide pins for holding the punch and die in alignment, straps *S* were used to hold up each end of the stripper plate in order to expose the ends of the punches when aligning them. These straps were used by forcing the stripper upward and inserting the ends of the straps in the holes *T*, as indicated by the detail view.

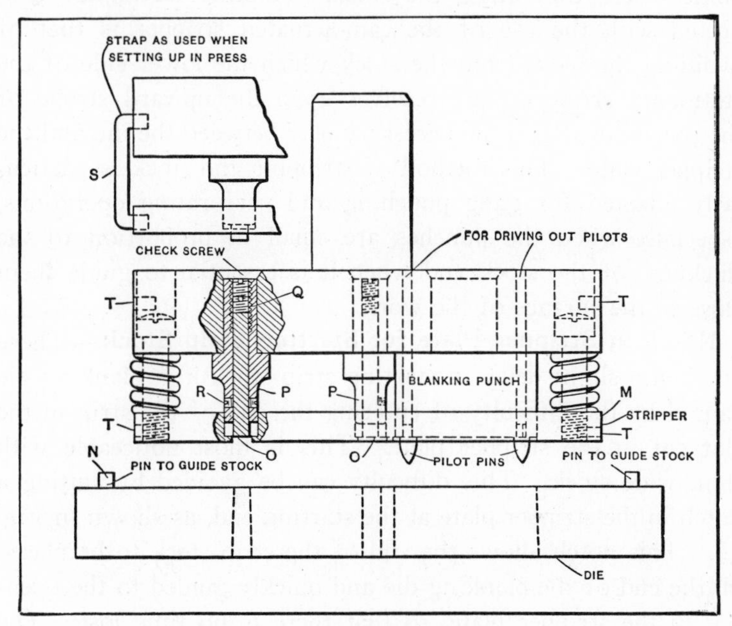

Fig. 16. Stripper Attached to Punch to Flatten out Stock and Hold It Securely

Presses with Cam-actuated Strippers.—Owing to the tendency which stationary stripper plates attached to dies have to distort pierced sheets, etc. (as explained in the foregoing), some presses are equipped with cam-actuated stripper plates. The stripper plate is attached to vertical rods which extend up above the press slide. When the press is in operation, the stripper, actuated by cams on the press shaft, descends first and clamps the stock before the punches enter the work. As the stripper plate is suspended above the die, a clear space is left between the punch and die, so that the operator has an unobstructed view. The stripper plate moves up and down with the punches, so that the latter may be made shorter than would be possible with a stationary stripper, thus increasing their rigidity and durability.

A smaller hole in proportion to the thickness of the stock may be pierced when using a stripper of this kind, because of the close support which the stripper gives the punches up to the point where they enter the stock. Another advantage connected with the use of the cam-actuated stripper is that of avoiding the blow from the stock which the lower side of the stationary stripper plate receives upon the upward stroke of the punch, owing to the necessary play between the die and the stripper plate. This method of stripping the stock is particularly adapted for gang punching and perforating operations, especially when the punches are small in proportion to the thickness of the stock and when it is essential to guide them close to the surface of the work.

Notch in Stripper Plate for Starting Strip Stock.—There is often a slight delay in starting strip stock in a blanking die caused by the difficulty of entering the end of the strip in the slot cut in the stripper plate. This is most noticeable with thin, wide stock. This difficulty can be avoided by cutting a notch in the stripper plate at the starting end, as shown in Fig. 17. This notch allows the end of the strip stock to be placed on the end of the blanking die and quickly guided to the opening in the stripper plate, so that there is no time lost. The illustration shows the stripper plate arranged for feeding the stock from right to left. The same principle applies, however, if the stock is fed from left to right, but in that case the left-hand end of the stripper would be notched or cut away.

Stripping Work from Single Piercing Punches.—In piercing small work, such as washer blanks, where a single punch is used, a piece of cushion rubber placed on the punch after it is set up will force the blank off the punch as it rises out of the die. This is an old device, but nevertheless is unknown to many. When rubber is not available corks will give the same result when the piercing punches are ¼ inch or less in diameter and the stock is not over 0.030 inch thick. Placing a spiral spring around the punch, holding it in position by wire, will accomplish the same result. If a washer is clamped in such a position that the punch travels through its center, the work will be stripped as the punch travels back through the washer. A piece of flat stock with a hole drilled in it can be used for the same purpose, and is often much easier to arrange than a washer. These methods will be found of value in shops where a great deal of special work and job-

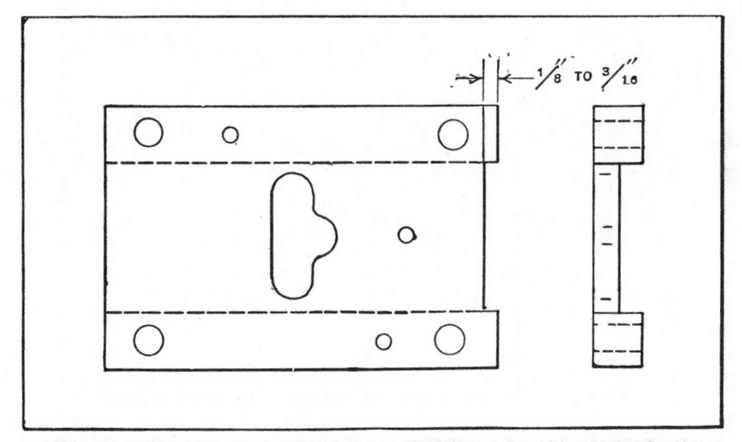

Fig. 17. Stripper Plate Notched to Facilitate Starting Strip Stock

bing is done and the tools cannot be made and kept on hand for each piece of work that comes along.

Self-adjusting Spring Guide.—In connection with combination blanking and piercing dies, it is frequently desirable to provide a self-adjusting stock guide to compensate for variation in the width of the stock. To this end, the spring guide shown in Fig. 18 was designed. The holes in the guide strip *A* through which the screws pass that secure the stripper to the die-block, are bored over size, so as to permit the bushing *B* to be inserted. All the holes on one side of the die are treated similarly, and are elongated to permit a small coil spring *C* to be inserted. The bushings are longer than the thickness of the guide strip, so that the strip will not be bound tightly between the die-block and the stripper, thus permitting any variation in the width of the stock to be compensated for by the yielding construction of the guide strip.

Stock-clamping Device for Piercing Die.—The work shown at *A* in Fig. 19 was bent or deformed, as shown at *B* when the slot was pierced. As this was objectionable, it was decided to provide means for clamping the work on the sides as the punch passed through. This necessitated an arrangement that would hold the work securely and still release it automatically to permit its removal.

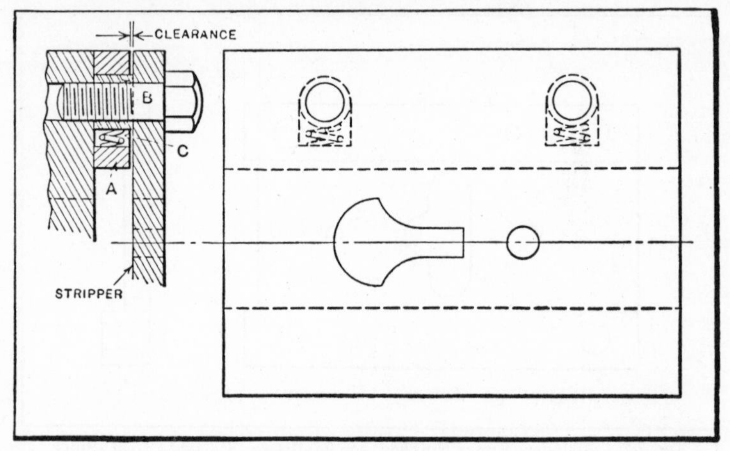

Fig. 18. Construction of Compensating Spring Guide for Blanking and Piercing Dies

The illustration shows a sectional view of the die which was designed for the work and which proved satisfactory. The die member *C* is constructed in the conventional manner. The stripper plate *D* is provided with guide plates *E* and *F*. Plate *E* is held stationary by a pin which enters the die. This plate is grooved, as shown at *L* to permit the tongue of the punch to pass through. The groove is made to correspond accurately with the outline of the die, so as to form practically a continuation of the die, although it does no cutting. Plate *F* slides in a groove in stripper plate *D*, and is provided with a heel at its back end. The back face of this heel is ground to an angle of 5 degrees with its base. In back of plate *F* is screwed an angle-piece *G*, which carries a sliding plate *H*. Plate *H* is ground at its lower end to an angle of 5 degrees, so as to coincide with the heel of plate *F*. The punch-holder *I* carries the punch *J* and the plunger *K* which is free to slide in its shank and is backed up by a spring. The work *W* is shown in position between the guide plates.

As the ram of the press descends, plunger *K* comes in contact with sliding plate *H* and forces it downward. Plate *H*

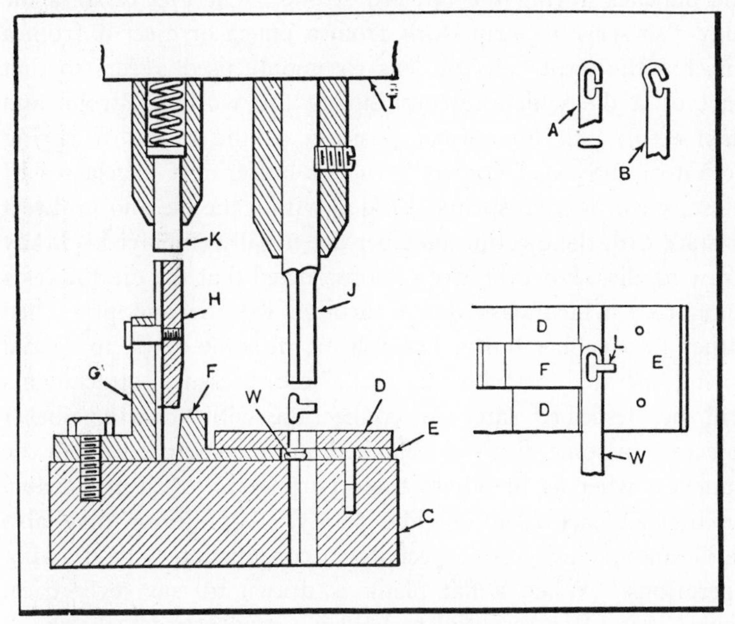

Fig. 19. Punching Die Provided with Clamping Arrangement Designed to Prevent Work from Being Deformed

comes in contact with the heel of plate *F*, and, owing to the angularity of the two surfaces in contact, plate *F* is moved to the right, pressing the work against plate *E*. At this point punch *J* has not yet entered the stock. When the punch enters the work, the stock is prevented from being distorted by plate *F*, which is wedged against the work by plate *H*. The angular faces on plates *F* and *H* permit the latter plate to serve as a wedge in back of plate *F*, so that motion cannot be imparted by plate *F* to plate *H*. The result is that plate *F* becomes immovable when it touches the stock, holding it so securely that it will not be bent. As the ram ascends, plates *F* and *H* are returned automatically to their original positions by springs (not shown in the illustration).

Ejectors for Punches and Dies.—The term "stripper," as applied to a blanking die is a plate on a die which is located above the stock and has openings through which the punches pass and against which the stock strikes for stripping it off of the punches during the upward stroke. The *ejector* of a die may also serve to strip work from a punch or eject it from a die, but the term "ejector," as commonly used, refers to that part of a die which recedes during the working stroke and then returns to its normal position as the result of spring action or the expansion of a rubber buffer. If all classes of dies are considered, springs located within the die and in direct contact with the ejecting member are usually employed. Many drawing dies, however, are so constructed that the ejector rests upon pins which pass down through the die and press bed either to a rubber buffer beneath or, in some cases, to special spring-operated attachments. (These pressure attachments will be described later in connection with drawing dies.) Ejectors in some dies strip blanked and pierced parts from the punches, whereas in others their purpose is to eject a drawn or formed part from the die cavity. An ejector may also serve another purpose, especially in conjunction with drawing operations. When a flat blank is drawn to, say, cylindrical shape, it is often essential to hold it firmly between the upper surface of the drawing die and that of the ejector, which, in this case, becomes a blank-holder as well. During the return stroke, the ejector spring forces the drawn parts off of the punch as the parts return to their normal position. Ejectors of the type which strip the work from the punches have already been shown in connection with various dies illustrated in preceding chapters, and the application for ejecting and holding the blank during drawing will be shown later in conection with various designs of drawing dies. The term "knock-out" is commonly applied to ejecting devices, especially when they are operated mechanically or in a positive manner, instead of relying upon spring action.

Automatic Ejector for Piercing Dies.—The device here described may be applied to almost any piercing die and will save a great deal of time by ejecting the work after it has been stripped from the punch without the necessity of removing it from the nest by hand. This ejector is positive in action and can be readily applied for ejecting almost any type of small work. After the work has been pierced and while it still sticks to the punch, it travels up with the punch and bears against the inclined face of the ejector *B* (Fig. 20), forcing this member back against the tension of the leaf spring *F*. As soon as

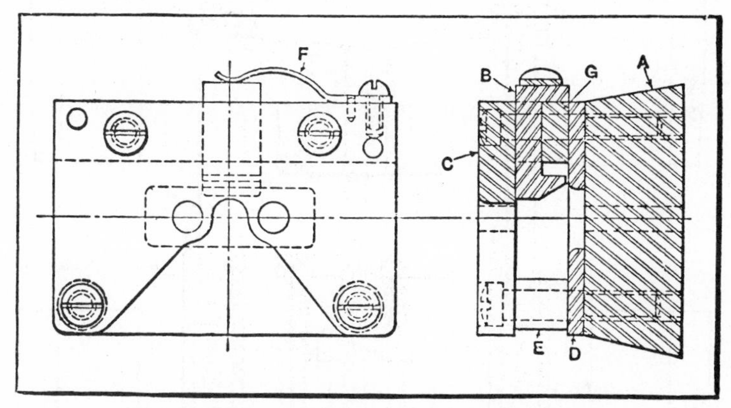

Fig. 20. Device for Ejecting Work from Punch Press

the work has been stripped, the spring immediately snaps the ejector forward and knocks the work clear of the die, so that if a deflector plate or some other arrangement is employed, the part can be deposited by means of a chute into a suitable receptacle. When applying this ejector, the riser or separator strip *G* must be made slightly higher than in the usual construction, so as to allow it to be slotted for the reception of the ejector *B*. The stripper is supported at the front of the machine by means of bushings *E*. It is well, if practicable, to cut away the stripper in front, as shown in the illustration, to facilitate loading. If the production is large enough to warrant it, a magazine and automatic feed may be advantageously used, and for such a combination this ejector adapts itself admirably. If so desired, the attachment may be applied on either side of the die instead of at the back as shown.

Ejectors or "Knock-outs" of the Positive Type.—A difficulty sometimes encountered in the use of spring-actuated ejectors is that, since the spring operating the ejection device is usually compressed by the down stroke of the press, ejection

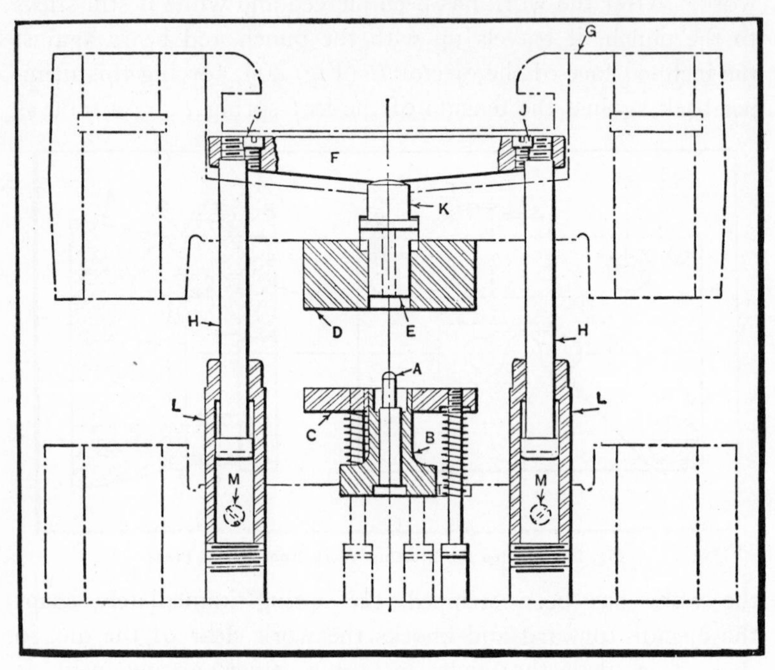

Fig. 21. Shaving Die Equipped with Positive Knock-out

starts immediately upon the release of the pressure on the spring at the beginning of the up stroke, and in some cases, the work may be of such a nature that its ejection from the punch or die should be delayed until a portion of the up stroke has been completed. Spring-actuated knock-outs are undesirable in such instances, and a further disadvantage is that they are not positive in their action. Mechanical ejection devices, or "knock-outs," can be utilized to better advantage in cases of this kind, owing to their positive nature and the varying adjustments that they permit.

In Fig. 21 is shown an adjustable positive knock-out applied to a shaving die for small gears. The piece to be shaved is located on the pin *A* which is held in punch *B*. The spring-actuated stripper *C* strips the shaving from the punch while the part shaved is carried up with the die *D*. Near the top of the stroke the piece is ejected from the die by the positive knock-out *E*. Delaying the ejection of the part from the die permits the shaving to be removed from the top of the stripper by a blast of air and allows the press to be operated at a higher speed. The press is inclined so that the part drops out into a receptacle provided for it.

The knock-out, in this case, consists of a cross-bar *F* which floats in a recess milled in the punch-holder *G*. The two actuating plungers *H* are secured in place by lock-screws *J*. The cross-bar is in contact with button *K* and shedder *E*, which, after the piece has been ejected, is flush with the lower surface of the die. Plungers *H* extend down through the punch-block into the two bushings *L*, which are bored out to receive the plunger heads. Bushings *L* are milled to a hexagonal shape at the top to permit adjusting them with a wrench. When adjusted, these studs are locked in place by set-screws *M*.

The action of the ejector is as follows: As the die shaves the work on the down stroke, shedder *E*, button *K*, and cross-bar *F*, with the plungers *H*, recede until the completion of the down stroke of the press. On the up stroke, the work is carried up with die *D* until the heads of plungers *H* strike the end of the enlarged holes in bushings *L*. When this takes place, the upward movement of cross-bar *F*, button *K*, and shedder *E* is arrested, and as the die is still in motion on the upward stroke, the part is ejected from the die, leaving it ready to receive another part on the next shaving stroke.

Knock-out for Swaging Die.—In Fig. 22 is shown a knock-out that has been successfully applied to a swaging die. The punch and die shown is used for swaging the part *A*, Fig. 23, from the blank *B*. This type of gear has the teeth on the

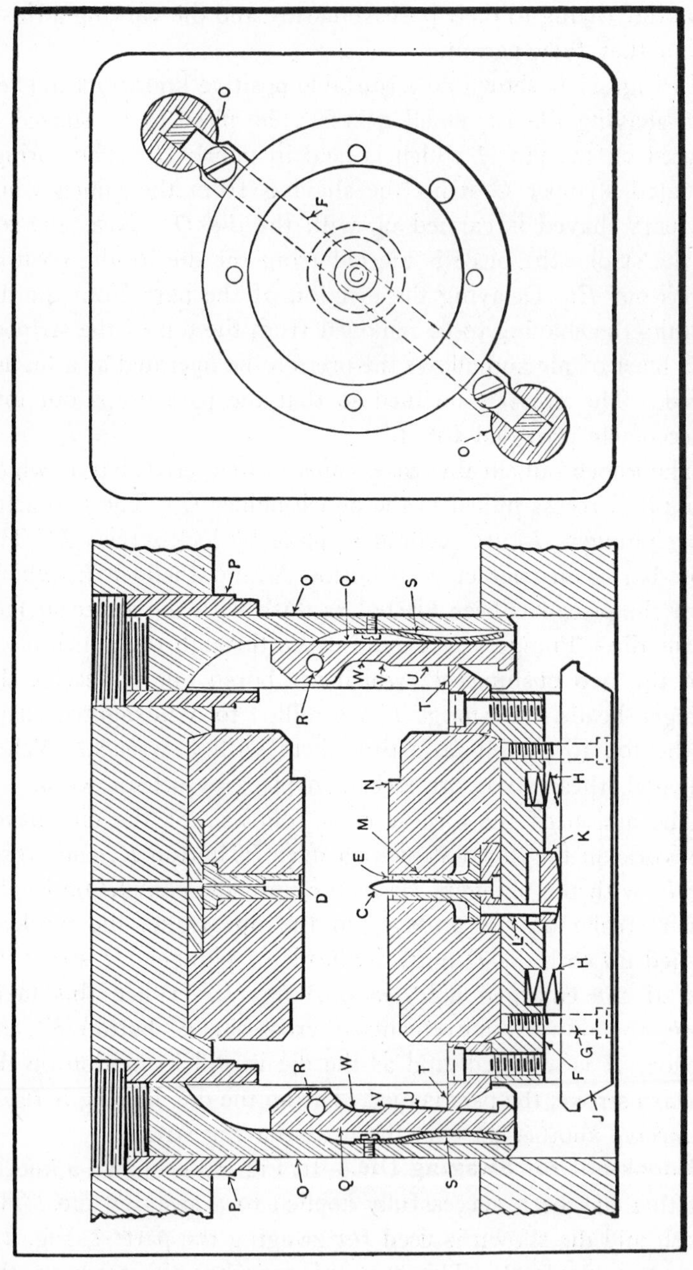

Fig. 22. Swaging Die Provided with Positive Type of Work Ejector

central flange sized in a shaving or trimming die, such as shown in Fig. 21. The blank *B*, Fig. 23, is located on the pin *C*, Fig. 22, for the swaging operation, in which the two hubs are swaged down into recesses at *D* and *E* in the upper and lower dies. As the swaging action closes in the metal around pin *C* (to insure accurate sizing of the hole) it is necessary that a device be used to eject the piece from the lower die. After ejection, the mechanism drops down to avoid interference when locating the next piece to be swaged.

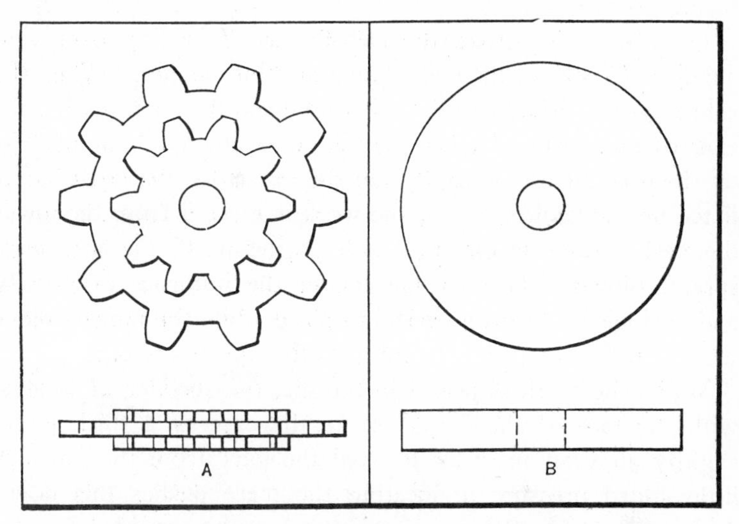

Fig. 23. Work Swaged on Die Shown in Fig. 22 and the Blank Before Swaging

The ejection arrangement includes a cross-bar *J*, set in a recess or slot in the die-block. Adjustment screws *G* control the location of the bar, while springs *H* return it to the lower position after the piece has been ejected. In contact with the upper surface of the cross-bar *J* is a button *K* carrying shedder pins *L* which engage the shedder *M* in the die *N*. Two posts *O*, carried in adjustment bushings *P* in the punch-holder, have a longitudinal groove milled in them, in which are carried the ejection latches *Q*, pivoted on pins *R* and actuated by latch springs *S*. Two cam-fingers *T*, placed diametrically opposite each other on the top of the die-holder, enter the groove in posts *O*, and it is against the ends of these fingers that latch springs *S* hold the ejection latches *Q*.

Posts *O* are adjusted vertically to obtain the proper point of ejection on the up stroke, by turning adjustment nuts *P*, which have a right-hand thread on the outside and a left-hand thread on the inside. Nuts *P* are milled to a hexagonal shape on the lower end so that they are easily turned by a wrench, and they are locked by set-screws (not shown) in the punch-holder. Posts *O* are prevented from turning by the cam-fingers in the grooves.

On the down stroke the cam-fingers *T*, riding over cam surfaces *U*, spread the ends of the ejection latches. When the cam-fingers reach the inclines *V* leading to the surfaces *W*, the ends of the ejection latches snap in below the overhanging lugs on the ends of cross-bar *J*. On the up stroke the cross-bar is lifted by the latches so that the work is ejected from the lower die, and as the cam-fingers *T* ride up incline *V*, the latch ends spread allowing the cross-bar, under the influence of gravity and springs *H*, to drop back into place while the punch-holder which carries the posts *O* continues the upward stroke.

When the work is placed in the die, the shedder *M* is level with the face of the die *N*, or in the case of a thick piece, slightly above it in order to shed the part from the pin. A little added pressure in locating the piece pushes this down flush with the die. No spring return can be provided for the shedder on this type of swaging die, since pressures as high as 350 and 400 tons are used. The die must, therefore, be constructed very solidly.

Positive mechanical ejectors such as the ones described can be used as valuable auxiliaries in pushing or ejecting parts from the dies into spring fingers on transfer arms, slides, etc., where the work is moved to a spot outside the dies, to be dropped into a magazine for subsequent operations or to be removed by hand.

Knockout Operated by Crank on Press Shaft.—The mechanically operated knockout shown applied to a punch-press in Fig. 24 operates more satisfactorily than a rubber

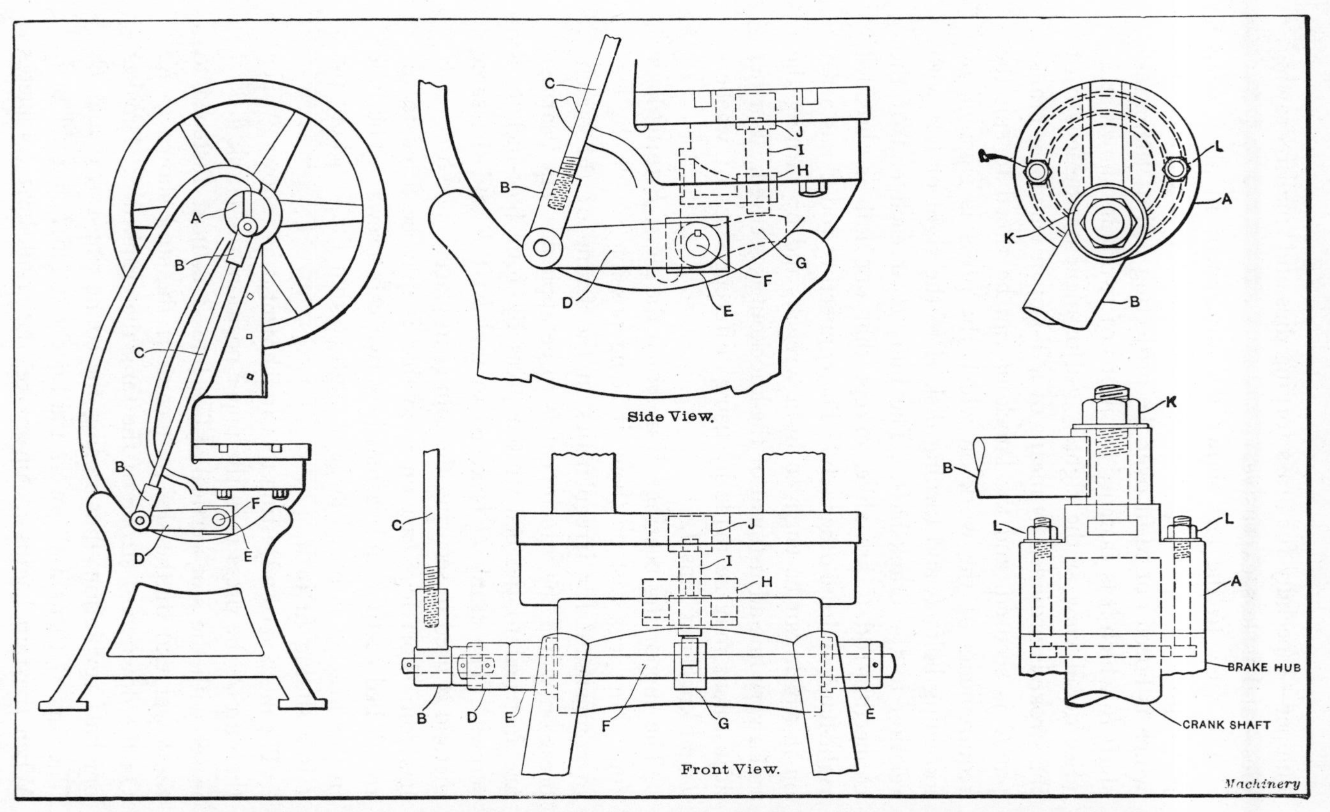

Fig. 24. Power Press Equipped with Mechanical Knock-out, and Views Showing Details of Design

bumper—especially for brass forging dies and small redrawing dies—and is less expensive.

The view to the left shows the attachment in place on a punch-press. Referring to this illustration, *A* is a crank disk which is bored out to fit over the projecting end of the crankshaft to which it is fastened by means of two bolts shown at *L*. (See detail view at the right.) Adjustment of the length of the stroke is provided by means of a T-slot in which the crankpin *K* is secured, and the knockout can be timed to suit the requirements of the work on which the press is engaged by loosening bolts *L* and turning disk *A* to the right or left with relation to the crankshaft. The hubs *B* at each end of the connecting-rod *C* are alike, except that one hub is threaded right-hand and the other left. The connecting-rod *C* has a flat on it which can be engaged by a wrench, and by turning the rod a very fine adjustment of the knockout is secured. Further adjustment may be made by using different sizes of washers *J* and knockout pins *I*.

The supporting bearings *E* in which the shaft *F* turns have four short legs cast on them, it being possible to file the legs to compensate for irregularities in the frame of the punch-press on which the attachment is to be applied. The bearings are fastened to the bed of the press by four half-inch cap-screws. The crank *D* is keyed to the shaft *F* and the same method is used in securing the cam *G* in place. The bracket *H* has four short legs cast on it so that it may be fitted to the rough bed casting and fastened by two cap-screws. The hole in this bracket is bored large enough so that the knockout pin *I* is a sliding fit in it.

The method of adjusting this attachment is as follows: When the ram of the press is in the upper position, the crank disk *A* is set with the slot vertical. The hub *B* is next fastened to the lower end of the slot by means of the stud shown at *K*. On the downward stroke of the ram, the crank disk *A* makes one-half revolution, thus raising the connecting-rod *C* and *D*. The cam *G* turns and lowers the knockout pin *I* and collar *J*. When the ram begins its up-stroke, the crankshaft completes

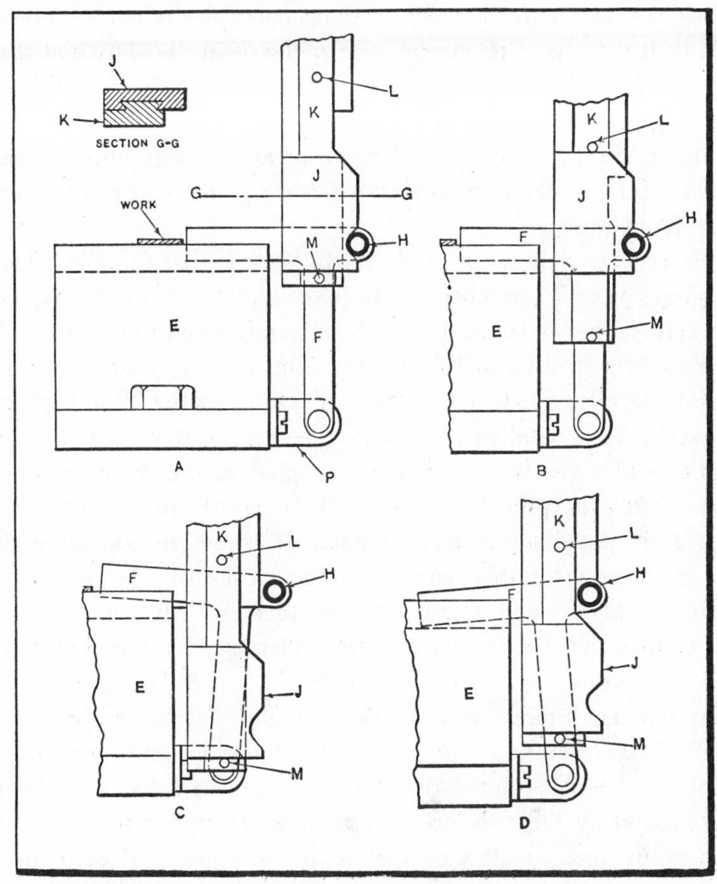

Fig. 25. Diagrams Showing Successive Positions of Knock-out of Kicker or Pusher Type

the revolution, pushing down the connecting-rod *C* and the crank *D*, and raising the pin *I* and collar *J* through the action of the cam *G*. In this way, the work is ejected from the die. In some cases corrugations are milled on the inside of the crank disk and the brake hub, to prevent the collar from slipping.

Knock-out of Kicker or Pusher Type.—The diagrams in Fig. 25 show the construction of an ejector or knock-out which receives its motion from the press ram. The final operation is one of forming, which makes it impossible to push the blank through the die. The view at *A* shows the knock-out device in the position that it occupies when the press ram is at the top of its stroke. At *B* the device is shown at the beginning of the down stroke, and at *C* the knock-out is shown as it appears at the end of the downward stroke. The view at *D* shows the position of the knock-out at the beginning of the upward stroke when the kicker or pusher *F* has just ejected the part from the die.

Referring to the view at *A*, it will be seen that the die *E* has an angle-piece *P* attached to its base which carries the kicker *F*. The kicker is pivoted at its lower end, while the upper end swings in a groove in the die *E*. The back end of kicker *F* carries a roller *H*, which rests in a pocket in the sliding piece *J*; part *J* is dovetailed to part *K* (see sectional view *G-G*) so that it slides freely. Part *K* is fastened to the punch-holder, and carries the pins *L* and *M*. Pin *L* comes in contact with part *J* on the down stroke, and pin *M* comes in contact with the lower edge of this part on the up stroke of the press. A spring (not shown) serves to hold kicker *F* in the forward position so that the pressure of the roller against *J* will sustain this part while part *K* descends with the punch-holder.

When the knock-out is in the position shown in the view at *B*, the press ram is approximately at the center of its down stroke. It will be noted that the sliding piece *J* has been kept in position by the pressure of the roller *H* in the pocket. At this point pin *L* makes contact with the upper end of *J*, and as the ram continues to descend, it carries part *J* along with part *K* so that roller *H* rides out of the pocket and along the outer edge of *J*.

When the ram has reached the bottom of its stroke, roller *H* has run off the edge of part *J*, which then drops by gravity, allowing roller *H* to rest on the back edge of part *K*. As the ram ascends, roller *H* drops into the depression in *K*, causing kicker *F* to strike the work and eject it from the die. Pin *M* causes part *J* to be carried along with part *K* on the upward stroke of the ram, so that roller *H* rides up the incline on the upper end of part *J* until at the top of the stroke roller *H* again drops into the pocket in *J*.

Knock-out Attachment of Cam and Spring Type.—Fig. 26 shows the construction of a die equipped with a knock-out mechanism which has a spring that is compressed by a cam action prior to the ejecting movement. In the upper left-hand corner is shown a front elevation of the punch and die, while directly below is a plan view of the die. A side view of bar *L* which actuates the knock-out mechanism is shown in the upper right-hand corner. The work is formed from soft iron stock 0.250 inch wide by 0.060 inch thick. The stock is fed from the right-hand side of the die, between the guide plates *A* and against the stop *B*. When the ram descends, the stock is pierced by the punches *C* and *D* and cut off by the punch E while the 90-degree bend is formed by the punch *F*. As the ram ascends, the work is thrown out by the knock-out plunger *G*.

The interesting point in this die is the knock-out mechanism, which is shown with the ram in its extreme upper position. The knock-out plunger *G* slides in another plunger *H*. Plunger *H*, in turn, slides in a groove in an angle-piece *I* which is carried on the back of the die-bolster. Plunger *G* is held in its extreme forward position by the spring *J*, while plunger *H* is held in its extreme backward position by the springs *K*. Each of these plungers carries a stop-pin (not shown) which limits its motion. The bar *L* has a cam action on the downward stroke, imparting the necessary motion to plunger *H* by passing through the oblong hole *P*. The dotted lines at *M* show the position of the stock when the punch begins its descent. It will be seen by referring to the illustration that plunger *G* is so located that it just clears the edge of the stock.

When the ram has descended until the forming punch *F* comes into contact with the stock *M*, the punches *E*, *C*, and *D* will have just passed through the stock. The cam surface of the bar *L*, in its downward travel engages the forward edge of the oblong hole in the plunger *H*, causing it to move forward a distance equal to the throw of the cam surface. As plunger *G* is also carried on plunger *H*, it also has a tendency to move forward, but is prevented from doing so by coming into contact with the edge of the stock *M*, as shown.

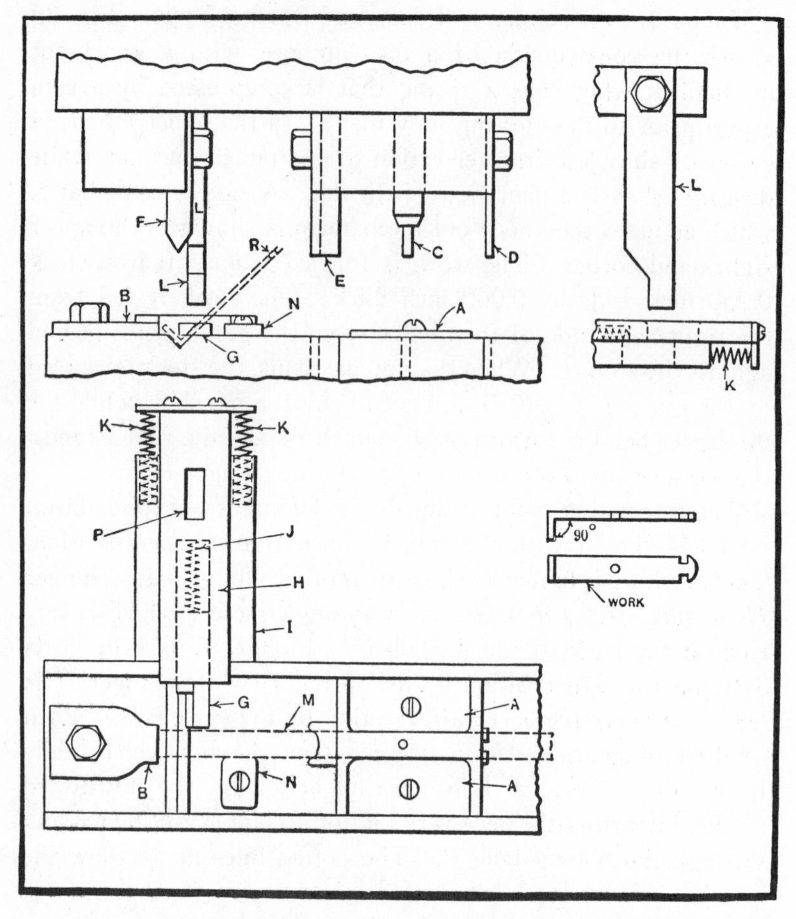

Fig. 26. Die Equipped with a Knock-out, the Spring of Which is Compressed by Cam Action Prior to the Ejecting Movement

The stock *M* is held in position by the guide plates *A* and the stop *N*. In this position, the spring *J* is compressed, and pressure is exerted on the stock through the plunger *G*. Continued downward travel of the ram brings the forming punch *F* into operation, with the result that the stock is raised on one end so that it clears the stop *N*, as shown by the dotted lines at *R*, and is bent to the shape indicated. The pressure of the forming punch *F* on the stock is sufficient to overcome the action of the spring plunger *G* on the edge of the stock.

As soon as the ram starts on its return stroke, the pressure of the punch *F* on the stock is released, and the spring *J* actuates the plunger *G*, throwing the work clear of the die. The springs *K* then return the plunger *H* to its original position. When the press is running at a speed of 150 revolutions per minute, which is the speed regularly employed with this die, the work is thrown clear of the press bed, and into a hopper placed in a convenient position to receive it.

Sectional Rubber Pressure-Pads.—The rubber pressure-pads used on some types of drawing dies for supplying the necessary pressure to the blank-holder should be built up of separate sections instead of being formed of one solid piece of rubber, provided a comparatively large size is required. One advantage of the sectional form is that the smaller sections will not "settle" and lose their resiliency as soon as the large solid piece of rubber, because the smaller sections are of better quality. The use of sections also makes it convenient to build up the pressure-pad until the required size is obtained. The sections can also be utilized on different dies in many cases.

Ejecting Press Work with Air Blast.—An arrangement for blowing work from a forming die in a punch-press, by means of compressed air, is shown in Fig. 27. It is simple and durable, and is used on about forty presses in a large plant, with satisfactory results. The illustration shows a plain forming die in position under the plunger of a press, while at the left of the plunger is the air valve *A* with its attachments. This valve is a Lunkenheimer whistle valve. It is held by the pipes which are screwed into each end, these pipes being held by the brackets which are screwed to the frame of the press. Below the valve there is a union and some other connections, and a bent tube which may be turned so as to apply the jet of air most advantageously. In some cases two unions are used to facilitate the adjustments. The lever of the whistle valve has been removed and in its place the trigger is mounted. This trigger is so designed that it remains vertical when not in action; it is seen in position against the plunger of the valve. The trigger is operated by the pawl *C* which is mounted on the bracket

D. The bracket is made of angle iron and is provided with two long slots for adjustment when the dies vary in thickness.

As the plunger descends, the end of the pawl *C* rises, as shown by the dotted outline, and passes below the head of the trigger *B*. On the upward stroke the end of the pawl engages the cam on the end of the trigger and thus operates the valve.

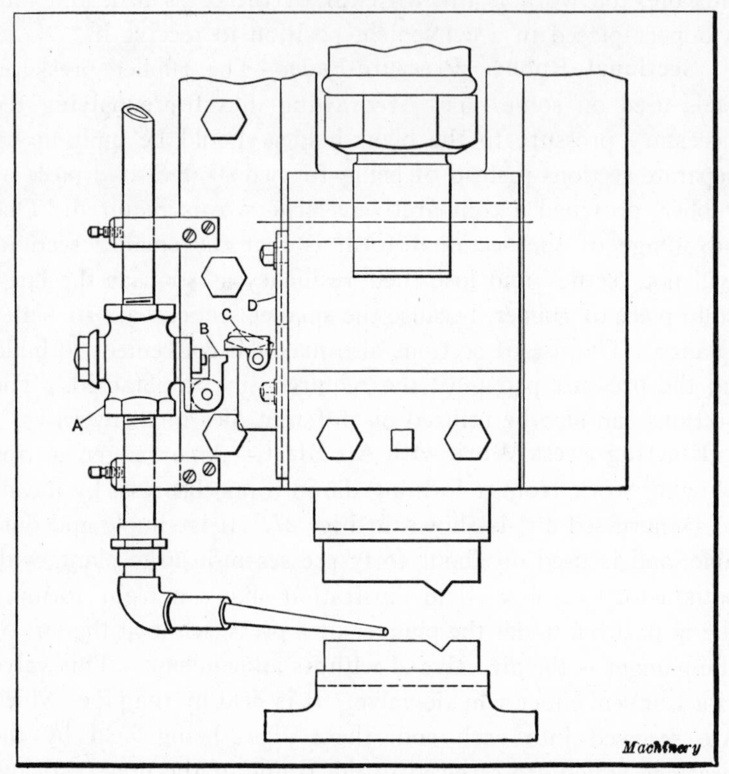

Fig. 27. Pneumatic Press Attachment for Automatically Removing Work

In this way a jet under full pressure is suddenly directed against the work, blowing it out of the operator's way before the plunger reaches its highest position.

Another arrangement for blowing away finished stock from a punch-press is illustrated in Fig. 28. As there was no compressed air of sufficient pressure available, an independent pump was attached to the press, as shown. The piston-rod of this pump is connected to the cross-head of the press, and, consequently, the pump has the same stroke as the throw of the crankshaft. The air is compressed on the up-stroke, and it is delivered against the work by means of a 1/8-inch pipe which is fitted on the end with a nozzle. The pump cylinder is made of a piece of 3-inch brass tubing which is screwed into a baseplate, as shown in the enlarged sectional view. This tubing is fitted with a head containing a stuffing box, and a 1/8-inch pipe outlet. The piston is a regular 3-inch hydraulic

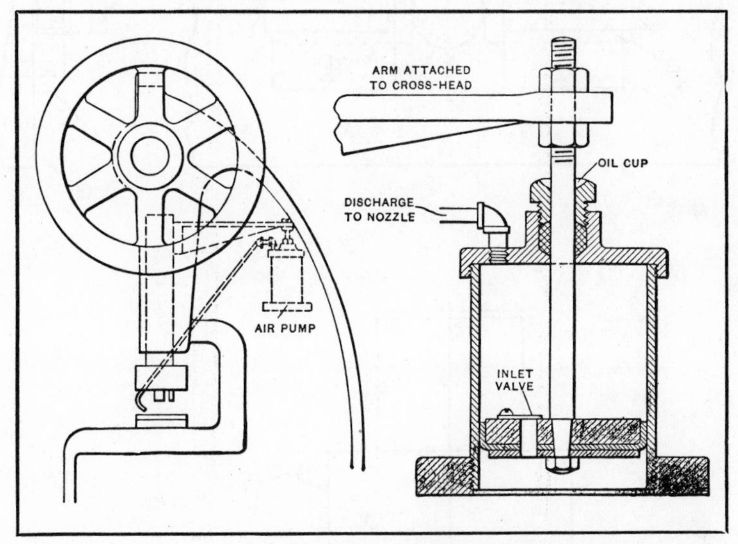

Fig. 28. Press Equipped with Air Pump for Ejecting Work—Enlarged Section of Pump

cup, and a piece of leather belting is used as packing. A piece of leather fastened by one screw to the inside of the piston, acts as an inlet valve.

Receding Guides for Locating Work in Coining Die.—A large number of disks such as shown in Fig. 29 at *A*, which had been stamped from sheet steel, were required to be coined to the form shown at *B*. Although the coining operation itself is not unusual, the fact that the stamped blank is considerably smaller in diameter than the coined piece and is reduced in thickness at the edges, makes the locating of the blank under

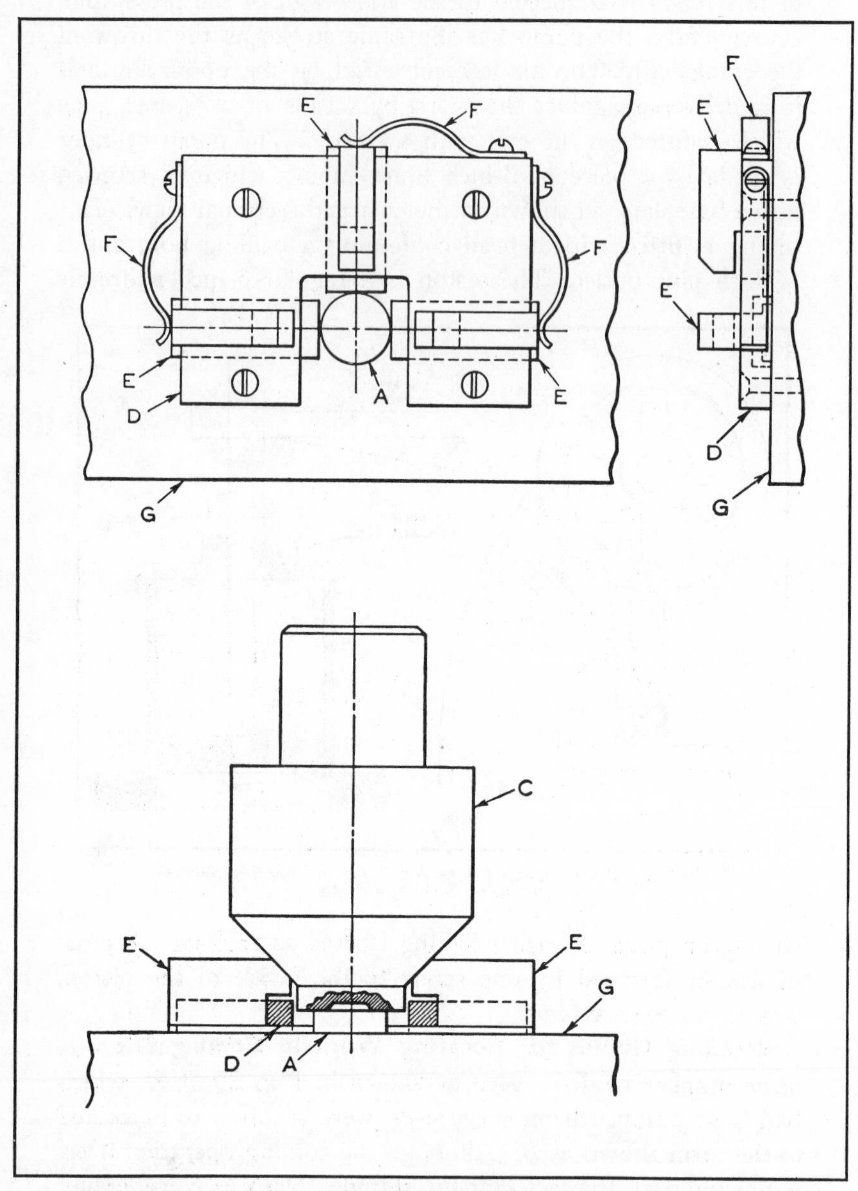

Fig. 29. Coining Die Equipped with Guides which Recede as the Punch Descends

the coining punch with a reasonable degree of accuracy somewhat of a problem. The solution of the problem was accomplished by providing guide surfaces which withdraw from under the punch as the latter descends.

Disk *A* is located by the three guides *E*, which slide in plate *D*, fastened to die *G*, and are held at their inner positions by the flat springs *F*.

In the partial sectional front elevations of the die (lower diagram), punch *C* has descended to a position in which it is in contact with disk *A*. At this point the angular surface of punch *C* has come in contact with the angular surfaces on the inner ends of guides *E*. From this point until the completion of the stroke, disk *A* cannot move out of position, as it is held by punch *C*. It will be noted that the inner ends of guides *E* which come in contact with disk *A* are reduced in thickness. However, they cannot be reduced in thickness to an extent that will permit the guides to remain in position until the end of the stroke. Therefore, they are caused to withdraw by the action of the angular surface of punch *C* on the angular surface of guides *E*. When the ram has completed its stroke guides *E* are withdrawn to a point outside of the working surface of punch *C*. On the up stroke of the ram, the coined piece *B* is removed and guides *E* return to their original positions.

CHAPTER V

STOPS FOR CONTROLLING POSITION OF STOCK

THE stop or stop-pin on a die is a device for controlling the position of the stock as it is moved along after each successive stroke of the press, so that the spacing of the openings cut into the stock will be uniform and a predetermined distance apart. Various forms of stops are used. A very simple inexpensive form consists merely of a fixed pin which projects slightly above the level of the die and comes into contact with successive openings in the stock. While this simple form is often used on dies of cheap construction, the stock is liable to catch at times on a fixed stop of this kind, and if this occurs quite frequently it is evident that the press makes many idle strokes and production is lowered. A more efficient type of stock and one requiring less concentration, in case the stock is fed by hand, is so arranged that the stop, which is pivoted, is automatically lifted to permit the bridge of metal between successive openings to pass under it, as the stock is fed forward; the stop then drops down in time to engage the edge of the following opening. Properly designed stops of this general class may be used in conjunction with an automatic roll feed, as well as when feeding by hand. Several ingenious modifications of this general type of stop will be described and illustrated after describing some of the simpler forms of stops. It will be noted that an important feature of any design is to so arrange the action of the stop that it will not interfere with the forward feeding movement.

Plain Fixed Stop-pin.—A plain fixed stop-pin is indicated in Fig. 1. This stop is best suited for use with strip stock in simple dies, because a miss will cause no serious delay. The time between finishing one strip and starting the next affords the necessary rest for the operator. The concentration required is intense—especially for the novice. When but a few blanks are made from a die at one time, and when changes of dies are frequent, this simple stop-pin is economical. Of course, it would not be feasible to use this stop-pin for coiled stock and expect the operator to finish the coil without a rest or a miss. One method of using this stop which permits of a maximum output, is to allow no metal between the blanks, assuming that the shape of the blank permits this. Then the stop-pin will extend clear up to the die and be high enough so that the stock cannot jump it. Each blank will then part the scrap at the stop-pin and allow the stock to be pulled along to its next position. This arrangement is shown at *A* in Fig. 2, with the stock parting at the pin *P*. This method is widely

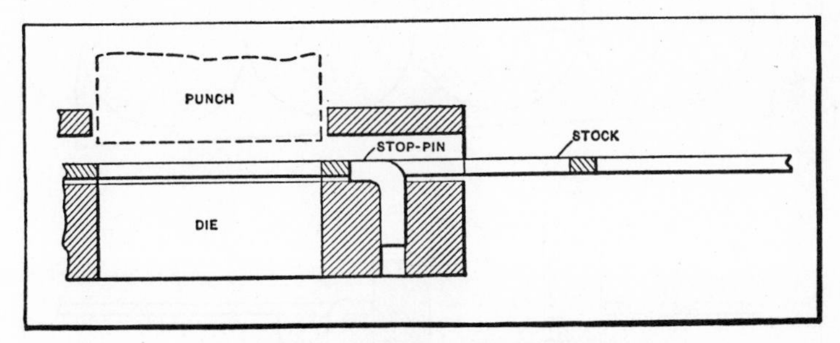

Fig. 1. A Plain Fixed Stop-pin

used on simple work where the edge of the blank does not have to be perfectly uniform. Small drawn cups are made in this way. The blank is cut by the first punch and held by it while a second punch, within the first, draws the blank through another die and forms the cup. This is shown in Fig. 2 at *B*. The stock feeds to the right and each cup, as formed, pushes the one ahead of it through the die as indicated by the dotted lines. Where the die has least to cut it will wear away most on account of the thin pieces of stock that crowd down between the punch and the die.

The common way to make a fixed stop-pin is to bend over a piece of steel rod and drive it into the die. The difficulties and disadvantages connected with making a bent stop-pin are as follows: First, the difficulty of bending the pin at right angles without breaking it or bending the part to be driven into the die; second, after the pin has been made and hardened it is apt to break in driving it home to its place in the die because of its uneven shape; third, in driving the pin into the die it is liable to swing around out of its proper position, making it necessary to knock it around again and thus increasing the chances of breaking it. Every time the die is ground, this difficulty is experienced and the result is frequent breakage and consequent

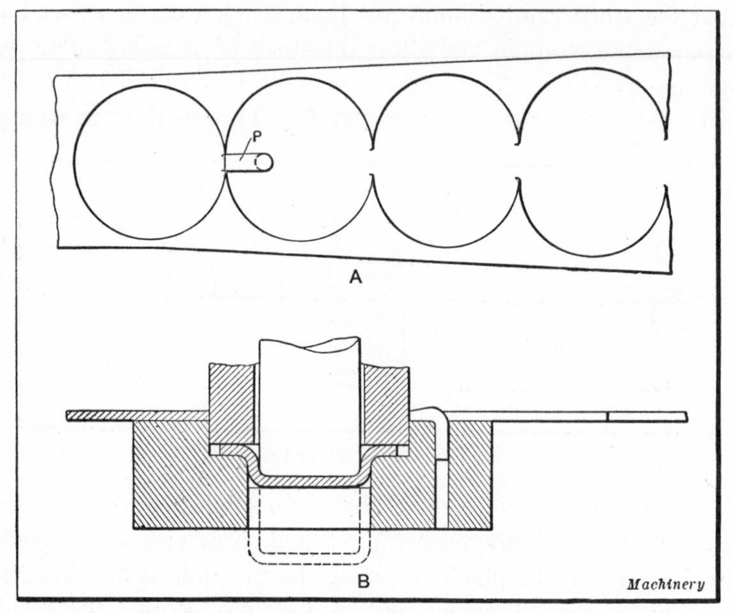

Fig. 2. (A) Fixed Stop-pin Set close to Blanking Die Opening. (B) Example Illustrating Application of Stop-pin Set as Shown at A

loss of time in waiting for new stops. All these difficulties are overcome by making the style of pin shown in Fig. 3. This is simply a shoulder pin turned to a nice snug fit in the die. The shoulder, which acts as the stop for the stock, may be made larger or smaller in diameter according to the width of scrap desired between blanks. This stop is quickly and easily made, is easily taken out and put back again after grinding the die, and will last as long as the die itself. It is a good idea to cut a hole through the stripper *A* directly over the stop-pin as shown at G, so that the operator can see the pin when the press is in operation.

Bridge Stop-pin.—The bridge stop-pin shown in Fig. 4, is easy to operate and simple in design. The stop-pin P projects downward from a bridge B that extends over the stock which is fed to the left. Provision is made for the blank (or scrap, as the case may be) to fall out under the bridge. The use of this type of stop-pin is limited to that class of work which cuts the

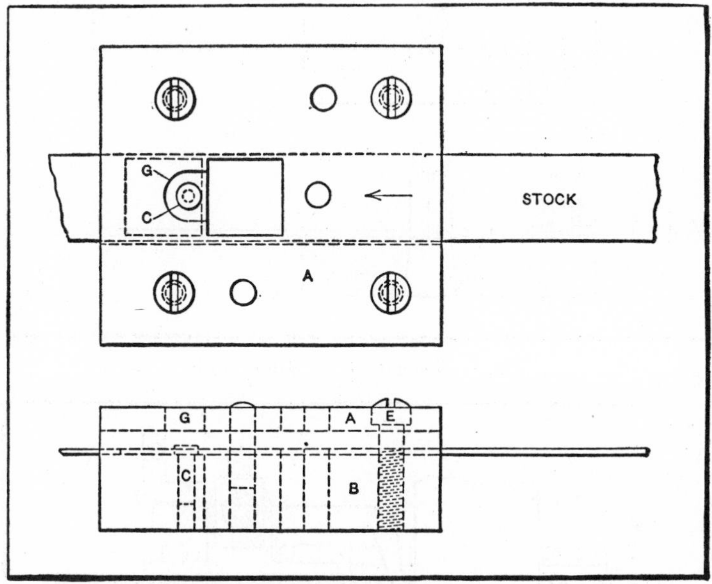

Fig. 3. Improved Form of Fixed Stop-pin

stock clear across and uses its edges as part of the finished blank. As here shown, the scrap is being punched through the die, and the blank, when cut, falls down the inclined end of the die. When the blanks are simpler and have straight ends, the die may be so arranged that each stroke finishes two blanks, one being punched through the die and the other falling outside down the incline. The operator simply has to be sure to push the stock up to the stop-pin at each stroke.

The Simple Latch Form of Stop.—The simple latch or pivoted form of stop is shown in Fig. 5. It is suited for dies that have pilot-pins. The latch is lifted by the down stroke of the punch and is lowered again as the punch rises; hence it is evident that, if used with dies without pilot-pins, the

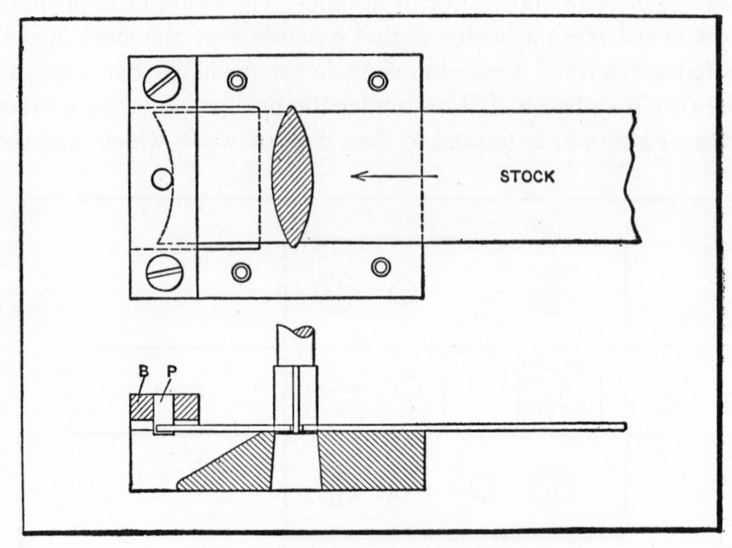

Fig. 4. Stop-pin of the Bridge Type

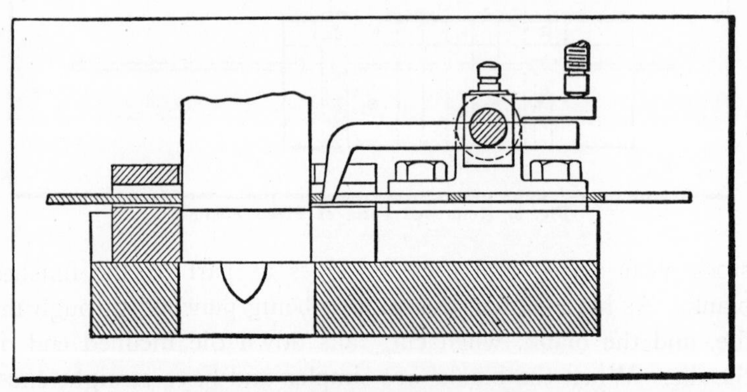

Fig. 5. Simple Latch Form of Stop

punch must reach the stock and hold it before the latch lifts. When its lifting is thus delayed it will lower before the punch withdrawals from the stock and will fall in the same place it lifted from so that the stock cannot be fed along. On the other hand, if a pilot-pin is used, which enters the guide hole just before the latch lifts, the latch may be set to lift before the punch reaches the stock. It will then fall after the punch withdraws from the stock, and sufficient time may be allowed for the operator to feed the stock along. This device is best suited for use with automatic feed rollers because the timing of the operations is uniform; if the operator does not pull the stock with uniform speed the latch is apt to drop too soon or

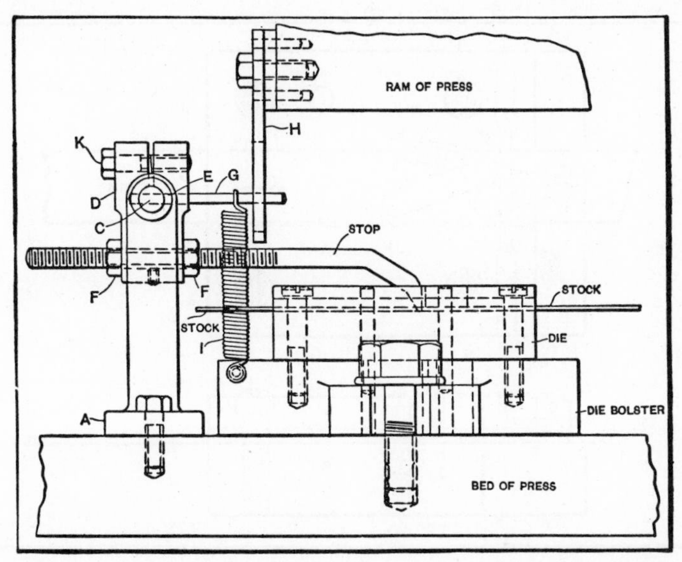

Fig. 6. Latch which is Operated by Slotted Arm Attached to Punch

too late. Another manner of operating this simple latch is to give it its motion by means of a cam or eccentric on the press shaft. When thus driven its motion can be very carefully timed, irrespective of pilot-pins. This style is also best suited for automatic roll feed. New presses are often provided with this attachment.

Another simple form of latch which differs somewhat from the one just described is illustrated in Fig. 6. There are two brackets *A* which form bearings for rod *C*. The stop is attached to rod *C* by a split knuckle *D*, this knuckle being held to the rod by means of the cap-screw *K*. Two washers *E* are fastened to each end of the rod on the outside of the brackets to obviate any longitudinal movement, but allowing it to rotate easily. The stop can be adjusted through the knuckle *D* by means of the adjusting nuts *F*. The manner in which this stop operates is as follows: As the ram of the press ascends, the arm *H*, which is fastened to the ram, as shown, and has a longitudinal slot in it, raises the pin *G*, which extends through the rod *C*. As this pin is lifted it rotates the rod *C* and, con-

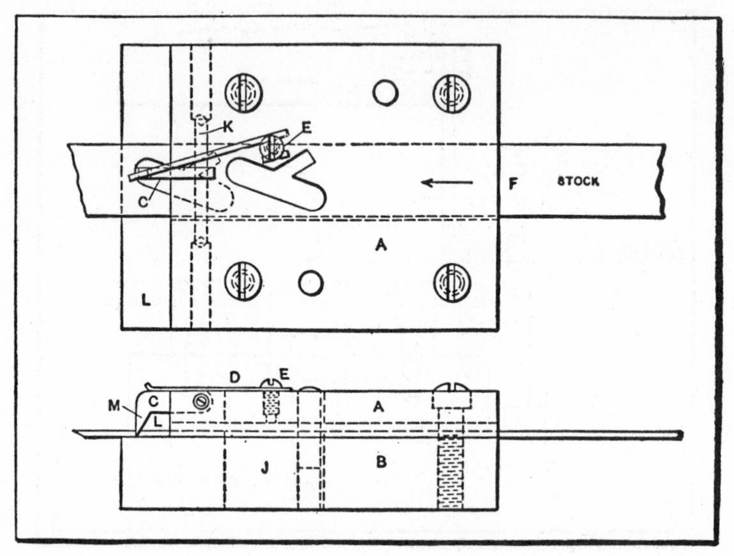

Fig. 7. Latch Stop which is Operated by Feeding Movement of Stock

sequently, raises the stop against the tension of spring *I*. When the stop is raised, the feed-rolls force the stock through the die, but the stop descends before the stock has been fed the required distance. The feed used is the ordinary ratchet feed and is set so that it feeds 1/16 inch further than the required distance to compensate for any slip, such as often takes place in ratchet feeds which are used for punch and die work. This extra feeding movement insures bringing the stock into proper contact with the stop.

Latch Stop Operated by Stock and used for Hand Feeding Only.—The stop shown in Fig. 7 is excellent because of its simplicity, and also because of the great variety of work to which it may be applied. This stop is of the latch variety, but it differs from most stops of this type in that it requires no mechanism to lift. It is not operated by the action of the press nor by the punch, as is generally the case with latches. A hole is drilled through the stripper *A* to receive the pin *K* which passes through a hole in the stop *C*. The stop swings upon this pin. A light flat spring *D* is fastened to the top of the stripper so that the end of the spring rests on top of the stop. In securing this spring to the stripper, it is only necessary to place one end under the head of the screw *E* with a piece of the same material under the opposite side of the screw as shown in the plan view. By this method the spring can be quickly and easily attached or removed, and a straight piece of spring material can be used. The stripper should be cut off at the stop end as shown at *L* so that the stop will be outside of the stripper and in full view of the operator.

The action of this stop is as follows: The stock *F* is fed to the left, and as the punched strip passes the stop, the point of the stop *M* drops or rather springs into the hole made by the blanking punch. The operator then pulls the strip back against the straight outer edge of the stop, and holds it there until the next blank is punched. This process is repeated at each stroke of the press, the scrap between the blanks being pushed past the stop each time and then pulled back against it. The inner beveled edge of the point *M* causes the stop to lift as the scrap between the blanks is pushed against it, while the outer edge, which is at right angles with the die, prevents the stop from lifting when the edge of the scrap is pulled back against it. It will be evident from this that a double movement is required, *i.e.*, to first push the stock ahead more than the required distance and then pull it back into contact with the stop. An operator can make about 40,000 blanks per day with dies fitted with this form of stop on a press making about 100 strokes per minute. These stops are used only on hand-fed work.

The Spring Toe Latch.—The spring toe latch involves but little change from the simple latch. Fig. 8 shows it clearly with an enlarged detail of the spring toe. This latch may be used very successfully with hand feed and there is little danger of the stock getting by it too fast. Its operation is as follows: As the punch lowers and starts to cut the blank, an adjustable screw on the ram or punch plate lifts the latch. Its spring toe snaps forward and when the latch lowers, it rests on the scrap left between two blanks; hence it cannot fall back into its former place. When the operator pulls the stock along, the latch toe drops into the next hole and brings the stock to a

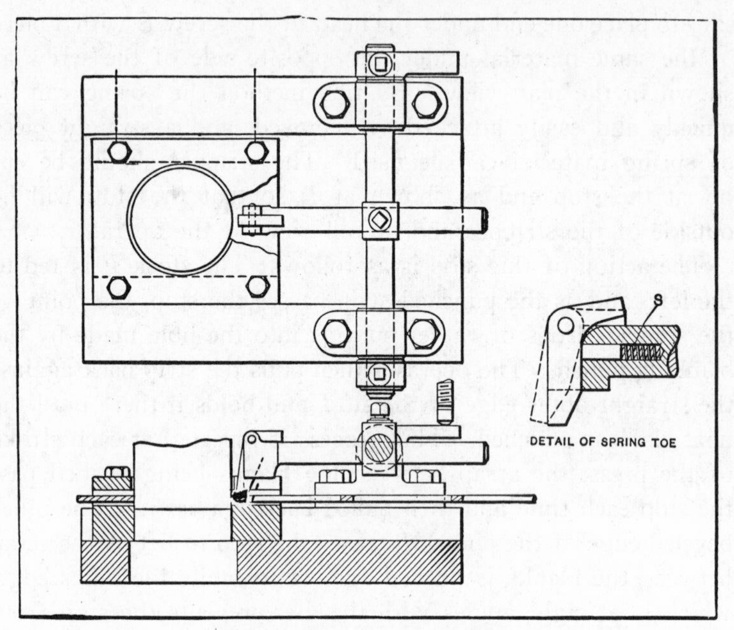

Fig. 8. Spring Toe Latch Stop

stop at the proper point, compressing the light spring *S* as it does so. This design is simple, rigid and effective.

The Danly Automatic Gage.—The Danly automatic gage illustrated in Fig. 9 is a commercial design of gage or stop which may be applied to any type of blanking die, such as simple, progressive, and compound dies. The lever *A*, which is engaged by a set-screw in the punch holder, is pivoted at *B* and has in its end a spring plunger *C*. The spherical end of this plunger engages the gage or stop-pin *D*. This stop pin has about $\frac{1}{32}$ inch play in the hole, which, in conjunction with the spherical connection with plunger *C*, permits a slight swinging or lateral movement of the stop, which constitutes an important feature. The operation is as follows: As the stock is fed forward against the gage pin, the latter is tilted to the position shown by the sectional view. The set-screw in the punch holder next strikes the outer end of lever *A*, thus lifting the gage pin *D* so that it clears and snaps over on top of the

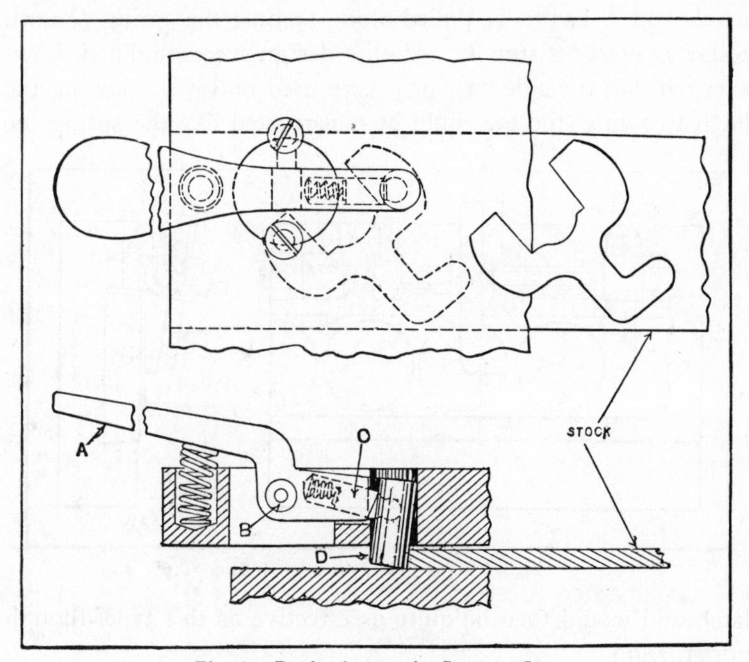

Fig. 9. Danly Automatic Gage or Stop

stock during the down stroke of the press. Since the end of the stop is now on top of the stock, the latter is free to move forward as soon as the punch clears it on the up stroke. As this forward movement occurs, the gage pin drops into the opening just blanked and the stock moves forward to the next blanking position. The operation of this gage as applied to compound dies is practically the same as just described, excepting that the gage is mounted in the pressure pad so that the lever strikes a set-screw mounted in the die shoe.

The Side-Swinging Latch.—A side-swinging latch is shown in Fig. 10. When the punch descends, an adjustable screw hits lever *L* and lifts the latch. The whole rod *R* then springs forward till collar *C* stops against *B*. When the latch lowers it rests on the stock as did the spring toe latch. As the stock is pulled along, the latch drops into the next hole and acts as a stop again. With this style of latch the tension on the stock must be greater than with the spring toe latch, because the whole rod *R* has to be pulled along against the spring *Q* until collar *D* engages stop *E*. If this design were modified, however, so that the side bearings were used only for allowing the latch to swing, the toe could be constructed like the spring toe

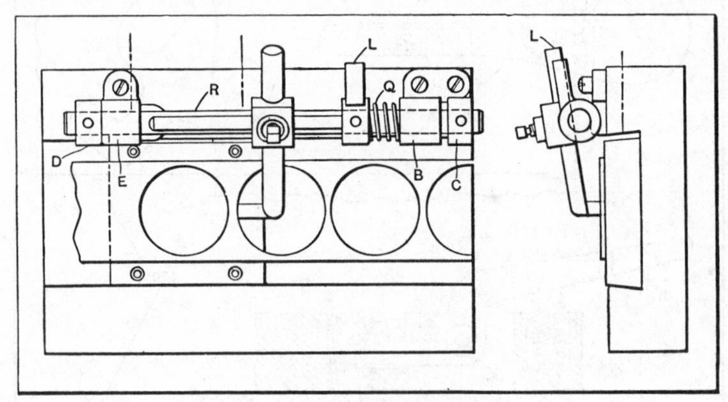

Fig. 10. The Side Swing Latch Stop

latch and would then be quite as effective as this type, though not so rigid.

Another design of side-swinging latch is shown in Fig. 11. This stop mechanism consists of a latch or trigger *A* which is pivoted on the pin *B*. The latch works in a tapered slot in the stripper plate which allows it a sidewise movement of about 1/32 inch. A helical spring *C* pulls the point of the latch down and tends to hold it on the side of the slot nearest to the advancing stock. A trip-screw *D* is screwed into the upper member of the die directly over the latch, and is so adjusted that it will cause the point of the latch to be raised as soon as the punch has started operating on the stock. The method by which this mechanism operates is as follows: When the stock is pushed forward against the latch, the latter is moved over to the far side of the tapered slot and the stop locates the stock in the required position for punching. As soon as the punch engages the stock, the trip-screw *D* strikes the latch and raises its point

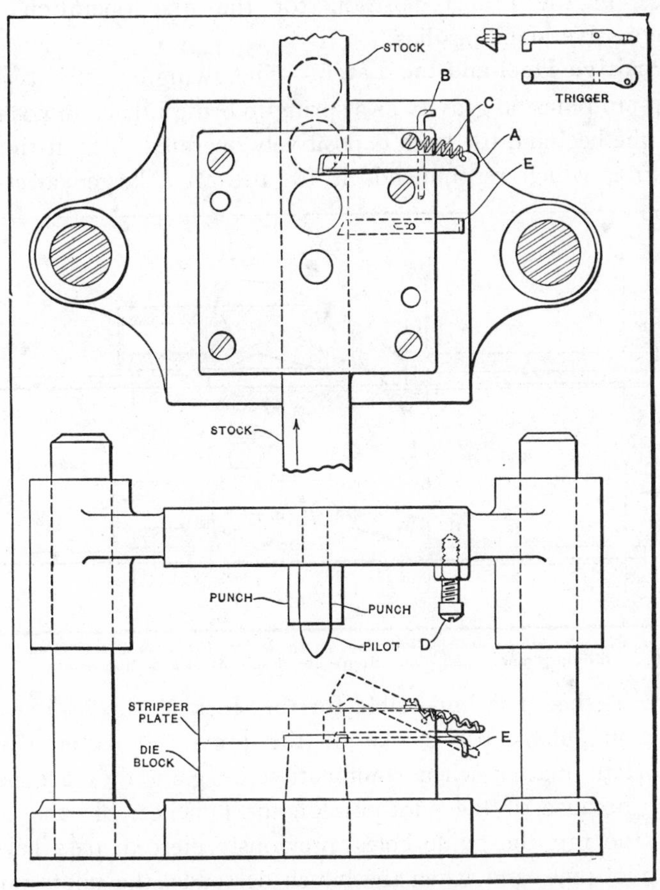

Fig. 11. Another Stop of the Side Swinging Type

out of contact with the stock; then the spring *C* pulls it to the opposite side of the tapered slot so that when the punch rises and the latch is allowed to drop, the point comes down on top of the stock instead of in the hole produced by the blanking operation; consequently, the stock can be pushed forward until the stop drops into the next hole and the movement of the stock is then continued to the position for the next punching operation. The point of the latch is beveled at the back to provide for withdrawing the stock if necessary. The sliding stop *E* is placed in the stripper plate to locate the end of the stock in the proper position for the first operation with progressive blanking dies.

Positive Heel-and-toe Latch.—The swinging latch type of stop-pin relies on gravity or a spring to bring it back in position, but the heel-and-toe latch is positively operated. Its distinctive feature, which recommends it for use on a large variety of

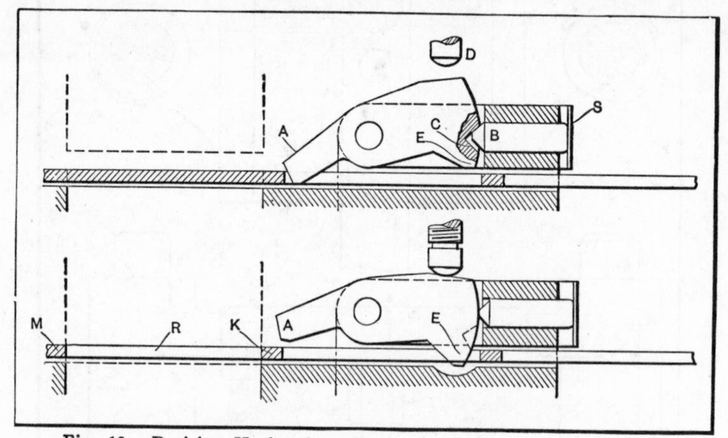

Fig. 12. Positive Heel-and-toe Latch which Prevents Stock from Moving more than One Blank for Each Stroke of the Press

work, is that it is impossible for the stock to slip by it faster than one blank per stroke of the press. This is a very important matter when combination or gang dies are being used, because of the pilot-pins on the punches. If the stock slips too far, the guide holes, previously pierced, pass beyond the pilot-pins, and when the punch descends, the pilots punch their own holes, form a heavy burr, and cause delay.

The upper view in Fig. 12 shows the catch in position to stop the movement of the stock at its point *A*. The stock is being fed to the right. The conical-pointed pin *B* is pushed by the spring *S* so that it engages a conical depression *C* in the end of the catch. By this means the toe of the catch is pressed against the die. As the punch descends to cut the next blank, an adjustable crew on the punch plate presses on the top of the catch at *D* and causes the heel to lower and the pin *B* to disengage from the notch *C*; the position of the latch is then as shown in the lower view. Its heel *E* has been lowered into the hole left by the previous blank and it is held in this position by the pressure of the point of *B*. While this is sufficient to hold the catch in its new position, it offers but little resistance to its return to the original position. The stock may now be moved along. The metal *K*, left between two successive blanks, engages the heel *E* of the latch and lifts it easily. This causes the notch *C* to engage with the pin *B* and the catch snaps back into its first position. The toe *A* falls into the new opening *R*, and *M* comes to a stop against it. Since the metal *K*, between two successive blanks, cannot pass the heel of the latch without raising it, and since the heel *E* cannot rise without lowering the toe *A* far enough to catch the stock, it is evident that the action is positive; hence the stock cannot jump ahead faster than one blank at a time.

In constructing a stop of this kind, care must be taken to allow under the heel *E* but little more height than the thickness of the stock. The length of the latch from toe to heel should be less than the opening left by one blank; then there will be no difficulty in starting the new ends of strips or coils. If necessary, however, the latch may be made so as to measure a little less than two (or more) openings in the stock. In such a case the latch would have to be tripped by hand until the first piece of stock *K*, between two blanks, had passed under the heel *E*. This would cause delays which would amount to considerable in the case of strip stock.

This style of stop has been used successfully with gang dies cutting blanks from brass 1/32 inch thick, and cold rolled steel 1/64 inch thick. In the case of the steel blanks, reels were used and the scrap was wound on a reel as it came from the die. By keeping the proper tension on the scrap, the stock was pulled through the die and kept against the stop. Four thousand blanks per hour were made by this means. In view of the thin stock used and the fact that the dies were of the combination type, this was considered very good. The stop had to be set accurately because the thin stock prevented the pilot-pins from shifting it much when aligning. Other precautions taken on account of the thin stock were to make the toe broad and to fit the stripper close to the front edge of the toe.

Starting Stop for Follow Die.—The devices so far described serve to stop the stock when it has passed the blanking punch, but there are many cases where two or more operations are performed on a piece before it reaches the blanking die and the

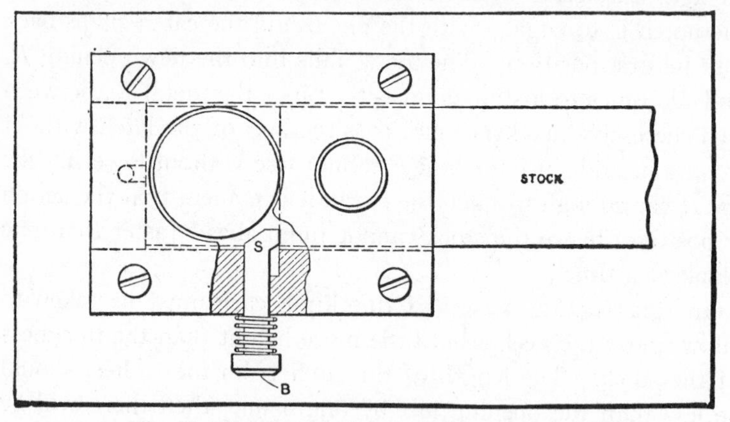

Fig. 13. Stop for Starting Stock in a Follow Die

usual stop-pin. The operator may gage the proper positions by watching the end of the stock through openings in the stripper, but it is better to have temporary stop-pins that can be used for that purpose. Fig. 13 shows a starting device for a follow die with two punches. When starting a strip the button *B* should be pressed. This brings into action the temporary stop *S*, which locates the stock properly for the first operation. It is then released and springs back out of the way. The stock is then advanced to the regular stop-pin.

Position of the Stop-pin.—The exact position of the stop-pin or that part of the pin which engages the stock depends, of course, upon the lay-out of the die and the amount of stock that is to be left between the punched holes. The width of this strip or bridge w (see sketch A, Fig. 14) between the punched holes is usually approximately equal to the thickness of the stock; it should not be less than this amount and for very thin material should exceed the thickness slightly. When there is not sufficient stock between the openings, the punch, which tends to draw the material in when passing through it, may actually draw it to such an extent as to cause damage. While it is common to allow the thickness of the stock, this rule should not always be applied. For instance, when narrow strips, 1/4 inch wide by 3 inches long, were blanked out crosswise of the strip, it was found that by allowing only the thickness of the metal the punch sheared off toward the scrap side because the end cuts were so narrow that they did not support the punch against the thrust resulting from the shear on the solid side of the strip. When using dies of the general shape referred to, it is advisable to allow at least 1 1/2 times the thickness of the stock between the blanks.

The position of the stop for a simple blanking die may be determined as follows: Draw outlines representing the two holes that are punched successively, so that they occupy the same relative positions as required for the holes in the stock; then draw a line parallel to the edge of the stock as at a—a and measure the distance along this line between corresponding points on the outline, thus obtaining dimension x. This dimension equals the amount that the stock must be moved for each stroke of the press, and, therefore, the distance that the stop-pin should be located from that edge of the hole which is to come against the stop-pin. Assuming that the shaded area represents the hole in the blanking die and that point y on the stock is to engage the stop, then the stop-pin s should be located a distance x from this point, in the direction in which the stock is to be fed through the die.

In case the stock is to be passed through the die twice, as indicated at B, Fig. 14, in order to cut it more economically and without making a multiple die, the openings which are punched successively or those which occupy the same position relative to the edge of the stock must be considered when locating the stop-pin. For instance, if edge y is to engage the stop-pin, the latter should be located a distance x equal to the distance from edge y to the corresponding edge of the next hole which is cut during this same passage of the stock. The position of the stop-pin relative to the hole in the stock,

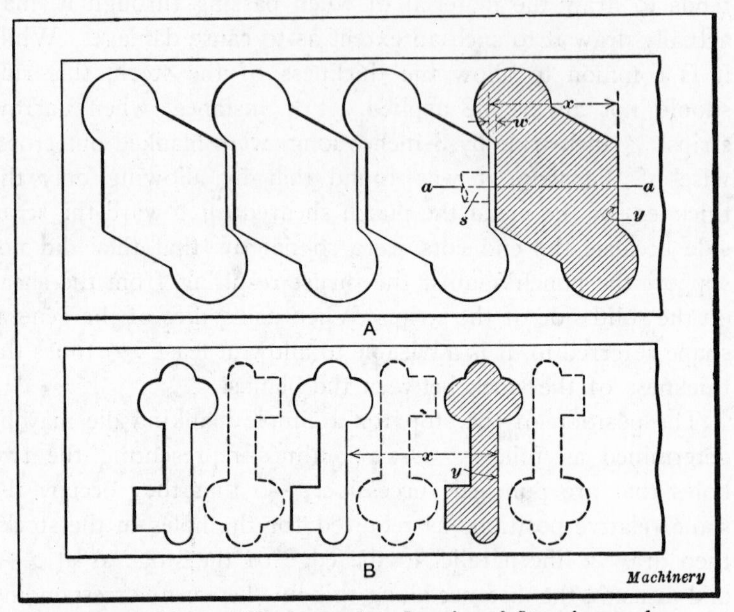

Fig. 14. Diagrams Illustrating how Location of Stop-pin may be Determined

depends upon the shape of the hole. It should be placed so as to engage whatever part of the edge will provide the best contact point for the stop-pin, a straight part of the hole being selected in preference to an irregular section if convenient. Whenever possible, however, the point should be in such a position with relation to the hole that when the stock is pushed against it, the tendency will be to force the stock over towards the guide strip. When punches are equipped with pilots the stop-pin in the die should be so located that when the pilots enter the pierced holes they will tend to move the stock slightly away from the stop-pin. If the stock were crowded against the stop-pin, a sheared die or a burred hole where the pilot enters would be the result.

CHAPTER VI

SECTIONAL PUNCH AND DIE CONSTRUCTION

MANY dies are formed of sections instead of being cut out of a solid piece of steel. This sectional construction is employed more particularly for large dies, especially when the form is complicated. There are two principal reasons for using the "split" or sectional die. One is that it sometimes happens that the blanks to be cut are of such a shape that the die can be made more quickly and cheaply by making a split die than by making a solid or one-piece die. The other reason is that when the required blank must be of accurate dimensions, and there is a chance of the solid die warping out of shape in hardening, the split die is preferred, because it can be much more easily ground or lapped to shape; moreover, a solid die is liable to be cracked by the hardening process, and in the case of a large die of complicated form this, of course, means a considerable loss. Some dies are also provided with one or more sections, at points on the die-face where the work is severe, so that the die can easily be repaired by simply replacing these sections when they have been worn excessively.

Not only is the cost of making sectional dies reduced in many cases and the machining of the impressions simplified, but also repairs may be readily made without the expense of replacing an entire die member. No essential points of die design should be sacrificed, however, in order to use a built-up construction in place of a solid die.

Examples of Sectional Die Construction.—Fig. 1 shows the manner in which the ordinary split die is sometimes made. After the die is worked out, it is hardened and ground on the top and bottom. The two sides *A* are then ground at right angles to the bottom. The cutting parts of the die, *B*, are next ground at an angle of 1¼ degree to the bottom, so as to give the necessary clearance in order that the blanks may readily drop through. The key *D* is now set in place, and the die is keyed in the die-bed by the aid of a taper key. The key *D* prevents the die from shifting endwise; the keyway should have rounded corners as shown, which not only give added strength, but also act as a preventive to cracking in hardening. The last operation on this particular form of die is to grind the two circular holes. This is done by first lightly driving two pieces of brass or steel rod into the holes until they are flush with the face of the die. The exact centers are then laid out and spotted with a prick-punch, care being taken to get the centers central with the sides *B*. The die is now fastened to

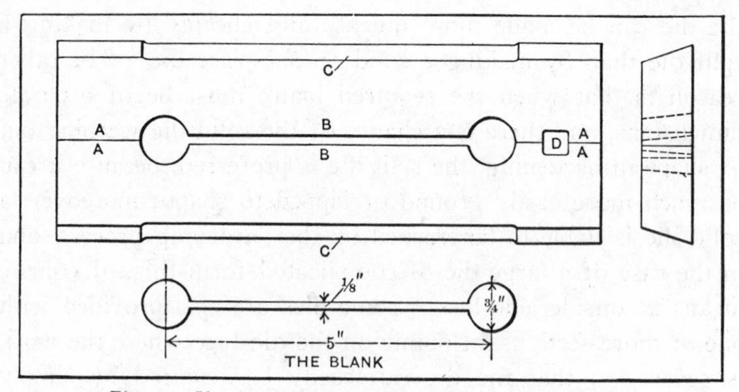

Fig. 1. Simple Example of Sectional Die Construction

the face-plate of a universal grinder, and the center mark is trued up with a test indicator until it runs exactly true. The brass piece is then driven out, and the hole ground to size, with 1½ degree taper for clearance in this particular case. The other hole is next ground out in a similar manner, which completes the operations so far as the die is concerned. It often happens with a die of this kind that when it is placed in the die-bed and the key driven in place, it will "close in." To overcome this, the die is relieved after the manner shown at *C*, which does not in any way prevent it from being securely held in place when in use.

Fig. 2 shows a rather novel form of split die; this die with a slight change practically takes the place of two dies. It is used for piercing slots in brass plates. The size of the slot for one style of plate is 4⅜ inches long by ¼ inch wide; for the other plate the slot is 4 inches long by 5/16 inch wide. The cutting part of the die is made in four sections, *A*, *B*, *C*, *D*. When cutting the 4⅜-inch plates, sections *C* and *D* are used, whereas, when cutting 4-inch plates, sections *E* and *F* are inserted between the parts *A* and *B*. The soft steel bushings *G* (through which dowel-pins are inserted) are used to allow for the distortion of the parts *A* and *B* in hardening. It may be added that the four bushings shown in the piece *A* were driven in first; then solid pieces were driven in the part *B*;

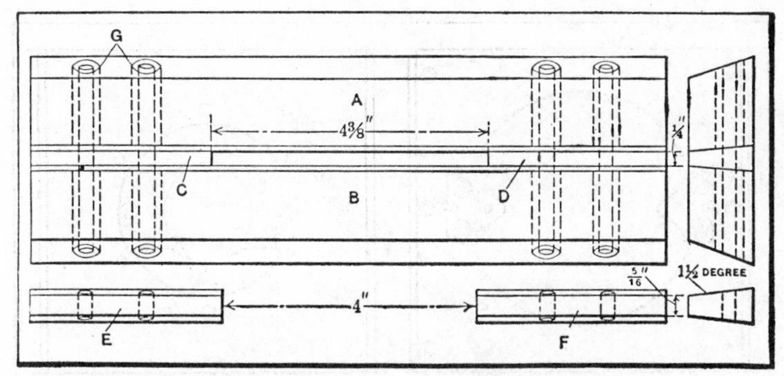

Fig. 2. Sectional Die having Interchangeable Parts so that Two Sizes of Blanks can be Punched by Changing the Central Pieces

then the holes were drilled in these latter pieces, being transferred from the bushings in the part *A*. The sections *C*, *D*, *E*, and *F* are hardened only at the cutting ends.

The dies shown at *A* and *B*, in Fig. 3, illustrate how the sectional construction may facilitate making the die and also lessen the danger of spoiling it in hardening. The punch for die *A* was made before the die. This punch consists of a cast-iron holder to which is attached a steel plate forming the punch proper. After the punch was hardened and attached to the holder by screws and dowel-pins, the outside was ground to the required diameter; then the die was machined and, after hardening, ground to fit the diameter of the punch. The sections *a* and *b* were then fitted to the die and fastened with screws and dowel-pins, as shown. The cutting edges of these sections were then sheared to the required form by means of the punch. As these inserted parts were small they did not change to any appreciable extent in hardening. The punch for the die shown at *B* was also made first. After hardening it and grinding the circular part, the die was ground at *c* to fit the punch. The sections *d* were then fitted to the die and the cutting edges sheared by the punch. In hardening these sections, one of them changed so much at the point *e* that it had to be discarded and another one made. This did not require any great amount of work, however, but if the die had been solid, obviously, it would have been entirely spoiled.

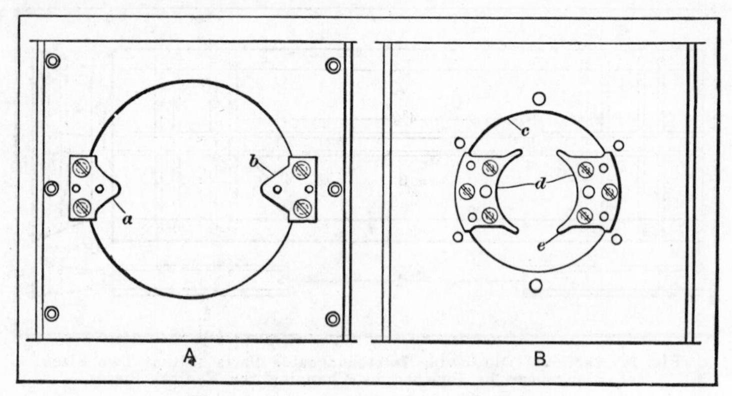

Fig. 3. Dies Having Inserted Sections

Sectional Die for Square Washers.—The sectional die shown in Fig. 4 is so designed that all the cutting edges and the inside of the die can be machined and ground to the required dimensions without requiring any hand work. This construction makes the punch and die inexpensive to produce, and in event of its being damaged during the hardening process or when placed in operation, the damaged parts can be renewed at a relatively small cost. The punch and die are used in manufacturing laminated copper washers in large numbers. These washers are square and have a square hole in the center; they are produced from sheet copper 0.020 inch in thickness. An inclined power press with automatic roll feed is used, and the finished work slides into a receptacle located at the rear of the press.

By referring to the plan and sectional views of the die, it will be seen that there are three piercing and three blanking dies carried on one bolster. The die is made up of fifteen sec-

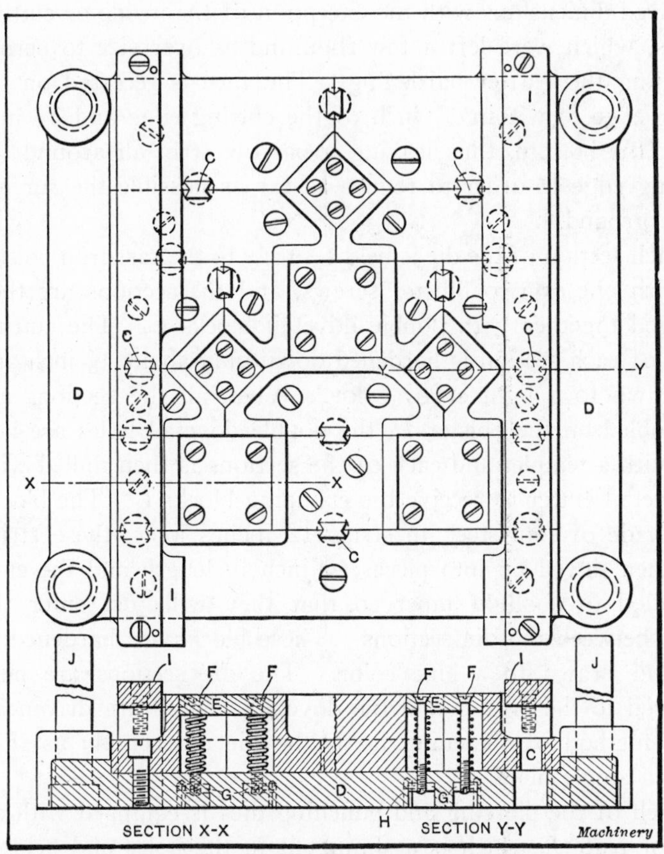

Fig. 4. Blanking and Piercing Die of Sectional Construction

tions which are held together by double dovetail plugs fitting into corresponding holes. When ribbon stock is fed through the die, the holes in three washers are pierced at the first stroke of the ram, and at the next stroke the blanking punch cuts away three washers with the holes in their centers which were produced by the preceding stroke; at the same stroke, the holes are pierced for the next three washers. The diagram, Fig. 5, shows the order of the piercing and blanking operations. None of the sections of the die have been drawn in detail as they will be readily understood from the assembly drawing. All of the die sections are machined approximately to the required dimensions with the exception of the inside or cutting edges, which were left a few thousandths over size to permit grinding them after hardening. The face is recessed on the outer edge to within 1/4 inch of the cutting edge and 5/8 inch from the bottom, thus leaving a narrow strip all around the cutting edge in order to reduce as far as possible the surface to be ground.

Each section of the die is held securely to the cast-iron bolster *D* with one or two fillister screws, and the sections are then wedged together with double dovetail blocks *C*. The cutting edge of each section is hardened down only about 3/8 inch and is drawn to a light straw color. When all the sections are assembled on the bolster *D*, the double dovetail holes are laid out with a templet and each of the sections is then milled with a dovetail cutter to receive the clamping blocks *C*. The blocks are made of tool steel, in strips 12 inches long; these strips are then sawed up into pieces 5/8 inch in length and the ends are filed to a slight taper so that they will just enter the holes between the die sections. These blocks are hardened in oil and drawn to a blue color. The die sections are next screwed to the bolster and the dovetail wedges are driven in. This method of fastening holds the die as securely as if it were a single piece.

Each of the piercing and punching dies is equipped with an ejector plate *E* which is a sliding fit in the holes and held in position with four flat-head screws *F*. Spiral springs are placed around these screws to hold the ejector plates in position. The screws *F* extend through the bolster and carry adjusting nuts *G* which fit in counterbored holes in the under side of the bolster. Small holes are drilled in the under side of the bolster, before the counterbored holes for the adjusting nuts are bored. These small holes are then plugged up to keep the drill from running out while counterboring the larger holes for the nuts *G*. When the plugs are removed from the small holes, the portion of the hole which was not removed during the counterboring operation serves as a guide in drilling a hole to receive the small pin *H* which is tapped into the nut *G* and keeps it from turning. The ejectors are adjusted by means of the screws *F* so that they are about 1/32 inch above the cutting edge of the dies. A long guide plate *I* is placed at each side of the die and fastened in position with fillister screws and a dowel-pin on each end.

The cast-iron bolster plate *D* is planed on the bottom and top and also across the bosses. The four holes in each corner are next drilled, reamed, and counterbored to receive the guide pins *J*, similar holes being made in the punch-holder after the punch and die have been assembled. The sub-press pins *J* are made of tool steel hardened up to the head; the heads are ground to a driving fit in the die-bolster and the pins are ground to a sliding fit in the punch-holder. To locate the holes for these pins in line with each other, and also to have them square with the punch and die, the following method was used: After the punch and die were hardened and assembled, two parallels were placed between the bolsters. The punch was placed inside the die and the punch and die clamped together with four C-clamps. After the work had been clamped in this way the holes were bored in the punch-holder through the holes in the die-bolster, and were consequently in accurate alignment.

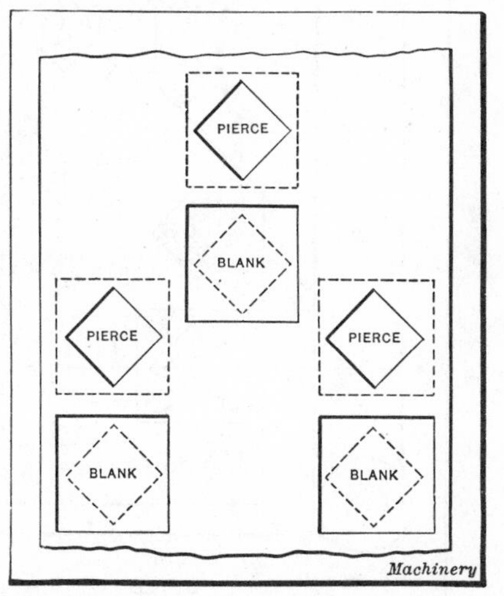

Fig. 5. Diagram Illustrating Piercing and Blanking Operations Performed in Die Shown in Fig. 4.

Fig. 6 shows plan and sectional views of the blanking and

piercing punches *A* and *B*, which are made of tool steel and left soft. These punches are secured to the cast-iron holder *C* by means of two fillister screws and two dowel-pins. In order to locate the punches in proper alignment with the die, the punches are first marked so that they can be replaced in the same

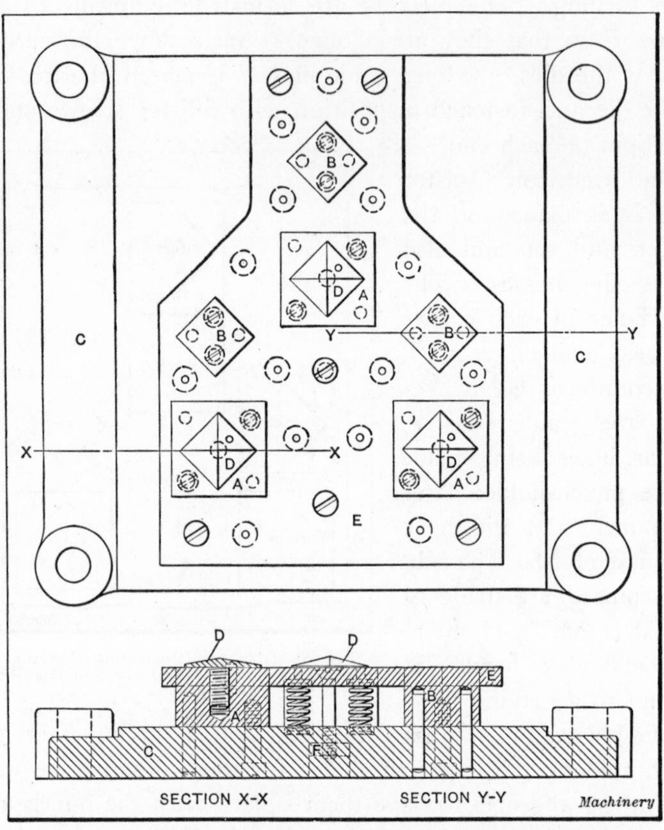

Fig. 6. Plan and Sectional View of Blanking and Piercing Punch for Die Shown in Fig. 4

positions. The ejectors are then taken out of the die, and blocks made of ¾-inch cold-rolled steel are placed in the die holes in their places. These parallel blocks are faced off to the proper height to bring them 1/16 inch below the cutting edge, all six of the blocks being of the same height. The punches are next placed in their respective die holes and the punch-holder *C* is then slipped over the four sub-press pins in the die-bolster and lowered onto the punches. With a right-angle scratch-awl, lines are marked on the punch-holder to locate the four sides of each punch, the scriber being worked through the screw holes in the die-bolster. The punch-holder is next withdrawn, and from the outlines of the punches on the holder the four holes for each punch are located, drilled, and counterbored to receive the two set-screws and the two dowel-pins. When all of these holes are drilled in the holder, the latter is once more replaced on the punches and secured with four C-clamps. Care must be taken not to twist the punches and also to see that the two bolsters are parallel with each other. All of the screw and dowel-pin holes are now drilled into the punches to a depth of about 1/32 inch, the holes in the punch-holder serving as a guide. The C-clamps are now loosened and the punch-holder removed; all of the punches are then taken out of the die and the holes are drilled to the required depth, after which the screw holes are tapped. When this work has been finished, the punches are replaced in their respective positions on top of the blocks in the die. Care must be taken to have all the chips removed and the work perfectly clean. The punches are secured with screws and the two bolsters again strapped together with four C-clamps; straight dowel-pin holes are then reamed through the bolster into the punches. In this way all of the punches and sub-press pins are finished in accurate alignment.

Pilots *D* are screwed on top of the three blanking punches to guide the metal during the blanking operation. These pilots enter the holes in the washers which were pierced by the preceding stroke of the ram, and prevent the work from twisting. The pilots are held in place by a screw and a dowel-pin. A stripper plate *E* made of 5/16-inch cold-rolled steel surrounds the punches and is held in position by the tension of fifteen springs. This stripper plate is made to fit between the guides *I* (Fig. 4) on the die and is a free fit on the outside of the punches. The stripper plate is adjusted by the flat-headed screws and nuts *F*. It will be noticed that there is a small hole in the center of each spiral spring seat. These holes are made in the following manner: All of the holes in the stripper plate are laid out in the usual way and drilled through with a 1/8-inch drill; the stripper is then placed on the bolster with all of the punches in position and the holes are transferred through onto the bolster. The spring seats can now be counterbored on the stripper and bolster and by this means all of the spring seats will be in accurate alignment with each other.

Piercing Die of Sectional Construction.—Points that should not be overlooked in designing dies especially when

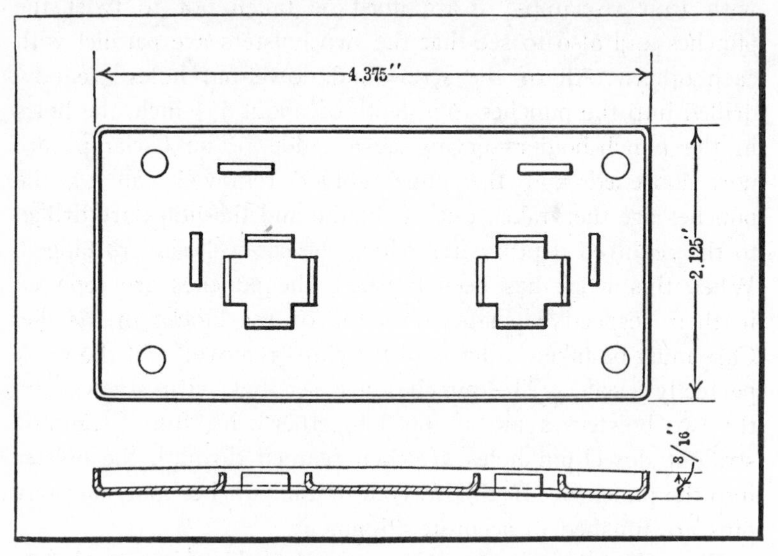

Fig. 7. Rheostat Base Produced with Dies of Built-up Type

they are to be used for quantity production, are: (1) The safety of the operator; this is of first importance, because it is very easy for an operator to be injured for life while feeding a power press. (2) Rapidity of operation; the dies should be designed to enable the operator to perform the work as rapidly as possible. (3) The combining of operations; this should be done whenever possible, but not to such an extent that the design will become so complicated as to cause the cost of repairs to amount to more than the net savings derived from combining operations.

The points of design mentioned have been incorporated in a set of dies for producing the rheostat base shown in Fig. 7 and it is believed that these dies are so constructed that the productive and repair cost is much less than for dies of solid construction. The rheostat base is made from a strip of soft cold-rolled steel, 5 inches wide by 0.035 inch thick, and there are four sets of dies used in completing the base. First the stock is pierced, then blanked, formed, and finally the lugs are produced.

The first die used in the operations on this part is a piercing die of built-up construction. This is used for piercing four small round holes, two square holes and four slots in the strip, as shown in Fig. 8. The position of the stock before it is fed into the dies is shown by a heavy broken outline; the outline of the blank and the position of the holes pierced are also indicated. The die consists of a cast-iron shoe milled to receive die-block *A*, into which a center block *B* is fitted. The shape of this center block is shown in the lower right-hand corner of the illustration. It will be seen that the slots and openings that produce the square holes in the die can be readily milled in this block. The simplicity of producing the die openings in this way greatly reduces the cost of construction over that required when each opening is cut from the solid.

The center block is a press fit in block *A*, and both these members are made from oil-hardening tool steel. The larger block is fastened to the die-shoe by machine screws and dowel-pins. The stock is fed between two cold-rolled steel guide strips *C* and *D*, over which, at each end of the die the machine-steel members *E* and *F* are bridged. The guide strips are 1/8 inch thick, which provides sufficient clearance for the stock to pass under the bridge pieces. The guide strips and the bridge pieces are fastened to the die-shoe by machine screws and dowl-pins. Bridge piece *F* contains a slot in which the stop-finger *G* is held. This stop is operated at every downward movement of the press ram, by means of a trip screw attached to the punch holder.

The stripper *H* is of the familiar spring type, and is attached

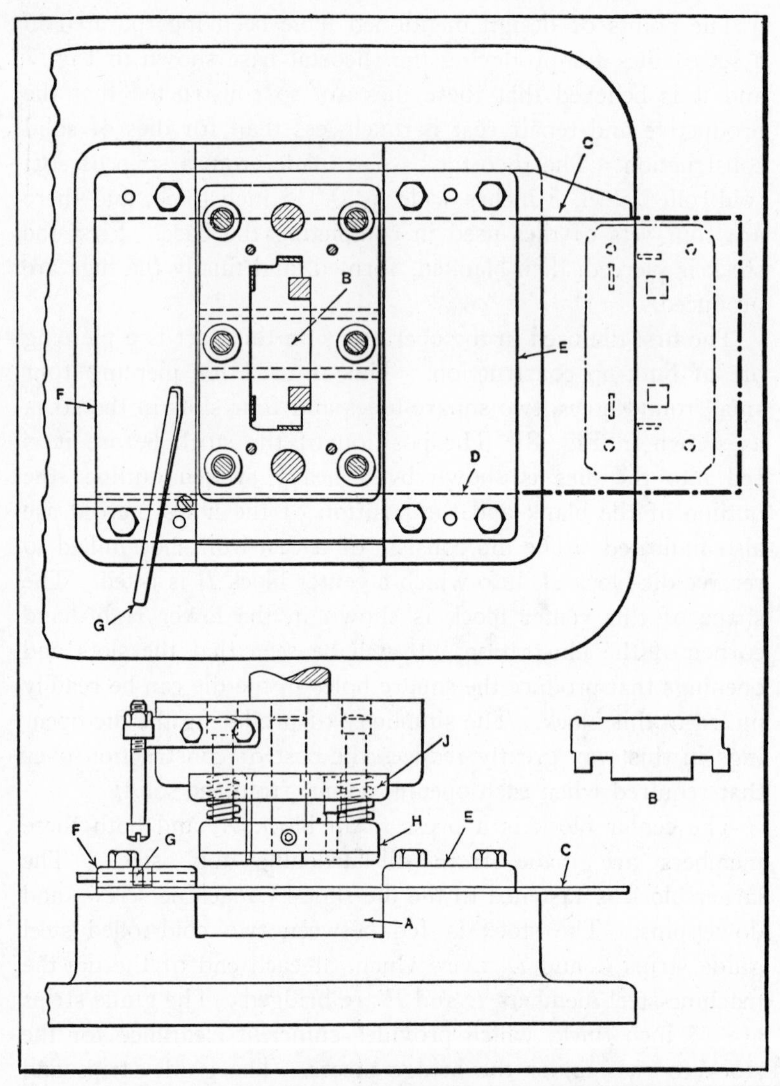

Fig. 8. Piercing Dies Having Openings Formed by Machined Blocks Set into the Die-shoe

to the cast-iron punch-holder by screws, and guided by two posts which are a press fit in the stripper and a slip fit in the punch-holder. The stripper is operated by six coil springs of square-section wire. Both the punch pad *J* and the stripper are of the same construction as the guide blocks; that is, they are each made in two parts. By this construction, the center block for the die and the ones used in the stripper and punch pad may be milled as one piece, thus insuring perfect alignment of the punches with the holes in the stripper and die-block. The flat punches for piercing the slots are made of B & S ground stock; they are riveted over in punch pad *J* and are well supported by the stripper. Excellent results have been obtained with this construction.

In setting up the die in the press, the stripper springs are compressed enough to allow the punches to protrude beyond the stripper about 3/16 inch, in which position they are temporarily held by set-screws tightened against the shoulder screws that hold the stripper to the punch-holder. After the punches have been aligned with the die holes, these set-screws are released.

Sectional Die for Blanking Rheostat Base.—The second operation in the manufacture of the rheostat bases consists of blanking the pierced stock in the die shown in Fig. 9. The general construction of this die is not greatly different from that of the piercing die. It is of built-up construction, the die opening *A* being made of four sections, two straight pieces for the sides and two end pieces *B* in which the contour for the corners is milled. The shape of these end pieces is shown in the lower right-hand corner of the illustration. Each of the four sections is fastened to the die-block by two 1/4-inch fillister-head machine screws and one dowel-pin.

The stripper plate *C* is made of machine steel, and it bridges the front and rear guides, after the general construction shown in Fig. 8. The slot for the feed-stop is cut in this stripper plate. Punch *D* is a solid piece of tool steel, fastened to the cast-iron punch-holder, and contains two pilot pins, which locate the stock from two punched holes diagonally opposite each other. In the operation of both the piercing and the blanking die, the strip stock is continuously fed through being automatically stopped at each operation of the ram by the stop-finger. The press on which these dies were used operated at a rate of 112 strokes per minute on this job.

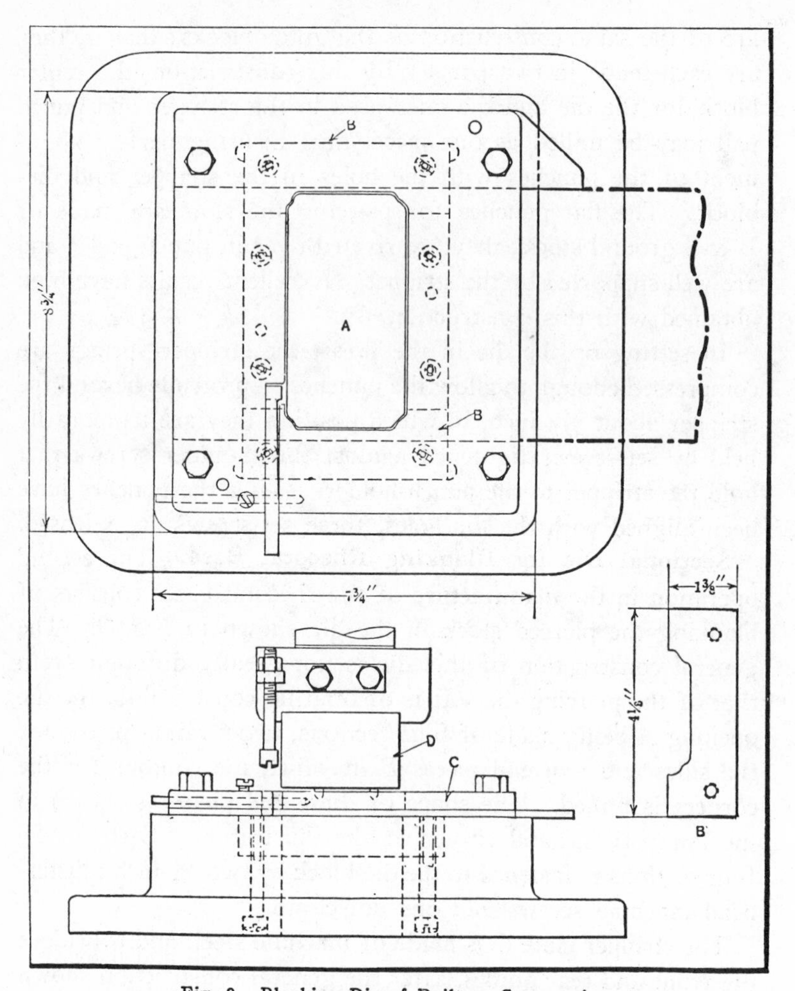

Fig. 9. Blanking Die of Built-up Construction

Construction of the Forming Die.—The design of the forming die for flanging the rim of the base (as shown in Fig. 7) is not illustrated. The cast-iron die-shoe is cut out to receive four steel strips, which, when assembled, form the upper corners of the die opening, in which a weight-operated pressure block is a sliding fit. The pressure-block and the four forming strips are of hardened tool steel. There are two gage strips fastened to the die-block by screws and dowel-pins at each side of the die opening, these strips being shaped to serve as stops when the blanks are fed into the die. The contour of the surface of these strips is the same shape as the corners of the blank (see Fig. 9). These strips are located back from the die opening enough to allow stock to form the sides of the rheostat base.

Above these gage strips, and also located on the sides of the die opening, are two stripper blocks, each of which has two projections extending in toward the die opening sufficiently to engage the formed side of the rheostat base and strip it from the punch on the upward stroke of the press. The screws and dowel-pins used to attach the gage strips also fasten the stripper blocks in place. The punch is of tool steel, and is attached to a cast-iron punch-holder by means of two dowel-pins, which also act as pilots to locate the blanks from the two square holes.

The die is provided with a feeding device of the chute type, which is capable of accommodating three blanks at a time. In operation, this feeding device is loaded and the blanks pushed along until one has been properly stopped under the punch. While this blank is being formed, the operator places a fourth blank at the edge of the chute so that as soon as the ram has ascended the next blank may be fed along to the operating position.

The formed work is blown from the die by compressed air and deposited in a container at the back of the press. The valve for controlling the compressed air is operated by the slide on the upward stroke. The weight-actuated pressure-block, previously mentioned, ejects the formed blank, bringing it to the level of the die so that the compressed air can remove it from the face of the die. There is little danger of injury to the operator with a die which is operated and constructed in this manner. When a formed part is produced at every stroke of the press ram, the rate of production is about thirty per minute.

Dies for Shearing and Forming the Lugs.—The final operation in making the rheostat base is performed in the die illustrated in Fig. 10. The point of special interest in the construction of this die is that the die-block *A* is made in two pieces, as shown in the sectional view in the center of the illustration. Each of these pieces can then be readily milled to produce the die openings, which are in the form of a cross. These two blocks are set into the cast-iron die-shoe, and fastened by four fillister-head machine screws and two dowel-pins. Within the cross-shaped die openings there are two plungers *B*, each of which is actuated by a coil spring made of square-section wire. These coil springs surround the shank of the plungers, and a plate is set into the bottom of the die-shoe to support the springs. The springs furnish enough tension to eject the formed piece of work from the die.

The punches *C* shear the two square holes at the corners and bend the lips thus produced to a 90-degree angle to form the lugs. These punches are made of tool steel, and are provided with a 30-degree angle shearing edge at the corners, while at the ends there is a clearance of 0.035 inch (equal to the thickness of the stock) so that there may be space for the lug to be formed. The corners of the die *A* over which these lugs are bent are slightly rounded to facilitate the operation. The punches are set into the machine-steel punch-pad *D* and riveted over, and are provided with tool-steel pilots of sufficient length to project 1/32 inch beyond the lug formed on the work. The purpose of this is to force plungers *B* down ahead of the lugs being formed so that they will not interfere with the free cutting and forming action.

The punch-pad is of two-piece construction like the die-block *A*, and the two pieces of the pad and of the die-block are all milled at one time. This gives the required alignment and also saves considerable time in machining. The punch stripper *E* is a machine-steel part, held in place by the customary arrangement of screws, and operated by four coil springs.

The formed work is placed over the die-block, which is an easy fit inside the work. Any play between the work and the die-block is compensated for by the pilots on the punches which enter the square holes before they are pierced, and

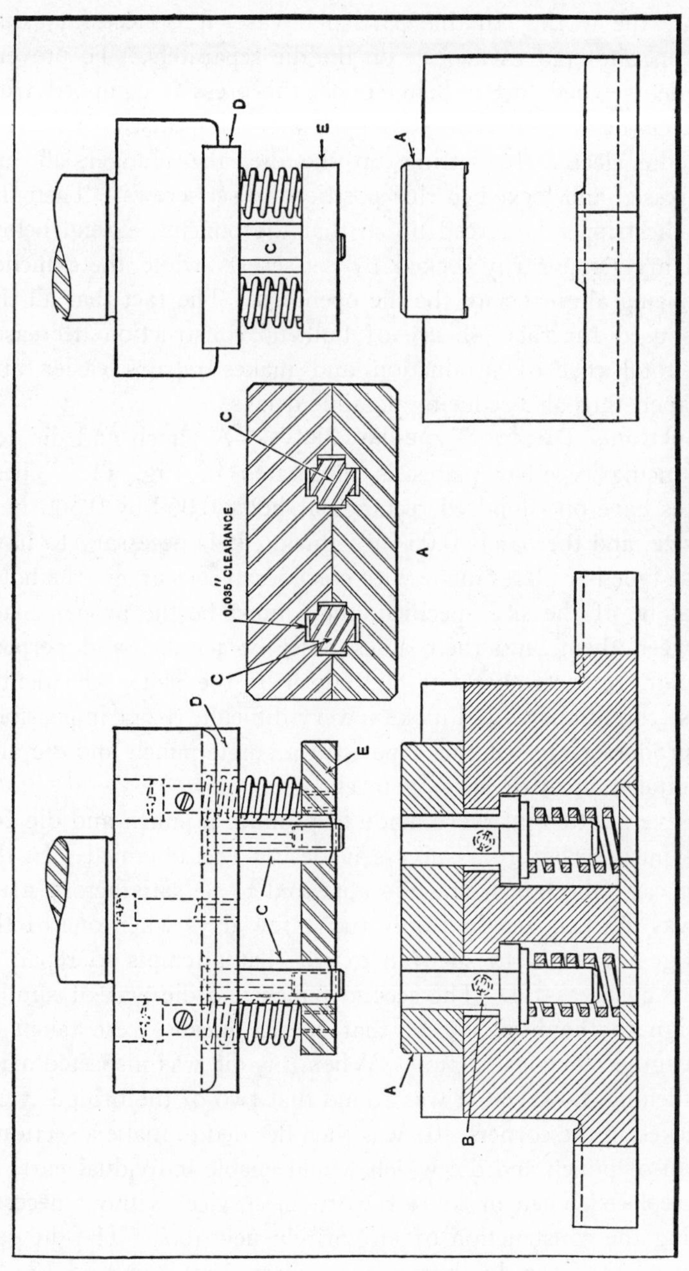

Fig. 10. Shearing and Lug-forming Die, also of Built-up Construction

locate the work. In this particular case, it is necessary that the operator put each piece on the die separately. To prevent accidents when this is being done, the press is equipped with a safety device. It is also equipped with compressed air to keep the die clean. In setting up the die, the plungers *B* are depressed and locked in this position by set-screws. Then the punch stripper is forced up so that the punches extend below and are temporarily locked by set-screws while the punches are being aligned with the die openings. The fact that all the dies used for this job are of built-up construction decreases the total cost of production and makes repairs easier and cheaper, thus also reducing possible delays.

Sectional Die for Type-bar Plates.—A punch and die for producing type-bar plates is illustrated in Fig. 11. These plates have one hundred rectangular holes 0.060 by 0.360 inch in size, and the bar is 0.03 inch thick. It is necessary to have these type-bar plates made with considerable accuracy; the holes must be of the size specified, there must be the proper space between them, and their sides must be parallel and perpendicular, respectively, with the edges of the plate. Evidently these conditions would make it very difficult, if not impossible, to produce plates of this type with a single punch and die and a suitable form of spacing mechanism.

Several attempts were made to produce a punch and die for this purpose before a successful design was obtained. In the first case, the punch and die appeared to be satisfactory after it was finished, but had only run a few days when one of the bridges caved in to such an extent that attempts to repair it were unsuccessful. The second punch and die was of similar design to the first, except that special means were taken to strengthen its construction. When this die was inspected after hardening, however, it was found that two of the bridges were cracked in the corners. It was then decided to make a sectional form of punch and die which would enable individual parts to be replaced when broken or worn in service, without necessitating the construction of an entirely new tool. The die section adopted for this purpose is indicated at *B* in Fig. 12. It

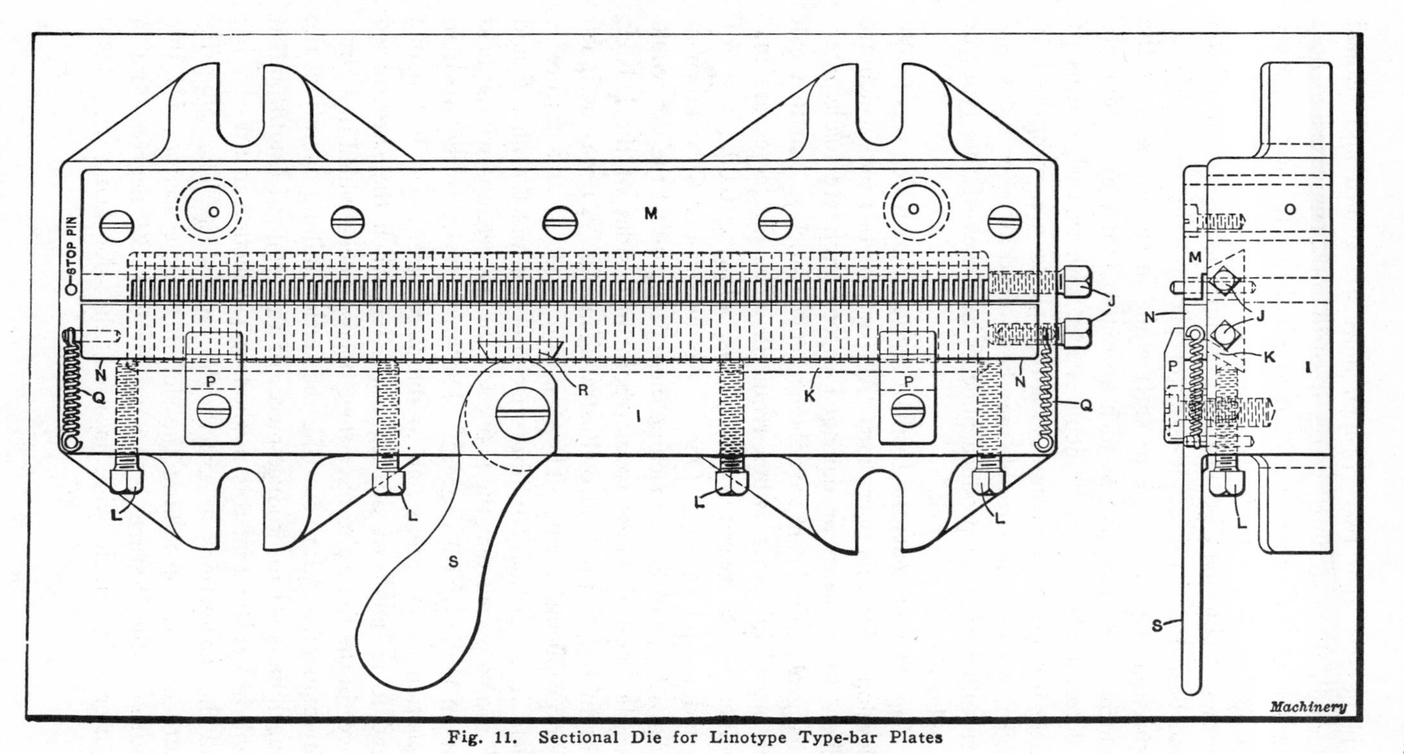

Fig. 11. Sectional Die for Linotype Type-bar Plates

will be seen that two 5/16-inch holes are drilled and reamed through these sections, pieces of drill rod being used to hold the sections together in a 30-degree bolster; the sections were wedged in this bolster by means of a suitable gib and set-screws. This die also proved a failure because no provision had been made for guide-posts or pilots. The result of this omission caused the die to shift while in service, so that the punches were stripped to such an extent that they became absolutely useless. The difficulties met with in early forms of dies for producing these type-bar plates are mentioned in order that the same trouble may be avoided by other shops that are called upon to produce punches and dies of this type for similar classes of work.

Fig. 11 represents the form of sectional die which was finally developed for this operation. All parts of this tool which are likely to be worn or damaged in operation are made interchangeable, duplicate parts being kept in stock so that they can be placed in service when required. The die pieces are machined to the required dimensions, allowing 0.005 inch for grinding and lapping. One of the die sections *C* is shown in Fig. 12. In order to machine these parts so that the slot would be the same distance from the inclined sides of the bolster, the milling fixture (also illustrated in Fig. 12) was designed for producing them. The cast-iron block of this fixture is held in an ordinary milling machine vise and the pins *E* and *F* are so placed that the blank for the die sections will be held at an angle of 60 degrees. The strap *G* holds the work in position while milling; all of the pieces are first milled at one end to an angle of 30 degrees, after which they are turned over in the fixture to have their opposite ends milled in a similar manner. Before starting the section milling operation, the machine is set to produce pieces of the required length, and it will be evident that this method of production insures having all the die sections of exactly the same size. The same fixture is used for milling the slot in the die section; for this purpose the fixture is swung around 30 degrees and a cutter 0.360 inch wide is used, the slot being cut 0.060

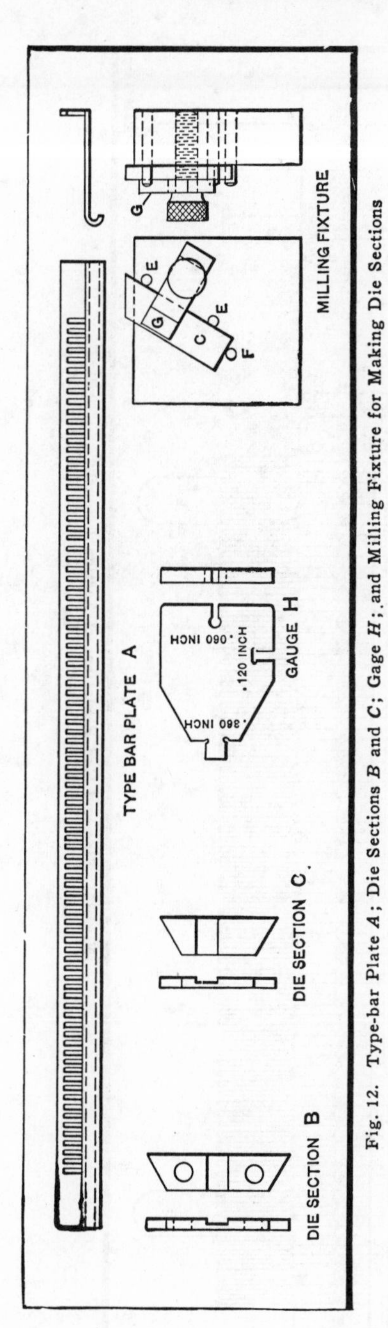

Fig. 12. Type-bar Plate *A*; Die Sections *B* and *C*; Gage *H*; and Milling Fixture for Making Die Sections

inch deep. The three sides of the slot are now relieved with a file and after being hardened and drawn to a light straw color, the sections are ground on both sides so that the section through the slot will just enter the 0.060-inch space in the gage *H* and the thicker section will enter the 0.120-inch space. The bottom and angles are not ground, but the tops of all the sections are ground when they are assembled in the cast-iron bolster *I*, Fig. 11. Two set-screws *J* are provided to take care of the end-thrust on the die sections. The length of the die is 9 inches, but if it is found that this dimension is slightly exceeded, it is an easy matter to lap the sections off on the sides to reduce it the required amount.

The cast-iron bolster is held securely to the press bed by means of four 5/8-inch hexagon screws. The gib *K* runs though the entire length of the die-bolster and is held against the die sections by four set-screws *L*. On top of the bolster, there are two soft-iron plates *M* and *N*. The plate *M* is held in position by five fillister screws and acts as a stop-wall for the work to rest

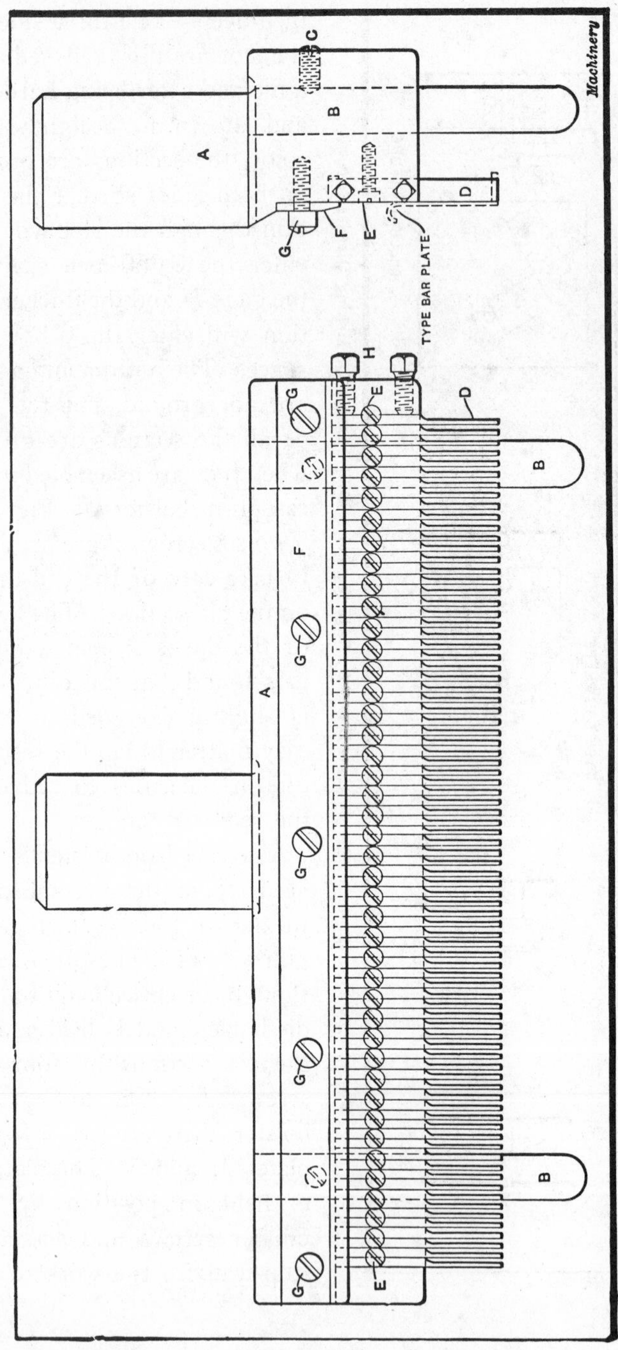

Fig. 13. Side and End Elevations of Sectional Punch

against the die. This plate has slots milled along its edge which correspond with the die section, only they are a few thousandths larger than the punches; the plate *M* also acts as the stripper for the punch. The plate *N* slides back and forth on the bolster under the strap *P*, its movement being controlled by the cam and lever *S*. The hardened wedge *R* is driven into the middle of the plate for the cam *S* to rest against and when the cam is swung around to bring the flat section into engagement, the springs *Q* at each end of the die pull the plate *N* back so that sufficient space is made to lift the finished work out of the die.

There are two ¾-inch holes *O* provided in the bolster to receive the pilots *B* of the punch-holder, Fig. 13. These holes have hardened bushings driven into them which can be replaced when they become worn to an objectionable extent. The punch sections are held in a machinery steel holder *A*. This holder is finished all over, great care being taken to secure the necessary alignment. The guide pins *B* are hardened, ground, and lapped to exact dimensions and the same gage *H* (Fig. 12) that was used for measuring the die sections is also used in determining the accuracy of the punch sections. These punch sections are secured to the holder by fillister screws *E*, a single screw being used between two sections in the manner shown in the illustration. The clamp *F* runs the entire length of the holder and is held in position by the fillister screws *G*. Two set-screws *H* are provided to take up any end-thrust in the punch sections.

The forming of the type-bar plates *A* (Fig. 12) is done in two operations. The stock is rolled on a spool and held in the proper position to be received by a powerful trimming press. In the first operation, the stock is cut off and formed to the right angle; the downward stroke of a roller at the back of the die then curves the other edge of the plate upward to form a quarter segment. The second operation is done separately in a clamping die and forms the plate to the required shape.

CHAPTER VII

BLANKING DIES FOR ROTOR AND STATOR LAMINATIONS

In determining upon the type of die to be built for producing laminations used in electrical equipment, the factors of design, construction, maintenance, and economy of production should always be given careful consideration. Before these factors can be considered intelligently, production requirements must be ascertained and the design and thickness of the lamination determined. All four factors will be taken into consideration in discussing various types of dies used to produce laminations in the metal stamping department of the Westinghouse Electric & Mfg. Co., East Pittsburgh, Pa. The principles of construction embodied in the numerous dies used are based on experience that has extended over many years. A few of these dies are shown in Figs. 1 to 10 inclusive, to illustrate important principles in the designs used.

Multiple-purpose Dies for Laminations.—In order to expedite the manufacture of laminations for special apparatus, meet low production demands, or furnish laminations for standard apparatus before the completion of single-purpose dies, a variety of multiple-purpose tools have been constructed. With these dies almost any design of rotor or stator lamination can be manufactured upon short notice by a number of simple operations. These simple dies consist of a male and a female part, and perform a single operation. The punch or male member is usually the moving part, and the female member the stationary part. These simple tools consist of round-hole, ventilating, keyway, and slot dies.

A round-hole die is used for piercing the center from a piece of sheet steel. The hole produced may be either the bore or shaft fit of a rotor or the inside hole of a stator lamination.

This type of die may be inverted and used for trimming the periphery of a rotor lamination or for trimming a stator lamination to fit the frame. Round-hole dies range in size up to 36 inches in diameter.

Ventilating dies may be made either in groups or as a single die provided with a hand indexing mechanism. The center hole previously blanked in the material is used for locating the ventilating holes.

Keyway dies may be used to cut a keyway either around the bore of a rotor lamination or on the stator edge which fits the frame.

Dies employed for notching teeth on a rotor or stator lamination are set up in special automatic notching presses. The rotor lamination is placed over a plug which fits into the bore and keyway of the lamination, and the latter is held securely by friction while it is indexed for slotting. The stator lamination is placed in a ring under two spring clamps made to suit the outside of the stator iron, and this lamination is also driven at the keyway.

Certain standard dimensions of laminations occasionally present an opportunity for economy through the possibility of constructing one die to pierce the bore, vent holes, and keyway in one operation. The material is then trimmed to the proper diameter with a round-hole die, and the coil slots are notched in an automatic indexing press.

Round Hole or Outside Trimming Die.—When piercing a hole with a round-hole or outside trimming die, the male part is the upper moving member and the female part the lower stationary member. When the die is inverted for a trimming operation, the female part is the moving member and the male part, the stationary member.

Fig. 1 illustrates the most important details of a round-hole or outside trimming die. Shoe 2 is drilled and reamed to hold liner pins 10, and recessed to receive punch ring 6 and gage ring 7, which are held to the shoe by means of cap-screws. Gage plug 9 fits in the tapered hole of gage ring 7. The outside stripper consists of plate 4, which is supported by com-

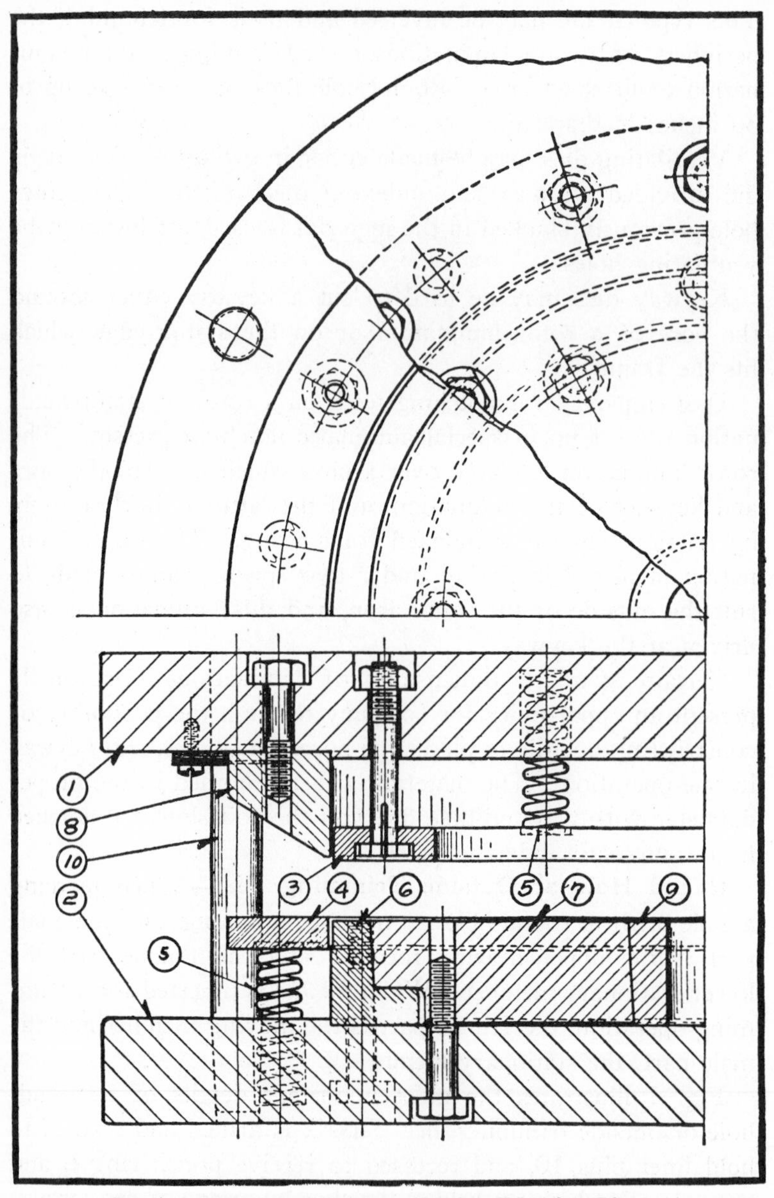

Fig. 1. Typical Round-hole or Outside Trimming Die

pression springs 5, and held by stripper bolts. A shoulder is turned on shoe 1 to fit die ring 8, which is fastened in position by means of cap-screws. The inside stripper 3 is supported by stripper bolts, as shown, and held apart from shoe 1 by means of compression springs 5. Plates which fit gage plug 9 are used for locating the center hole of the work when a trimming operation is to be performed. These plates are of various diameters.

All parts of the die are made from machine steel, except punch ring 6 and plug gage 9 (which are made of tool steel and hardened and ground) and die ring 8 (which is also made of tool steel, but not heat-treated). Ring 8 is kept in cutting condition by peening the shearing edge until it is necessary to grind the surface of punch 6. When die ring 8 becomes badly worn, it can be refaced on a boring mill.

Fig. 2 shows a combined keyway, bore, and ventilating-hole die of simple construction. Die 5, punches 6, 7, and 8, and key 9 are made of tool steel. These parts are all hardened and ground except die part 5, which is kept in cutting condition by peening the cutting edges.

General Features of Compound Dies.—Compound dies are used for blanking rotor, stator, segmental, pole, and spider laminations. In dies of this classification, the female part is the moving part for cutting the outside of a lamination, and the male part is stationary; while for piercing the bore, ventilating, and bolt holes, the male part moves and the female part is stationary.

The lamination is cut between the die part carried in the upper or moving shoe and the punch held in the lower or stationary shoe. The punch also serves as a die to receive the piercing punches carried in the upper die part. The lamination is stripped from the moving part by a stripper actuated by springs, or by the ram through the lower knocker attachment. Slugs from the piercing punches are disposed of by gravity through the stationary die part, shoe, and bed.

On account of the extreme accuracy required in diemaking, and the different contours and angles to which parts must be

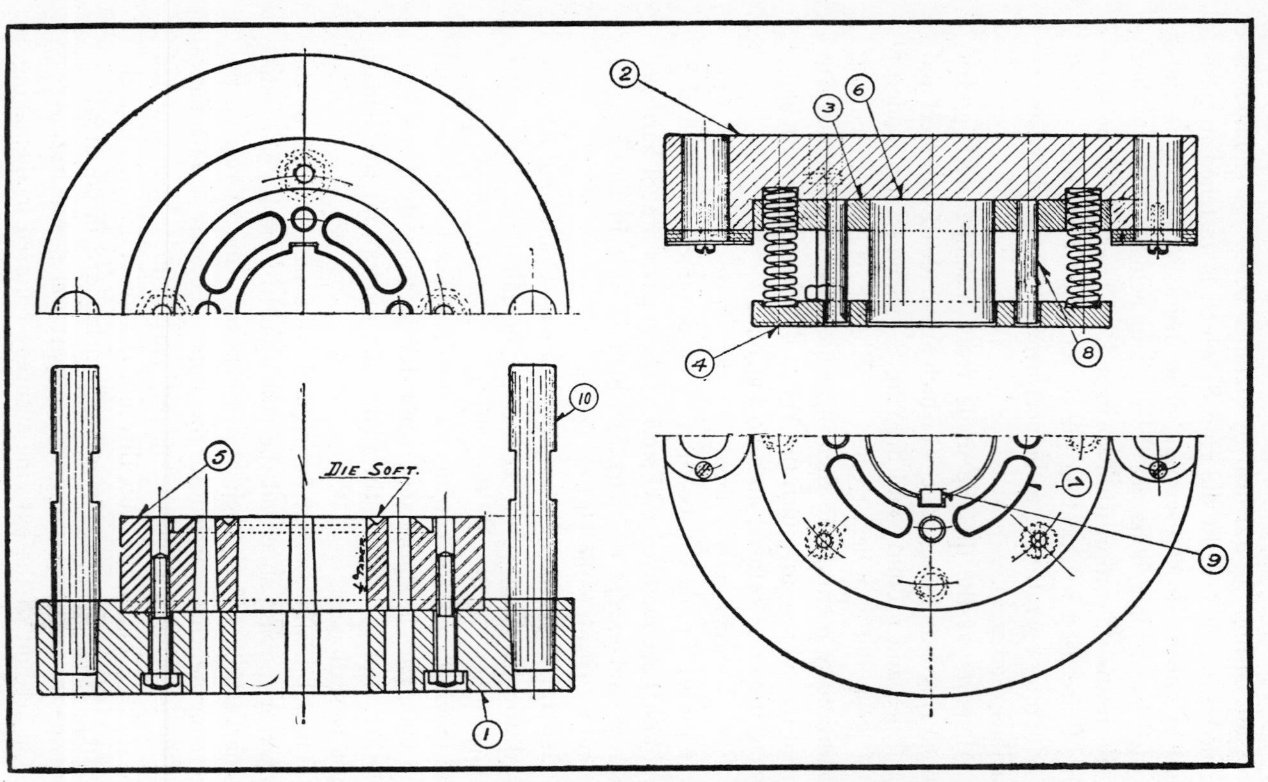

Fig. 2. Combined Keyway, Bore, and Ventilating-hole Die, of Simple Construction

machined, economy in die construction and maintenance may often be obtained through sectional or composite construction. The various parts of a composite die may be replaced readily if a section becomes damaged, and extra parts may be carried in stock for active dies, in order to expedite repairs.

Three Types of Compound Dies.—There are three types of compound dies, which have been designated *A*, *B*, and *C*. Type *A* dies are designed to produce a lamination complete in one operation, and type *B* dies to produce a lamination as nearly complete as is practicable in one operation. Because of die construction and maintenance, or economy in production, it is frequently desirable to perform a second operation to complete a lamination. This subsequent operation may consist of trimming the teeth on the periphery of a rotor lamination when a delicate tooth tip is required, or of piercing the center from a stator lamination. Die types *A* and *B* are used when production requirements demand quantity output.

Type *C* dies are constructed when the standardization of certain dimensions permit them to be used for the primary operation on a number of different laminations. A variety of laminations may be produced with this type of die by performing a subsequent operation. For example, certain rotor laminations may differ from each other only in number of teeth. Stator laminations may also differ merely with regard to the number of teeth. The outside diameter, bore, keyway, ventilation and bolt holes of rotor laminations and the outside diameter or contour and bolt holes of stator laminations are standardized. A type *C* die is designed for economy in investment, and is employed instead of several simple dies when there is a sufficient variety of laminations, each possessing certain similar dimensions.

Types *A*, *B*, and *C* dies, besides being designed for the economies to which reference has been made, are conveniently operated in a press, from the viewpoint of production. The operation of picking a lamination from the sheet of material after it has been blanked is performed at the same time that another lamination is being blanked. On the return of the ram, the sheet of material is stripped from the stationary part of the die and the lamination is knocked out of the moving part, falling on the sheet of material. Then, simultaneously with the advance of the material by hand to the next position, the blanked lamination is carried from under the moving part of the die, where it is conveniently picked up by the operator, whose hands are outside of the danger zone.

Compound dies used for blanking rotor, stator, and segmental laminations are designed for material from 0.014 to 0.017 inch thick. These dies are of essentially the same construction as the dies designed for producing various other laminations. The high quality required of laminations necessitates accurate and careful workmanship in order to insure alignment of the working parts of the dies.

Since laminations must be produced practically without burrs, no clearance is allowed between the moving and stationary parts of the dies used in making laminations from 0.014 to 0.017 inch thick. When a die is first set, a slight pressure is required as the moving part engages with the stationary part. The fit between the two parts is obtained by hammering or peening the stationary part around the cutting edges with an ordinary hammer. The hammer marks may be removed with a flat file. Any slight excess of material which may be hammered in around the cutting edges of the stationary part is sheared off when the moving part enters the stationary part. The latter is kept in operating condition by removing it from the press and hammering and filing any part of the cutting edge that shows excessive wear. This method is used until it is necessary to grind the moving part of the die.

The stationary part of the die is hardened only in cases where it is difficult to maintain the cutting edges, and then it is not hardened to the extent that it will resist a chisel or file. The solid section around the slots, holes, and edges is cut away at an angle of 45 degrees, but about 1/16 inch of flat surface is left around all cutting edges. Individual sections of the moving part of a die are hardened before they are assembled and are kept in operating condition by grinding.

Compound Die for Stator Laminations.—Figs. 3 and 4 show the general design of the lower and upper members of a type *B* compound die for blanking a stator lamination. The construction is suitable for laminations ranging up to about 30 inches in diameter. A subsequent operation is required to pierce the center from the lamination. This center is used to make the rotor in a manner to be described later. The small hole pierced in the lamination by means of die part 18 and

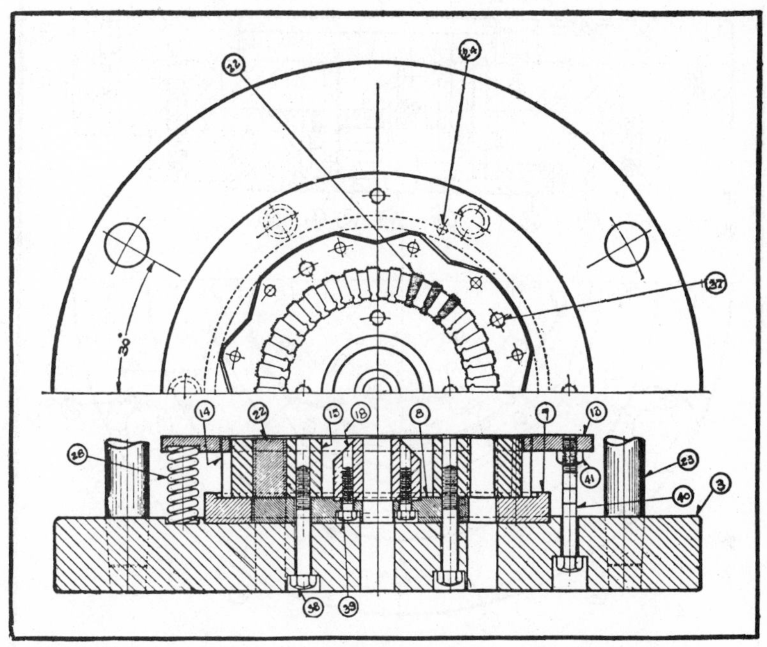

Fig. 3. Lower Member of Compound Die for Blanking Stator Laminations

punch 19 is used for accurately locating the lamination in the die employed to pierce out the center, the hole being used in conjunction with a locating pin in the upper part of the die. This small hole is also the means of centering the disk in the same manner when the rotor is produced.

The lower part of the die illustrated in Fig. 3 is assembled on shoe 3, which is drilled and reamed to hold liner pins 23; drilled and counterbored for screws 37, 38. and 40; counterbored for compression springs 28; drilled and slotted to permit the passage of slugs; and counterbored to receive raising plates 7 and 8. These plates are machined to permit the assembly of punch ring 14, die ring 15, and die pieces 22. The die pieces rest on the solid tooth section of raising plate 8, and are held securely in position by a shrink fit between punch

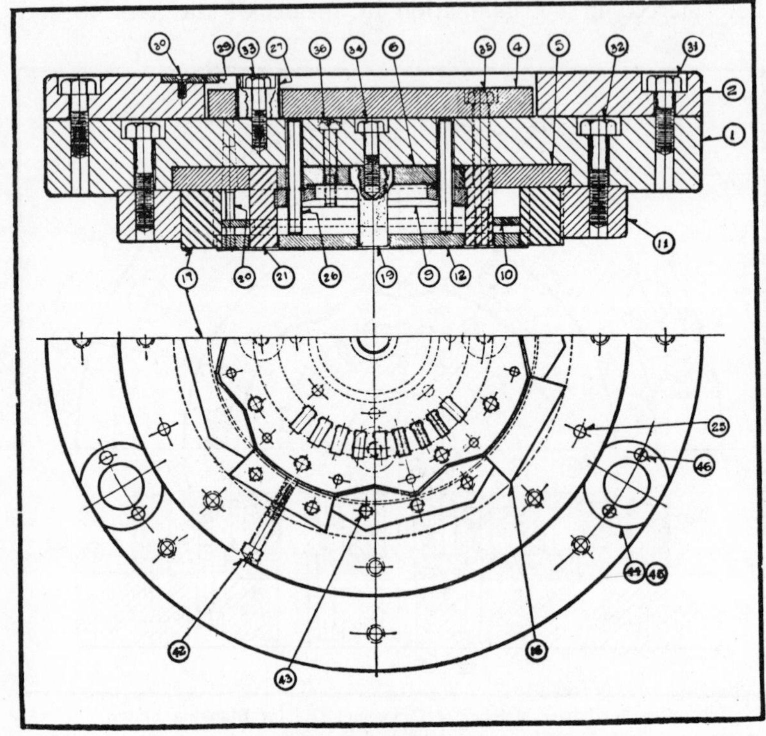

Fig. 4. Upper Member of Compound Die

ring 14 and die ring 15. Die piece 18 fits in the recess of raising plate 8, and is held by means of screws 39.

This composite unit is fastened to shoe 3 by means of cap-screws 37 and 38 and dowel-pin 24. When sufficient economy in the use of tool steel cannot be obtained by making die piece 18 a separate part, the inside diameter of die ring 15 should be made the desired inside diameter of die piece 18. Parts 14, 15, 18, and 22 are made of tool steel, but are not hardened.

A flat surface $\frac{1}{16}$ inch wide is left around their cutting edges.

The bottom stripper consists of outside plate 13, which is actuated by springs 28. The plate is counterbored for these springs, and drilled and tapped for screws 40. Nuts 41 prevent the screws from working loose.

The upper part of the die (Fig. 4) is mounted on shoe 1 and top plate 2. The shoe is drilled and tapped to permit the assembly of felt washers 44, steel retaining washer 45, and screws 46; drilled and tapped for screws 31 and 33; drilled and counterbored for screws 32, 34, and 36; drilled for knockout pins 26 and screws 35; recessed to suit punch-holder plates 5 and 6.

Die ring 11 also fits into a counterbore in shoe 1, and is held in place by means of screws 32. It is located by dowel-pins 25. Punches 21 are pressed into slots in punch-holder plates 5 and 6, and supported by distance rings 9 and 10. Ring 9 is held by screws 36, while ring 10 is a press fit between punches 21 and die pieces 16 and 17. These die pieces are fastened to plate 5 by screws 42 and 43. Punch 19 is fitted to plate 6 and held by screws 34.

Punches 20 extend through tapered holes in plate 5 and into shoe 1. Top plate 2 is fastened to shoe 1 by screws 31. The shoe and plate are assembled and drilled and reamed together for the liner pins of the lower unit. The top stripper is actuated by a knocker bar attachment, and includes knocker pins 26, stripper plate 12, and knocker plate 4 (all held in place by screws 35), distance pieces 27, and retainer piece 29. The distance and retainer pieces are held in place by screws 33 and 30, respectively. The parts of this die that are hardened before assembly are 16, 17, 19, and 21, all of which are made of tool steel. Six distance blocks 27 are used. They are intended to strengthen the unit directly over the punches.

Die of Compound Design for Rotor Laminations.—A type *A* compound die for producing rotor laminations of the open-slot style is shown in Fig. 5. For this style of lamination, a solid punch and die section 13 constitutes the most economical design. Compound dies are used for producing rotor laminations only when the centers from the stator laminations are not available.

Shoe 3 of the die illustrated is drilled and reamed to hold liner pins 19; drilled and counterbored for screws 27; drilled and tapped for screws 25; drilled for knock-out pins 20 and bolts 26; machined to permit the escape of the slugs produced by punches 14, 15, 17, and 18; and counterbored for the combined punch and die part 13. The latter is held in position by screws 27. Bottom plate 4 is drilled and counterbored and fastened to shoe 3 by means of screws 25.

The bottom stripper, which is actuated by a mechanical knock-out, consists of knocker pins 20, stripper plate 11, and knocker plate 5. These parts are fastened together by screws 26. Lock-nuts 28 limit the height to which plate 11 can be lifted. Punch and die part 13 is not hardened. It is machined below the top, 1/16 inch of flat surface being left all around the cutting edge, as on other non-treated tool-steel parts previously referred to.

Shoe 2 of the upper unit of the die is drilled and tapped for screws 22; drilled and counterbored for screws 24; drilled for screws 23 and knock-out pins 21; and recessed to admit punch-holder plates 7 and 8. The tooth punches 16 are assembled in punch-holder plates 7 and 8 and are held against die ring 12 by distance ring 9. This distance ring also acts as a support for ventilating-hole punches 17, bore punch 14, and keyway punch 18, all of which are assembled in punch-holder 8. Bolt hole punches 15 are driven into tapered holes in shoe 2 and plate 8, and they are also supported by distance ring 9.

Top plate 1 is fastened to shoe 2 by means of screws 22. Both the shoe and the top plate are drilled and reamed to a working fit for liner pins 19. The shoe is also drilled and tapped to permit the assembly of wiping pads, which consist of felt washers 31, iron washers 30, and screws 29.

The top stripper, which is actuated by a top knock-out for shedding the lamination, comprises top stripper 10, knocker plate 6, and pins 21. This unit is held together by screws 23 which are screwed into stripper plate 10. The sectional tool-

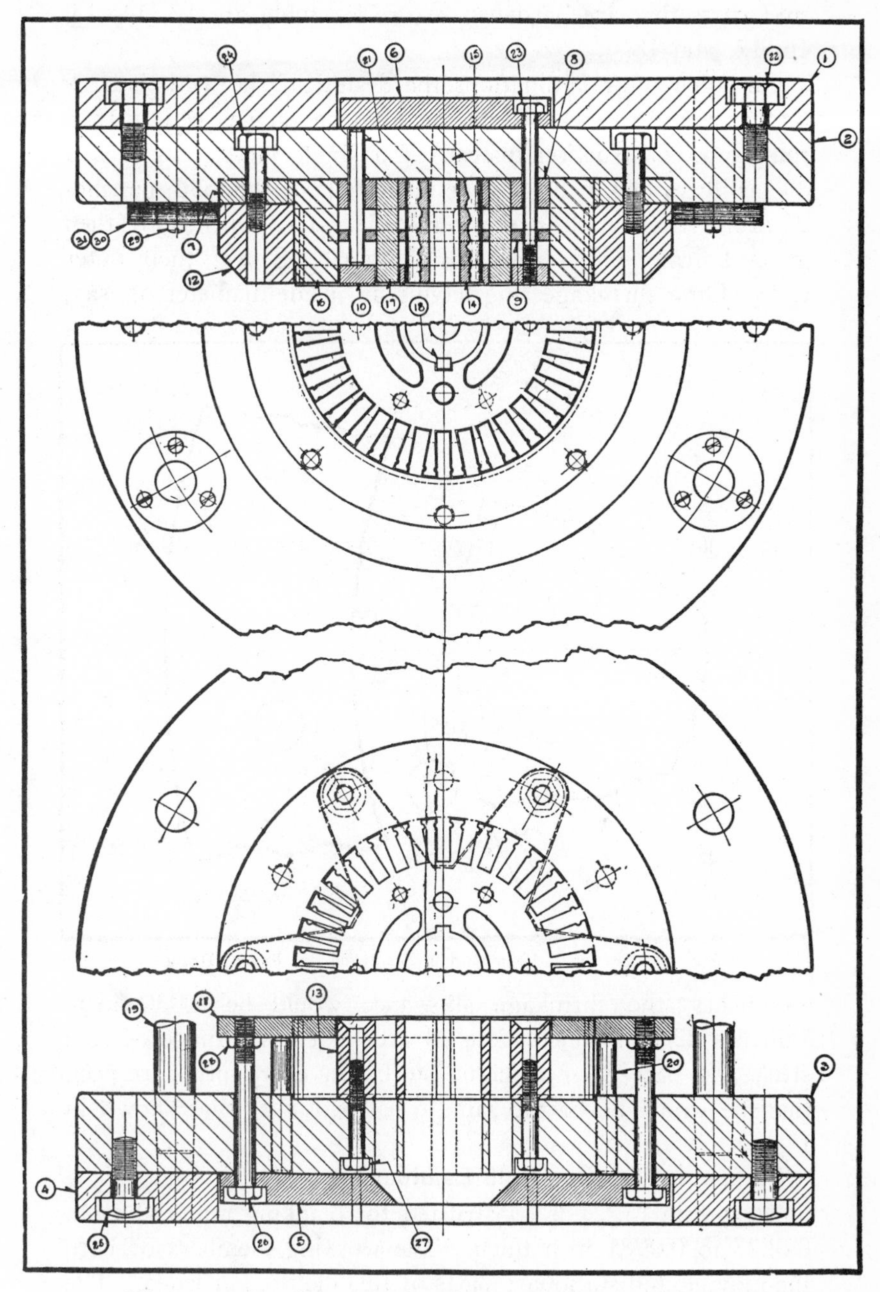

Fig. 5. Another Compound Die which is Used for Producing Open-slot Rotor Laminations

steel parts that are hardened before assembly are 12, 14, 15, 16, 17, and 18.

On some rotor laminations the design of the teeth is such that economy can be effected by making punch section 13 a composite construction instead of a single piece. In such a die, as illustrated in Fig. 6, the inner ends of the tooth punches 22 are inserted in slots of a center 23. The punches are then gripped firmly in place by shrinking ring 8 over their outer ends. On a shrinkage ring having an inside diameter of, say,

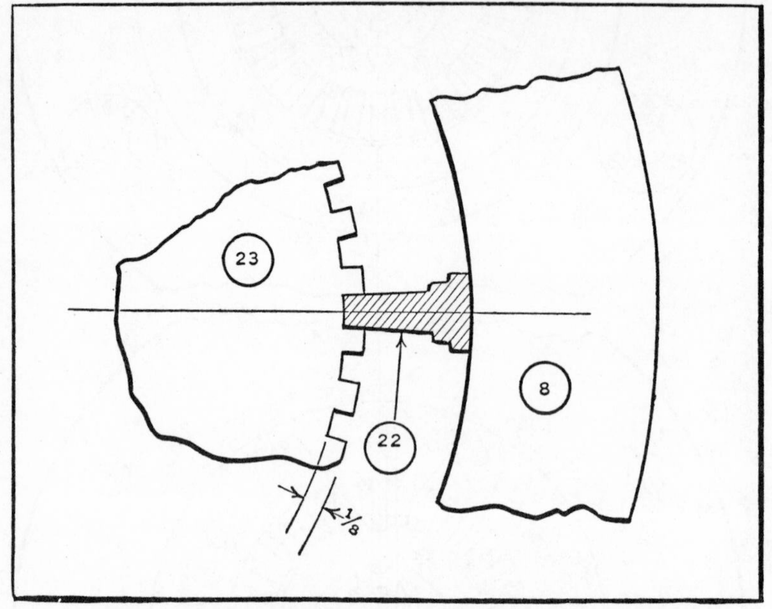

Fig. 6. Sectional Construction Employed in Punch Design

14 inches, the shrinkage allowance would be 0.030 inch. Punches 22 and punch piece 23 are, of course, made of tool steel, and part 8 of machine steel. In every other respect, this die would be of the same construction as that shown in Fig. 5.

Compound Die for Pole Laminations.—The compound die illustrated in Fig. 7 is constructed for blanking material from 0.0625 to 0.0981 inch thick. The working members of both the moving and stationary parts of this die are hardened. The

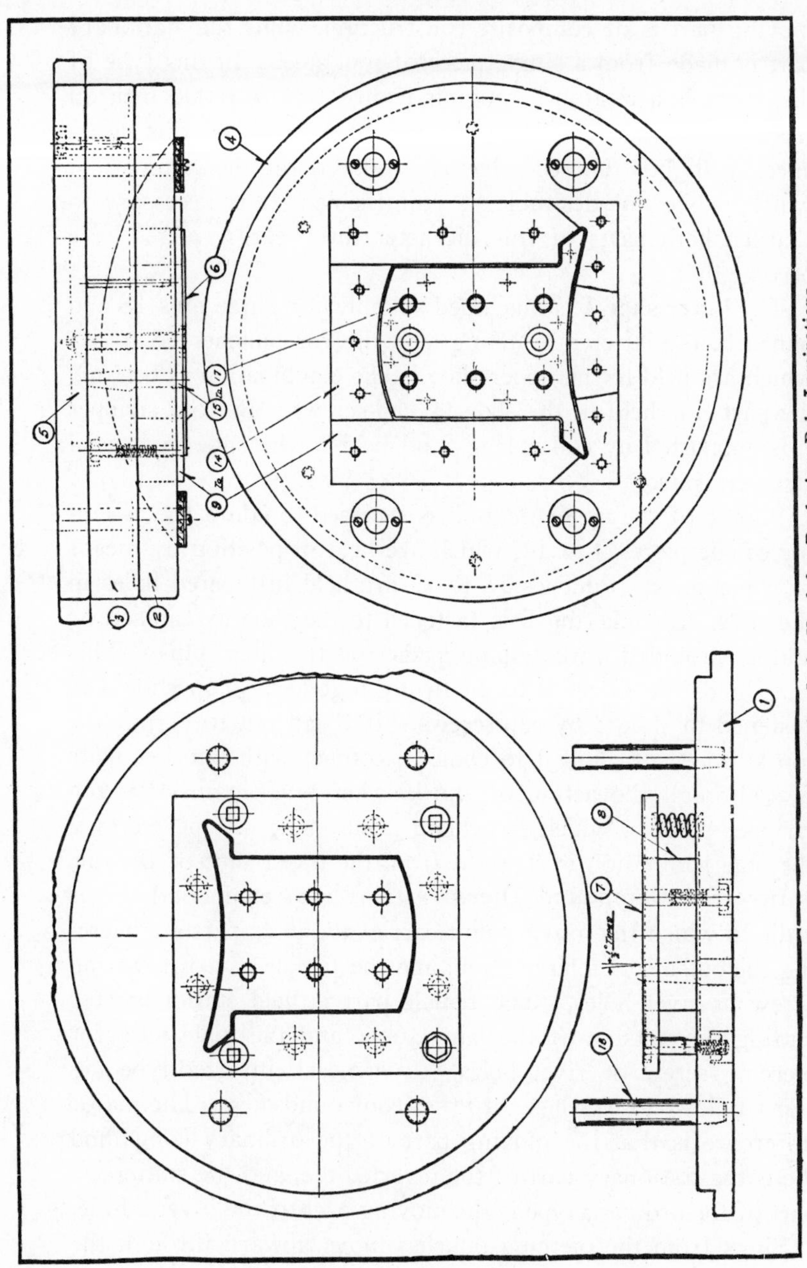

Fig. 7. Compound Die of the Style Used for Producing Pole Laminations

moving part is of composite construction, while the stationary part is made from a single piece of tool steel. In this type of die, there is a clearance ranging from 0.004 to 0.006 inch on the diameter between both parts. As a result of this clearance, a slightly burred edge is produced on the lamination, which, while not desirable, is permissible. It is necessary to sharpen both parts of this die after the shearing edges have become dull.

The lower shoe 1 is machined suitably for guide pins 18 and punch 8, the latter also acting as a die for punches 15 to 17, which are held in the upper shoe. The combination punch and die part 8 is held in the shoe by cap-screws. Bottom stripper 7 is supported by coil springs and held to the shoe by special stripper bolts.

Shoe 3 of the upper die unit is recessed to admit the assembly of die pieces 9 to 14, which are held in position by means of cap-screws. Punches 15 to 17 are held in tapered holes in the shoe. Shrink ring 2 is fastened to the shoe by cap-screws and is provided with wiping pads for the liner pins. This ring holds die pieces 9 to 14 firmly together. Top shoe 4 is fastened to shoe 3 by cap-screws. It is cut out to permit the top knocker attachment to come in contact with knocker plate 5. Through the action of the knocker pins against the top stripper plate 6, which is held in position by stripper screws, the pole lamination is stripped from the upper unit of the die.

Inverted Compound Dies.—An inverted compound die is a die in which the moving unit carries the male part for piercing the outside of a lamination, and the female part for cutting screw or rivet holes. The female part is held stationary for cutting the outside of the lamination, and the male part for piercing screw or rivet holes. In general, inverted-type designs follow closely those of other compound dies. The major difference is that the moving part of the ordinary compound die is the stationary part of the inverted die, and the stationary part of the ordinary type is the moving part of the inverted die.

Slugs from the piercing punches move upward through the moving part of an inverted die, passing through channels to one or both sides of the shoe, from which they escape. Ejection of the lamination from the stationary part is accomplished by means of an inside stripper actuated by springs. The scrap is forced from the moving part by an outside stripper, which is operated by springs or a knocker attachment in the ram.

Dies of this type are intended for small detail laminations, and hence there is no necessity for composite construction. While extreme accuracy of dimensions is required, this can usually be attained by making the major parts of the upper and lower units from single pieces of steel. The part attached to the upper or moving shoe is not hardened. There is little clearance between the upper and lower die parts, and the product is practically burrless.

Inverted compound dies are used for blanking laminations of irregular shapes, magnets, cut-out switches, and transformers. They produce a lamination complete at one stroke of the press, and are employed when the lamination cannot be picked from the strip of material simultaneously with the advance of the material for the next operation. During the process of blanking laminations, the stripper on the stationary part of the die pushes the blanked lamination back into the strip of material. Then, when the material is advanced by hand the proper distance, the lamination drops from the material on a pile in front of the die.

Blanking Die of Simple Design.—In a blanking die, the punch or male part is usually the moving member, and the female part the stationary member. Three types of blanking dies are used by the Westinghouse Electric & Mfg. Co. for segmental laminations. Of these, type *A* is constructed to produce a lamination complete in one operation, and is termed a "complete" blanking die. It is designed to meet large production requirements. Type *B* is called a "partial" blanking die. All dimensions are fixed, except the width of the lamination and the size and shape of the winding slots. Locating pins are set at suitable distances on the bottom plate to limit the width of the segment. A subsequent operation, which consists of trimming and slotting the teeth simultaneously, is performed in an automatic slotting press to finish the lamination. This type of die may be used for producing laminations of various widths, containing different winding slots, when production requirements are small.

The type *C* die is called a "closed" blanking die. All of its dimensions are fixed, except those relating to the shape and number of coil slots. A subsequent operation, also performed in an automatic slotting press, is necessary to complete laminations produced in this type of die.

Construction of a "Complete" Segmental Blanking Die.—A type *A* segmental blanking die is shown in Fig. 8. The lower part has a shoe 1 which is machined to fit the tool-steel punch 16 and two pieces dovetailed to the punch, all three of these parts being fastened to the shoe by cap-screws. The punch is not hardened. It is recessed about 3/8 inch deep, a shearing edge about 1/16 inch wide extending around the perimeter. From this edge the metal tapers 45 degrees to the bottom of the recess. Stripper 7 is supported by coil springs, and held in position by special stripper screws. Liner pins 18 are fastened in the corners of the shoe.

The upper unit contains shoe 2, which is machined to admit die-piece holders 8 and 9. These holders support tool-steel die members 12, 13, and 14, and filler pieces 11. The tooth die pieces 15 are fitted into slots in holder 8 and held securely by calking. Pieces 8, 9, 12, 13, and 14 are held in position by cap-screws. Top plate 3 is fastened to shoe 2 by means of screws. The top stripping device includes top knocker 4, knock-out pins 17, distance block 5, and inside stripper 6.

Both "partial" and "closed" blanking dies follow closely the design of "complete" blanking dies.

Progressive Dies for Laminations.—A progressive die consists of a series of simple dies arranged on one shoe for performing operations in sequence at the different stations of the die. Progressive dies are used for blanking rotor and stator laminations, both at different stations of the same strip and separately. E-plates and pole laminations are also produced in dies of this class.

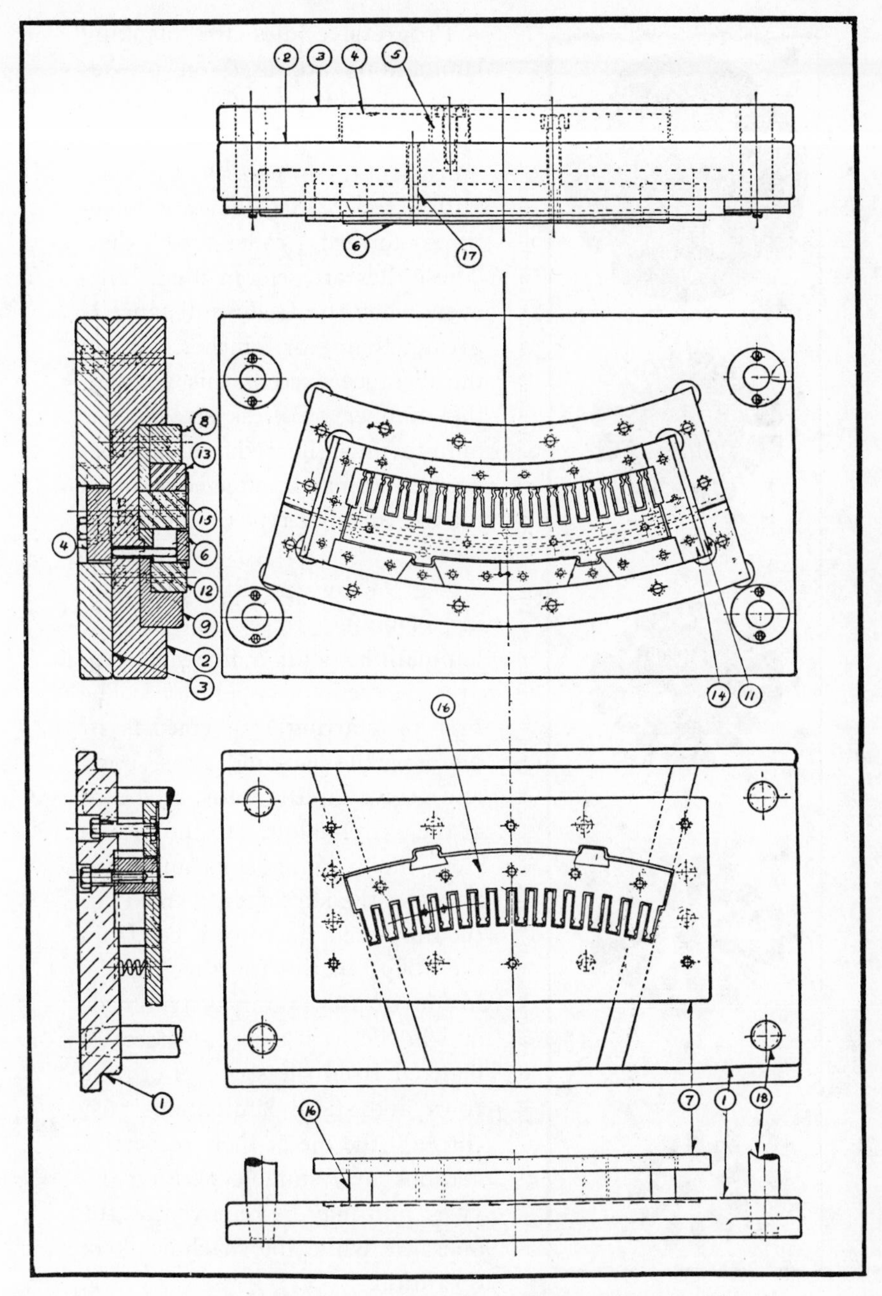

Fig. 8. Construction of a "Complete" Segmental Blanking Die

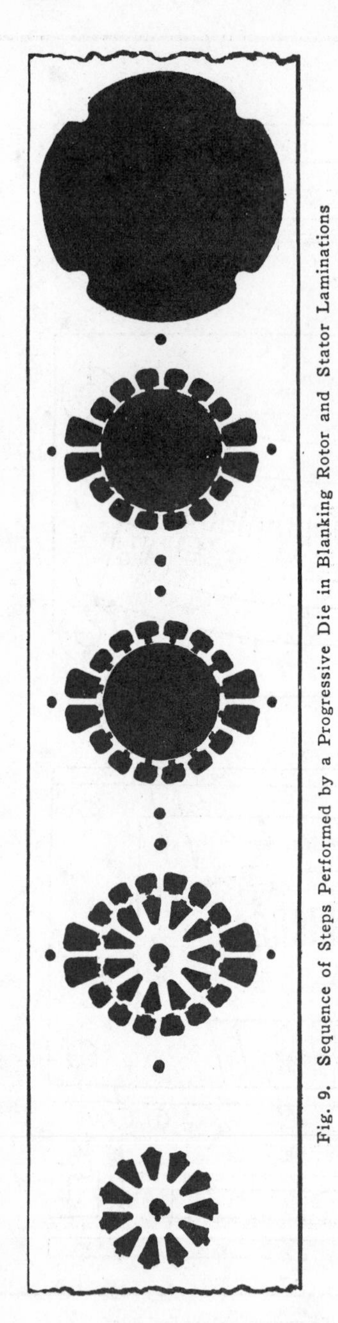

Fig. 9. Sequence of Steps Performed by a Progressive Die in Blanking Rotor and Stator Laminations

Progressive dies for blanking laminations are used on presses equipped with an automatic feed; when constructed to meet the requirements of presses equipped with a roller feed, they are sometimes termed "roller-feed" dies. These dies are seldom used, however, when the feeding distance is greater than 6 or 7 inches. When the distance exceeds this amount, the number of press strokes per minute must be reduced, and so economies may be effected through the use of other type of compound dies.

Fig. 9 shows the different stages in blanking rotor and stator laminations with a five-step progressive die in one operation. The first or starting step consists of piercing the winding slots, bore, and keyway in the rotor, as shown at the extreme left. In the second step, the winding slots and rivet holes of the stator are pierced; in the third step, the rotor is cut from the strip; in the fourth step, the inside of the stator is trimmed; and in the fifth step, the stator is blanked from the strip. Both the rotor and stator laminations pass through the die at their respective stations into suitable packing devices, and may be removed by the operator while the machine is in operation.

Both the male and female parts of the die used in this operation are hardened. The female part is usually made from a single piece of tool steel, while the male part is of composite construction.

Piercing Die for Rotor Laminations.—The piercing die shown in Fig. 10 is designed to produce a rotor lamination from a disk cut from the center of a stator lamination. It will be obvious that economy of material is attained by this practice. The general design of the die follows closely the design of the compound die for rotor laminations, which is shown in Fig. 5. In designing this die, provision had to be made for disposing of the slugs obtained in perforating the coil slots. These slugs pass through holes in sections 13 and out of openings in raising plate 6. The rotor lamination produced from this die is of the closed-slot design, which makes composite construction of parts 5, 12, and 13 the most economical.

Shoe 1 is drilled and reamed to hold liner pins 26, and is drilled and counterbored to receive raising plate 6. Die part 12 is fitted into the counterbore of the raising plate, and the sectional die pieces 13 are fitted into slotted sections of part 12. These die pieces are held in position by shrink ring 5, which is supported by blocking pieces 24 and held to the shoe by screws 31 and 33 and dowel-pin 23. Gage 37, which provides a means of locating the disk approximately, is fastened by means of screws 35 and dowel-pins 21. Die parts 5, 12, and 13 are not hardened. The die is under-cut, 1/16 inch of flat surface being left around all cutting edges.

The upper unit of the die has a shoe 2, which is drilled and tapped for cap-screws 29 and 34; drilled and counterbored for screws 30; drilled for screws 32, and knock-out pins 36; recessed to admit punch-holder plates 1 and 8; drilled and taper-reamed to receive punches 18; and drilled above center pin 20. Plate 9 is held in position by screws 30, which also hold punch-holder plates 1 and 8. The tooth punches 16 are assembled in punch-holder plates 1 and 8, and ventilating punches 17 also fit in plate 8.

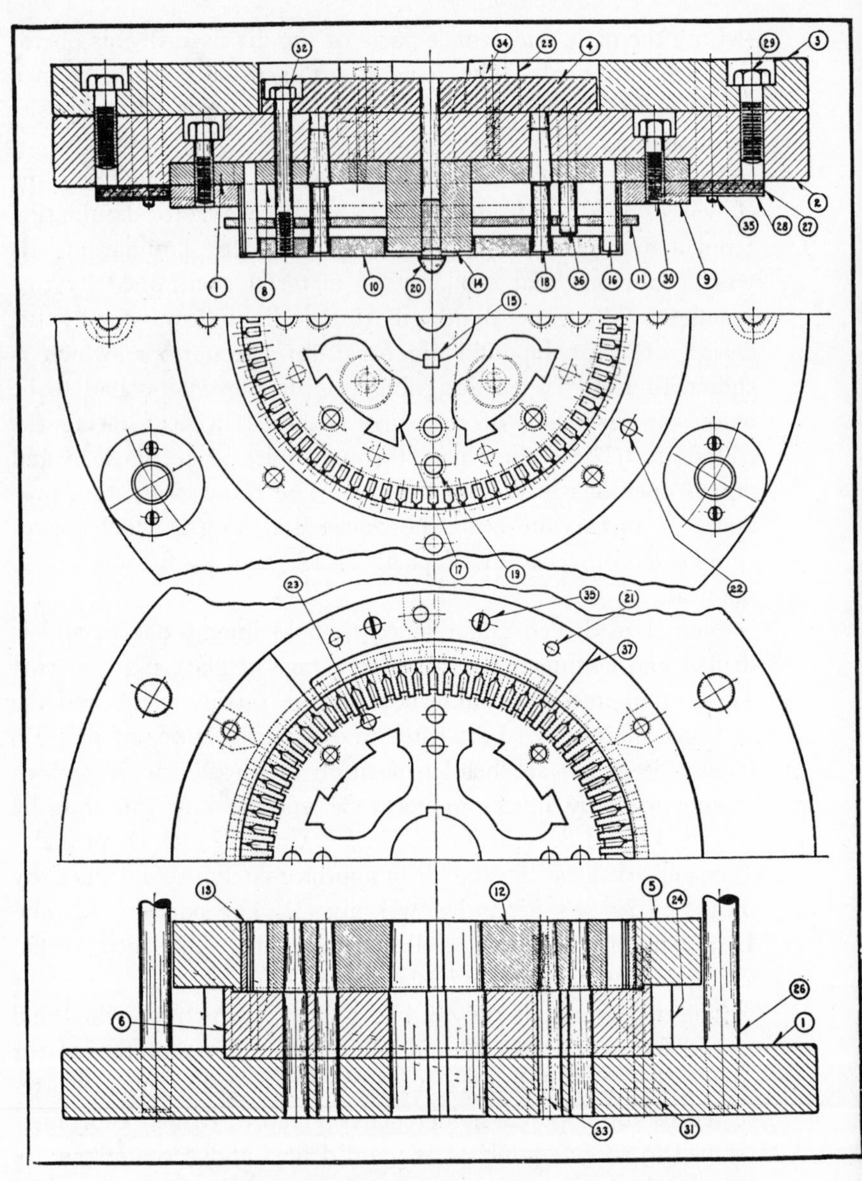

Fig. 10. Piercing Die Designed for Blanking a Rotor Lamination from a Disk Cut Out of the Center of a Stator Lamination

Punches 18 for bolt holes are held in tapered holes in plate 8 and shoe 2. Distance plate 11 supports punches 16 and 17, bore punch 14, and keyway punch 15. Center pin 20 accurately locates the blank. Top plate 3 is fastened to shoe 2 by means of screws 29. Both the shoe and top plate are drilled and reamed for liner pins 26 of the lower unit. Shoe 2 is also drilled and tapped to permit the assembly of felt washers 27 and steel washers 28 by means of screws 35.

The top knock-out comprises stripper 10, knocker plate 4, and pins 36. This unit is held together by bolts 32 which pass through holes in plate 4, shoe 2, plates 8 and 11, and are screwed into stripper plate 10. Distance blocks 25 support ventilating-hole punches 17, and are fastened by screws 34. The sectional tool-steel parts are hardened before assembly include parts 14, 15, 16, 17, and 18.

Advantages of Sectional Construction.—The compound stator-stamping die shown in Fig. 11 is another example of a design for producing laminations. This die, like many others used for stamping laminations, is of sectional construction. Certain advantages are claimed for the sectional stamping die over the solid die. In making repairs on dies of this type, it is only necessary to remove the damaged section and replace it with a new part. Other things being equal, this is a decided advantage. Furthermore, difficulties encountered in hardening a large solid die-block are not met with in the case of the sectional die; and each section can be accurately ground and fitted after hardening, thereby correcting errors due to distortion in hardening. In this way, each section can be made identical with every other. In the case of solid dies, errors due to distortion produced by the hardening process are exceedingly difficult to correct.

The accuracy that can be obtained in making sectional dies is also of importance. In order to finish the slots in the solid die accurately, a great deal of difficulty and considerable expense are involved. In fact, the inaccessibility of the surfaces to be finished in a solid die adds to the cost of manufacture sufficiently to balance, in large measure, the expense incident

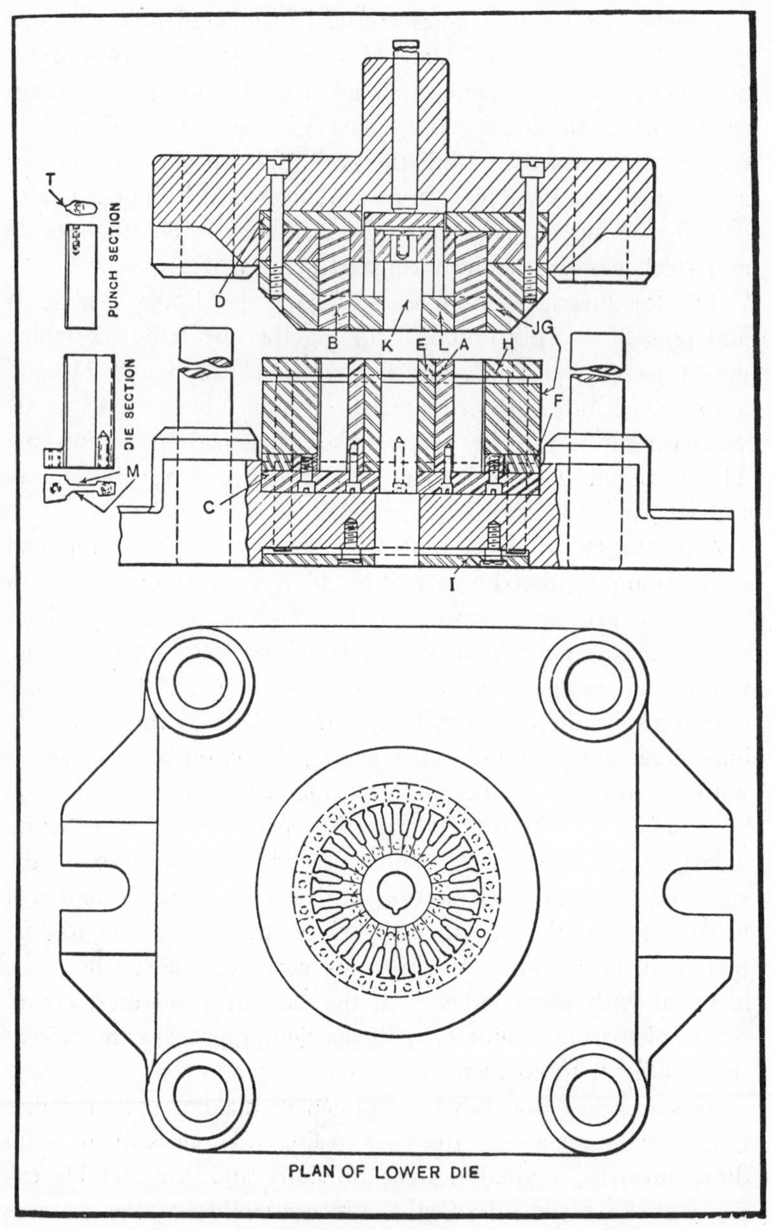

Fig. 11. Compound Blanking and Perforating Die of Built-up Construction

to finishing every member of a sectional die. It is also claimed that with the sectional construction the dies can be made thicker than when made solid, which allows for many regrinds and greatly increases the life of the dies.

The die sections *A* and punches *B* (there are twenty-five of each), are fastened by machine screws to plates *C* and *D*. The die sections fit around a central die bushing *E*, and a spacer ring *F* is used to build up the die to the level of the fastening lugs on the sections, thereby furnishing a locating surface for the soft steel shrink ring *G* which is assembled around the die sections. By making this ring of unhardened steel, it may be faced off when the length of the die sections has been reduced by grinding to such a degree that there is no longer space for the blanking stripper plate *H* to operate. This plate strips the blanked stock, and is operated by a knock-out mechanism on the press through the medium of plate *I* and the rods extending from it through to the stripper *H*.

The blanking die *J* is fastened to the upper die member by bolts passing through the multiple punch-plate *D* and the plate that carries center-punch *K*. This die has a working clearance for punches *B*. The descent of the press ram causes the blanking die to depress stripper *H* as it blanks the stock, at the same time that the punches perforate the stock and enter the lower die openings. The scrap from the perforating operation is ejected by positive knock-outs which operate in the lower die openings, and the scrap from the center hole drops through the die.

Center-punch *K* is surrounded by a soft steel punch stripper *L*, which operates freely over the center-punch as well as over the punches *B*. Its purpose is to eject the stator stamping from the upper die member, and it is operated by the upper knock-out on the machine. The pins that back up this stripper extend through the center-punch plate and are of such length as to allow an air space between the punch-plate and the stripper. As the punches and the die *J* are reduced by grinding, it becomes necessary, of course, to shorten these pins in order to bring the face of stripper *L* into the same plane as the ends of the punches and die. The punch-block and the die-block are made of cast iron or soft steel, and are aligned by means of four posts as indicated by the plan view of the lower die.

Use of Water-hardening Steel.—The sections of the die shown in Fig. 11 are made from a high-carbon water-hardening tool steel having a carbon content of from 1.3 to 1.4 per cent. This material is used on account of the extreme hardness and durable quality which it has when properly hardened and tempered. Some manufacturers do not advocate the use of a water-hardening steel for dies, principally on account of the difficulty encountered in hardening, but in the case of a sectional die where distortion can be corrected by grinding all over, water-hardened steel is preferred by some die-makers. Motor builders using these sectional dies report that from 50,000 to 100,000 motor stampings have been produced with one set of dies without regrinding. Furthermore, the length of the die sections permits grinding away about 1½ inches of metal, which, under normal conditions, removing about 1/64 inch per grind, would be equivalent to ninety-six regrinds.

The steel is heated to about 1450 degrees F. and quenched in brine, which gives extreme hardness, but which sets up a severe molecular strain in the material. To relieve this strain, the work is tempered in oil at a temperature of 425 degrees F. for approximately thirty minutes. Any distortion resulting from heat-treatment is immaterial, at this stage of manufacture, as this is afterward corrected by grinding. Each part must pass a scleroscope hardness test before delivery to the grinding department. Not only is it important that the proper degree of hardness be obtained, but aslo that each punch and die section in a die have the same hardness. It will be readily understood that if any one of the sections is not as hard as the others, a vulnerable spot is produced which wears quickly.

Dies for Small Rotor and Stator Laminations.—Economy in punch press work demands that the scrap be reduced to a minimum. There is perhaps no better example of the maximum utilization of stock than in the practice commonly followed in punching rotor and stator laminations for induction motors. It is customary to punch both laminations from one strip, those for the rotor being punched along the center line of the strip at a center-to-center distance slightly greater than the outside diameter of the stator laminations, and the latter being punched around those for the rotor. The only scrap is the small amount blanked around the stator laminations.

Sometimes the holes and slots are punched before separating the laminations from each other and from the strip, while in other instances they are punched afterward. The rotor and stator laminations for small motors of 1/8, 1/6, and 1/4 horsepower capacity, as made by one manufacturer, are pro-

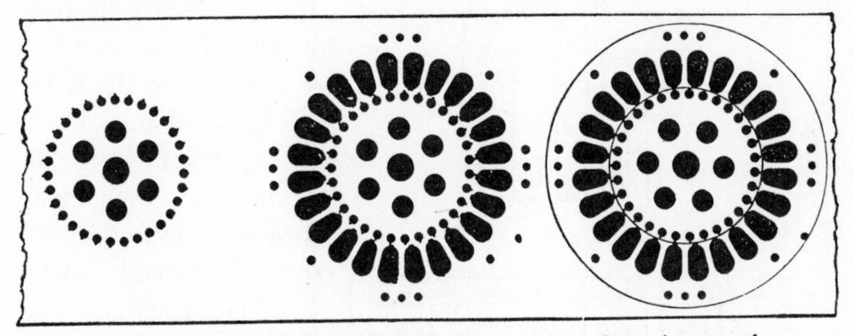

Fig. 12. Diagrammatic Views of the Sequence of Operations as the Strip Stock is fed from Right to Left through Three Power Presses

duced by the first of these two methods. The construction of the dies used will be described. Each of these dies averages about 40,000 punchings between regrindings.

Electric sheet steel stock, 0.022 inch thick, which comes in sheets 34 inches in width and from 5 to 8 feet in length, is used for the laminations. These sheets are run through a gang shear, which cuts them into five strips 6 5/8 inches wide. The strips are then brought to a row of three power presses, two of which are equipped with dies for piercing the various holes and slots, while the third is supplied with blanking equipment. The sequence of operations is illustrated diagrammatically in Fig. 12. As the stock is fed from right to left the rotor holes are punched by the first machine, the stator holes and slots by the second machine, and the parts are separated by blanking in the third machine. The diameter of the rotor laminations is 3½ inches, and that of the stator laminations, 6⅜ inches.

The press and die employed for punching the rotor holes is equipped with an automatic feed, which has a finger that engages one of the punched holes and, through a bellcrank lever, pulls the strip of stock to the left between the strokes of the press, to bring it into position for each successive stroke. The rotor die is shown in Fig. 13. It will be seen that the punches for producing the holes are held in a block *A*, which is attached to the punch-holder by means of fillister-head machine screws. The holes are pierced as the punches enter the holes of die *B*, which is a press fit in ring *C*. Stripper plate *D* is located above the die-block the desired amount by means of blocks *E*. The production on this machine is 1900 laminations per hour.

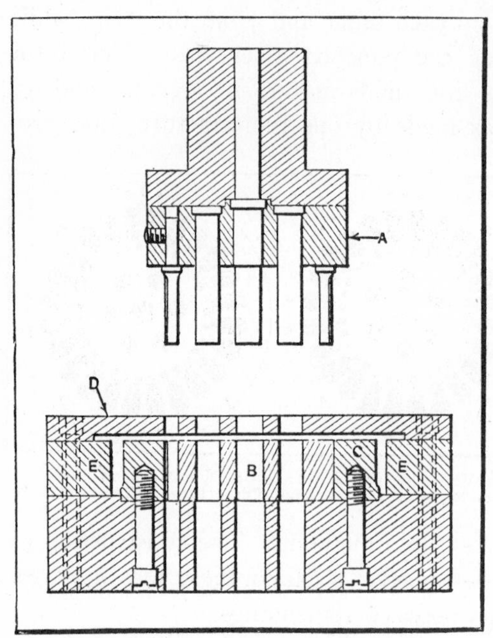

Fig. 13. Construction of Die for Punching the Rotor Holes

Die for the Stator Laminations.—In the second operation, as will be seen by referring to the central diagram in Fig. 12, twenty-four elongated holes, or slots, are punched immediately around the thirty-one outer holes of the rotor, and there are seventeen small-diameter holes located outside the ring of slots. One of the interesting features of the stator die is that the row of punches *A*, Fig. 14, for the slots, are integral with block *B*. The smaller-diameter punches are inserted pins held in a ring *F* in which block *B* is a press fit. An advantage claimed for this construction is that a larger number of regrindings can be obtained than with a sectional punch. The punches are hardened by dipping to a depth of ¾ inch in a lead pot, and quenching in oil. This procedure hardens the point and leaves the remainder of the punch soft, so that in case a punch breaks off it may be readily milled out and a new one substituted. The punch and die members are made to size

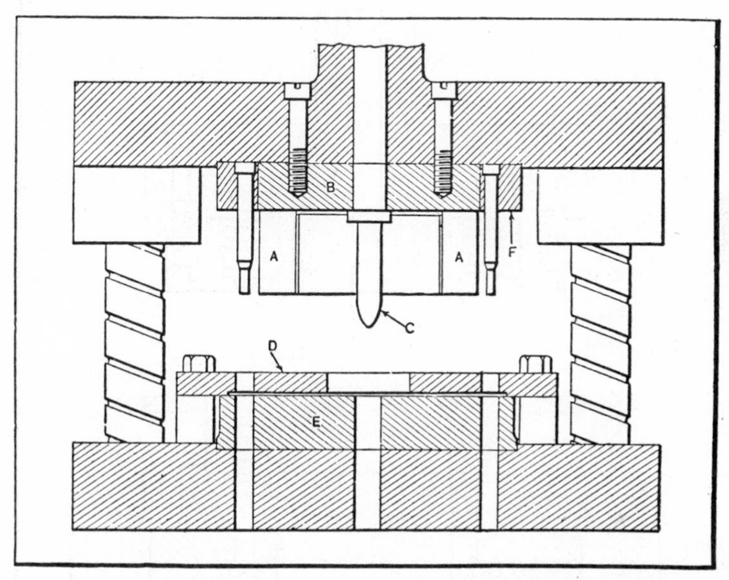

Fig. 14. Stator Die in which All the Punches for the Slots are Integral with a Block, and the Die Member is made of a Solid Piece of Steel

and then hardened, there being practically no shrinkage in hardening.

The pilot that aligns the strip on the downward stroke of the press ram is indicated at *C*. The punch-holder is held in alignment with the die by two guide posts 1⅜ inches in diameter. Pilot *C* is a press fit in block *B*, and stripper plate *D* is supported on the die-block by four posts which are screwed into the block. Die *E* is machined from one solid piece, and is hardened all the way through. Approximately 1500 punchings are made per hour with this equipment.

Blanking the Laminations from the Strip.—The separation of the two laminations from each other and from the strip stock is accomplished by means of the die shown in Fig. 15. The strip is also aligned for this operation by a pilot entering the central hole, on the downward stroke of the ram. The rotor lamination is blanked as the face of punch *B* passes the inner cutting edge of die *C*, and the stator lamination is blanked

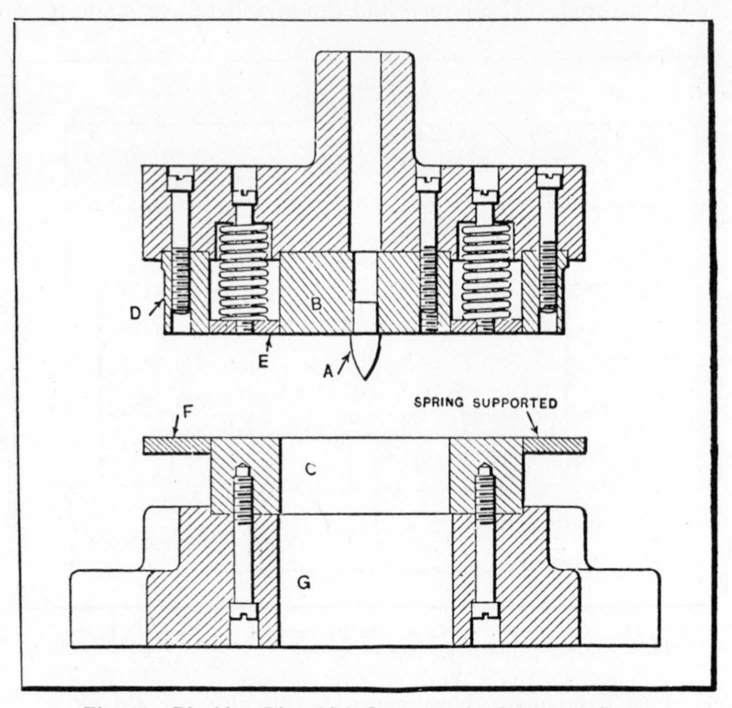

Fig. 15. Blanking Die which Separates the Rotor and Stator Laminations from Each Other and from the Strip of Stock

simultaneously, as the face of ring *D* passes the outer cutting edge of die *C*. Stripper ring *E* which is acted upon by eight compression coil springs, holds the stator lamination firmly against the face of die *C* during the blanking, and at the same time stripper ring *F* holds the stock that surrounds the stator lamination firmly against punch ring *D*. Stripper ring *F* is supported by four coil springs and is attached to the die-block *G* by machine screws that pass through the springs.

As the rotor laminations are blanked they drop through the die and die-block and are automatically stacked on a round rod which is replaced from time to time as it becomes filled. Similarly the stator laminations slide through the inclined frame of the press after they have been separated from the strip and are automatically stacked on a rod at the back of the machine. By stacking the laminations in this manner, they may be conveniently handled in subsequent steps. This blanking press is operated at about 1300 strokes per hour. The laminations as they come from this operation, are clean cut without burrs either around the edge or around the pierced holes, and may be assembled without filing.

Dies for Laminations of Sewing Machine Motors.—In manufacturing the stampings for a small sewing machine motor, known as the SA type, a series of four-pillar sub-presses is employed. Fig. 16 shows a view of the upper and lower members of the sub-press employed in the first operation. This is a compound blanking die which produces the stator stamping, and the rotor stamping in its first stage. Dies used in the following operations are employed in finishing the rotor stamping, the stator stamping being completed in one operation in the die shown. These stampings are made from sheet steel, 0.025 inch thick.

The upper and lower holders *A* and *B*, respectively, carry all the operative parts and hold them in perfect alignment. This is the feature of sub-presses which makes them particularly suitable for the manufacture of laminations for electric motors. Barring very slight variations in the laminations due to wear on the cutting edges of the die, duplicates can be produced, so that when assembled the laminations show no variation in contour or alignment of holes. The upper and lower holders are made of cast iron; the punches, dies, and bushings of tool steel, hardened and ground; and the punch-plates, knock-out parts, and strippers, of machine steel. The upper holder carries die *C* and punch *J*, and between these parts the knock-out *N* operates. The feathered punches *M*, of which there are thirty-seven, and the four plain punches *L*, are attached to the punch-plate *P*, between which and the knock-out a space is provided to enable the knock-out to operate. The knock-out is operated by suitable pins extending through the upper member to the knock-out plate *K*.

Referring to the lower member, punch *G* is held fixed, so that as the ram of the press descends it will pierce the center hole in the blank and enter a steel bushing in the upper member, while the die *C* in passing down over the blanking punch

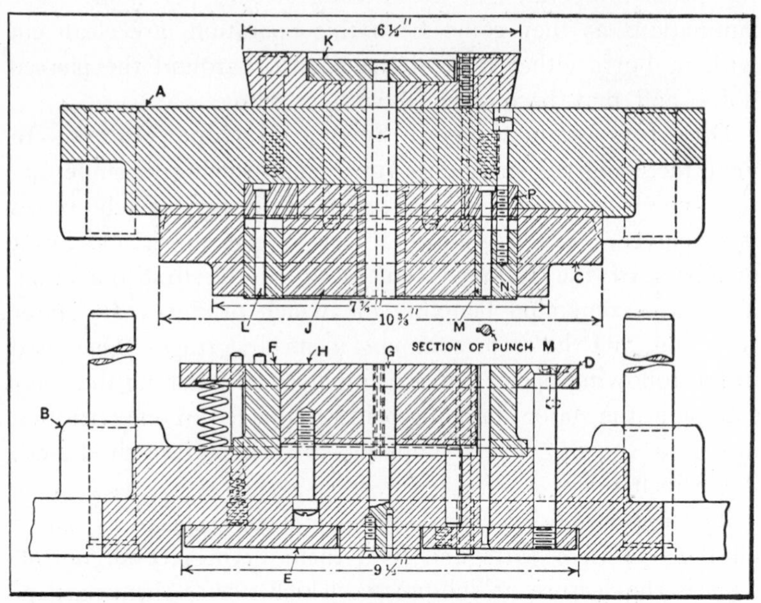

Fig. 16. Sectional View of Pillar Type of Sub-press Die for Rotor and Stator Stampings

F blanks out the stamping. Simultaneously, punches *M* and *L* of the upper member pierce the smaller holes in the work. An arrangement similar to that employed in the upper member is used to support the lower knock-out, and a corresponding opening between this part and the lower holder is also provided as the illustration clearly shows. As the knock-out *H* is permitted to descend when the spring-supported stripper *D* and knock-out plate *E* (on which the knock-out pins rest) are lowered by die *C*, space is provided for the feathers on punches

M to protrude into the space that was formerly occupied by the knock-out.

Dies for Repunching and Trimming Rotor Stampings.— The sub-press dies employed to perform the second operation on the rotor stampings are shown in Fig. 17. This operation is that of punching six holes. The dies employed are of simple construction; in the upper holder *A*, the punch-plate *C* is carried for holding six punches *D*. Between the punch-

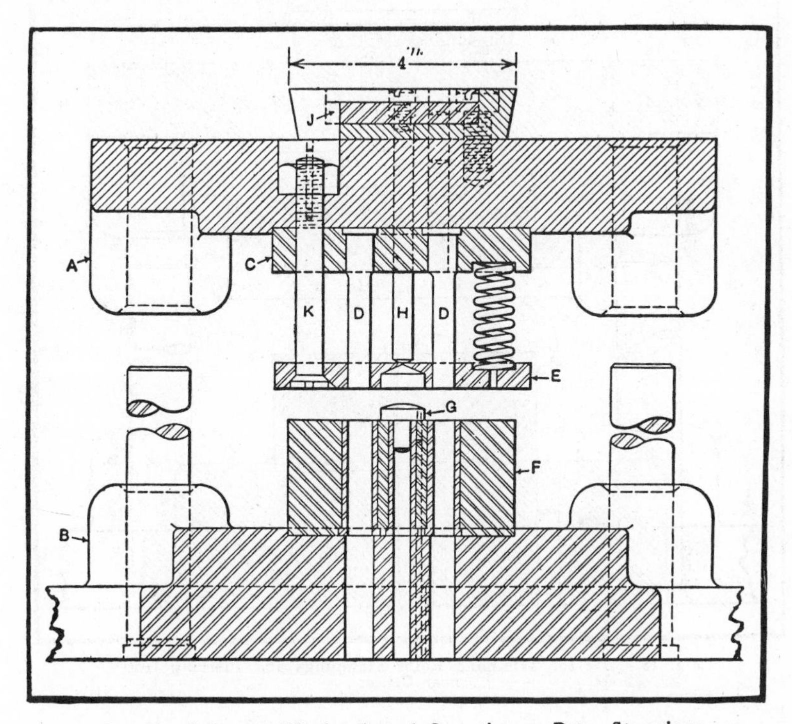

Fig. 17. Sub-press Die for Second Operation on Rotor Stampings

plate and the stripper *E*, the customary spring construction is employed. The three knock-out pins *H*, extending from the stripper to the knock-out plate *J* in the head-block of the upper holder, are a part of this familiar type of stripping mechanism. The three screws *K*, which maintain the desired alignment between the operative parts of the upper section of the sub-press, are provided with a locking arrangement for the nut so that as they operate through holes in the holder *A*, there will be no danger of turning and causing trouble. The die-block or bushing holder *F* of the lower member carries suitable steel bushings in which the punches operate, and a locating pin *G* by means of which the blank from the previous operation is located by its center hole.

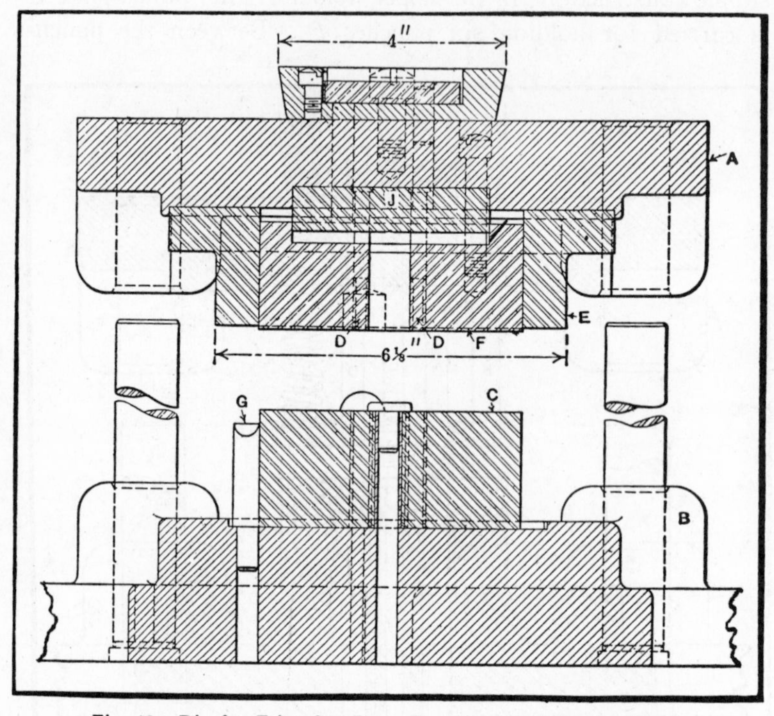

Fig. 18. Die for Trimming Rotor Stampings and Piercing Holes near Center

The third operation is performed with the dies shown in Fig. 18, and consists of trimming the blank and of punching three small holes near the center. The upper holder *A* carries the trimming die *E* and the punch-plate *J* in which punches *D* are secured. The knock-out *F*, through holes in which the punches operate, functions through the familiar pin and knock-out plate arrangement. As the upper member descends, die *E* trims the blank with the aid of trimming punch *C*, on which the work is located by means of two pins, one for the center hole of the stamping and the other for one of the six holes previously punched. As the blanks are being trimmed, the narrow rings of scrap are forced down around punch *C* until they are severed by cutter *G* located in the lower holder. Since this sub-press was designed a series of vent holes has been added in punch *C* which do not show in the illustration.

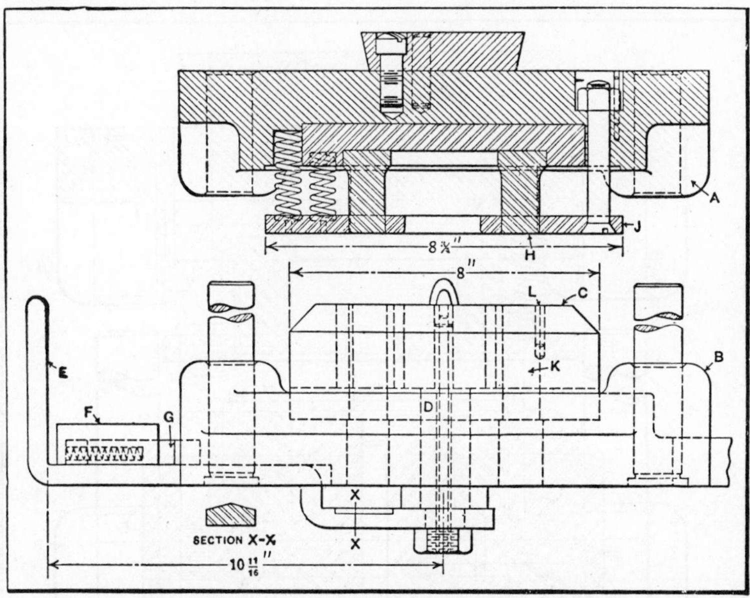

Fig. 19. Detailed View of a Two-stroke Multiple Slotting Die for Rotor Stampings

Two-stroke Indexing Type of Multiple Slotting Die for Rotor Stampings.—The two-stroke die shown in Fig. 19 has an indexing feature so that only one-half as many die openings are required as would be the case with a single-stroke die of this type. This provides greater strength for the die sections, which otherwise would be rather frail unless this or some other means of reinforcing these die sections were employed.

The stripper *J* is attached to the upper holder *A* in the regular way, and through it the twenty-four slot punches *H* held in the punch-plate operate. Die-block *C* in the lower holder *B* carries twenty-four die segments *K* which are set into the die-block and secured by four pin-keys *L*. For the purpose of indexing the die one-half space preparatory to punching the intermediate slots during the second stroke of the press ram, the handle *E* is attached to the center stud *D* beneath the lower holder, and is offset so as to operate in a recess cut in the holder, as shown. This handle carries a

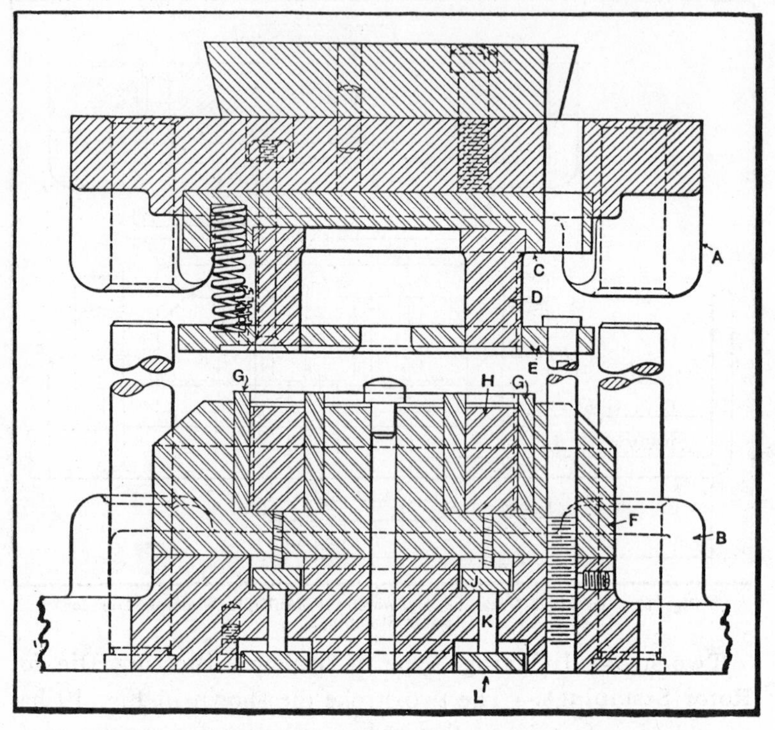

Fig. 20. Single-stroke Multiple Slotting Sub-press Die for Rotor Stampings

detent block *F* in which the spring-actuated detent *G* is carried, which engages notches in a steel plate attached to the lower casting. Attention is called to the shape of the handle at section *X-X*; it is made this shape in order to prevent congestion of the scrap stock which falls through the openings in the die. If some such means of relief were not provided, the scrap would pile up between the handle and the lower holder as the handle is brought back and forth under the openings in the holder.

Single-stroke Multiple Slotting Die.—The multiple slotting die illustrated in Fig. 20 is a modification of the die just described and is used in performing the same operation. In this design forty-eight punches *D* are carried in the punch-plate *C* instead of twenty-four, as in the other die. The stripper *E* is backed up by one set of four coil springs, instead of two sets of sixteen as in the other case, and is connected with the lower holder *B* by means of two machine-steel stripper rods, which furnish additional stability to the punches. Forty-eight die sections *G* are set into the die-block or plate *F*, and the knock-outs *H* which operate in the die openings are supported by pins which rest on three knock-out plates *J*. These knock-out plates form a ring and are set into the lower holder, each ring section being, in turn, supported on the knock-out ring *L* by means of the two supporting pins *K*.

A positive knock-out mechanism on the machine is employed to operate the knock-out ring for the purpose of ejecting the scrap material from the die openings on the upward traverse of the press ram. This knock-out mechanism (not shown in the illustration) is connected by rods to the press ram and functions with it on every ascent. In this respect it will be seen that the design is quite different from that shown in Fig. 19, and that the narrowness of the knock-out sections makes it imperative that rather slender supports be used, so that the interposition of the knock-out plates is necessary to provide a more substantial construction.

CHAPTER VIII

PIERCING AND PERFORATING DIES

MANY of the dies described in preceding chapters are equipped with punches for piercing holes or irregular openings into parts which are either blanked during a following press stroke, as in a progressive die, or which are blanked at the same time, as when a compound die is used. In this chapter several designs of dies intended especially for piercing holes or other openings will be shown. These designs will be followed by others used for perforating operations. The terms "piercing" and "perforating" sometimes are used interchangeably, but according to the more common usage, piercing refers particularly to the punching or cutting of a hole or opening, or perhaps several holes or openings, in a very wide variety of parts which may either be flat, cylindrical, or of irregular form. The term "perforating," while sometimes applied to the piercing operations just referred to, relates more especially to the dies used for making such products as perforated screens, strainers, colanders, and similar parts having numerous uniformly spaced holes or other openings or perforations.

Relation between the Punch Diameter and the Stock Thickness.—The smallest hole that can be punched in stock of a given thickness, depends upon the hardness of the stock, and it may also be influenced decidedly by the design of the punch and die as, for example, when sub-press dies are used. However, a good general rule which applies under average conditions and when using ordinary dies, is to limit the diameter of the hole to the thickness of the stock. It might be possible to punch holes having a diameter of, say, only three-quarters of the stock thickness, but when the diameter is so small in relation to the thickness it may be cheaper to drill the holes; in fact, usually it is the practice to drill holes in sheet stock when the diameter of the hole is less than the thickness of the stock. If certain departures from the ordinary construction of press tools are made, it is not difficult to pierce, in moderately hard stock, a hole having a diameter equal to three-fourths the thickness of the material. These modifications of ordinary practice are: increase in clearance between punch and die; special pointing or grinding of the punch; and the use of special punch steels.

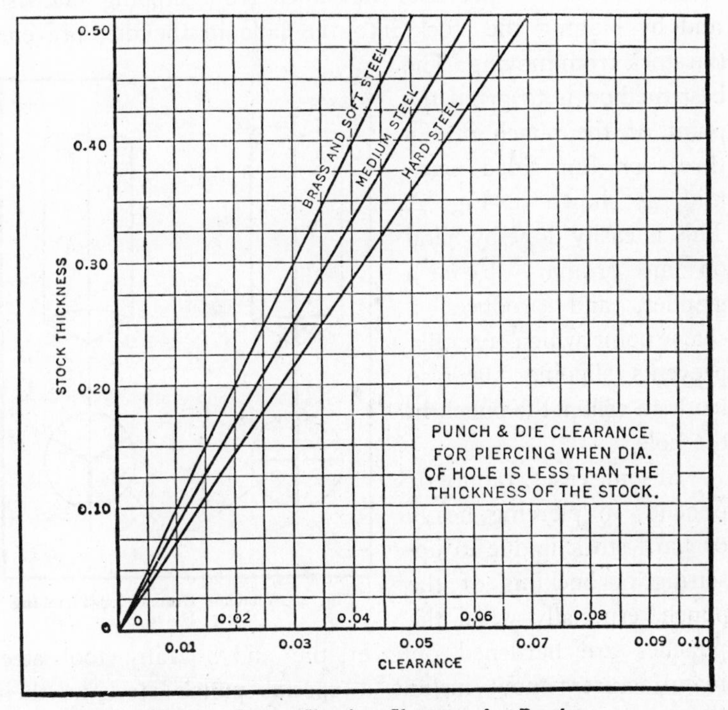

Fig. 1. Curves Showing Clearance for Punches

The first of these methods—increase in clearance between the punch and die—has the apparent disadvantage of producing a cone-shaped hole. However, this disadvantage is more apparent than real, unless the hole is to be used as a bearing, when it is usually necessary to ream out even a drilled hole. A little care in deciding which side the stock should be pierced from will ordinarily avoid any objections to this method. The clearance between the punch and die should be twice that ordinarily used. The set of curves, Fig. 1, show the clearance between punch and die required for heavy piercing. The difference in diameter is twice the clearance.

Piercing Punches Ground to Obtain Shearing Action.—It is common practice to give shear to punches in order to reduce the pressure required for piercing the stock. In this case, the shape of the nose of the punch has two other important functions. It prevents the punch from slipping sidewise, and by bulging the stock into the hole in the die, prevents the stock from moving. The best method is to grind the point of the punch into a three- or four-sided pyramid, as shown in Fig. 2. This is easily done by hand on an ordinary bench grinder, and produces a sharp point which not only prevents slipping but also tends to center the punch in the hole.

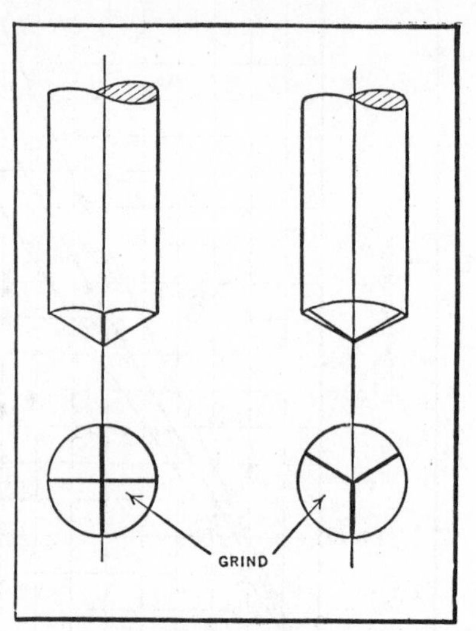

Fig. 2. Punches Ground for Punching Deep Holes

In some cases, failure of punches in piercing heavy or hard stock is due to upsetting or buckling of the punch, especially when the punches are hardened only at the end. Many tool steel manufacturers now include a special punch steel in their lines. As the most prominent characteristic of these steels is their strength, punches made from them are very stiff and sturdy, and withstand the impact of heavy, fast piercing very well. Instructions for hardening them should be obtained from the steel maker. A certain amount of experimenting in the application of the foregoing methods is required to get their full benefit, but the saving that is made possible by substituting the punch press for the drill press is marked.

Die for Piercing Heavy Stock.—Considerable trouble was experienced in piercing holes 0.120 inch in diameter in metal stock 1/8 inch thick due to the breaking of the punches. Punches made from various kinds of steel were tried out without satisfactory results. Finally the redesigned die shown in Fig. 3 was used and then no more trouble was experienced.

The stripper plate *A* was drilled, and fitted with hardening bushings *B*, which were a push fit over the punches. As trouble was experienced in lining up the punches, clearance holes were made in the punch pad *C* as illustrated. After

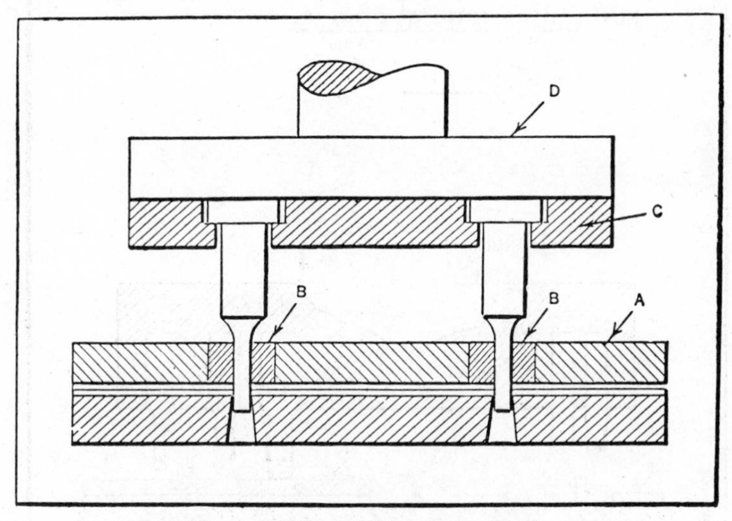

Fig. 3. Die for Piercing Heavy Stock

placing the punches in the pad with the latter member loose, the punches were passed through the stripper plate *A* and into the die, after which the punch pad was tightly clamped to the holder *D*. The punches were thus clamped securely while lined up in the holes in the die and in the guide holes in bushings *B*.

Punching Instead of Drilling.—In attempting to produce an experimental lot of 500 contact springs, such as shown at *A* in Fig. 4, considerable difficulty was experienced in drilling the No. 76 (0.020 inch) holes *h* for the contact wire *b*. The springs are made from No. 20 B. & S. gage (0.032 inch) spring phosphor-bronze. Modern high-speed sensitive drilling machines were employed, as well as many different kinds of lubricants, and the drills were carefully sharpened; yet the results were not wholly satisfactory, particularly with the objective of quantity production in mind.

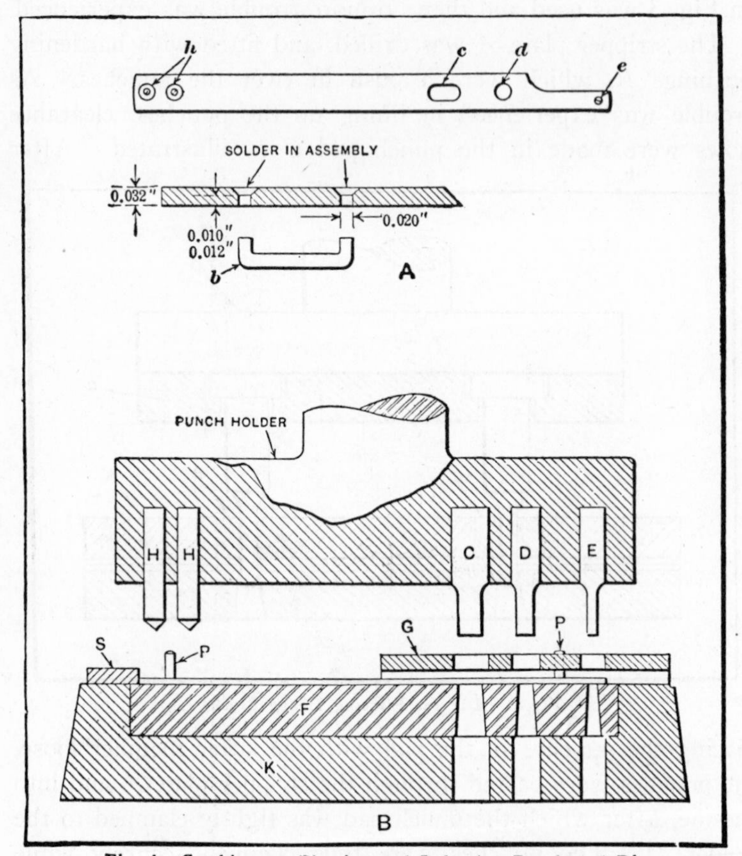

Fig. 4. Combination Piercing and Indenting Punch and Die

The piercing die, which was primarily used for piercing holes *c, d* and *e,* was accordingly remodeled to perform the indenting operation required to form the tapered portion of holes *h.* After the blanks were indented, a piercing punch and die of conventional design was made to pierce the holes. The construction of the indenting punch and die after the equipment was remodeled is shown at *B*. The delicate 0.020-inch punches were sufficiently supported to complete the lot without replacement, by using a close-fitting stripper plate. The illustration shows the indenting punches *H* and the work in place located by the end-stop *S* and the gage pins *P*. The die *F* is carried in the cast-iron holder *K* which is provided with suitable clearance holes, and to which the stop *S* and the stripper plate *G* are attached. The slight burr produced by the piercing die was of little consequence, and the contact wire was assembled without difficulty.

Piercing and Countersinking in One Operation.—The views at *A* and *B*, Fig. 5, show the usual method of piercing

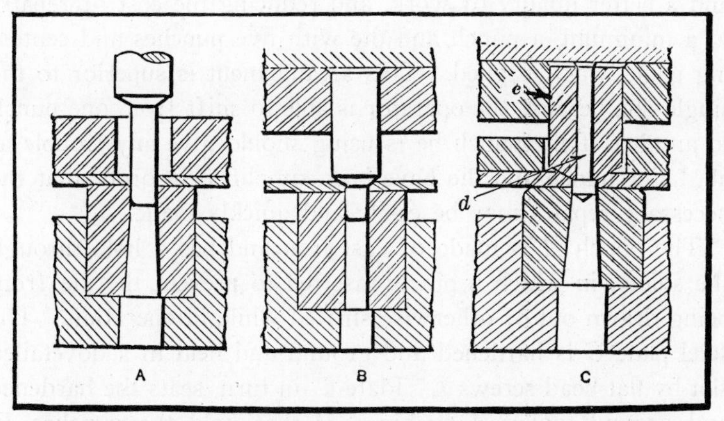

Fig. 5. (A) Die for Piercing Sheet Metal for Screw Holes; (B) Countersinking Die; (C) Die Combining the Operations of Dies *A* and *B*

and countersinking holes in sheet steel. This method is a costly one. The method illustrated at *C* eliminates one die by combining the two. The piercing punch *d* is turned down to a diameter smaller than the pierced hole, and shoulders against the bottom of taper punch *e*. The work is slightly embossed below the countersink, and the metal is bulged out along the edge of the metal (No. 18 gage), as the center of the hole is about 9/32 inch from the edge. This, however, also happens when dies *A* and *B* are used, and is not objectionable in this case. The elimination of one operation has reduced the cost of this work 50 per cent.

Extra Piercing Punches to Increase Production.—In Fig. 6 is shown a small stamping that must be produced in large quantities, but as the shape permits this part to be made from the scrap from other jobs, it has been found more economical to make the part in two operations. As the thickness of the metal exceeds the punch diameter, a great strain is placed on the piercing punch, resulting in its occasional breakage. This, with the necessity of punching a clean hole, made it necessary to replace or grind the punch a number of times a day, thereby holding up production, as well as increasing the cost of grinding and replacing the punch. In order to keep the press operating more steadily, getting more production and a better quality of work, and reducing the cost of repairs to a minimum, a punch and die with five punches and centering gages was designed. This arrangement is superior to the single die, because the operator is able to shift from one punch to another if the punch he is using should give any trouble at all. The punch and die have been simplified in order that the necessary repairs may be easily and quickly made.

The punch *A* is made of cast iron and has a hole through the shank, in which a pin is inserted to prevent the die from being drawn out or otherwise shifted while in operation. The steel plate *C* is hardened and ground and held in a dovetailed slot by flat-head screws *I*. Plate *C*, in turn, seats the hardened and ground tool-steel bushings *D* that hold the punches *E*. The punches *E* are made from standard drill rod and their heads are upset. They are hardened and drawn to a light straw. The die *B* is made of cast iron and the bushings *F* are made from tool steel and are hardened and drawn to a light straw. Bushings *F* must have plenty of clearance so that the slugs will discharge freely; otherwise too great a tension may be put on the already overburdened perforating punch by reason of too many slugs being in bushing *F* at one time. The stripper *G* is held in position by flat-head screws *H*; it is made of machinery steel and is carburized. The tool-steel gage *L* is hardened and ground and is held in position by the stripper *G* and screws *H*. A guard *J* prevents the operator

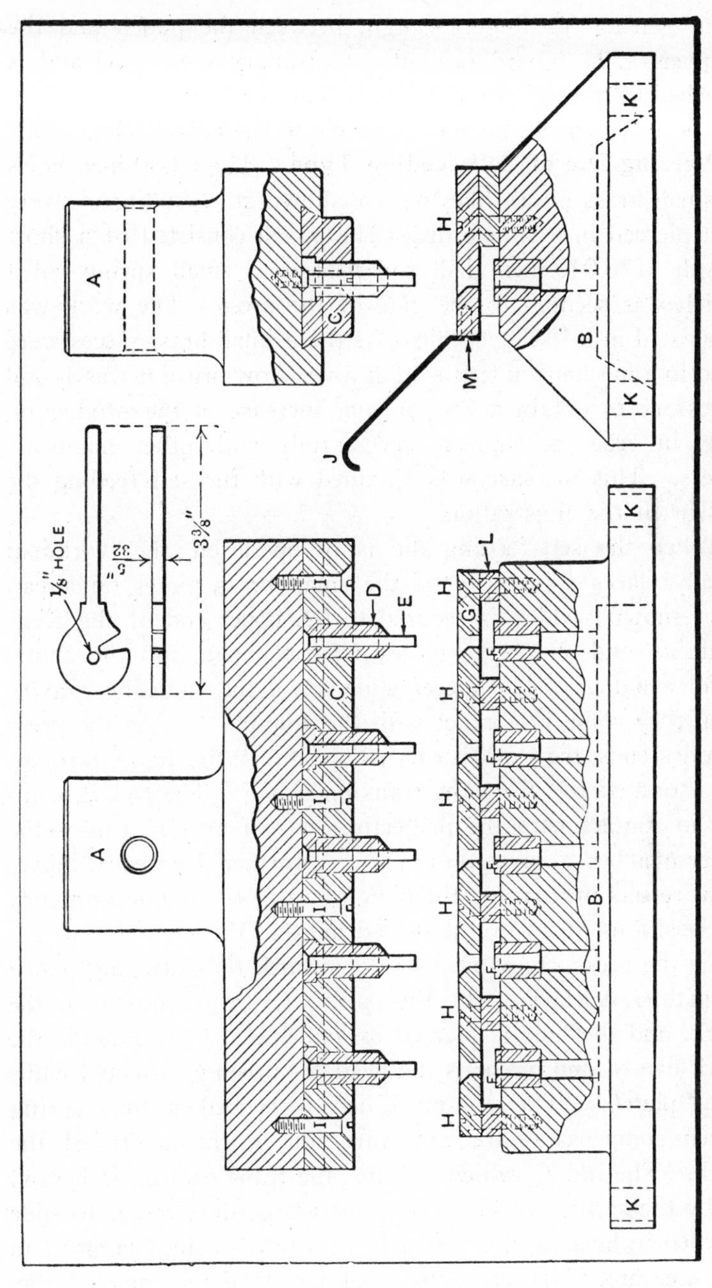

Fig. 6. Piercing Die Equipped with Extra Punches which are Used Until all Require Grinding

from getting his fingers caught between the punch and the stripper. This guard is made of ordinary sheet steel and is attached to the stripper *G* by small flat-head screws *M*. Holes *K* are provided for fastening the die to the bolster plate.

Piercing Die of Self-feeding Type.—The 0.040-inch holes in small brass pieces like the one shown at *A* in Fig. 7, were first pierced in a simple die. The punch consisted of a short length of 0.040-inch drill rod held in a small spring collet which was secured to the gate of the press. The work was supported in a V-shaped die. As these small brass pieces were used in a mechanism that sold at a very low price, it was found necessary to obtain a 75 per cent increase in the production rate, in order to compete successfully with other manufacturers. This increase was obtained with the self-feeding die shown in the illustration.

When the self-feeding die is in operation, the workman simply places a quantity of the small brass pieces on a pan (not shown) which is secured to the upper end of the feed-chute *B*, and slides the pieces from the pan into the chute, small end first. The pieces slide down the chute by gravity until they come in contact with the stop-pin *C*. As the press ram descends, the work is carried up against the die *D*, through the action of rod *E* on the transfer arm *F*. The rod *E*, coming in contact with the projecting end of arm *F*, causes the latter member to pivot on pin *G*. A further downward movement results in carrying the piece of work *W* to approximately the position shown by the dotted lines at *Y*.

As the press ram continues downward, the flattening punch or pad *H*, backed up by the spring *I*, presses down on the work, and the hole is pierced by punch *J*. Pad *H* holds the work firmly, and prevents the head from being distorted while being pierced. The stop-pin *C* is also backed up by a spring which compensates for any variation in the length of the work. The rod *E*, which actuates the transfer arm, is backed up by the spring *K*. This construction permits rod *E* to slide upward in bushing *L*, if a piece of work becomes jammed in the die, and thus prevents breaking or damaging the die.

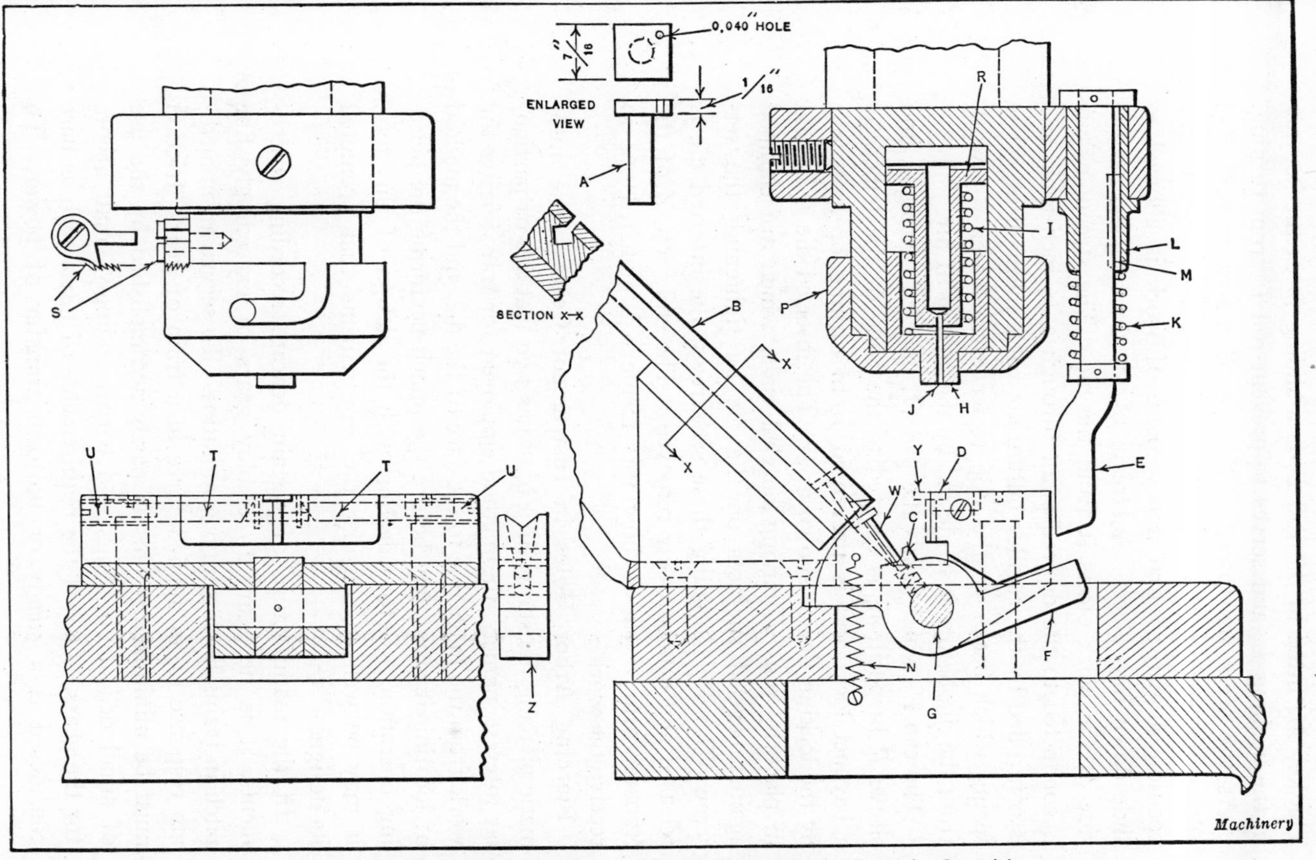

Fig. 7. Self-feeding Piercing Die for Handling Small Brass Parts in Quantities

The key *M*, fitted in the rod *E*, is a sliding fit in the keyway in the bushing *L*, and serves to prevent rod *E* from turning.

As the press ram ascends, the rod *E* moves upward and allows the spring *N* to bring the transfer arm back to the position shown, so that a new piece of work is allowed to slide down into place. A stream of air directed against the side of the work ejects it from the die. The stream of air is conducted to the desired point through a 1/8-inch tube, and is controlled by the regular button air valve mechanism. The spring which backs up the stop *C* serves to loosen the work from the die before it is ejected by the stream of air.

The cap *P*, which holds the pad *H*, punch *J*, spring *I*, and sleeve *R* in position, is secured to the body of the punch by a bayonet lock, and is prevented from turning or loosening by the locking device shown at *S*. The inserted die *D* is held in place by pins *T* having beveled ends, which are clamped against beveled surfaces on the die by tightening the set-screws *U*. By loosening these set-screws, the inserted die is released and can be easily removed. The end view *Z* of the transfer arm *F* shows how this member is notched out to receive the work.

Piercing Arbor Holes in Instrument Gears.—The automatic piercing die shown in Fig. 8 has two features of particular interest, namely, the method employed for transferring the work from the magazine to the face of the die, and the method of locating it accurately before the punch performs the piercing operation. Before dealing with the design of this tool, it may be well to consider the requirements that prompted its design.

In the manufacture of certain delicate recording instruments, it is necessary to employ gears of exceedingly fine pitch in trains having high gear ratios. To secure an immediate response to an applied force in a train of gears, friction must be minimized. This is partly accomplished by the use of small delicate bearings and correspondingly small arbors for the gears. One of the requirements of gears such as here considered is a steady or uniform transfer of power. To accomplish this, the teeth are cut automatically with a fly cutter, the blank being indexed by an accurate spacing device. Obviously, the central hole in the blank, as shown in the enlarged view in the upper right-hand corner of Fig. 8, is too small to permit the gear to be adequately supported by an arbor during the tooth-cutting operation, and since this operation must be done as cheaply as is consistent with the required accuracy, the blank is prepared for the tooth-cutting operation by piercing or blanking out the spaces between the arms, leaving the central hole to be pierced in a later operation. The pieces thus blanked out are mounted on a split arbor, sixty at a time, and the teeth cut.

The outside diameter of the arbor used for the tooth-cutting operation is a good fit for the surface *A* of the rim of the blank. It has been found, that when the central hole and the spaces between the arms are pierced at one time, the pitch circle does not run true or concentric with the shaft, even when the teeth are cut with the work mounted on an accurate arbor, as described. It must be borne in mind that, due to the exceptionally fine pitch, the pitch circle must be concentric with the bearings within close limits of accuracy.

Formerly it was the practice to pierce the central hole for the arbor about 0.010 inch smaller than the finished size, and after cutting the teeth, mount each gear separately in a chuck. The chuck employed gripped the work on the finished tooth surfaces, so that the hole could be bored out true or concentric with the pitch circle. This method, although it generally gave good results, was too slow and sometimes caused the teeth to be marred or distorted. As the teeth were formed or finished on the top surfaces by the cutter, it was decided that a bell center descending in advance of the piercing punch and receding under spring pressure could be used to locate the gear under the center-piercing punch. Accuracy in the size of the hole was essential, as the arbor was required to be a good drive fit in the hole. The piercing die designed for this operation is shown in Fig. 8. The upper member, which carries the punch assembly and the cam *K* for operating the slide.

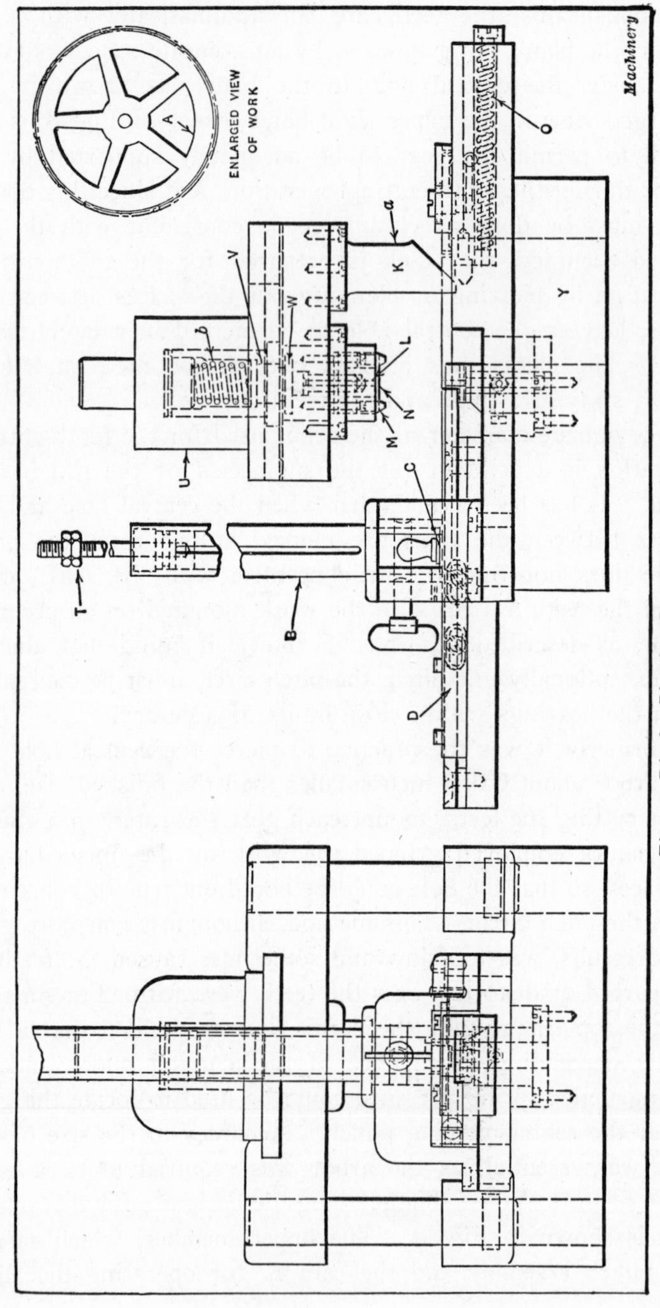

Fig. 8. Die for Piercing Shaft Hole in Gear

is shown at *U*. The lower member *Y*, with the piercing die and the magazine feed, is shown in Figs. 8 and 9.

Operation of Magazine Feed.—The first step in placing the die shown in Fig. 8 in operation is to fill the magazine *B* with gear blanks and place the magazine in position on the die bed. The slide *C* is moved from the bottom of the magazine, allowing the gear at the bottom to rest on the surface on which it slides when fed into position under the piercing punch. The secondary slide *D* caries two thin members *E*, shown in the plan view of the die, Fig. 9, which are beveled at the edges and which come in contact with the gear teeth. These members centralize the blank when it is pushed under the punch. As the guide is made slightly thinner than the gear, only one gear is transferred from the magazine to the piercing position at each stroke of the press.

The secondary slide *D* is connected to the primary slide *F* by the rack *G* and the compound gear *H* on the primary slide. One part of the compound gear meshes with the rack *G* on the opposite side of the primary slide, so that when cam *K*, held in the punch member, descends and pushes the primary slide backward, the gear rotates and imparts a movement of greater magnitude to the secondary slide; in other words, a 1-inch movement of the punch moves the gear a distance of about 3 inches from the magazine to a position directly under the piercing punch.

The approximate location of the gear under the piercing punch at the end of the movement of the feed slide is obtained by properly adjusting the screw *X*. The transfer movement described takes place before the piercing punch *L* and the bell center *M* which precedes it come in contact with the gear. The conical or beveled surface of the bell center accurately centers the gear under the piercing punch, after which the stripper *N* strikes the gear, clamping it securely while the punch *L* pierces the hole true with the pitch circle.

The bell center is milled away, as shown in the view in the upper right-hand corner of Fig. 10, in order to provide clearance for the transfer pieces *E*, Fig. 9. It will also be

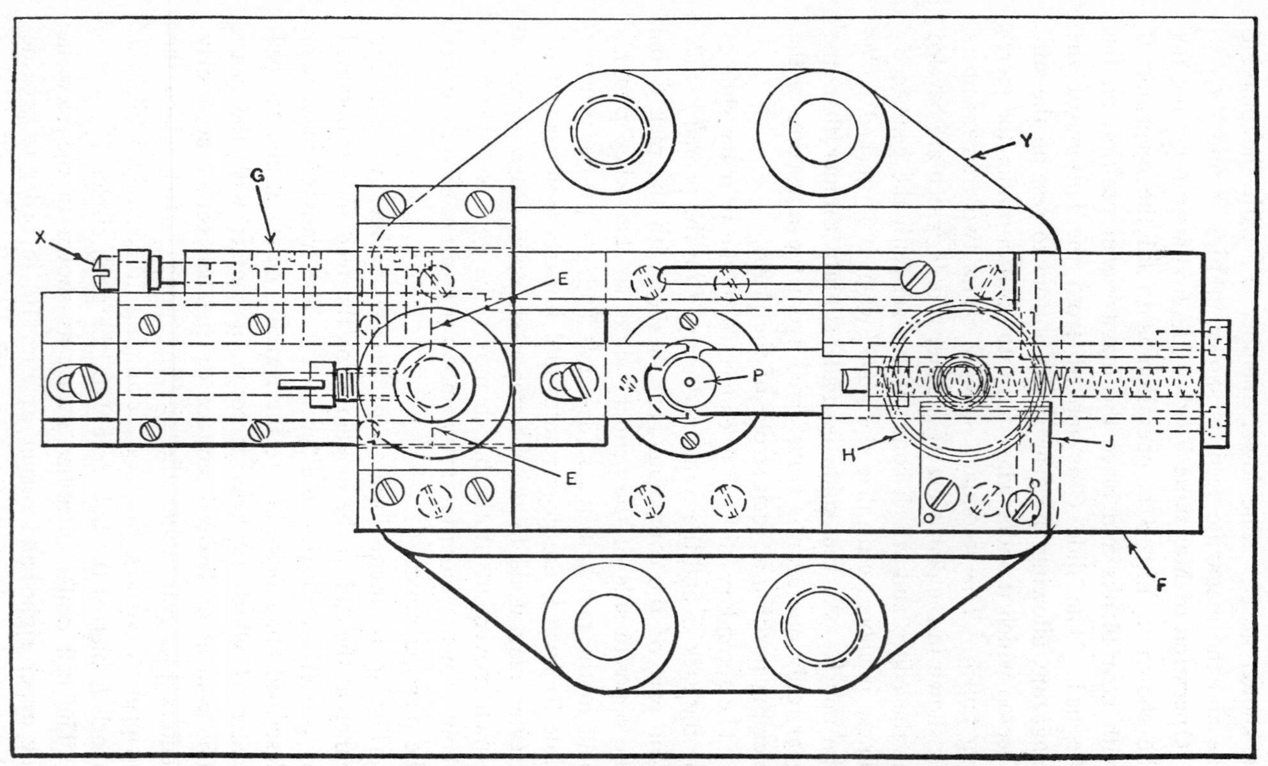

Fig. 9. Plan View of Die, Showing Automatic Feeding Mechanism

noticed that the cam *K*, Fig. 8, has a relieved portion above the end of the inclined face at *a*. This relieved portion causes the secondary slide and transfer pieces to recede slightly after reaching the end of the feeding stroke. This allows the gear to be moved in any direction by the bell center. If the cam *K* were not relieved at *a*, it is possible that the gear would be fed past the center of the die, in which case it could not be properly located by the bell center.

On the up stroke, the spring *O* on the primary slide returns the feeding members to their former positions, and another gear is picked up and transferred to the piercing position, the pierced gear being pushed off the die by the gear which precedes it and dropped through an opening in *Y*.

Construction of Punch and Die.—The construction of the punch and die members is shown clearly in the enlarged view, Fig. 10. The die *P* is threaded at *R* and can be turned or adjusted in the holder until its top surface is on a line with the lower surface of the transfer member. The die is locked in this position by means of the set-screws *S*. This adjustment insures a level and unbroken surface which permits the gear to be fed into place.

A weight *T*, Fig. 8, is placed on the top of the gears in the magazine to insure proper feeding. This weight also serves to close an electric circuit when it reaches the bottom of the magazine. The closing of this circuit operates an electric magnet which stops the press. Thus the press is automatically stopped when all the gears have been drawn from the magazine. The die is so designed that the punch, the die members, and the magazine can be easily removed from their holders. By providing suitable tools, one housing can be utilized for piercing several sizes of gears. There is no direct connection between the spring *b* in the stem of the holder *U* and the stripper which surrounds the punch. The stem is a floating member carried in a T-slot in the punch-holder, and for this reason it will not become cramped on the pillars as the result of play in the punch slide. The button *V* projects downward and makes contact with button *W* carried in the punch body,

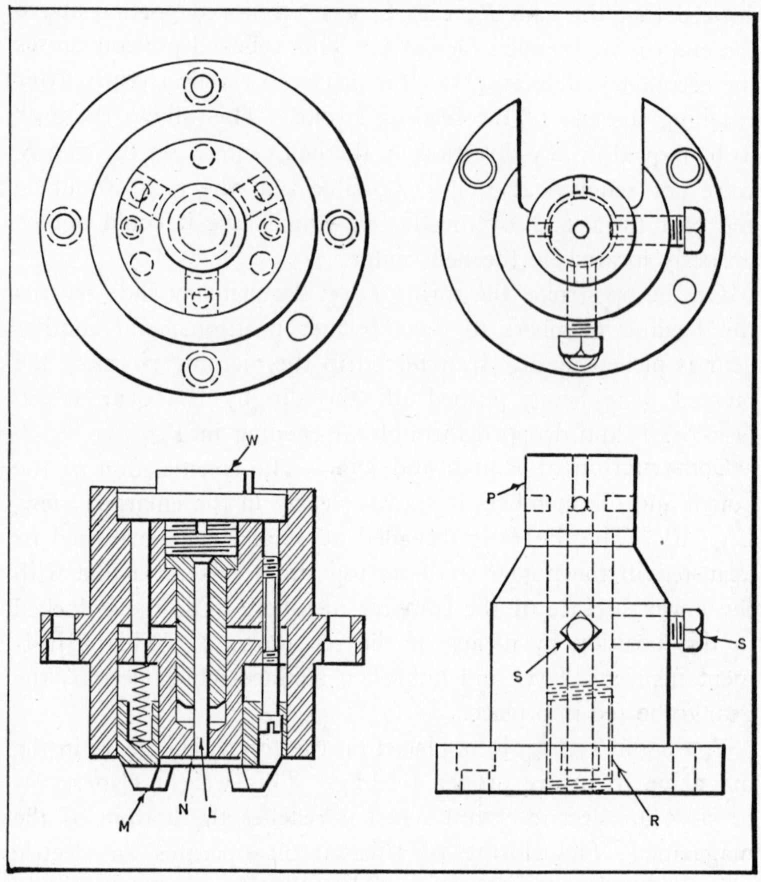

Fig. 10. Work-centering Punch and Die Members Used in Piercing Shaft Hole in Gear

when the stem and punch-holder are properly located or aligned with each other. One of these buttons is larger in diameter than the other one, so that some misalignment of the stem and punch slide may exist without impairing the transfer of spring pressure to the stripper *N*.

In cases where it is desired to locate holes accurately in a piece having an irregular contour, a bell center having a contour which matches that of the work is employed. When the work is placed on the face of the die by hand, limiting or gage pins can be used to locate the part within 1/32 inch of the exact piercing position. These pins should be so arranged that they will prevent the work from being placed on the die in a reverse or incorrect position. As the ram descends, the centering device accurately locates the work and holds it until clamped securely in place by the pressure ring which precedes the piercing punch. This method of locating the work is faster than the usual method in which the work is placed in a tightly fitting profile cage or nest. When the latter method is used, a piece frequently becomes wedged in the locating nest and time is lost in removing it. With the improved method, no difficulty of this kind is experienced.

Piercing Die Hinged at Side for Inserting and Removing Work.—The die for piercing four holes through the back of an automobile lamp on a short-stroke punch press is shown in Fig. 11. A novel feature of this die is that the die-block *A* is pivoted on pin *B* in such a manner that when latch *C* is pulled back from contact with the base of the die-block, the latter can be tilted forward in the direction indicated by the arrow. This is accomplished by pressing down on lever *D*. The purpose of this arrangement is to bring the die-block into such a position that work can be readily placed on it or removed without interfering with stripper *E* when punch-holder *H* has been raised its maximum height. If this feature were not employed, it would be necessary to use a punch press having a comparatively long stroke or have the die designed in such a way that it could be swung sidewise from under the punch in order to remove or mount work on die-block *A*. Latch *C* is pivoted on pin *F* and is held in contact with the die-block by the expansion coil spring *G*. While this spring is of such size and strength that it will readily snap latch *C* forward when die-block *A* is lowered to its working position, it can be easily held back by one hand while operating lever *D* with the other hand in tilting the die-block.

In the operation of this die, stripper *E* first comes in contact with the work as punch-holder *H* descends on the downward stroke of the press ram. The holes are next pierced in the work by punches mounted in the punch-holder, as they are forced through the stripper and work into corresponding holes in die *I*. On the return stroke of the press ram, stripper *E* is held in contact with the work by means of expansion coil springs *J*, until the punches are entirely removed from the work. When this has occurred, the bottoms of the counterbored holes in which the fillister-head machine screws *K* which secure stripper *E* to the punch-holder *H* are contained, come

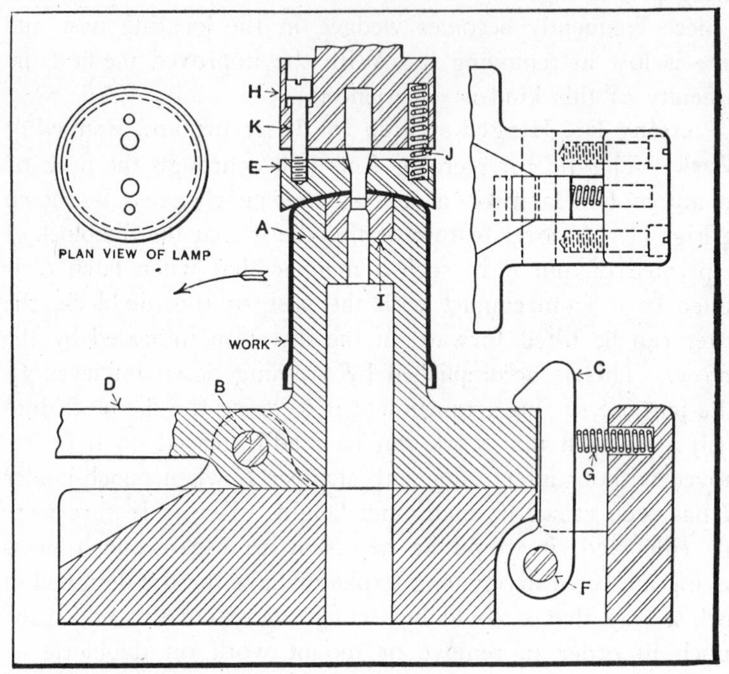

Fig. 11. Tilting Piercing Die Used in Operation on a Short-stroke Punch Press

in contact with the heads of these screws. This causes screws *K* and stripper *E* to be raised as the punch continues to ascend.

Horizontal Cam-operated Side-piercing Punches.—The die illustrated in Fig. 13 was designed for piercing the four holes *a, b, c,* and *d* in the shell shown in Fig. 12. The shape or construction of some of the parts of this die are shown more clearly in Fig. 14. In the latter illustration the parts are identified by the same reference letters as are used in

Fig. 13. The shell to be pierced is placed on the die-block *E* which is provided with four piercing dies, *a*, *b*, *c*, and *d*, Fig. 14. The piercing punches *A* and *B* are held in bushings *L* inserted in the block *F*. The punches *C* and *D* are held in the slide blocks *G* and *H*, respectively. The slide blocks are constructed exactly alike, as are also the punches *C* and *D*.

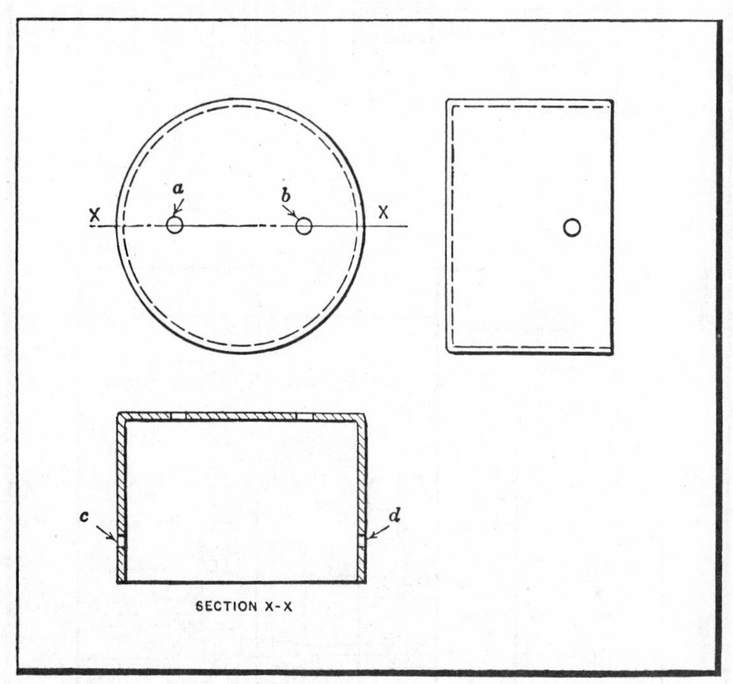

Fig. 12. Shell in which Four Holes are Pierced by Die Shown in Fig. 13

These punches are held in place by pins *J* which are backed up by screws *K*.

On the down stroke of the press ram, the beveled portions *N* of the cams *M* and *O* force the slide blocks *G* and *H* inward so that punches *C* and *D* enter the dies inserted in the sides of die-block *E* and thus pierce the two holes *c* and *d*, Fig. 12. The holes *a* and *b* are also pierced on the down stroke by the punches *A* and *B*, Fig. 13. On the up stroke the outer ends of the punch releasing dogs *P* and *Q* are forced upward by

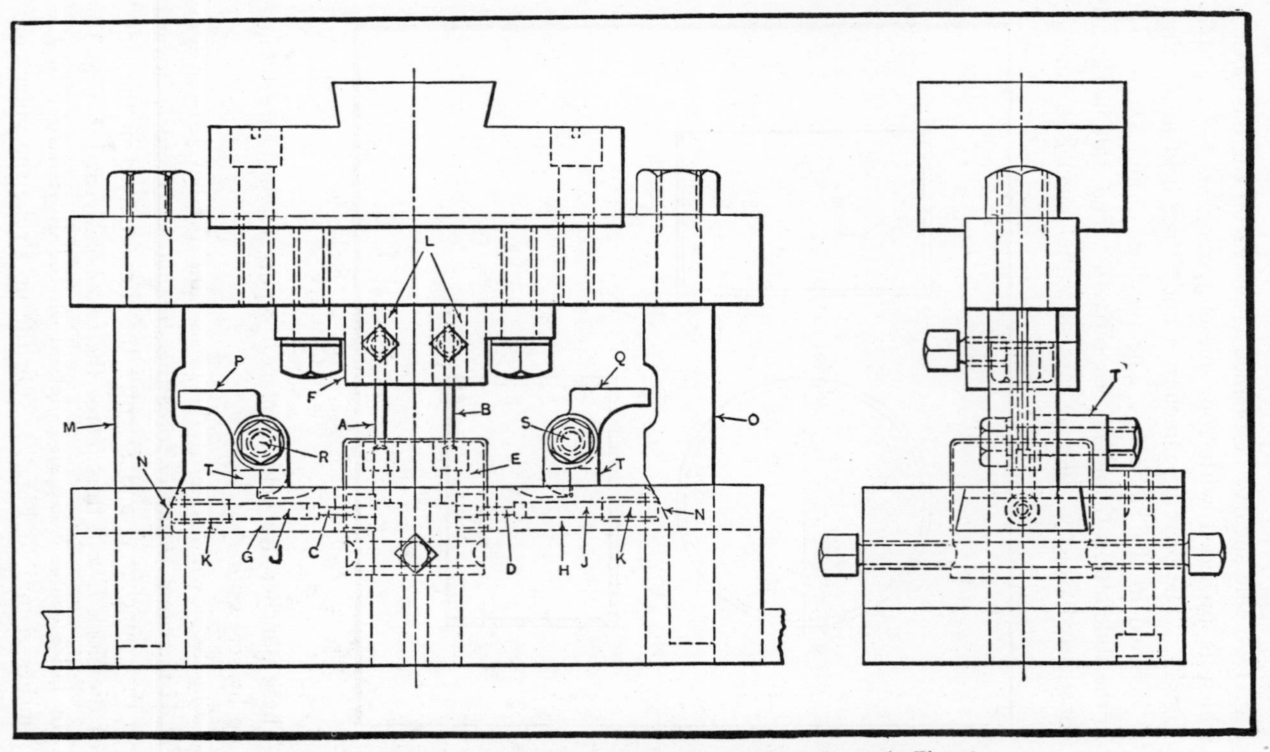

Fig. 13. Die Designed for Piercing Four Holes in Shell Shown in Fig. 12

the lower ends of the notches on the inner sides of cams *M* and *O* coming in contact with them. This action causes the dogs to pivot on studs *R* and *S* so that their lower ends will come in contact with the notches in the slide blocks *G* and *H* and force the latter outward, thus withdrawing the punches *C* and *D* from the holes in the shell. It will be noted that the

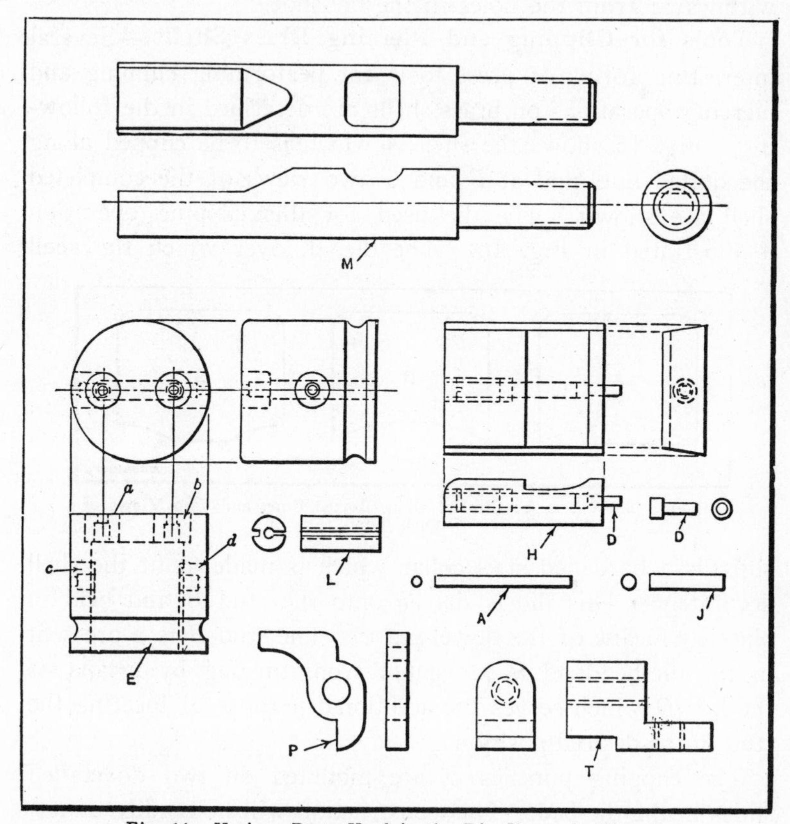

Fig. 14. Various Parts Used in the Die Shown in Fig. 13

releasing dogs are mounted on blocks *T* which are secured to the die-shoe by fillister-head machine screws.

Dies of the same general design as the one illustrated can be made for piercing a greater or smaller number of holes in the ends and sides of shells. For instance, four slides like the one shown at *H*, Fig. 14, could be used so that four holes would be punched simultaneously in the sides of the shell. Three holes could also be punched by using three of these slides. Again it is possible to use thicker slides, so that two punches can be mounted one above the other. In setting up a die like the one described, care should be taken to have the stroke short enough to prevent the cams *M* and *O* from being withdrawn from the holes in the die-shoe.

Tools for Clipping and Piercing Brass Shells.—Several interesting forms of press tools for performing clipping and piercing operations on brass shells are described in the following. Fig. 15 shows the shell *A* which is to be clipped along the dotted line, and at *B* and *C* two views of the completed shell are shown. The die used for this clipping operation is illustrated in Fig. 16. The die *A*, over which the shell

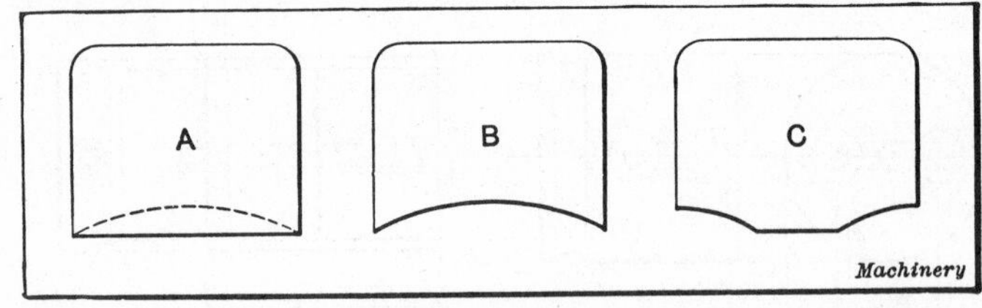

Fig. 15. Shell *A* to be Clipped along Dotted Line, and Two Views of Clipped Shell

slips, is a hardened steel collar which is made to fit the shell accurately. This die is driven onto the stud *B* and held in place by means of the dowel-pin *C*. The stud *B* is a press fit in the die-bed and is prevented from turning by means of the key *D* which serves the additional purpose of locating the stud in the desired position.

The clipping punches *E* are mounted on two dovetailed slides in the die-bed. This construction will be readily understood by referring to the cross-sectional view of the die-bed along the line *X-X*. Allowance is made for any adjustment of the punches that may be necessary on account of grinding, by the provision of elongated holes for the screws which secure the punches to the slides. In case any adjustment is made, a shim of sheet steel of the required thickness is placed between the back of the punch and the slide. This gives the

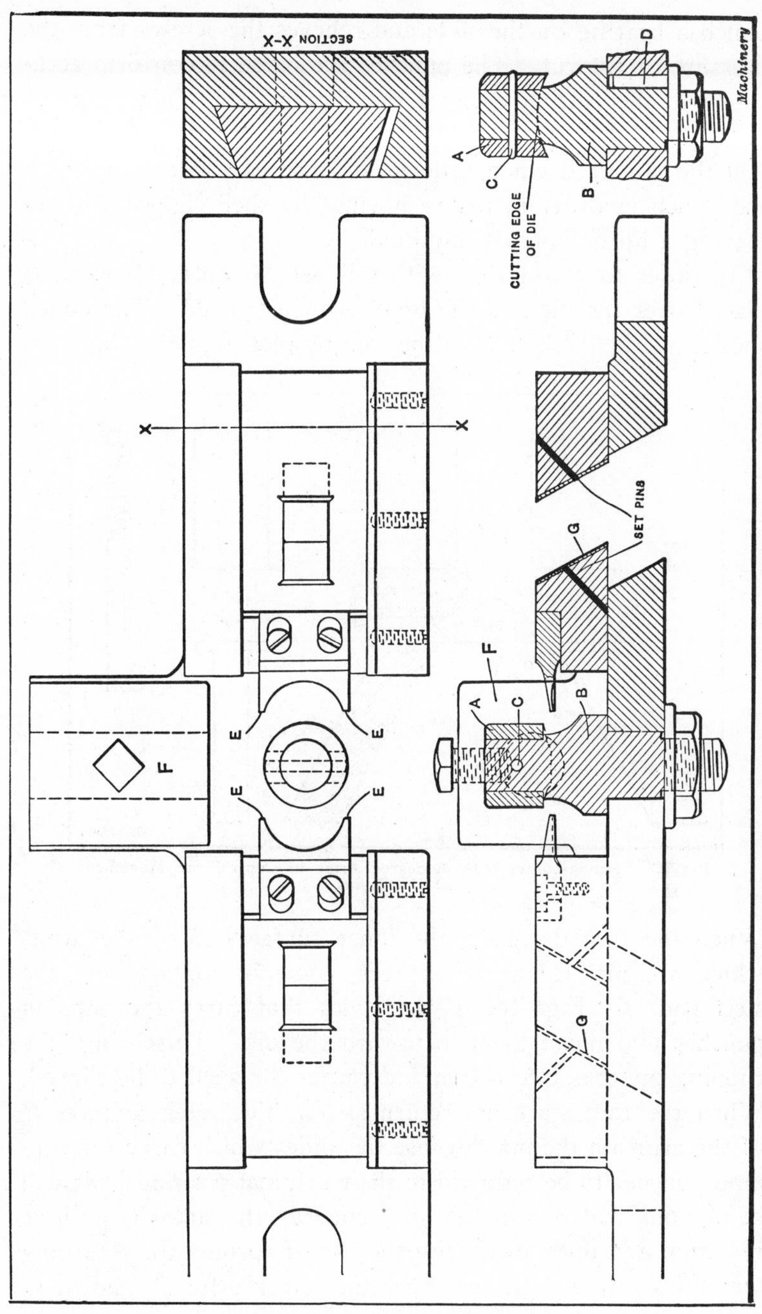

Fig. 16. Die-bed Equipped with Tools for Clipping Shell Shown in Fig. 15

punch a bearing on the slide and relieves the screws from the pressure of the cut. The punches are made to conform accurately to the cutting edge of the clipping die. The faces of the clipping punches conform to the circumference of the shell and the points *E* cut a little in advance of the remainder of the punch in order to insure having the shell clipped without leaving a fin or burr of any kind.

In order to clip a shell with this set of tools, the work is placed over the die and the press is then tripped. The punch shown in Fig. 17 is held in the ram by means of the shank *A*.

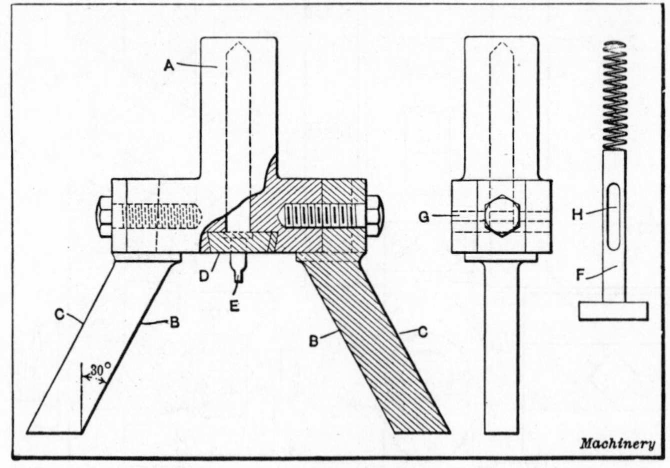

Fig. 17. Punch-holder with 30-degree Arms to Control the Movement of the Slides

When the ram descends, the inner surfaces *B* of the arms, which are inclined at 30 degrees, come in contact with the steel pads *G*, Fig. 16, in the slides that carry the clipping punches and move them in toward the die. This brings the clipping punches into action and causes the shell to be clipped. When the ram starts its return stroke, the outer surfaces *C* of the arms on the punch cause the slides which carry the clipping punches to be returned to their original positions. It will be obvious that this method of actuating the slides is positive in action and does away with the use of springs for returning the slides. It will be seen that the punch-plate *D*, shown in

Fig. 17, has a small piercing punch *E* mounted in it. This piercing punch is used in an operation that will be described later. When the tool is used for the clipping operation, the piercing punch *E* and the punch-plate *D* are removed from the punch and the "hold-down" *F* is mounted in their place. This hold-down is held in place by means of a pin *G* which fits in the slot *H*, the length of the slot being sufficient to allow the hold-down the necessary amount of movement. This hold-down moves a little ahead of the clipping punches and thus comes into contact with the top of the shell and holds it

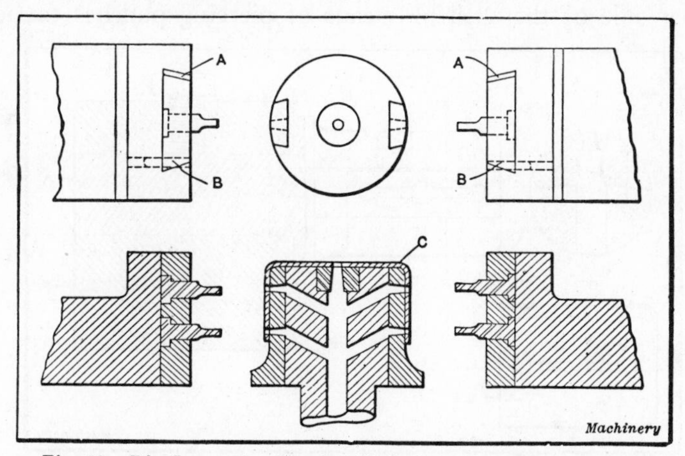

Fig. 18. Die Set up for Piercing Shell Held in Vertical Position

securely in place so that it cannot be raised off the die when the clipping punches begin to cut.

The shells that are clipped or pierced on the die-bed shown in Fig. 16 are ordered in lots of not over 25,000. This fact made it desirable to make a die-bed that could be used for both clipping and piercing operations, and this advantage is obtained by the design shown. This would not be of much advantage, however, if the work had been ordered in large quantities which would require the same set of tools to work day after day. In some cases, it was found desirable to provide special slides for a given set of punches, and the clipping punches shown in place on the die-bed in Fig. 16 are an example of this kind. When these punches are removed, the slides are taken off with them and the regular slides can then be put in place on the die-bed in order to allow other tools to be set up. It will be seen that gibs are provided to enable any wear which may develop in the slides to be taken up.

The construction of the die-bed is such that shells can be held in either a horizontal or vertical position. This will be better understood by referring to Figs. 18 and 19 which show shells mounted in the vertical and horizontal positions. The shell *C*, which is shown in position on the die in Fig. 18, has five holes pierced in it. Two of these holes are pierced in either side of the shell by means of piercing punches carried

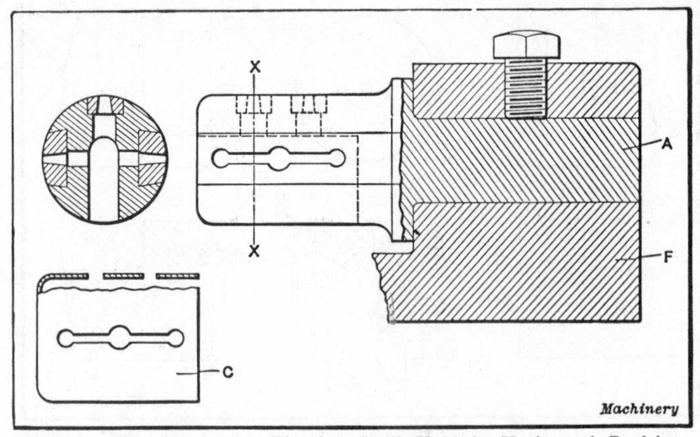

Fig. 19. Die Set up for Piercing Shell Held in Horizontal Position

in the slides of the die-bed, while the fifth hole is pierced in the top of the shell by means of the piercing punch *E*, which is shown in position in the punch-holder in Fig. 17. The piercing punches for working on the sides of the shell are mounted in regular slides of the die-bed shown in Fig. 16. Referring to the top view in Fig. 18, it will be seen that these punches are mounted in dovetail holders which are held in the desired position by means of keys *A*. The pins *B* locate the punches in their proper positions and are particularly convenient in obtaining the desired alignment when setting up the tools after they have been removed for sharpening.

Fig. 19 not only shows the construction of the piercing die for piercing the shell *C* (shown at the left-hand side of the illustration) but also illustrates the way in which the work is held in a horizontal position in the same die-bed that is used for holding work in a vertical position. Referring again to the illustration, Fig. 16, it will be seen that the part *F* at the back of the die-bed has a hole in it to receive the shank *A* of the piercing die-holder which is held in place by means of a set-screw. The shell *C* which is pierced on this die could be pierced in a vertical position but this would necessitate a three-slide die-bed. With the method now in use, the slot at either side of the shell is pierced by punches carried in the slides of

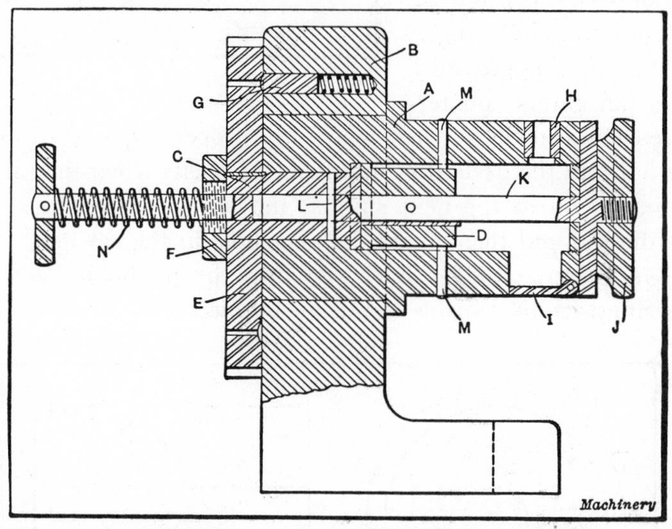

Fig. 20. Type of Die Used for the Piercing Operation Shown in Fig. 21

the die-bed and the two small holes at the top of the shell are pierced by two punches carried in the punch-holder mounted in the ram of the press. In the case of the die used for piercing this shell, and all of the other dies referred to, it will be seen that a space is provided to allow the scrap and dirt to drop out at the bottom of the die.

Piercing Holes Located on a Helical Curve.—The die illustrated in Fig. 20 was designed for perforating shells similar to the one shown in Fig. 21, having holes extending along a helical curve. It will be seen that the tool consists of a die-holder *A*, which is carried by the die-bed *B*. This die-holder is counterbored to receive the mandrel *C* and cam *D* which control the movement of the shell to obtain the desired location for the holes. An index ratchet *E* is keyed to the left-hand end of the mandrel and held in position by a nut *F* which holds it against the die-bed. This ratchet is operated by a pawl carried by the ram of the press. In order to take up any backlash and secure accurate indexing, a spring pin *G* is provided. This pin enters counterbored holes in the ratchet, which are properly spaced to locate the holes in the desired positions in the shell; when the ratchet is moved on to the next station, the pin is forced back into the die-bed and then enters the next hole in the ratchet.

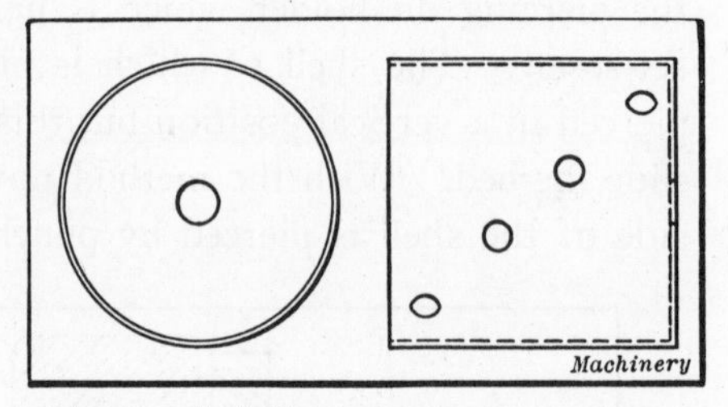

Fig. 21. Shell Having Perforations Along a Helical Curve

The piercing die *H* is driven into the die-holder and the piercings are held inside the drum by means of a trap door *I*,

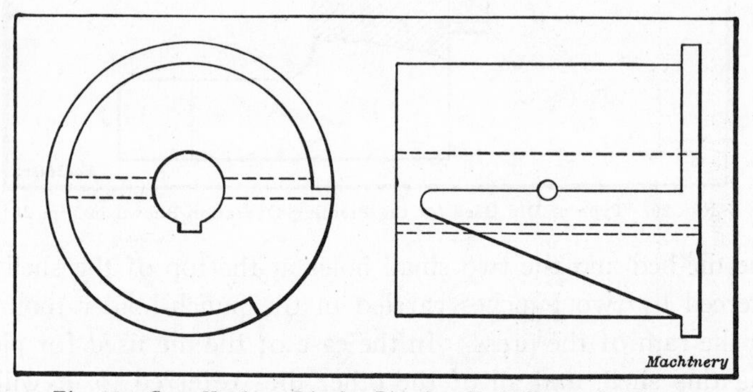

Fig. 22. Cam Used on Die for Piercing Shell Shown in Fig. 21

until all of the holes have been punched. The shell is held in position by nut *J* carried at the right-hand end of the shaft *K*. Cam *D*, which controls the movement of the shell, is secured to the shaft *K* by means of a key and pin. (This cam is shown in detail in Fig. 22.) Four pins *M* extend into the bore of the die-holder and these pins are engaged successively by the cam *D*. The left-hand hole of a series is first pierced; the ratchet then rotates the shell and the action of the cam moves it to the right. The indexing is effected as previously described, one hole being pierced at each station. After the four holes on one curve have been pierced and the ratchet starts to index for the next hole, the pin *M* slips over the point of the cam and the tension of the spring *N* then returns the cam and the work to the extreme left where the cam is engaged by the next one of the pins *M*. This process is repeated four times to complete piercing the holes on the four helical curves. The longitudinal movement of the shell is limited by the pin *L* which fits in a slot in the shaft K. This die proved very satisfactory for this perforating operation.

Perforating Dies.—As explained previously the dies used for punching large numbers of holes or perforations in sheet metal, for producing strainers, sifting devices, etc., and also the dies used for cutting ornamental shapes around the edges of lamp-burner shells, etc., are commonly known as perforating dies. The type of die used for perforating sheet stock is in reality a multiple or gang die, but as a general rule the work of a perforating die differs from a gang die in that it is used to punch a large number of holes, whereas a gang or multiple die, as these names are ordinarily applied, means the type that is used to blank out a number of duplicate parts. There may be exceptions, however, to this general classification. Some perforating dies, such as are used for perforating sheet metal or other materials, have hundreds of punches which are arranged in rows and operate simultaneously.

Perforating Presses.—The perforating of shells and flat sheets is done either in presses of ordinary construction fitted with special attachments or by means of special perforating presses. For perforating lamp burner gallery shells and other circular shaped parts, an attachment is used which is designed with reference to the particular part to be perforated. The perforating die, with a chuck of suitable shape, is mounted on a die-holder and a ratchet wheel is arranged to rotate the shell at each stroke of the press slide, the ratchet having teeth spaced to suit the spacing of the holes desired. Perforating by this method may be done at the rate of from 150 to 200 strokes per minute, according to the size and shape of the shell. Special attachments may be designed to suit parts of special shape. For perforating tapering shells, the die-holder is located at an angle to the slide, so that the punch is square with the part being perforated. These presses may be equipped with an automatic clutch release which automatically stops the press after one revolution of the shell or perforating die.

Perforating Flat Sheets.—One type of perforating press for operating on flat stock is arranged to perforate the entire width of the sheet at each stroke. The stock is fed forward automatically after each stroke by a double-roll ratchet feeding mechanism. For instance, after perforating a double row of holes simultaneously, the stock is fed in the required distance for perforating the next double row, and so on. For perforating very heavy sheets, or when only a small number of the same pattern or design are required, it usually does not pay to make dies extending across the entire width of the sheet, so that the latter may be finished in one passage through the dies. For work of this kind, the press sometimes used has a sliding table to which the sheet is clamped. The latter is then automatically fed under the press slide which carries from one to fifty punches, the number depending upon the design or quantity of perforating necessary. The table feed is automatic, and some machines are provided with a special slide which permits the punching action to be stopped while the table feed continues, in order to produce blank spaces between the perforated portions.

Another design of perforating press is so arranged that the feed-rolls have a side motion which automatically shifts the sheet sideways at each stroke for the purpose of perforating a staggered pattern, by means of a single-row die. This reciprocating motion which shifts the feed-rolls and sheet being perforated may be adjusted for different patterns. This lateral motion makes it possible to use a comparatively cheap die.

since the latter only requires one-half the holes and punches that would otherwise be necessary. Moreover, since the die holes are spaced farther apart, tool-steel bushings inserted in a machine-steel holder can ordinarily be used. The advantages of this construction are apparent to those who are at all familiar with die work.

There is still another type of perforating press which has, in addition to the double-roll feed with lateral motion, a device for varying the feed, thus enabling the sheet being perforated to move an equal distance for two or three strokes, and then a greater or less distance. For instance, during three strokes of the press slide, the rolls may be fed two short distances and one long one, or *vice versa,* or all three spacings may be alike. By substituting other cams and gears of different proportions, a number of combinations may be obtained, thus securing a considerable variety of spacing or grouping of the rows of holes. Perforating presses have cam-actuated strippers such as are described in connection with multiple or gang presses. With an ordinary fixed stripper plate attached to the die, more or less clearance space is required for the work, and the result is that the stock before being stripped is carried up against the under side of the plate and causes considerable shock when the stock is heavy. With the cam stripper, this blow against the lower side of the stripper plate is obviated.

Tools for Perforating Cylindrical Work.—The punches and dies used for perforating the sides of cylindrical work are similar to blanking punches and dies, except for the modifications necessary, owing to the fact that the metal is circular in form instead of being flat. In perforating a shell similar to the one shown in Fig. 23, the shell is first slipped over the die-holder (Fig. 24) in such a manner as to allow the elongated slot *A* in the bottom of the shell to engage with the projecting tongue of the driving arbor. The press is then tripped and the punches, at the first stroke of the press, cut out two of the irregular shaped perforations *B* in the shell. On the upward stroke of the press, a ratchet mechanism, revolves the driving arbor, a part of a turn and as a slot in the bottom of the shell is engaged with the tongue of the driving arbor, the shell is indexed with the arbor before the punch descends again. These operations are continued until the press, in this case, has made fourteen continuous strokes, when it is automatically stopped and the perforated shell removed. The stopping of the press is effected by a cam which automatically releases the driving clutch when the required number of strokes has been made. The construction of the tools and the manner in which they are made will be treated later.

Fig. 25 is shown another set of perforating tools for perforating the gallery fence of a lamp burner shown in Fig. 26.

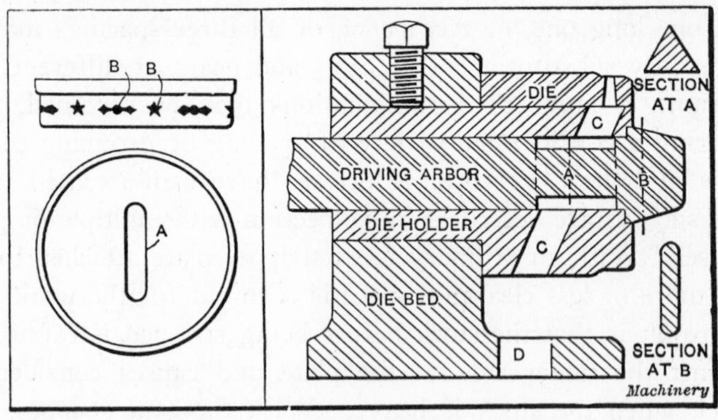

Fig. 23. Example of Shell to be Perforated

Fig. 24. Section of Die-bed, Holder and Die for Perforating Shell Shown in Fig. 23

The gallery fence of a lamp or gas burner holds the lamp chimney or globe in place by the spring pressure exerted by the perforated part. The metal must be hard in order to impart the required spring pressure and is, therefore, on the better grade of burners, burnished before perforating, which not only hardens and toughens the metal, but also produces a brilliant finish. On the cheaper grade of burners, the shells from which the gallery fences are made are passed through an extra redrawing operation, the shells not being annealed, but left hard. The difference in the diameter of the shell before and after redrawing is about $\frac{1}{32}$ inch, while the difference in the thickness of the metal is about 0.0005 inch.

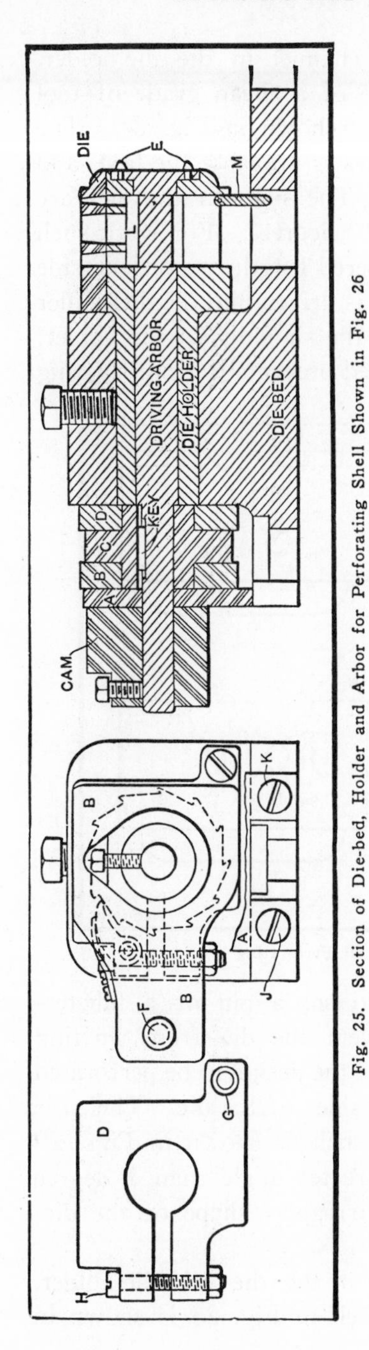

Fig. 25. Section of Die-bed, Holder and Arbor for Perforating Shell Shown in Fig. 26

This treatment of the metal not only imparts the required springiness, but also makes the perforating operations easier, because hard metal is more readily perforated than soft.

The ratchet *C*, Fig. 25, is keyed to the driving arbor, and when the tools are set up in the press they are set with the face of the die-holder turned towards the right, instead of facing the operator. The perforating operation, however, is similar to the one already described. The effect of the successive strokes of the press is indicated in Fig. 26. At the first stroke of the press, the four shaded areas at *F* are punched out. At *G* can be seen the appearance of the shell after the second stroke. In order that no burr or fin may be left on the top points of the scallops, the die is made so that the punch will cut a trifle past the center of the point as shown at *H*. The shell is rotated towards the left by the driving arbor, and a simple holding device, not shown in the illustration, is used for holding the shell in place on the arbor.

Construction of Perforating Tools.—In Fig. 27 the perforating die for the shell in Fig.

23 is shown held in a dovetail channel in the die-holder. The die-holder is preferably made of a cheap grade of tool steel, and is held in the die-bed as shown in Fig. 24. The dovetail method for holding the dies is probably the best, and is the one most commonly used. The sides of the dies are beveled at an angle of from 5 to 10 degrees. For work such as shown in Fig. 23, the die is tapered lengthwise on one side with a taper of about 1 degree, and is driven into the die-holder from the back and left flush with the shoulder of the holder, so that, when in position, the die-bed prevents it from shifting

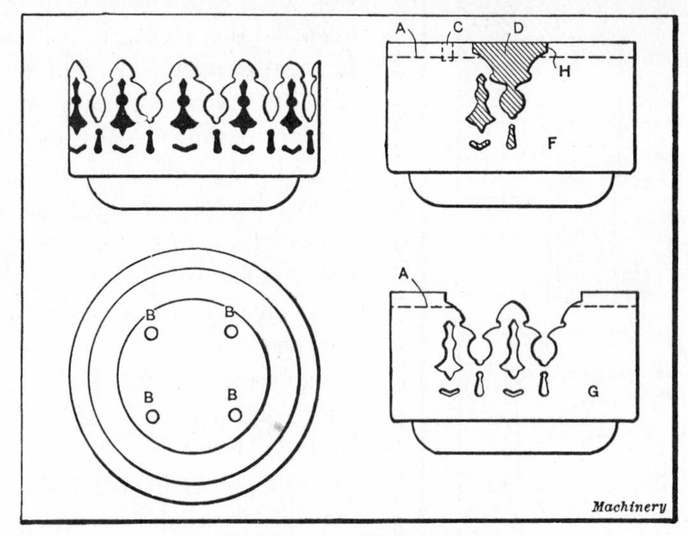

Fig. 26. Example of Shell Perforating

back. When it is possible to do so, a pin or a fillister-head screw may be used to prevent the die from shifting endwise. The shape of the shell and the design to be perforated sometimes govern the taper of the sides of the die. This, for example, is the case where shells such as shown in Figs. 29 and 30 are perforated, when a greater angle than 1 degree must be used on account of the irregular shape of the die-holder and dies.

The longitudinal cross-section of the die-bed, die-holder, and driving arbor used for the shell in Fig. 23 is shown in

Fig. 24. Section *A* shows how the arbor is milled at the neck *A* in order to allow the scrap punchings to drop through. A section of the tongue of the arbor which engages the slot in the end of the shell, by means of which it is rotated, is shown at *B*. This tongue is tapered as shown, to facilitate the putting on and taking off of the work. A scrap escape hole *C* is drilled in the die-holder at an angle as shown, so as to prevent the scrap punchings from coming in contact with the shell while it is rotated around the die. An escape hole drilled in this manner can be used only on short shells and when the scrap punchings are small, or, if they are large, when they are few in number. Hole *D* in the die-bed permits the scrap punchings to readily fall out of the way.

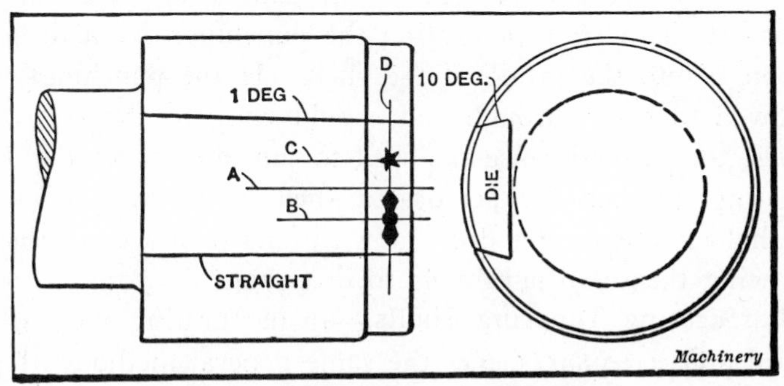

Fig. 27. Die in Position in Die-holder

The construction of the tools shown in Fig. 25 is somewhat different. Two small pins *E*, which are used in the face of the driving arbor, act as driving pins for rotating the shell. These enter into pierced holes in the bottom of the shell as shown at *B*, Fig. 26. The pawl which operates the indexing ratchet is fastened to part *B* in Fig. 25, which is made to fit the shoulder of the ratchet and oscillates in order to provide for the required indexing. This oscillating motion is imparted to *B* by fastening a handle *F* to an adjustable connecting-rod which, in turn, is fastened to the crankshaft of the press. Part *D* is a friction collar which prevents any backlash in the driving arbor. This collar is fastened to the die-bed by a screw at *G*. The hole in the center of the collar fits the shoulder on one end of the ratchet. The brake or friction effect is obtained by screw *H*. Part A acts as a steadyrest for the driving arbor; and is fastened to the die-bed by screws *J* and *K*.

The cam fastened to the end of the driving arbor causes the press to stop automatically by coming in contact with a lever connected to the driving clutch. The driving arbor is relieved at *L* to prevent the congestion of the scrap punchings. The hole for the driving arbor in the die-holder is also recessed at this place in order to give the scrap punchings, which, in this case, are rather large, ample room to pass the arbor. When the device is in operation, a shutter *M* closes up the bottom of the scrap escape hole in the die-holder. When the shell is slipped over the latter, the shutter is forced up and thus acts as a trap, preventing the punchings from dropping through into the inside of the shell. If the punchings were allowed to drop through and should cling to the perforated holes, they would cause the shell to jam and prevent it from rotating. When the perforated shell is removed from the die-holder, the shutter drops down of its own accord, thereby allowing the scrap punchings to drop out.

Perforating Tapering Shells.—In perforating shells of tapered and irregular shapes the same general methods of procedure as already described are used, with the exception that the die-holder is held in the die-bed at an angle of 5 to 70 degrees or more with the bottom of the die-bed, the angle depending on the shape of the shell and the perforations to be made in it. In Fig. 28 is shown a die, die-holder, and die-bed for work of this kind. The angle at which the die-holder is set should be such that if the outer ends of the two extreme holes in the perforating die are connected by a straight line, this line would be parallel with the bottom of the die-bed, as indicated in Fig. 29, where the points *A* and *B* are on the line which should be parallel with the base of the die-bed.

In Fig. 28 may also be seen the shell which is perforated by the die. The shell is rotated around the die by the tongue of the driving arbor engaging in an elongated hole in the bottom of the shell. The arbor is relieved at *A* in the usual manner to allow the scrap punchings to escape. No shutter is used, as the open end of the shell does not come near the scrap escape hole. The ratchet *B*, which is operated by a pawl, not shown, is keyed to the driving arbor, while the friction used for controlling the backlash bears upon the shoulder of the ratchet as indicated. This shell has two rows of perforated holes, fifty-two holes in each row. Eight holes at a time are cut, or four holes in each row. The reason that four holes in each row are cut at each stroke, instead of five,

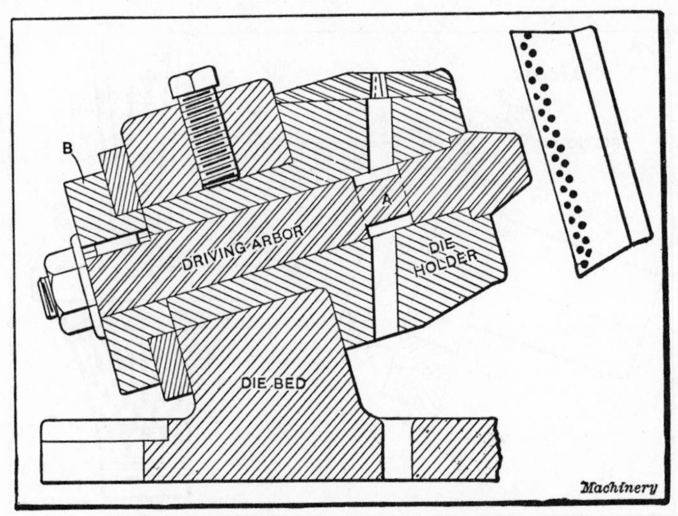

Fig. 28. Die, Die-bed and Holder for a Tapered Shell

six, or eight, is, in the first place, that the number of holes cut at each stroke of the press must be such that the total number of holes in each row is a multiple of it. In the second place, it is not possible to get good results if the end punches are too far away from the center of the work, as these punches would strike a glancing blow. These holes would be somewhat elongated and "burry" instead of being clean, round, and free from burrs. In this case, four holes in each row is as much as is practicable. Of course, if the holes are small in diameter and close together, a greater number can be cut at one time than when they are larger and further apart. If the diameter of the shells is large, a greater number of holes can also be cut at one time than with shells of smaller diameter, other conditions being equal.

Methods of Rotating Shell to be Perforated.—A method commonly used in connection with perforating tools for rotating the shell to be perforated is the dog-notch method. A dog *C*, Fig. 29, is fastened to the ratchet by screws or dowel-pins. The end of this dog fits a notch *D* in the shell, called the "dog-notch." The shell is slipped over the die-holder in such a manner as to cause the dog-notch in the shell to engage with

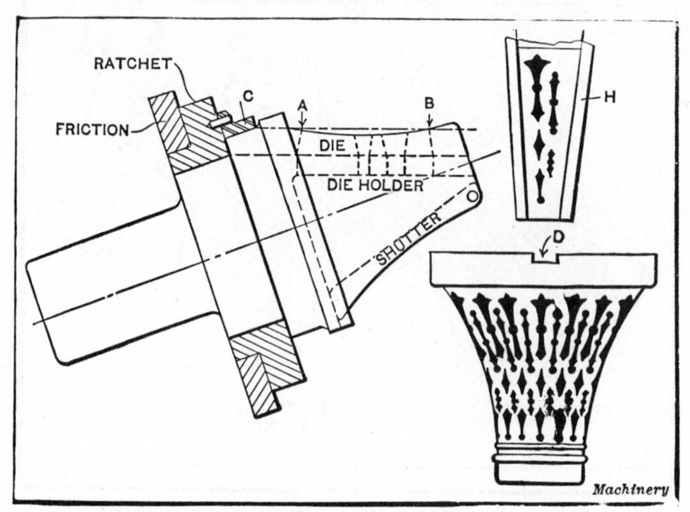

Fig. 29. Die and Holder for Perforating Shell Shown to the Right

the dog on the ratchet. In this way the ratchet can index the shell directly around the die-holder.

There are also a number of other methods used for rotating shells to be perforated. Besides those already described, one may make use of an irregular shaped hole in the bottom of the shell in connection with the driving arbor. Sometimes an irregular shaped hole is required in the bottom of the shell, and in such a case the tongue of the driving arbor may be made to fit this hole, which affords a good driving means. Sometimes use is made of a coaster brake device fastened to the ratchet. The tools used in connection with this device are similar to those already described, having the ratchet in the front of the die-bed, as shown in Fig. 29, with the exception that instead of using a dog, a device working on the principle of a coaster brake, such as is used on an ordinary bicycle, is fastened to the ratchet. With this device, no notch in the shell is required, as the open end of the shell is simply slipped into this device and given a part of a turn, causing it to be tightly gripped. The press is then tripped and the shell rotated around the die in the usual manner. In cases where a dog-notch is used and where there is a tendency on the part of

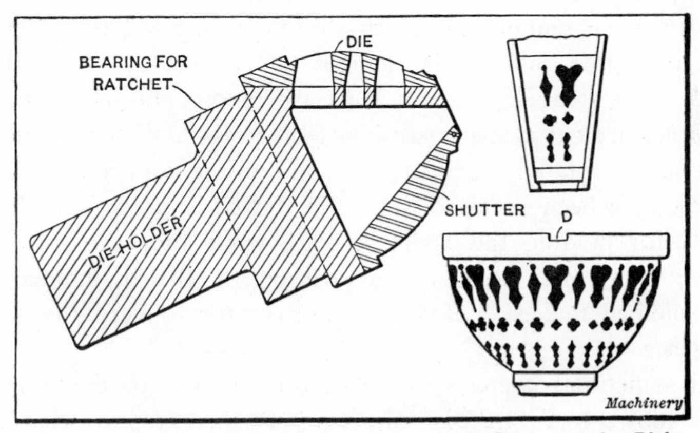

Fig. 30. Die and Holder for Perforating Shell Shown to the Right

the shell to slip in between the dog and the die-holder, which would prevent the shell from being properly rotated, the die-holder is turned down as shown and the dog is made to just clear the holder. This prevents the shell from slipping in under the dog.

The perforating die shown at *H* is held in the die-holder in the usual way, and is tapered lengthwise at a suitable angle as indicated. In order to afford a support for the die when in use, the bottom of the dovetail channel upon which the die rests is worked out so as to conform to some extent to the shape of the bottom of the die. This is done on dies where the holes are close together, so as to support the narrow bridges that separate the irregular shaped holes in the die. The best way to do this work is to first work out an open space under the dovetail channel. This space is used for holding the scrap punchings that are prevented from dropping through by a shutter. In working out this space enough stock is left under the dovetail channel to support the die properly, as indicated in Figs. 29 and 30, after which the openings through which the scrap punchings from the die drop are worked out. The shutter, which is shown closed, swings open on the shutter pin as soon as the perforated shell is removed from the die-holder.

The construction of the tools in Fig. 30 is similar to that of those just described. At the right is a plan of the die, showing the manner in which the die is tapered lengthwise, which in this case is six degrees on each side. When the tools shown in Figs. 29 and 30 are in operation, two rows of holes are cut at every stroke of the press until the shell has completely rotated around the die and all the required rows of holes have been punched out. No device is used with these tools for holding the shells in place while they are rotating around the die, because the position of the die-holder in the die-bed makes it easy for the operator to keep the shell in place.

It sometimes happens that a perforated shell of the general type shown in Fig. 26 is required, with the exception that the bottom is left intact and therefore cannot be used in connection with a driving arbor for rotating the shell. In such a case, the shell is dog-notched and rotated in the manner already described, with the exception that the locating of the dog on the ratchet preparatory to perforating the shell forms an important part in the successful operation of the tools. The reason for this is that when cutting out the scallops of the shell the dog-notch *C*, which is used for rotating the shell, must necessarily be cut away from the shell, and must, therefore, be placed in such a position that it will come in the center of the large scrap punching which will be cut out at the last stroke of the press, completing the operation. If the shaded portion shown at *D* is the punching resulting from the first stroke of the press, and if the blank is rotating from right to left, then the dog-notch must be located at *C*, central between the two scallops completed by the last stroke of the press, after the whole shell has been perforated.

In order to present the punch *A*, shown in the upper right-hand corner of Fig. 31, which cuts out the scrap punchings *D*

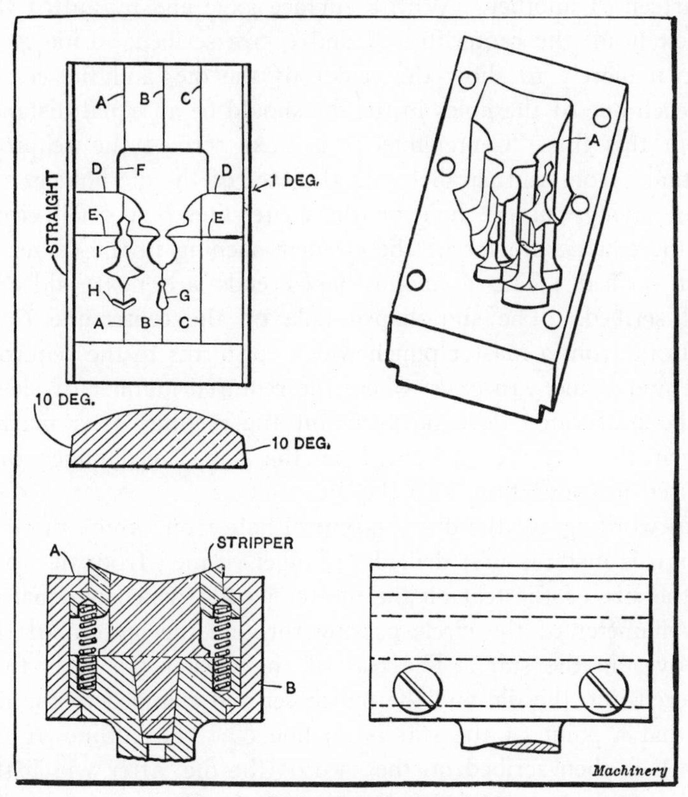

Fig. 31. Perforating Punch and Die

Fig. 26, from coming in contact with the dog, a short slot is milled in the center of the face of the punch at the back end near the ratchet, so that the punch will clear the dog when that part of the shell containing the dog-notch is cut out.

Lay-out of a Perforating Die.—Preparatory to laying out the die shown in Fig. 27, the die blank is carefully fitted to the dovetail channel in the die-holder, after which it is turned up in the lathe in place and highly polished. It is then removed from the die-holder and blued by heating, and again driven into the die-holder, after which it is ready to be laid out. The die-holder is then mounted in the milling machine, the index-head in this case being set for twenty-eight divisions, as there are fourteen perforated holes of one design and fourteen of another. With a surface gage and by aid of the index head, the centerlines *B* and *C* are scribed. Line *A* is drawn merely to show the center of the die, and the center of each one of the holes in the die should be an equal distance from this line. Center-line *D* is next scribed the required distance from and parallel with the face of the die-holder.

In laying out the hole on the center-line *B* a small circle of the exact diameter of the circular opening in the center is first scribed. The diamond-shaped ends are next laid out and scribed. The star-shaped hole on the center-line *C* is laid out from a master punch which conforms to the required size and shape. In cases where the required number of shells to be perforated does not warrant the making of a master punch, the dies are laid out from the star-shaped punch that is used in connection with the die.

In working out the die, the central hole from which the star design is made is first drilled and taper-reamed from the back to the size of the teat on the master punch, which is equal to the diameter of the circle passing through the bottom of the grooves in the star. The teat of the master punch is then entered into the die and the punch set and clamped to the die so that a point of the star is on line *C*. The outline of the punch is then scribed on the face of the die, after which the die is worked out and fitted to the punch. In order to facilitate matters, the punch is used as a broach after the die is filed to shape. In working out the outer hole in the die, on line *B*, a hole is first drilled and taper-reamed from the back for the circular opening in the center. Two holes are drilled and reamed in the center of the diamond-shaped ends. The surplus stock between the drilled holes is then removed and the hole filed to the desired shape.

There are two ways in which a die such as that shown in the upper left-hand corner of Fig. 31 may be laid out. One is to lay out the die on a milling machine in a manner similar to that already described. The other, which is most commonly used, is to lay out the died by scribing the design on its face from a master shell slipped over the die-holder which has the shape to be perforated worked out upon it.

The master shell itself is laid out as follows: The shell is fastened to the die-holder by a few drops of soft solder to prevent it from moving. The die-holder is then mounted in the milling machine. The index-head in this case is set for twenty-four divisions. In Fig. 31 is shown the laying-out of the die, but the same method applies to the shell. With a surface gage used in connection with the index-head, the lines *A, B,* and *C* are scribed on the shell. Lines *A* and *C* represent the centers of two adjoining scallops, and line *A* is also the center for the two holes *I* and *H*, while line *B* is exactly in the center between two scallops and constitutes the center-line for hole *G*. The lines *E* and *D* are next scribed on the shell, the former representing the height of the ears of the projecting scallops, while the latter shows the height at which the lower curved portions of the pointed scallops converge. After these construction lines are scribed on the shell, the design is readily laid out. The shape of the design is then worked out by drilling and the surplus stock is removed by means of a jewelry saw. The shell is then filed to the desired shape and when completed should be a duplicate of the portion cut out by the first stroke of the press, as shown at *F* in Fig. 26. In filing out a design, care should be taken to file out the holes central with the center-lines, *A, B,* and *C,* and also parallel with a plane passed at right angles to the center of the design, through the shell, in order that the holes may be at their exact required position on the inside of the shell.

It will be noted in Fig. 31 that the large hole *F* in the die is extended past the line *D*; this is done in order to make sure that the large scrap punching *D*, Fig. 26, will be completely cut from the shell. This is especially necessary when the shells vary in length. The dotted line *A*, Fig. 26, is drawn so as to more clearly show the length of the twelve pointed scallops and their relation to the top of the shell.

In drilling and working out the surplus stock in the die, Fig. 31, the same general methods that are used for working out an irregularly shaped blanking die are used. First, remove as much of the surplus stock as possible by drilling. When drilling out the surplus stock in the hole *F*, the smaller of the two circular openings between the scallops is first drilled out and taper-reamed from the back to the finish size. After this, the hole is plugged with a small taper pin that is filed to fit it, and the large hole is drilled and taper-bored in a lathe. The round corners at the opposite end of the hole are then drilled out. These corners are left circular in order to add to the strength of the die and to prevent cracking of the die in hardening. The remainder of the hole is drilled and worked out in the usual way. In working out the small holes *G* and *H*, the opposite ends are first drilled and taper-reamed to the finish size, after which other holes are drilled and reamed and the surplus stock is removed with a small broach or jewelry saw preparatory to filing out the die. Hole *I* is drilled out and the surplus stock removed in a similar manner.

Filing the Die Shape.—A die used for perforating the sides of cylindrical work is rather awkward to hold, either in the vise or in die-clamps, while being filed out, owing to the fact that the face of the die is circular in shape and the sides are dovetailed. For this reason, a die-holding fixture, shown in Fig. 32, is used to hold the die in the vise, die-clamp, or filing machine while it is being filed out. The device shown is adjustable to accommodate various widths of dies. The most essential points to be remembered when filing out a perforating die are: Use a coarse file for the rough filing and finish with a smooth one. Take care to have the clearance filed straight in order to prevent the congestion of scrap punchings in the die; perforating dies as a rule are not very strong and are often cracked and broken because of neglect on this point. The clearance should not be filed over 1½ degrees, in order to make the die as strong as possible; in cases where the holes in the dies are close together even less clearance is necessary, and a very narrow wall that separates two holes is filed almost straight on each side, with just enough of a taper to clear. Care must be taken while filing to prevent the back or the sides of the file from running into the finished part of the die.

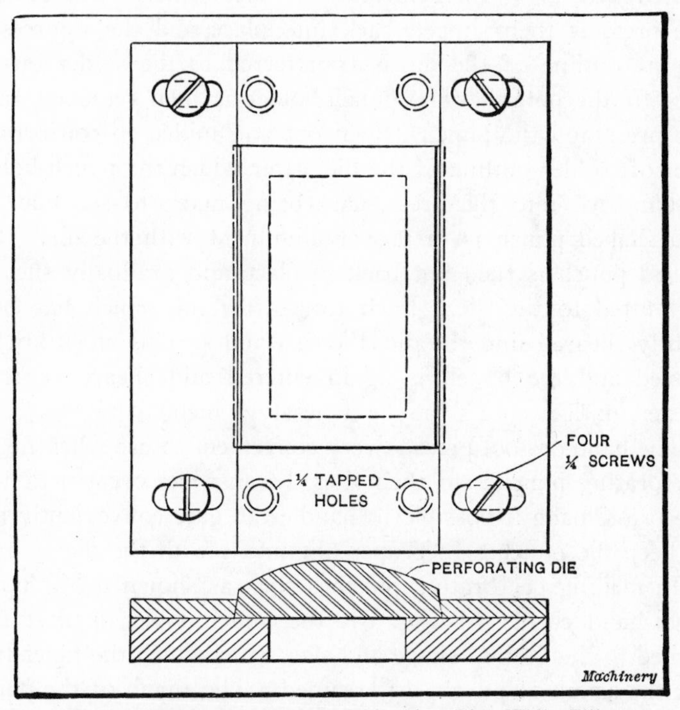

Fig. 32. Device for Holding Perforating Dies While Filing

Making the Punch for a Perforating Die.—The punch used with the die shown in Fig. 27 is comparatively simple in its construction. It consists of the usual form of punch-holder into which the two perforating punches are driven. The star-shaped punch, after it is fitted to the die and hardened, is driven into the punch-holder in such a position that when it is entered into the die the sides of the punch-holder will be in a straight line and parallel with the die-bed. The tools are then set up in a hand or foot press so that the die and star punch are in proper alignment with each other. The foot treadle of the press is then disconnected from the gate so that the gate which holds the punch-holder in place can be withdrawn from the press without disturbing the punch-holder or the ways upon which the gate slides. The other punch, in its unfinished state, is then driven into the punch-holder and the face is coated with a 1/16-inch thickness or soft solder. The gate of the press is then slipped back into place and the impression of the outline of the die is transferred to the solder on the face of the punch. The punch-holder is then removed from the press and the punch driven out and milled to conform to the soft solder outline of the die, after which the punch-holder is put back into the press, care being taken to see that the star-shaped punch is in proper alignment with the die. The milled punch is then put back in place and gradually sheared and fitted to the die. Each time after the punch has been lightly sheared into the die, the fins and surplus stock are removed and the punch is again entered and sheared a trifle deeper, until it enters the die at least 1/4 inch.

The hand or foot press is very convenient to use when fitting perforating punches to their dies, because the construction of the press make it possible to handle the gate conveniently and to keep the punches in proper alignment with the die.

In making perforating punches such as shown in the upper right-hand corner of Fig. 31, the punch-holder is first machined to the desired shape and size, after which the taper hole for the shank of punch *A* is reamed. The shank of the punch is then turned and fitted to the punch-holder and driven into place. The face of the punch is made to conform to the outside diameter of the shell and is then clamped to the face of the die and the outline scribed on it, after which it is milled to shape and sheared and fitted to the die. Before scribing the outline of the die on the face of the punch, care must be taken to see that the punch is set in the proper relation with the die, so that, when the finished tools are set up in the press, there will be no necessity for elongating or widening the slots in the die-bed used for clamping the die to the bed of the press, due to the punch not being laid out central with the die.

After the first punch *A* has been fitted to the die, the holes for the other three punches are laid out so that the cutting part of the punches will be as nearly central with the shanks as possible. Holes are then drilled and reamed for the shanks, and when this is done punch *A* is hardened. The reason that this punch is hardened before the other punches are fitted to the die is that if the punches were all sheared and fitted together and then punch *A* should spring in hardening, it would cause great difficulties in again bringing the punches into proper alignment with the die. After punch *A* has been hardened and driven back into the punch-holder, the shanks of the other three punches are turned up and fitted to the respective holes into which they are afterwards driven. The shanks of these punches may be made either straight or tapered, but should be a good driving fit and should have shoulders bearing against the punch-holder.

Before the punches are driven into place, the die and punch *A* are set up in the foot press and properly aligned with each other. The gate of the press is then withdrawn, the three punches are driven into place, and the faces coated with soft solder. The gate of the press is then slipped back into place and the outline of the die transferred to the punches, after which they are driven out and milled separately in the milling machine. Sometimes the punches cannot be driven out from the back of the punch-holder, because if the holes for these punches were drilled through they would run into and weaken the shank of the holder. In such cases holes are drilled from the side to meet the shank holes, in order to allow a taper drift to be used for starting the punch so that it can be removed.

After the punches have been milled, they are driven back into the punch-holder and are sheared and fitted into the die, as previously described. The punches, of course, are lined up perfectly with the die so as to enter into their respective holes as one single punch. After the punches are hardened they are sharpened by holding the punch-holder in a special grinding fixture and drawing the punches back and forth across the face of a wheel of about the same diameter as the shell to be perforated. The bases of the punches are strengthened by milling the punches so that there is a liberal fillet between the shoulder of each punch and the milled-out shape. This also tends to prevent distortion in hardening.

The Stripper of a Perforating Die.—The stripper serves three purposes: It strips the metal from the punch; it supports the small punches by preventing them from springing; and it tends to keep the perforated shell in shape by preventing it from bending. The commonly used stripper construction is shown by the lower view, Fig. 31. The face of the stripper conforms to the outside diameter of the shell. It is drilled and worked out so that it is a sliding fit on the punches. The shoulder part of the stripper bears against the bottom lugs of the side pieces *A* and *B*, which are fastened to the punch-holder and prevent the stripper from being forced off the punch. Six spiral springs exert the required pressure on the stripper. When setting up the tools in the press, the stripper is forced back about ⅛ inch and two pieces of, say No. 31 drill rod are placed between the stripper and the bottom lugs of the side pieces, which keep the stripper out of the way while the punch and die are aligned with each other.

Perforating dies of the type described are sharpened on universal grinding machines. Owing to frequent sharpening it is sometimes necessary to raise them slightly by putting shims of sheet steel under the dies. These shims are drilled and filed out to conform to the holes in the dies, in order that the scrap punchings may drop through.

CHAPTER IX

SUB-PRESS OR SELF-GUIDING DIES

THE term "sub-press" does not indicate a type of die but rather a method of constructing dies so that the upper and lower members are combined in one self-contained unit and are held in accurate alignment. A typical form of sub-press construction for the smaller classes of dies is shown in Fig. 1. The frame or barrel *A* is fitted to the base and serves as a guide for plunger *C*, which holds the upper die member and slides vertically in an adjustable babbitt bearing. The plunger head or "button" *D* engages a T-slotted block held by the press slide. This form of connection allows any slight floating movement which may be necessary to allow the sub-press to adjust itself and maintain its alignment independently of the alignment of the press proper. The compound type of die is commonly used in sub-presses, because these presses are used ordinarily for the most accurate classes of die work, but various other types of dies are applied to sub-presses.

The term "sub-press" is often applied to dies, the upper and lower members of which are held in alignment by guide pins or pillars. Usually there are two of these guide pins, but comparatively large dies have four guide pins to provide better support. Dies of this general class, which will be described later, are often referred to as "pillar dies," owing to the use of the pillars or guide pins for holding the upper and lower members in alignment.

Advantages of Sub-press Construction.—The sub-press die was originated in watch and clock factories for performing blanking operations requiring great accuracy, and, at the present time, dies built on the sub-press principle are employed for a great variety of work and in connection with many different lines of manufacturing. The sub-press is invaluable not only for blanking the delicate wheels and gears of watch and clock movements, but for producing the numerous small parts, such as are required for time-recorders, electrical instruments, meters, cyclometers, and a great many other similar devices. In fact, the extensive use of parts stamped or cut from sheet metal, in many delicate forms of mechanism, has been made possible by the sub-press, owing to the accuracy

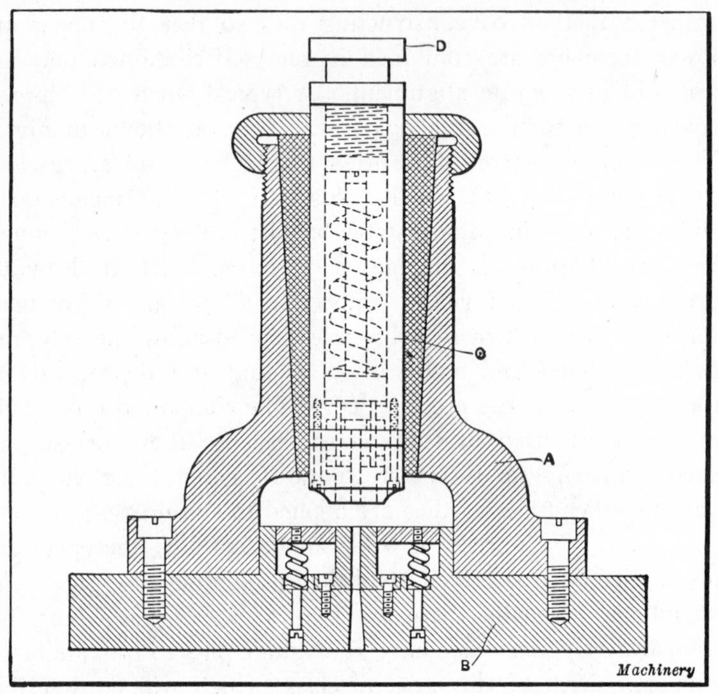

Fig. 1. Sub-press for Aligning and Guiding Upper and Lower Members of Compound Dies

which can be obtained; moveover, the rapidity with which the parts can be produced has resulted in a great reduction in the cost of manufacture. The fact that the sub-press is a self-contained tool and is not dependent upon the power press in which it is used (except for motion), combined with the ease with which a sub-press can be arranged for use, means not only accuracy but a great saving in time, because in setting up the sub-press it is simply necessary to slide the head of the punch plunger into a T-slot of the press slide, clamp the base to the bed of the press, and adjust the stroke. The sub-press is not only a time-saver but possesses another distinct advantage in that the unit construction makes it unnecessary to align the upper and lower die members. Still another point in favor of the sub-press is that this construction makes it possible to pierce smaller holes in thick stock than is possible with other dies, because the small punches are supported along almost the entire length. It is not unusual to punch holes in stock having a thickness which is over twice the diameter of the pierced hole. With sub-press dies a narrower "bridge" can also be left between blanks and a much better blank obtained than with any other form of die. The blanks are always of a uniform size, the die being straight instead of having clearance, as in the case of an ordinary die through which the blanks must pass; therefore, the first blanks punched from the new sub-press die are practically exact duplicates of those obtained when the die is about worn out; obviously, this means that a large quantity of work can be done in a sub-press die before it is unfit for use.

Owing to the large number of parts of which most sub-press dies are composed, the first cost is, of necessity, much higher than that of ordinary dies, but when we consider that the sub-press die, if properly made, will run ten hours per day for weeks at a time, without grinding, the initial cost does not seem so important. When using an ordinary follow die, it is almost impossible to obtain two blanks that are duplicates within very close limits of accuracy. One reason is that the stock to be punched is more or less wrinkled and does not lie flat on the face of the die; the result is that after the peircing punches have pierced the wrinkled stock and it is then flattened out, there is a slight variation in the distance between the holes. Moreover, the pilot-pins on the blanking punch, that are depended upon to locate the stock, cannot do this with extreme accuracy, since they are made a little smaller than the piercing punches to provide clearance. On many classes of work, following dies are entirely satisfactory, but when the parts to be produced are small and delicate, and especially when great accuracy is necessary, a die of the sub-press type should be used.

Although, in some cases, one sub-press can be made to take several sets of punches and dies, it is customary, and generally advisable, to have a separate sub-press for each set, as one of the advantages gained in using the sub-press is in being able to quickly change from one die to another; when separate sub-presses are used this can be done by simply loosening the clamps, changing the presses and re-clamping. In addition to this advantage, there is no time wasted in aligning the punches and dies; moreover, the danger of shearing the punch or die, as a result of careless alignment, is entirely eliminated.

Another advantage of the sub-press, dependent in part on the accuracy of alignment provided, and the corresponding accuracy in fitting which can be given to the cutting edges, is that the work is remarkably free from fins and burrs. A consideration of the action of the press will show that there is practically no chance for burrs to form in a piece even where they would in an ordinary blanking die. It is necessary for the die to descend until the punch has all but entered it, if clean work is to be produced. There is a slight difference in the practice of different operators in this respect, although this difference in practice would be expressed in the dimensions of only 0.002 or 0.003 inch, perhaps. Some of them adjust the stroke so that the die does not quite meet the punch. Others prefer to have them meet and even enter by very slight amount. The only objection to the use of sub-presses is the extra cost, and this is often more apparent than real. The difference in cost is more noticeable in a simple, low-priced die than in a compound die, and, in fact, in the latter case it often occurs that a complicated die can be made with less expense by using a sub-press than by any other method.

Typical Sub-press Die Construction.—A brief description of a sub-press die for producing the blank shown at *A*, in

Fig. 2, follows: The upper half of the casting or cylinder *B* is shouldered onto the base *C*, to which it is attached by screws *D*; it is also doweled in position by the two pins *E*. The plunger *F* runs in a casing of babbitt shown at *G*, the wear in which is taken up when necessary by screwing down the tightening nut *H*, which forces the babbitt down and in at the same time, as the cylinder is bored on a slight taper. The plunger has three semi-circular grooves milled along its length to prevent its turning. Attached to the plunger is the die *I*, which cuts the outside of the blank, and the small punches *J* which are held in the back-plate *K* and supported by the shedder *L* which is backed up by the heavy spring *M*. The tension on this spring is obtained by screwing down screw *N* which has a small hole running through it to allow the air to escape. The center piece *O* and the three pins *P*, placed between the spring and shedder, supply the tension necessary to operate the latter. The hardened disk *Q* is pressed into the plunger behind the back-plate, as indicated, to take the thrust of the small punches. The base *C* is recessed to receive the base of the larger punch *R* which has three openings for the three small punches *J*, clearance being provided to allow the scrap punchings to pass through. The stripper in the lower member is shown at *S*, the resistance from the Springs *T* doing the work. The most important parts are also shown in detail and are marked with corresponding reference letters.

In operation the plunger descends with the ram of the press and the stock caught between the two flat surfaces is held firmly in position, thereby preventing any creeping or distortion of the metal during blanking. The outside of the blank and the pierced holes are cut simultaneously, the die being a compound type. Upon the return stroke of the ram, the tension from the small springs *T* forces the stripper *S* back over the punch *R* which still has the blank pressed firmly against its face by the shedder *L*, forcing the blank back into the scrap from which it is afterwards removed.

Another sub-press of the common cylindrical type is shown in Fig. 3. To the base *B* is screwed and doweled the cylinder

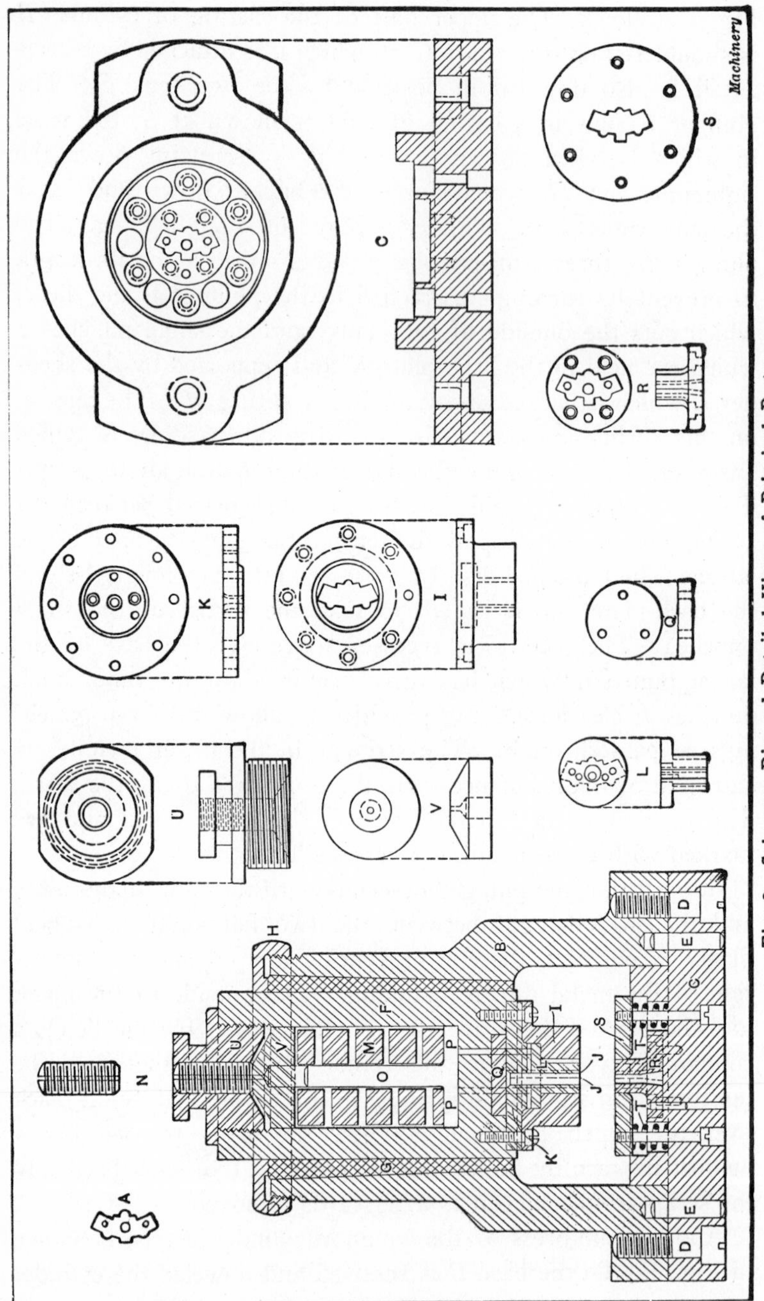

Fig. 2. Sub-press Die and Detailed Views of Principal Parts

A lined with babbitt, as shown at *C*, this lining being provided with ribs which engage corresponding grooves in plunger *D*, which works up and down within the babbitt lining under the action of the ram of the press in which it is used. Nut *U* furnishes an adjustment for tightening the babbitt lining to take up all slack due to wear, as fast as it is developed. The die *K* is screwed and doweled to plunger *D*. Accurately fit-

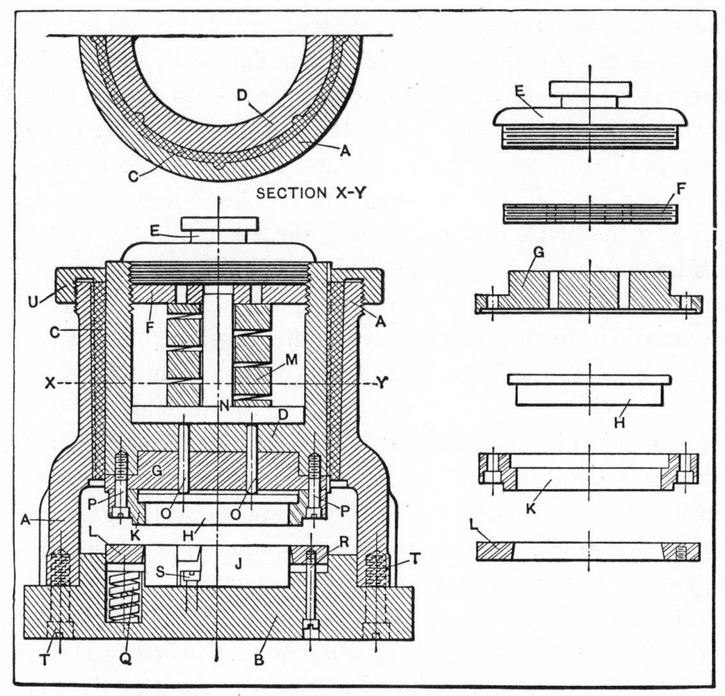

Fig. 3. Another Sub-press Die of Typical Design

ting the opening in this die is the shedder *H*, which is normally forced downward with its face flush with the face of the die by the action of spring *M*, which acts through the plate *N* and pins *O*. A similar construction is used in the bottom member: *J* is the punch, screwed and doweled to the base; and *L* is the stripper, surrounding the punch and accurately fitting it, and held firmly at the upper extremity of its movement by the pressure of suitable springs. This is restrained with its face flush with that of the punch, by the heads on stripper screws *R*. Thus it will be seen that the faces of the punch with its stripper and the die with its shedder may be ground off smooth and flush with each other, presenting to the eye the appearance of two solid plates of metal, the division between the fixed and spring-supported members scarcely being visible if the fitting has been well done.

With this construction in mind, the enlarged details of the punch and die shown in Fig. 4 will be readily understood. Similar letters in each case refer to similar parts, but only the members of the device which actually work on the metal are shown. The outline of the punching made in this die is indicated by the outline of the punch and its stripper, as shown in the plan view. There are two small holes *c* and one larger hole *b* in the blank. For punching these small holes, in addition to the simple arrangement shown in Fig. 3, openings in the punch are necessary, and small piercing punches have to be placed within the aperture of the die, passing through holes in the shedder; the holes in the punch are continued through the base of the sub-press, so that the waste material drops through beneath the machine. The piercing punches in the upper member are held to die pad *G* by holding screws *g* which draw these parts up into their tapered seats against the shoulders formed on them for the purpose. The fitting at all the cutting edges is done with great accuracy. The punch *J* fits die *K* very closely, and the shedder *H* is also closely fitted to the die. The stripper *L* is fitted to the punch, and small punches *f* are accurately aligned and closely sized to their corresponding openings in the face of main punch *J*. The pins *h* are used to guide the strip of stock, and are pressed down by the descent of die *K*, returning under the action of their springs as the ram ascends.

With the stock in place, die *K*, and with it small punches *f*, descend, the latter passing through the stock until they almost meet the corresponding cutting edges in the lower member. As soon as shedder *H* strikes the stock, its motion is arrested, and it remains behind until the blank is cut, being meanwhile

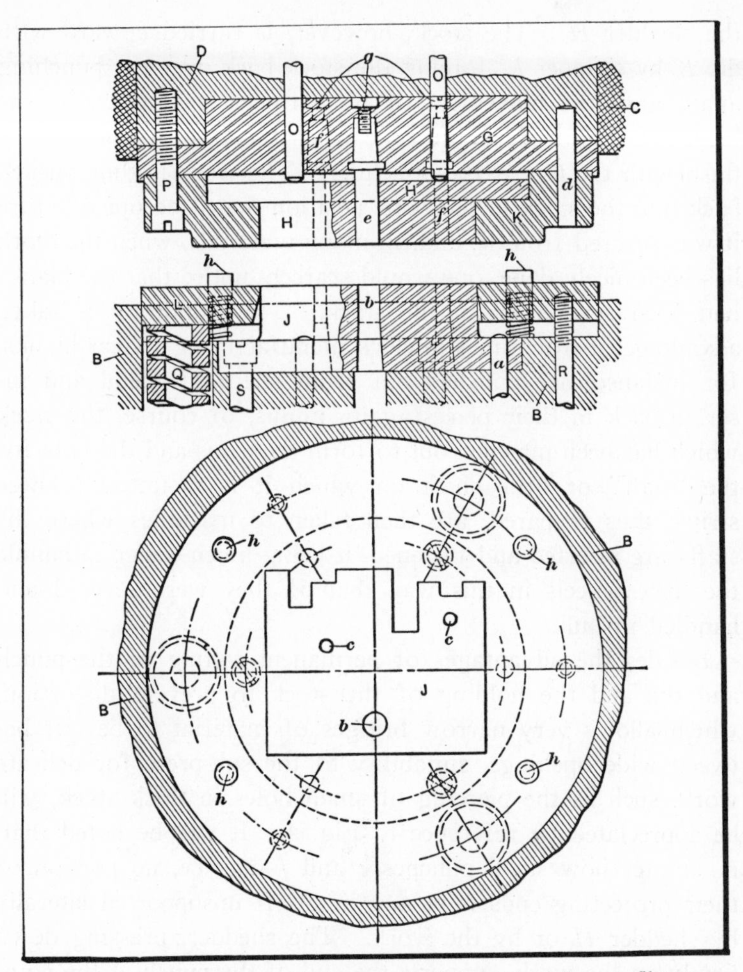

Fig. 4. Enlarged Views of Compound Die used in Sub-press Shown in Fig. 3

powerfully pressed upon the work by spring *M*. As the stock, while being sheared, is pressed down around the blank, it carries with it stripper *L* which also, by the influence of springs *Q*, exerts a heavy pressure on the stock. The whole area of metal being thus firmly held between plane surfaces, there is no danger of buckling or distortion of the stock as would otherwise be likely. As the ram moves upward again the blank is still firmly held on the stationary top of punch *J* by the shedder *H*. The stock, however, is carried upward with die *K* by stripper *L*, forcing the stock back over the punching again until the movement of the stripper is arrested by the heads of screws *R*, at the time when the face of the stock is flush with the top of the punching. The work is thus pushed back into the stock in the same position that it occupied before it was severed from it, and, in many materials, when the work has been nicely done, one would scarcely notice that the blanks had been severed from the stock. This condition is taken advantage of oftentimes in clock manufacturing. Gear blanks, for instance, are punched out from strips of metal and inserted back in their places again, minus, of course, the stock which has been punched out to form the arms and the hole for the "staff" or little shaft on which it is mounted. These strips, thus prepared, are then taken to machines where the staffs are inserted and fastened, it being much easier to handle the little wheels in this way than if they were severed and handled in bulk.

Besides the advantages of permanent setting of the punch and die and the holding of the stock to prevent distortion, which allows very narrow bridges of material to be left between wide openings, suitability of the sub-press for delicate work, such as the piercing of small holes in thick stock, will be appreciated by reference to Fig. 4. It will be noted that, no matter how small punches *e* and *f* may be, no portion of their projecting ends is at any time left unsupported laterally by shedder *H* or by the work. The shedder, pressing down firmly on the work, supports the end of the punch at the point where the pressure is applied. It is thus possible to employ a much more slender punch for a given thickness of stock than can be used in ordinary dies.

General Procedure in Making Sub-press Dies.—The making of sub-press dies requires both skill and experience, but a general idea of the method of procedure may be obtained from the following description which applies to the principal operations connected with sub-press die construction. As the practice referred to is that of the shop or tool-room in which the die under consideration was made, it may not conform altogether with the methods employed elsewhere, although an attempt has been made to present only approved practice.

In making the sub-press die shown in Fig. 3, the base *B* and cylinder *A* are first machined and fitted together according to methods that would naturally be pursued by any good mechanic. The inner surface of the cylinder is grooved lengthwise (as shown by the section X-Y) so that the babbit may be securely locked against rotary movement. Plunger *D* is then machined, and the outer surface ground and fluted lengthwise with semi-circular grooves. Especial pains are taken to have these grooves parallel with the axis of the plunger in both planes; if this is not done the die may be given a slight twisting movement instead of the perfectly straight forward one that is required, since upon these grooves depends the angular location of the punch and die with relation to each other. The plunger is now inserted within the cylinder and, with proper precaution, the space between them is filled with babbitt which flows into the grooves in the cylinder and those in the plunger as well, locking with one and guiding the other. After being cooled, the plunger is worked up and down to test the bearing which is then scraped to obtain free movement and to insure a more perfect bearing. The nut *U* is screwed down until all slack is taken up. Die *K* is now made to accurately fit the templet or model furnished the toolmaker as a sample. After it has been completed, it is hardened and fastened in place. Then the model is inserted within it, and such holes as may be required in the blank are transferred to die pad *G*. This is done by punches with outside diameters ground to fit the holes in the templet, and provided with sharp points concentric with the outside. The pad, after being thus prick-punched, is put on the face-plate, the slight punch marks are carefully indicated, and the holes are carefully bored to a taper to fit the punches which are to be inserted in them. The punches are finished by grinding on centers after they are hardened. They are supported at the shank by a male center, while the opposite end is temporarily ground to a point which revolves in a female center in the other end of the grinder. The punch may thus be ground all over with the assurance that the pointed end is true with the exterior —a necessary provision, as will appear later.

It might be noted here that no draft is given to any of the cutting edges of these tools, since they do not enter each other, at least not to any appreciable extent, and since the stock in entering and leaving the cutting edges is positively moved, no clearance is necessary, and the die cuts practically the same kind of a blank throughout its life. Shedder *H* is fitted to die *K* and the holes for the punches are transferred to it in the same way as for the die pad, by means of carefully machined prick-punches which fit the holes in the models, these prick-punch marks being afterward indicated to run true on the faceplate. The punch is now worked out a very slight amount larger in all its outlines than the die. The model is laid upon it and the holes transferred to it, as in the case of the other parts; these holes are then indicated and bored out, but not ground in this case, being left three or four thousandths of an inch smaller in diameter than finished size. The punch is fastened in place in the base and aligned as nearly as possible with the die. The ram is forced downward in a screw press until the punch enters the die very slightly, cutting a thin chip from its sides to bring them to the shape required. The punch is then worked down to this point all around and again entered in the die a short distance further, the operation being repeated until the two parts fit perfectly.

In finishing the holes in the punch, after the hardening process, small brass plugs are first driven into each hole. The punches *f*, Fig. 4, still with their ends pointed concentric with their outside surfaces, are fastened in position in the upper member, and the ram is brought down until these punches mark slight centers in the top of the brass plugs, when the ram is again raised and the punch *J* (Fig. 3) removed. The punch is then strapped to the faceplate and each of the small plugs is in turn indicated from the prick-punch marks, when it is removed and the hole is ground to size with a steel lap charged with diamond dust in an internal grinding fixture. The stripper is fitted to the punch in the usual manner. With the parts thus made and fitted great accuracy is obtainable.

Construction of a Sub-press Die for Washers.—In order to further illustrate the general procedure in sub-press die construction, the die used for punching an ordinary washer has been selected for an illustration. Having selected a frame or "barrel" of the circular form shown in Fig. 5, it is placed in a chuck, being held by the upper end, and faced off on the bottom; the recess *A* is also bored to fit snugly the corresponding boss on the base of the press. This base is finished on both top and bottom, and the boss on it is turned to fit the bottom of the frame. The center of the base is recessed to receive the stripper plate and blanking punch, and a hole is drilled completely through to allow scrap punchings to fall to the floor. The base and frame are then fastened together by means of bolts and dowel pins, as shown. Together they are clamped to the faceplate of the lathe, being centrally located by means of a plug center which fits into the lathe spindle and passes through the hole in the center of the base. In this position the frame is bored out to a taper of about one-half inch per foot. After boring, a splining tool is substituted for the boring tool, and with the lathe locked by means of the back-gears, three or four grooves *B* are cut the entire length of the bore by sliding the carriage back and forth. At the same setting the upper end of the frame is faced off and threaded to receive the cap which is screwed on the frame. After the cap is in place, the hole for the plunger in this cap is bored out to the required size. This insures the hole in the cap being central with the inside of the frame.

The plunger (which is also shown in detail) is the next piece to receive consideration. After being centered and rough-turned, it is put in the center-rest, and the hole *C* bored and threaded and fitted with the button by means of which connection is made with the press slide. The internal thread in the plunger is carried down to a considerable depth in order to allow of the insertion of a tension cap, by means of which a sufficient tension is placed upon the stripper spring to force the punching back into the stock upon the return stroke of the press. A dog is fastened to the button and the plunger turned to fit the hole in the cap, great care being exercised to keep the sides perfectly parallel. After turning, the lathe is blocked by the back-gear, and three grooves *E* are splined, about 1/16 inch deep, for the entire length. It is essential that these grooves be parallel with the axis of the plunger. Before the plunger is completed, a ring, 3/4 inch wide, is made of machine steel and forced onto the lower end of it. The outside of this ring is trued up, using the plunger as an arbor, after which this end of the plunger is placed in the center-rest, where the ring prevents it from being scored or injured by the center-rest jaws. In this position the recess *F* is bored to receive the punch-holder *K*.

The punch-holder is made, as are also the die stripper and piercing punch, by turning from a bar held in the chuck and finishing complete before cutting off. The recess which receives the head of the piercing punch should be bored at the same time to insure its being central with the rest of the die. The stripper, which is placed inside the blanking die, should be made of tool steel and left large to allow for grinding after hardening, while the hole is bored sufficiently small to allow for lapping to exact size. The blanking punch, which also forms the piercing die, is made of tool steel in the same manner, being finished completely before it is cut off, and it is left with sufficient stock to grind after it has been hardened. The holes *H* are drilled and counterbored for screws to hold the punch to the base.

After the parts are hardened, the blanking die is the first to be ground. It is gripped in a chuck, upper end outward, and the large hole *J* is ground out to fit the step *K* on the punch-holder. Then the hole *L* is ground perfectly straight and of the same diameter as the master templet. The top face is also ground off, thus completing the die. In the stripper, the hole *M* is lapped to the same dimension as that in the templet. A round piece of cold-rolled steel is gripped in a lathe chuck and turned to fit closely the hole in the stripper. Without disturbing the chuck, wring the stripper onto this arbor and grind the

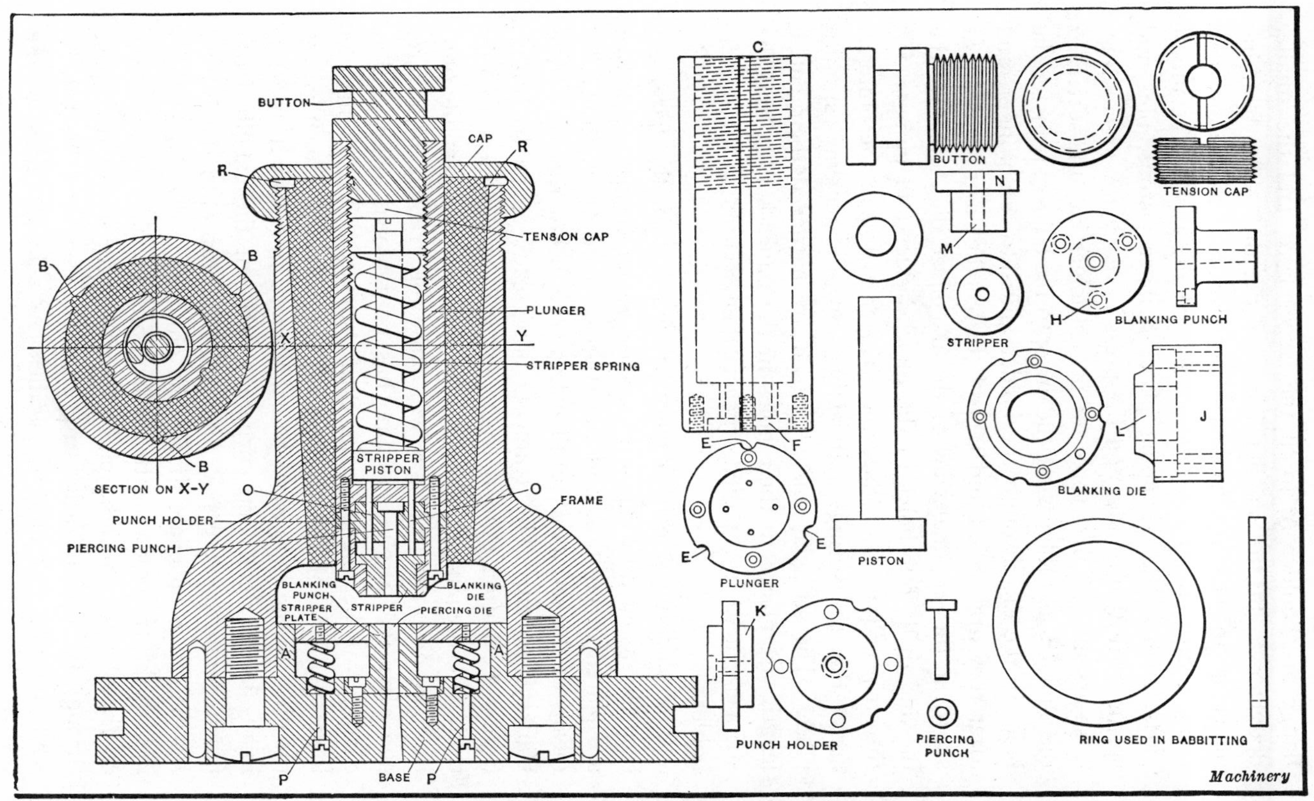

Fig. 5. Sub-press Die for Blanking and Piercing Washers

flange or shoulder *N* to fit the larger bore, and the smaller diameter to fit the smaller bore, of the die. The blanking punch is finished in exactly the same manner as the stripper, being ground to fit the recessed seat in the base. The minor parts, such as the stripping plate, stripper pistons, pins and springs, are then made, and the press is ready for assembling.

In assembling, first force the punch-holder into the seat *F* of the plunger, and then force the die onto the holder; transfer the holes in the die through the holder and into the plunger, and after they are drilled and tapped, fasten the parts together as shown in the sectional view of the assembled die. Remove the die and drill four holes in the punch-holder and plunger for the stripper pins *O*. Place the stripper piston in the plunger, above this the spring, and lastly screw the tension cap into place. The stripper pins *O*, which are hardened their entire length, are placed in their holes in the punch-holder, and the stripper placed in the die, which is then secured to the punch-holder.

The blanking punch is placed in its seat in the base and securely fastened by cap-screws, after which the springs shown are placed in position and the stripper plate drawn down by means of the screws *P*, until it is a trifle below the top of the blanking punch. The frame is now ready to be babbitted. Screw the button onto the plunger, and with a piece of oily cloth wipe the plunger all over, then sprinkle flake graphite onto it. The oil on the plunger will cause the graphite to adhere, and after the surplus graphite has been blown away, a thin coating will be left over the entire surface. The plunger is lowered inside of the frame until the blanking punch enters the die. In the cap insert the babbitting ring(shown in detail in the lower right-hand corner) to prevent the babbitt from flowing into the recess *R*, and screw the cap onto the frame. As the cap is an exact fit for the plunger, it therefore aligns it with the frame and with the blanking punch. The grooves on the plunger must be plugged with putty where they pass through the cap, in order to prevent the escape of the babbitt while pouring. A pair of parallels, of a height equal to the projection of the button beyond the top of the cap are now placed on the bench, and the die is placed in an inverted position upon them. Great care should be taken to avoid any vibration during pouring, as very little will affect the alignment of the plunger. Before pouring, heat the frame with a torch or jet of gas, and when the babbitt has attained the proper heat, which is a very dark red, pour in from both sides of the die simultaneously. Allow it to remain until thoroughly cool, then remove the plunger, strap the frame to the faceplate of a lathe, and cut a spiral oil groove the entire length of the babbitt.

As the blanking punch has already been ground, the next step is to grind the faces of the blanking die, piercing punch, and stripper, while all are in their proper positions in the plunger. They should be ground so that the face of the stripper, die, and punch are all flush with each other. After grinding, the parts should be taken from the plunger and thoroughly cleaned, so that there will be no abrasive in the working parts. Oil all of the running parts in a thorough manner, then put them together in their proper positions, and replace the plunger in the frame. In setting up a sub-press die, care should be taken to have the punch come only to the face of the die, and not enter it to any appreciable extent.

Sub-press Equipped with Die for Blanking and Forming Copper Cups.—The die shown in Fig. 6 was designed to blank and draw a copper cup or capsule used in the manufacture of balance wheels for watches. The copper strip is fed into the press, which then blanks out and draws the metal into the shape shown at *R*, at the same time punching the center hole. Referring to the illustration, *A* is the base of the sub-press, *B* the body, *C* the cap, and *D* the plunger, all these being of cast iron machined to size. The body and base are held together by two screws *E* in the usual manner; *F* is the buffer plug which receives the thrust of the press ram; *G* is the babbitt lining of the body *B*; *H* is the outside diameter die, held in place by four screws and two dowel-pins; H_1 is the outside diameter punch, also held in place by four screws and two dowels; I is the die for cutting out the center hole, and J is the punch for this hole. The parts H_1 and I also serve as forming dies in bringing the metal to the proper shape. The "shedders" or strippers K and L are supported by four push-pins, those of the former resting upon springs, the tension of which is controlled by short threaded plugs, as shown, and those for the latter abutting against the piston M, which is

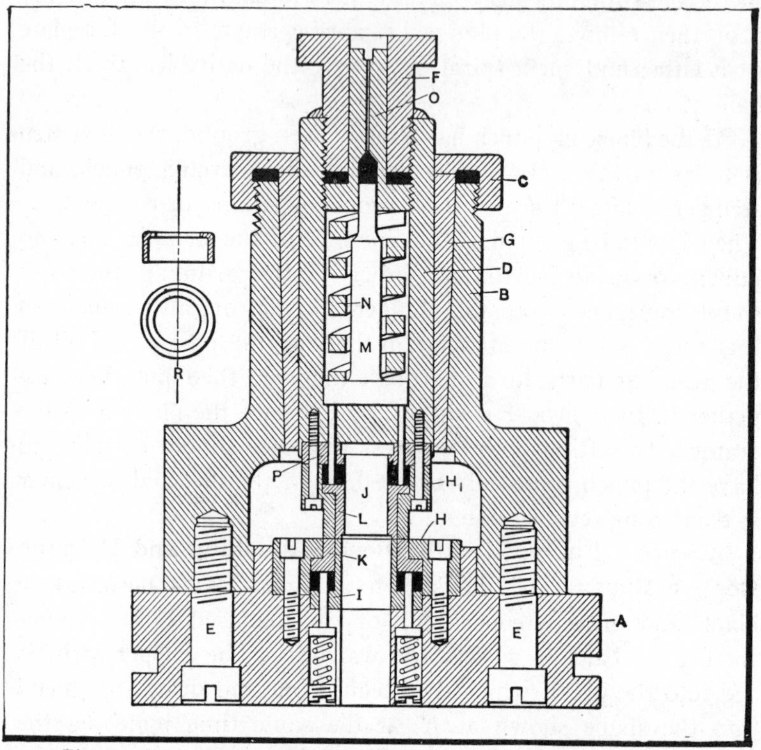

Fig. 6. Sub-press for Blanking, Piercing, and Drawing the Copper Cup Shown at *R*

pressed down by the large spring N, the tension of which is controlled by the plug O. The block P is used merely to hold the punch J firmly in place.

The operation of the die is as follows: The press ram being at the top of the stroke, the strip is fed in across the top of H, and as the ram descends, the blank is cut from the strip by the punch H_1 and drawn to a cup shape between the inside edge of H_1 and the outside edge of *I*. Simultaneously, the center hole is punched by *J* and *I*. As will be seen by referring to the illustration, *J* is made a trifle short, so that the drawing operation will have begun before this hole is punched; this prevents any distortion of the piece by the punch *J*. A little trouble was experienced with this tool at first, on account of the air in the hollow plunger *D* forming a cushion when it was compressed by the rising of the piston *M*, thus preventing the proper working of the die. This was finally obviated by making a small groove at the side of the piston where it worked in the plug *O*, and drilling a vent hole through *O* as shown. This allowed free communication to the atmosphere, and from then on the die gave complete satisfaction. The variation in size among the cups, or capsules, as they are called, is never more than 0.001 of an inch either in diameter or in length.

Modified Type of Sub-press.—The modified design of sub-press shown in Fig. 7, is employed to shave the triangular pin hole in a balance hub and roller which is used in high-grade watch movements. The delicacy of this operation is indicated by the size of the drilled hole which is 0.015 inch in diameter. This hole is shaved to a triangular shape 0.0252 inch wide by 0.0142 inch deep, one side of which is formed to a radius of 0.0536 inch.

The sub-press consists of a solid stand *A* containing the punch and the die bearings; a cylinder *B* operated directly under the slide of the press; and a pillar *C* which maintains alignment of the punch with the die located in the base of the stand. The simplicity and low cost of construction will appeal to those well versed in punch and die design. The stand, being made of one piece of ribbed design, can be mounted on a lathe face-plate, and the plunger bearing, hole, and face for the die all machined at one setting so that proper alignment is insured.

After the cylinder bearing has been bushed, the yoke *D* is secured to a standard plug to which size all cylinders are lapped. This plug enters the cylinder bearing, and after yoke *D* has been clamped securely to stand *A*, the pillar hole is machined through the yoke down into the stand. The hole in the yoke

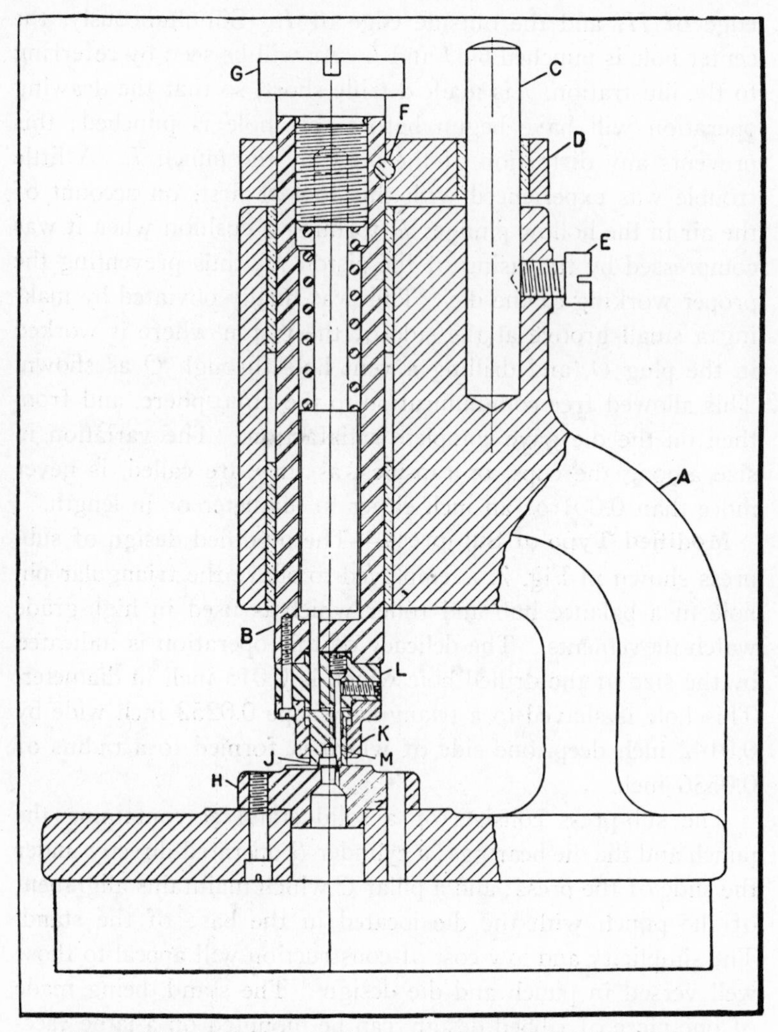

Fig. 7. Modified Design of Sub-press for Shaving Hole in Watch Part

for the pillar is provided with a bushing which is a sliding fit on the pillar. The pillar itself is ground and lapped its entire length, and is a light drive fit in the stand; it is finally secured by a set-screw *E*. In the assembly, the yoke is keyed to the cylinder by a taper pin *F*, and the cylinder is provided with the usual button *G*. If an accurately trued-up faceplate is used in boring the cylinder bearing and pillar hole, no difficulty will be experienced in machining these holes parallel.

The space between the upper and lower bushings on the cylinder is used as an oil well for lubrication. In this connection, attention is directed to a common practice in pillar sub-press design which is faulty. A great many designers provide a spiral groove on the pillars to assist lubrication. This opening affords access to grit and dirt which soon destroy the fit of the cylinder in the bushings. If the cylinder is properly fitted and the oil supplied from an internal reservoir, all dirt and grit will be excluded from the bearings and long life insured. This type of die is recommended for a great many press operations where a self-contained unit is desired for accuracy and rapidity in set-up, and where initial cost and upkeep are the prime considerations. It should, therefore, replace either the cylinder or the true pillar type in many instances.

Secondary Ejector for Sub-press Die.—Every diemaker or press hand is familiar with the troublesome, disastrous effect of having drawn and blanked pieces cling long enough to the ejector, or knockout, for the punch to descend upon a new piece of stock and also the punching just made. The outcome is likely to be a broken die. When using a sub-press die similar to that shown in Fig. 8, which is for blanking and drawing shallow cups, many thousand cups may be drawn without any mishap, especially if little or no oil is used on the stock, but without oil the life of the drawing die is shortened, or if copper or brass is being drawn, the metal tends to amalgamate with the die which, at intervals, must be taken down in order to remove this amalgamated material. On the other hand, if enough oil is put onto the stock to keep the dies in good condition, the cups or blanks may adhere to the face of the knock-out long enough to cause trouble. The simple device shown will prevent difficulty from this cause. The cast-iron plunger *A* carries the hardened drawing die *B* into which the knockout *C* is inserted for pushing the drawn piece from the die. If the cup *D* should cling to the face of the knockout by oil contact, the secondary knockout pin *E*, operated by a flat spring (see enlarged view), would force the work away from the face of the knockout as soon as the cup was pushed out of the drawing die. As spring *F* is strong enough to break any oil contact, the work is caused to drop immediately and the result is that the die can be operated at a much higher speed. The particular cup shown is 1¾ inches in diameter, ⅜ inch high, and 0.02 inch thick.

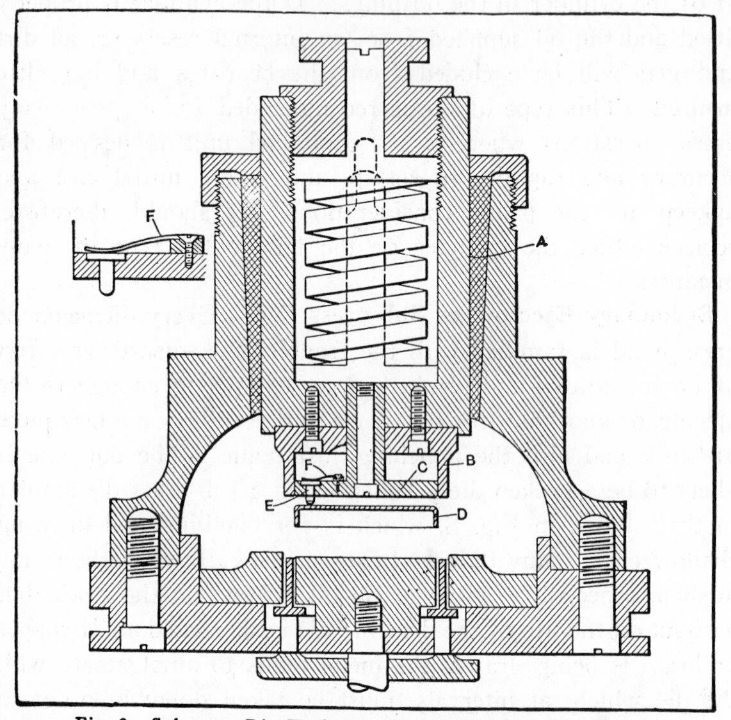

Fig. 8. Sub-press Die Equipped with Secondary Ejector Pin *E*

Commercial Die Sets.—Commercial "die sets" have been placed on the market by several manufacturers. A die set consists of a punch-holder, a die-holder or die-shoe, and two or more guide pins or leader pins for accurately holding the punch-holder and die-holder in alignment and also forming a complete unit which may readily be applied to a press. Die sets of this general type are manufactured in quite a number of different forms or designs and in many different sizes, which are standardized by the different manufacturers. These die sets are ready to be equipped by the purchaser or user with whatever punches and dies are required for a given operation. Figs. 9 to 12, inclusive, show the principal types or designs of commercial die sets.

The one illustrated at *A*, Fig. 9, has a die-holder which is nearly square and, as the plan view shows, there are two guide pins which are placed at the rear so that the front space between the punch and die is entirely open. A die set of this kind

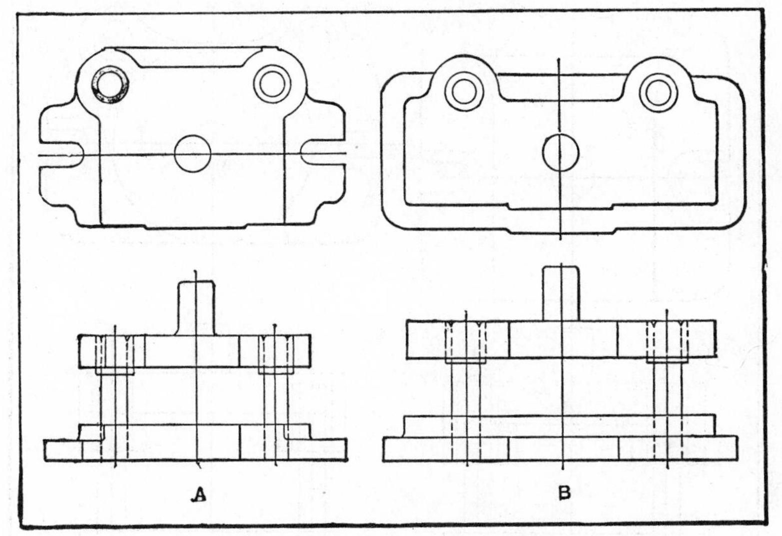

Fig. 9. Commercial Die Sets Made in Standard Shapes and Sizes

may not only be made in a series of sizes, but also with variations as to the thickness of the punch-holder and the die-holder. For example, both the punch-holder and die-holder may be made as thin as possible, without sacrificing the strength required, when the die set is to be used on a press having a comparatively small "shut height." (The definition and method for obtaining the "shut height" is given on page 56.) Other die sets have a thick die-holder and a comparatively thin punch-holder, and this order may also be reversed. A thick die-holder may be used to increase the strength, and a thick punch-holder may be needed to provide room for ejector springs or other moving parts.

The diagram *B*, Fig. 9, shows a long or narrow die set such as would be used for blanking parts which are comparatively long or for use with progressive dies. At *A* in Fig. 10 is shown a form that is wider from front to back than longitudinally, and at *B* is shown a die set having a circular die-holder for dies of circular form.

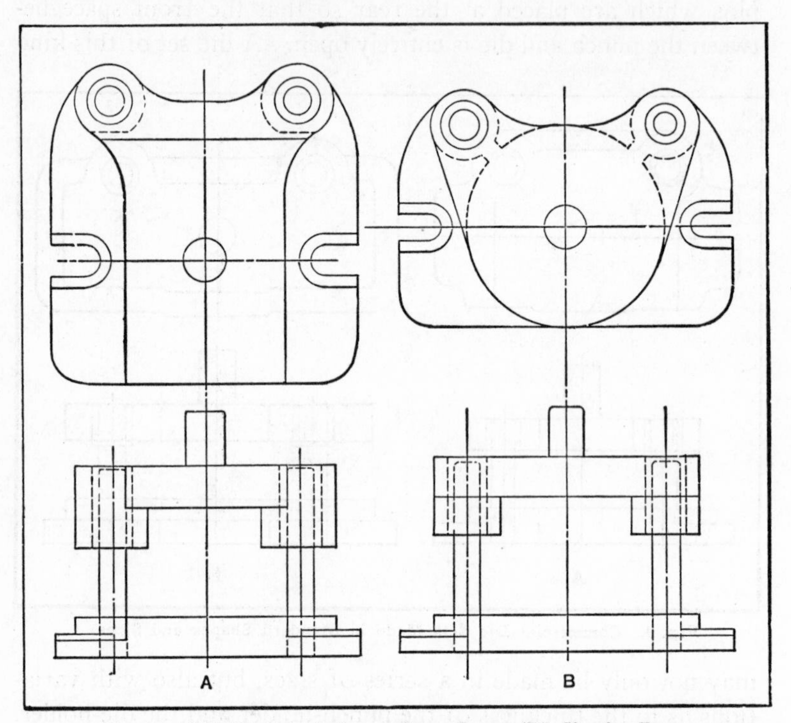

Fig. 10. (A) Die Set of Narrow Deep Form; (B) Circular Form

The designs illustrated in Fig. 11 are known as center-pin types, because the guide or leader pins are located on the center-lines. This arrangement brings the guide pins in line with the punch and die, thus eliminating overhang and providing a better support. Dies of this general class, although not as open and accessible as those having guide pins at the rear, are preferable for very precise work.

At *A* in Fig. 12 is shown the diagonal or staggered guide pin design. This general style has been widely used. The guide pins are in line with the punch and die, like the center-pin types, but the die is more accessible than the one shown at *A*, Fig. 11, and it is also adapted for feeding strip stock from the side. When dies are comparatively large, it is preferable to have four guide pins, a die set of this general type being shown at *B* in Fig. 12.

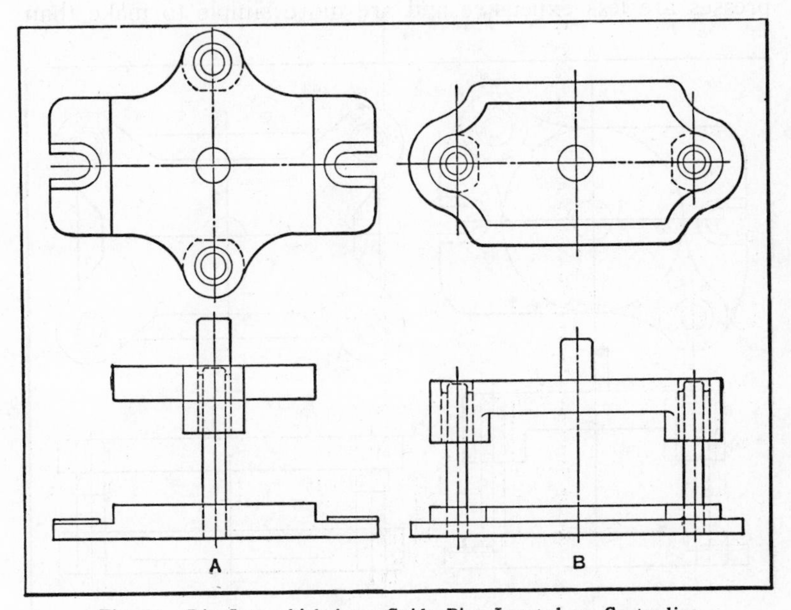

Fig. 11. Die Sets which have Guide Pins Located on Center-line

The punch-holders and die-holders of these commercial die sets are made ordinarily of semi-steel and the guide pins are of low-carbon steel, which is case hardened and ground. Hardened and ground bushings are also used in the punch-holder and many die sets are equipped with means for lubricating the guide pins and bushings. The lubricating device may consist of an enclosed oil wick surrounding the guide pin, or an oil wick may be inserted in a hole in the center of the pin, lateral holes and oil grooves being provided to convey oil to the outer surface.

The use of die sets with guide pins is an application of the sub-press construction and it insures accurate alignment, increases the life of the dies, reduces the number of grindings necessary, and also reduces the total die cost for the average user, because the main parts of commercial die sets are manufactured on a quantity basis. Dies equipped with guide pins are often called "pillar dies."

Advantages of Pillar Type of Sub-press.—Pillar sub-presses are less expensive and are more simple to make than

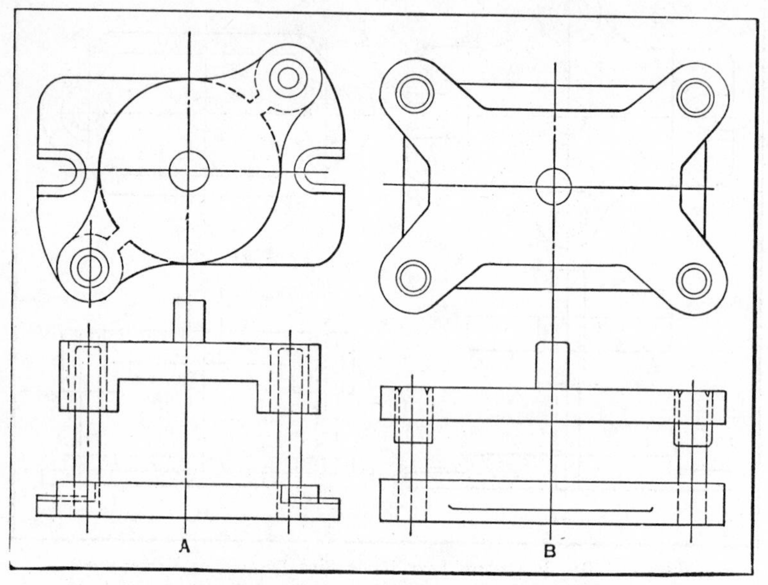

Fig. 12. (A) Guide Pins Located Diagonally; (B) A Larger Die Set Which Has Four Guide Pins

those of the cylinder type. They have the distinct advantage of more die space. It may be claimed that the pillar type of sub-press lacks adjustability for wear. If properly made, there will be no cause for this claim. Guide posts also facilitate lining up the parts in setting up the punch and die for an operation. Without them, the average set-up man rarely gets a die so lined up that the clearance is equal around the punch, and when there is unequal clearance, poor work, and not infrequently, broken punches and chipped dies are the result. When a die is equipped with guide posts, the proper clearance is insured around the working elements until enough wear has taken place on the guide posts or in the guide bushings to permit the die parts to shift. An additional advantage of guide posts is that they make a die set more or less self-contained so that the different parts are held together when off the press. Thus there is less trouble from chipped, jammed and misplaced parts.

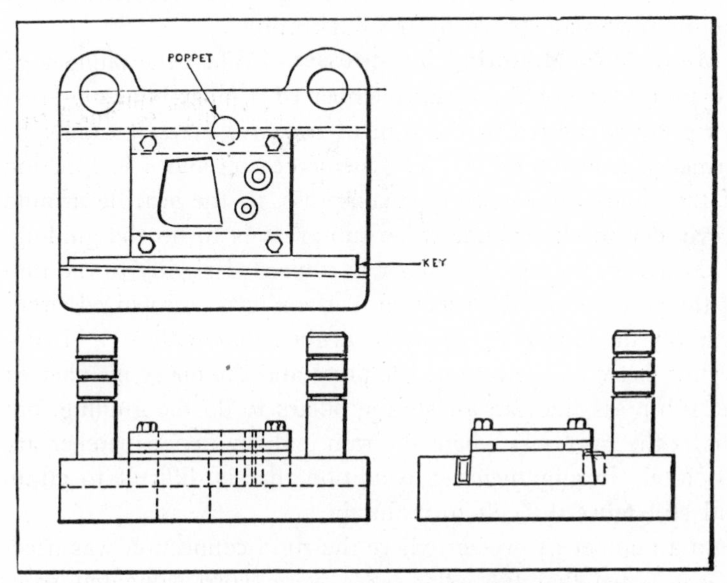

Fig. 13. Pillar Die Set so Constructed that Punch and Die Members may be Removed Readily for Regrinding

Pillar Die Arranged for Quick Removal of Punch and Die Members.—In spite of the many advantages of pillar die sets, they have several disadvantages which often limit their use. The first of these is the cost, especially in the case of small dies, where the expense is often twice as great as that of the ordinary type. Dies of the pillar type are also more difficult to grind, as they must either be taken apart for regrinding or be ground on a much larger machine than would otherwise be required.

The method illustrated in Fig. 13 of mounting the die and

punch in the die set was especially worked out to overcome these difficulties. The punch and die can easily be removed for grinding without taking the shoe from the press. As there is a minimum number of holes in the die sets, it is a simple matter to change from one set of tools to another. This construction also reduces the expense for die-shoes. The method is an adaptation of two well-known devices, the taper key method of holding dies, and the cylindrical "poppet" or dowel used to prevent drop-forged dies from shifting. The construction of the die is clearly shown by the illustration.

Methods of Mounting Sub-presses.—When the plunger of a cylinder-type or the upper member of a pillar-type sub-press is rigidly connected to the ram of a power press it cannot be termed a true sub-press. The prime reason and sole function of the pillars on a pillar-type sub-press, or the bearing around a cylinder of the cylinder-type sub-press is to do the guiding. If, however, the upper member is connected rigidly to the ram of the power press the function of the pillars is impaired either partially or entirely. It may be argued that with a rigid connection between the ram of the press and the upper member of the sub-press the ram assists the pillars to do the guiding, but this is the case only where the ram and the upper member are absolutely in alignment—a condition that is difficult to attain and still more difficult to maintain.

In a number of presses where the rigid connection was used, it was noted that the pillar holes were worn elongated from the continuous cramping action on the pillar. In some cases where a shank or plug connection was used, the shank was sheared off. On the other hand, in a pillar-type sub-press with an adapter that had $\frac{1}{32}$ inch or more play, or in other words, a floating connection, it was found that the pillar holes were 0.001 inch larger than the pillars, and this was an instance in which the press was in almost continuous operation for ten years. Therefore it would appear to be the best practice to employ a floating connection and use the pillars solely for the purpose they are intended for, namely *to do the guiding.*

Fig. 14 shows the usual type of shank or plug connection

for the upper member of a pillar type of sub-press. Fig. 15 shows the dovetail type. Another method of connecting is to bolt the upper member to the ram without any means of locating. These three types illustrate the usual practice for making a rigid connection. Fig. 16 shows a pillar-type sub-press

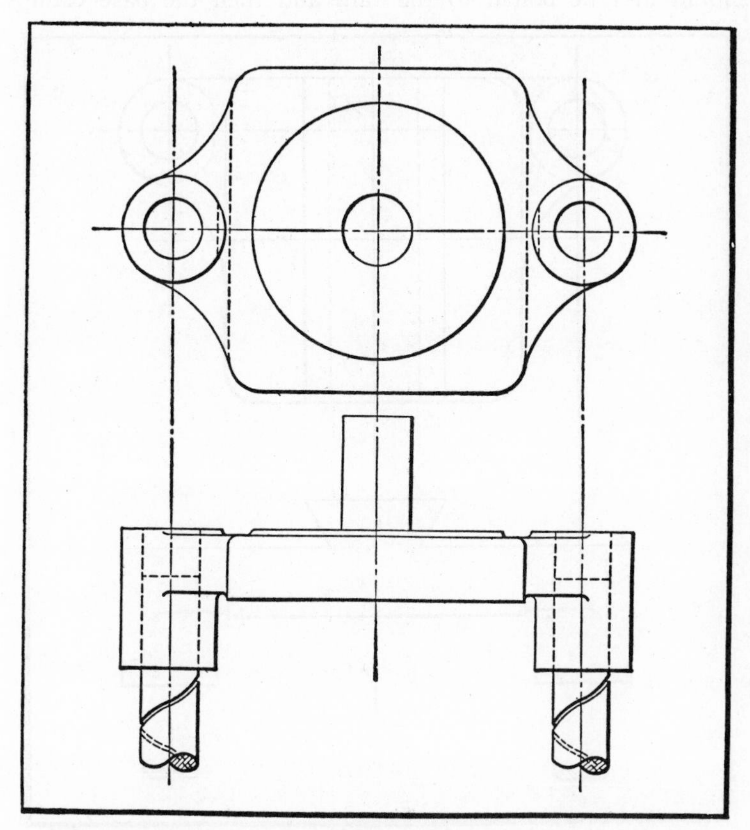

Fig. 14. Upper Member of Sub-press Having Usual Type of Shank or Plug Connection

arranged for a floating connection between the ram and the upper member.

When dies are equipped with guide posts, the base block should not be bolted to the press in the usual manner, but should be held down instead by clamps. If bolts are used, some careless operator will bolt the block to the table without first run ning the punches up and down in the dies a few times to test the setting. Then the result will probably be sprung guide posts or a broken die or machine, and in any event, wear will be considerably increased if the die parts bind in operation. When the base block is simply clamped in place, the punch-block should first be bolted to the ram and then the base clamps

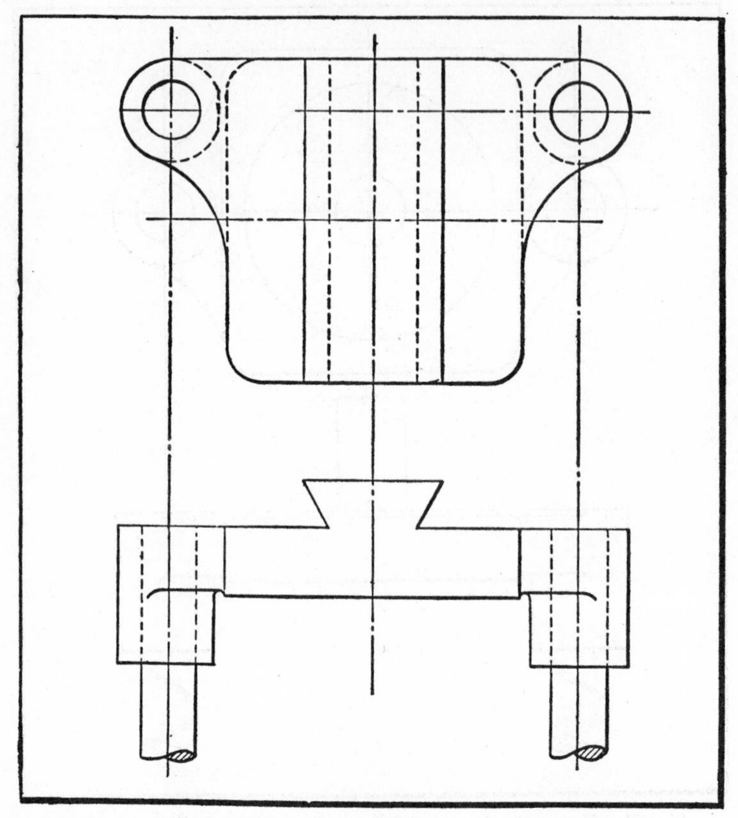

Fig. 15. Offset Type of Upper Member which is Dovetailed to Press Ram

tightened. Should the die parts then bind in a preliminary test, the base block will shift sufficiently to remedy the condition.

Sub-press Blanking, Drawing and Piercing Die.—A sectional view of a sub-press die of the two-pillar type employed in a watch factory for blanking, forming and piercing the

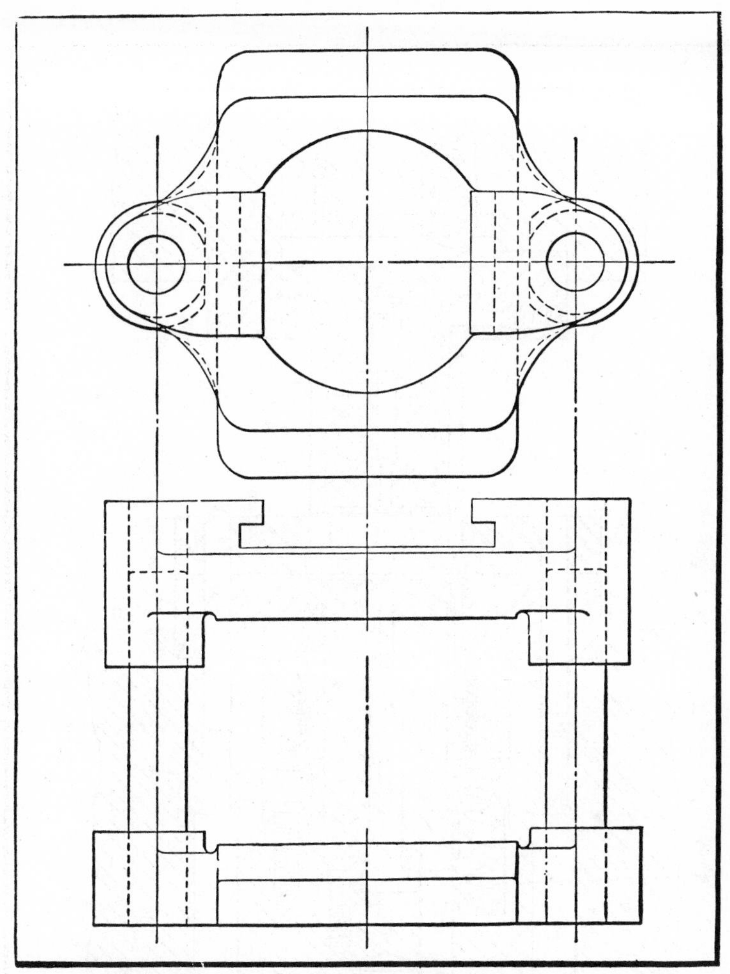

Fig. 16. Upper Member Designed for a Floating Connection to Press Slide

barrel drum of a watch is shown in Fig. 17. At the left in Fig. 18 is shown a sectional and plan view of the barrel drum. The diameter of the blank before being drawn or cupped is 0.825 inch. The stock used is Bessemer steel, ⅞ inch wide by 0.016 inch thick. Before the die shown in Fig. 17 was designed for this work, it was the practice to blank and draw the piece and then pierce and size it in a separate operation. Both of

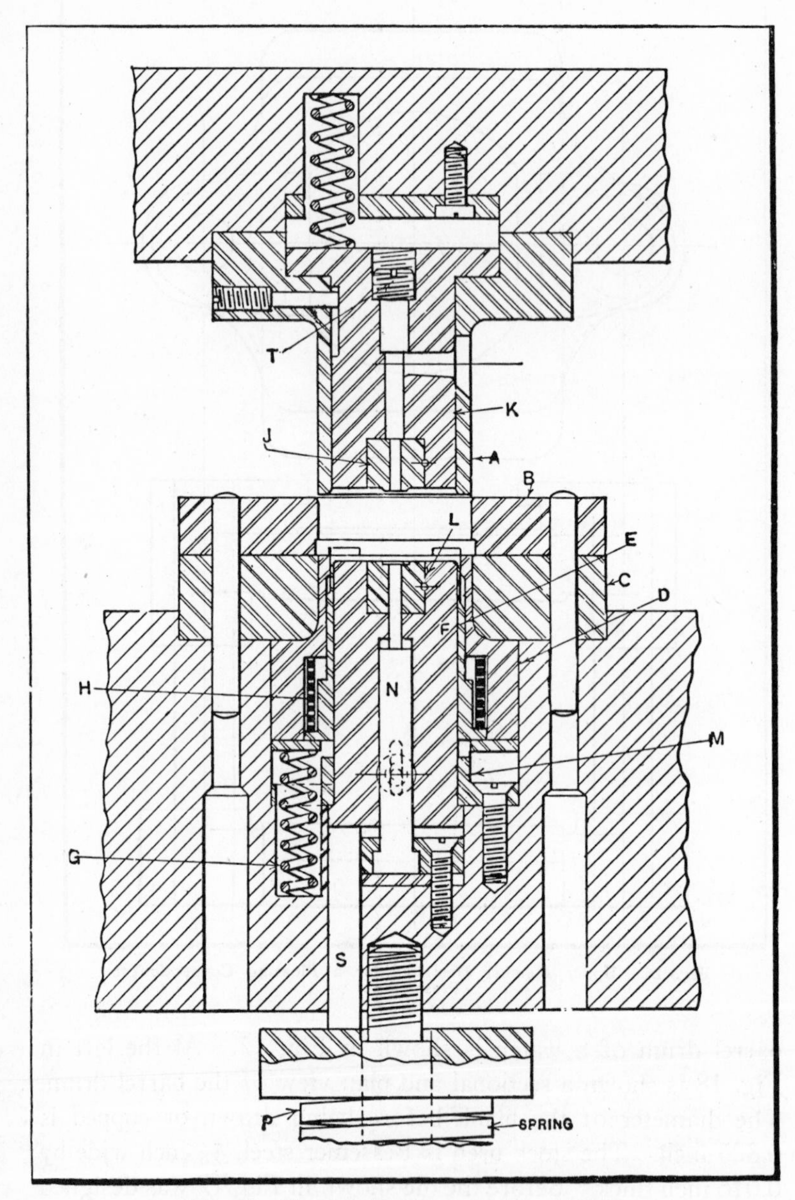

Fig. 17. Blanking, Drawing, and Piercing Die

these operations were performed in sub-press dies of the cylindrical type; thus two operations were required to do the work accomplished in one operation by the new die.

The sectional view at the right in Fig. 18 shows the blanked, formed, and pierced barrel drum *W* in the position it occupies when the ram of the press has reached the end of its downward stroke. The construction of the punch and die, however, is more fully illustrated in Fig. 17. On the downward stroke of the ram, punch *A* passes through stripper *B*, and, entering die *C*, blanks the piece. Part *D* is forced downward by punch *A* as the latter turns down the outer edge of the blank. Parts

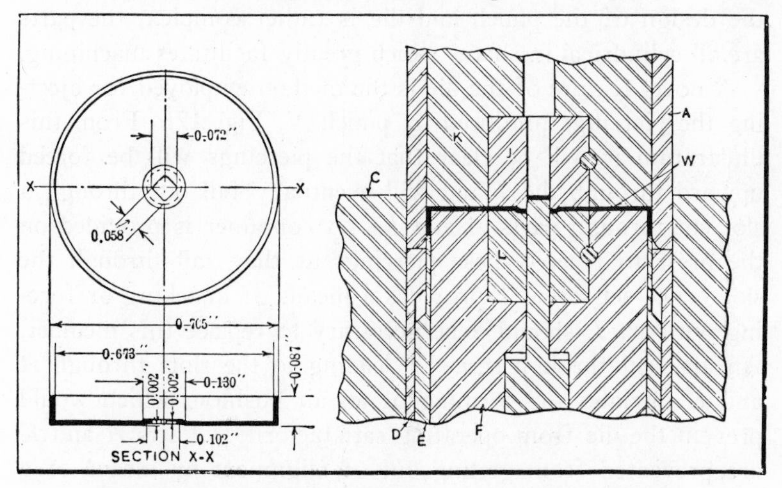

Fig. 18. Enlarged View of Work and Punch and Die Members

E and *F* recede with part *D* due to the pressure of punch *A*, which acts against the pressure exerted by springs *G* and *H*. When the end of the downward stroke is reached, part *E*, having come in contact with part *M*, will have upset the flange, thus producing a square edge at the bottom. Piercing punch *N* will have entered piercing die *J*, and part *K* will have receded the required distance in punch *A*. At the right in Fig. 18 is shown a detail view of the most important members of the punch and die.

On the upward stroke of the press, the finished piece is pushed out of the die by the action of the heavy sub-press spring *P* and the springs *H* and *G*, which act against parts *D* and *E*. It will be noted that spring *P* exerts pressure on the die member *F* through pins *S*. In order to prevent interference of the work with the top of the stripper, the latter member is cut away, as shown at *X*, Fig. 19. The problem of ejecting the work was solved by the use of four spring-actuated pins, one of which is shown at *Y*. These pins are designed to raise the stock just enough to permit it to contact with the center of the rim of the finished piece at *Z*. The stock, when fed in for the succeeding stroke of the press, serves to push the finished piece out of the die. It will be noted that although the design of the punch and die is rather complex, the parts are all cylindrical in shape, which greatly facilitates machining.

A novel feature of the die is the method employed for ejecting the piercings produced by punch *N*, Fig. 17. From this illustration it will be clear that the piercings will be forced upward through die *J* and will eventually fall out through a slot cut through parts *A* and *K*. A container is provided on the press to receive these piercings as they fall through the slot. The set-screw *T* provides a means of knocking or forcing out part *J*, should it be necessary to replace this member. An air vent through screw *T* leading to the slots through *A* and *K* obviates the forming of an air cushion, which would prevent the die from operating satisfactorily. Parts *A* and *K* are prevented from getting out of alignment by means of a pin and keyway as shown. Parts *J* and *L* are pinned to prevent them from turning in their holding members.

Two-pillar Sub-press for Watch Part.—In Fig. 20 is shown a small blanked and pierced part which is used in the watches made by a large watch manufacturing concern. The "click," as this part is called, works in conjunction with the ratchet wheel attached to the main spring of the watch, its function being to prevent the spring from unwinding. Heretofore it has been the general belief that it was next to impossible to produce the teeth on these parts by the blanking method, the usual practice being to cut the teeth on a generating machine. However, the pillar type of sub-press die which is shown in

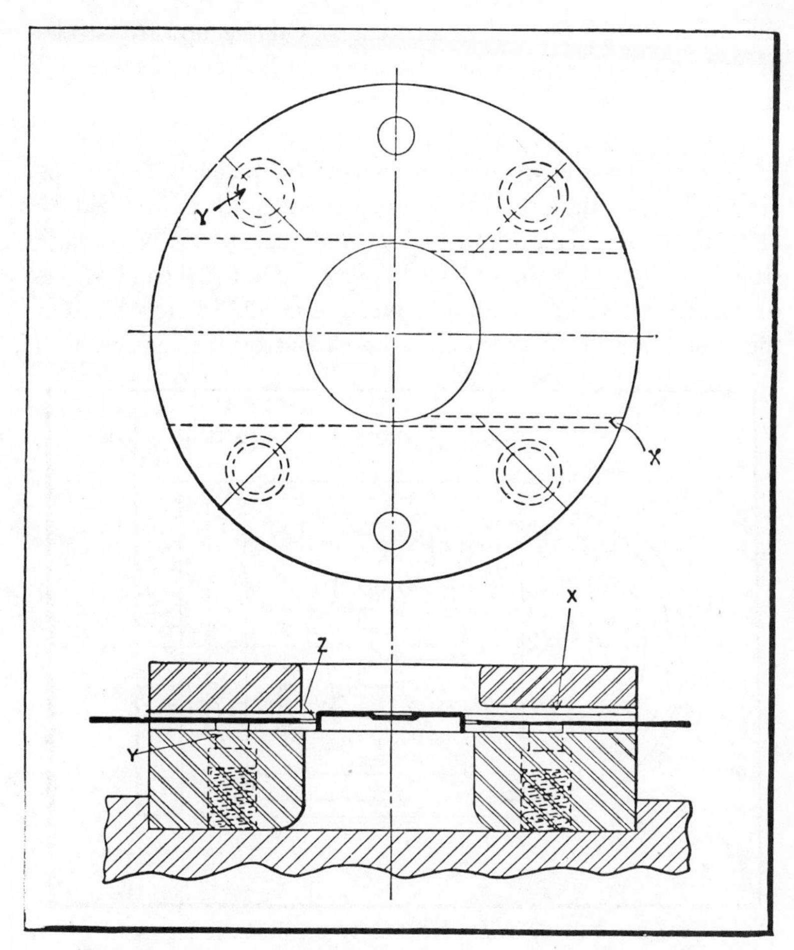

Fig. 19. Diagram Showing Work in Position to be Pushed from Die

Fig. 21 has been successfully employed to produce these teeth. At one stroke of the press this die blanks the teeth, pierces the holes, and pushes the finished piece from the stock by means of a separate attachment termed a "knock-out." The material used for the watch part is Bessemer strip steel, $5/16$ inch wide by 0.029 inch thick. It will be clear from Fig. 21 that on the downward stroke of the ram, the upper member or die *A* compresses stripper *B* and punch *C* enters die *A*. The stripper or shedder *D* is then pushed up into die *A*, compressing the sub-press spring *E* in the ram plate. On the upward stroke of the press the blank, which has been pushed out of the stock into die *A*, is pushed back into the strip by shedder *D* through the medium of spring *E*.

In Fig. 22 is shown the plan view of the punch. Two stops are used in the design of this punch. The stock is first fed by hand up to the temporary stop *K* and then to the automatic stop *L*, after which the roll feed is used. On the second stroke of the press the strip is pulled over the pin *M* in stop *K*. On the fourth stroke of the press a knock-out on the upper mem-

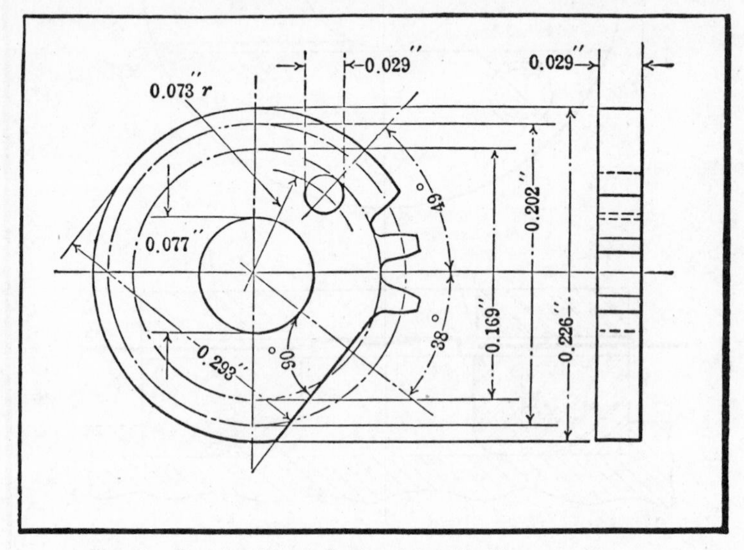

Fig. 20. Part for Watch Produced by Die Shown in Fig. 21

ber comes into use. This knock-out pushes the blanked piece from the stock through tube *N*, a receptacle being provided under the press to catch the finished pieces. At the sixth stroke of the press the temporary stop *K* is pulled back and clamped in position by screw *P*. The automatic stop *L*, shown in Figs. 22 and 23, is of the trigger type, having a projecting end which is operated by the adjustable striking screw *Q* held in the die-block. The plate *R* of the automatic stop is ground down each time the punch is ground so that the stock will not be bent where it passes from the blanking die to plate *R*.

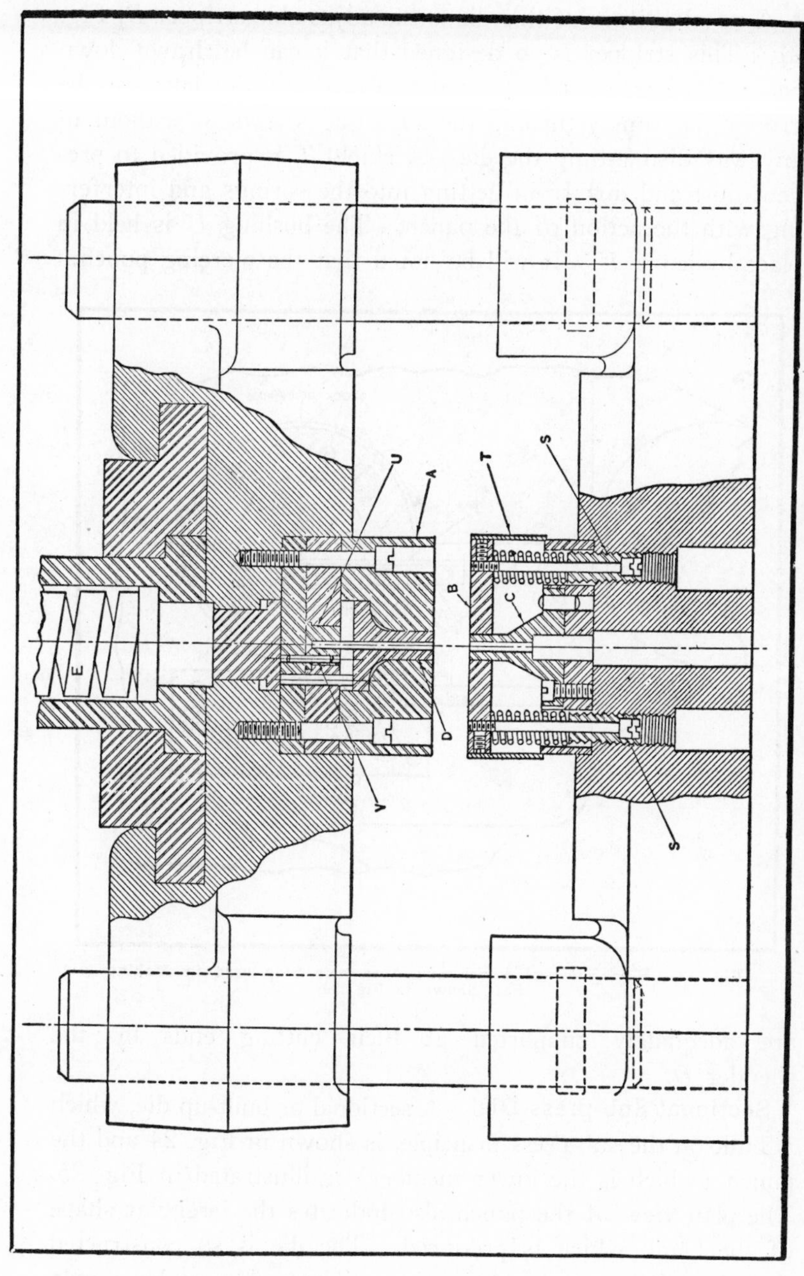

Fig. 21. Sub-press Die for Producing Watch Click Shown in Fig. 20

A novel feature of this die is the adjustable stripper *B*, Fig. 21. This stripper is so designed that it can be drawn down below the surface of the punch, to permit the latter to be ground, by simply turning the adjusting screws *S*, without in any way dismantling the die. A shield *T* is provided to prevent dust and dirt from getting into the springs and interfering with the action of the punch. The bushing *U* is held in place by a pin *V*. It will be noted that the piercing punches

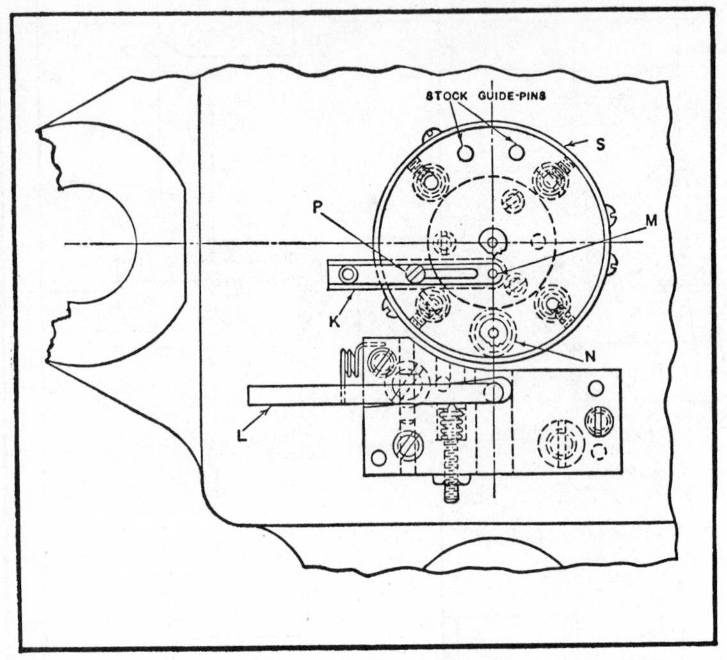

Fig. 22. Plan View of Punch and Automatic Stop used in Making Part Shown in Fig. 20

are adequately supported at their cutting ends by the shedder *D*.

Sectional Sub-press Die.—A sectional or built-up die, which is built on the sub-press principle, is shown in Fig. 24 and the punch (which is the lower member) is illustrated in Fig. 25. The plan view of the punch also indicates the irregular shape of the blank which is produced. The die is so constructed that the blanks can be changed to different shapes by simply

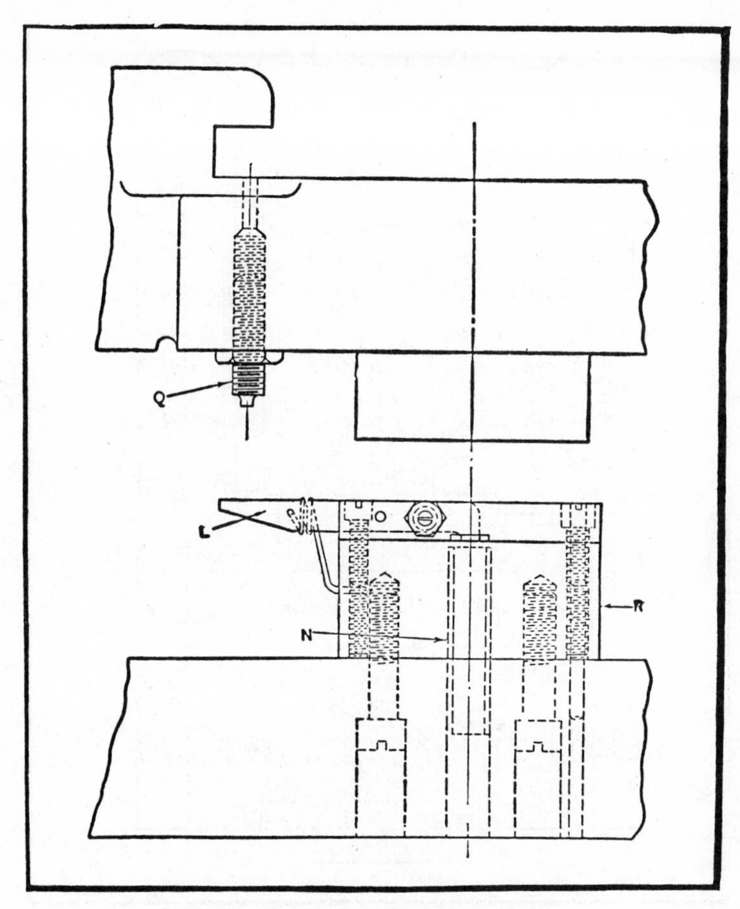

Fig. 23. Combination Knock-out and Stop

inserting different die sections in different places in the die. At *A*, Fig. 26, is shown a modification of the blank, possible with this die. Another of the principal features of this sub-press sectional die is the means for stripping the scrap and ejecting, when it is wanted to produce punchings in quantities. The die may appear to be unduly light in construction, but several sets have been built on these lines and have given full satisfaction. Their light weight materially lessens the cost of handling, as well as the cost of making. The holder *C* is of good, close-grain cast iron planed on both sides. At the top.

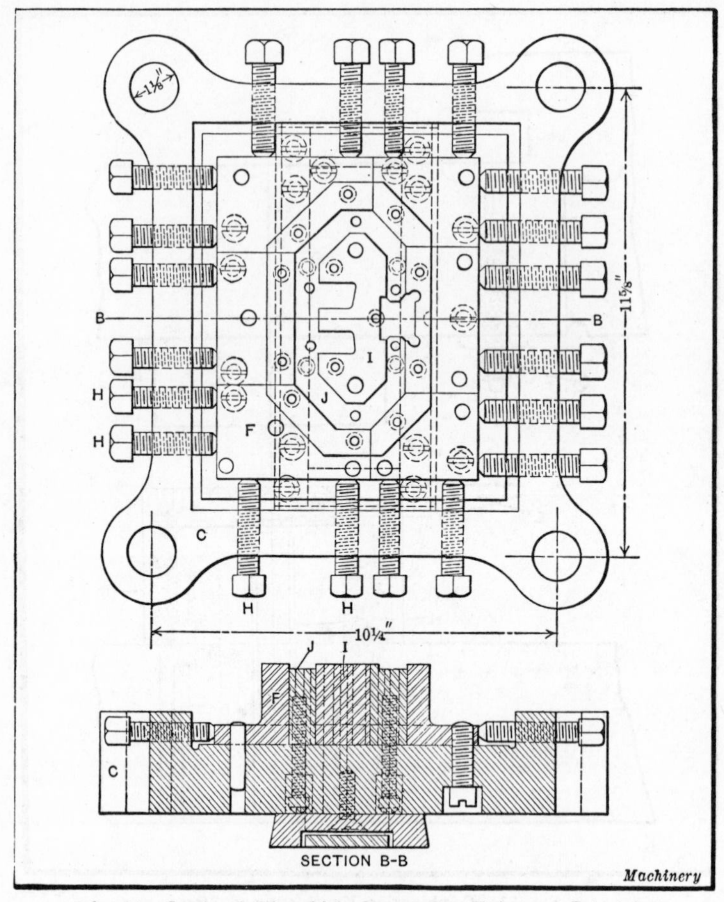

Fig. 24. Sectional Die which Operates on Sub-press Principle

a recess is milled with an end-mill in a vertical miller. In this recess are held the sectional parts of the die, which are fastened to the body from the bottom. After having made the necessary templets, the various die sections are shaped. A few thousandths of an inch are left on the adjoining surfaces to permit finishing by grinding. The cutting edges of the die sections must be left as hard as possible. Die section *F* is shown in detail Fig. 26. It will be noticed that two small holes are drilled in the center of the two screw holes in the piece *F*. This is done to enable transferring the screw holes to the cast-iron holder when assembling the die. The bottoms of the die sections are left soft in order to be able to drill all the screw and pin holes through the cast-iron holder at the same setting. Each section is reinforced on the two outer sides by four set-screws *H*, as shown in Fig. 24. In the center of

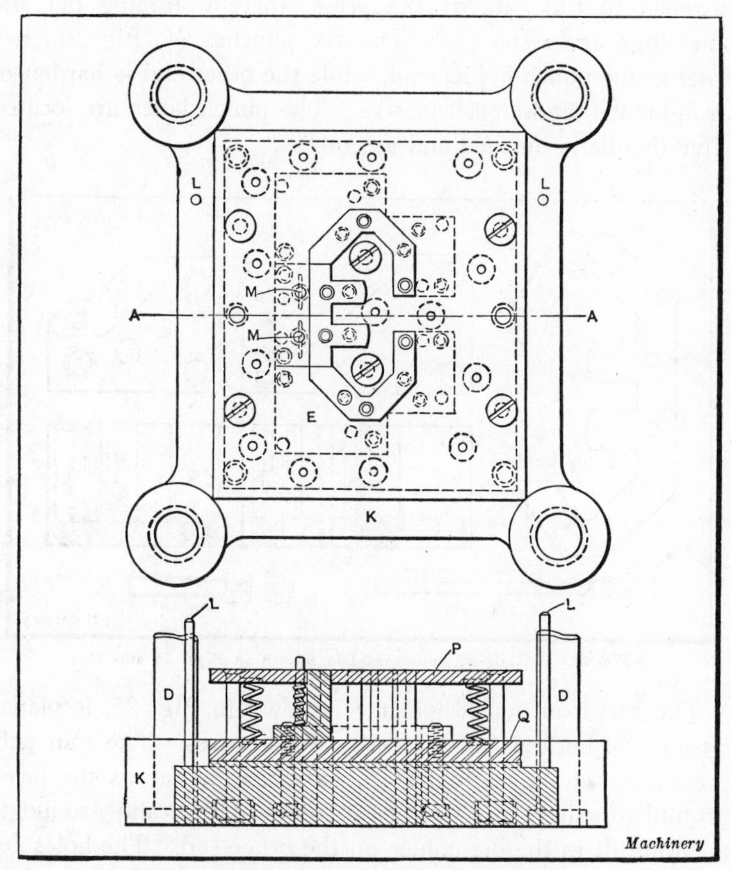

Fig. 25. Punch for Die Illustrated in Fig. 24

the die a solid block *I* is fastened with three screws and two dowel pins. This block is hardened and ground all over to the shape of the templet. The ejecting or stripping device *J* for the die is made of a solid tool steel piece to the same shape as the templet, but is a very free fit. This part is left soft and is located a few thousandths of an inch more than the thickness of the punching below the top of the die. When the die is sharpened, the stripper is ground off the same amount. No springs are used with the stripper, it being actuated by two 1-inch studs fastened with screws on the stripper. These studs pass through the die and holder, and are actuated by a bar fastened to the gate of the press, thereby forcing out the punchings from the die. The six punches *N*, Fig. 26, are upset at the punch-holder end, while the other end is hardened, straightened, and lapped to size. The punch holes are located after the die is finished and assembled.

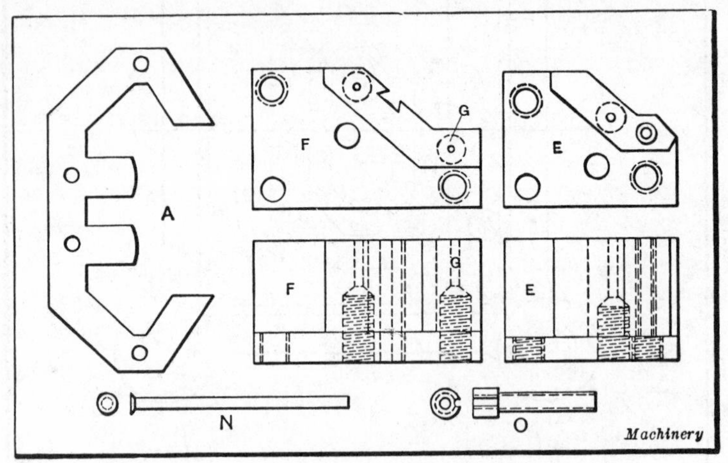

Fig. 26. Details of Sub-press Die Shown in Figs. 24 and 25

The cast-iron punch-holder *K*, shown in Fig. 25, is planed on top and bottom and across the four bosses. The four sub-press pins *D* are of tool steel, hardened as far as the head, ground to a light driving fit on the head end, and ground to a sliding fit in the die-holder on the other end. The holes for these pins were located so as to come in line with each other, and at the same time square with the punch and die. After the punch and die parts were hardened, they were placed together with two parallels between the castings, the punch being entered into the die, and the two clamped together with four C-clamps. In this way the holes for the four guide-posts were machined so as to be in accurate alignment.

A punch part is shown at *E*, Fig. 26. In locating the positions for the piercing bushings *O* (see detail view) it sometimes happens that the holes for the bushings are so numerous and small that they cannot be conveniently bored. The holes are then transferred by a drill that runs through the die and is of the same size as the piercing plug, the die being used as a drill jig. After drilling, the holes are counterbored to the right size for a driving fit for the bushings. The latter are hardened and ground all over, and the holes in them taper one-half degree. A straight dowel pin, driven in so as to be located halfway in the bushing, and halfway in the section *E*, holds the bushing in position while in operation. A stripper plate *P*, Fig. 25, is placed over the punch sections and has a free fit on both the inside and outside. It is held by flat-head screws which are adjusted with nuts from the bottom of the holder. Between the stripper and the punch-shoe *Q*, which is made of tool steel and hardened, sixteen spiral springs are placed to strip the metal. The punch-shoes are secured to the cast-iron holder *K*.

Two guide pins *L*, for the stock, are driven into the top of the cast-iron holder *K*, and two gage pins *M* are located 1/16 inch from the cutting edge. A small wire is driven through the gage pins, below the stripper, having a spiral spring underneath, which latter is seated on the punch-shoe. When the die comes down, forcing down the stripper plate, the gage pins follow, coming up again on the upward stroke.

Making a Sub-press Die of the Four-post Type.—A sub-press die of the four-post type is shown in Fig. 27. This sub-press is used for making a part having rack teeth, the shape being indicated by the illustration. The punch and die are finished before the upper and lower members are aligned with each other. When aligning them, the punch is entered into the die, the faces of the two parts being parallel with each other; then bushings *A* are slipped over the guide-posts until they rest in the bottoms of the cast counterbores of the die-holder *B*. (See upper left-hand sectional view.) This counterbored space has large pockets gouged out at the sides for the babbitt to flow into and form anchorages. The helical oil grooves, with which these posts are subsequently provided, are not yet cut, the posts being smooth and true as left by the grinding operation. After the space C is filled with babbitt, the punch and die are securely held in alignment with each other. The guide-posts are then removed and the helical grooves for oil distribution are cut in them.

One of the noticeable features of this die is that the section of the cutting edge which shears out the rack teeth is built up of small segments, each containing two teeth only, these segments being dovetailed into the larger piece, K_5. Each of these small pieces, K_8, is secured by two dowels which lock the parts firmly together. This costly and difficult construction was necessitated by the demand for accuracy in the spacing of the teeth. With the sectional construction shown the parts are not affected sensibly in the hardening. That piece K_5 may not be warped out of shape, it is ground to size on all its surfaces, top, bottom, sides, and even on the dovetail, so that when completed its plane surfaces are straight and parallel. The dovetail of the die sections K_8 are next machined to fit the groove in K_5. The holes in K_5 are then continued to pieces K_8, which are taken out and hardened, and returned to be doweled in place. It will be seen that this die is constructed on the sectional plan throughout. This makes it possible to finish most of the cutting edges on the surface grinder. Troubles due to distortion in hardening are thus entirely avoided. The proper end measurements between important points in the model are also preserved by leaving a slight amount of stock where two sections of the die come together, the parts being ground away at this point until the proper dimensions are obtained.

In the few cases where the grinding wheel will not finish the cutting surface, extended use is made of diamond laps, these being in the form of steel sections of proper contour to fit the part of the die they are working in, these steel pieces being charged with diamond dust and reciprocated vertically in filing machines. The little dovetail in which part K_7 is inserted, for

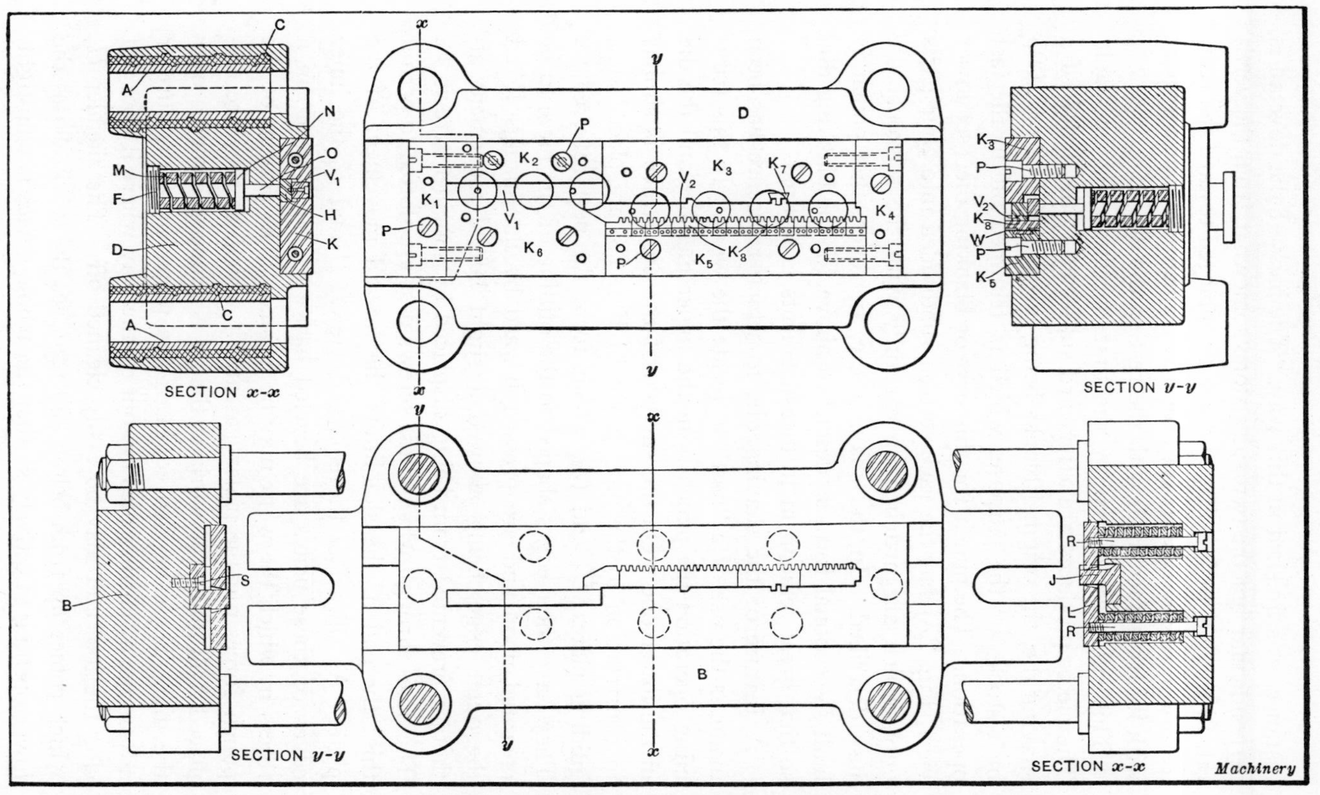

Fig. 27. Sub-press Die of Sectional Construction

instance, was finished in this way. The back of the dovetail is perpendicular but the two sides slope somewhat from the vertical, forming a wedge-shaped opening enlarged toward the rear. Section K_7 is driven in from the rear, finished off, and ground with its front face flush with the rest of the die.

This sub-press die is for the first operation on the blank. The pieces produced are afterward subjected to the action of a shaving die, the original blanks being left with 0.002 or 0.003 inch stock for the purpose, which is trimmed off in the last operation. The punch for this first or blanking die (see lower view, Fig. 27) has the rack section subdivided into four parts only, which are matched up carefully with the sectional die just described. In the shaving die, however, this punch is built in sectional form as described above for the blanking die, so that great refinement in measurements is secured.

A feature of the shaving die, to which reference has been made, is the use of a "nest" to locate the work. In this trimming operation the punch is in the upper member and the die in the lower one. On the surface of the die, which is similar in construction to the one shown in Fig. 28, are placed steel guiding plates, U_1 and U_2, which form the nest referred to. They have their edges shaped to the outline of the piece to be operated upon and are pressed inward by flat springs *W* at the outer edge, being allowed a slight lateral movement although prevented from being displaced by shoulder screws *V*. The holes through which these screws pass are slotted to permit this; the end of the slot limits the inward movement of the plate. As shown in the enlarged views, *A* and *B*, the inner edges of these plates are beveled backward so as to form a recess in which the work may be located. The descent of the punch forces out the plates (as at *B*) which, as they are displaced, still guide the work so that it is properly centered over the die. These beveled edges of the plates have the further advantage of curling the chip out of the way where it does not clog the tool and may be easily cleaned off. The shedder *H*, which comes up from below and removes the work, closes the lower opening effectively so that the whole device is chip-tight.

Even greater accuracy is advisable in the fitting of the punch and die in this shaving sub-press than is necessary in the one used for blanking only, if it is desired to produce clean work free from burrs. The necessity for this will be appreciated upon examining detailed section *B*, which shows in magnified form the action of the cutting edges. If the punch does not match up closely with the edge of die *K*, the stock is bent

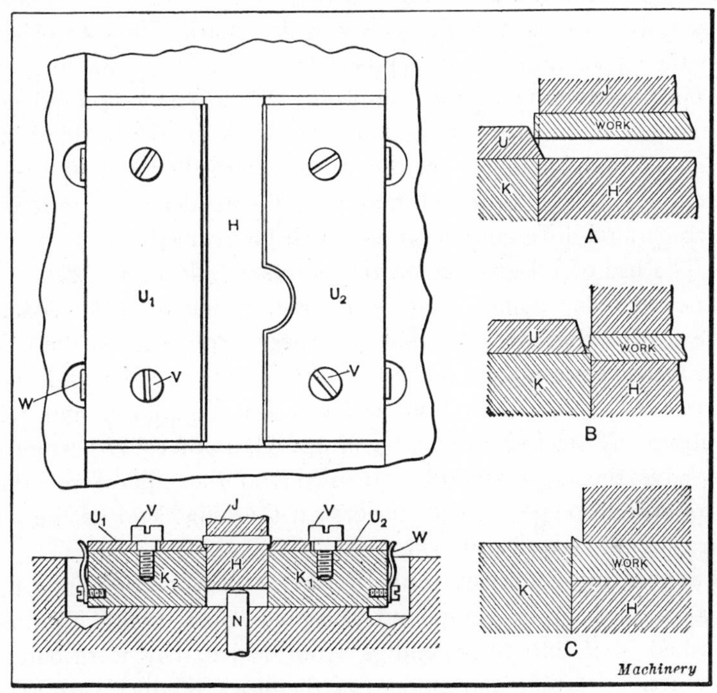

Fig. 28. Shaving Die with Nest for Locating Work—Detailed Views Illustrating Action of Locating Plates

upward, leaving a sharp burr, while the punch impresses the outline of its cutting edge on the top surface of the blank.

Details of Pillar-type Sub-press Construction.—For the upper and lower members of a pillar-type sub-press, either a good grade of charcoal iron or semi-steel should be used. After rough-machining, allow the casting to season and then machine the faces parallel to within limits of 0.0005 inch. The pillar holes should not be cored, as better results are obtained by drilling from the solid. For the pillars use machine steel. After turning, pack-harden, rough-grind, and season. Finish-grind and lap to a sliding fit in the upper member (which may or may not have bushings) and grind to a driving fit in the lower member of the sub-press.

In some cases, two different size pillars are used in the same sub-press in order to prevent the improper setting of the punch and die in relation to each other. Where the same size pillars are used, some distinguishing mark should be placed on the upper and lower members, furnishing a guide for the proper assembling of the sub-press. These marks should not be small or in an inconspicuous place. A good practice is to number both members on the front where they can be easily seen. By using different numbers, the tendency to mix the members of different sub-presses will be avoided.

The use of oil-grooves on the pillars should be avoided. A grooved pillar makes a first-class lap, which tends to reduce the life of the bearing. This has been proved to be the case by actual experiment. The use of bushings or liners is not necessary, as the cast-iron bearings become glazed and will outlive any steel or bronze bushings. It is of course essential to have the holes smoothly reamed and the pillars smoothly ground and lapped. The corners on the upper end of the pillars should be well rounded.

Separating Sub-press Die Blanks from Scrap.—When flat blanks are cut in compound sub-press dies, the blanks are pushed back into the openings from which they were cut by the action of the stripper, and if the stock is much over 0.02 inch thick, considerable trouble is sometimes experienced in removing the blanks. Fig. 29 shows a machine that is used for forcing the blanks from the strip of stock without marring them. This machine is equipped with a soft rubber wheel *A* which, as the illustration shows, is supported on the sides by steel flanges which are quite large in diameter in proportion to the diameter of the wheel. The table of the machine is formed by a knee or angle iron which is provided with adjustable guides, and is recessed to receive bushings *B* having different sized holes. Before using this machine, a bushing is inserted in the table having a hole somewhat larger in diameter than the diameter of the blanks to be forced out of the stock. The guides are then adjusted to allow the strip to slide through freely, after which the table is raised until the rubber wheel bears against the stock with a slight pressure. The wheel is

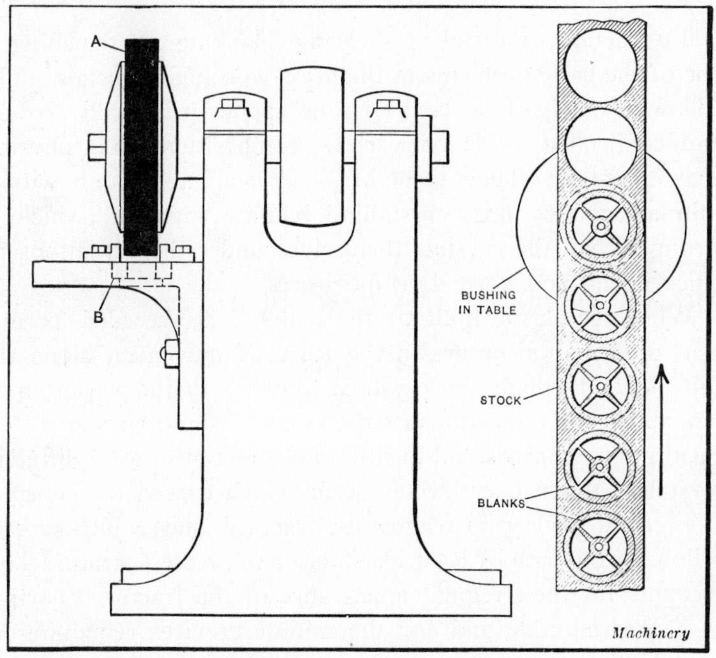

Fig. 29. Machine for Separating Blanks from Stock which has Passed Through Sub-press Dies

then rotated by power, and it is simply necessary to place the end of the strip under the wheel which will then automatically feed it along, at the same time forcing out the blanks through the hole in the bushing. The diagram at the right illustrates how the blanks are fed out of the scrap as they pass between the bushing and the rubber wheel.

CHAPTER X

ACTION OF METAL IN SHEARING AND WEAR OF CUTTING EDGES

THE action of metal in shearing, blanking, or punching is one of the basic problems in the press-working of metals. The following analysis by E. V. Crane applies principally to hot- and cold-rolled steels of various compositions and physical characteristics. Their structure is crystalline, though with a thin amorphous intra-crystalline binding material, which is stronger than the crystals themselves under the conditions of quick action and normal temperatures.

When the elastic limit of the material is exceeded, permanent deformation occurs in the form of movement along the slip planes through the crystals. Owing to the variation in size and relative positions of the crystals, slip occurs at different times and speeds and in different directions in the different crystals. When overstresses occur which exceed the cohesive strength of the crystal fragments, fractures start which spread, following the path of least resistance and greatest strain. This accounts for the irregular appearance of the fractured portion of a sheared edge and for the minute crevices remaining to start further fractures.

The principal factors affecting shearing work are thickness and physical properties (especially hardness) of the metal; size, shape, subsequent operations, tolerances, and finish of the job; and clearance, shear, relief, and condition of the tools. Press selection is also of extreme importance, but that should be considered as a separate subject. Most of the variables mentioned can be isolated sufficiently to ascertain their characteristics and effects. The various samples and some of the curves to be referred to were selected from experimental results obtained in the E. W. Bliss Co.'s laboratories.

Shearing Action in Blanking a Disk.—The blanking of a disk from sheet material has been taken to illustrate shearing action. The material is soft ¼-inch hot-rolled steel. The diagrams in Fig. 1 show the stages of the punch progressing through the sheet to illustrate the action upon the metal in shearing.

The upper diagram represents the stage at which the elastic limit of the material is just beginning to be exceeded, the principal action being bending. In the second diagram, the punch has penetrated just far enough to start the fracture. There is a normal pinching or compressive stress between the edges of the punch and die, and a tensile stress along the strata lines. The metal has been elongated locally along all these lines, and especially in the top and bottom strata. Here the ultimate strength has been exceeded over the corners and fracture has started. As the punch advances (see lower diagram), the fractures spread quickly from each edge, the load dwindling finally to what is necessary to overcome friction in pushing the blank through the die.

Effect of Clearance between Punch and Die.—The first example, just referred to, represents practically an ideal condition for shearing, as regards clearance (distance between die and punch all around). The two fractures met, giving a clean break and a minimum power requirement. When a disk is blanked with insufficient clearance for its thickness and softness, Fig. 2 illustrates what occurs. The fractures start from the corners, as before, when the surface material has been elongated beyond its ultimate strength. Instead of meeting, however, they pass, leaving a ring of material which must again be stressed to the point of fracture, with a further expenditure of energy; also there is a ragged fringe left around the disk, which tends to wedge against the die as it is pushed through, adding to the power required.

There is a "rule of thumb" that the clearance should be about one-eighth to one-tenth of the thickness of the material, depending upon its hardness. Hard stock does not require nearly so much clearance for a clean fracture as soft stock.

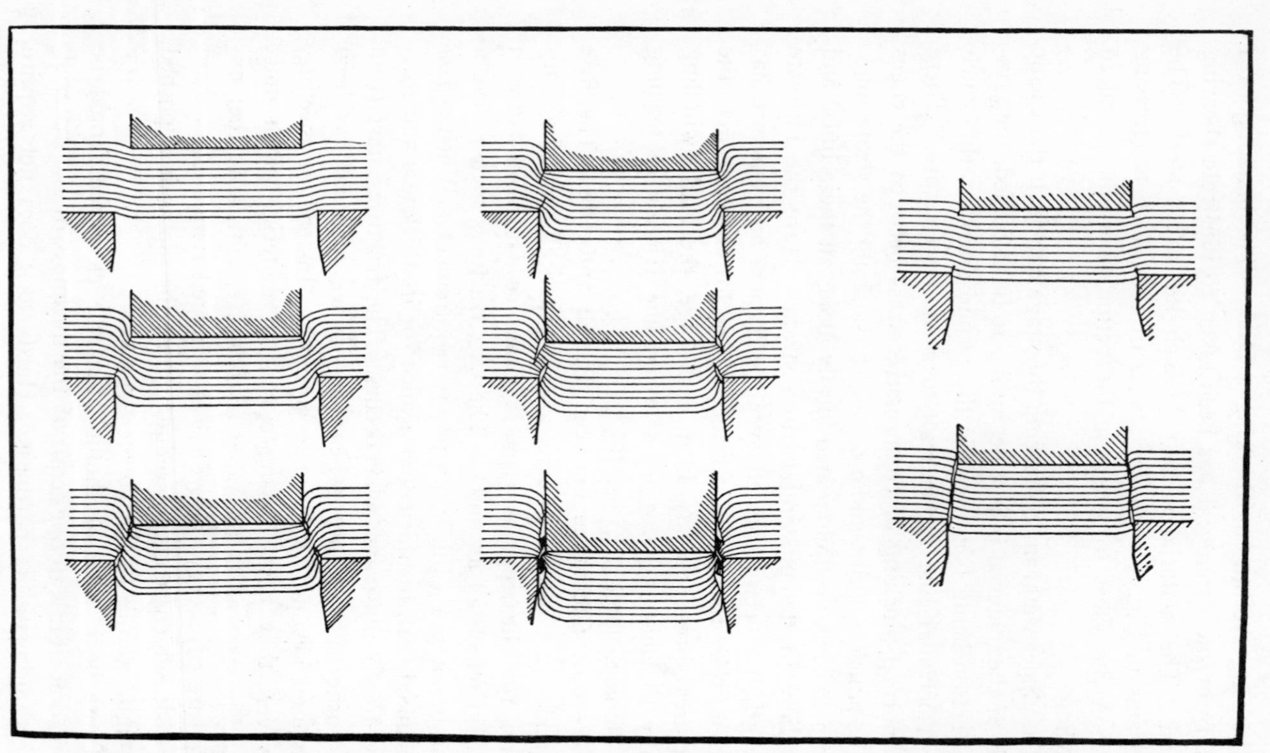

Fig. 1. Shearing Action when Punch and Die Have Proper Clearance

Fig. 2. Shearing Action when Punch and Die Have Insufficient Clearance

Fig. 3. Shearing Action in Blanking a Moderately Hard Steel Disk

As illustrated in Fig. 3, the punch enters but a short distance, stretching the surface strata comparatively little before the fractures start. And, again, due to the hardness of the material, the break is completed almost instantly, so that the disk is completely severed before the punch has entered more than a quarter of the thickness of the stock. For softer metals, the punch must enter farther to cause fracture, in some cases even passing all the way through the sheet and actually pinching the blank out.

A little variation in clearance around a die makes the difference between a clean fracture and a poor one. A clean fracture causes less wear on the dies, and insufficient clearance may become so small as to permit of actual contact between the cutting edges. It is well known that cutting part blanks may cause breakage or at least excessive wear on punches. Off center spring, due to unbalanced loading in too light a press, is equally capable of shifting the clearance with detrimental effect on the tool life.

Pressure and Power Variations.—A disk was blanked in an Olsen testing machine, with load readings taken every 0.005 inch. This particular disk may be classed with Fig. 2, since there was not sufficient clearance between the punch and die to permit a clean fracture. The material was about 0.12 per cent carbon hot-rolled plate, 0.245 inch thick, showing, when subjected to a tensile test, an elastic limit of about 32,000 pounds per square inch, an ultimate strength of about 47,000 pounds per square inch (on the original area), and an elongation of about 27 per cent in 2 inches. The diameter of the punch was 1.434 inches, and the stress on the metal actually in shear at the point at which the facture started figured about 53,000 pounds per square inch (which on the original area, amounts to 39,000 pounds per square inch).

In Fig. 4 is shown the curve obtained from this test, which indicates the way in which the pressure rises to the elastic limit, holds constant as the area is reduced until fracture starts, and then falls away. The hump on the way down is due to a repetition of the shearing action, since the clearance was insuffi-

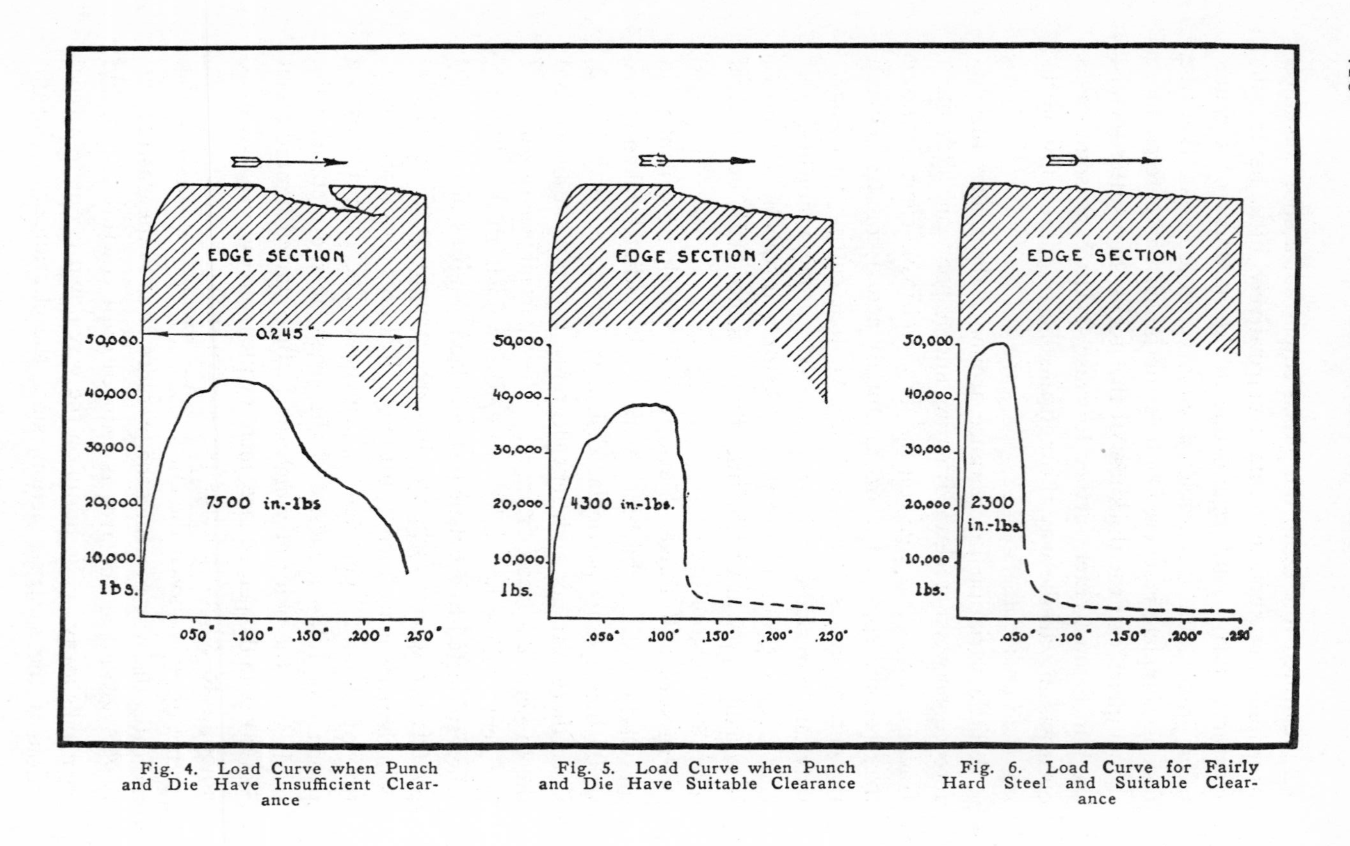

Fig. 4. Load Curve when Punch and Die Have Insufficient Clearance

Fig. 5. Load Curve when Punch and Die Have Suitable Clearance

Fig. 6. Load Curve for Fairly Hard Steel and Suitable Clearance

cient for the original fractures to meet. A cross-section of the edge of the metal is shown above the curve and drawn to the same scale, so that the change in load may be compared with the progress of the punch.

Figs. 5 and 6 are arranged in the same way and to the same scale as Fig. 4 to permit easy comparison. Fig. 5 illustrates the effect of blanking the same soft material as before, but, in this case, with suitable clearance in the die. This is the same condition as was illustrated in Fig. 1. Fig. 6 shows conditions prevailing in blanking hard material of similar actual ultimate strength to that previously used. (See also Fig. 3.) The pressure required to cause fracture is greater than for the softer steel, but fracture begins sooner, and once started, is more quickly completed. The clearance is less than in Fig. 5, but is ample for the material.

The energy required to perform the work of punching out the blank is represented in each case by the area under the curve. The common method of approximating this value would be to figure the force required, at about 25 tons per square inch, on the area to be sheared, and multiply it by the thickness of the stock. This gives about 13,500 inch-pounds, whereas the actual power consumed varied from about one-sixth (Fig. 6) to a little over one-half (Fig. 4) of this theoretical value.

Fig. 7 shows three indicator diagrams taken from a report by Professor Gardner C. Anthony of his investigations in punching boiler plate. The equipment used was an Olsen testing machine with a hydraulic cylinder connected with a regular steam engine indicator. These diagrams were taken while punching mild steel plate 0.315 inch thick. The die diameter was 0.767 inch, and the punch diameters were 0.702 inch for card *A*, 0.738 inch for card *B*, and 0.750 for card *C*. The clearance between the punch and die, in per cent of metal thickness, was 10.3 per cent for card *A*, 4.6 per cent for card *B*, and 2.7 per cent for card *C*.

Card *A* is quite typical of a clean fracture with proper clearance. The jump of the indicator pencil at the bottom of

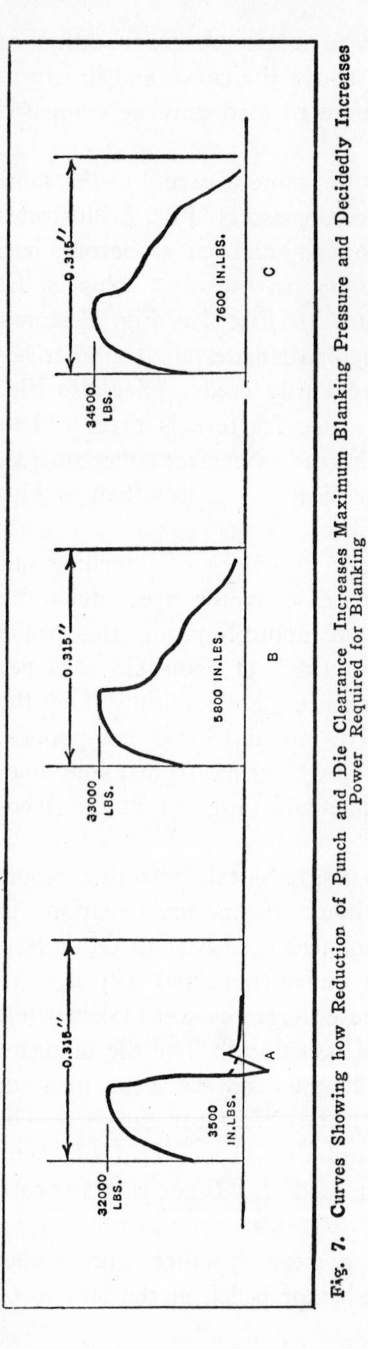

Fig. 7. Curves Showing how Reduction of Punch and Die Clearance Increases Maximum Blanking Pressure and Decidedly Increases Power Required for Blanking

the fracture was probably due to spring in the machine as the break released the pressure. Decreasing the clearance below the proper amount for the metal caused an increase both in the maximum load (required to cause fracture) and in the power requirements, shown in inch-pounds on the diagrams.

Condition of Sheared Edge.—The condition of the edge of the sheet, blank, or strip after the shearing action explains a number of points in press operations. Examine, for instance, the edge as shown in Figs. 1 and 5. The unsupported surface of the metal is drawn down in an easy curve to the edge. Then follows the polished portion of the edge, indicating the depth of penetration before fracture occurs, which is drawn smooth against the surface of the die or the punch. The remainder is the rough fractured surface containing many fine crevices and breaks which will serve as the starting point for further fractures. Where the fracture joins the other surface, the edge may be either a square break, if the tools are sharp, or a jagged burr, if they are worn.

Where to Apply Clearance.—In blanking or punching accurately to size, the clearance must obviously be taken into account. Fig. 1 is a good illustration of this point. The die is larger than the punch by an amount sufficient to give a clean fracture. Note that if the hole is to be held accurately to size, the punch must be that size, and the amount of the clearance added to it to determine the die size. Conversely, if the disk or blank must be punched to an accurate size, that is the size of the die. The clearance allowance would then be deducted from this to determine the punch size.

Where to Apply Shear.—It is fairly common practice to give a die or punch shear by beveling off the face at a slight angle, so that cutting does not occur on the whole cutting edge at once, thereby reducing the peak load. In this case, note that the metal follows the contour of the punch or die, depending upon which has shear. If a flat blank is desired, the punch should be flat and the shear should be on the die, where it will deform only the scrap. Conversely, if a hole is being punched in a sheet so that the metal punched out is the scrap, the die should be flat and the shear should be on the punch.

While discussing shear, it is well to comment that the conventional method of figuring it, although safe, is too inaccurate for particular applications. In Fig. 8, at *A* is an illustration commonly used to represent full shear; that is, beveling one cutting edge with respect to the other by an amount equal to the thickness of the metal. This is supposed to reduce the maximum area in shear, at any one time, to half the total area, and thereby to reduce the total load to half of the theoretical maximum. This may be nearly true for some unusual cases and materials, but for example, for mild steel (requiring a penetration to effect shearing of about a quarter of the metal thickness, and with proper clearance in the dies), the load rises to a peak and then falls to practically nothing in a quarter of the stock thickness. Then the "full shear" condition is better indicated at *B*, and the total load at any instant would be less than one-eighth of the pressure required with no shear—that is, with a flat punch and die.

Load Distribution in Multiple Punching.—In perforating work with a number of punches, each punch or group of punches is sometimes made shorter than the preceding punch or group by the thickness of the metal (as shown at *C* in Fig. 8) to obtain the effect of shear. A better condition is obtained by stepping the punches or groups of punches only by an amount equal to the penetration required to effect a clean fracture. Such a condition is illustrated at *D*, where the length variations are such that one punch finishes its work as the next begins. In either case, the load curve for the individual punch

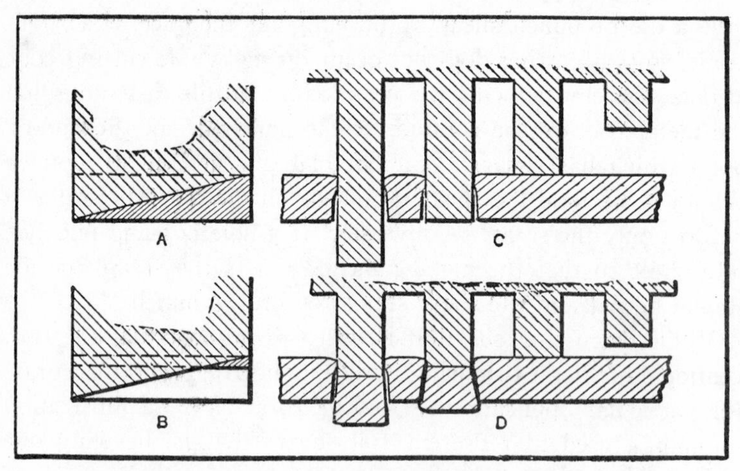

Fig. 8. (A and B) Diagrams Representing Full Shear; (C and D) Methods of Distributing Load in Multiple Punching Operations

(with proper clearance) would be similar to that in Fig. 6 or card *A* in Fig. 7. Adding the individual punch curves would give very nearly a smooth curve for arrangement *D*, Fig. 8, but arrangement *C* would result in a series of jumps from peak load to no load and back to peak load. This, combined with spring in the press, would bring the punches down upon the metal with a snap which would certainly reduce their life materially.

This plan of varying the punch lengths not only reduces the peak working load from the total for all punches to that of the individual punch, or approximately so, but there is another distinct advantage, and sometimes a greater one: As a punch progresses through a sheet of metal from its surface to the point at which the fracture starts (see central diagram, Fig. 1) there is a squeezing or pinching action between the corners of the punch and die, tending to squeeze out or spread the surrounding metal in the sheet. The result of this is indicated by the buckling of the perforated sheet. It is also apparent when perforating or punching comparatively thick metal with a number of small-diameter punches placed close together, the

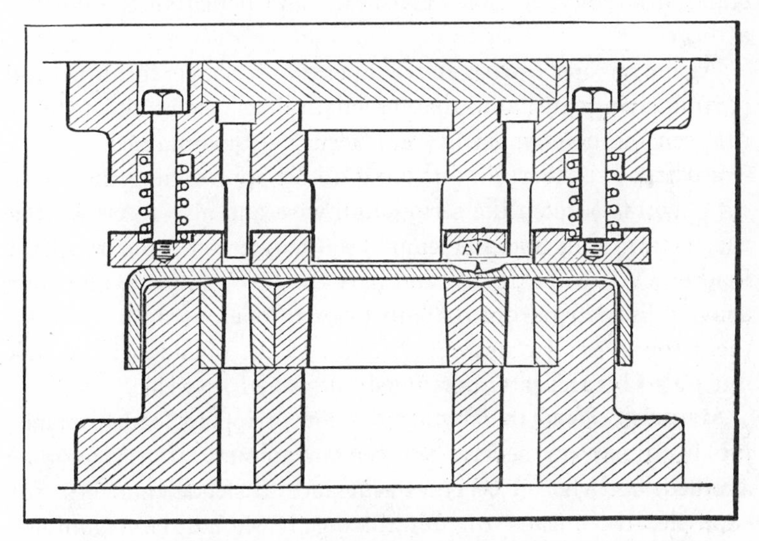

Fig. 9. For Brake Drum Perforating, Small Punches are Shortened an Amount Equal to One-third or One-fourth the Stock Thickness to Prevent Punch Breakage

tendency of this crowding action being to spread and break the punches. As soon as a punch has penetrated the sheet far enough to start the fracture, it ceases to crowd out the metal around it. Thus, for example, in perforating a break drum, Fig. 9, an effort to punch the large center hole and the small holes around it simultaneously, with all punches ground to the same level, would result in excessive breakage of the small punches; however, if the small punches were ground shorter than the large one by an amount A equal to one-quarter or one-third the thickness of the metal (as required), there would be no possibility of the center punch crowding metal out against the small ones.

There are other cases, also, where the crowding out of metal in punching seriously affects the product, and must be taken into account. Thus, in punching a series of notches in one side of a straight and narrow strip, if the notches are punched one at a time, that side of the strip will be so badly stretched as to bend the whole strip considerably. The way to accomplish the operation is to reinforce the punches to stand any crowding that may occur, and punch all the notches at once.

Again in such progressive operations as perforating and parting strip material in making chain links, the center distance between the holes must be very accurately maintained. There is a marked tendency in punching a hole approaching the width of a strip to stretch the strip lengthwise and also to crowd out the metal. One method employed to overcome the resultant inaccuracy is to perforate and part the link complete, and then shave a little metal out of both holes in one operation to make them round and accurately spaced. If the outside of the link must also be accurate, that must be shaved as well.

Stripping Load in Blanking.—The stripping load in blanking is often very severe. A certain amount of it cannot be avoided, but when it becomes a menace to slender punches, for example, the means of minimizing it should be examined. First. to account for resistance to stripping, examine Fig. 1. As the punch penetrates the metal, it bends down, squeezes, and stretches the surface strata until the fracture starts. When the fracture does occur, it releases the tensile strain in this strata (and in the others to lesser extent as they approach the center). The result is a tendency, due to elasticity of the metal, to spring back somewhat or to shorten in the long direction and to thicken up in the normal direction. At the fractured edge of the top strata this tends to make the hole smaller; consequently on the up stroke of the punch the metal tends to compress the fractured edge of the top strata around the punch. Clearly, any roughness on the surface of the punch, or a slight shoulder or tool mark around the punch, would add to the existing frictional resistance. Note also that the natural tendency of steel to "pick up" on steel in stripping, is increased by pulling the punch back against the pinched and roughly fractured edge of the hole.

There is also a tendency in the surface strata of the disk punched out to expand at the edge as the fracture releases the tensile stress. This tends to increase the diameter of the disk at this point and creates a resistance to pushing the disk through the die, for which reason the die is tapered larger at a slight angle (say about 2 degrees) from a short distance below the surface. The fact that the resistance to pushing the slug through the die is not so great as the stripping resistance is clearly due to the relative direction of motion with reference to the fractured edge.

Dullness of Cutting Edges.—Dullness of the cutting edges is of interest as regards burrs and increased load and power requirement. Note in Fig 1 that sharp cutting edges must localize and intensify the stresses that cause the fracture to start. Thus the tensile stress in the surface strata will be much more severe over a sharp corner than over a rounded or dull corner, at any point in the progress of the punch. Again, the pinching effect or compressive stress between the cutting edges of the punch and die is more highly localized, and hence more intense, between sharp edges than between rounded ones, at the same point of progress. Then, if the edges of the punch and die are dull or rounded over, the punch must penetrate farther to cause a fracture to start, increasing the load duration and hence the power required. Also, the compressive stress is spread both ways over a larger area, increasing the crowding effect and also the peak load.

The burr left by a dull edge is merely due to the fact that the metal, as it is pulled down to the point of fracture, follows the shape of the edge. The fracture starts, not from the center of the radius on a dull edge, but from the point where that radius joins the outside surface of the punch or the inside surface of the die. Thus if a punch face is flat, with a square edge, the edge of the punching is flat and fractures at that square edge. If the edge is rounded (dull), a burr remaining on the punching fits this radius very closely.

This may be made use of in some special cases where it is desired to dish or form the edges slightly while punching. If the punch face or the die is shaped as desired, the metal will follow that shape closely as it is drawn during the portion of the stroke that the punch is penetrating to effect shearing. Applications of this principle are not common except in a general way in connection with hot work and in drawing and pinching-off paper shells.

Single-edge Shearing.—Single-edge shearing, as in squaring shears and bar shears, requires little additional comment. Harder metal will require less clearance and will shear squarer on the edge than softer material. An unsupported portion of a bar or sheet will bend away from the blade (changing the relative angle of the fracture) during the penetrating portion of the shearing stroke before fracture occurs. Rake, or beveling the blade back from the edge instead of grinding it square, tends to reduce this somewhat. An unrestrained bar or sheet will move away from the cutting line of the blades in shearing due to the pinching action between the edges. This tends to give a cleaner fracture, but in soft metal, causes some change in the angle of the burnished portion of the edge relative to the surface of the metal. Shear on either blade, as in punching, shapes the metal in contact with it. Thus in shearing a long narrow strip from the edge of a sheet of metal, with the shear blade set at a considerable angle, the strip will be badly distorted by the progressive bending action of the blade as it is sheared off. The angle of shear should be based upon the depth of penetration rather than upon the total metal thickness, as discussed with reference to diagram *B* in Fig. 8.

Wear Resistance of Cutting Edges of Blanking Dies.—The following information on wear resistance of blanking dies and shear blades, is from a paper by W. J. Merten, presented before the American Society for Steel Treating.

It is universally recognized that shearing and blanking of

sheet steel covered with hammer or roll scale will dull or wear down the cutting edge of die parts and shear blades and produce a burr sooner than when there is no scale. Hammer scale is an abrasive material, and quite hard, as compared with the hardness of low-carbon steel. However, as it is impractical to obtain a scale-free material for economic and commercial reasons, the use of heavy, clinging, or highly adhesive greases as lubricants has been found to practically neutralize the scoring tendency of the scale.

It has also been recognized that the embedding of the crushed crystals of iron-oxide scale and the prevention of their pulverization, spreading, and lodging between the cutting edges is responsible for improved performance. Iron silicide crystals (FeSi) in 4 per cent silicon sheet having a considerably greater abrasive quality than iron scale, affect the cutting edges of tools similarly, and the tendency to dull the edge is very pronounced if a crushing or pulverizing of the crystals takes place and precedes the shearing of the sheet. Evidently, any process or method resulting in a splitting of the iron silicide crystals without powdering or severe fragmentation aids in the retention of a sharp cutting edge and prolongs the life of the die or shear blade.

To bring about the splitting of hard crystals of iron oxide or iron silicide, instead of crushing them, is accomplished by various methods:

1. By baking on a coat of lubricating enamel.

2. By inserting a layer of paper on the top of the sheet or between the punch and the sheet.

3. By dipping sheets into a solution of hot copper sulphate ($CnSO_4$) or lead acetate ($PbC_2H_3O_2$), thus depositing a soft metallic coating of copper or lead on the surface.

All these methods have the same object, namely to fill the small surface cavities and lock or embed the exposed hard and brittle particles, thereby preventing their fragmentation or powdering and spreading just prior to subjecting the softer ground mass of the sheet to the shearing stresses. The more secure such embedding or locking is, the greater the life and the better the performance of the cutting edge. Deposits of metallic copper or lead obtained from dipping the sheets in a solution that precipitates these metals on the sheets should give most satisfactory results. This method is not favored, however, on account of the high cost of these materials and the more expensive method of application.

A striking illustration of the effect of brittle crystals rendered weak and fragile by removing from them their supporting matrix, the soft iron, is the low production and rapid dulling of the cutting edge from punching pickled sheets. Pickling acid (H_2SO_4) obviously acts only on the iron matrix, iron silicide being practically acid-proof. The dissolving of the iron naturally exposes the iron silicide crystals still more and weakens their resistance to crushing stresses, and it is practically certain that excessive powdering and spreading takes place before actual shearing of the sheet starts. Consequently a very short production-life was obtained from the dies.

The facts mentioned explain why fluid lubricants, which give merely a wet film, are not successful in solving these problems. A substantial and viscous lubricant is needed to embed and hold the fragments of the split crystals.

Should Punch or Die be Hardened?—The successful performance of a die for large production in blanking operations was at one time synonymous with the producing of a hard stationary die plate and a soft punch or moving die part of quenched and tempered tool steel. The latter would permit the greatest number of peening or refitting operations without splitting, breaking, or chipping the edge. This practice was quite generally accepted as giving the best results and long die life. With the advent of very hard but tough and highly abrasive-resistant alloy steels, the hard punch and die plate combination has supplanted the old method in all but a few special cases.

The type of steel adapted for blanking dies and shear blades is the high-carbon high-chromium type of tool steel of the following approximate analysis: Carbon, from 2.00 to 2.25 per cent; chromium, from 10 to 12 per cent. This steel has a scleroscope hardness of from 85 to 95 when oil-quenched from 1800 degrees F. and tempered at 600 degrees F.

The successful application of a hard punch and die plate, or highly and uniformly hard movable and stationary die parts, depends to a large degree upon the rigidity of the punch while blanking. On outline dies or on dies where the entire perimeter of the punch section is used as a cutting edge, the tendency to produce a side thrust is practically nil, and a hard-punch hard-die plate combination will work out ideally.

For dies where the punch cuts on one side of the cross-section only, the soft punch is still employed. Since no clearance can be allowed between punch and die plate, and since a tremendous pressure is exerted upon the cutting side of the punch, a hard punch introduces a grinding effect upon the cutting edge of the die plate or stationary part, producing a burr after comparatively few strokes. The softer punch, naturally having less abrasive action on the cutting edge of the die plate, insures longer life and therefore is favored on dies of this class.

There is, however, a very important consideration outside of the producing of a burr caused by dull cutting edges of the die, namely, the crushing of the hard crystals and the plastic flow and deformation of the metal held between and sheared by the very hard cutting edges, as compared with the deformation when held between and sheared by cutting edges, one of which is comparatively soft and the other hard. To investigate this difference, if any, a series of blanks were selected. One set was blanked with a newly ground (therefore sharp) soft punch and hard die-plate combination die. Another set was blanked with a newly ground hard punch and hard die-plate combination die. The third set was blanked with the dulled edge of the hard punch and hard die-plate die.

It was quite evident that the sharp but soft punch and hard die-plate combination die produced a considerable dragging effect, extending quite a distance into the blank. This type of plastic deformation, because of its depth, did not show this drag in the form of a burr, although its deleterious effect upon the electrical and magnetic characteristics may be as bad or worse than that of a dulled-edge hard punch and hard die-plate combination die, where plastic deformation is concentrated and localized near the edge of the blank, as evidenced by a burr.

The decidedly advantageous results from a hard punch and die-plate die combination, in producing the minimum plastic deformation of the sheared section and the immediate adjacent material were plainly and strikingly apparent.

A summary of the results of the investigation involving wear resistance of cutting edges of blanking dies and shear blades show that:

1. The application of highly viscous lubricants aids performance and lessens abrasion or dulling of cutting edges by preventing powdering and spreading of hard and abrasive constituent of sheets.

2. Uniformly and fully hard die parts offer many advantages with regard to quality of blank produced and quantity of production; however, the designer is called upon to use his ingenuity in designing an outline die in which the perimeter of the entire cross-section performs during the shearing of the blank, without excessive scrap metal from the sheet.

3. Plastic deformation not evidenced by burr formation is produced by the use of soft punch parts; this deformation may at times be more detrimental than a more localized drag resulting in a burr.

In concluding, it should be stated that there are obviously other factors outside of those related to tool maintenance, life of die, and quantity production to be considered in a final analysis and solution of the problem of increasing the wear resistance of cutting edges of blanking dies. Some of these are:

1. Better results in the assembly of the blank in the apparatus or machine.

2. Greater uniformity of grain structure of blank due to less deformation in blanking.

3. Lower annealing temperatures for restoration of normal crystal structure.

CHAPTER XI

BENDING AND FORMING DIES

BENDING dies are designed for bending sheet metal or wire parts into various shapes which are usually irregular and are produced either by pushing the stock into cavities or depressions of corresponding shape in the die or by the action of auxiliary attachments such as slides, etc., which are operated as the punch descends. A simple form of bending die would be one having an upper part or punch shaped to correspond with a depression in the die face; such a bending die is sometimes employed for bending flat, sheet-metal plates into an irregular shape. When the material to be bent is elastic or spring, the die must be made to allow for this, or so that the part is bent slightly beyond the required shape or angle to compensate for the backward spring when the pressure is released. Determining this allowance is, of course, a matter of experiment.

The terms "bending" and "forming" are often used interchangeably as applied to dies which produce parts by a bending action. If a sheet metal blank is formed by confining it between a punch and die, the shapes of which are directly reproduced by applying pressure, then the die would be classed as a forming type. On the other hand, if the action is more nearly pure bending, as for example, when a bending punch moves past some part of a die and bends a lug or other part at an angle, the die is generally classed as a bending type, because in this case the shaping of the part is due chiefly to the movement of the punch relative to the die and the shaping of the work may not be a reproduction of the shape of the punch and die.

While it is possible, in certain cases, to bend articles during the operation of punching, it is usually necessary to make a separate operation of bending. It is sometimes possible to make the dies so that the various operations can be done in different parts of the same die-block, the piece of work being changed from one portion to another in order, as the various operations are gone through. At other times it is necessary to make several sets of bending dies, the number depending on the number of operations necessary. When a given quantity of work has been run through the first die, it is removed from the press and the next in order placed in, so continuing until the work has been brought to the desired shape. When a comparatively small number of pieces are to be bent to a shape that would require a complicated and, consequently, costly die, in order that the bend might be made in one operation, it is sometimes considered advisable to make two dies for the operation, which are more simple in form and inexpensive to make. At times the design of the press is such that a complicated die could not be used; and, consequently, dies of a simpler form, which can be fitted in the press, must be made.

Simple Types of Bending Dies.—The simpler forms of bending dies will be described first. The diagram *A*, Fig. 1, represents a die used in bending a piece of steel *a* to a V-shape, as at *b*. In the case of a die of this form it is necessary to provide an impression of the proper shape as shown; this impression, if the die is to be used for bending stiff stock, must be of a more acute angle than if stock having little tendency to spring back when bent to shape is used. Under ordinary circumstances the upper portion or punch would be made of the same angle as the die. It is necessary to provide guides and stops to locate the work properly. If the stock used in making the pieces is of a high grade and the product is a spring or similar article which must be hardened, it will be found necessary to cut away the die somewhat in the bottom of the impression, to prevent crushing or disarranging the grain of the steel to an extent that would cause it to break when in use. If the die is of the form shown at *B*, the width *x* of the punch should be slightly less than the width of the die minus twice the thickness of the stock. If possible, the upper corners *d* of

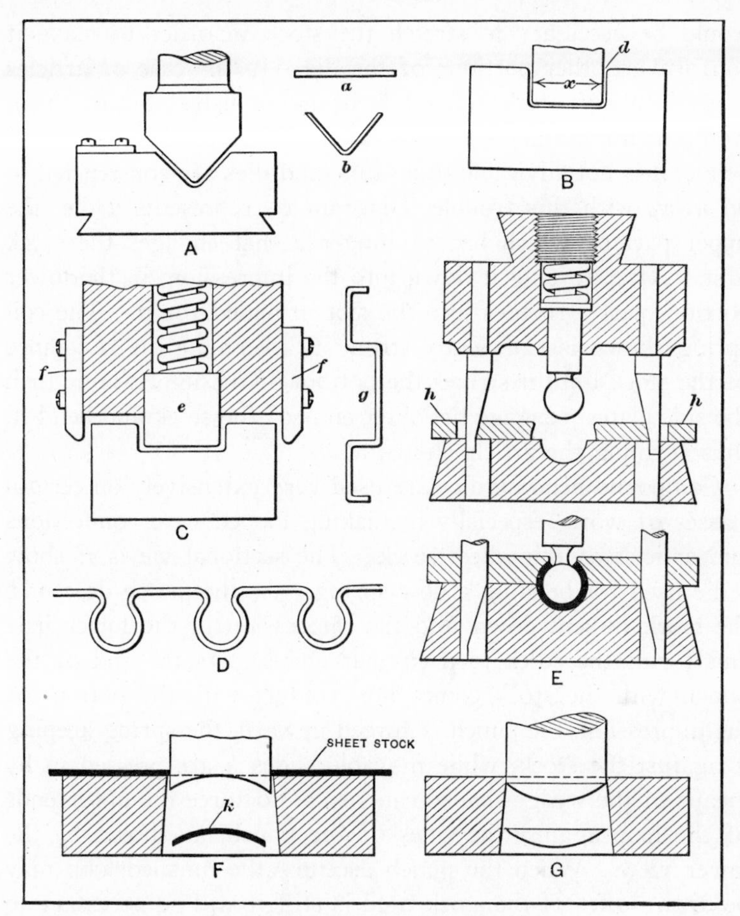

Fig. 1. Simple Types of Bending Dies

the die should be rounded somewhat, as the stock bends much easier and with less danger of mutilating the surface than when the corners are sharp. When bending thin ductile metal the corners need but little rounding; if the stock is thick or very stiff, a greater amount of rounding is needed.

When bending articles of certain shapes, it is necessary to design the tools so that certain sections of the piece will be bent before other portions. If an attempt were made to make the tools solid and do the work at one stroke of the press, the piece of stock would be held rigidly at certain points and it would be necessary to stretch the stock in order to make it conform to other portions of the die. In the case of articles made from soft stock, this might be accomplished, but the stock would be thinner and narrower where it stretched; however, as a rule, it is not advisable to do this, and dies are constructed to do away with this trouble. Diagram *C*, represents a die, the upper part of which has a plunger *e* that engages the stock first. After forcing it down into the impression, in the lower portion, part *e* recedes into the slot provided for it. The coil spring shown is sufficiently strong to overcome the resistance of the stock until it strikes the bottom of the impression; then the side plates *f* engage the outer ends of the stock and bend it. thus forming the article shown at *g*.

Compound bending dies are used very extensively on certain classes of work, especially in making looped wire connections and articles of thin sheet stock. The sectional views *E* show a die used for bending a bow spring. As the punch descends, the stock is bent down into the impression in the lower half and forms the stock to a circular shape. As the end of the punch with the stock comes into contact with the bottom of the impression, the punch is forced upward, the spring keeping it against the stock, while movable slides *h* are pressed in by means of the wedge-shaped cams so as to force the upper ends of the loop against the sides of the punch, as shown by the lower view. When the punch ascends, the finished loop may be drawn off. If the stock used is stiff it will be necessary to make the punch somewhat smaller than the finished size of the spring, because the latter will open out somewhat when the pressure is removed.

When making looped wire work, a loop may be formed and the wire moved along against a stop, another loop formed, and so on, as indicated at *D*. When forming looped wire work it is customary to make the punch ball-shaped rather than cylindrical. The ball answers well on wire work and allows of the easy removal of the loop. It is sometimes desirable to close the upper end of an article nearly together, and if the stock used is extremely stiff, such as that used for bow springs made from tool or spring steel, it may be necessary to heat the bow (which has previously been bent) red hot, and finish-bend it by a special operation. A great variety of work may be done by modifications of the methods for bending shown. Where but a few pieces are to be bent it is not advisable to go to the expense of making costly bending dies, but when the work is done in large quantities, such dies will produce work uniform in shape at a low cost.

Blanking and bending dies are made which not only punch the article from the commercial sheet, but bend it to the desired shape in the same operation or by utilizing the blanking punch. As a rule, it is advisable to blank the article in one operation and bend it in another, but there are certain forms of work where it is possible to do it in a satisfactory manner in one operation and at a cost not exceeding that of the ordinary blanking operation. This also effects a saving in the cost of tools, as the special bending die is dispensed with. Diagram *F* represents a punch and die used in punching the shoe *k* to the proper shape shown, whereas *G* illustrates a method of producing the spherical tension washer shown. Gun and other irregular shaped springs are often punched to form by dies of this type, although, when stock suitable for use in making springs is employed, it will be found necessary to make the face of the punch somewhat different in shape from that desired, as the piece will straighten out more or less after it is punched.

In producing a short bend in blanks in such a position and of such a nature that the blank slips away from under the punch when it is descending into the die, a spring pad is fitted into the die with the lower part of the bend shaped into it, and flush with the top surface of the die. This holds the metal securely against the punch in its descent into the die and insures perfect duplicates of the product. Where holes in a blank come near a bend, a strain in the metal is set up during the bending operation which elongates the holes. This makes it necessary sometimes to pierce the holes slightly oval in the opposite direction before forming.

Allowances for 90-degree Bends in Sheet Metals—1

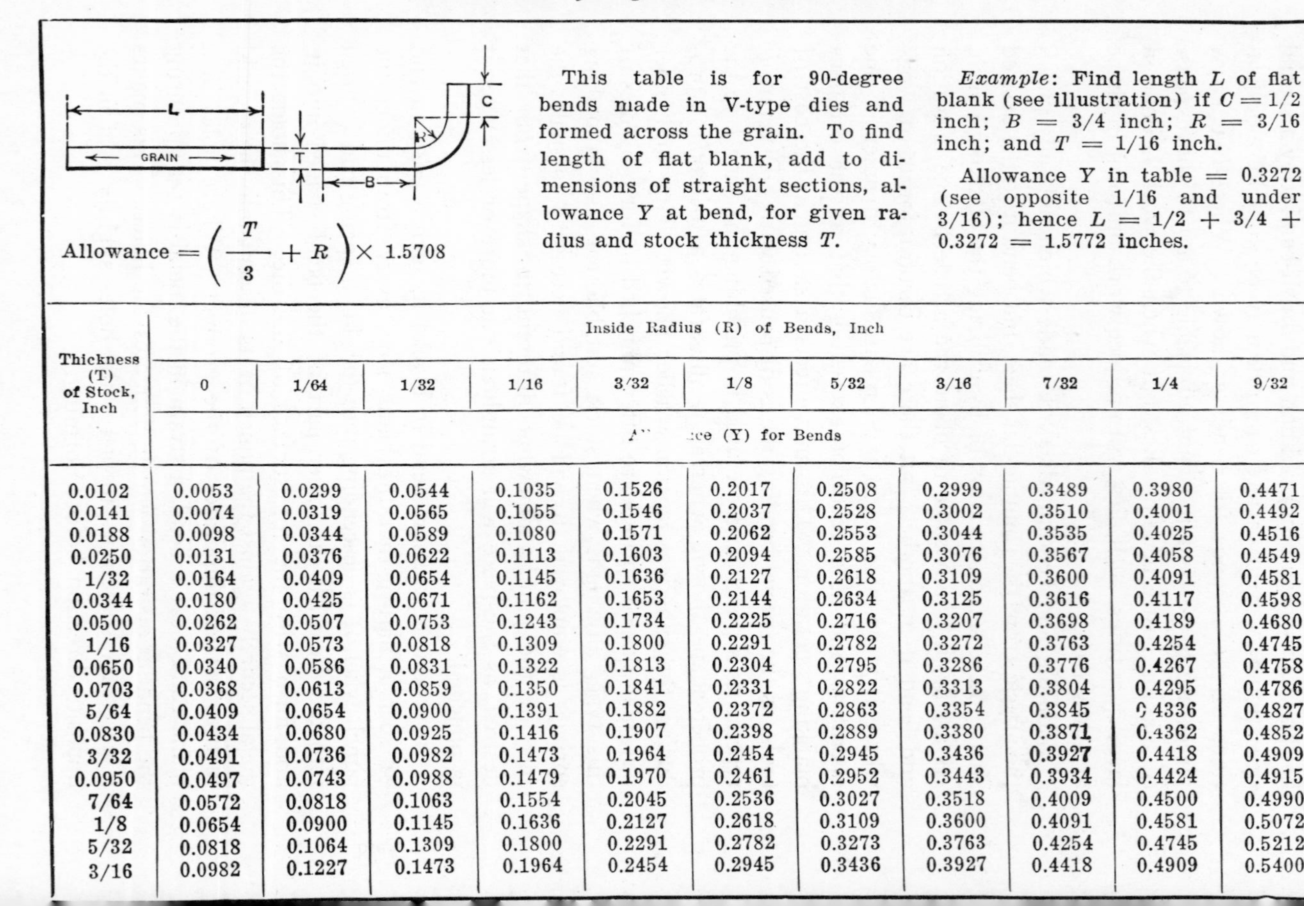

$$\text{Allowance} = \left(\frac{T}{3} + R\right) \times 1.5708$$

This table is for 90-degree bends made in V-type dies and formed across the grain. To find length of flat blank, add to dimensions of straight sections, allowance Y at bend, for given radius and stock thickness T.

Example: Find length L of flat blank (see illustration) if $C = 1/2$ inch; $B = 3/4$ inch; $R = 3/16$ inch; and $T = 1/16$ inch.

Allowance Y in table $= 0.3272$ (see opposite 1/16 and under 3/16); hence $L = 1/2 + 3/4 + 0.3272 = 1.5772$ inches.

Thickness (T) of Stock, Inch	Inside Radius (R) of Bends, Inch										
	0	1/64	1/32	1/16	3/32	1/8	5/32	3/16	7/32	1/4	9/32
	Allowance (Y) for Bends										
0.0102	0.0053	0.0299	0.0544	0.1035	0.1526	0.2017	0.2508	0.2999	0.3489	0.3980	0.4471
0.0141	0.0074	0.0319	0.0565	0.1055	0.1546	0.2037	0.2528	0.3002	0.3510	0.4001	0.4492
0.0188	0.0098	0.0344	0.0589	0.1080	0.1571	0.2062	0.2553	0.3044	0.3535	0.4025	0.4516
0.0250	0.0131	0.0376	0.0622	0.1113	0.1603	0.2094	0.2585	0.3076	0.3567	0.4058	0.4549
1/32	0.0164	0.0409	0.0654	0.1145	0.1636	0.2127	0.2618	0.3109	0.3600	0.4091	0.4581
0.0344	0.0180	0.0425	0.0671	0.1162	0.1653	0.2144	0.2634	0.3125	0.3616	0.4117	0.4598
0.0500	0.0262	0.0507	0.0753	0.1243	0.1734	0.2225	0.2716	0.3207	0.3698	0.4189	0.4680
1/16	0.0327	0.0573	0.0818	0.1309	0.1800	0.2291	0.2782	0.3272	0.3763	0.4254	0.4745
0.0650	0.0340	0.0586	0.0831	0.1322	0.1813	0.2304	0.2795	0.3286	0.3776	0.4267	0.4758
0.0703	0.0368	0.0613	0.0859	0.1350	0.1841	0.2331	0.2822	0.3313	0.3804	0.4295	0.4786
5/64	0.0409	0.0654	0.0900	0.1391	0.1882	0.2372	0.2863	0.3354	0.3845	0.4336	0.4827
0.0830	0.0434	0.0680	0.0925	0.1416	0.1907	0.2398	0.2889	0.3380	0.3871	0.4362	0.4852
3/32	0.0491	0.0736	0.0982	0.1473	0.1964	0.2454	0.2945	0.3436	0.3927	0.4418	0.4909
0.0950	0.0497	0.0743	0.0988	0.1479	0.1970	0.2461	0.2952	0.3443	0.3934	0.4424	0.4915
7/64	0.0572	0.0818	0.1063	0.1554	0.2045	0.2536	0.3027	0.3518	0.4009	0.4500	0.4990
1/8	0.0654	0.0900	0.1145	0.1636	0.2127	0.2618	0.3109	0.3600	0.4091	0.4581	0.5072
5/32	0.0818	0.1064	0.1309	0.1800	0.2291	0.2782	0.3273	0.3763	0.4254	0.4745	0.5212
3/16	0.0982	0.1227	0.1473	0.1964	0.2454	0.2945	0.3436	0.3927	0.4418	0.4909	0.5400

Allowances in this table are for stock drawn over edge of die and across grain. Allowance $= \left(\frac{T}{4} + R \right) \times 1.5708$

Thickness (T) of Stock, Inch	Inside Radius (R) of Bends, Inch										
	0	1/64	1/32	1/16	3/32	1/8	5/32	3/16	7/32	1/4	9/32
	Allowance (Y) for Bends										
0.0102	0.004	0.0285	0.0531	0.1022	0.1512	0.2003	0.2494	0.2985	0.3476	0.3967	0.4458
0.0188	0.0074	0.0319	0.0564	0.1055	0.1546	0.2037	0.2528	0.3019	0.3510	0.4001	0.4491
0.0250	0.0098	0.0344	0.0589	0.108	0.1571	0.2062	0.2552	0.3043	0.3534	0.4025	0.4516
1/32	0.0123	0.0368	0.0613	0.1104	0.1595	0.2086	0.2577	0.3068	0.3559	0.405	0.4540
0.0344	0.0135	0.0380	0.0626	0.1117	0.1607	0.2098	0.2589	0.3080	0.3571	0.4062	0.4553
0.0500	0.0196	0.0442	0.0687	0.1178	0.1669	0.2160	0.2651	0.3142	0.3632	0.4123	0.4614
1/16	0.0245	0.0491	0.0736	0.1227	0.1718	0.2209	0.2700	0.3191	0.3681	0.4172	0.4663
0.0703	0.0276	0.0521	0.0767	0.1258	0.1749	0.2239	0.2730	0.3221	0.3712	0.4203	0.4694
5/64	0.0307	0.0552	0.0798	0.1288	0.1779	0.2270	0.2761	0.3252	0.3743	0.4234	0.4725
3/32	0.0368	0.0613	0.0859	0.135	0.1841	0.2332	0.2822	0.3313	0.3804	0.4295	0.4786
7/64	0.0429	0.0675	0.0920	0.1411	0.1902	0.2393	0.2884	0.3375	0.3866	0.4356	0.4847
1/8	0.0491	0.0736	0.0982	0.1473	0.1963	0.2454	0.2945	0.3436	0.3927	0.4418	0.4909
0.1406	0.0552	0.0798	0.1043	0.1534	0.2025	0.2516	0.3007	0.3497	0.3988	0.4479	0.4970
5/32	0.0613	0.0859	0.1104	0.1595	0.2086	0.2577	0.3068	0.3559	0.405	0.4540	0.5031
3/16	0.0736	0.0982	0.1227	0.1718	0.2209	0.2700	0.3191	0.3681	0.4172	0.4663	0.5154
0.2031	0.0798	0.1043	0.1288	0.1779	0.2270	0.2761	0.3252	0.3743	0.4234	0.4725	0.5215
0.2188	0.0859	0.1104	0.135	0.1841	0.2332	0.2822	0.3313	0.3804	0.4295	0.4786	0.5277
0.2344	0.0920	0.1166	0.1411	0.1902	0.2393	0.2884	0.3375	0.3866	0.4356	0.4847	0.5338
0.2500	0.0982	0.1227	0.1473	0.1963	0.2454	0.2945	0.3436	0.3927	0.4418	0.4909	0.5400
0.2656	0.1043	0.1288	0.1543	0.2025	0.2516	0.3007	0.3497	0.3988	0.4479	0.4970	0.5461
0.2813	0.1104	0.1350	0.1595	0.2086	0.2577	0.3068	0.3559	0.405	0.4540	0.5031	0.5522
0.3125	0.1227	0.1473	0.1718	0.2209	0.2700	0.3191	0.3681	0.4172	0.4663	0.5154	0.5645

Examples of Right-angle or V-die Bending.—Some interesting examples of various types of bends that may be made in a V-die are shown in Fig. 2. The construction of the die and punch is such that it will permit a large variety of right-angle bends to be made on angular strips of sheet metal. The die shown in the six cross-sectional views is about 2 feet long. A plan view of the die is shown at *G*, in the lower right-hand corner of the illustration. The member *I* is held in the die-bed of the bolster plate of the press. Two operations performed in this die are indicated in view *A*.

The first operation consists of laying a piece of flat strip stock on top of the die *I*, where it is located by a suitable gage secured to the die. After the strip is in place, the punch *H* descends and forms a right-angle bend, leaving one side straight, as indicated by the dotted lines. After all the parts are bent in this manner, the locating gages are removed from the top of the die and replaced by other gages that hold the work in the proper position while the next operation is performed. The latter operation consists of bending the piece to the U-shape indicated by the full lines. It will be noted that the punch is cut away at *X* to provide a clearance space for the work.

The type of gage generally used for locating the work on the die is indicated diagrammatically in the plan view at *G*. A strip of stock is indicated at *W*. The stock is simply dropped between the locating plates or gages *Y* and *Z*, which are held in place by screws. These locating plates are removable, and are cut from flat stock about 1/8 inch thick. They are also cut at the end to suit the particular strip to be bent.

In view *B* is shown a bending job which differs from the one described in that one side of the finished work is longer than the other. The blank on which the bends are made is first laid on top of the die and the short end bent up at *J*, at which time the other side or end remains in the position shown by the dotted lines at *K*, the short side stopping at point *L*.

The work is next placed on the die, where it is positioned by locating plates *Y* and *Z* (view G) which have narrow gage

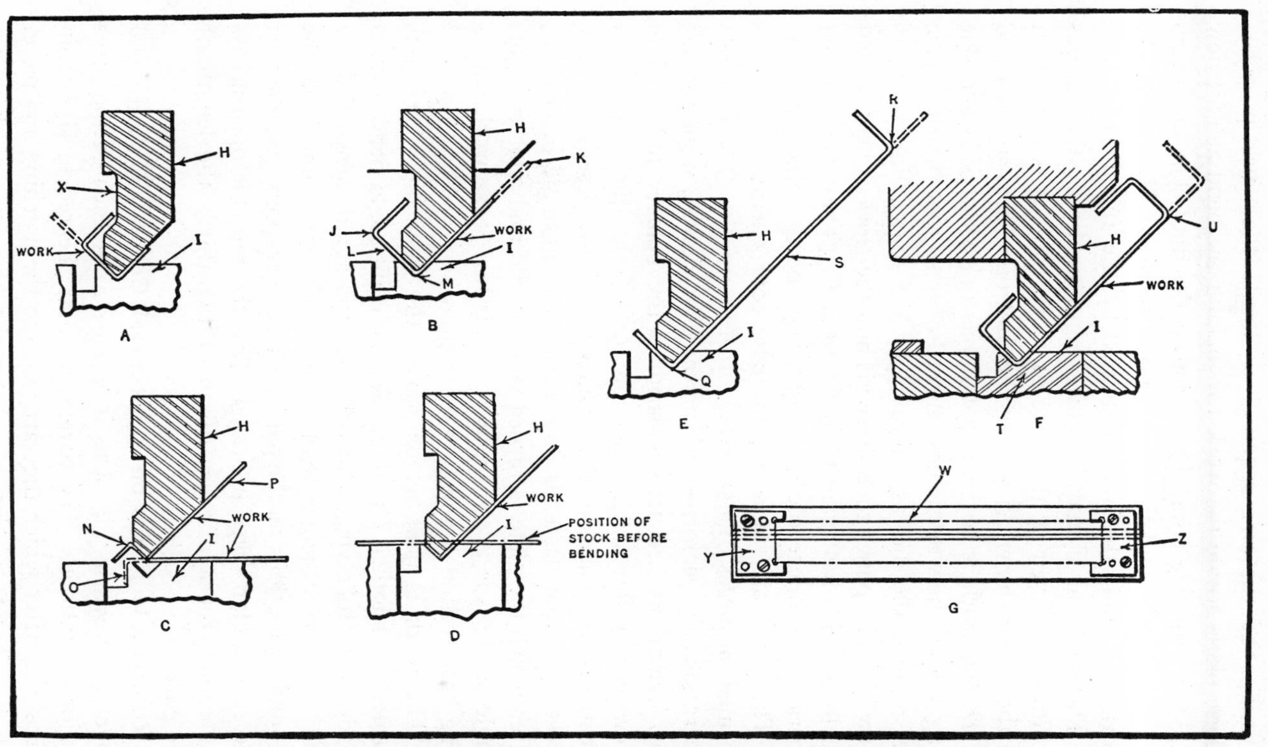

Fig. 2. Various Types of Bending Operations Performed on a V-die

openings of the size required to locate the work properly. These plates locate the work for making the bend at *M* (view *B*), the long side lying flat on top of the die. The press ram again descends and the final bend is made at *M*, causing the work to assume the shape indicated by the full lines.

The views at *C* and *D* show diagrammatically the various positions assumed by the piece of work while it is being bent to the shape shown at *N*. In the first operation, as indicated at *D*, the work is so bent that it has one short side and one long side. The work is next turned over so that the short side lies against the die, as indicated by the dotted lines at *O* in view *C*. The punch then descends and the stock is bent so that the longer side lies against the die, as at *P*. These two bending operations produce the two right-angle bends indicated at *N*.

The views at *E* and *F* show how four operations are performed on pieces of flat plate, 2 feet in length. The first two operations are performed as indicated in view *E*, while the last two operations are accomplished in the manner indicated in view *F*. A flat plate is laid on top of the die, where it is located by the gages in the manner previously described. The press ram then descends and makes a right-angle bend at *Q*, after which the plate is turned end for end and another right-angle bend made as shown at *R*. This leaves the work with a long base section *S* and two short sides.

The work is next set on top of the same die where it is located by another set of gages. A right-angle bend is then made at *T*, following which the work is again turned end for end and a right-angle bend made at *U*, thus completing the bending operations on the part. These operations give the part the rectangular shape indicated, with the top side open across the center for a distance of about two-thirds the length of the part.

Right-angle Bends on Sheet-metal Cover.—A sheet-metal cover is shown in Fig. 3 as it appears after each of the three major operations. The covers are first sheared to size from flat stock, after which they are put into the notching and piercing die shown in Fig. 4. After the piercing and notching operations, the pieces are bent, as indicated by the second-operation diagram in Fig. 3, by the forming die shown in the upper view of Fig. 5. The final bending operation is then performed as shown in the lower view of Fig. 5.

Referring to the detail construction of the die shown in Fig. 4, *B* is a cutting die, secured to the bed *A* by machine screws

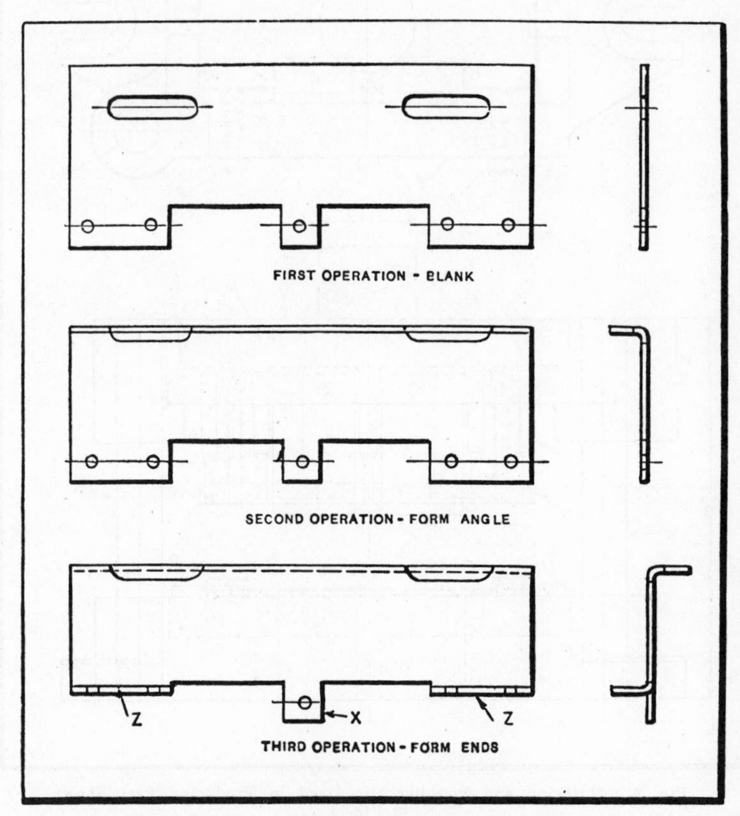

Fig. 3. Steps in the Production of a Sheet-metal Cover

(not shown in the illustration). The corner pieces *C* and *D*, which are secured to the top face of the bed, serve to locate the blank in the correct position for notching. The two spring pins E serve to push or hold the work back against the locating pieces *C* and *D*. This method of locating the work insures uniform positioning of the pierced holes and notches.

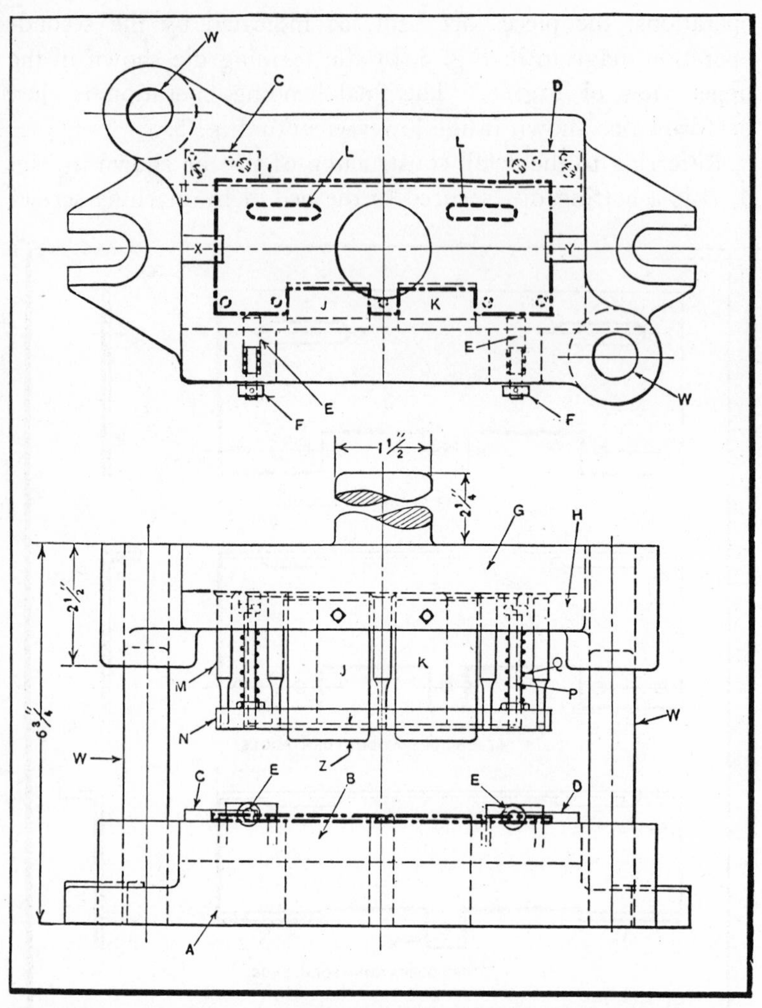

Fig. 4. Notching and Piercing Die Used in Producing Part Shown in Fig. 3

The collars F, which are pinned to the spring pins, allow the latter members to spring forward for a distance of only about 1/16 inch when the work is removed from the die. When loading the die, the work is slipped into the corner gages C and D, and then pressed down against the chamfered ends of the spring pins until it snaps into the correct position. The punch-holder G contains a block H which is held in position by machine screws. On block *H* are mounted the two large punches *J* and *K*, which notch the front edge of the work while the two punches *L* cut the elongated holes in the plate, and a group of five round punches *M* pierce the small holes.

All the punches are fitted into the block *H* before it is placed in the punch-holder *G*. Screws at the front side of the holder *G* are used to clamp punches *J* and *K* against block *H*. These punches are also locked in the block in such a manner that they will not be loosened or pull out. The punches for the elongated slots and for the small holes are headed over at the top to prevent them from being pulled out of the block. The stripper plate *N* forces the work from the punches as it ascends after the holes are pierced. The screws *P* prevent the stripper plate from sliding off the punches.

As the punches descend, the stripper plate *N*, being suspended slightly below the cutting edge of the punches, holds the work down on the die while it is being pierced and notched. The stripper plate springs *Q* are compressed when the piercing and notching operation takes place. The work has a tendency to cling to the punches as they ascend, but is prevented from doing so by stripper plate *N*, which is actuated by springs *Q*. The finger grooves at *X* and *Y* permit the operator to grip the work and lift it from the die. The notching punches *J* and *K* have a step-down surface at *Z*, the object of which is to allow the ends of the punches to enter the die-holder before their cutting surfaces come in contact with the work. With this construction the punches are backed up or braced so they will not spring away from the work. Guide pins at *W* are used to hold the punch-holder and die-holder in accurate alignment.

The second operation—that of forming the angle—necessitates the use of a V-die as shown in the upper view of Fig. 5. The die member *A* has a groove *B* of the required angle. A stop-plate *D* is secured to the top face of die *A*, against which the back edge of the work is located. The punch member consists of a block *E* which matches the die groove. To complete the forming of the part, the opposite side is bent up on the same forming punch by locating the work in the position shown by the heavy dot-and-dash lines at *N* in the lower view. Punch *E* is thus employed for both bending operations, but a different die member *K* is used for the second operation. Die *K* is beveled at *L* for a length *M* at the center so that the end of the work not formed will remain flat while the ends *Z*, Fig. 3, are being bent or formed.

Dies for Accurate Right-angle Bending.—Bending dies for accurate work have always been a source of trouble to toolmakers. There are so many methods of bending a part and

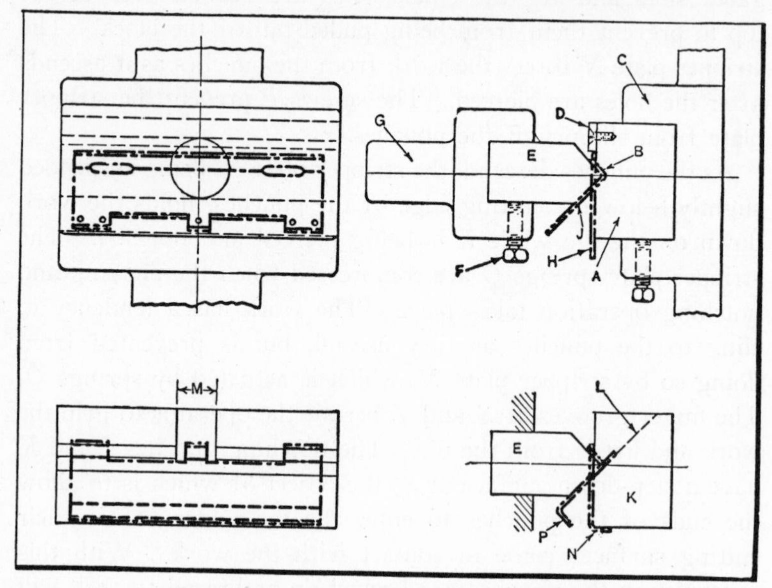

Fig. 5. Die for Bending Part Shown in Fig. 3

so many different kinds of metal that no fixed rule holds good for determining the amount of metal to allow for a bend. Generally, the holes are pierced and the form blanked before the bending operation is performed. For this reason, accurate information regarding the change produced in a part by bending must be had before the blanking die is made. The V-notched die, in many cases, will not bend two successive blanks alike. However, it answers for work not requiring great accuracy.

As a result of the demand for greater accuracy, the dies to be described were developed. These dies have proved very satisfactory. The die shown in Fig. 6 is designed for making right-angle bends in a lock part. It has a steel block *K* with a slot sawed in it to receive and locate the work during the bending operation. If the part to be bent is of irregular shape, it may be necessary to place a form *L*, of corresponding shape, in the bottom of the slot. A square or oblong hole *M* of suitable size is cut vertically through the die to receive the pilot *N*

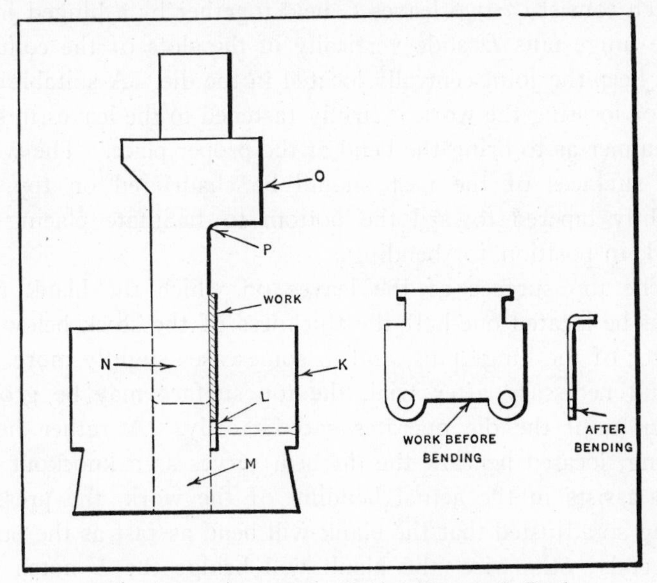

Fig. 6. Punch and Die for Making Right-angle Bend

of the punch *O* and to prevent the punch from backing away from the work. The punch is made with a radius surface *P* in the working corner to suit the radius of the bent piece. This radius can be determined by bending a piece of the same kind of stock in a vise. As the punch descends, the corner of the blank is pushed to one side by the radius surface. After the bend is started, the straight surface finishes the right-angle bend. This die is particularly adapted for producing parts in which the bend is required to be accurately located with respect to one side only. A greater allowance for bending is necessary when this method is used, as much as the full thickness of the stock often being required for the bend.

Another successful bending die of novel design is shown in Fig. 7. This die is more expensive to build than the one shown in Fig. 6, but it possesses features that warrant the additional cost. It produces work of surprising accuracy if properly made. The die consists of a base *A* with a V-cut of suitable size across the upper surface. A column *B* is fastened at each end to give support to the working members, which consist of two leaves *C* held together by a hinged joint. The hinge pins *D* slide vertically in the slots of the columns and keep the joint centrally located in the die. A suitable nest *E* for locating the work is firmly fastened to the leaves in such a manner as to bring the bend at the proper place. The working surfaces of the nest should be chamfered on top and slightly tapered toward the bottom to facilitate placing the work in position for bending.

The top surface of the leaves on which the blank rests must be located one-half the thickness of the stock below the center of the hinge pins, and in some cases slightly more. If found necessary after trial, the top surface may be ground down until the die operates satisfactorily. A rather heavy spring, located beneath the die-bed, serves as a knockout and also assists in the actual bending of the work, the pressure being so adjusted that the blank will bend as fast as the punch descends; otherwise, the blank will bridge the V-notch and exert pressure against the locating nest. Punch *F* is the design usually employed for V-shaped bending dies.

The die is mounted in a pillar die set to secure perfect alignment. The same die may be used for bending different shapes at right angles by supplying a separate nest for each shape. When the thickness of the stock varies, the leaves should have inserts of the proper height for each kind of stock. This is very important, as the blank will be stretched or crushed if the working surface is too low or too high.

When the die is in operation, the work is placed in the nest while the leaves are in the "up" position. The leaves are

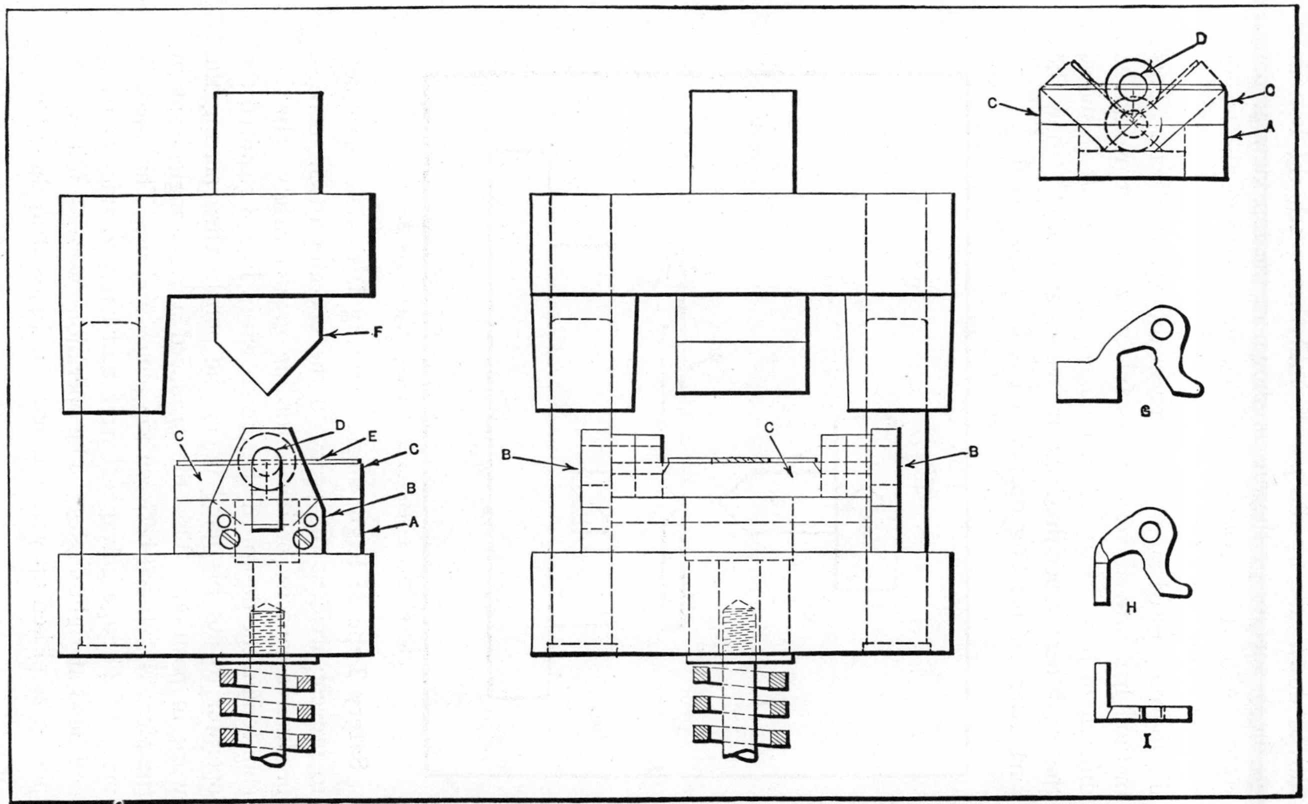

Fig. 7. Die for Bending Accurately the Part Shown at *G* to the Shape Shown at *H* and *I*

moved downward by the punch until they reach the bottom on the V-surface of the die as shown in the top view at the right. After the work is bent, the spring returns the leaves to their original position, and the work may be blown off the die by compressed air or removed in the ordinary way. This method has proved very successful on work that would be difficult to bend in the usual manner. The view at *G* shows the blank before bending, and the views at *H* and *I* show the part after the bending operation has been completed.

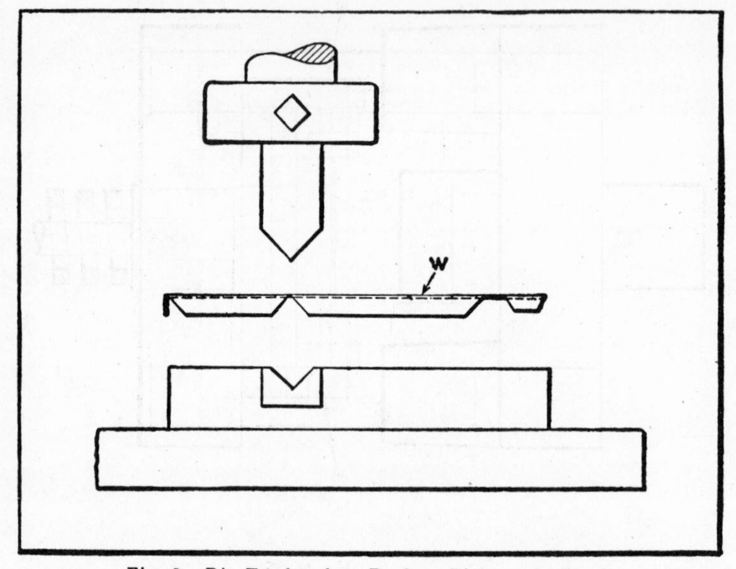

Fig. 8. Die Employed to Produce Right-angle Bends

Safety Type of Right-angle Bending Die.—Dies designed to prevent accident or injury to the operator often increase productive capacity besides affording greater safety. In this connection, the design of the die shown in Fig. 8 required the operator to put his hand under the punch when placing the work in position. This die produced a right-angle bend in the piece *W*, shown between the punch and die. This piece is made of 24-gage galvanized iron, and has two sides and one end bend at right-angles. The operations were as follows: A piece was picked up with one hand and passed to the other in the correct position for placing in the die, and with the index finger extending along the piece. While held in this manner, the piece was pushed to the left, knocking the finished piece from under the punch. It was then placed in the correct position over the die and slid to the right, the end flange acting as a stop to locate it longitudinally. In grasping the piece, the operator frequently caught hold of it with his index finger extending so far along the piece that there seemed danger of its becoming caught between the punch and die. It was therefore decided to change the die so that it could be operated under an inclinable press, as it could then be fed by gravity. The positions of the punch and die were reversed in the new design, shown in Fig. 9. This arrangement permits the work to slide down the guides with the flanges up. There is a guide at each end of the work made of two angle-irons *A* and *B*, formed from 14-gage sheet iron and riveted to short pieces of 1½-inch angle-iron *D*. The two lower guides *A* extend beyond the end of the upper guides *B*, thus forming a table on which the work is placed when the slide is being filled. The guides *A* end at the beginning of the bottom former *F*, but the upper guides *B* continue far enough to allow the work to slide over the bottom former and against the stops located at *E*. The work will then rest on the bottom former, and as the right-hand side is longer than the left, the left side will tip up until it bears against guide *B*. There being no lower guides at this place, space is allowed for the ends to pass down as they are formed by the punch. The finished work can then pass out of the back of the press.

After this die had been in operation for a short time the operator suggested that a stop be put on the slide in such a position that it would prevent any piece of work from being placed incorrectly in the slide. By referring to the illustrations it will be seen that the height of the flange on the right-hand end of the work is less than that of the other flanges of the piece. By making a stop *C* to catch any piece that might enter in a reverse position, all loss from this source was stopped. With this die, the operations consist

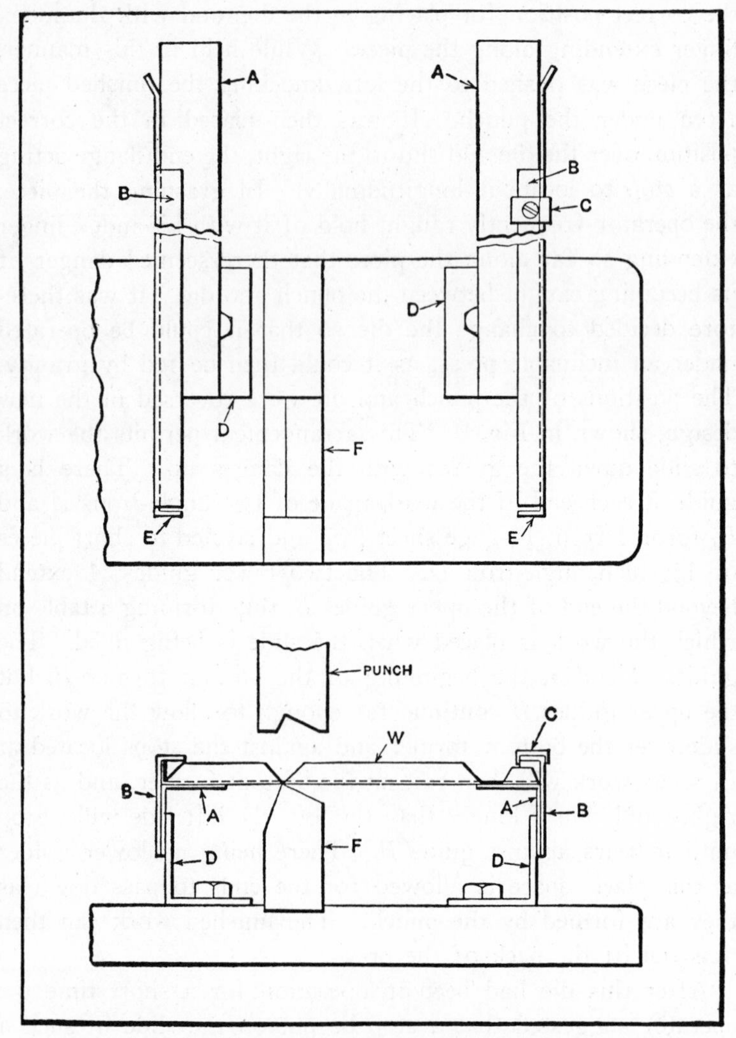

Fig. 9. Improved Design of Bending Die, Which Reduced the Possibility of Injury and also Increased Production

merely of placing the pieces in the slide and allowing the press to run until the slide is nearly empty, at which time the press must be stopped and refilled. This is necessary because the pieces cannot be placed in the guides as fast as the press operates. This scheme proved entirely satisfactory

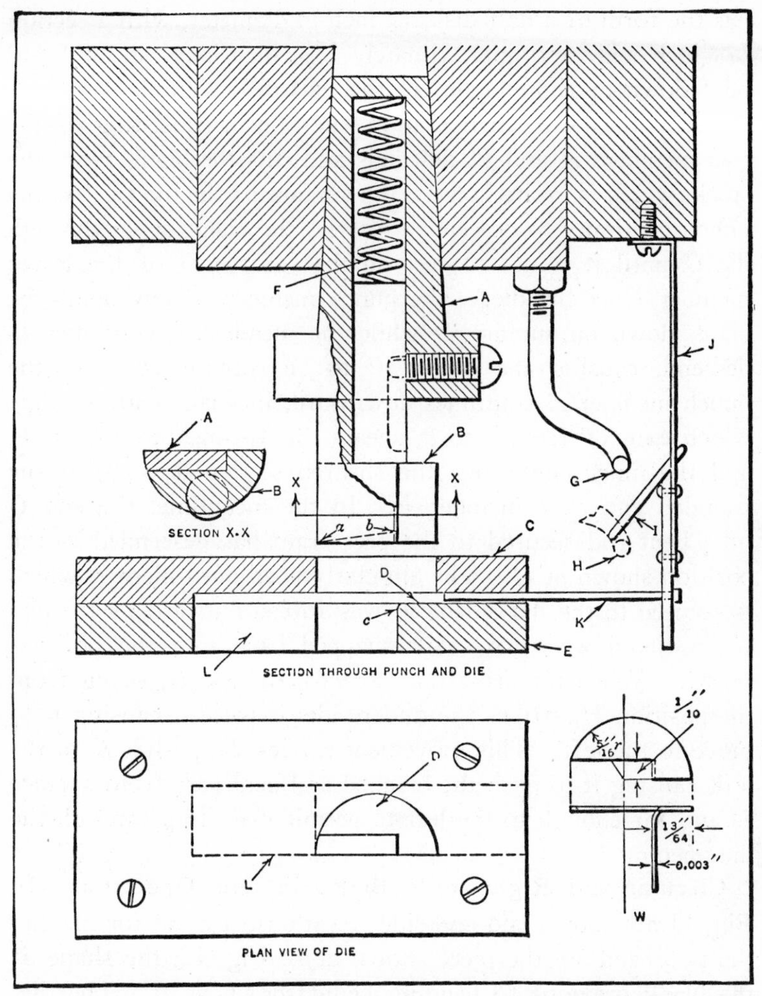

Fig. 10. Blanking and Bending Die for Producing Part *W*

from a safety point of view and has also more than doubled production.

Combination Blanking and Right-angle Bending Die.—The die shown in Fig. 10 is for a foot-operated press having a stroke of 1 inch. The die is used to produce the part shown at *W* in one operation. The platinum stock from which this part is blanked is 0.003 inch thick. The blanked and bent part has the form of a half-disk, 5/8 inch in diameter, with a section 1/10 inch wide and approximately 15/32 inch long, sheared and bent down at right angles to the half-disk section.

When the die is in operation, the punch, consisting of the two members *A* and *B*, descends and cuts the blank from the stock, which is located on the top surface of the die *C*. As the punch continues to descend, it carries the blank down through die *C* until it comes to rest on the surface *D* of the lower member *E* of the die. The punch member *B* now holds the blank down on surface *D* while the member *A* continues to descend, causing the spring *F* to be compressed. As the punch member *A* continues downward, its inner cutting edge, which extends from *a* to *b*, shears the 1/10-inch wide section, and the inner end bends the sheared section down over the rounded end *c* of member *E*. In the meantime, the end *G* of a bent rod secured to the press ram has descended to the position shown at *H*. The angularly positioned piece *I*, which is secured to the flat spring *J*, was forced outward by the end *G* on the down stroke, but snapped back into the position shown. When the press ram ascends, the end *G*, rising from the position *H*, strikes the under side of piece *I*, causing it to move to the left. This movement carries the pusher *K* to the left, causing it to push the blanked and bent part from surface *D* and far enough to the left to permit it to drop through the die opening *L*.

Circular and Right-angle Bends in One Operation.—In Fig. 11 are shown end and side elevations of a die for making the two bends in the piece shown at *B*, Fig. 12, the shape of the blank previous to bending being shown at *A*. The die-bolster *A* is bored out to receive the two guide-rods *B*, which are made a sliding fit in the die-holder *A*. It will be noticed that the bosses on the die-holder *A* are made large, sufficient material having been left so that they could be bored for bushings. However, in this case it was not thought necessary to use bushings, inasmuch as the die was not intended for continuous operation. The stud or cam *D* held in the punchholder, presses on a block *E*, which, in turn, operates

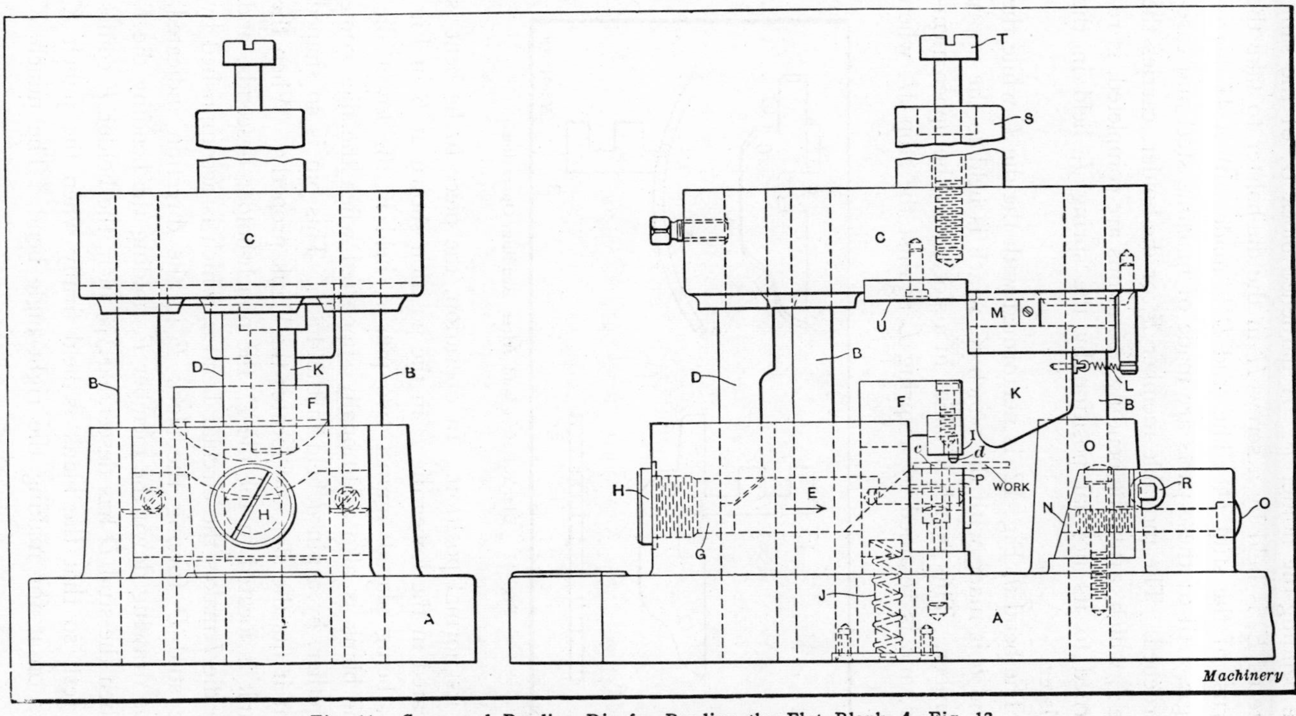

Fig. 11. Compound Bending Die for Bending the Flat Blank *A*, Fig. 12

the bending-die holder *F*. A hardened block *G*, of the same size as *E*, is held by a screw *H* in the die-bolster to take the thrust of the stud *D*. The stud *D* is made with a 45-degree angle. All of these parts are made of machine steel and case-hardened. The movable member *F*, or die-holder, carries the die *I*, which, after the bending operations are completed, is returned to its normal position by the spring *J*, held in the bolster.

The bend *a*, Fig. 12, is performed with the die *I*, while the bend *b* is made with the punch *K*, which is held to the upper member. This punch *K* slides in a slot cut in the upper member, and is retained by a spring *L* against the stop *M*, when

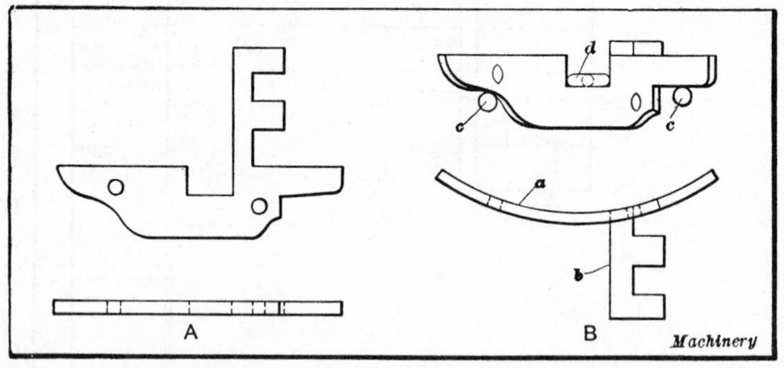

Fig. 12. Blank Before and After Bending Operation

in its normal position. In operation, the piece to be bent is located in the lower die *P* in the position shown at *B* in Fig. 12, being placed against two pins *c*, held in the lower die. The blank is also additionally supported when the dies come together, by a pin *d* held in the die *I*. This pin is so shaped that it fits the slot and locates the blank properly. When the blank is located in the die *P*, the punch-holder descends, and the die *I* makes the circular bend *a*, which is accomplished by the stud *D* forcing the block *E* in the direction indicated, thus drawing down the member *F*, holding the bending die *I*. When the stud *D* has descended 7/16 inch, the holder *F* comes to rest, so that the blank is held firmly when the punch *K* acts on it for making the right-angle bend. The punch *K* then comes in contact with the blank and the adjustable block *N*. The block *N* is tapered as shown, and deflects the punch *K* inward, so that it slides in the punch-holder, and in its descent bends the blank at right angles. The block *N* is held to the die-bolster *A* by means of three screws *O*, and is adjusted inward by a tapered gib operated on by a screw *R*. Having the block *N* adjustable in this manner makes provision for the blank to be bent to such shape that after the punch retreats it will spring back to the angle desired. The shank *S* is held to the punch-holder *C* by screw *T*. A hardened block *U* held to the punch-holder *C* comes in contact with the holder *F*, and gives the final blow to the blank.

Bending Circular Clamp-collar.—It is frequently required to make a formed sheet-metal collar similar to that shown at *A* in Fig. 13. This piece can be easily formed in one operation if the quantity of pieces required is sufficient to warrant the manufacture of an expensive forming punch and die equipped with side-acting cams. However, if such expense is not warranted, the following method can be used: A forming punch and die is made to form the blank in the first operation to the shape shown at *B*. The dimension *h* should be made slightly greater than one-half the outside diameter required for the finished piece. This dimension will vary, depending upon the quality of the stock. After forming, the piece is shaped by a punch having a removable pin around which the collar is shaped by pressing the formed piece into a U-shaped die. These simple devices are very inexpensive tools to make.

Bending Square-cornered Offset.—A shape that is often troublesome to form in one operation is that shown at *C*, Fig. 13. This and similar shapes are frequently required in large quantities. For performing this operation, the punch and die shown at *D* and *E* are used. The construction is simple and inexpensive. At *D* the forming dies *f* are shown raised by the action of the spring plunger *g* and supporting the work previous to starting the forming operation. At *E* the punch *p* has descended and formed the piece, the plunger *g* having been forced down. On the upward stroke of the punch the spring which controls the plunger forces it up and ejects the work.

Adjustable Strap-bending Dies.—In Fig. 14 is shown a die for piercing, bending, and cutting off pieces like the ones shown in Fig. 15. The dies are of the progressive type, and can be adjusted to produce the various sizes of straps shown. It will be noticed that the dies are provided with four scales *A*, *B*, *C*, and *D*, each of which is graduated from 3/16 to 3½ inches. Three of the scales are located on the die member shown in the lower view, and one on the punch member, a plan view of which is shown.

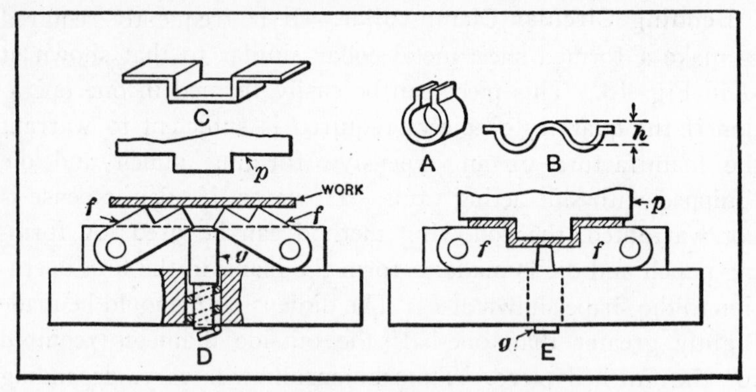

Fig. 13. Simple Punch and Die for Bending Part *C*

The die member consists of the adjustable piercing die *E*, the piercing and parting die *F*, the knock-out pin *G*, the bending block *H*, and the gage *I*. These tool-steel parts are all hardened and mounted on the die-shoe. The punch consists of the adjustable block *J*, with piercing punch *K* and the stamp bumper *L*, piercing punch *S*, and parting punch *M*, and a bending punch *N*. These members are also of hardened tool steel.

The adjustable members *E*, *H*, *I*, and *J* are provided with zero point indicators or lines. The method of setting the dies is as follows: First, loosen the set-screws *P*, and set members *E*, *H*, *I*, and *J*, with the aid of the zero lines, to suit the size of strap to be produced. The proper size bending

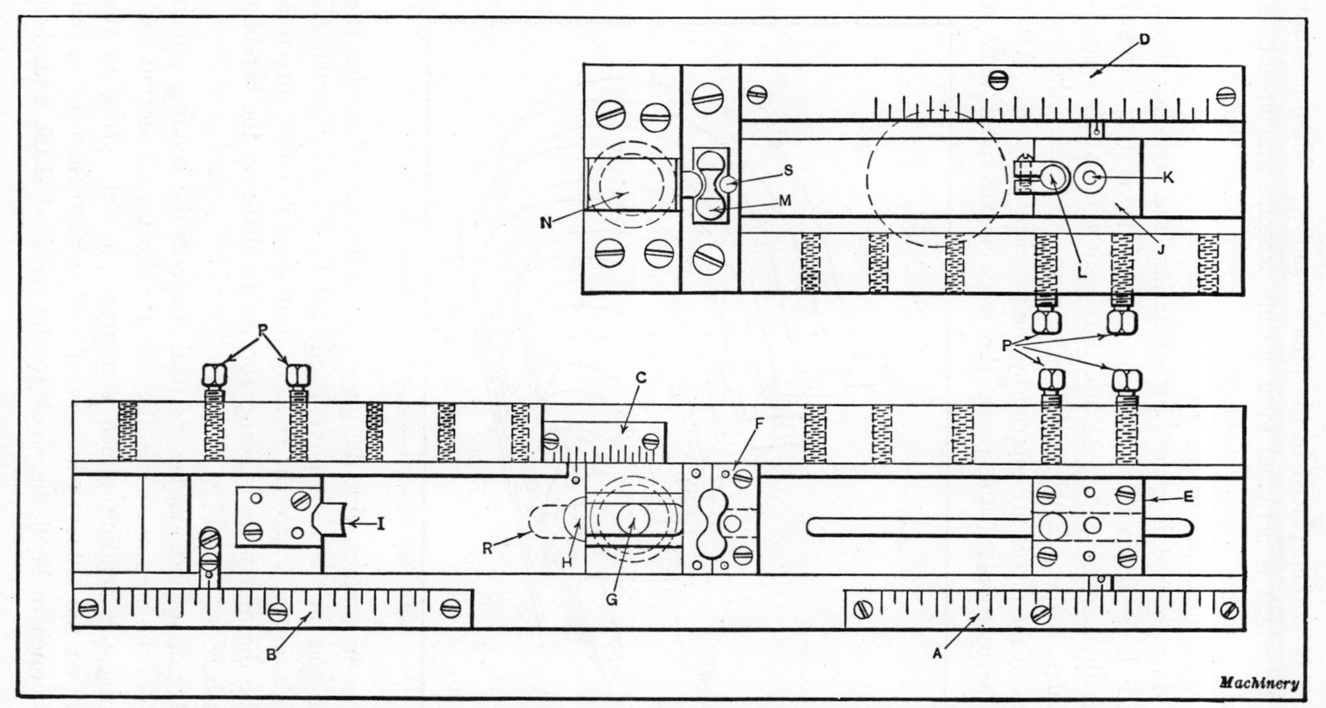

Fig. 14. Punch and Die for Piercing, Bending and Cutting off the Straps Shown in Fig. 15

punch *N* is then placed in the punch member. The knockout pin *G*, which is actuated by a spring pressure attachment, is adjusted to the correct position in the slot *R*, so that it is in line with the center of the bending punch *N*.

When the die is ready for operation, the strip of stock, which is 1/32 inch thick and 5/16 inch wide, is fed forward until the parting punch *M* and die *F* cut the end to a semicircular shape. During the cutting-off operation, the two holes in the pieces are pierced by the punches *S* and *K*. After the first stroke of the press, the stock is advanced until it

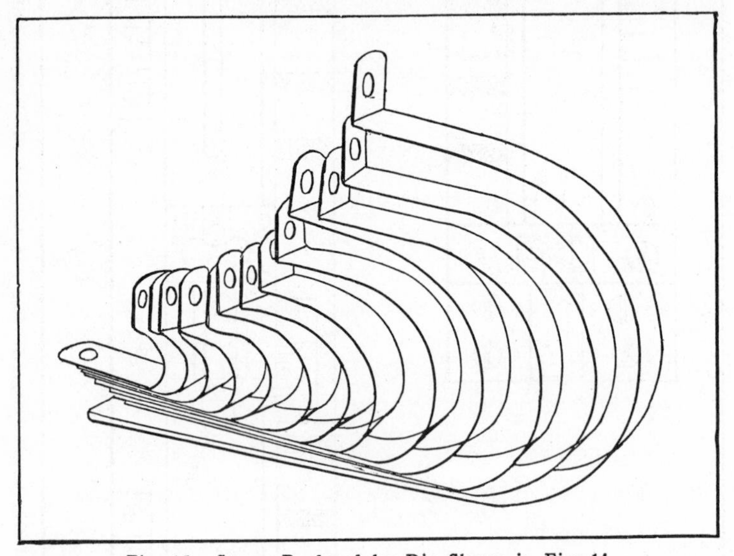

Fig. 15. Straps Produced by Die Shown in Fig. 14

comes in contact with the gage *I*. At the second stroke, the first hole in the next piece is pierced by the long punch *K*, which serves to hold the strip from moving in either direction while the first piece is being formed to shape by the bending punch *N*.

The first piece reaches its final shape as the bending punch strikes the bottom of the die. As the downward motion continues, the bending punch compresses a coil spring in the body of the holder, which is of sufficient stiffness to permit the punch to bend the work to the required shape and then allow it to dwell during the remainder of the downward stroke while the parting and piercing punch *M* operates. On the upward stroke of the press ram, the finished piece is lifted from the die by the knock-out pin *G* and ejected by air pressure.

Bending Die Having Pivoted Arm Which Swings into Under-cut Die Cavity.—An interesting design of bending die is shown in Fig. 16. As will be seen, a swinging arm is pivoted at one end of the punch; this arm carries a steel roller *B*. When the punch descends, this roller bends the stock down into the die at *C*. When the downward travel of the roller is

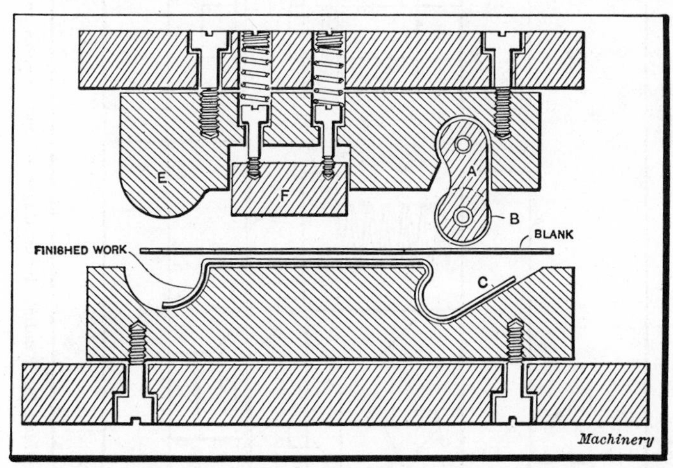

Fig. 16. Bending Die of Pivoted Arm Type

checked by the die, the arm *A* swings to the left and continues to move in this direction until the roller has formed the work into the die, as shown by the lower finished part. The left-hand end of the work is formed between the die and the extension *E* of the punch. Before the punch has reached the end of its downward travel, the gripper *F* engages the work and holds it in position through the tension of the two springs shown in the illustration. This prevents any movement of the blank during the final stages of the bending operation.

Die Having Cam-operated Slides for Bending Edges 150 Degrees.—The die shown diagrammatically in Fig. 17 is used

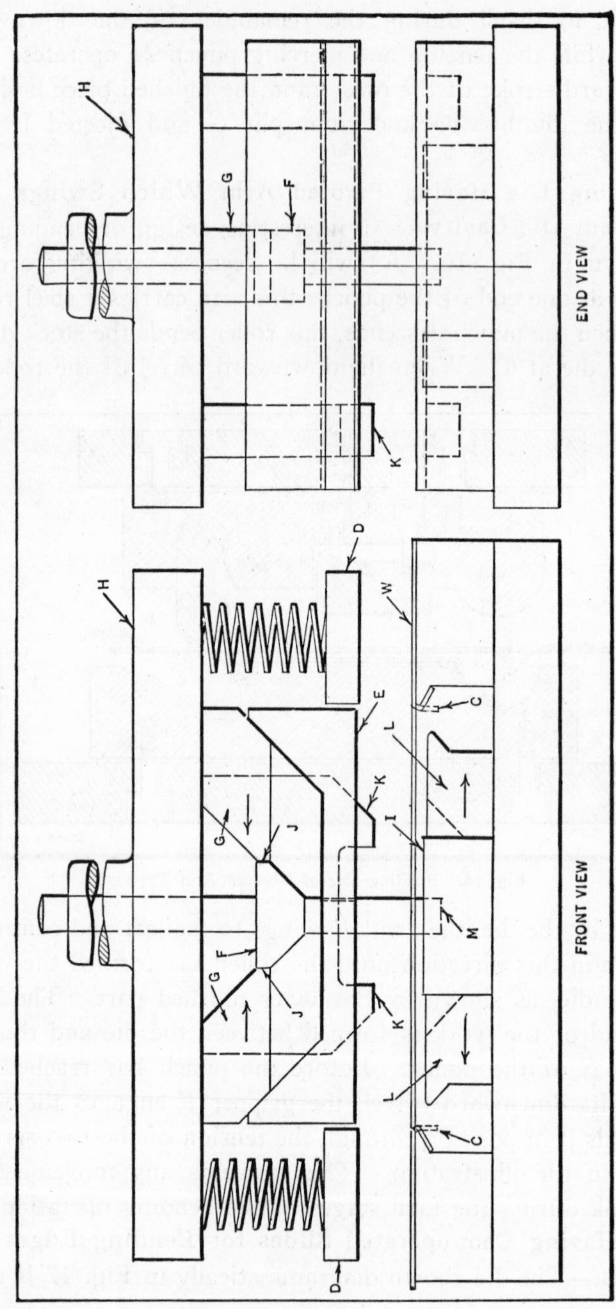

Fig. 17. Die Used for Bending Inner Edges of Part Shown in Fig. 18

on a single-action press for bending the inner edges of the cut-away portion of a sheet-metal part. One of the sheet-metal pieces on which the inner edges *A* and *B* have been bent or formed to the required angle of 150 degrees is shown in Fig. 18. The piece to be bent is placed on the die, as shown at *W* in Fig. 17. When the press is tripped, the two spring pads *D*, descending slightly in advance of the bending punch *E*, come in contact with the work and hold it in place while the bending die forms the right-angle bends at *C*.

As the punch continues its downward movement, the end *M* of the central member *F* comes in contact with the base of the

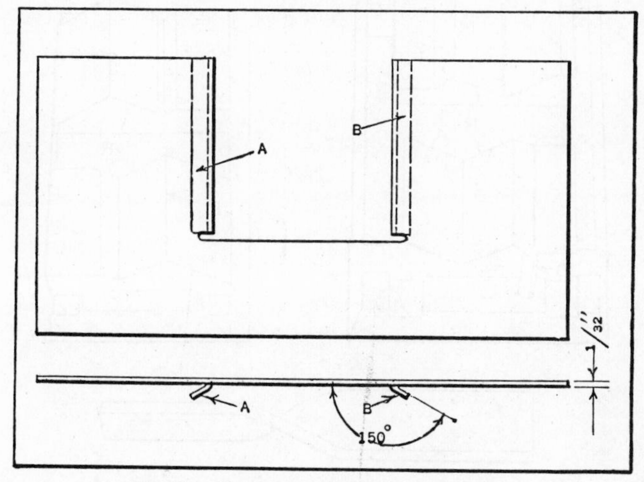

Fig. 18. Sheet-metal Part with Bent Edges

die. Member *F* then remains stationary while the bending member *E* and the two members *G*, which transmit the required bending force from the punch holder *H* to member *E*, continue to move downward. This movement continues until a point is reached where the inner ends of members *G* slide past the ends *J* of the member *F*. The parts *G* are then allowed to slide inward, which, in turn, permits the bending member *E* to remain stationary when it comes in contact with part *I* of the die after completing the 90-degree bends.

In moving inward, the parts *G* slide on the lower side of

the punch-holder *H*, being forced over by the cam or wedge surfaces of part *E*, which remains stationary. The lower end of part *F* is of such length that the ends *J* will pass out of contact with members *G* immediately after the 90-degree bends are completed and just before part *E* comes in contact with the members *I*. A further downward movement of the punch brings the wedge or cam surfaces of the pieces *K* into contact with the bending members *L*, causing them to slide outward

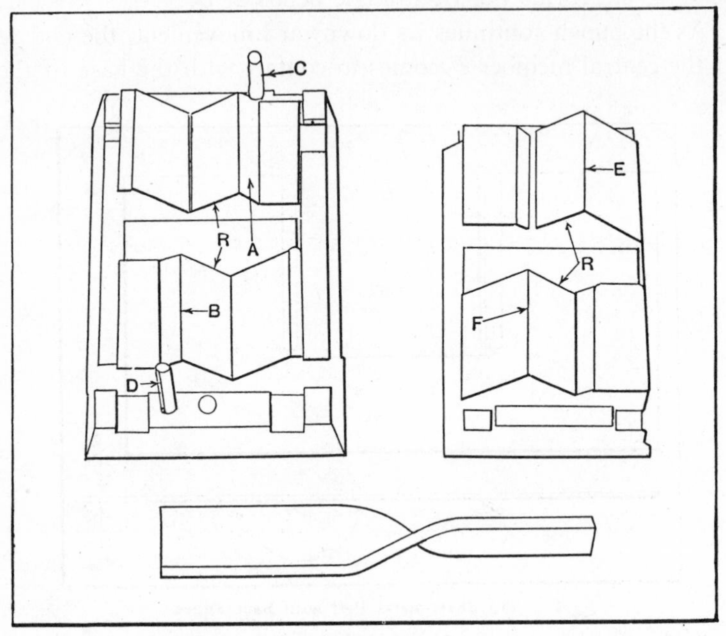

Fig. 19. Die and Punch for Twisting Flat Stock as Shown by Sample

and complete the bending operation. At the end of the upward stroke of the press ram, the upper end of the central member *F* comes in contact with a knock-out bar, causing the sliding members *G* to resume their normal operating positions, ready for the next bending operation.

Twisting Die for Flat Bar Stock.—The die shown in Fig. 19 was designed and made to twist flat bars, although the principle can be applied in other types of dies, for twisting blanks of various shapes and sizes. The die is very rugged and will withstand any strains that an ordinary V-shaped forming die will stand. It is very simple in construction and action, and can be designed to give the stock either a right- or a left-hand twist of any desired amount. The work is laid on the die in a horizontal position so that it rests on the edges *A* and *B*, and against the gage pins *C* and *D*. A stop (not shown) is employed to locate the work endwise. When the punch descends, the points or edges *E* and *F* strike the work, forcing the edges downward.

At *G*, Fig. 20, is shown diagrammatically, a section of the work in the position it occupies at the completion of the stroke.

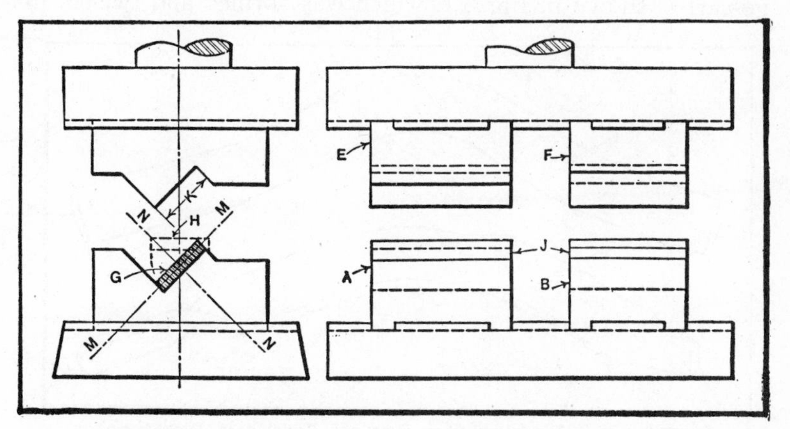

Fig. 20. Assembly View of Die for Twisting Flat Bar Stock

The dotted lines at *H* show the position of the same section at the beginning of the stroke. The lengths of the different sections of the work can be varied by changing the lengths of members *A* and *B*. The length of the twisted part can be varied by changing the distance *J* between the members *A* and *B*. Although the die here described was designed to make but one twist, any number of twists can be obtained by adding more members such as *A*, *B*, *E* and *F*.

The inside edges *R*, Fig. 19, of the die and punch members over which the different sections rub when being twisted, should be rounded. This rounding of the edges must be considered when designing the dies if the twisted parts are to have the correct length. The dimension *K*, Fig. 20, should be the same as the width of the work so that the edges of the work will be automatically kept in proper alignment.

By exercising care in laying out the die-blocks and keeping the blocks properly centered on the point of intersection of the center lines *M-M* and *N-N*, all the members can be machined from one piece at one setting, the piece being parted to make the required number of die members. The same practice, of course, applies to the punch-blocks.

Combination Bending and Twisting Die.—A latch for a go-cart is shown in Fig. 21, which was formed and twisted in

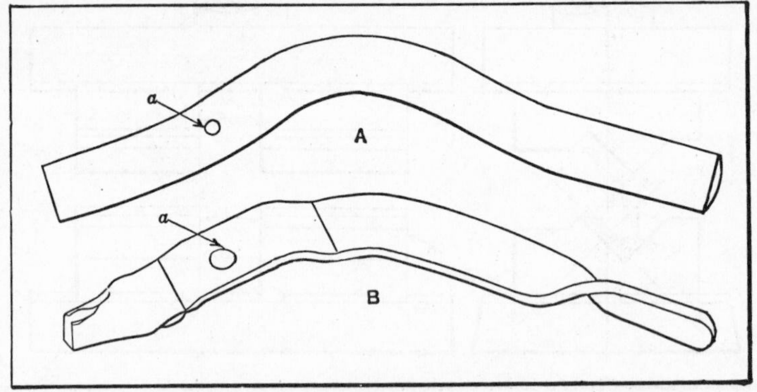

Fig. 21. Steel Latch which is Bent and Twisted in Die Shown in Fig. 22

the die shown in Fig. 22. This latch is first cut off and formed to the shape shown at *A*, Fig. 21, after which it is placed in the die and is bent and twisted to the required shape shown at *B*. The lower bending die *A*, Fig. 22, is held in a cast iron base *B*, and pins *C*, driven into the former, extend down through the base and come in contact with a pressure plate *D* operated by a rubber pad *E*. The top forming die *F* is held by screws and dowels, as shown, to the holder *G*, which has a shank to fit the hole in the ram of the press. This holder *G* is lined up with the base *B* by standards *H*, and holds two pins *I* which operate the lower twisting dies *J* and *K*. The twisting dies *J* and *K* correspond in shape to the dies *L* and *M*, which

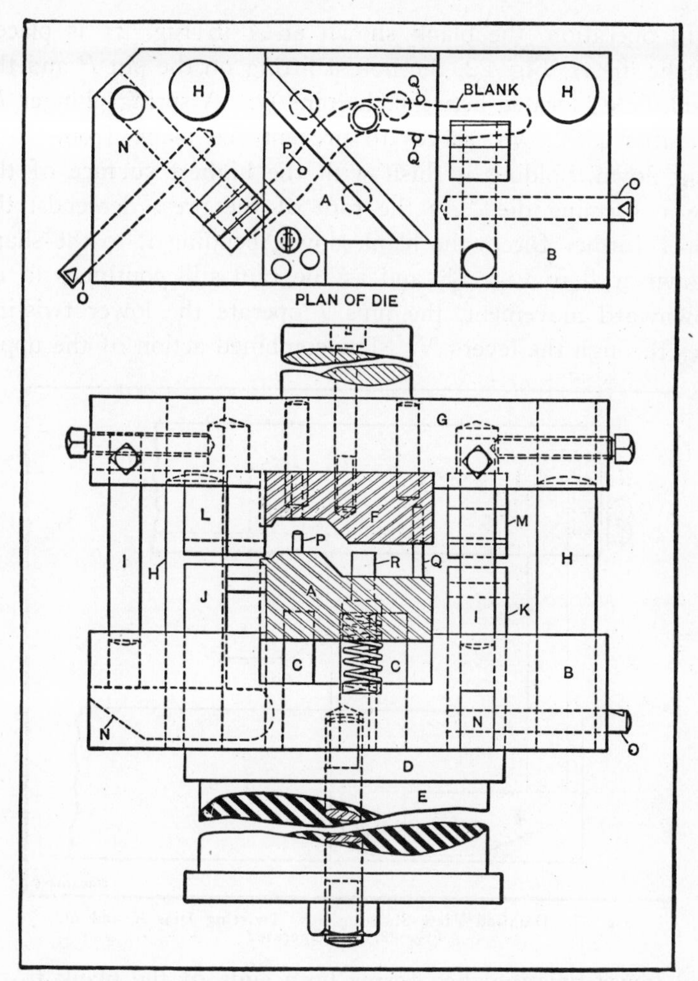

Fig. 22. Elevation and Plan of Combination Bending and Twisting Die

are provided with shanks and are held in the holder *G* by screws and dowels.

The lower twisting dies *J* and *K* are given a slight upward movement by means of the pins *I*, which come in contact on the downward stroke of the ram with fulcrumed levers *N* held on pins *O*. These fulcrumed levers are connected to the twisting dies by pins, as shown more clearly in Fig. 23, where the operation of the twisting dies *K* and *M* is illustrated.

In operation, the blank shown at *A* in Fig. 21 is placed on the die *A*, Fig. 22, the hole *a* fitting on the pin *P* and the blank being located between the pins *Q*. A spring plunger *R*, operated as shown, serves to prevent the blank from dropping down, holding it flush with the highest surface of the lower forming die. As the ram of the press descends, the upper former forces the blank down, bending it to the shape shown at *B* in Fig. 21, and as the ram still continues in its downward movement, the pins *I* operate the lower twisting dies through the levers *N*. The combined action of the upper

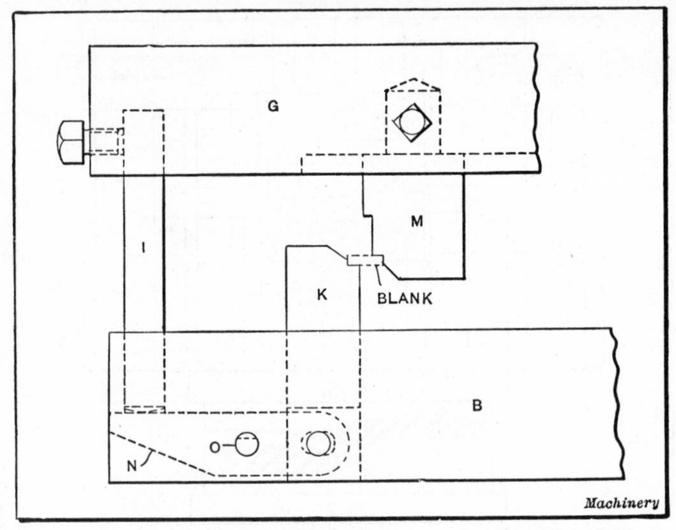

Fig. 23. Detailed View Showing how Twisting Dies *K* and *M*, Fig. 22, are Operated

and lower twisting dies forms both ends of the blank to the shape shown at *B*. The lower die *A*, while the twisting operation is taking place, has been forced down to the lowest point of its travel, compressing the rubber pad *E*, which returns it to its former position when the ram of the press ascends.

Progressive Dies for Piercing, Right-angle Bending and Blanking.—Parts that in the past have required the use of several separate dies are now made by a series of operations in one die that produces a finished part at each stroke of the press. A die of the latter type, as explained in Chapter I, is sometimes called a "follow" or "progressive" die. A die of this kind employed to produce the locating bracket shown in detail in Fig. 24 is described in the following. This piece is used in an electrical device, and as it forms a certain part of a magnetic circuit, it is required to be made of Norway iron. The stock is obtained in strips 10 feet long, 0.110 inch thick by 2¹¹⁄₁₆ inches wide. The metal strip is fed into the press from right to left by means of a double roll feed. The press

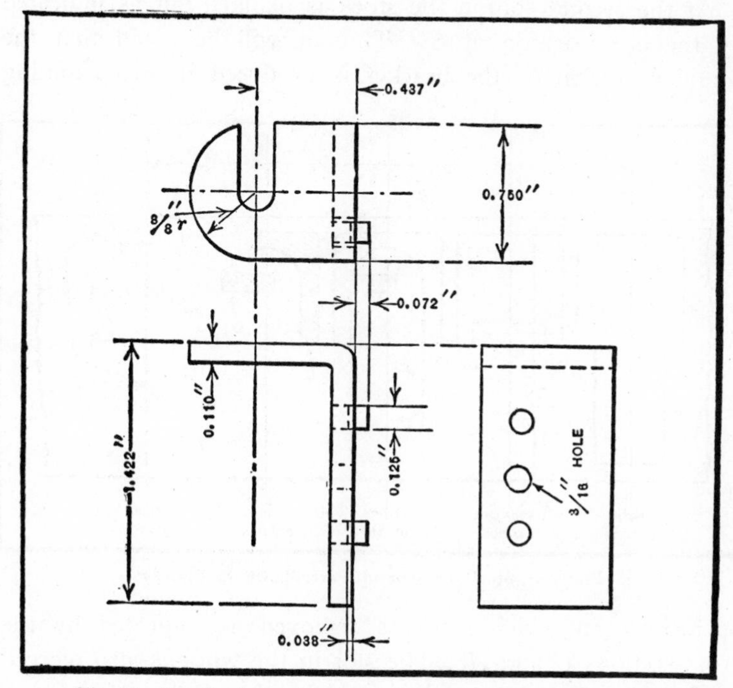

Fig. 24. Details of Bracket Produced in Progressive Type of Die

is operated at a speed of 120 strokes per minute, and the gross production per hour is 6500 finished parts.

In Fig. 25 is shown the stock lay-out of the part. It will be noted that there are five stations, the stock from which a single part is punched being successively located in five different positions on the die. It was found that about 107 feet of stock was required to make 1000 pieces, and that the approximately weight per thousand pieces was about 106 pounds. The nature of the operation performed at each station of the die will be described in the regular order in which the work progresses. At the first station, located at the extreme right-hand side of the die, part of the stock is blanked out to form the rounded section of the end of the piece shown bent at right angles to the main body in Fig. 24. The part blanked out in this operation is shown in cross-section at *A*, Fig. 25. The three holes *B* are also pieced at the first station.

At the second station the stock is blanked out as indicated by the cross-section at *C*. Thus it will be noted that the rounded section of the bracket is produced in two blanking

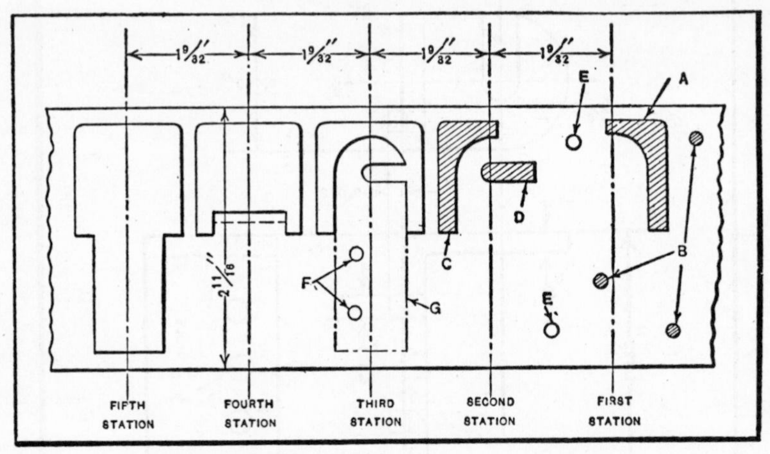

Fig. 25. Stock Lay-out of Part Shown in Fig. 24

operations, in which stock is removed as indicated by the cross-sections *C* and *A*. The slot in the work is also pierced at the second station, as indicated by the cross-section at *D*. In this operation, the stock is located by pilots *E*, which enter two of the holes *B* pierced at the first station. At the third station, the two projecting pins or bosses *F* are pressed up from the stock. At the fourth station, the rounded end of the part is bent down, and at the fifth station the piece is blanked out. Referring to Fig. 26, the dotted lines at *D* indicate that a slot is cut in the die which extends from the die opening at the fourth station to that of the fifth station. This slot is made wide enough to clear the bent down end of the piece as the stock is fed forward to the next position. The stripper plate is shown in this plan view of the die. It will be noted that the stock guides *A* are actuated by springs *B*. These guides keep the stock pressed against the opposite side *C* of the guide strip shown at *U*, Fig. 27. The plate *O*, Fig. 26, was required to be cut away, as indicated by the dotted lines at *E*, in order to provide clearance for the scrap.

Referring to the front elevation of the punch and die shown in Fig. 27, parts *A* and *C* are the punches that blank out the

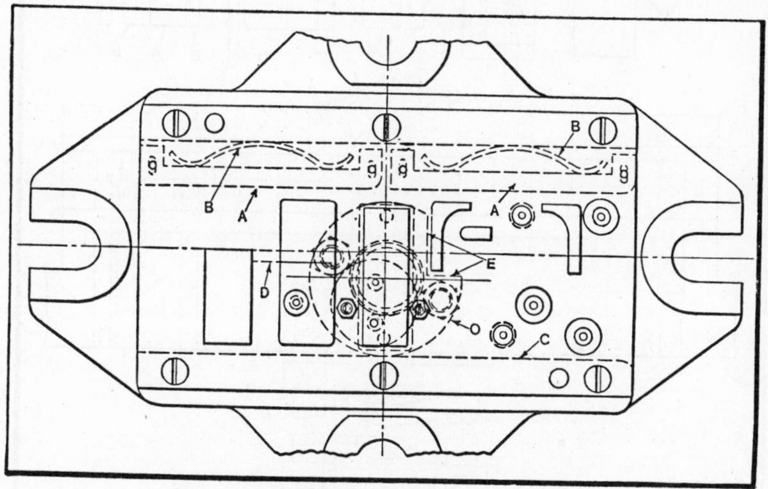

Fig. 26. Plan View of Die Shown in Fig. 27

part of the stock indicated by the cross-sections shown at *A* and *C*, Fig. 25. The punches *B*, Fig. 27, pierce the holes *B* shown at the first station Fig 25. Part *D*, Fig 27, is the punch that pierces the slot in the bent-up end of the piece. Part *E* is one of the pilots that enter the holes pierced by the two outside punches *B*. The punch *G* partly pushes the section shown by dot-and-dash lines at *G*, Fig. 25, out of the stock, in order to force up the metal that forms the projecting pins or bosses.

The part *H*, Fig. 27, bends the rounded end of the piece down at the fourth station. This punch is provided with a

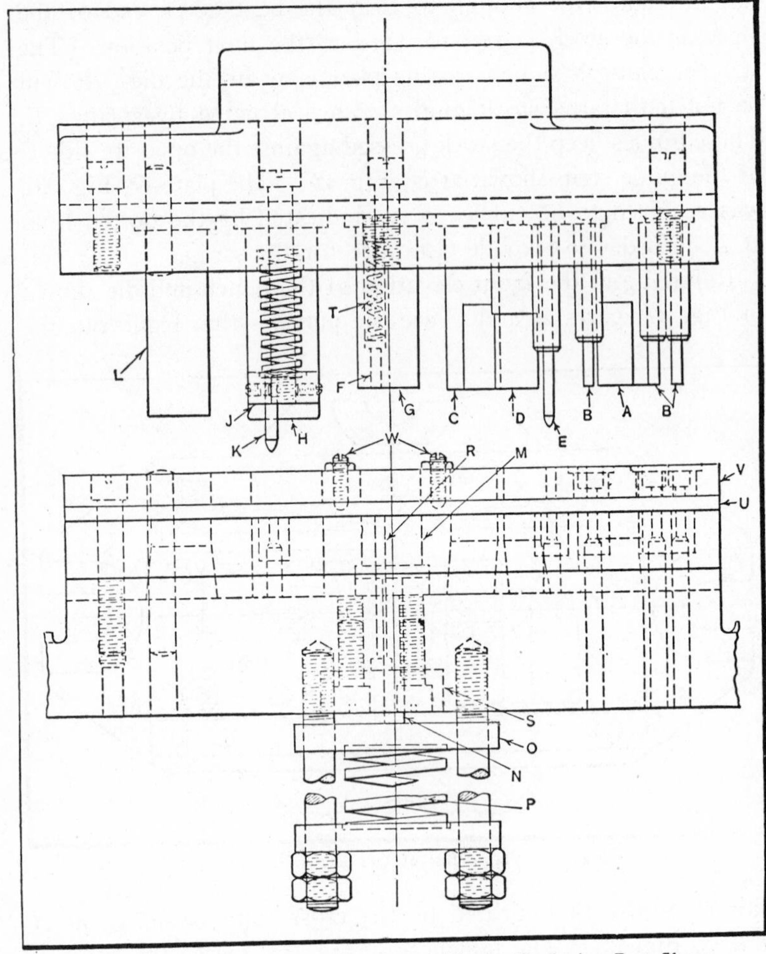

Fig. 27. Front Elevation of Punch and Die for Producing Part Shown in Fig. 24

step that is designed to strike the outer point of the rounded end before the bending operation actually begins. It will be noted that a spring-actuated pad *J* is provided for punch *H*. This pad, with the pilot *K*, which enters the central hole *B* (Fig. 25) pierced at the first station, prevents the metal from being drawn or pulled to one side. The pilot *K* thus prevents the projecting bosses or pins from being damaged. The incorporation of the bending punch *H* in the die is a feature of particular interest in view of the fact that follow-dies of this type are generally used for work that requires only piercing and blanking operations. The pieces are blanked by punch *L*, and fall through the die into a receptacle under the press. It was found necessary to support the piercing punches *B* at the first station by inserting bushings in the stripper plate *V*.

A novel feature of the die is the method employed for forcing up the metal that forms the projecting pins or bosses. On the downward stroke of the press, the punch *G*, Fig. 27, pushes the section indicated by dot-and-dash lines *G* in Fig. 25 partly through the stock, or a distance of 0.072 inch, thus causing the part *M*, Fig. 27, to recede into the die. Pins *N*, in turn, cause plate *O* to compress spring *P*. The punches *R*, being stationary and backed by the plate *S*, push up the two bosses on the work when the sheet metal stock is pressed down over them. This also causes the two spring-backed pins *F* to recede into punch *G*.

The two adjustable screws *W* were provided in order to hold the stock down flush on the die, for on the upward stroke of the press the heavy sub-press spring *P* reacts against plate *O*, and the pins *N*, which are in contact with part *M*, push the section shown in dot-and-dash lines *G* in Fig. 25 back into the stock, thus leaving the bosses on the upper side of the stock. The spring-backed pins *F*, Fig. 27, in punch *G* are returned to their normal positions by the action of springs *T*.

In Fig. 28 is shown the plan view of the punch-holder block. The holes *T*, shown in part *J*, clear the bosses or projecting pins formed in the preceding station, so that the entire face of part *J* is in contact with the stock during the bending operation.

Another Example of Piercing, Right-angle Bending and Blanking.—The die shown in Fig. 29 is for producing the part illustrated at *A* in Fig. 30, which also shows the successive piercing, bending, and blanking operations. The stock is fed through the die in the direction indicated by the arrow, Fig. 29. On the first stroke the piercing operation at *B*, Fig. 30, is performed by a punch of corresponding shape. On the next stroke a bending punch turns over the part *C*, making a right-angle bend, and, finally, the finished piece *A* is blanked out. Of course these operations all take place simultaneously, except when the stock is first being started, so that a finished piece is blanked out at each stroke.

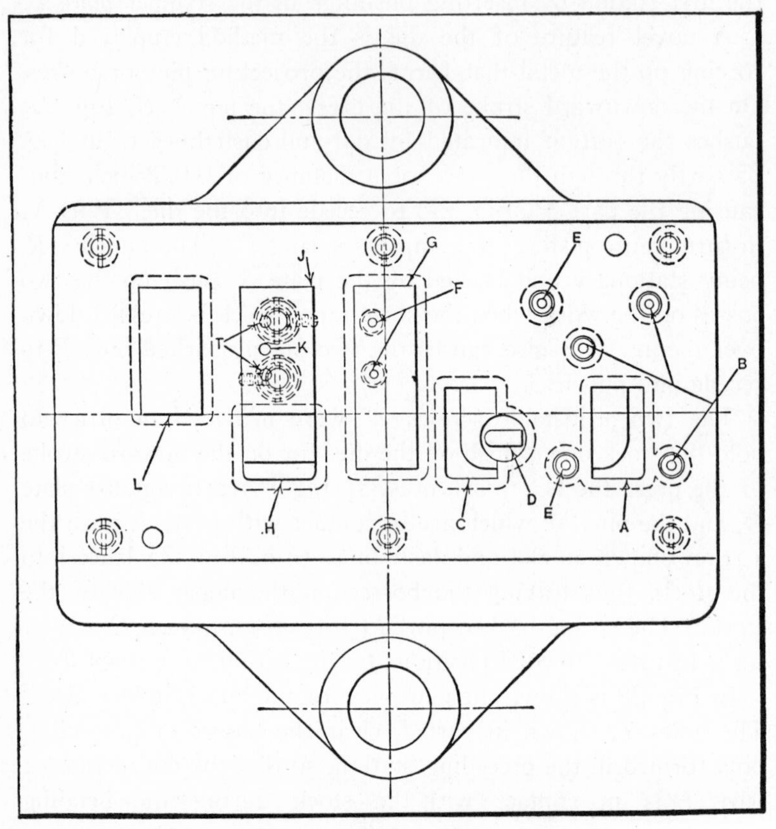

Fig. 28. Plan View of Punch Shown in Fig. 27

One of the interesting features of this die is the method of stopping the stock as it is fed forward. After the bending operation, which takes place at b_2 on the die, the bent end which projects downward below the surface of the die, is fed forward through channel *d* until it comes against the end d_1 which forms a positive stop. By this simple method, the stock is located

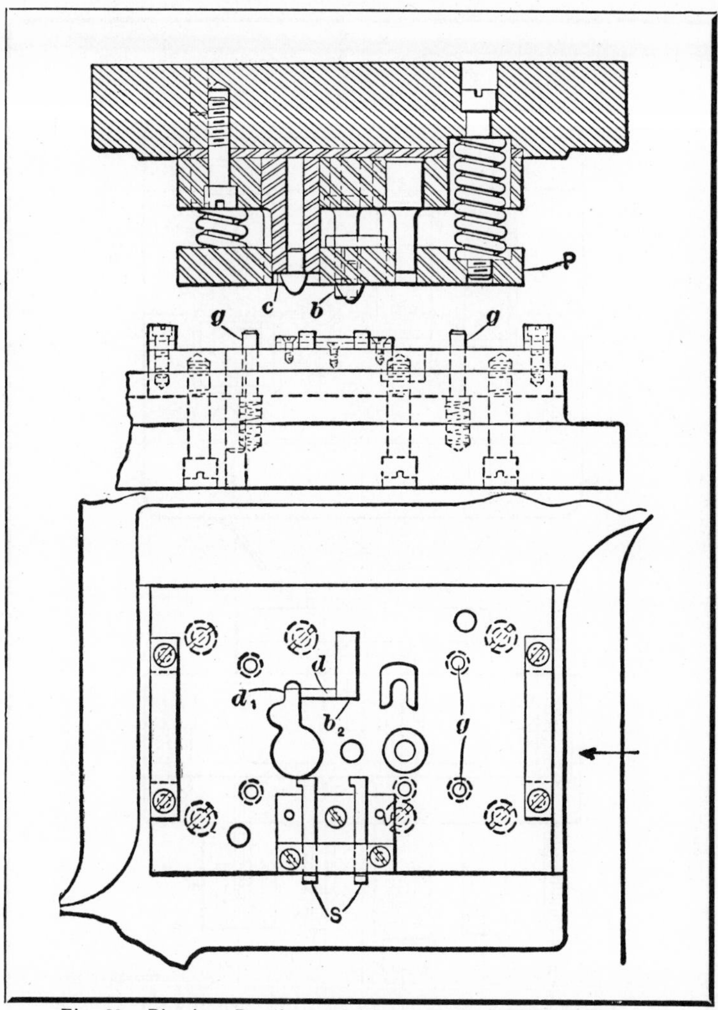

Fig. 29. Piercing, Bending and Blanking Die for Part *A*, Fig. 30

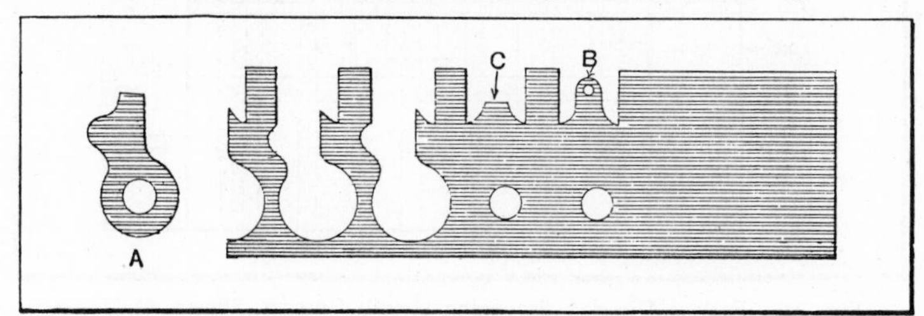

Fig. 30. Order of Operations in Producing Part *A*

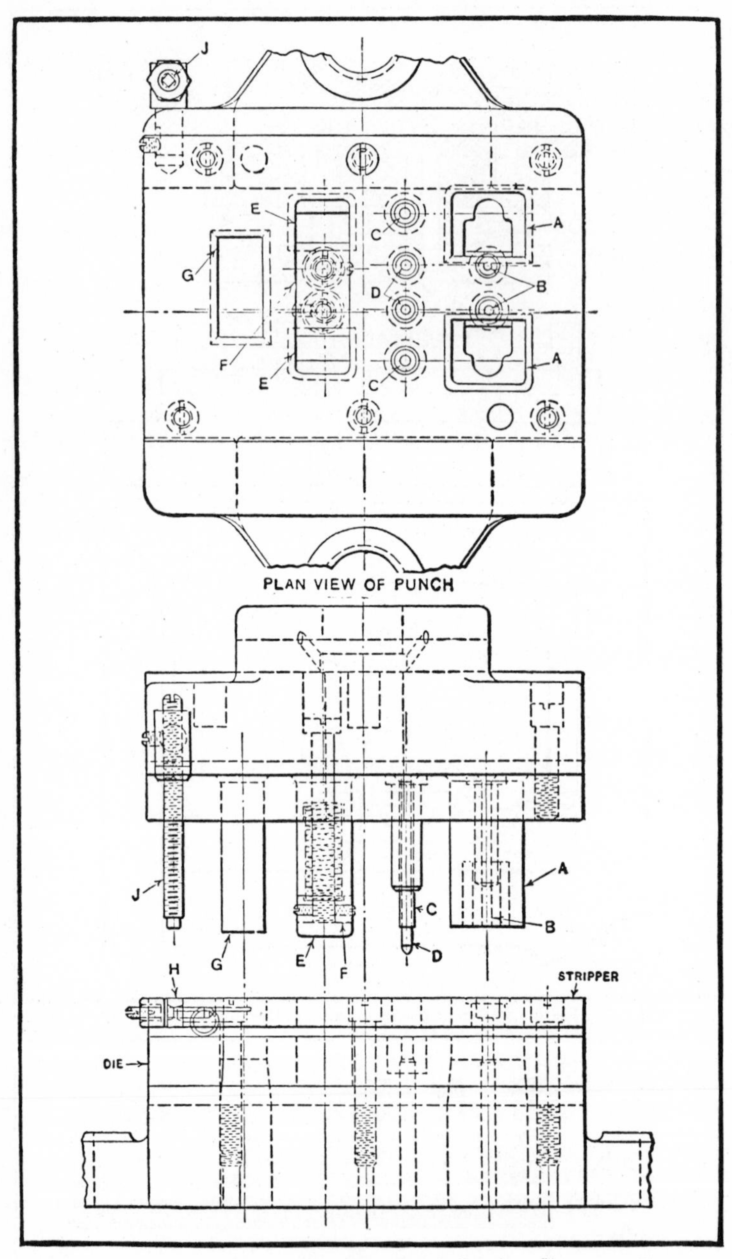

Fig. 31. Follow Die for Producing Small Bracket Shown at Upper Part of Fig. 32

for the pilot-pins which accurately position it for the blanking operation. By means of the spring pressure-pad *P*, the stock is held firmly against the die, so that it will not be buckled by the bending operation. When the stock is first being started through the die, stops *S* are used for locating the stock for the first and second operations.

Follow-die for Piercing, Double Right-angle Bending and Blanking Small Parts.—One die of the follow type, in many instances, can be used to pierce and blank work in one operation, which formerly required the use of several dies. Fig. 31 shows the general construction of the follow-die used to produce the part shown in the upper view of Fig. 32. This part is known as a bracket support, and is used in an electrical device, the nature of which requires that the part be of Norway iron. The stock is obtained in 10-foot lengths, 3 inches wide by 0.093 inch thick. It is fed to the press by means of a double roll feed. The speed of the press is 90 strokes a minute, and the gross production per hour is approximatley 5000 finished pieces. About 95 feet of stock is required for 1000 pieces.

Referring to Fig. 32, it will be noted that the ends of the piece are bent at right angles to the central section. The provision of the bending punches *E*, Fig. 31, is a feature of particular interest in view of the fact that follow-dies are generally used for work that requires only piercing and blanking operations. The die lay-out is shown in Fig. 32. It will be noticed that this lay-out provides for four distinct stations. At the first station the stock is blanked out at each side to form the rounded sections of the bent-up ends shown in the view of the finished piece. The part blanked out in this operation is shown in cross-section at *A*. The two holes *B* are also pierced at the first station. At the second station the two outside holes *C* are pierced, the stock being located by pilots *D* which enter the holes pierced in the first position. At the third station, the two ears or ends are bent down, and at the fourth station the piece is blanked out.

A plan of the die is shown in Fig. 33. Part *A* (Fig. 31)

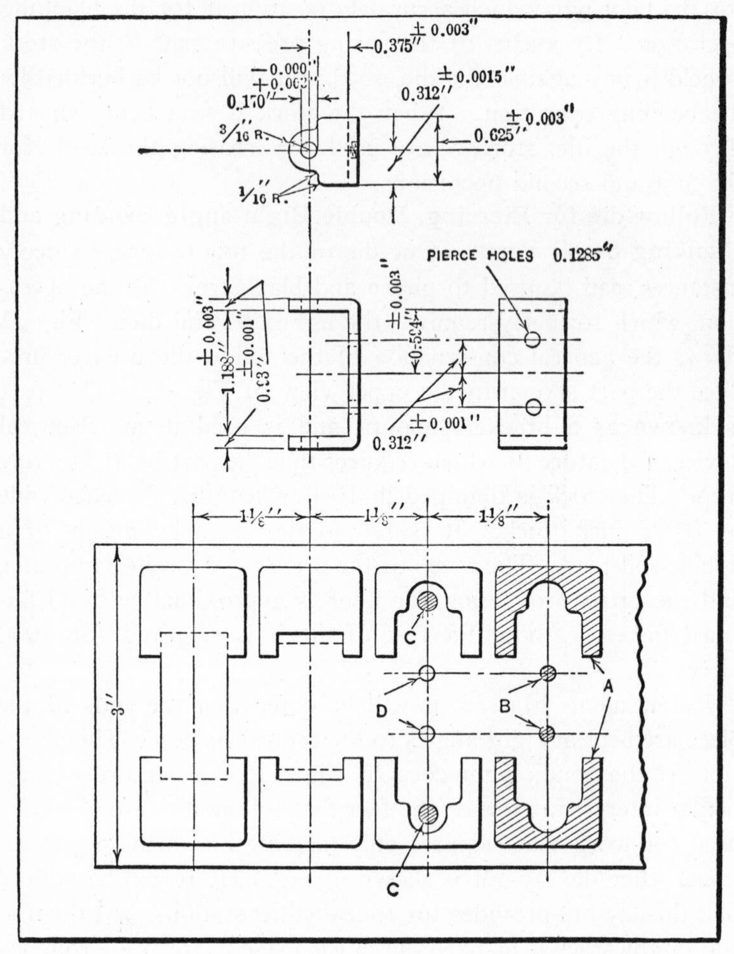

Fig. 32. Bracket Support and Diagrams Showing How it is Blanked, Pierced and Bent

is the punch which blanks out the part of the stock indicated by the cross-section *A* in the lower view of Fig. 32. Punches *B* pierce the two central holes, the holes in the ends of the stock being punched in the second position by punches *C*. In this position the stock is located by pilots *D* which enter the central holes. The punches *E* that bend down the ends or ears are provided with steps designed to strike the outer points of the ears before the bending operation actually begins. It will be noted that a spring-actuated pad *F* is provided in the third position. This pad prevents the metal from being drawn or pulled to one side, and thus assists in obtaining a clean bend. The pieces fall through the die into a receptacle as they are blanked by punch *G*. A stop *H* (see also Fig. 33) locates the work after each feeding movement. The trip *J* which actuates stop *H* is mounted in a block attached to the punch-holder.

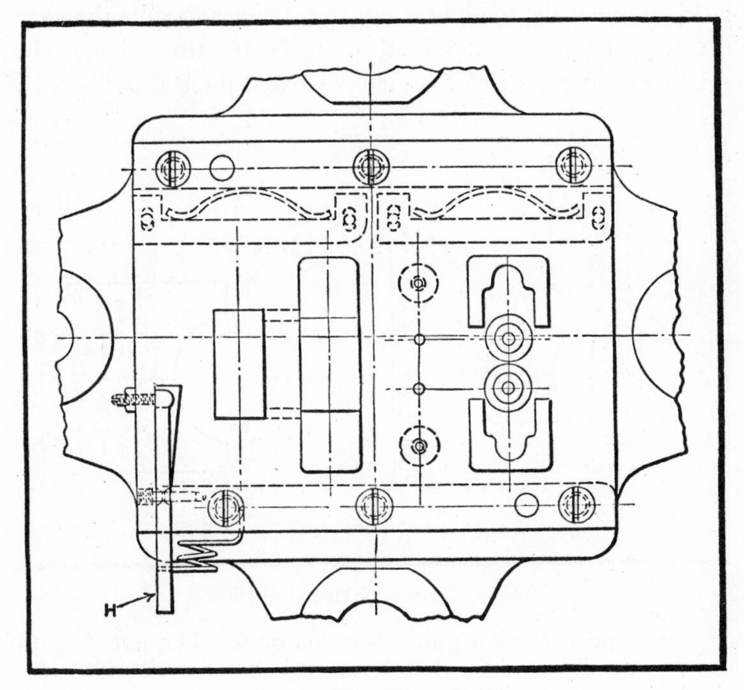

Fig. 33. Plan View of Die

Die for Special Washer With Two Right-angle Bends.—The original method of producing the washer shown completed at *A*, Fig. 34, was to pierce and blank the piece in one operation, and bend the ears in a second operation. The cost of the bending operation was many times that of the piercing and blanking one, because, in forming, it was necessary for the operator to handle each washer separately. In order to eliminate the second operation, the die shown in Fig. 35 was designed. This die produces one complete washer at each stroke of the press. The die-block *A* is of tool steel and is fastened to the cast-iron die-shoe *B* by three 1/4-inch fillister-head screws, four 1/4-inch hexagonal-head cap-screws and two dowel-pins. The fillister-head screws are screwed into die-block *A* from the bottom, while the cap-screws enter the castings from the top side. The cap-screws also serve to hold the stripper *C* in place. Spacers or strips 1/16-inch thick are placed between the die-block and the stripper to give the clearance required to permit the stocks to be fed through the dies. One of the spacer strips *D* extends beyond the end of the stripper plate, and acts as a guide for the stock when entering the die.

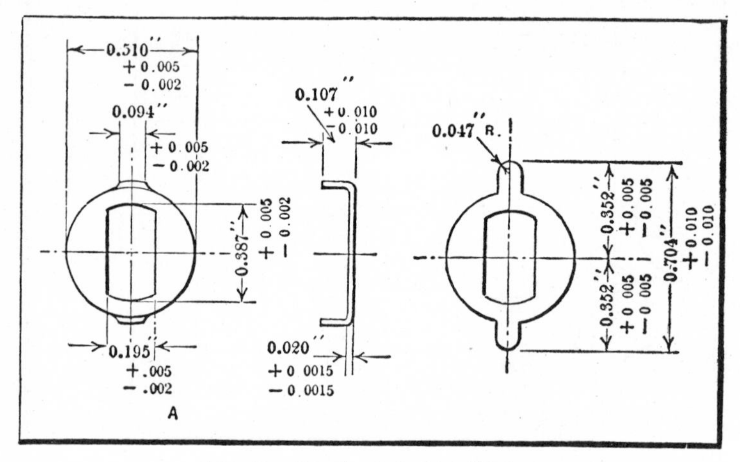

Fig. 34. Details of Special Washer

The punches are set in a machine-steel part *E* and are riveted over at the top of this member. The part *E* is mounted on a cast-iron punch-holder *F*, and held in place by four 5/16-inch fillister-head screws and two dowels. The punch *G* and the forming punch *H* are kept from turning by small headless set-screws. The stock is fed into the die against the finger-stop *J*, which is normally held in the outward position by a small coil spring. When starting a new roll of stock, this stop is held in by the operator so that it serves to locate the stock while the elongated hole is pierced by punch *G*. The

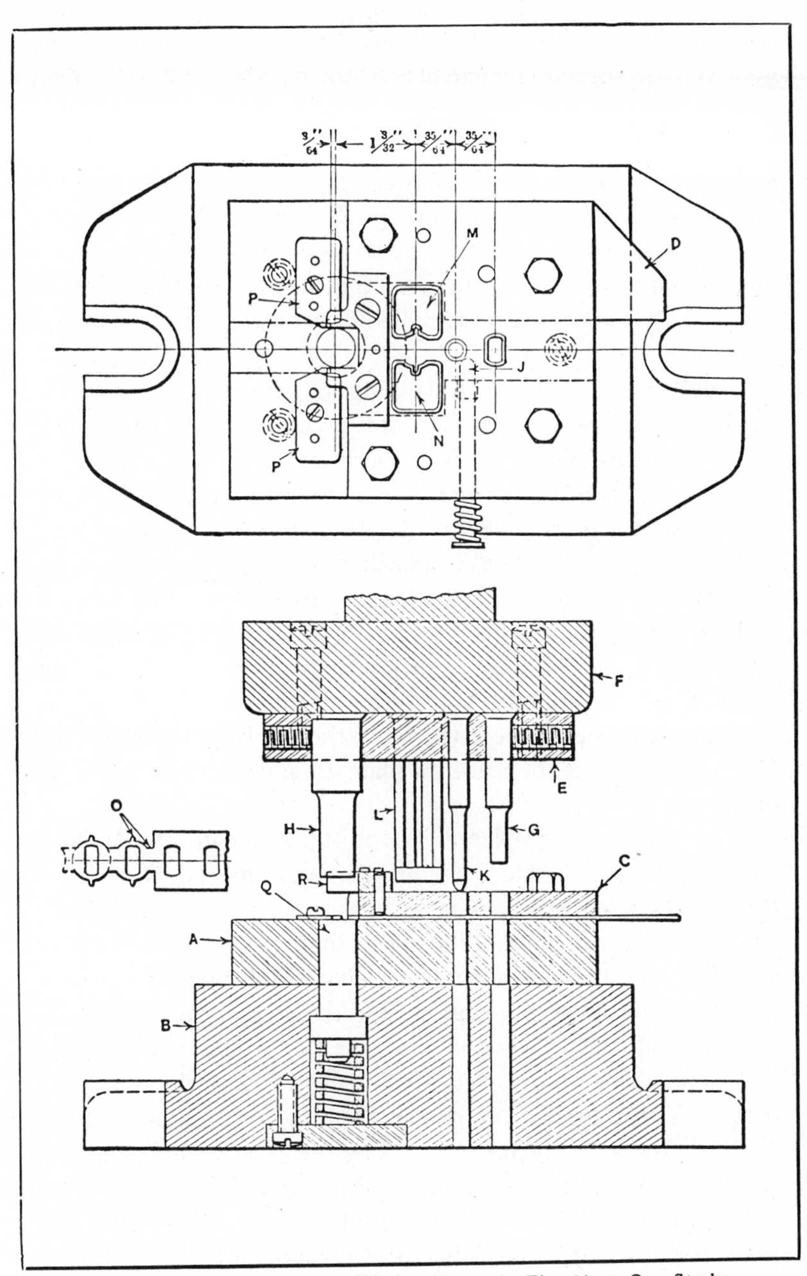

Fig. 35. Die for Producing Washer Shown in Fig. 34 at One Stroke of the Press

stock is then fed in so that the pierced hole lines up with the pilot *K*. A second elongated hole for another washer is next pierced by punch *G* while pilot *K* holds the stock in place. The stock is then fed into the third position, and the first step or blank is trimmed by punches *L*, which enter the die member at *M* and *N*. (See upper view.) This punch leaves the ears and a small web in the center of the strip as shown at *O*. An idle or blank space is left between punches *L* and *H* to provide ample wall thickness for the die-block between the trimming and forming openings.

When fed in to the final blanking and forming position, the small ears on the work are brought in contact with the locating gages *P* so that the stock is properly centered. The edges of the forming punch *H* which are in contact with the ears are slightly stoned or rounded, while the remaining part is ground to a cutting edge. As this punch descends, the blank is cut free from the web and the ears are bent or formed. It will be noted that punch *H* acts against the spring-backed plunger *Q*. The blank is stripped from punch *H* by the stripper block *R* on the up stroke of the press, after which the blank and web are ejected from the die by compressed air. The stripper *R* is fastened to plate *C* and is made a slip fit on punch *H*.

Progressive Die for Double-bending, Piercing and Indenting.—A die for double-forming, piercing, and indenting brass electrical starter brackets is shown in Fig. 36. A finished bracket is shown at *A*. Formerly these parts were made in two dies; the first die formed the first bend, pierced the hole, and made the small indentation; and the second die formed the second bend. This was too slow for the production required, and hence, the progressive die illustrated was designed and built. With this die, the press is operated continuously, a roll feed for the stock being used. The die *B* is of built-up construction, to simplify machining and repairs. The several parts are screwed and doweled to the die-bolster *C*. There are two punches *D* and *E* attached to the punch-block *F*. Punch *D* forms the first bend, punch *E* cuts off the stock to length and

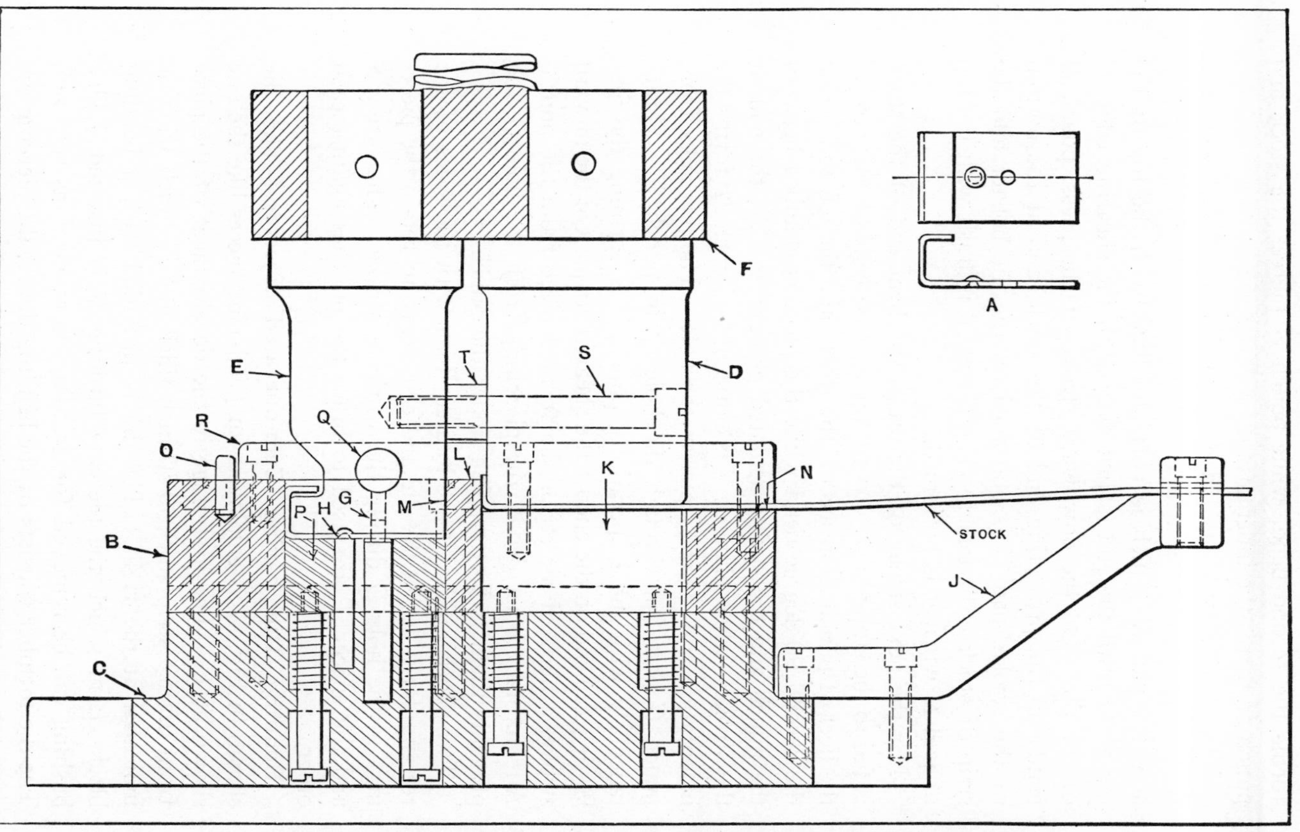

Fig. 36. Die for Forming, Piercing and Indenting Electrical Starter Brackets

forms the second bend, while punch *G* pierces the stock and punch *H* forms the indentation.

The strip of stock is fed through the die as follows: It is passed through guide arm *J* and over the top of the spring-actuated pad *K*, which is normally flush with the top of the die at *L*, until the end is just even with the shearing edge *M* of the die. On the downward stroke of the press, punch *D* bends up the projecting end of the stock, and at the bottom of the stroke, pad *K* is bottomed on the die bolster and the strip of stock is flattened. The die at *N* is flush with the top of pad *K* when it is bottomed.

For the next stroke of the press, the bent end of the stock is fed to the stop-pin *O*. As the punches descend on this stroke, the heel of punch *E* shears off the stock, and the toe end forms the second 90-degree bend while the piece is clamped between the punch and the spring-actuated plunger *P*. At the end of the stroke—when plunger *P* is bottomed—punch *H* forms the indentation and punch *G* pierces the hole. The piercings from punch *G* pass out through the hole *Q* in punch *E*. Simultaneously with these operations, punch *D* is forming the first 90-degree bend on the end of the sheared strip. On the upward stroke, a blast of air strips the formed piece from the punch. An auxiliary blast drives the piercings from the hole *Q* and prevents them from dropping under the punch.

Two stock guides *R* are located flush with the sides of the rectangular holes in the die and also serve to retain the piercings in the hole *Q* during the working stroke. The screw *S* and the spacer *T* are used to brace the punches against each other.

Bending Die having Cam-operated Ejector.—The die shown in Fig. 37 is employed for producing pieces like the one shown at *V*. The first stage in the development of the piece from bronze strip stock, 0.30 inch thick and 9/32 inch wide, is indicated at the right. The die is provided with a bending block *A*, in which the piercing bushing *B* is inserted. This bushing can be removed for grinding or renewal, as required. The die member consists of the bending die *A*, the piercing die

B, the cutting-off die *D*, and the final bending die *E*, which is equipped with the pressure pad *F*. The pressure pad is backed up by a spring *G*. The stop or gage *H* serves to locate the piece for the final bending operation. All the tools in the die member, as well as those in the punch member, are of hardened tool steel.

The punch member consists of the bending punch *J*, piercing punch *K*, the parting blade *L*, and the final bending punch *M*. On the bending punch *M* is located the ejector *N*, which is made up of two flat bars having a roller *C* at the outer ends.

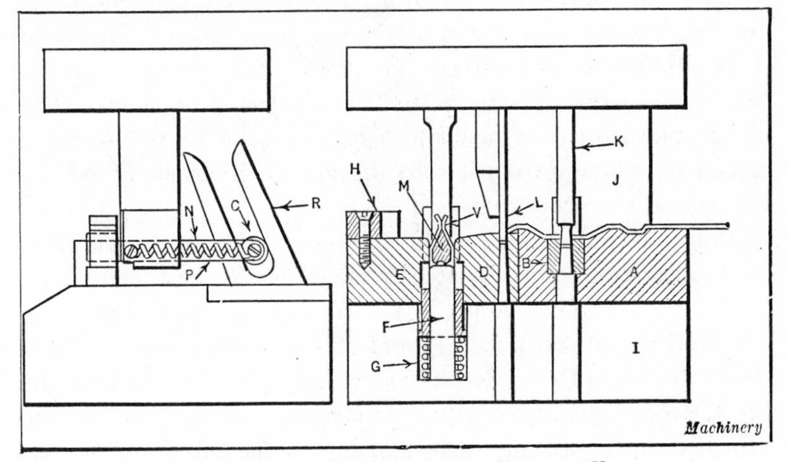

Fig. 37. Die for Producing Part Shown at *V*

As the press ram descends, the ejector is withdrawn or carried to the right by the action of the cam *R*. On the upward stroke, the cam *R* causes the ejector to slide to the left and force the formed piece from the punch *M*. Following this, one piece is finished by each down stroke of the press ram. In order to have the upper ends of the piece closed in properly at *V*, the pad *F* and the bending punch *M* are machined to a radius which forms the part slightly at this point. This slight forming of the part causes the ends to spring together after the piece has been ejected from the punch or when the assembly screw is tightened down on the formed portion.

Bending Operation after Piercing and Cutting-off.—An interesting point in the design of the die shown in Fig. 38 is that it pierces and cuts off the piece from the strip stock, as shown at *Y*, before forming or bending, as at *W*. The forming is done in the last stage because the spade-shaped ends cannot be cut to the required outline without completely severing the pierced part from the strip stock.

As the piercing punches are of conventional design, they will not be described. When the die is in operation, the stock is fed in from the left side and is pierced by the punches *A*, *B*, *C*, and *D*, being located in its proper position at the second stage by the pilot *E*. Plan views of the punch and die are shown in Figs. 39 and 40, respectively. Punch *F*, Fig. 38, separates the flat blank from the strip at the third position or stage. The flat blank is then formed into a hairpin bend by the forming punch *G*, which forces it into the groove in block *H* on the descent of the press ram.

Punch *G* is provided with ribs which increase its rigidity. A small prick-punch is located in the center of the forming end of punch *G*. This punch is set so that it strikes the stock ahead of the cut-off punch *F*, and thus serves to keep the blank from moving after it has been cut off. It also prevents the stock from drawing unevenly during the bending operation, which is an important factor, owing to the proximity of the two holes to the bend.

In Fig. 38 and in the view at the left in Fig. 41, the ram of the press is shown in its extreme upper position. At this point, the ejector *I* is at its extreme forward position. Ejector *I* is actuated by the cam groove in block *K*, which operates lever *J* through contact with its roller *L*. As the ram descends, the cam groove in block *K* causes ejector *I* to recede to the extreme rear position, as shown in the view at the right, Fig. 41, at which point it remains at rest until the ram has reached about the mid-point of the upward stroke. As the punch *G* forces the flat blank into the groove in block *H* in making the first bend, it passes between two guides or strippers *M*, which prevent the formed blank from being lifted with punch *G* on the upward stroke. It will be noted that block *H* is grooved at *T*, Fig. 40, to permit the rear rib of punch *G* to enter, while the front rib has been cut away at the bottom to avoid the necessity of providing another groove in block *H*. This also avoids restriction of the movement of the work when it is pushed forward by the ejector *I*.

On the up stroke of the ram, ejector *I* remains at rest until the roller on lever *J* reaches the angular portion of the cam

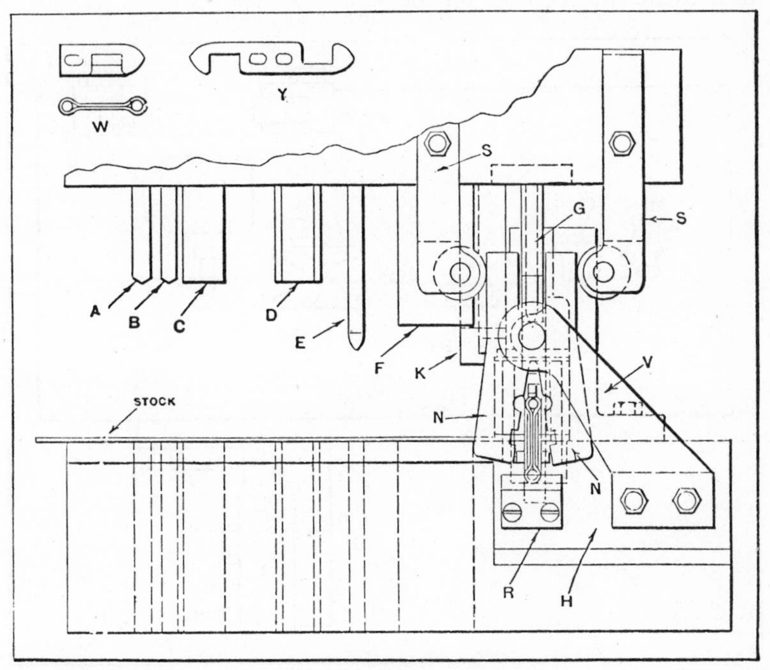

Fig. 38. Follow-die and its Product

groove in block *K*, at which time the front flange on punch *G* entirely clears the work, leaving it free to be moved forward. As the ram continues upward, ejector *I* moves forward, pushing the work ahead of it, through the bridge *O*, until, at the extreme upper end of the stroke, the work is located between the forming jaws in readiness for the final forming.

The final forming is done by the jaws *N*, which press the work around the cylindrical projections on plate *P*, Fig. 41.

Guide plates *Q* prevent the work from springing open when it is being entered between jaws *N*, while the piece *R*, Fig. 40, supports the work during the forming operation. The jaws *N* are supported on the bracket *V* and are closed on the down stroke by the rollers carried on the arms *S*, Fig. 41, as they pass over the angular surfaces of the jaws. This arrangement insures a positive movement. As the ejector *I* could be made only as thick as the stock, ribs were attached to its outer sides to provide the required stiffness.

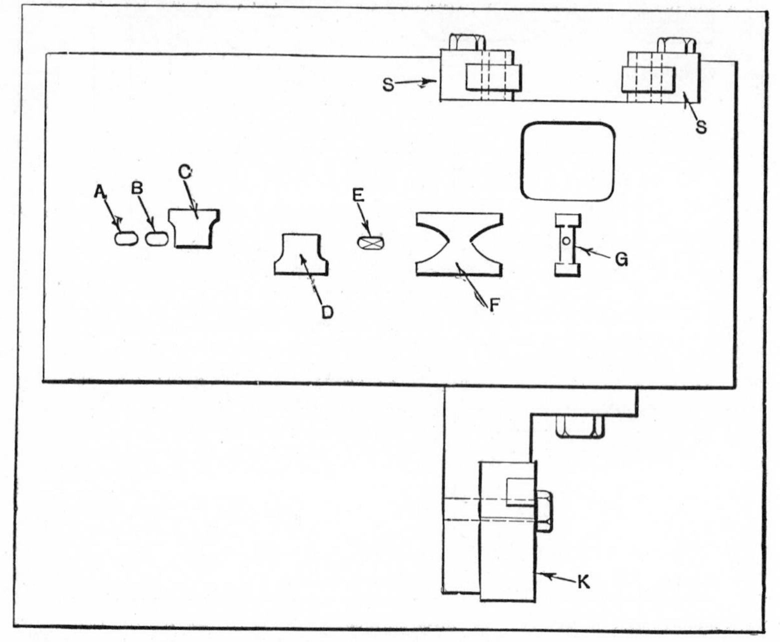

Fig. 39. Plan View of Punch Shown in Fig. 38

Lever *J* is hinged and provided with a spring *Z* so that it will spring backward, rendering the ejector *I* inoperative in case one of the blanks should stick. After the work has received its final forming, it remains in position until the next upward stroke of the ram, when it is moved forward by the following piece of work. In the front view, Fig. 38, and in the end view shown at the left, Fig. 41, the die is shown with the ram at the top of its upward stroke and with a finished piece in the forming position. In the view at the right, Fig. 41, the die is shown with the ram at its lower position. As the ram ascends, the piece, which has received its initial bend, will be pushed forward by the ejector *I*, replacing the piece which has just received its final forming operation. The die described is used on a single action punch press which operates at a speed of 160 strokes per minute.

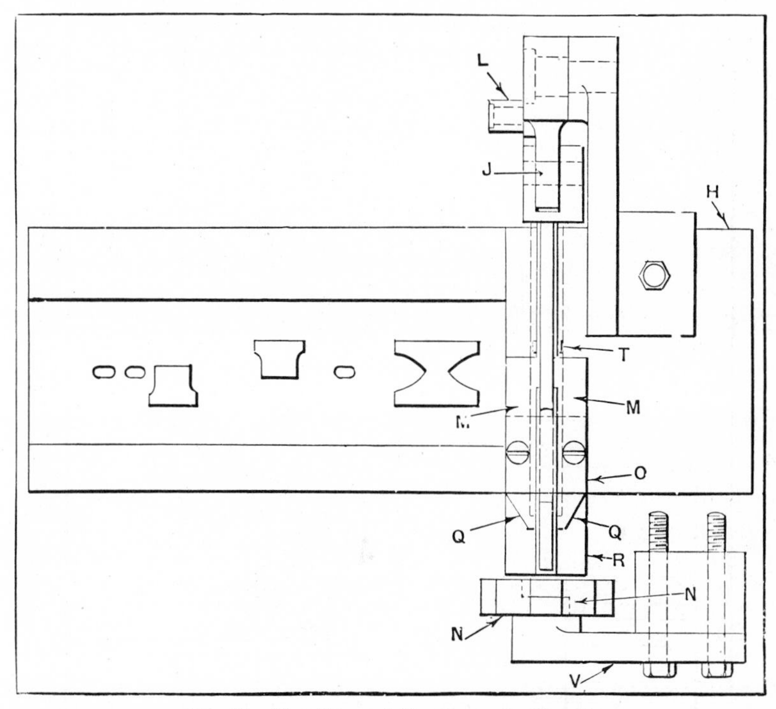

Fig. 40. Plan View of Die Shown in Fig. 38

Die for Making Four Bends.—The die shown in Fig. 42 was designed and made for the third and last bending operation on the piece shown at *A* in Fig. 43. The metal is $\frac{1}{16}$ inch thick, of soft composition, and easy to bend. The first and second operations are performed in two dies of the usual type, blanking or cutting from strip stock being done in one die, and the bending of the blank to a U-shape, as shown at *B* in the other. No description of these tools will be given here as

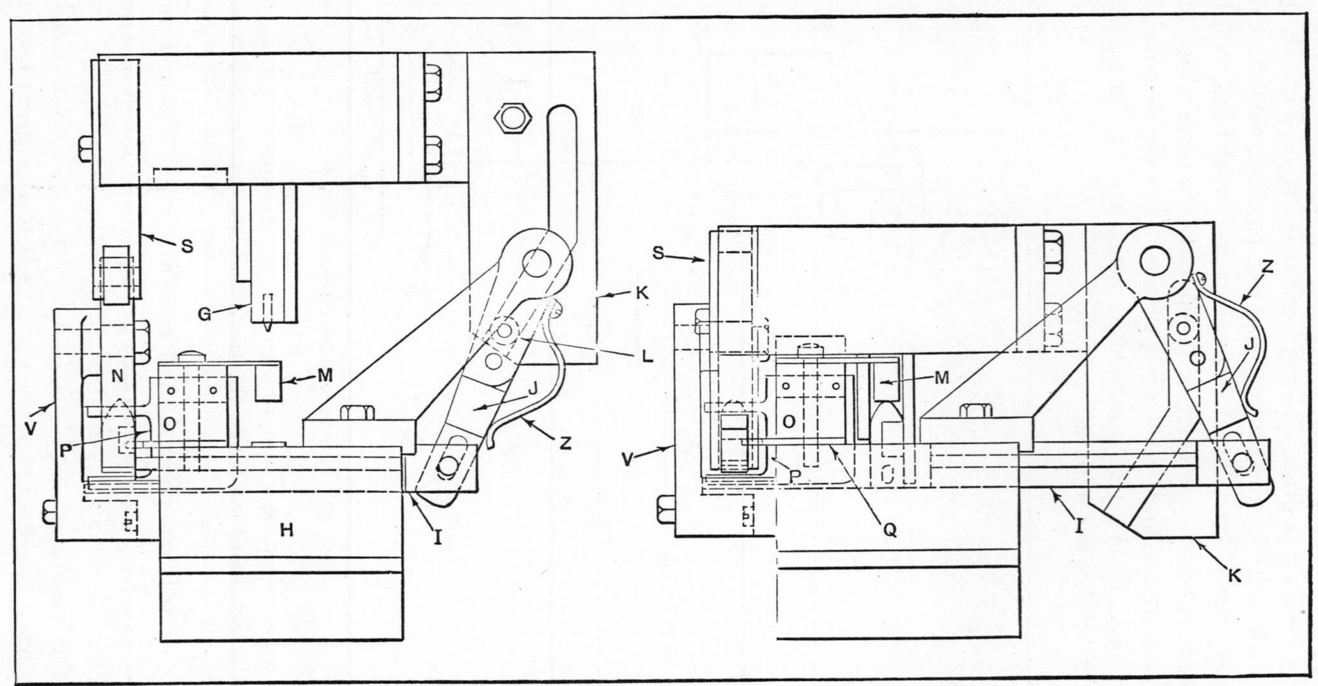

Fig. 41. Views Showing Punch in Upper and Lower Positions

they are of simple construction and readily understood by those who are at all familiar with die designing and die making.

The tool under consideration, shown in Fig. 42, has, of necessity, several movable parts in order to make the four bends required to complete the work. All the members are of simple outline and easy to make and assemble; therefore no detailed description of the methods of machining each part

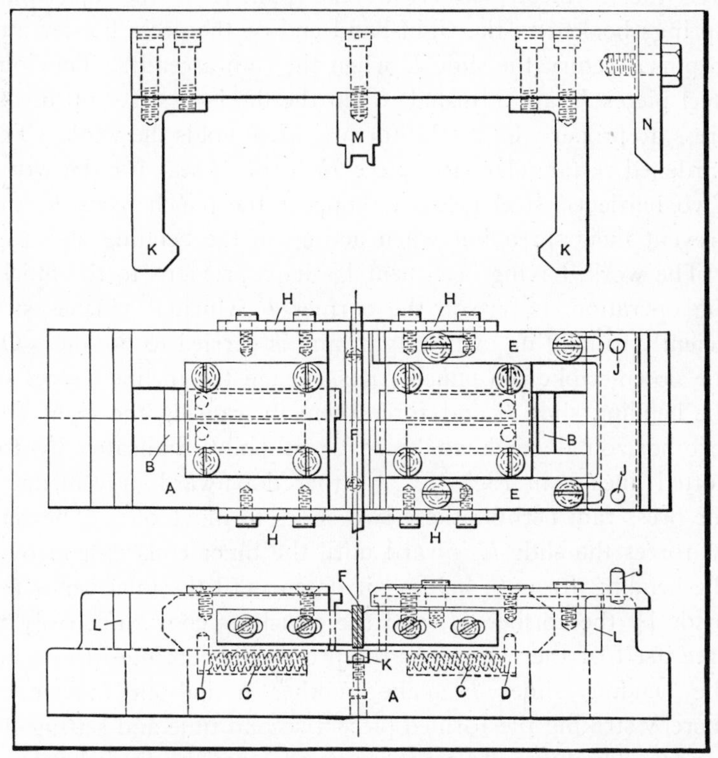

Fig. 42. Bending Die and Punch for Forming Piece Shown in Fig 43

will be given. The holder *A* is of cast iron and is machined on the bottom, top, and sides to receive the several steel parts. The two bending slides *B* are located in finished seats in the holder and secured in place by plates 1/4 inch thick, each of which is, in turn, fastened by four 5/16-inch countersunk screws. The slides *B* have a close running fit, and are forced in, to make the right and left bends, by the cams *K* on the punch;

their opposite or outward movements are made to take place by four compression springs *C*, located in the holder and acting against the pins *D* which are tightly driven into slides *B*. The third slide *E*, which has slotted holes to allow it to move in and out a limited distance, begins to operate after the other two have done their work; the object of this latter slide is to hold the steel form *F*, upon which the work is mounted, down, and free the formed piece from the punch on the up-stroke. Springs hooked to the right-hand end of the press bolster and to pins *J* return the slide *E* when the ram ascends. The four steel pieces *H* are adjusted, when the die is first set up in the press, to properly locate the form *F* whch holds the work. The hardened rectangular steel piece *K* forms a seat for the work. Two hardened steel pieces *L* support the punch parts *K* and prevent their spreading when acting on the bending slides *B*.

The work, having been bent U-shape previous to the finishing operation, is put on the former *F* which it pinches sufficiently to hold its own weight, and is carried to the die. On the down-stroke the punch parts engage the inclined faces of the bending slide *B* and force them in, causing the right and left horizontal bends to be made at points indicated by the dotted lines *x* in Fig. 43. Further downward movement of the press ram permits these two slides to move out. The cam *N* forces the slide *E* inward until the inner ends extend over the bending form *F*, holding it down until the final bends are made by the former *M*, and the punch ascends sufficiently to free itself of the work. As the press slide continues to go up, the bending slides *B* make another in-and-out movement, thereby striking the formed piece a second time and setting the bends. The finished part is removed from the form by dropping the latter into a yoke secured to the press in a convenient position, and giving a slight pull, thus stripping the work. It has been found advisable to taper the forms slightly from the section where the work is located, to the rear, to facilitate the removal of any material, after it is bent, that has a tendency to hug and not spring away. A suitable handle should be on the front end of the form, for the comfort and convenience of the press-man, and it should extend to the front of the die sufficiently to make it absolutely unnecessary for the operator to incur any danger of accident by putting his hands between the working parts of the tool. The press in which this type of die is used is usually run at about 100 strokes per minute, and has a slide movement of three or four inches.

Die for Making Five Bends.—The making of the five bends in the piece shown at *D* in Fig. 44 was thought at one time to require a very expensive punch and die. Upon laying it out, however, it was found that while there were a large number of parts required and various movements to be provided for, the

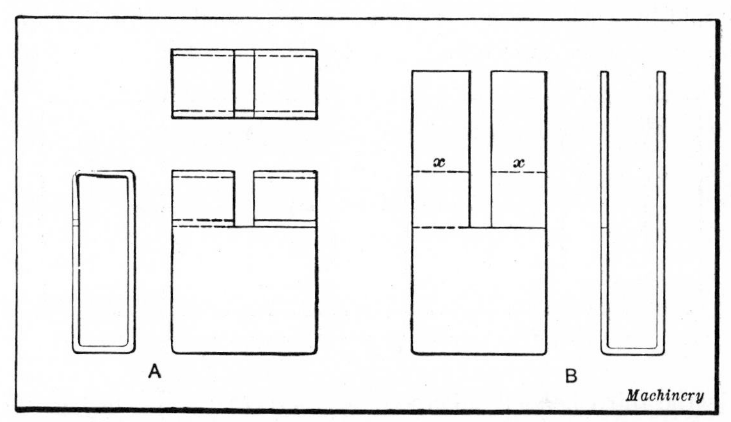

Fig. 43. Bending Operation Performed in Die Shown in Fig. 42

punch and die would not be at all complicated, and would come within the limit of cost that was allowed for this operation. The stock from which this piece *D* was to be made was one-quarter hard brass, ½ inch wide and about 0.023 inch thick. The stock was received in strips of the correct width, and, previous to bending, it was cut to required length. After the pieces were cut to the required length, holes were drilled and countersunk for wood-screws. As the positions of these holes were not always the same, it was decided to drill them instead of piercing them, while cutting the blanks off.

A front elevation of the punch and die used for completing the bends in the piece shown at *D* is shown in Fig. 45. This punch and die was provided with two 1-inch guide-posts for retaining the alignment. These guide-posts are not shown in the illustration, but were located at the rear of the moving parts, so as to be out of the way of the operator. In designing this punch and die the usual plan of bringing all the working parts to the front was observed. This facilitates the operating of the die and obviates the chance of the operator putting his hand in a dangerous position. Referring to the illustration, *A* is the cast-iron body of the die, which is machined to receive the spring pad *B* and the bending slide *C*. The pad *B*, as shown, is actuated by a coil spring *D*, and is retained in its upward position by the two fillister-head screws *E*. This spring *D* should be weak enough, so that it will be easily compressed by the punch when descending into the die. The slide *C* for mak-

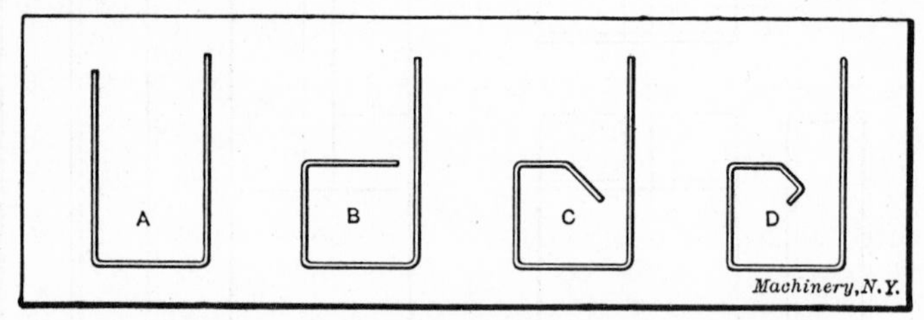

Fig. 44. Successive Bending Operations Effected by Die Shown in Fig. 45

ing the third bend is advanced by the cam *F*, fastened to the punch-holder as shown, and is retained in its backward position by a coil spring *G*, which bears against a pin G_1, located in the base of the slide.

Attached to the punch-holder is the punch *H* which forms the first two bends in the blank; the third bend is accomplished by the slide *C* in the die; the fourth bend is made by the punch *I*, and the fifth bend by the punch *J*. The punch *H* slides on two dowels or guide pins *K* (one of which is shown) and works against a coil spring *L*. Two fillister-head screws *M* (one of which is shown) limit the movement of this punch. The forming punch *I* slides on two dowels or guide-posts *N* and is operated by a coil spring *O*. The downward movement of this punch is limited by two fillister-head screws, not shown. The swinging punch *J* rotates on a stud *P*, and is retained by a closed spring *Q*. This punch J is fastened by the stud *P* to the block *R*, which, in turn, is held to the punch-holder by two fillister-head screws, as shown.

In operation, the strip is placed between the locating pins *S* and also between other locating pins not shown, which hold the blank in the correct position. Then as the ram descends the punch *H* forces the blank down into the die on top of the

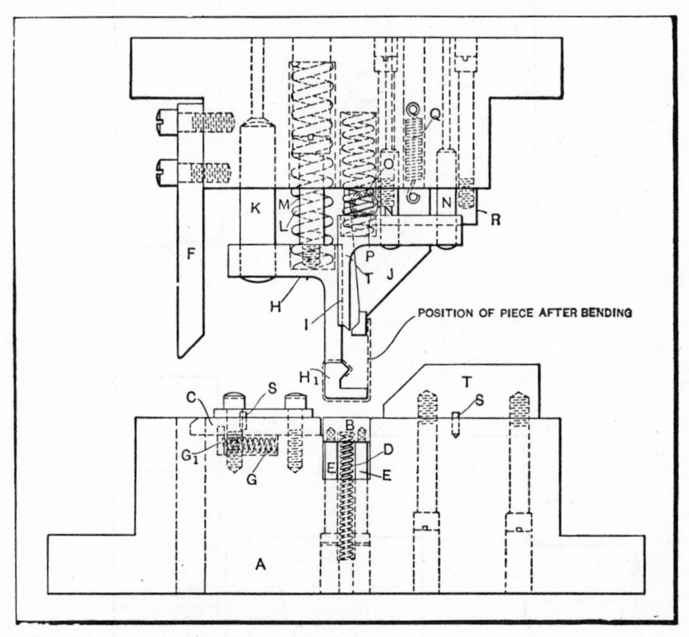

Fig. 45. Punch and Die for Making and Bending the Part Illustrated in Fig. 44

pad *B*. This forms the blank into the shape shown at *A* in Fig. 44. On further movement of the ram, the cam *F* comes in contact with the slide *C* forcing it in and bending the blank over the projected part H_1 of the punch *H*. This forms the blank to the shape shown at *B*. As the ram descends still further, the punch *I* bends the blank around the punch H_1, giving it the shape shown at *C*. The fifth bend is made by the punch *J*, and is accomplished as follows: As the ram still continues in its downward movement, the punch *J* comes in contact

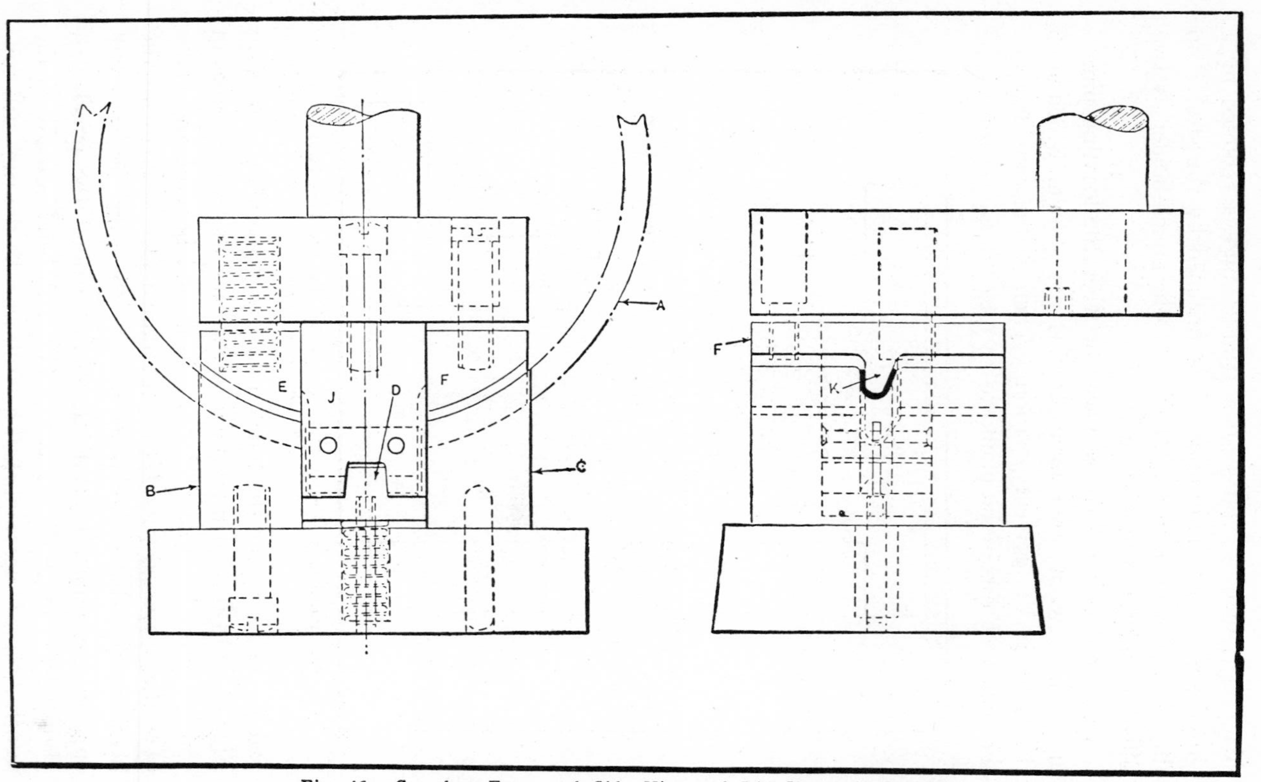

Fig. 46. Complete Front and Side Views of Die Shown in Fig. 48

with the block T, fastened to the die-block as shown. This block T rotates the punch J on the stud P, and forces the blank around the punch H_1. On the up-stroke of the punch-holder, all the slides and punches are returned to their normal positions, the projection H_1 on the punch H carrying the blank out of the die and leaving it in the position shown by the dotted lines (Fig. 45), when it is removed by hand. The forming part of the punch J is offset from the main body of the punch, as can be seen, so that the blank will slide up past it. The forming part H_1 of the punch H is also offset, thus allowing the blank to be bent around it.

All the springs in a punch and die of this description should be of the best quality and well tempered, so that they will not become fatigued to such an extent as to render any part of the mechanism inefficient to even a slight degree.

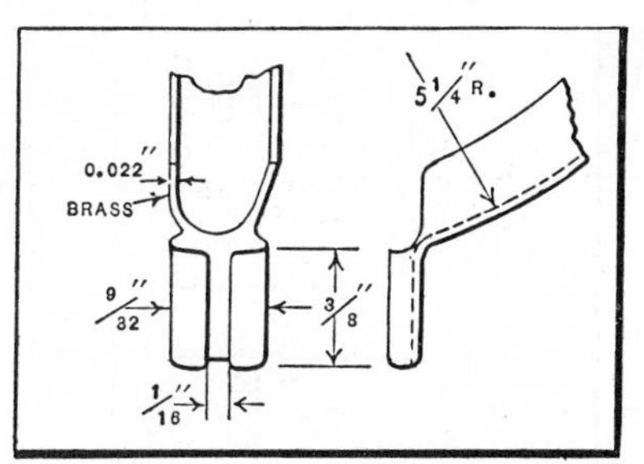

Fig. 47. Formed End of Rim

Curling Ends of Circular Rim.—The die shown in Fig. 46 was designed for the purpose of bending the ends of the rim A to an angle of approximately 90 degrees and at the same time forming or curling the sides of the bent portion as shown in Fig. 47. The formed ends are subsequently pierced so that they serve as eyelets for screws that fasten the rim to another member.

In performing the bending and forming operation, the rim is located in grooves in the die members B and C with the ends in contact with the locating pad D, as shown in Fig. 48. When the punch descends, the hold-down blocks E and F, backed up by springs G and H, come in contact with the work and press it down firmly in the grooves in blocks B and C while the punch J forms or curls the sides of the ends, and bends the ends down. Referring to the side view in Fig. 46, it will be noted that the hold-down blocks E and F have a projecting rim at K, which fits the inner side of rim A so that it is held securely in place.

In Fig. 48 it will be seen that there is a groove across the end or bottom of punch *J* and at both sides. The place *L*, which is set in a slot in the end of the punch and riveted in place, extends into the grooves at the end and sides of the punch. This plate is 1/16 inch thick, and serves to keep the curled sides of the bent ends 1/16 inch apart when the ends are forced against it and ironed out at the completion of the downward stroke of the punch. It will be noted from Fig. 46 that the punch is offset so that the work clears the ram when it is properly located in the die.

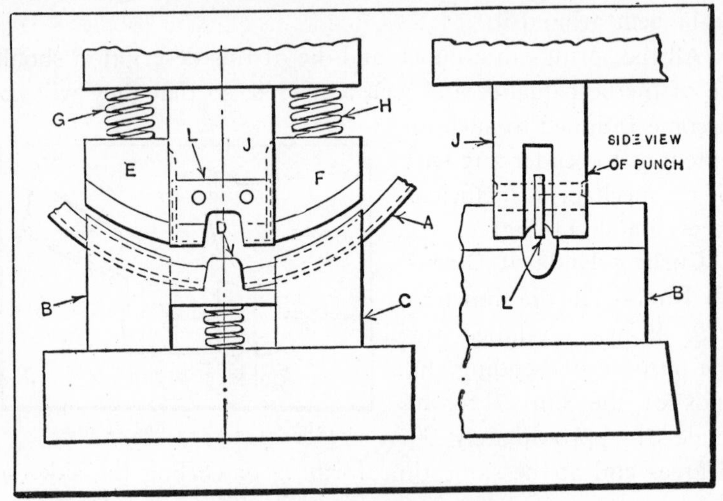

Fig. 48. Rim-end Forming Die

Forming Wheel Arm into a Rectangular Section.—Two dies of unusual design are employed to form steering wheel arms into a box or rectangular section. The die shown in Fig. 49 bends it into the channel shape indicated by the heavy solid lines and dotted lines *X*. The forming is accomplished as punch *A* enters die *B* and bends the blank between the walls of the punch and die. Pressure is exerted on the work by die-block *C* so that it is held firmly against the lower face of the punch during the operation. This pressure is derived from a spring buffer which actuates pins *D*. Die *B* is made in four sections, as may be seen in the plan view.

At the right-hand end of the die, there is a block *E* which is held stationary on the die-shoe. In this block is a small plug which is adjustable vertically by means of screw *F*. Attached to punch *A* directly above block *E* is a block in which there is a small punch that mates with the plug in block *E*, for form

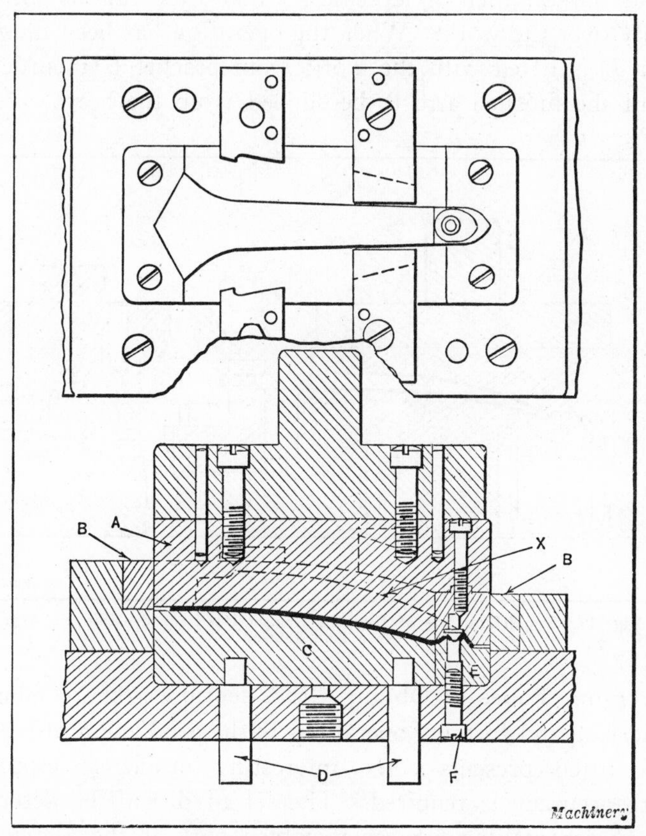

Fig. 49. Die for Forming the Arm into a Channel Section and for Partly Shaping One End

ing the end of the arm that is attached to the wooden rim when the steering wheel is assembled. Blocks in front and in back of the die opening locate the blank for the operation.

Closing the arm into the box section is completed by means of the die illustrated in Fig. 50. For this operation, the stamping is laid in die-block *A*, and then arbor *B* is projected over it by seating the horn in bracket *C*. On the downward stroke of the press ram, punch *D* closes the channel sides of the arm on top of the arbor, as shown in the sectional view at the right-hand side of the illustration. From this sectional view it will also be seen that punch *D* is made in two parts which are spread out on their inner side so that they can be lowered readily over the work. When the operation has been finished, arbor *B* is lifted with the work from bracket *C* in order to permit the finished arm to be slipped from the horn.

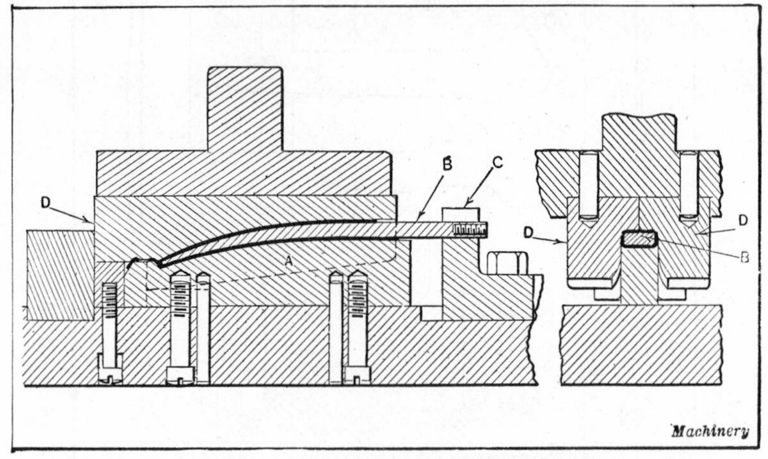

Fig. 50. Punch and Die of Unusual Design Used for Closing the Arm into a Box Section

Forming Tubes of Oblong Cross-section.—The combining of piercing and forming operations in the production of tubular work often presents some interesting problems, especially where accuracy is required. The set of dies to be described is used for making a piece in which part of the piercing is done in the flat stock before it is formed, and duplicates of these pierced holes are produced in the other half or side of the tube after it is formed in order to bring both sets of holes into alignment.

In Fig. 51 the work is indicated by heavy dot-and-dash lines. The strip stock is fed from right to left. Two punches *A* pierce holes through the strip of stock, after which it is fed forward a distance equal to the length of one piece. As the ram of the press again descends, the wide punch *B* cuts off the end of the strip, following which the long forming punch *C* turns up the edges of the work which is to form the tube shown by the dot-and-dash lines at *N*, Fig. 52. The forming punch *C*, Fig. 51, operates in conjunction with the die *E*, and the end of the stock is fed against the stop *F* which determines the length cut off. The piercing die consists of a block *G* in which two die bushings *H* are placed, together with a com-

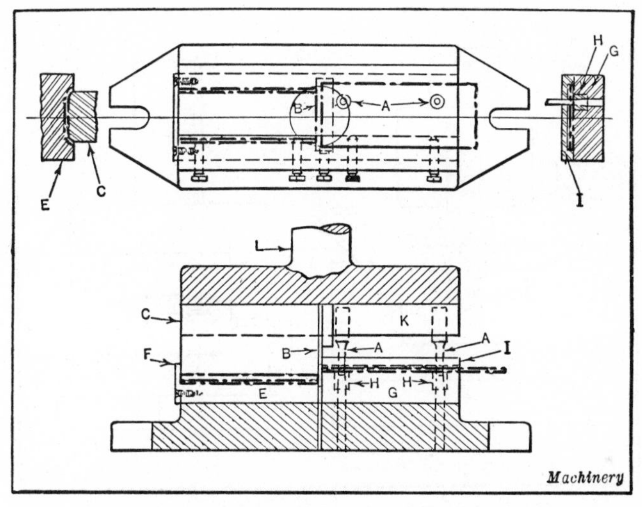

Fig. 51. Die for Piercing, Cutting Off, and Bending Operations

bination stripper and guide plate *I* through which the stock passes.

The forming portion *E* of the die and the cutting-off and piercing unit *G* are secured to a cast-iron holder by screws, and the piercing punches *A* are held in the block *K*. Block *K* and forming punch *C* with its shearing edge *B* are held to the upper member *L*, which is secured to the ram of the press. After the work has been pierced and the edges formed, it is placed in a forming die of the type shown at the left in Fig. 52.

The work is placed across the top of this die between the plates *A* and *B*, which locate it over the forming die. When the forming punch *E* descends, it forces the blank into the groove *D* cut in the die *C*. This operation forms the work to the shape shown by the dot-and-dash lines. Punch *E* is clamped in the slot in holder *G* by screws *H*. The hooked ends of the work cling to the punch, so it must be slid off endwise.

The next operation is performed on the die shown at the right in Fig. 52. The upper die *L* and the lower die *K* are similar, and give the work its finished shape when formed over the arbor *R* which is placed inside the work after it has been

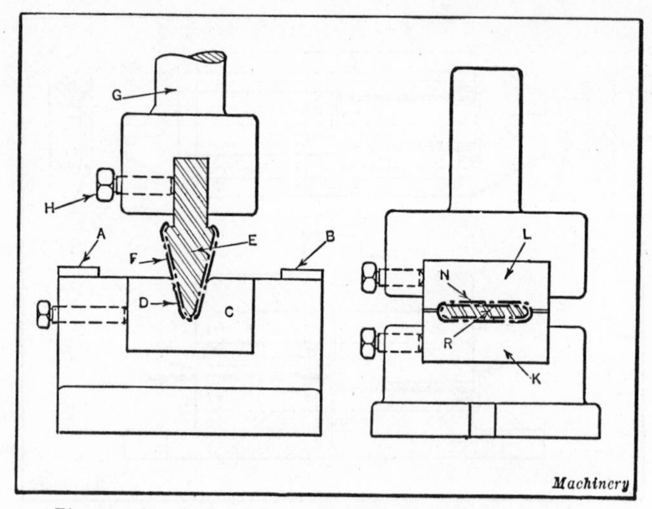

Fig. 52. Bending and Forming Dies for Flat Tubular Piece

removed from punch *E* of the forming die shown in the view at the left.

The die shown in Fig. 53 is employed to punch two holes in the blank side of the formed piece. These holes must align with the previously pierced ones on the opposite side of the tube. Only one hole is punched at a time, the hole on the opposite side being used to locate the work. Referring to the lower view, one of the pierced holes in the tube *A* shown by dot-and-dash lines, is located over the punch *B*. When the ram of the press descends, punch *B* pierces the hole in the upper side of the work, forcing the slug up into the die clamped in

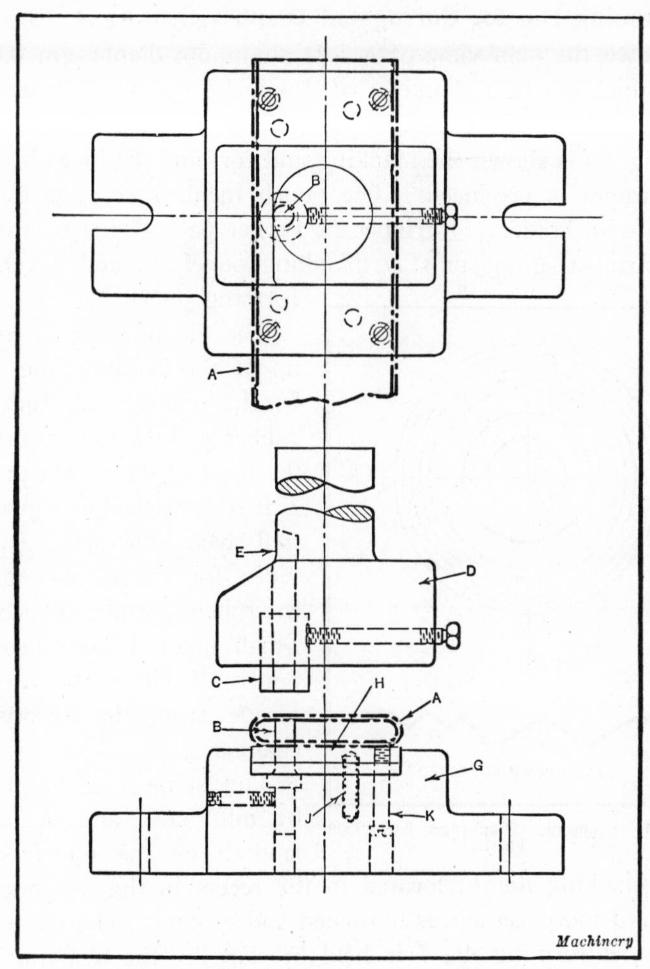

Fig. 53. Die for Final Piercing Operation

the holder *D*. The hole at the other end of the work is pierced in the same manner. The slugs punched from the work pass upward through the die bushing *C* and out through the hole *E* cut in the holder *D*. The holder *G* is provided with a plate *H* which is free to slide up and down. Plate *H* is forced upward by a series of springs *J*. The four screws *K*, however, limit the upward travel of plate *H* which acts as a stripper to force the formed tube *A* from punch *B*.

Forming Die for Corrugated Diaphragm.—At *A*, Fig. 54, is shown the plan view of a soft aluminum diaphragm 0.002 inch thick having a diameter of 2⅛ inches. The cross-section *X-X* of one-half the diaphragm is shown to an enlarged scale. In Fig. 55 is shown the blanking and forming die in which the diaphragm is produced. The punch member consists essentially of a holder *A*, stripper *B*, rubber pads *C* for operating the stripper, guide pins *D*, blanking punch *E*, and a rubber forming punch *K*.

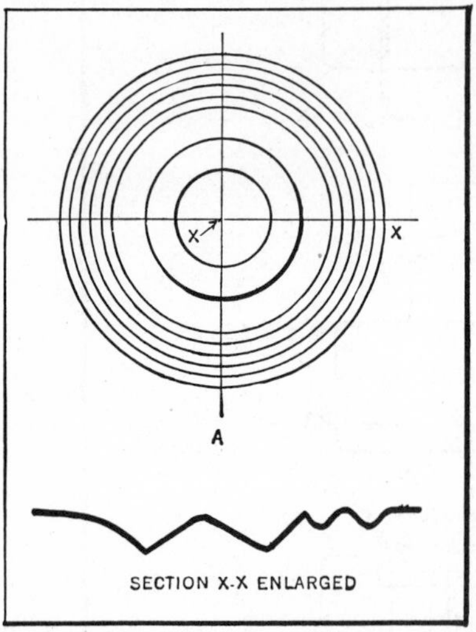

Fig. 54. Aluminum Diaphragm 0.002 Inch Thick

The die member is made up of the blanking die ring *F*, the die-shoe *G*, and the rubber pad *H* for operating the forming die *I*. The punch *E* is of hardened and ground tool steel. The space *J* provides for the expansion of the rubber forming punch *K*. Small holes drilled through punch *E* allow the air to escape from the expansion chamber.

The stripper *B* is made of mild steel and is faced smooth on the under side. The blanking die *F*, located in the recess in the die-shoe, is made of tool steel and is hardened and ground. The hardened tool-steel forming die *I* is held in place by the blanking die ring *F*. The forming die is backed up by the rubber pad *H*, which fits into recesses in the forming die and the die-shoe. The space at *L* provides for the necessary travel of the forming die *I*. Small holes, not shown, permit the air to escape from the chamber *M*.

When the die is in operation, the upper member, on its downward stroke, causes the rubber pad *K* to partly form the diaphragm and hold the stock in place while punch *E* blanks the part. The downward movement is continued until pad *K* completes the forming operation. Before the die described was adopted for this work, a steel forming punch was employed. The steel punch was slightly distorted during the hardening operation, with the result that it frequently caused the diaphragms to break through at the sharp bends.

Wire-forming Die for V-shaped Part.—The wire-forming die shown in Fig. 56 was designed for forming large quantities of wire pieces to the shape indicated at *A*. The die consists of a shoe *B* in which a slot is cut for the back slide *C*. To this sliding piece is fastened a forming tool *D*. The slide

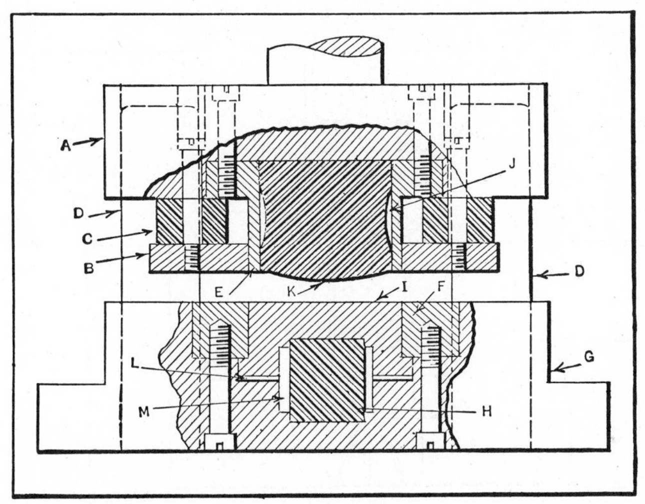

Fig. 55. Die Employed in the Production of the Diaphragm Shown in Fig. 54

C is normally held back against a stop-pin by a compression spring located on its under side. The forming pin *E* is made from 5/8-inch drill rod, turned down to a diameter of 3/16 inch at the top end. The base of the pin is shaped as shown and inserted in the die-shoe, where it is backed up with a tool-steel piece *F* which is also inserted in the die-shoe. The upper surface of piece *F* is machined to a V-shape which conforms with the angle formed by the two straight sections of piece *A*.

Two hardened steel pieces *G*, with their inner ends beveled to an angle of 30 degrees, are inserted in the die-shoe. The beveled ends serve as cams to force the two hinged fingers *H* of the punch member inward, so that the wire is formed around the post *E* and against the V-shaped part of piece *F*. The hinged fingers *H* are normally held apart by a small compression spring *J*, against the stop-pins *K*. The ends of pieces *H* are formed to an angle of 30 degrees on their outer sides

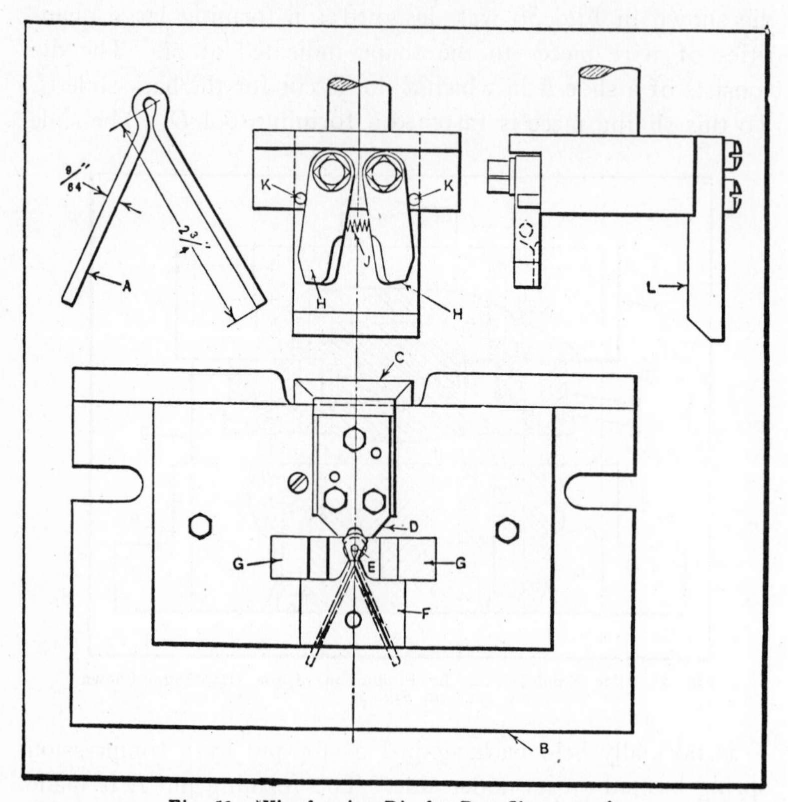

Fig. 56. Wire-forming Die for Part Shown at *A*

to correspond with the beveled ends of the pieces *G* inserted in the die-shoe. The inner ends of the hinged fingers are shaped to fit the contour of the formed wire.

The piece of wire that is to be formed is placed on the die in contact with the back side of the pin *E* and between two stops that are not shown in the illustration. As the ram of the press descends, the slide-operating finger *L* comes in contact with the beveled end of slide *C*, forcing the latter member inward so that it forms the wire around the pin *E*. Slide *C* then remains stationary with the wire firmly pressed against post *E*, upon the continued downward movement of the ram, while the finger *L* simply slides over the end of part *C*. As the ram moves downward the two fingers *H* are brought in contact with the beveled ends of pieces *G*, so that the fingers are closed in around the wire, thus completely forming the eye of the work. After the ram has returned to the upper position, the operator removes the piece from the post *E* with a screw-driver. About 8000 pieces can be formed in a ten-hour day by an experienced operator.

Die for Bending U-shaped Staple.—The die illustrated in Fig. 57 is used to bend the staple shown dotted at Y in the illustration, from the 3/16-inch diameter cold-rolled steel piece shown at *W* in the plan view. The pieces of stock are turned down on the end to a diameter of 1/8 inch and a length of 3/16 inch, and are cut off on an automatic screw or pin machine. It is essential that both legs of the staple be of equal length and this design provides for properly centering the work in the die regardless of any slight variation in the length of the stock.

The hardened tool-steel forming block *A* on which the staple is shaped contains a semicircular groove corresponding with the radius of the inside of the staple. This block has a flange at its lower end by means of which it is seated in the die-block, being secured in place by means of screws and dowel-pins. The stripper B is made of cold-rolled steel and serves the double purpose of locating the work and stripping it after it has been formed. A rectangular slot is cut in the center of this stripper in which block *A* is a sliding fit. The recoil action of the stripper is actuated by two springs *C* and limited by the four stripper-screws *D*. In order to locate the work centrally above the forming block, regardless of any slight variation in the length of the stock, two V-blocks *E* are secured to the stripper plate. The 90-degree groove in these blocks has a 30-degree inclination toward the bottom, as clearly shown in the illustration. The upper forming die *F* contains a semi-circular

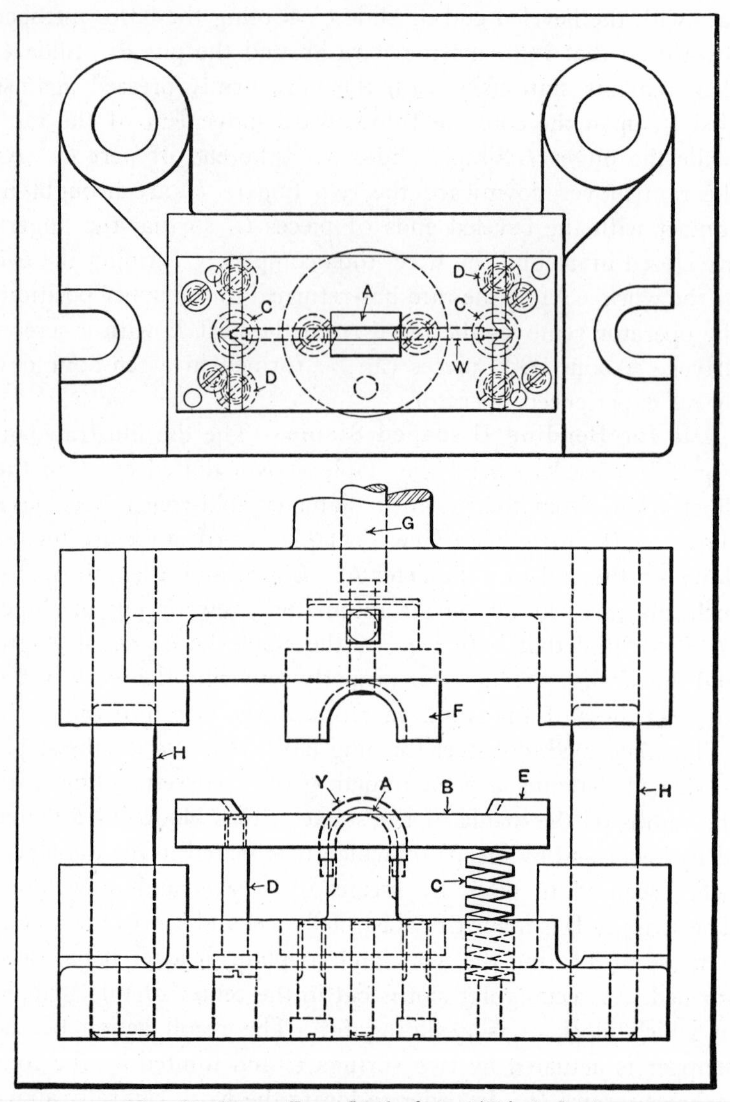

Fig. 57. Die to Form Staple from 3/16-inch Stock

groove similar to the one in block *A*, and of a suitable radius to conform to the outside radius of the staple. This upper forming die is held in the punch-head by means of a set-screw, and is provided with a positive knock-out pin for *G* for stripping the staple from the die. The upper and lower members of this die are held in alignment by means of two posts *H*.

Bending Die for Staples made from Sheet Steel.—The die shown in Fig. 58 was designed for bending a large number of staples that were to be made of 0.025-inch sheet steel. The cast-iron punch-holder *A* carries the tool-steel punch *B*, which has ejector bar *C* running through its center. The outside bending die *D* is provided with nests *E* for locating the blank in the required position preparatory to bending. The taples are bent over the inside former *F*, which is riveted to tool-steel pins *G*, which are a sliding fit in the die-shoe *H*.

The detail views *A*, *B*, and *C*, Fig. 59, illustrate steps in the downward stroke of the punch. At *A* the blank is shown in position in the nest ready for the punch to descend upon it. Sketch *B* shows the punch after it has carried the blank down between the side bending dies and brought it into contact with the inside former, and at *C* the punch has descended a little further, with the result that the blank is partially bent over the former. At the conclusion of the downward stroke, the two sides of the staple will be bent into close contact with the former. This is the position shown in Fig. 58.

On the upward stroke of the punch the inside former *F* rises with the punch until it is flush with the top surface of the die, this movement being imparted by the springs *I* that act against the lower side of the pins *G* on which the former *F* is mounted. The staple is held in the punch *B* until the punch has almost reached the top of its stroke. At this point a knock-out bar on the punch press strikes the ejector bar *C* and ejects the staple from the punch. The press is inclined so that the work drops clear of the die.

Wire Forming on a Punch Press.—The die to be described was designed to replace a hand-operated wire-bending fixture in order to increase production and secure more uniform results. The round tool-steel wire *W*, Fig. 60, is 0.075 inch in diameter, and is required to be formed as shown at *W*, Fig. 62. The die-bolster carries the forming block *N*, the cut-off die *O* and the guide block *M*. The guide block *M* carries the

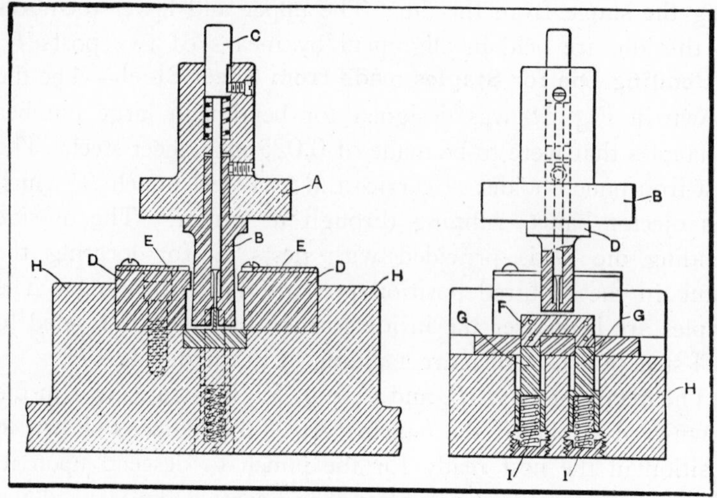

Fig. 58. Sectional Views of Staple Bending Die

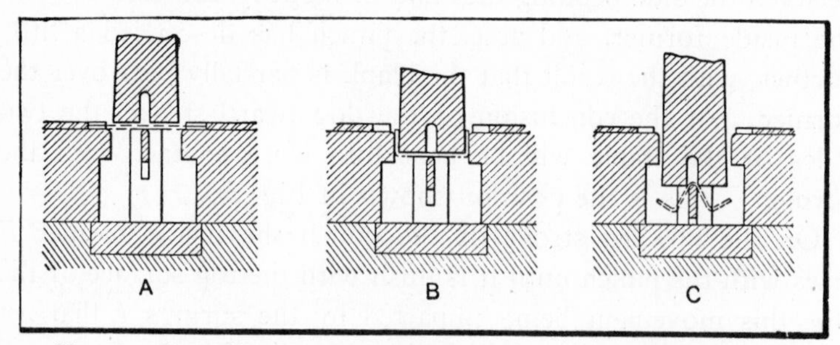

Fig. 59. Successive Stages in Bending Staple in Die Illustrated in Fig. 58

grooved block *P* through which the wire passes. Block *M* is held in its upper position, as shown in Fig. 60, by a spring which permits it to travel downward into the bolster when struck by the cutting-off punch *C*, as shown in Fig. 61.

The forming block *N* carries a slide-block *L* which travels in a groove in block *Q*. Block *L* is held in its extreme left-hand position by a spring. At the outer end of slide *L* is a roller *R*. On the rear side of the die-bolster is mounted the block *B*, upon which the forming block *A* is free to slide in a vertical direction, being held in its upper position by a spring. The latch *F*, which is pivoted in block *B*, serves to lock the

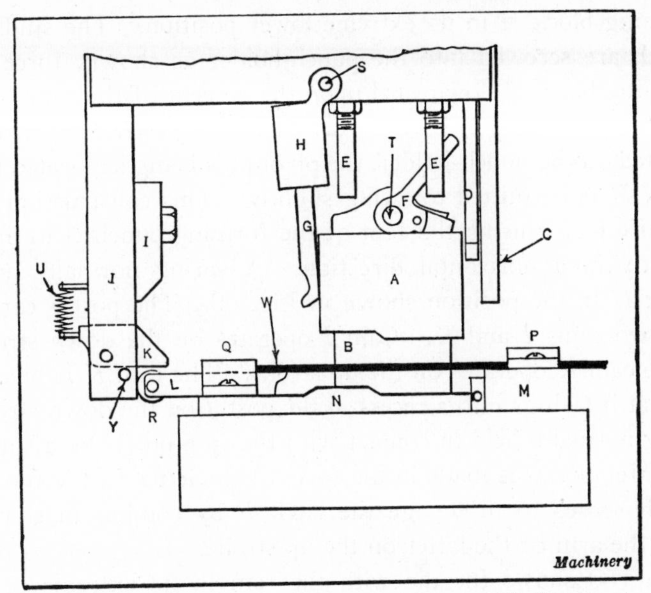

Fig. 60. Wire Forming Die for Part Shown at W, Fig. 62

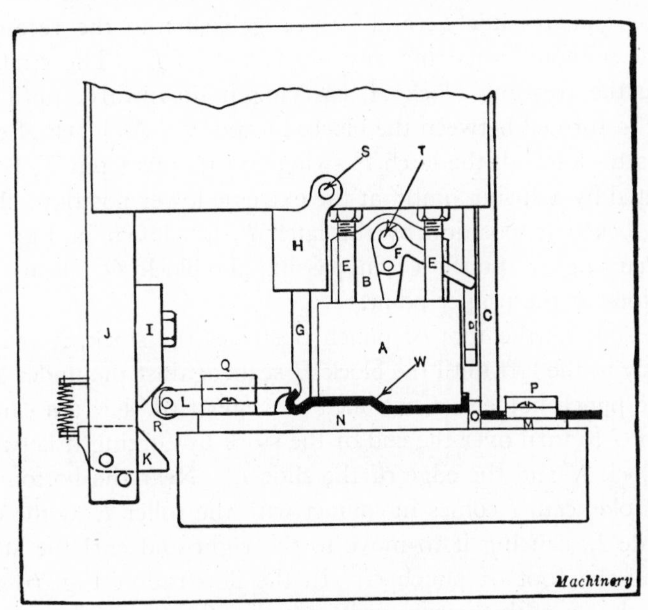

Fig. 61. Forming Die at End of Down Stroke

forming block *A* in its extreme lower position. The studs *E*, which are screwed into the punch-holder as shown, force the forming block *A* downward upon the descent of the ram.

The forming punch *G* is carried in the block *H*, which is pivoted on the punch-holder, the pivot pins being so located that block *H* is permitted to swing slightly. This construction has the effect of causing the foot of the forming punch *G* to move slightly in a horizontal direction. A spring normally holds block *H* in the position shown in Fig. 60. The post *J* carries the two cams *I* and *K*. Cam *I* operates on the down stroke, while cam *K* operates on the up stroke. The cam *K* is pivoted so that it swings into a recess in the post *J* on the down stroke, being normally held in contact with the stop-pin *Y* by a spring *U*. Member *D* is made in the form of the letter L, the foot of which serves to disengage the latch *F* by coming in contact with the arm of the latter on the up stroke.

Fig. 60 shows the die with the ram in its extreme upper position. As the ram descends, the cam *K* passes the roller *R* on the end of slide *L*, and is swung back into the recess in post *J* without imparting any movement to *L*. The studs *E* strike the forming block *A*, carrying it downward, until the stock is formed between the blocks *A* and *N*. As block *A* continues to descend, the latch *F* swings on its pivot pin *T*, being actuated by a spring, until, at the extreme lower position, block *A* is locked in position by the latch *F*, as shown in Fig. 61. The cutting-off punch *C*, in passing die-block *O*, shears off the stock at the proper point.

As soon as the foot of punch *G* strikes the stock, it swings slightly to the left until the block *H* seats against the under side of the punch-holder. Continued movement of the ram causes punch *G* to turn over the end of the stock by forcing it between the block *N* and the edge of the slide *L*. Near the bottom of the stroke, cam *I* comes in contact with the roller *R* at the end of slide *L*, causing it to move to the right and curl the stock around the foot of punch *G*. In the illustration Fig. 61 the die is shown with the ram in its extreme lower position.

As the ram begins to ascend, the slide *L* again returns to

its left-hand position, while punch *G* moves lightly to the right, which permits its foot to slip out of the hook formed on the end of the stock. Block *A* is held in its lower position by the latch *F*, and serves to act as a pressure-pad to hold the stock for the final curling operation, which occurs on the upward stroke when the cam *K* forces the slide *L* to the right, as indicated in Fig. 62, where the die is shown with the ram nearing the end of the up stroke. Continued movement of the ram

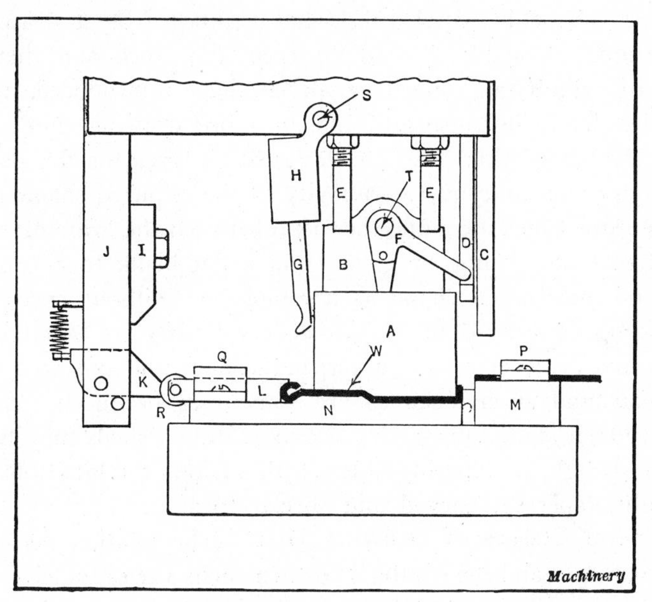

Fig. 62. Punch Member Nearing End of Up Stroke

causes roller *R* to ride off cam *K*, and slide *L* to again return to its left-hand position.

The foot of the L-shaped member *D* makes contact with the arm of latch *F*, unlocking the block *A* which returns to its extreme upper position, thus completing the cycle of operations. The operating leg of the latch *F* is hinged, so that when the slide *A* is unlocked, the leg will swing slightly at the hinge, thus avoiding frictional resistance, which would otherwise be present were the foot of the latch *F* forced to slide on block *A*.

CHAPTER XII

CLASSES OF DRAWING DIES AND GENERAL DESIGNING INFORMATION

MANY products made from sheet metals are given the required shape by employing what is known as a drawing operation. A blank is first cut from flat stock and then a shell of cylindrical, conical or special shape is produced from this flat blank by means of one or more drawing dies. In general, dies of this class are designed to force the flat blank through an opening or into a cavity of the required shape, and at the same time so confine the metal between the drawing surfaces that the change in form from a flat blank to a cup or shell of the desired shape, is accomplished without excessive wrinkling or other defects. Most drawn parts are of circular form in a transverse section perpendicular to the axis, but rectangular and special shapes are sometimes produced. In a longitudinal plane intersecting the axis, drawn shells may have either straight or tapering sides, with various combinations of straight, tapering, curved and special forms.

General Classes of Drawing Dies.—The relation between the diameters and the depths of drawn shells varies widely, and this relationship is an important factor in the design of drawing dies, as illustrated by the examples in the following chapters. It is evident that the changing of flat blanks into shallow shells having comparatively little depth, is less of a mechanical problem than the drawing of deep shells, and the smaller the diameter in proportion to the depth the more difficult the operation becomes as a general rule. The thickness of the stock, its ductility or susceptibility to drawing, and its strength for resisting the stresses resulting from the drawing operation are additional factors which have to be taken into account in designing drawing dies. Since these varying conditions and other factors not mentioned all govern the design of drawing dies, it will be seen that such dies cannot be laid out according to fixed rules, although there are certain principles which are generally applicable; consequently, to obtain a definite knowledge of the subject of drawing die design, it is essential to study the arrangement and proportions of drawing dies which have proved to be successful in practice. In the various chapters to follow, drawing dies for a wide variety of operations will be illustrated and the important features described. Before presenting these different designs, some information will be given about drawing dies in general, including certain rules and features of drawing die construction which may be applied to various classes.

Any classification of drawing dies must necessarily be of a very general character, because the designs differ widely and many dies are so arranged as to combine with the drawing operation some other operation, such as blanking, forming or embossing. There are, however, several distinct types. The simplest type is a plain drawing die without a blank-holder. The flat blank is given a cup shade as the punch descends and pushes it through a hole in the die. Unless the stock is quite thick, a blank-holder is required to prevent the blank from wrinkling as the outer part is contracted to the form of a cup or shell having possibly about one-half the diameter of the undrawn blank. If the die has a self-contained blank-holder and provision for cutting out and drawing the blank by using a single-action press, it is called a combination die. Double-action dies, which represent another distinct type, are so named because they are used on double-action presses having two slides. According to a typical arrangement, a combined blanking punch and blank-holder is attached to one slide and a drawing punch to the other slide. The blanking punch moves slightly in advance of the drawing punch and after the blank is cut, the blanking punch continues to descend until the blank is closely confined between the lower end of the punch (which serves as a blank-holder) and the die. The blanking punch slide then remains stationary while the drawing punch descends.

Triple-action dies, for use in triple-action presses, have three independent movements obtained from an equal number of slides. With such dies three operations, such as blanking, drawing, and embossing may be performed. With the plunger, carrying the embossing die, located beneath the drawing die, the drawn part is pushed through and delivered below the die instead of ejecting it upward as when using a solid bottom die. This makes it possible to produce the drawn parts more rapidly.

Many parts cannot be drawn from a flat blank to the diameter or shape required, in one operation; consequently redrawing dies are used for reducing the cups or shells obtained from the first operation dies. Some redrawing dies resemble first operation dies, whereas others differ in design, especially when equipped with an inside blank-holder, such as would be required for supporting on the inside a comparatively thin shell as it is being pushed through the die for reducing the diameter.

Classification of Forming and Drawing Dies.—The parts produced by some forming dies are quite similar in appearance to those produced in drawing dies; however, according to the general and approved usage of the terms "forming" and "drawing," there is an important distinction between these two classes of dies. The term "forming die" should be applied whenever the design is such that the shape of the punch and die is directly reproduced on the work by a bending action. For example, when a sheet-metal part is pressed by the punch down into the die cavity, and both punch and die are formed to suit the shape required, the die is a forming type. Thus, a forming die shapes the work principally by bending it. The part produced in a forming die may not, however, be confined between a punch and die shaped to correspond with the form required on the work. For example, some sheet-metal parts are given angular or other bends as the result of the movement of the punch (or of an auxiliary slide) relative to the die. In such a die the shape frequently is not a reproduction of the shape of the punch and die, as when the metal is confined between formed surfaces; however a die which operates by pure bending is commonly known as a bending type, although the term "forming" is frequently applied even to dies which are more nearly in the bending class.

The difference between a forming die and a drawing die is that a forming die, as just explained, operates chiefly by bending, whereas a drawing die produces the required shape by a drawing or flowing of the metal, as for example, when the downward movement of the punch forms a cylindrical or other shape by drawing or folding a flat blank as the sheet of metal slides over the drawing edge and downward while confined in a space between the punch and die equal approximately to the stock thickness. In some cases it is difficult to draw a definite dividing line between forming and drawing dies because drawing and forming or bending actions may be combined in the same die. With such dies the common practice is to classify the die as a drawing type provided the chief action is one of drawing, and as a forming die provided the bending action predominates. Drawing dies have sometimes been classified as dies equipped with a blank-holder for exerting pressure on the flange or outer surface of the blank as it is drawn inward, to prevent excessive wrinkling. A blank-holder, however, is not used on all drawing dies, as many cups or shells of simple form and comparatively shallow in proportion to the diameter, may be produced by drawing and without excessive wrinkling in a die not equipped with a blank-holder. Examples of both types of dies, that is, the plain die and the blank-holder type, will be shown later.

Simple Design of Drawing Die.—A very simple design of plain drawing die is shown in Fig. 1. The blank to be drawn is first cut in an ordinary blanking die; it is then laid in the drawing die, being located centrally with the die opening by an annular recess in the die face. After the clutch of the press is engaged, the punch descends and forces the flat blank through the die opening (as indicated by the right-hand view), thus forming it into a cup or shell of cylindrical shape. As the punch ascends, the drawn part is stripped from its end. This stripping may be caused by the contact of the upper edge of the cup with the lower edge of the die; some dies are also equipped with pivoted dogs or fingers which tilt downward as the punch descends and then swing in above the edge of the cup, thus stripping it off of the ascending punch. This form of die (commonly known as a "push-through die") is inexpensive as compared with some other designs and is often used for drawing operations, especially when the stock or metal is quite thick. Such dies are not adapted to drawing stock thinner than, say, 3/32 or 1/16 inch.

Most first-operation dies, or those for drawing parts from flat blanks, are equipped with a blank-holder which presses against the outer part of the blank while the punch forces it through the die opening. The advantage of using a blank-

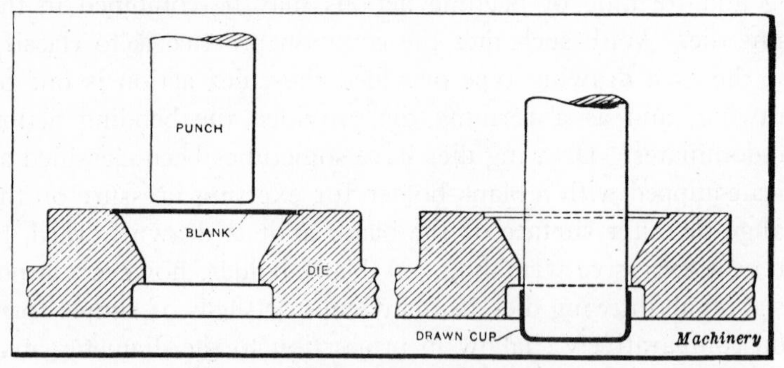

Fig. 1. Simple Type of Drawing Die

holder is that when the blank is being drawn radially inward, it is confined between the top surface of the die in a blank-holder or "pressure pad," wrinkles cannot readily form. The method of confining the blank and drawing it, or, in other words, the design of the die, depends upon the conditions, such as the number of parts to be drawn, the amount or depth of the draw, type of drawing press available, etc.

Drawing Die Equipped with Blank-holder.—A simple and inexpensive form of drawing die of the type having a blank-holder is shown in Fig. 2. This die also draws a blank which has been cut out in another die. The blank to be drawn is placed in a recess in the die face, and when the press ram descends (after the clutch has been tripped by the operator) the blank-holder *D* first engages the blank; then, as the downward movement continues, the rubber pressure-pad *F* is compressed so that the blank is held firmly by the blank-holder while the drawing punch *E* forces it through the cylindrical opening in the die. In this way, a cylindrical cup is formed from the flat blank, as indicated at *A*, *B*, and *C*, which show the blank, the half-drawn cup, and the finished cup. The cup is stripped from the ascending drawing punch by coming into contact with the lower edge *G* of the die opening. If a smaller and deeper cup is required, additional drawing operations in separate redraw-

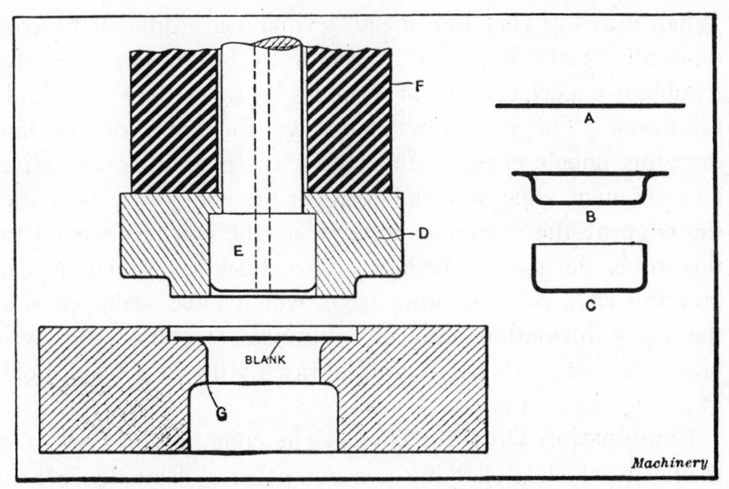

Fig. 2. Plain Drawing Die Equipped with Blank-holder

ing dies are necessary. Some dies of the type shown, instead of having a rubber buffer, are equipped with a strong spring for operating the blank-holder.

Formation of Wrinkles in Drawing.—When a flat blank is drawn either in a combination or double-action die, the outer part is subjected to pressure by the blank-holder; consequently, no wrinkles can form if the die is properly constructed, and all the movement must be radially inward (provided a circular or cylindrical shape is being drawn), but when the metal passes from under the blank-holder and over the edge of the die, it is no longer confined and, as it is being drawn into a smaller circumference, the natural tendency is to wrinkle. These are sometimes known as "body wrinkles" to distinguish them from the "flange wrinkles" which result when there is insufficient pressure between the blank-holder and die.

As the stiffness of sheet metals increases approximately as the square of the thickness, thicker metals also offer more resistance to a buckling or wrinkling action when being reduced to a smaller circumference, than comparatively thin stock. For this reason, stock thicker than 1/16 or 3/32 inch is often drawn in plain push-through dies that are not provided with a blank-holder, and there is little or no trouble due to wrinkling. When drawing very thin metal, wrinkles are difficult to avoid, especially if the diameter of the work is quite large. More trouble is experienced from wrinkles on taper than on cylindrical parts. The reason is that when the point of the taper drawing punch engages the stock, there is a comparatively large annular zone of metal between the end of the punch and the edge of the drawing die, and, as the stock is forced into this zone, the natural tendency is to buckle. When drawing tapering cake pans or other parts which have scalloped sides, the wavy formation naturally eliminates trouble from wrinkling; in fact, such parts can be drawn without a blank-holder in a single-action press.

Combination Drawing Dies.—The combination type of die is one in which a blanking die and either a drawing or forming die are combined so that the blank is cut out and drawn or formed to shape in one stroke of the press. Owing to the construction, a combination die can be used in a single-action press, or one having a single slide. A typical combination die of the blanking and drawing type is illustrated in Fig. 3. Its operation is as follows: When punch *F* descends and enters die *E*, it cuts out the blank and forces the blank-holder *G* downward against the tension of the rubber pressure attachment *H*, the blank-holder being supported upon the connecting pins *J*. As the downward movement continues, the blank is drawn to a cylindrical shape between the bore of the blanking punch *F* and the drawing punch *D*.

When the ram of the press ascends, the shell is stripped from punch *D* by the blank-holder *G*; the shell is also ejected from the blanking-punch *F* by the "knockout" *K*. The stem of this knockout extends up through the punch and has either a cross-pin or nuts at its upper end to hold it in place. The usual method of operating the knockout is to force it down positively. This may be done by means of a stationary arm or bar which extends through an elongated slot in the slide. When

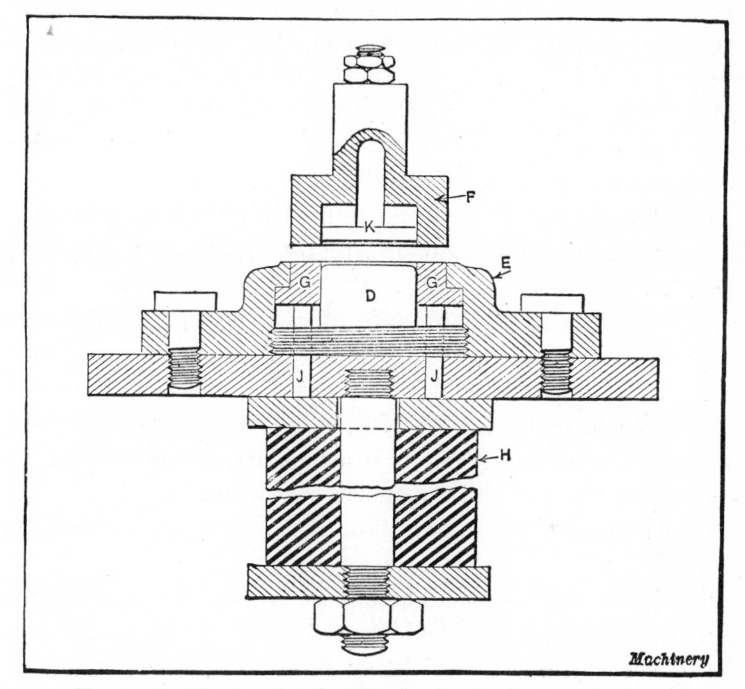

Fig. 3. Combination Drawing Die for Use in Single-action Press

the punch ascends, the upper end of the knockout stem strikes this stationary arm and in this way the knockout is forced down, thus ejecting the drawn cup from the inside of the punch. Another arrangement is as follows: A bar of rectangular section extends laterally through an elongated slot in the slide and engages the top of the knockout stem. When the punch ascends, the outer ends of this cross-bar strike set-screws so that the knockout is forced down. These set-screws are adjusted according to the stroke of the press. A rubber pressure attachment is generally applied to dies of this type instead of a spring, because the rubber is more durable and gives a more uniform pressure.

In most cases, articles made in combination dies are in the form of shallow cups, etc., such as can tops and bottoms, pail bottoms and a variety of similar parts which frequently are not over 1/4 inch in depth. Dies of this class are also used for deeper articles, such as boxes and covers for blacking, salve, tobacco, etc., with depths up to about one inch. Most combination dies are so arranged that the finished article is automatically pushed out from the dies by the action of a stripper, as previously described; with a press set on an incline, the finished work will, therefore, slide back by gravity.

Combination dies that are to be used for blanking and forming parts of either conical or irregular shapes are frequently made on the same principle as the one just described. Punch *D*, however, is shaped to conform to the shape to which the cup is to be drawn and on the under side of knockout *K* there is a cavity or pocket which fits over the punch and forms a seat into which the work is forced. When the die is in use, the blank, after being cut, is drawn and formed between the face of knockout *K* and the punch. If the part is not too deep, it can be blanked and drawn in one operation in a die designed in this way.

Double-action Dies.—These dies are known as a double-action type because the blanking and drawing punches have independent movements which are derived from the two slides of a double-action press; hence, the name of the die, in this case, indicates the type of press in which it is used. A double-action die of the "push-through" type is illustrated at *A* in Fig. 4. The combined blanking punch and blank-holder *c* is operated by the outer slide of the double-action press and moves slightly in advance of the drawing punch *d*, which is actuated by the inner slide. The outer slide is so arranged that, after making its stroke, it stops during about one-quarter of a revolution of the crankshaft. The blank, after having been sheared from the sheet by the outer edge of punch *c*, is held between the end of punch *c* and the seat in the die, during the dwell of the outer slide. While the blank is thus held under a pressure which can be regulated to suit the special requirements of each case, the drawing punch *d* continues its downward movement, thus drawing the metal from between *c* and the die, into the form of a cylindrical cup. The drawing punch is so timed or adjusted that it will not reach the blank until the latter is subjected to sufficient pressure by the blank-holder for the drawing operation.

While this type of die requires a double-action press, it is very much simpler in construction than a combination die which, as previously mentioned, is used in a press of the single-

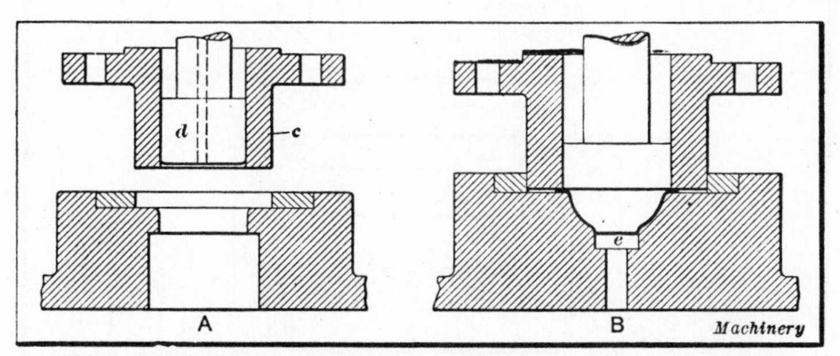

Fig. 4. Double-action Drawing Dies of "Push-through" and "Solid-bottom" Types

action type. The design of die shown at *A* is suitable for cylindrical articles which can be pushed through the die; hence, it is sometimes called a "push-through" cutting and drawing die, to distinguish it from the solid bottom type shown at *B*, which may be used for producing a cup of the shape illustrated. As will be seen, both the drawing punch and die conform to the shape of the part to be drawn. This type of die is equipped with knockout or "push-out plate" *e* at the bottom of the die, which rises on the upstroke of the press and lifts the drawn part from its seat in the die. This push-out plate, which is also called a "knockout," may be either spring actuated or positively operated from beneath (as in the case of the die illustrated) by connection with the press.

Triple-action Die.—A triple-action die, as the name implies, is one having three independent movements. This class of dies is used to produce articles requiring three operations, such as cutting or blanking, drawing, and stamping or embossing. They are frequently used in preference to a solid bottom, double-action die of the type shown at *B*, Fig. 4, because they deliver the finished part *below* the drawing die instead of pushing it up, thus enabling the operator to feed continuously and without waiting for each piece to be ejected before blanking for another operation. A triple-action die is illustrated in

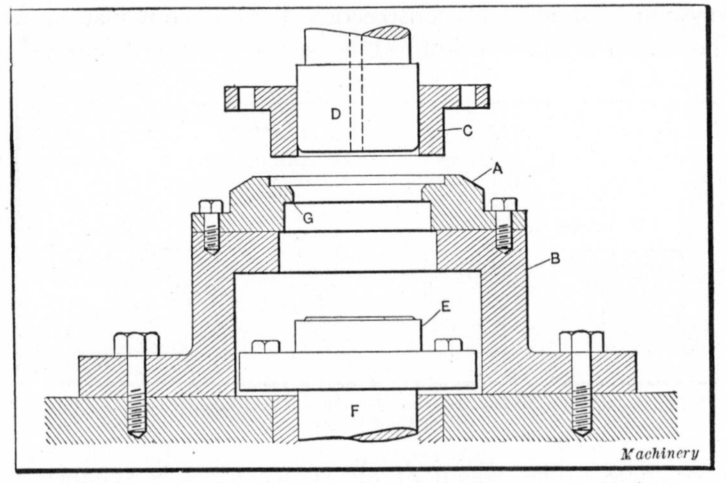

Fig. 5. Triple-action Die for Blanking, Drawing, and Embossing

Fig. 5. The cutting and drawing die *A* is mounted on a raised bolster *B*; *C* is the blank-holder and cutting punch; *D*, the drawing and embossing punch; and *E*, the embossing die.

In the operation of this die, the blank is cut by punch *C*, which acts as a blank-holder, while the cup is drawn by punch *D*. As the drawing punch continues to descend, it carries the drawn cup downward until its lower surface engages the embossing die *E*. The latter is mounted on plunger *F*, and on its upstroke imparts to the work the required impression, which may be a fancy design, lettering, etc. On the up-stroke of the punch, the finished article is stripped by edge *G*, and, if the press is set on an incline, the work slides back by gravity beneath the raised bolster *B* into a box. With a die of this type, drawn and embossed articles can be produced as rapidly as plain covers in "push-through" dies. Triple-action dies are especially adapted for such work as drawing and embossing lettered covers for blacking boxes, baking powder cans, covers for lard pails and also for articles such as seamless sardine boxes, etc.

Selecting Type of Drawing Die.—The type of die to use depends primarily upon the shape of the drawn part and the nature of the drawing operation, although the quantity of parts required may also affect the design of the die. If comparatively shallow cups or shells, such as can or box covers, were required in quantity, a combination die and a single-action press would ordinarily be used, whereas, if the cups were quite deep or simply the first of a series of operations, a double-action blanking and drawing die would usually be employed. On the other hand, if comparatively few drawn parts were needed, it might be advisable to do the work in two operations by first cutting out the blank in a plain blanking die and then drawing it in another die of the simple push-through type. Such a die, however, should only be used for metal having a thickness of at least 1/16 inch and for producing shallow cups.

When designing drawing dies the number of drawing operations necessary must also be considered. If a deep shell is to be drawn and a double-action drawing die is used to form the cup, redrawing dies will be necessary to gradually lengthen and reduce the diameter of this cup, in order to form the shell.

Dies for Drawing a Cylindrical Shell.—A set of drawing dies for producing a cylindrical steel shell, 4 inches in diameter and 8 5/8 inches long, is shown in Fig. 6. The successive operations are illustrated in Fig. 7. The flat circular blank from which the shell is drawn is made of sheet steel, 1/16 inch thick and 12 3/4 inches in diameter. This flat blank is first drawn into the form of a shallow cup *B* which is reduced in diameter and lengthened to the required size by operations *C*, *D*, and *E*, as Fig. 7 indicates. The first drawing or cupping die is illus-

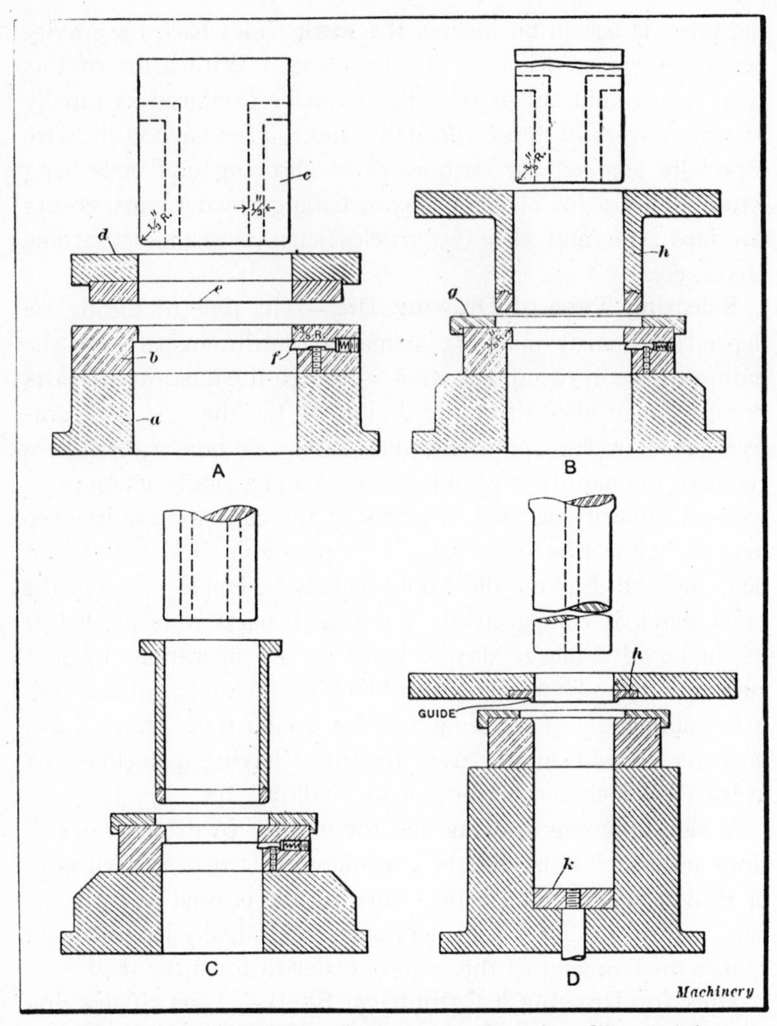

Fig. 6. Drawing Dies for the Successive Operations Illustrated in Fig. 7

trated at *A,* Fig. 6. The die-bed *a* is made of cast iron and the drawing die *b,* of machine steel, pack-hardened. The punch *c* is also made of machine steel and pack-hardened, whereas the blank-holder *d* is of cast iron faced with a hardened machine steel ring *e.* The cup is stripped from the punch by means of fingers *f* which are backed up by a spiral spring and engages the top of the drawn part when the punch ascends, thus stripping it off. Many dies do not have these stripping fingers, the work being removed from the punch, when the latter ascends, by contact with the lower edge of the die. The use of stripping fingers, however, gives a more positive action and they are particularly desirable for deep drawing operations.

The construction of the die for the second operation (see view *B*, Fig. 6) is practically the same as the one just referred to, except that it is provided with a gage plate *g* for centering

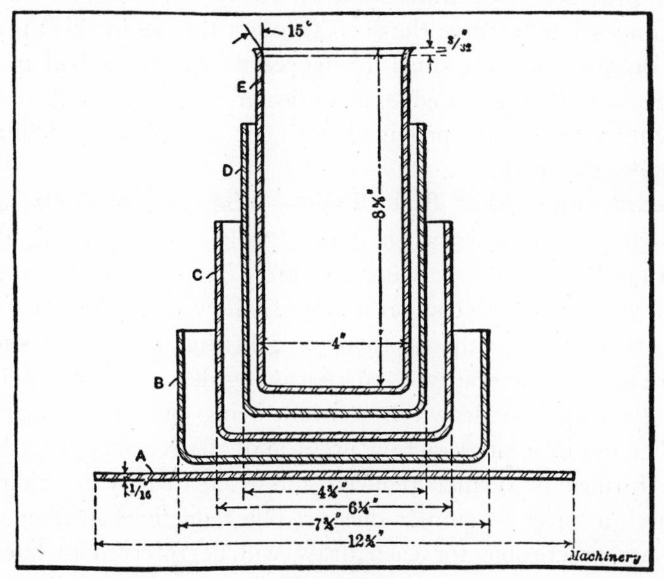

Fig. 7. The Blank and Successive Drawing Operations for Producing Steel Shell *E*

the cup with the die. An inside blank-holder *h* is also used for steadying the cup while it is being redrawn. The size of the shell produced in this die is indicated at *C*, Fig. 7. After these two drawing operations the shell is annealed and is then put through die *C*. As will be seen, this die is also equipped with an inside blank-holder and a gage plate for centering the shell to be redrawn. The cup *D*, after the third drawing operation, was too long to be inserted in the press available for the fourth drawing operation, and had to be trimmed to a length of 7½ inches. It was then redrawn in die *D*, Fig. 6. The shell is kept in an upright position in the die by guide *h*, which fits in the top of the shell and holds it while the punch descends. The distance between the bed and ram of the press was not sufficient to allow the use of this guide without trimming the shell; this operation, however, could have been dispensed with if a suitable press had been available. Prior to the final drawing operation, the shell was annealed and after being drawn was trimmed to the required length. This last drawing die is provided with a knockout *k*, which is necessary because it is impossible to force the shell through the die in this operation on account of a small 15-degree flange which had to be formed around the top edge, as indicated in Fig. 7. All of the drawing punches are provided with air passages to facilitate stripping the work.

Redrawing Dies of Plain Type.—After cups or shells have been drawn in either a plain or double-acting drawing die, what are known as redrawing dies are often used to reduce the diameters of these comparatively shallow cups and at the same time increase the depth or length, thus forming a shell. There are two general types of redrawing dies. In the simplest type the cup is redrawn by simply being pushed through a smaller die in a single-action press and, if necessary, the shell thus formed is further reduced and elongated by pushing it through a series of similar dies. (The reductions in diameter that are practicable for each draw will be referred to later.) This simple form of redrawing die is used for small parts, especially when the metal is comparatively thick and does not wrinkle to any great extent while being drawn. Some redrawing dies do not differ essentially from an ordinary plain drawing die, as will be seen by referring to sketch *A*, Fig. 8. In this particular design, the cup is located in the die by an annular recess above the drawing surface and it is reduced in diameter and lengthened by simply being pushed through the die. There is, of course, a limit to the amount of reduction which can be obtained in a single drawing operation, and when a long shell is required, a series of redrawing dies are necessary, the steps or reductions in diameter being varied according to the thickness and quality of the metal being drawn.

Redrawing Dies of the Blank-holder Type.—Sketch *B*, Fig. 8, shows another type of redrawing die, which is especially adapted for drawing large cylindrical parts when considerable reduction is required and when the stock is thin and liable to wrinkle. In this case, the cup to be redrawn is held by an inside blank-holder *C* as it passes between the lower beveled edge of the holder and the die, as the drawing punch descends. For large thin work, redrawing dies having inside blank-holders are commonly used. The blank-holder prevents the formation of body wrinkles as the work is being pushed

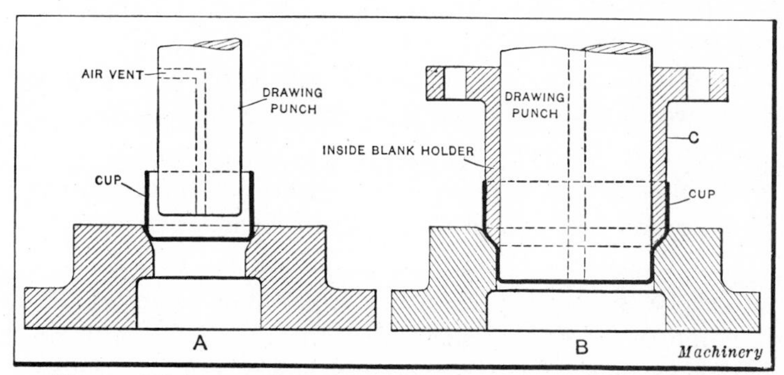

Fig. 8. (A) Plain Redrawing Die. (B) Redrawing Die with Inside Blank-holder

through a smaller opening and this support to the body also allows a greater reduction of metal to be obtained in one drawing operation. Redrawing dies having blank-holders should be used when work is large and especially if the stock is thin in proportion to the diameter.

A double-action press must be used for a die of this kind, one slide operating the blank-holder and the other the drawing punch. The blank-holder presses against the cup and prevents the formation of wrinkles while the punch draws it into a deeper shape of less diameter. These dies, especially when used for large work, are frequently made of cast iron, treated in such a manner as to give a very dense and uniform texture to the metal at the working surfaces. Sometimes a steel ring is set into a cast-iron holder to form the drawing part of the die, and the blank-holder is made of a steel casting, which adds considerable to the durability of the tools. For articles which have to be very accurate in diameter, a hard steel sizing punch and die are sometimes used after the last redrawing operation.

Depth of the First Drawing Operation.—When a shell or cup is to be drawn from a flat blank, the diemaker or designer must decide how many drawing operations will be required. Shallow cups, can covers, etc., can be drawn in one operation, but, when a comparatively deep shell is required, two or more operations are necessary, the number depending upon the quality and kind of metal, its thickness, the slant or angle of the dies, the amount that the stock is thinned or ironed in drawing and the thickness of the metal in proportion to the diameter of the work.

According to a commonly used rule, a plain cylindrical shell should not be drawn to a depth exceeding three-fourths its diameter and in some cases the depth should not exceed one-half the diameter. When an attempt is made to draw a blank too deeply, so much pressure is required to contract the flat sheet into a cylindrical shape that the tensile strength of the metal is exceeded. It is impossible, however, to determine the maximum depth by a general rule, because the greatest depth which can be obtained safely depends not only upon the properties of the metal being drawn but may be affected decidedly by the type of die used. An ordinary combination die, which would be used in a single-acting press, cannot draw as deeply as a double-action die because the pressure between the draw ring and blank holder gradually increases with the depth, provided there is increased compression of a rubber or spring. Many dies, however, now used in single-acting presses are equipped with special pressure-compensating attachments (described later) for maintaining practically a constant pressure throughout the drawing operation. When such an attachment is used, often it is possible to draw in one operation to a depth about equal to the diameter; hence, it will be seen that the rule for maximum depth is subject to modification owing to varying conditions. If a shell is to have a flange at the top, it will not be practicable to draw as deeply as when there is no flange, because the stock is subjected to a higher tensile stress owing to the larger blank which is necessary for forming the flange.

Diameter Obtained in One Drawing Operation.—The diameter which can be obtained from a flat blank in one operation varies somewhat, owing to differences in the physical properties of the sheet metals used for drawn parts and also because of certain other variable factors related to the die itself. These variable conditions account for the fact that there is a certain range between the maximum depth and minimum diameter which it is practicable to obtain in one drawing operation, when considering different dies and sheet metals of different kinds. In general, there are three points to be considered. One pertains to the minimum diameter which is practicable when a shell is drawn from a flat blank. Another point is in regard to the maximum depth that is feasible in one drawing operation, and finally, the third point relates to the amount that a previously drawn shell can be reduced in diameter in connection with a redrawing operation. The following rules and information should be regarded as applicable under ordinary conditions, but they are subject to change due to different conditions, as for example when a drawing die is equipped with a modern pressure attachment or "die cushion." The stock ordinarily used for drawn parts may be drawn from a flat blank to a diameter equal to the blank diameter multiplied by 0.55. Under favorable conditions the diameter might be as small as 0.4 of the blank diameter, and when conditions are less favorable, it would be safer to limit the diameter to from 0.60 to 0.65 of the blank diameter.

According to the practice followed by some die designers and diemakers, it is assumed that steel, copper, brass, and aluminum shells can be drawn in the first die to a diameter ranging from 0.55 to 0.60 times the blank diameter, whereas zinc can be drawn to about 0.65 times the blank diameter. All rules for determining the relation between the blank diameter and the diameter of the first drawing die are subject to variations owing to differences in the physical properties of the metals to be drawn.

Tables of Drawn Shell Dimensions.—The accompanying tables "Approximate Dimensions of Drawn Shells" give the diameters and heights of shells drawn from various blank diameters and to various percentages of the blank diameter. To illustrate the use of the table, we shall assume that the blank diameter is 5 inches and that the first drawing die diameter is to equal 0.60 times the blank diameter. By locating the blank diameter, or 5, in the first column and following horizontally to the shell dimensions under 0.60, it will be seen that the die or shell diameter equals 3 inches and the height of the shell 1.33 inches. These figures are based upon the assumption that the area of the drawn shell equals the area of the flat blank. Thus, if the shell diameter is 3 and the height 1.33, then

$$\text{Blank diameter} = \sqrt{3^2 + (4 \times 3 \times 1.33)} = 5 \text{ nearly.}$$

Amount of Reduction in Redrawing Dies.—When a shell is to be reduced by using redrawing dies, the reduction which may be obtained satisfactorily in one redrawing operation depends upon the physical properties of the stock, its thickness, the type of die used, and other factors. As a general rule, the percentage of diameter reduction for different thicknesses of good drawing steel is about as follows, when using single-action presses: For steel stock of a thickness up to about 1/16 inch, 20 per cent reduction in diameter or 0.80 of the diameter left by the preceding die; for stock between 1/16 and 1/8 inch, 15 per cent reduction; and for stock between 1/8 inch and 3/16 inch, 12 per cent reduction. These reductions may be increased about 50 per cent when using double-action dies, the inside of the shell being supported by a bushing or blank-holder. This 50 per cent increase also applies when redrawing suitable brass stock in single-action presses. When the *reverse* drawing method is employed (as described in Chapter XIV) a reduction of 25 per cent may be practicable.

Approximate Dimensions of Drawn Shells—1

Diam. of Flat Blank	When Diameter of First Drawing Die Equals Blank Diameter Multiplied by ——							
	0.70		0.65		0.60		0.55	
	Shell Diam.	Shell Height	Shell Diam.	Shell Height	Shell Diam.	Shell Height	Shell Diam.	Shell Height
1	0.70	0.18	0.65	0.22	0.60	0.27	0.55	0.32
1¼	0.88	0.23	0.81	0.28	0.75	0.33	0.69	0.40
1½	1.05	0.27	0.98	0.33	0.90	0.40	0.83	0.48
1¾	1.23	0.32	1.14	0.39	1.05	0.47	0.96	0.55
2	1.40	0.36	1.30	0.44	1.20	0.53	1.10	0.63
2¼	1.58	0.41	1.46	0.50	1.35	0.60	1.24	0.71
2½	1.75	0.46	1.63	0.56	1.50	0.67	1.38	0.79
2¾	1.93	0.50	1.79	0.61	1.65	0.73	1.51	0.87
3	2.10	0.55	1.95	0.67	1.80	0.80	1.65	0.95
3¼	2.28	0.59	2.11	0.72	1.95	0.87	1.79	1.03
3½	2.45	0.64	2.28	0.78	2.10	0.93	1.93	1.11
3¾	2.63	0.68	2.44	0.83	2.25	1.00	2.06	1.19
4	2.80	0.73	2.60	0.89	2.40	1.07	2.20	1.27
4¼	2.98	0.77	2.76	0.95	2.55	1.13	2.34	1.35
4½	3.15	0.82	2.93	1.00	2.70	1.20	2.48	1.43
4¾	3.33	0.86	3.09	1.05	2.85	1.27	2.61	1.51
5	3.50	0.91	3.25	1.11	3.00	1.33	2.75	1.59
5¼	3.68	0.96	3.41	1.17	3.15	1.40	2.89	1.66
5½	3.85	1.00	3.58	1.22	3.30	1.47	3.03	1.74
5¾	4.03	1.05	3.74	1.28	3.45	1.53	3.16	1.82
6	4.20	1.09	3.90	1.33	3.60	1.60	3.30	1.90
6¼	4.38	1.14	4.06	1.39	3.75	1.67	3.44	1.98
6½	4.55	1.18	4.23	1.44	3.90	1.73	3.58	2.06
6¾	4.73	1.23	4.39	1.50	4.05	1.80	3.71	2.14
7	4.90	1.28	4.55	1.55	4.20	1.87	3.85	2.22
7¼	5.08	1.32	4.71	1.61	4.35	1.93	3.99	2.30
7½	5.25	1.37	4.88	1.67	4.50	2.00	4.13	2.38
7¾	5.43	1.41	5.04	1.72	4.65	2.07	4.26	2.46
8	5.60	1.46	5.20	1.78	4.80	2.14	4.40	2.54
8¼	5.78	1.51	5.36	1.83	4.95	2.20	4.54	2.62
8½	5.95	1.55	5.53	1.89	5.10	2.27	4.68	2.69
8¾	6.13	1.60	5.69	1.94	5.25	2.34	4.81	2.77
9	6.30	1.64	5.85	2.00	5.40	2.40	4.95	2.85
9¼	6.48	1.69	6.01	2.06	5.55	2.47	5.09	2.93
9½	6.65	1.73	6.18	2.11	5.70	2.53	5.23	3.01
9¾	6.83	1.78	6.34	2.17	5.85	2.60	5.36	3.09
10	7.00	1.82	6.50	2.22	6.00	2.67	5.50	3.17
10¼	7.18	1.87	6.66	2.23	6.15	2.73	5.64	3.25
10½	7.35	1.91	6.82	2.33	6.30	2.80	5.78	3.33
10¾	7.53	1.96	6.99	2.39	6.45	2.87	5.91	3.41
11	7.70	2.00	7.15	2.44	6.60	2.94	6.05	3.49
11¼	7.88	2.05	7.31	2.50	6.75	3.00	6.19	3.57

The figures in the body of this table represent the diameters and heights of cylindrical shells drawn from various blank diameters and to four different percentages of the blank diameter. Assume that the blank diameter is 2 inches; then if the diameter of the first drawing die equals the blank diameter multiplied by 0.60, the drawn shell will have a diameter of 1.20 inches and a height of 0.53 inch, provided there are no changes due to thinning or stretching of the metal.

Approximate Dimensions of Drawn Shells—2

Diam. of Flat Blank	When Diameter of First Drawing Die Equals Blank Diameter Multiplied by ——							
	0.70		0.65		0.60		0.55	
	Shell Diam.	Shell Height	Shell Diam.	Shell Height	Shell Diam.	Shell Height	Shell Diam.	Shell Height
11½	8.05	2.09	7.47	2.56	6.90	3.07	6.33	3.65
11¾	8.23	2.14	7.64	2.61	7.05	3.13	6.46	3.73
12	8.40	2.19	7.80	2.67	7.20	3.20	6.60	3.80
12¼	8.58	2.23	7.96	2.72	7.35	3.27	6.74	3.88
12½	8.75	2.28	8.12	2.78	7.50	3.34	6.88	3.96
12¾	8.93	2.32	8.29	2.84	7.65	3.40	7.01	4.04
13	9.10	2.37	8.45	2.89	7.80	3.47	7.15	4.12
13¼	9.28	2.42	8.61	2.95	7.95	3.53	7.29	4.20
13½	9.45	2.46	8.77	3.00	8.10	3.60	7.43	4.28
13¾	9.63	2.51	8.94	3.06	8.25	3.67	7.56	4.36
14	9.80	2.55	9.10	3.11	8.40	3.74	7.70	4.44
14¼	9.98	2.60	9.26	3.17	8.55	3.80	7.84	4.52
14½	10.15	2.64	9.42	3.22	8.70	3.87	7.98	4.60
14¾	10.33	2.69	9.59	3.28	8.85	3.93	8.11	4.68
15	10.50	2.73	9.75	3.34	9.00	4.00	8.25	4.76
15¼	10.68	2.78	9.91	3.39	9.15	4.07	8.39	4.83
15½	10.85	2.82	10.07	3.44	9.30	4.13	8.53	4.91
15¾	11.03	2.87	10.24	3.50	9.45	4.20	8.66	4.99
16	11.20	2.92	10.40	3.56	9.60	4.27	8.80	5.07
16¼	11.38	2.96	10.56	3.61	9.75	4.34	8.94	5.15
16½	11.55	3.01	10.72	3.67	9.90	4.40	9.08	5.23
16¾	11.73	3.06	10.89	3.72	10.05	4.47	9.21	5.31
17	11.90	3.10	11.05	3.78	10.20	4.53	9.35	5.39
17¼	12.08	3.14	11.21	3.84	10.35	4.60	9.49	5.47
17½	12.25	3.19	11.37	3.89	10.50	4.67	9.63	5.55
17¾	12.43	3.24	11.54	3.95	10.65	4.74	9.76	5.63
18	12.60	3.28	11.70	4.00	10.80	4.80	9.90	5.71
18¼	12.78	3.33	11.86	4.06	10.95	4.87	10.04	5.79
18½	12.95	3.37	12.02	4.12	11.10	4.94	10.18	5.87
18¾	13.13	3.42	12.19	4.17	11.25	5.00	10.31	5.94
19	13.30	3.46	12.35	4.23	11.40	5.07	10.45	6.02
19¼	13.48	3.51	12.51	4.28	11.55	5.14	10.59	6.10
19½	13.65	3.55	12.67	4.34	11.70	5.20	10.73	6.18
19¾	13.83	3.60	12.84	4.39	11.85	5.27	10.86	6.26
20	14.00	3.64	13.00	4.44	12.00	5.33	11.00	6.34
20¼	14.18	3.69	13.16	4.50	12.15	5.40	11.14	6.42
20½	14.35	3.74	13.32	4.56	12.30	5.47	11.28	6.50
20¾	14.53	3.78	13.49	4.61	12.45	5.54	11.41	6.58
21	14.70	3.83	13.65	4.67	12.60	5.60	11.55	6.66
21¼	14.88	3.88	13.81	4.73	12.75	5.67	11.69	6.74
21½	15.05	3.92	13.97	4.78	12.90	5.73	11.83	6.82
21¾	15.23	3.96	14.14	4.83	13.05	5.80	11.96	6.90

The figures in the body of this table represent the diameters and heights of cylindrical shells drawn from various blank diameters and to four different percentages of the blank diameter. Assume that the blank diameter is 12 inches; then if the diameter of the first drawing die equals the blank diameter multiplied by 0.65, the drawn shell will have a diameter of 7.80 inches and a height of 2.67 inches, provided there are no changes due to thinning or stretching of the metal.

That surface of a redrawing die over which the metal flows as it is being reduced to the smaller diameter, is usually conical or beveled. The angle of this conical surface, measured from the horizontal, is generally 30 degrees for stock having a thickness up to about 1/32 inch; 40 degrees for thickness between 1/32 and 1/16 inch; and 45 degrees for thicknesses above 1/16 inch.

Formulas for Drawing Die Diameters.—In order to determine more definitely the diameters that are practicable for drawing dies, several hundred tests were made on various thicknesses of steel stock, using different die and blank diameters. These tests showed that the ratio of $\frac{\text{die diameter}}{\text{blank diameter}}$ for the same thickness of metal is not constant (assuming that the same quality of drawn work is obtained in each case), but that an increase in blank diameter means an increase in ratio; in other words, the diameter of the first drawing die should be proportionately larger as the diameter of the blank increases. The following formulas for determining die diameters are the result of these tests and apply to drawing dies intended for soft steel or tinplate:

For first operation dies:

$$d = \frac{X \times D}{100 - 0.635D}.$$

For redrawing dies:

$$d_1 = \frac{X_1 \times d}{100 - 0.635d} \qquad d_2 = \frac{X_1 \times d_1}{100 - 0.635d_1}, \text{ etc.}$$

In these formulas,

D = the calculated blank diameter;
d = diameter of the first-operation drawing die;
d_1 = diameter for first redrawing die;
d_2 = diameter of following redrawing die;
X and X_1 = factors which depend upon the thickness of the metal to be drawn.

These factors X and X_1 for different thicknesses of stock are given in the accompanying table "Minimum and Maximum

Values for Die Diameter Formulas." The numerical values of these factors were found by making several hundred trial draws, using different blank and die diameters and different thicknesses of stock. It should be mentioned that the results

Minimum and Maximum Values for Die Diameter Formulas

<table>
<tr><th rowspan="2">Metal Thickness, Inch</th><th colspan="2">First-operation Die
X</th><th colspan="2">All Redrawing Dies
X_1</th></tr>
<tr><th>Minimum</th><th>Maximum</th><th>Minimum</th><th>Maximum</th></tr>
<tr><td>0.016 to 0.018</td><td>61</td><td>68</td><td>74</td><td>81</td></tr>
<tr><td>0.02</td><td>58</td><td>65</td><td>73</td><td>80</td></tr>
<tr><td>0.022 to 0.024</td><td>56</td><td>63</td><td>72</td><td>80</td></tr>
<tr><td>0.028</td><td>54</td><td>60</td><td>71</td><td>79</td></tr>
<tr><td>0.03</td><td>50</td><td>56</td><td>70.5</td><td>77</td></tr>
<tr><td>0.06</td><td>47</td><td>53</td><td>70</td><td>75</td></tr>
<tr><td>0.12</td><td colspan="2">51</td><td colspan="2">65</td></tr>
</table>

are correct only for dies used in double-action presses where the blank-holder pressure is constant and, in the case of redrawing dies, inside blank-holders having 45-degree drawing edges are employed.

How Formulas for Die Diameters Are Used.—To illustrate the use of the formula for first operation dies (see formula in preceding paragraph), assume that the blank diameter equals 5 inches and the metal thickness, 0.028 inch. The table shows that the metal thickness factor X for a thickness of 0.028 equals from 54 to 60. If we take the average value of 57 and insert it together with a blank diameter of 5 in the formula previously given, we have

$$d = \frac{57 \times 5}{100 - 0.635 \times 5} = 2\ 15/16 \text{ inches, approximately.}$$

The die diameter obtained in this particular case is about equal to 0.60 times the blank diameter.

Assume that the diameter of the first drawing die is made 3 inches in order to have an even dimension, and that the diameter of the finished shell is to be 1¾ inches; then the size of the first redrawing die can be determined by the formula previously given for redrawing dies. The metal thickness factor X for redrawing dies and for a stock thickness of 0.028 is found by referring to the table to range from 71 to 79. If the average of 75 is taken, then the diameter of the first redrawing die is determined as follows:

$$d_1 = \frac{75 \times 3}{100 - 0.635 \times 3} = 2.3, \text{ approximately}$$

The diameter of the second redrawing die is now obtained by inserting in the formula the diameter of the first redrawing die. Thus

$$d_2 = \frac{75 \times 2.3}{100 - 0.635 \times 2.3} = 1.75 \text{ inches.}$$

In this case the first redrawing die reduces the diameter from 3 to 2.3, which is equivalent to about 23 per cent reduction, and the second redrawing die in changing the diameter from 2.3 to 1.75 reduces the diameter about 24 per cent.

Determining Height of Drawn Shell.—The height of a shell which has been drawn to a given diameter may readily be determined by the following method, assuming that the main body of the shell is cylindrical. To illustrate the procedure, assume that the shell has a flange and that the radius at the bottom corner is large enough to be taken into account in determining the height. The first step is to find the area of the flange, the area of the rounded corner, and the area of the bottom. (A formula for determining the area of the rounded corner is given in Chapter II in connection with Fig. 10 in the table "Areas of Drawn Shells—2.") Assume that the total area of these three surfaces is 30 square inches and that the area of the flat blank is 50 square inches; then the difference of 20 square inches (50 — 30 = 20) represents the area of the cylindrical part of the shell. Now the area of a cylinder equals its circumference multiplied by the height; hence, the height equals the area divided by the circumference or in this case the height equals 20 ÷ circumference. When a series of redrawing operations is required to produce a shell of given diameter, the height after each redrawing operation may be calculated in the manner described. Tables of circumferences and areas, such as are found in MACHINERY'S

HANDBOOK, beginning page 55, will reduce considerably the figuring required for work of this kind, as many values can be taken directly from the tables.

Uniform Height for Shell Requiring Redrawing Operations.—Care should be taken that a shell which is the first of a series of operations is uniform in height all around, because a little unevenness will multiply as it passes through succeeding dies, thus requiring a larger blank than is necessary. This defect is often caused by the blanking ring not being concentric with the drawing die; the blank-holder may also bear harder on one side than on the other or a bad burr on one side of the blank may result in holding that side back.

Beveled Drawing Edges for First-operation Dies.—The shapes of the edges of drawing dies, for cylindrical work, vary somewhat even for dies of the same class. The shape depends, to some extent, upon the nature of the drawing operation, but the different forms of drawing edges in use, even for the same general class of work, are due in part to the difference of opinon among diemakers and also to a lack of specific information on this important point. When first-operation dies and those used for drawing cups from flat blanks are not equipped with a blank-holder, it has been found good practice to bevel the upper part of the die to an angle of about 60 degrees, as shown at *A*, Fig. 9 or to an angle of 30 degrees from the vertical center-line of the die. Some dies of this beveled form have an angle of about 65 degrees (when measured as shown at *A*) or 25 degrees from the center-line. The advantage of this steep beveled surface is that it tends to prevent wrinkling, although a die of this type or one not having a blank-holder should not be used on stock thinner than, say, 3/32 or 1/16 inch. The amount of bevel for a die of this class should be such that the flat blank will have a bearing *w* of about 1/8 inch on each side of the die opening. Some diemakers seldom make this width less than 1/16 inch or greater than 1/8 inch, whereas, others use a bearing varying from 1/8 to 3/16 inch, depending upon the size of the die and the thickness of the stock.

The upper and lower edges of the beveled surface are rounded, the radius depending somewhat upon the thickness of the stock. It has been found good practice to vary this radius from about 1/8 inch on a die for No. 16 gage stock to about 1/4 inch for dies intended for stock of, say, 1/4-inch thickness. The seat or nest for locating the flat blank concentric with the die opening is formed either by counterboring down into the die or by attaching a locating plate to the top of the die. Some first-operation dies that are not equipped with blank-holders have round edges instead of the bevel form. The latter is preferable as it will enable deeper cuts to be drawn and there is less tendency of the stock to wrinkle.

When using a plain push-through type of die, such as is shown at *A*, the relation between the blank and cup diameters is about the same as when using a double-action die. A cup drawn in a push-through die, however, will have a much more uneven edge along the top than if drawn in a die equipped with a blank-holder; consequently, if several redrawing operations were required, it might be necessary to trim the edge of the shell after the third or fourth draw in order to facilitate stripping the shell. It is the practice of one firm specializing in die-made products, not to use plain push-through dies for cups having a depth exceeding 1/2 inch, except when the stock is thicker than about 3/8 inch. When drawing a comparatively deep cup from stock varying, say, from 1/16 to 1/4 inch in thickness, without using a blank-holder, the metal tends to thicken or gather in folds toward the top and has to be ironed out, which may cause undue strain on the shell. The minimum stock thickness, when using a plain push-through die, depends somewhat upon the shell diameter.

Round Drawing Edges.—Most first-operation drawing dies are equipped with blank-holders and such dies have rounded drawing edges, as indicated at *B*, Fig. 9. When making a die of this form, the radius of the drawing edge is very important. Evidently, if this edge were left square it would tend to cut the metal and the latter would not flow over it readily, if at all; consequently, the stress upon the metal might exceed its tensile strength and the shell would be ruptured. By using a curved drawing surface, however, this difficulty is overcome because the curved edge offers less resistance to the inward flow of the metal. The effectiveness of a drawing die may depend upon the radius of the drawing edge. For instance, if the radius r is too large, the flat part of the blank will receive insufficient support from the blank-

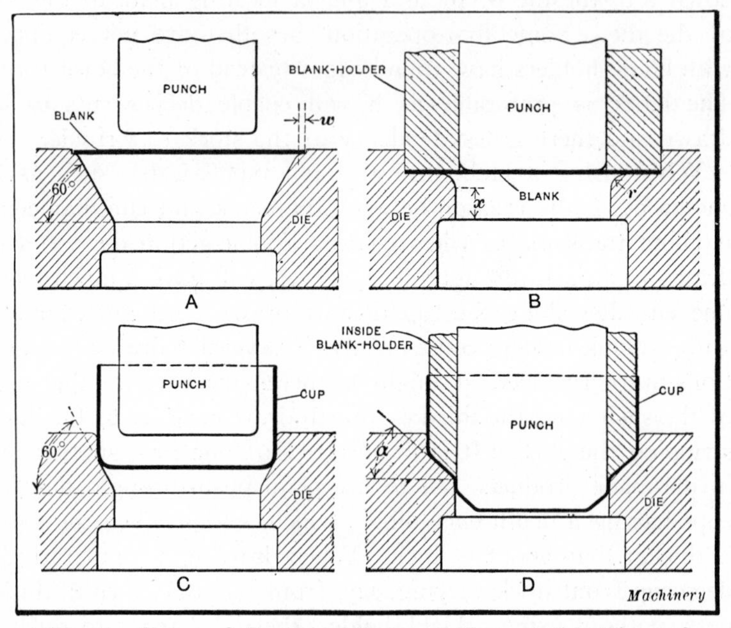

Fig. 9. Shapes of Drawing Surfaces of First-operation Dies and Redrawing Dies

holder and, as a result, the metal tends to wrinkle after the edge of the blank reaches the curved surface and the metal is no longer supported. If wrinkles form, they may be straightened out by the pressure of the drawing punch, but this operation is liable to develop flaws and minute cracks in the metal unless the latter is very ductile. The radius r depends upon the thickness of the stock and, to some extent, upon the nature of the drawing operation. A general rule that is used by some diemakers is to give the die a radius equal to from six to ten times the thickness of the stock.

When a part is drawn in one operation, or if the die is for a final operation, and it is especially desirable to secure an even top edge for the cup or shell being drawn, the radius of the drawing edge should be reduced as much as possible. When the outer edge of the blank after leaving the blank-holder begins to pass over the rounded part of the die, it is no longer supported by the blank-holder, and, consequently, is free to follow the natural tendency to wrinkle. Therefore, when it is essential to secure an even top edge, the radius should be reduced to a minimum. If this radius is made too small, however, there is danger of stretching and straining the metal excessively or even tearing it, because of the increased friction resulting from drawing the metal over too sharp an edge. On the other hand, if the radius is too large, the blank lacks the support necessary to prevent wrinkling, as previously mentioned.

For thin stock, this radius may be very small and, in extreme cases, the drawing edge is almost square, the advantage being that thin shallow cups drawn in such a die will have even top edges which, in many cases, do not require trimming. When the stock is thicker than about 3/32 inch, the radius can be made fairly large without trouble from wrinkling, because the heavier stock "clings" better to the drawing surface of the die. As a rule, cupping or first-operation dies for drawing cups or shells from flat blanks should always be equipped with blank-holders for stock thinner than 3/32 or 1/16 inch, although the diameter reduction that is necessary must, of course, be taken into consideration. The length x of the drawing surface of the die is usually made about 3/8 or 1/2 inch. If this surface is too long, it may increase the frictional resistance between the die and shell wall to such an extent that excessive stretching and straining of the metal occurs; moreover the pressure exerted on the metal when it is being drawn over the rounded edge tends to remove most of the lubrication, thus leaving very little for the straight surface; consequently, a scored shell is liable to be the result if the cylindrical part of the die is too long.

Radii of Drawing Edges for Different Stock Thicknesses.—The radius of the drawing edge over which metal can be drawn satisfactorily, has a direct relation to the gage of the metal. This radius, if too large, would start wrinkles in the shell that would be difficult to remove, while if too small, the metal might break in sliding over the corner on account of excessive friction. The same restrictions apply in a certain sense to the radius at the bottom of the shell.

A drawing edge radius that is too large will cause wrinkles from the bottom to the top of the work, while too sharp a corner might cause the punch to break through the bottom. As a general rule, the radius at the top or bottom has nothing

Radii of Drawing Edges for Different Thicknesses of Stock

Thickness of Stock		Radius of Drawing Edge		Thickness of Stock		Radius of Drawing Edge	
U. S. Gage	Inch	Min.	Max.	U. S. Gage	Inch	Min.	Max.
16	0.0625	1/4	3/8	23	0.0281	3/16	9/32
17	0.0563	1/4	3/8	24	0.0250	3/16	9/32
18	0.0500	1/4	3/8	25	0.0219	3/16	9/32
19	0.0438	3/16	5/16	26	0.0188	5/32	1/4
20	0.0375	3/16	5/16	27	0.0172	5/32	1/4
21	0.0344	3/16	5/16	28	0.0156	5/32	1/4
22	0.0313	3/16	5/16	......	......	......	......

to do with the diameter of the shell; nevertheless, it is customary in most shops to make the radii for large-diameter shells larger than for shells of smaller diameter. This is usually done either for the sake of appearance or because it facilitates later operations, such as beading. However, care must be taken not to use too much freedom in this respect, as the radii should be governed largely by the gage of the metal. The accompanying table can be used as a guide in determining the maximum and minimum radii that will produce satisfactory results.

Inserted Drawing-die Rings.—Many drawing dies are equipped with inserted removable rings instead of forming the die of one solid piece. One advantage of this construction is that the ring may readily be replaced if this should be necessary on account of wear. In addition, the cost of construction often can be reduced considerably, as, for example, when steel rings are inserted either in a cast-iron body or in one made of machine steel. Two forms of rings are shown in Fig. 10. The one at *A* has been counterbored in order to reduce the straight or cylindrical part of the die to a height of about 3/8 inch, as this height will be sufficient for most drawing operations. The lower edge or corner is sometimes beveled to an angle of 45 degrees, as shown, because if the

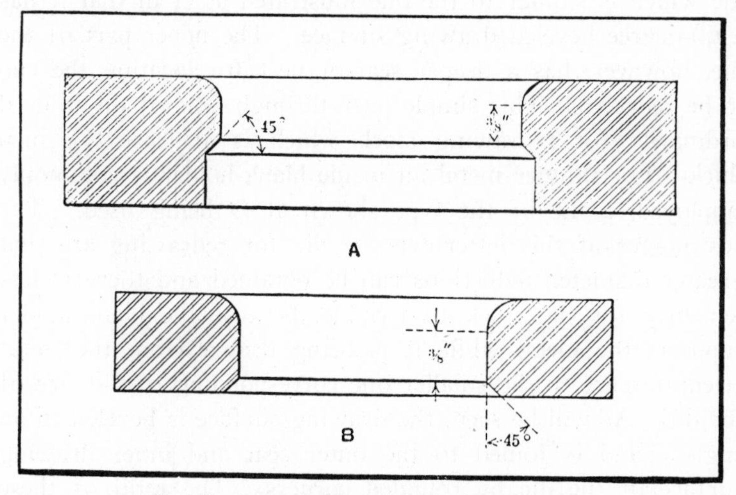

Fig. 10. Inserted Draw-rings for Drawing Dies

corners are left sharp, chips are liable to break off. Many drawing dies, however, have sharp or square corners as this corner is relied upon to strip the drawn shell from the punch during the upward stroke. This method of stripping is inferior to the use of stripping dogs which spring in over the top edge of the drawn shell and provide a positive means of stripping it as the punch ascends. The arrangement of these stripping dogs will be described later in this chapter. The ring shown at *B* is bevelled but not counterbored, as the height is not sufficient to warrant counterboring.

If the stripping is done by a sharp or square corner, this

edge is subject to considerable wear, and sometimes the wear is so great that the shell is drawn part-way into the die, where it sticks. If this occurs, a corner sharp enough for stripping may again be obtained by grinding the lower surface, but as such repairs interfere with the operation of the press, it is generally advisable to provide stripping fingers.

Drawing Edges for Redrawing Dies.—The shapes of the drawing edges for two commonly used types of redrawing dies, or those employed for reducing the diameters of cups or shells, are shown at *C* and *D*, Fig. 9. Sketch *C* shows a die which is similar to the one illustrated at *A* in that it has a 60-degree beveled drawing surface. The upper part of the die, however, has a deeper seat or nest for locating the cup to be redrawn. This simple push-through type of die is used ordinarily for redrawing stock which is at least 1/16 inch thick. For thinner metal an inside blank-holder is commonly employed, a die of the type shown at *D* being used. The advantages of this latter type of die for redrawing are that greater diameter reductions can be obtained and there is less tendency for the stock to wrinkle, because the blank-holder supports the metal while it is being drawn from the outer circumference to the smaller one corresponding to the size of the die. As will be seen, the drawing surface is beveled to an angle a and is joined to the outer seat and inner drawing surface of the die by rounded corners. The radii of these corners is generally made quite small, often being 1/8 inch or less. Some diemakers, however, increase the radii of these corners considerably as compared with the figure just given; in fact, in some cases the corners are rounded to such an extent that the straight beveled surface is entirely eliminated and the drawing surface of the die is simply a reverse curve. It is generally conceded, however, that the beveled edge is preferable. In the first place, it is claimed that the metal flows more readily over the beveled edge and there is another advantage in that the beveled surface forms a better seat for the shell, provided the end of the punch in the preceding die is given a corresponding taper.

The angle a of this beveled seat is generally varied according to the thickness of the metal to be drawn and ranges from 30 to 45 degrees, the thicker the metal the greater the angle. The following data taken from practice, show in a general way, the relation between the angle and stock thickness. For metal thinner than 1/32 inch, angle a is made 30 degrees; for metal varying from 1/32 to 1/16 inch, angle a is made 40 degrees, and for stock 1/16 inch and thicker, angle a is made 45 degrees.

Clearance for First-operation Drawing Die.—When a flat blank is changed into a cylindrical shape in the drawing die, the natural tendency of the annular part of the blank, which is compressed into a cylindrical shape, is to buckle and wrinkle, because it is changed from a flat to a circular form. Wrinkling is prevented, however, because there is not sufficient room between the die and punch to permit the formation of wrinkles, but the cylindrical wall of a cup which is drawn from a flat blank tends to increase in thickness during the drawing process, because the metal which is confined between the punch and die is compressed or upset circumferentially. Therefore, a first-operation drawing die, or "cupping die," as it is often called, is sometimes given a slight clearance to allow for this increase in thickness; that is, instead of making the space between the punch and die equal to the thickness of the stock, the diameter of the die is made equal to the diameter of the punch plus from 2.2 to 2.4 times the stock thickness. For some classes of work additional clearance is allowed to reduce the friction between the stock and the surfaces of the punch and die, the diameter of the die in some cases being made equal to the diameter of the punch plus from 2.6 to 3.2 times the thickness of the stock. For aluminum a clearance on each side of 1.25 times stock thickness is recommended, the die diameter equaling the punch diameter plus 2.5 times the stock thickness.

Insufficient clearance and the resulting increase of friction and wear affect the life of the tools and cause an unnecessary increase in the operating power. On the other hand, if too much clearance is given, the drawn shell will be somewhat conical in shape and full of wrinkles which cannot readily be ironed out by the redrawing dies. It is the practice of some diemakers to allow a slight clearance and then bevel the drawing surface of the die inward towards the bottom to iron out the metal and maintain the original thickness of the stock. If the die is used for a comparatively rough drawing operation, this ironing is not necessary and the stock is allowed to thicken.

The diameters of the punch and die should be measured occasionally to determine the width of the clearance space. If, as the result of wear, this clearance becomes excessive, the metal may thicken to such an extent that there will be difficulty in connection with succeeding drawing operations.

Ironing or Thinning the Stock.—When a cylindrical shell or similar part is to be drawn and a dead smooth finished surface is required, it is necessary to use stock that is one or two gage numbers heavier than the thickness of the finished shell to allow for the thinning or ironing out of the metal. For instance, if the wall of a shell is to be, say, 0.025 inch thick when drawn, the stock should be of No. 23 (0.0281 inch) or No. 22 (0.0313 inch) U. S. standard gage, so that it can be reduced in thickness while being drawn. Evidently, in order to produce this ironing effect, the space between the punch and die must be somewhat less than the thickness of the stock; that is, the diameter of the punch should be greater than the dimension obtained by subtracting twice the thickness of the stock from the die diameter.

The extent to which shells are ironed or thinned in one drawing operation varies somewhat with the thickness and kind of metal and also its qualities as to hardness and ductility. When the stock is ironed simply to secure a smooth surface and accuracy as to diameter, about 0.004 inch would ordinarily be allowed for No. 16 gage steel stock. In general, when ironing is required, the diameter of the punch should equal the diameter of the die minus twice the thickness of the stock plus from 0.004 to 0.008 inch. For the final drawing operation, when an extra fine finish is required, the allowances should not be over 0.001 inch on a side; that is, the diameter of the punch should equal the diameter of the die minus twice the thickness of the stock plus 0.002 inch. In many cases, the dies are so made that there is no ironing of the shell until the last drawing operation and then the stock is thinned from 0.001 to 0.003 inch, but this ironing is not done unless necessary. To reduce the thickness of the metal more than the amount specified, the shell should first be drawn to its finished inside diameter and then ironed by separate operations. When thinning the walls of the shell by ironing, it is advisable to run the press slower than for ordinary drawing.

While the foregoing figures apply to ordinary conditions and may not be an accurate guide in every case, they will serve to give a general idea of what is considered good practice. As previously mentioned, when the stock is to be ironed, this must be considered when determining the number of drawing operations, because ironing adds considerably to the pressure of the punch against the bottom of the shell. Therefore, the diameter reduction for each draw must be less when the metal has to be ironed out. It may be necessary to reduce the diameter reductions one-half of what would be practicable when drawing without ironing.

"Alligator Skin" Effect on Drawn Sheet Metal.—The peculiar mottled effect on drawn sheet metal, known in the sheet metal industry as "alligator skin," is noticeable only when the metal is drawn or stretched to a considerable extent, as in the formation of a deep cup. There have been many reasons given for this effect. In producing cold-rolled strip steel, the material is annealed previous to the last rolling operation, so as to eliminate brittleness as much as possible. The last rolling operation serves to brighten the metal and bring it to the correct thickness. For some work, however, it is necessary to secure a grade of sheet metal known as "skin hard." This cold-rolled strip steel has a comparatively hard surface, and, when the skin is not too deep, produces bright and nicely finished cold-drawn work. However, it is much more difficult to work than the softer grades of steel, and is used only when a hardened surface on the material is desired. It is when "skin hard" strip metal is being drawn up that the "alligator skin" effect is produced. If the metal, after annealing, is reduced too much in thickness in the final rolling operation, a hard surface is formed on the exterior which is much tougher than the interior; then, when the metal, in being worked up to the desired shape, is drawn to a considerable extent, the interior or center portion of the cup draws much more than the outer surface; hence the outer surface, or hard skin, pulls apart, as it will not stretch anywhere near as much as the inside. This leaves a peculiar looking surface slightly depressed in those portions where the skin has broken away. This "alligator skin" effect very seldom appears on soft sheet steel but is quite often present on "skin hard" steel. Manufacturers often find that this "skin hard" metal comes mixed up with soft stock, indicating that the rolling mill is at fault in allowing too much reduction in the final rolling operation.

Troubles Encountered in Drawing Light Gage Metal.— Some of the more common troubles encountered with drawing dies, especially when drawing thin stock, are as follows:

1. Continual tearing of the shells at one place is caused by high spots on the die or punch. Obviously the remedy for this trouble is to remove the high spots.

2. Breaking of shells at top or bottom corners is usually caused by attempting to form too sharp corners or corners with too small radii. However, before taking this for granted, it is well to relieve the pressure on the blank-holder slightly. If this causes wrinkles in the shell, it is certain that the first-mentioned trouble exists.

3. Difficulty in removing shells from the punch is often caused by lack of vent holes in the punch. The omission of vent holes may also be the cause of serious trouble in operating a die provided with a metal knock-out. On the down stroke of the press, the knock-out will compress the air in the die,

while on the up stroke it will form a partial vacuum that can be overcome only by the application of considerable force or pressure.

4. Trouble caused by bulging of the shell bottom is usually due to incorrectly designed knock-outs. At the completion of a long draw, the shell may be found to be very tight in the die and considerable pressure may be required to remove it. If the top of the knock-out is made flat, the bottom of the shell will be deformed. This trouble, however, will be eliminated if the knock-out is formed to fit the bottom of the shell.

In addition to considering carefully the troubles enumerated, when designing dies, it is well to remember that too great a reduction in the size of a shell should not be attempted in one operation. Drawing metal from too large a stock area is another thing that should not be done. Assume, for instance, that a blank is 8 inches in diameter, and that a cup 3 inches in diameter by 3/8 inch deep is required to be drawn at its center. It would at first appear that it would be an easy matter to draw such a shallow depression in the blank. As a matter of fact, however, it may be practically impossible to do this successfully in one operation. The 3-inch cup will be drawn from too great an area of metal and it may either break or wrinkle the flange excessively.

Formation of Air Pockets in Dies.—When making drawing and forming dies, it is important to provide vent holes wherever the air would be compressed excessively in the operation of the die, if such vents do not exist. Dies have often given trouble and even proved to be complete failures because of the formation of air pockets. Vent holes are needed, in some cases, to prevent the air from being entrapped between the work and the punch or die, and in other cases to facilitate removing or stripping a close-fitting cup or shell from a punch. For instance, if an air pocket is formed between the end of the cup and a forming punch, the air compression may be high enough to burst the end of the cup. The remedy is to drill a vent hole into the air pocket so that the air can escape. Drawing punches are often provided with small vent holes which extend from the end of the punch to some point beyond the top of the drawn shell. This vent allows the air to enter the space between the end of the punch and the bottom of the shell when the latter is being stripped, thus preventing the formation of a partial vacuum which would interfere with the removal of the work. The pressure-pads, or blank-holders, on dies of the combination type sometimes cause trouble by compressing the air as they descend during the drawing operation. This compression is, of course, more pronounced when the supporting pins which connect with the rubber pressure attachment are closely fitted to the holes in the base of the die. Air vents are sometimes formed for the space beneath the pressure-pad, by simply cutting small slots or grooves along the supporting pins, thus providing outlets for the air as the pressure-pad descends during the drawing operation. Much depends upon the location of the vent holes. For instance, sometimes when a vent is required at the end of the forming punch, it should be placed at one side rather than in the center of the punch, because the air is entrapped at the outer corner of the cup as the latter is pressed to its final shape. Before drilling vent holes, the action of the die should be carefully studied. The effect which a vent hole might have upon the strength of a punch or die should also be considered. When the parts of the die have not been closely fitted together (perhaps because accuracy was unnecessary) vent holes may not be needed.

Effects Produced by Trapped Oil, Air and Water.—Forming the piece shown at *A*, Fig. 11, which is made from 1/8-inch sheet brass, requires three operations, the last of which is done with a drop-hammer. After this part is formed, it has to be machined all over. A complaint was received that the thickness x was below size and that the parts could not be trued up. The stock was measured and also the piece before it went to the drop-hammer and both measurements indicated that it was O. K. Finally, the trouble was located and it was found to be due to the fact that the operator used too much oil in swabbing out the dies. This oil was trapped in the die and when the blow was struck, the pressure was so high as to reduce the original thickness from 0.005 to 0.008 inch. The surface of the metal was also made quite rough. The use of a light coating of oil eliminated the trouble.

Another unusual incident happened in connection with a compound blanking and drawing die. This was used in a press having an automatic roll feed and a compressed air pipe extending down from the ceiling. This air was used to blow the drawn cups away from the die into a box back of the

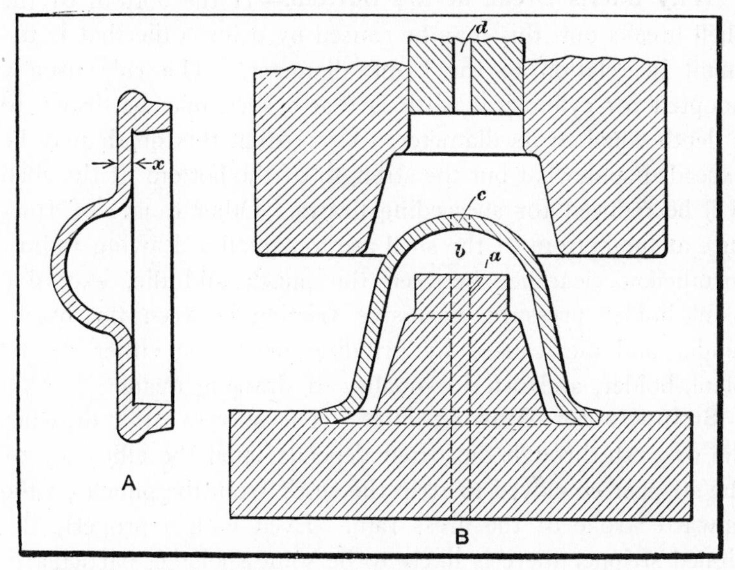

Fig. 11. (A) Part which was Unintentionally Reduced in Thickness by Oil Pressure (B) Die which Pierced Hole at *c* by Pressure of Air Trapped at *b*

press. One night the shut-off cock on the air pipe was not closed completely and water which had condensed in the line dropped on the die and flowed under the pressure pad, which was entirely housed in. When the press was rst tripped the next morning the shoe was pushed through the hole in the bolster plate because the water could not flow out quickly enough.

The action of air under high pressure is illustrated by another example. In making the die shown at *B,* Fig. 11, the diemaker failed to drill a vent hole through the punch, as indicated by the dotted lines *a*. The result was that when the press was tripped the air in space *b* was compressed to such a degree that a slug *c* was forced out into vent hole *d* in the knock-out. The material was No. 8 brass, B. & S. gage, and a hole was made as neatly as though it had been pierced by a punch. This indicates in a rather striking way how the lack of necessary vent holes increases the load on both the die and press.

Why Shells Break at the Bottom.—If the bottom of the shell breaks out, this may be caused by using a die that is too small in relation to the blank diameter. The rule usually adopted for cylindrical work is that a shell may be drawn to a depth equal to its diameter. Very often this depth may be exceeded somewhat but the strength of the bottom of the shell will be reduced for succeeding draws. Other causes of fracture at the bottom of the shell are too small a drawing radius, insufficient clearance between the punch and die, excessive blank-holder pressure, excessive friction between the blank-holder and die, caused by grinding marks on either die or blank-holder, and inferior quality of drawing metal.

Strippers for Drawing Dies.—The success of a drawing die or push-through die often depends upon the efficiency of the stripper employed to strip the stock from the punch on the upward stroke of the press ram. Even with a properly designed stripper there is likely to be some spoilage, particularly when drawing light gage metal. This spoilage is increased, of course, when the stripper is not the correct type for the work.

Stripper for Small Work.—The die shown in Fig. 12 is equipped with a type of stripper which has proved satisfactory for small work. This stripper, however, will seldom be found suitable for shells over 1 inch in diameter. A shell of 22-gage brass stock, ½ inch in diameter and 2 inches long is representative of the class of work for which this type should be used. The stripper consists of a split ring of tool steel composed of four parts or segments. As shown in the illustration, the segments are grooved to receive a circular wire spring *A* which holds them in place. As the shell is pushed through the die and enters the stripper, the segments are forced back allowing the shell to pass through. On the return stroke of the punch the segments grip the punch above the shell and thus serve to strip the shell from the punch. This stripper is not as positive as those shown in Figs. 13 and 14, and its success depends upon using it with shells of small diameter having thin walls. The stripper is held flat and in place by the tool steel forming plate *B*. This plate, in turn, is kept in position by the three clamps fastened to the top of the die, one of which is shown at *C*. By merely removing the clamps, the

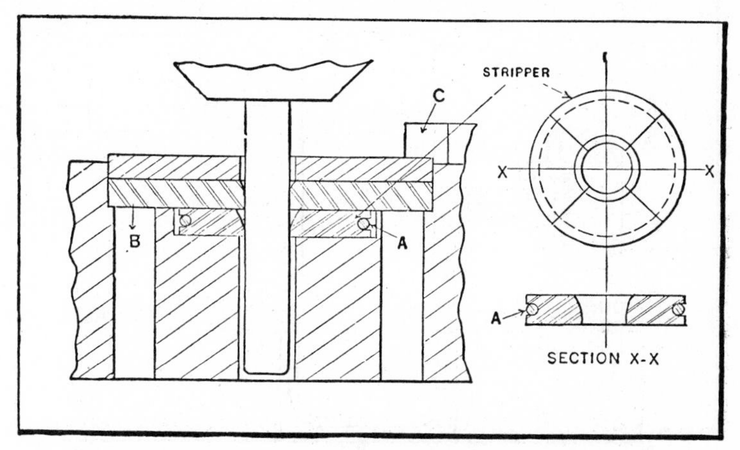

Fig. 12. Drawing Die Equipped with Stripper of Segment Type

forming plate and the stripper are left free so that they can be lifted from the die.

Stripper for Thick-walled Shells.—The die shown in Fig. 13 is equipped with spring-actuated strippers, and has been found to be best suited for use in dies employed for drawing thick-walled shells varying from 1½ to 5 inches in diameter that are less than 6 inches in length. This die is mounted on a machine steel base while the hardened and ground forming parts are of tool steel. The strippers *A* are also of tool steel, hardened and ground, and are kept in constant contact with the shell by the compression springs *B* which force them outward into the die opening. These strippers are provided with a shoulder so that they can extend into the die opening only a certain distance, and they are made a good sliding fit in the slots in ring *C*.

As these strippers have only a small bearing surface on the shell, it is necessary to make them rather sharp on the edges which come in contact with the work. As will be noted by referring to the view in the upper right-hand corner, the end of the stripper which bears on the work is not only rounded, but also beveled at an angle of 2 degrees. For this reason the stripping action is severe, and shells having thin

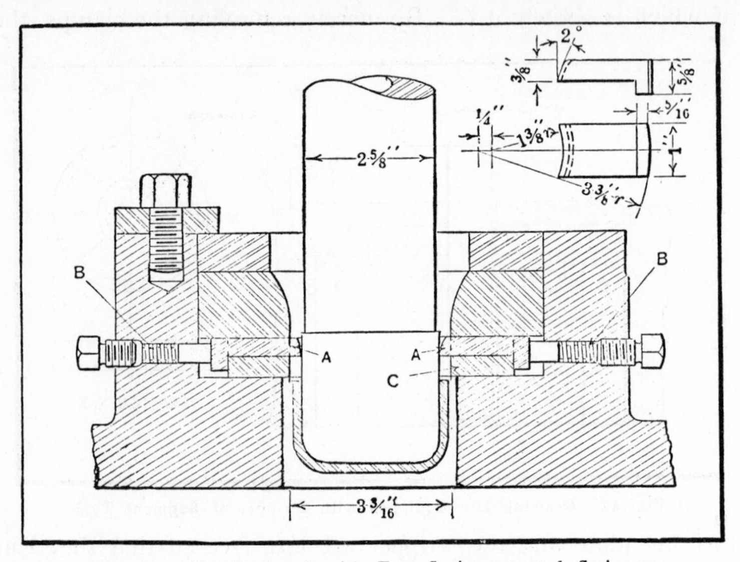

Fig. 13. Die Equipped with Two Spring-actuated Strippers

walls are found to tear and wrinkle badly when this type of stripper is used. This type, however, is positive and it has proved most successful when used on shells having a wall thickness of not less than 20 gage. A shallow 8-gage steel shell, for instance, is well handled by this stripper, whereas a stripper of the type shown in Fig. 12 would be entirely unsuitable.

Stripper for Large-diameter Thin-walled Shells.—The die shown in Fig. 14 is equipped with a stripper constructed on an entirely different principle from that of the strippers previously described. In the types described, spring pressure is applied at right angles to the part of the shell being pushed through the die. In the type shown in Fig. 14, however, spring *A* applies pressure in a direction parallel to the path of the shell, and the gripping action of the jaws *B* is similar to that of a collet. This die is held in a cast-iron base, the forming ring being tool steel, hardened and ground, as are also the gripping jaws. The plate *C* held to the bottom of the die by four ½-inch screws (not shown) is machine steel and holds the six action-pin springs in place.

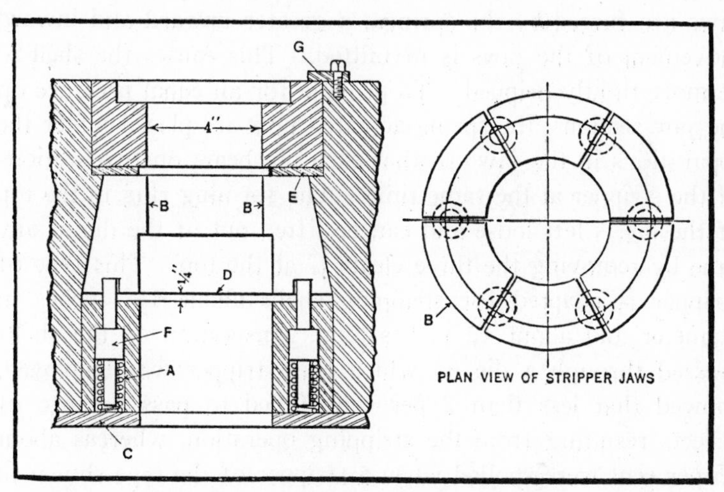

Fig. 14. Push-through Die Fitted with Stripper Adapted for Large Shells made of Comparatively Thin Stock

As the shell passes through the forming ring, it strikes the jaws of the collet and forces them down and outward. The ¼-inch clearance at *D* between the bottom of the jaws and the top of the machine-steel ring below them permits this downward movement. At the end of the downward stroke the top of the shell is still in contact with the base of the jaws, which, actuated by the constant spring pressure forcing them upward, grip the shell and hold it fast while the punch continues upward and thus strips the shell off so that it drops through the die at the next stroke.

The action-pins *F* are made from 1-inch cold-rolled stock

machined to ½ inch at both ends. A clearance of ⅛ inch is provided in the holes in which the pins enter the jaws. Without this clearance the jaws would not be able to expand or contract. The pins extending into the base of the jaws for about ½ inch serve to keep the jaws from moving in a circular direction. The compression springs used on the pins have an inside diameter of ⅝ inch and a length of about 2½ inches. The gripping power of the stripper is adjusted by the machine-steel ring *E* which lies on the top of the jaws. By grinding off the under side of this ring against which the jaws are forced by the springs, a greater upward and inward movement of the jaws is permitted. This causes the shell to be more tightly gripped. To provide for an equal pressure on the jaw sections, the spring-actuated pins are placed under the separations in the jaws so that each pin bears on two sections of the stripper at the same time. The forming ring in the top of the die is left loose and can be lifted out of the die at any time by removing the three cleats *G* at the top. This type of stripper is adapted for stripping shells about 4½ inches in diameter and about 12 inches long. Inspection of the shells pressed through a die on which this stripper was employed, showed that less than 2 per cent failed to pass because of defects resulting from the stripping operation, whereas about 15 per cent were spoiled when a stripper of the type shown in Fig. 13 was employed. The stripper shown in Fig. 14 is best suited for stripping shells of rather large diameter having comparatively thin walls. The reason that it is useful on such work is that it has a large bearing surface which comes in contact with the work during the stripping operation.

Pressure Attachments for Drawing Dies.—One of the important factors to be considered in the process of drawing various shaped parts from sheet metal is the pressure that must be applied on the outer surface or "flange" of the flat blank as the latter is drawn into the desired shape. This pressure should be just enough to keep the metal of the drawn shell smooth at all stages of the operation. If the pressure is too light wrinkles are liable to form. On the contrary, if the metal is unduly strained at any time, its toughness is lessened, which often results in the breakage of the shell during either the first or succeeding drawing operations. An excessive pressure is a waste of power, produces an avoidable strain on the machine, and causes a great amount of wear on the die parts, especially on the drawing ring and the blank-holder. Wrinkles which may be formed on the shell in any of the drawing operations are, of course, a disadvantage, but they are often tolerated when it is not absolutely essential that the finished article be entirely smooth, with the result that die parts also become excessively worn on this account. Thus it is important that some means be employed to regulate the pressure while drawing.

Many of the rubber or spring pressure-pads in use cause trouble when used for the deeper drawing operations because the pressure between the drawing die and the pressure-pad or blank-holder gradually increases as the part is drawn, owing to the increased compression of the drawing rubber or spring pressure attachment. The result is that the stress upon the metal being drawn increases rapidly as the drawing die descends, because the stress due to the drawing operation is unduly increased by the excessive pressure on the outer part of the blank. In other words, if the pressure upon the blank is sufficient at the beginning of the drawing operation, it rapidly rises as the pressure-pad or "drawing rubber" is compressed. On the other hand, when the pressure on the blank is regulated, a greater depth may be obtained in one draw, assuming that the same material is used in each case and that other conditions are equal.

In order to prevent an increase in pressure between the die and the blank-holder, some combination dies are equipped with a pressure attachment designed to give a uniform pressure; and one type to be described produces a decreasing pressure on the flange during the drawing operation. Some of these attachments are equipped with combinations of springs and links for varying the pressure, and others have pneumatic cushions.

Pressure-pad Supported Upon Receding Cross-bar to Prevent Excessive Pressure.—In order to prevent an increase in pressure between the die and blank-holder, some combination dies are equipped with a compensating attachment which has a cross-bar under the table. This cross-bar carries the rubber or spring pressure-pad and extends outward at each side. Vertical pins are attached to the ends and pass up through the press table. When the ram of the press descends, it begins to force these compensating pins downward as soon as the required blank-holder pressure is obtained. As the pins move downward, they also lower the cross-bar and rubber pressure-pad and, therefore, the blank-holder pressure remains more nearly constant. In other words, when there is sufficient pressure on the blank, the compensating pins are engaged by the slide and as the drawing operation continues, the blank-holder pressure does not increase excessively, because the rubber is carried down at the same rate as the press slide. The screws on the slide which engage the compensating pins are adjustable so that the rubber pressure-pad can be compressed the required amount before the compensating attachment comes into action. While this attachment has been used in many cases where it was desired to obtain an exceptionally deep draw in a combination die, the results obtained have not been altogether satisfactory, because it has been found difficult to obtain a uniform pressure on the blank; moreover, the compensating attachment is rather cumbersome and complicates the construction and it is preferable to use a well-designed commercial pressure-compensating attachment. By utilizing a properly designed pressure attachment it is possible not only to improve the drawing operation itself and reduce the number of operations in many cases, but also to employ a single-action press for a larger range of work. The initial cost of a single-action press is much less than that of a double-action press and the equipment is also less cumbersome and can be operated at higher speed. Proper regulation of the pressure also eliminates unnecessary strain on the press.

Toggle Type of Spring-pressure Attachment.—The toggle spring-pressure attachment shown in Fig. 15, has been developed for use with combination dies, particularly when lithographed metal is being handled. This attachment is designed to provide a uniform drawing pressure on the blank, and so increases the efficiency of the dies by minimizing the strain on the metal and reducing wrinkles and the breakage and wear of dies. The application of the toggle mechanism reduces the total rubber or spring compression. The reduced compression enables the economical manufacture of deep shells and a reduction in the number of operations required in cases where reducing operations follow the first blanking and drawing operation.

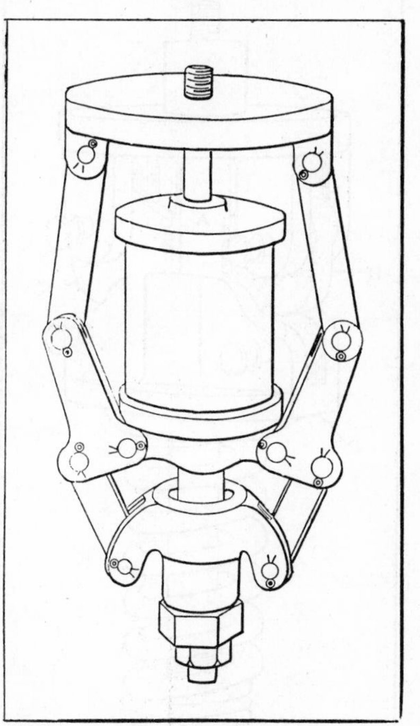

Fig. 15. Spring-pressure Attachment having Toggle Mechanism to Reduce Total Compression

Pressure Regulation by Rack and Segment-cam Mechanism.—The spring cushion or attachment shown in Fig. 16 is another design intended to maintain an even pressure throughout the drawing operation. This attachment is held in place by screwing the upper threaded end of the suspension bolt into a tapped hole in the bottom of the die or bolster plate. This suspension bolt extends through a sleeve *A* having teeth cut on its outer surface near the upper end which are engaged on opposite sides by the teeth of two compensating cams *B* and *C*. These cams swivel about their bearings when the draw-pins of the die are forced downward, the draw-pins resting on a plate and spacer block placed on top of the cam housing. Another housing *D* directly below the cam housing has two rollers that contact with the cams. The swiveling of the cams on their bearings causes a vertical movement of the rollers and so controls the compression of the spring *E*, this compression being less than if the spring was not provided with compensating members. When pressure is released from the draw-ring, the friction between the rollers and cams caused by the spring forces the cams to return to their original positions. The initial pressure on the spring may be regulated by means of an adjustable nut *F* placed on the lower end of the bolt.

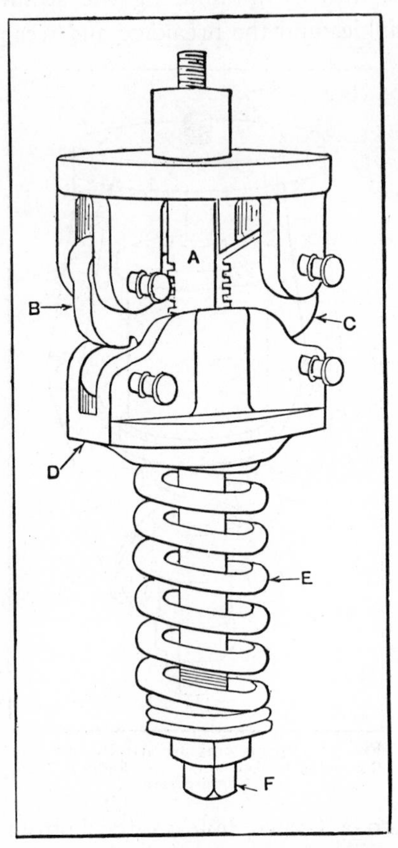

Fig. 16. Rack and Segment-cam Mechanism for Regulating Spring Pressure

Multiple-spring and Toggle-lever Device.—The attachment shown in Fig. 17 is known as a "pressure toggle" and is a development of R. D. King, Chicago, Ill. A multiple system of springs is employed in connection with a toggle lever mechanism which can be adjusted to maintain a pressure that is practically constant during the stroke of the drawing die, or it may be adjusted to gradually diminish the pressure as the drawing operation proceeds. The latter practice is recommended by the manufacturer in view of the fact that wrinkles form during the early stages of a drawing operation, whereas breakage usualy occurs near the completion of the stroke owing to excessive pressure. The percentage of pressure reduction which occurs as the flange decreases, as well as the intensity of pressure, may be regulated to secure the best results under different conditions. According to the manufacturer, the desirable percentage of decrease in flange pressure is not directly proportional to the decrease in the area of the flange owing to various conditions, such as hardening of the metal during the operation, change in shape of work, and the design of the die itself.

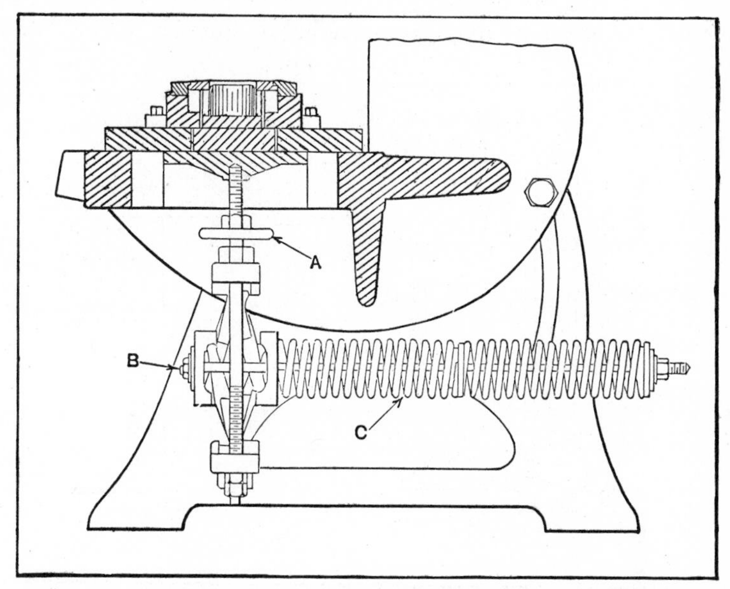

Fig. 17. Multiple-spring and Toggle-lever Mechanism for Pressure Regulation

These pressure toggles are made in various sizes. The maximum decrease in pressure during the entire stroke is 40 per cent for all sizes. In attaching the pressure toggle to the press the upper ends of two rods are screwed into the bolster or bed of the press. The downward movement of the draw ring is transmitted through suitable pins and plates to a central rod, which is threaded along the upper portion and carries the hand wheel *A* which is used to raise or lower the draw-ring and relieve the pressure when setting dies. Adjustment of the percentage of decrease of pressure is made by turning the rods *B* which compress the springs *C*, arranged in four parallel rows. When the springs are compressed one-tenth of their length at the beginning of the stroke, the pressure will be practically constant during the stroke. If they are compressed more than one-tenth of their length at the beginning of the stroke the pressure will decrease during the stroke. The more the springs are compressed at the beginning of the stroke the greater will be the percentage of decrease. By using one or more of the springs the desirable intensity of pressure may be controlled to suit the work.

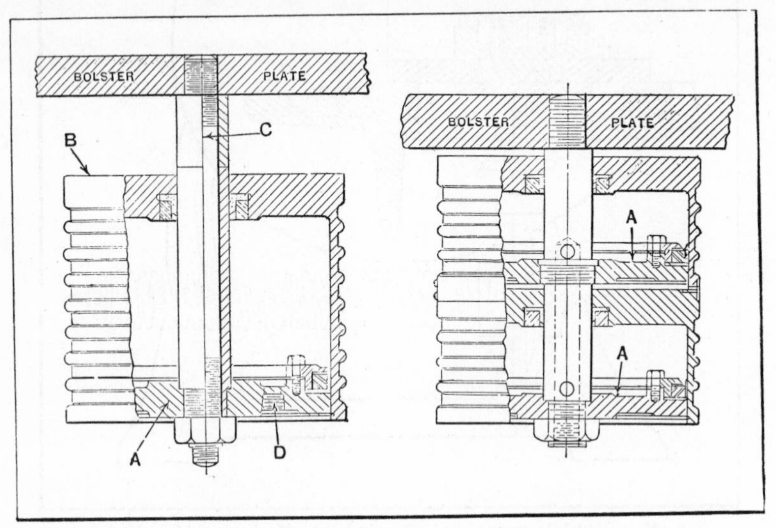

Fig. 18. Pneumatic Die Cushions for Small Work on Inclinable Presses

Pneumatic "Die Cushions" for Maintaining Uniform Pressure.—Pneumatic "die cushions" are widely used for maintaining uniform pressures for metal drawing on single-acting presses, and they have proved very satisfactory. Various types of these die cushions have been developed by the Marquette Tool & Mfg. Co., Chicago, Ill. One type is shown at the left in Fig. 18. This design is adapted for use on inclinable presses and is intended especially for small work. With this design the piston *A* is stationary and the cylinder *B* moves. The piston is supported by suspension rod *C*, which screws into the bolster plate. The lower ends of the draw-ring pins are supported either upon the upper surface of cylinder *B* or by an intervening plate, and air at the required pressure is admitted through piping connecting with the inlet *D*. Between this inlet and the main air line there is a tank and regulator valve so that the required pressure for each operation may be obtained. At the right in Fig. 18 is shown a modification of this design, there being in this case two pistons *A* for exerting twice the amount of pressure as required on inclinable presses of heavier construction. These pistons are also stationary and the cylinder moves.

The larger dies used on double-crank presses may require a battery of pneumatic die cushions, in which case a different type is used. The cylinder is stationary and a pressure-pad large enough to support all of the draw-ring pins is supported upon the piston shafts of the various pistons. The number of cushions used in any case depends, of course, upon the size of pressure-pad required. The pressure pad fits into the bed opening of the press. These die cushions are also made in the double piston design (see left-hand view, Fig. 19) for use in batteries on double-crank presses of medium weight. The presses may either be single- or double-acting. A three-piston design is made for heavy double-crank presses which may either be single- or double-acting. This three-piston design is of the same general construction as the type shown. If the shape of the product requires an uneven spacing of the draw-ring pins sufficient to cause uneven pressure and, consequently, tilting of the pressure pad, two cushions of the type shown at the left in Fig. 19, equivalent in capacity to a battery of possibly six or eight, may be used in conjunction with a pressure pad having special guide rods.

In order to permit blanking and drawing a cup or shell and at the same time pierce a central hole, a die cushion is made with a hollow shaft to allow the slug punched from the hole to drop through it. This design (see right-hand view, Fig. 19) has a stationary piston and a movable cylinder. The hollow shaft is shown at *A* and the cylinder is shown in the downward position, the shell having been drawn and the central hole pierced by the punch *B*. This sectional view also shows one of the draw-ring pins *E* which extends from the bottom of the draw ring *D* to the upper surface of the air cylinder. This hollow piston design is also made with two pistons to increase the pressure for heavier work.

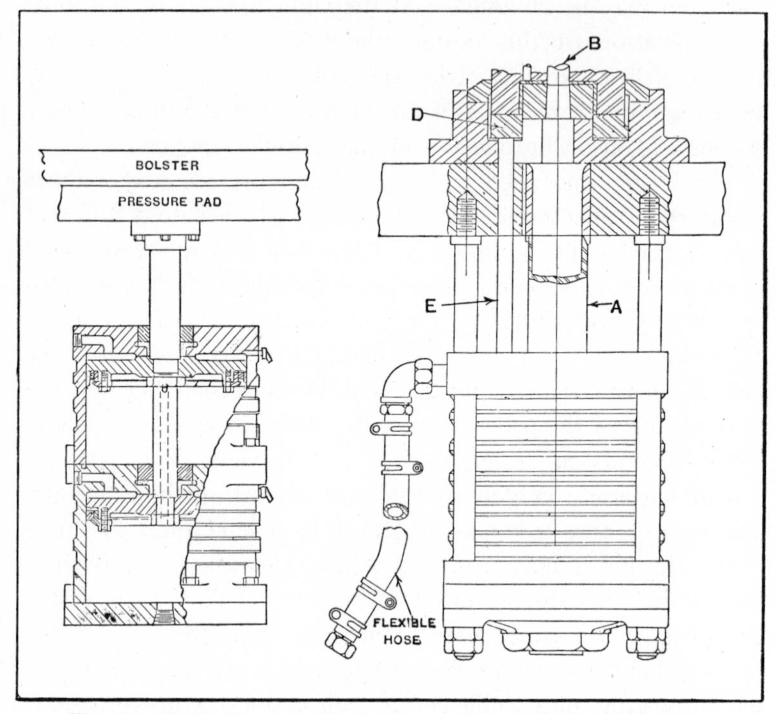

Fig. 19. (Left) Type of Die Cushion used in Batteries on Double-crank Presses; (Right) Hollow Piston Type for Drawing Shell and Piercing Central Hole Simultaneously

Another type of die cushion is equipped with a three-way valve to eliminate the pressure at any desired point during the stroke of the press. This equipment generally is supplied for double-acting toggle presses of light construction. All of these standard pneumatic die cushions are designed to work in connection with ordinary commercial air-compressing apparatus. In some cases it is necessary to provide blank-holding pressure ranges which are greater than can be obtained with air cushions, and the hydro-pneumatic type of cushion is designed to supply these higher pressures. This type, instead of using compressed air, operates with liquid which is stored in a tank and is admitted into the cushion through an operating valve which is timed from the crankshaft. When the ram descends, it moves the pressure pad against the liquid, which is forced through an air-controlled relief valve back again to the tank. This relief valve controls the resistance to the passage of the liquid and it is air controlled to secure accuracy and to make possible the recording of pressures used on various jobs.

These cushions have been applied to a large variety of metal-drawing operations with various modifications both of the pneumatic and of the hydro-pneumatic type.

Lubricants and Compounds for Drawing and Forming Operations.—Various classes of lubricants and compounds are used in producing pressed-metal parts. In connection with work of this kind, correct tool design is, of course, essential but the use of an effective lubricant is also very important. Commercial compounds are available which are adapted to all classes of press work, and, in lieu of the necessary experience, it is advisable to consult the manufacturers of such compounds in making a selection for a given drawing, forming, or other operation. This is especially important when a drawing or forming process is severe and the quality of the work and durability of the tools may depend to a considerable degree upon efficient lubrication.

In selecting a lubricating compound, the important general properties and requirements include (1) film strength that is high enough to withstand the maximum pressure and temperature resulting from a given operation; (2) oiliness or lubricity; (3) low surface tension and wetting ability so that the compound spreads readily over the surfaces of the material to form a protective coating; (4) non-corrosiveness as related both to material and dies; (5) stability and uniformity; (6) non-toxic property for the protection of workmen; (7) ease of application and cleaning; (8) economical not merely in first cost but when all factors have been taken into account.

Film Strength in Drawing Compounds.—The severity of the process determines the minimum requirements in the matter of film strength, one of the most important properties of the compound. The greater the deformation of the part being drawn, the higher must be the film strength of the compound, regardless of the metal used. Stainless steels usually require compounds of higher film strengths than carbon steels, brass, aluminum, and other non-ferrous metals, unless the milder alloys have been brought to a degree of greater hardness through heat-treatment or work-hardening.

The film strength is determined by the choice of basic ingredients and the alkaline saponification of the fatty materials used. It must be able to withstand the heat of the friction generated by the deformation of the metal. Pigments or fillers sometimes added to the various basic fatty ingredients increase the film strength and at times act as solid lubricants. As such, they prevent metal-to-metal contact, even in cases where the fatty lubricating film is ruptured.

Various mineral, animal, fish, and vegetable oils often are sulphurized or chlorinated to obtain greater strength of film. They may be used in such a "fortified" state or combined, in the form of soap, with minerals. While the latter practice is frowned upon for general machinery lubrication, because of the speed of the moving parts, it is satisfactory for drawing operations, because the relative speed of the rubbing surfaces in drawing is much lower. Since the coefficient of friction is not held to a minimum, the presence of pigments is not objectionable, but, on the contrary, in many cases is most desirable. The filler must be carefully selected to avoid the use of one that may be chemically active, highly abrasive, dangerous to the operators, or conducive to fermentation.

Oiliness of Compound and Friction between Die and Work.—Another of the key essentials of a drawing compound is its oiliness or lubricity. Friction between the die and work must be kept low, but zero friction is not to be considered a goal. A lubricant such as a straight oil or grease is not, in itself, a drawing compound. First, its lubricating properties may reduce friction to a point where it becomes too close to zero, at which point there is no control over the flow of metal as it is drawn. Such a condition results in excessive wrinkles and breakage, along with scored and broken dies. A certain amount of drag, to retard and restrict the flow of metal, is essential on difficult drawing jobs. Such control is not possible with an untreated lubricant.

What has been said is not intended to minimize the importance of the lubricity factor of the compound, but rather to emphasize the need for lubricity that is controllable with the aid of additives. The minerals and pigments would likewise be inadequate for the job if they were used without a lubricant. The fatty ingredients thus serve a dual purpose—acting first as a lubricant, and second as a medium to carry the necessary additives.

The lubricating properties and film strength are enhanced by inherent wetting-out properties in the compound, enabling it to adhere well to the work surface and increasing its ability to spread, under pressure, ahead of the working portion of the die to form a protective coating or film. The surface tension on which the wetting-out ability depends is controlled by the correct proportioning of saponified and unsaponified oil bodies.

Surface Tension and Wetting Property.—Surface tension is controlled by correct proportioning of the saponified and unsaponified oily bodies. The surface tension of good drawing lubricants should be low, owing to the fact that lubricants generally used for metal cutting and drawing purposes are efficient or inefficient in direct proportion to their wetting properties. The wetting property of any given lubricant is of extreme importance, and this factor is reflected in surface tension.

While the main requirement of a good cold-drawing lubricant is high film strength, it does not follow that any lubricant having this characteristic is efficient. A satisfactory lubricant must also have the right coefficient of friction, and surface tension which is as low as possible.

Stability and Uniformity of Compound.—For satisfactory results, a compound must be stable and uniform. Decomposition in storage is one indication of instability, a bad feature often disclosed by rancid odors. Each lot and drum must be free from separation characteristics, not only in storage, but in the working process itself, where the high heat and pressures involved tend to cause a breakdown of the compound. Some compounds may be unable even to withstand temperature changes in storage without showing a marked difference in effectiveness.

The uniformity of the product as it is shipped from the manufacturer is also of the utmost importance. A product manufactured under close laboratory control has a much greater chance of producing uniform results than one made on a less closely supervised basis.

Water-soluble Emulsions.—Lubricants prepared in the form of water-soluble emulsions are used extensively for cold drawing. There are several reasons for this; the principal one is the dependence placed upon the soap base of the lubricant. It is only by means of emulsification that the soapy materials can be uniformly dispersed throughout the unsaponified oily portion and maintained in that condition. Another reason for the use of water-soluble emulsions is that the suspension of the solid material is more readily accomplished and the compound is readily suited to various operations by water-dilution on the part of the user. Solubility in alkaline solutions is desirable in the interests of subsequent cleaning operations. Stability against separation is a necessary requirement.

Lubricants for Drawing Brass.—In order to determine what lubricant is generally recommended for use in connection with drawing operations on brass and copper parts,. this question was submitted to several manufacturers of sheet-metal products, and summaries of their replies follow, each paragraph containing the information secured from a different company:

1. For drawing operations on brass, copper, etc., we have used soap for many years. Ivory soap chips mixed with water and kept warm have proved very successful. The quantity of

soap used depends largely upon the thickness of the metal and the severity of the operation.

2. The lubricant used for drawing brass shells, such as cartridge shells, consists of a solution of soap dissolved in water, the consistency being changed to suit requirements. For heavy shells the solution should be thick—almost like gelatine —and for smaller shells, very thin, so that it will run through the feed-pipes without clogging. In the first cupping operation, oil, known under the trade name of "cupping oil" is preferred, as it has more body than the soap solution, and therefore has a better lubricating effect during the cupping operation, which is a heavy one, displacing considerable metal.

3. From experience we find the best lubricant for brass and copper consists of hard soap dissolved in equal parts of warm water and pure lard oil.

4. For working brass or copper, a solution composed of 15 pounds of Fuller's soap to a barrel of hot water (used hot), or any soap strong in rosin or potash, is cheaper and cleaner than oil. The stock should pass through a tank filled with this solution before entering the dies.

5. For heavy drawing work there are a number of lubricants on the market, all of more or less value on certain classes of work. One of the cheapest as well as most effective drawing solutions is a soap, oil and water emulsion. This is composed of equal parts of hard soap, lard oil and warm water, the hard soap being dissolved in the warm water first and the lard oil stirred in after. This is one of the best drawing solutions available for light brass and copper shell work, its only disadvantage being on work that has to stand any length of time between operations, the alkali in the soap having a tendency to corrode the brass; but on work where each operation is carried along to completion, this mixture will be found very satisfactory.

Lubricants for Drawing Steel.—For drawing steel, the following mixture is recommended as a lubricant: 25 per cent flaked graphite; 25 per cent beef tallow; and 50 per cent lard oil. This mixture should be heated and the work dipped into it.

Certain mixtures or compounds containing white lead have proved effective in drawing steel but the use of white lead has been discontinued in many plants because of possible lead poisoning. One white lead compound for drawing sheet steel of mild grade is made as follows: Mix one pound of white lead, one quart of fish oil, three ounces of black lead, and one pint of water. These ingredients should be boiled until thoroughly mixed. A mixture of white lead and kerosene is also used for steel, especially for heavy drawing operations. For heavy steel shell work a mixture of dry white lead and lard oil of about the thickness of heavy paint has proved satisfactory.

A drawing solution for heavy and light steel shell work alike consists of a mixture of lard oil and precipitated chalk. After a thorough mixing, this should stand over night to allow it to "jelly" or apparently grow softer; in fact, the longer it stands the better it gets, and it can be mixed to the right thickness to secure the desired results. The principle involved in shell drawing is to furnish a lubricant heavy enough and of the right nature to produce a film that will enter between the sides of the shell and the dies, thus lessening wear on the die and flaking of the metal resulting in scratches on the sides of the shell. These scratches are a grave defect on shells that are redrawn two or more times, as they cause the shell to split or crack open on the redraw.

When shells are annealed between operations, and the best results are desired, an acid pickle should be prepared to remove the scale. This is generally of the same composition as the "bright dip" or the "firing off" that is used in the plating room. The lubricant that is used should be kept clean and free from dirt, scale and sediment, even if straining is resorted to, as drawing solutions must be clean to do the best work. In very heavy boiler-plate punching, blanking and cutting, cylinder oil has proved successful. This is a heavy oil—almost a grease—and gives very good results.

Lubricants for Drawing Aluminum.—According to the Aluminum Company of America, mineral oils or compounded mineral oils are extensively used for drawing aluminum alloys.

A selection of a lubricant depends not only upon the extent or severity of the drawing operation but the thickness of the sheet, the finish, and even the die material are factors which should be considered. Among lubricants that have proved satisfactory the following are recommended:

For light drawing operations, light lubricating oil.

For medium drawing operations, medium lubricating oil.

For severe drawing operations, either heavy lubricating oil or 50 per cent mutton tallow and 50 per cent paraffin mixtures.

For very severe drawing operations, 30 per cent mutton tallow and 70 per cent paraffin mixtures.

Press tools made of cast iron and low-carbon steels require a heavier lubricant than hardened tool steels if scratching or scoring is to be prevented. The reduction per draw is another factor. The greater the reduction and the smaller the radius of the die, the heavier must be the lubricant; moreover, a comparatively thick sheet requires a heavier lubricant than a thin one. In drawing thick sheets, it is general practice to use a mutton tallow and paraffin mixture.

Petroleum jelly of a cheap grade is sometimes used when drawing aluminum. Lard oil is also applied to aluminum when drawing deep shells. Kerosene is used for drawing aluminum and is said to prevent the dies from becoming "loaded" as the result of the abrasive action of the metal. For comparatively deep drawing, a lubricant having more "body" should be used. A medium grade of cylinder oil is sometimes used. Incidentally, kerosene is also used when cutting aluminum in blanking dies. Aluminum should never be worked without a lubricant.

Other Methods of Reducing Resistance in Drawing Aluminum.—Pure aluminum and the less complex alloys are more plastic than steel or brass in the sense that they will accept a greater deformation without fracturing, and hence can be given a greater number of successive draws without requiring intermediate annealing.

The workability of any metal is, of course, limited by its mechanical properties, and different tempers of the same alloy will have different degrees of ductility. However, there is one property of aluminum and its alloys which introduces certain limitations and requirements. When planning the cold forming of aluminum, in comparison to the conditions selected for other metals, the most important characteristic to bear in mind is the coefficient of friction. Aluminum has a higher coefficient of friction than brass or steel, and in drawing it precautions must be taken to reduce resistance to the minimum. With this object in mind, the contact surfaces of the die and blank-holder must be put in a very smooth condition. In fact, for best results these surfaces should be polished. This reduction of frictional resistance is still further assisted by amply lubricating the surface of the sheet.

The pressure of the blank-holder could be so great as to prevent all lateral movement of the sheet, in which case the forming would proceed only up to the ability of the metal to actually stretch in its unconfined area. The pressure of the blank-holder, therefore, should be reduced to the minimum sufficient to keep the sheet flat. It will be clear from the foregoing that as the ultimate tensile strength of the metal increases, it can successfully overcome greater resistance against movement between the die and blank-holder. As the thickness of the sheet increases, the blank-holder pressure necessary becomes less because the metal in itself, being thicker, will tend to resist buckling.

In planning the drawing of aluminum shells, it is generally considered impractical to have the diameter of the shell in the first draw less than 0.6 of the diameter of the blank. If it is necessary to draw a smaller shell, recourse must be had to doing so in two or more operations.

The high plasticity of aluminum results in a greater thickening of the metal as it converges toward the die than occurs with steel and brass and this demands a slightly greater clearance between the punch and the die than is common for other metals. In other respects, the forming of aluminum and its alloys employs the same general principles used for other metals, with the exception, especially with the pure grade, that intermediate annealing between draws is usually not required.

The sharpness of the radius over which the metal can be drawn and the amount of work that can be done will depend on the mechanical properties of the metal. Information regarding tensile strength, yield point and elongation offers a fair criterion of the workability of the metal. A material possessing a high elongation will stretch more than one with a low elongation, and a material wherein the ratio of yield point to tensile strength is low can be worked far more severely than one in which this ratio is high. The same fundamental principles apply whether the work consists of drawing a shell or forming a right angle on a cornice-brake. In brake-forming operations, one must appreciate that as the ductility decreases the radius to which the metal can be successfully formed must be increased.

Lubricants for Zinc.—In drawing zinc, a solution of warm soapsuds has proved effective. The temperature of the metal is raised slightly by the warm solution which increases its ductility. Zinc may also be lubricated with kerosene, and, in this case, it is sometimes warmed as well as lubricated, to facilitate drawing. For many classes of die work, no lubricant is required, especially when the metal is of a "greasy" nature, like tin plate, for instance.

Lubricants for Drawing Magnesium Alloys.—Magnesium alloys should be well lubricated for drawing operations to prevent galling, scoring, and any adherence of metal to the die surfaces. For drawing or forming, the lubricant used should function properly when subjected to temperatures up to 600-700 degrees F. because such operations are performed at elevated temperatures. A lubricant should be applied not only to the material but to the die surfaces as well. A lubricant for the material that has been used extensively consists of about 2 per cent colloidal graphite suspended in a volatile carrier such as naphtha or alcohol. This mixture may be applied by spraying the stock with a standard spray gun such as is used for paint. The volatile carrier evaporates quickly and leaves a lubricating film of colloidal graphite for the drawing operation.

According to recommended practice of The Dow Chemical Co., the following cleaning solution should be used when stock has been lubricated with colloidal graphite:

Chromic acid, CrO_3 .... 1.5 lbs.
Calcium nitrate, $Ca(NO_3)_2\ 4H_2O$ ...... 4 oz.
or
Magnesium nitrate, $Mg(NO_3)_2\ 6H_2O$ ... 4 oz.
Water ....to make 1.0 gal.

Technical grades of the chemicals in the above formula are satisfactory.

The solution is maintained at room temperature and parts are immersed for 2 to 5 minutes. After cleaning, parts are washed in cold running water, followed by a dip in hot water to facilitate drying. This solution may also be used when oil type lubricants have been employed during the drawing or forming operation.

Both cleaning solutions must be kept in pure aluminum tanks. The usual precautions for the safe handling of the material used as the carrier for graphite, as well as chromic and nitric acids, should be followed.

When colloidal graphite is to be used, the sheet stock should be ordered in the oiled rather than the chrome-pickled condition because in the latter case removal of the graphite is difficult. If chrome-pickled stock must be used with colloidal graphite lubrication, remove the pickled surface before drawing or forming by immersing the material from one to fifteen minutes in a solution consisting of 1½ pounds of chromic acid (CrO_3) in one gallon of water. This treatment is followed by washing and drying.

For the drawing die a lubricating mixture of 20 per cent graphite suspended in tallow is recommended. This mixture is also applicable to magnesium sheets but the colloidal graphite and volatile carrier mixture previously mentioned is preferable. Another die lubricant for easing the flow of metal between the die surfaces consists of colloidal graphite in mineral spirits.

Cost Factors in Selecting Drawing Compounds.—In order to determine the true cost of one compound as compared with another, it may be necessary to take into account, in addition to the first cost, certain items or indirect costs which may be directly traceable to the use of a compound that is not adapted to a given class of work. The final or true costs are based upon the number of acceptable parts manufactured and upon such related items as the percentage of rejected pieces, the die life, the machine time lost due to die changes, the obnoxious or even harmful effects of certain compounds with the resulting reduction in quality and quantity of work, the possible corrosion or staining of work, and other factors. A drawing compound which keeps these factors at a low rate is, in all probability, far more economical than one less efficient in this respect, even if the latter has a lower initial cost.

A proper drawing compound has a marked effect in the prolongation of die life by smoothing the metal flow so that there is less wear on the die. Further, the plastic flow of the metal is so smoothed that a finer finish is obtained.

The use of any drawing compound that has a tendency to corrode or stain the work is not economical. Chemical reaction of sulphur on brass and of alkalies on zinc are examples; but cases such as these can be avoided through proper compound selection. The merits of any compound as regards rust inhibition should be evaluated with a view to ultimate economy in cost of production. Some compounds in the higher price brackets, because of their rust-preventive qualities, may be the most economical.

It is also false economy to buy compounds that require much labor and equipment for mixing or removal. The cost of many hours of labor to dilute a drawing concentrate or to clean it from the work may considerably increase the actual cost of the compound. Likewise, costly equipment and materials may be required, thus increasing both installation and operating costs. Those compounds that may be left on the work without pitting, rusting, or staining or those that can be easily cleaned from the work should be selected whenever possible.

Lubricants for Non-metallic Materials.—Non-metallic materials require a varied assortment of lubricants to gain the maximum efficiency. In blanking and piercing mica parts, gasoline or kerosene is used, preferably gasoline. The mica dust collects and clogs the stripper parts and piercing punches, and gasoline used freely washes away this dust and adds to the life and effectiveness of the tools. In the blanking of celluloid and other camphor gum compositions of a like nature, clean water may be used. Some of these compositions do not stick to the tools at all, while others are very troublesome. If the water is not effective, a very little lard oil on the punch once in a while will be of value. Leather, cloth and felt may be blanked dry. On rawhide and horn-fiber parts, wood alcohol has been used successfully. Wood alcohol also softens the rawhide for forming and cupping, dries very quickly, and does the material no harm whatever. Fibers, as a general rule, can be cut dry, but in some cases lubrication, or rather washing out of the dies with gasoline, is required occasionally. Gasoline is very effective in this instance and does the fiber no harm. Glass blanks can be pierced successfully by laying them in turpentine and then piercing on a quick-action press. A press having a speed of 1000 revolutions per minute or more is required.

Wood of certain kinds can be successfully pierced and embossed by first steaming or boiling, the work being done on a slow-action press with a long dwell, such as is used for cardboard forming. Foils, light tin, paper and cardboard, tapes and cambrics may be cut and blanked dry.

Annealing Shells which Require Redrawing.—When drawing steel, iron, brass, or copper, annealing is necessary after two or three draws have been made, as the metal is hardened by the drawing process. For steel and brass, anneal between every other reduction, at least. Tin plate or stock that cannot be annealed without spoiling the finish must ordinarily be drawn to size in one or two operations. Aluminum can be drawn deeper and with less annealing than the other commercial metals, provided the proper grade is used. In case it is necessary to anneal aluminum, this can be done by heating it in a muffle furnace, care being taken to see that the temperature does not exceed 700 degrees F.

Cold-working carried on to any considerable degree hardens steel, and it becomes necessary to soften it by raising its temperature to a point at which the hardness is removed before further operations can be performed satisfactorily. Where low-carbon steel is concerned, however, these apparently simple processes are sometimes exceedingly complex. In the first place, the annealing must be carried on with an exact temperature control and with uniformity. In the second place, careful attention to these factors will not necessarily insure uniform results, as low-carbon steel, under certain conditions, may undergo a peculiar change in its structure for which cold-working and annealing, as ordinarily applied, may be responsible.

Grain Growth and its Cause.—When low-carbon steel (that is, steel with a carbon content below approximately 0.20 per cent) is cold-worked within a certain "stress" range and is then annealed within a definite temperature range, a peculiar phenomenon occurs which is usually termed "grain growth." Under these conditions, the grains of steel may increase in size to a considerable extent, often reaching eighty times their normal size. While this condition will result only after annealing as indicated, the amount of cold-working to which the steel is subjected entirely controls the extent of the grain growth. A definite stress is necessary to produce a maximum grain growth. Any increase in the stress beyond this point will cause the grains brought out in the subsequent annealing process to decrease in size in inverse proportion to the applied stress. The stress may be increased to such an extent that no grain growth will be apparent even when annealing is carried on within the critical range previously referred to.

Annealing Temperature at which Grain Growth Occurs.—The temperature range mentioned, within which grain growth is produced, after the critical load has been applied, lies between 1290 and 1650 degrees F. Under these conditions, particularly following the lighter stresses, this range will be reduced to from 1290 to 1435 degrees F. To a limited extent grain growth will be found after annealing between temperatures of about 1250 and 1290 degrees F.

The grain growth in low-carbon steel may occur in a wide variety of products the manufacture of which requires cold-working and annealing operations. For instance, grain growth often occurs in low-carbon steel wire, tubing, and sheet or strip stock, and in all these materials, the grain growth may seriously affect production. The conditions under which grain growth occurs are to be found in the manufacture of stampings when cold-working operations are followed by annealing. The manufacture of stampings may perhaps be considered the most complicated of all the processes, as far as eliminating the trouble caused by grain growth is concerned, for not only may grain growth result from the operations performed in producing the stamping, but it may also be present in the raw materials. This is true of hot- as well as cold-rolled sheet and strip stock. It will be apparent, then, that this factor may increase to a considerable degree the difficulty of planning production methods.

Grain Growth in Hot-rolled Stock.—That grain growth may occur in hot-rolled sheet and strip stock may seem strange after considering the preceding explanations. The expression "hot-rolled," however, is purely relative in the sense in which it is used here, and covers material rolled under a range of temperature having an upper limit of about 1450 degrees F. This range may cover the temperature at which thin sheet or strip stock may receive its final rolling. Such material cools rapidly and may readily reach a temperature within the range at which grain growth occurs before the finish-rolling operation. At the end of the hot-rolling operation, the sheet or strip stock may retain its heat sufficiently long to admit of its being annealed within the grain growth range, particularly if it is placed in a pile while cooling.

If the grain growth has been moderate, subsequent operations may not be affected to any extent, but if the increase in the grain size has been large, the material will be exceedingly difficult to handle in the press room. Fortunately, much of the commercial sheet and strip stock is affected by grain growth to a very moderate extent so that further production processes may be carried on without any particular trouble from this source. Its occurrence is also usually limited to certain gages between approximately 1/8 and 1/80 of an inch in thickness. It seldom occurs in heavy or very thin stock.

Restriction of Grain Growth.—There has been considerable improvement in recent years in the restriction of grain growth in sheet metal, but its complete elimination as a commercial proposition is still to be accomplished. In spite of the increasing infrequency with which any great degree of grain growth occurs it nevertheless crops out occasionally in its worst state. With cold-rolled stock it is possible, by proper annealing methods, to eliminate this condition entirely and to produce material of high drawing quality. This is commercially feasible only in the case of products that can absorb the increased expense incurred. When the wide variation possible in the condition of sheet and strip stock is considered, the question of eliminating unsatisfactory stock by test naturally arises. The occurrence of grain growth can be readily detected by microscopic examination and in many cases by tensile or other physical tests. Such tests are not easily applicable under commercial conditions, but they are valuable in supplying data for further investigation.

From the commercial standpoint, the information most desired is that which will distinguish between good and bad raw material. For this purpose several methods of testing have been introduced, nearly all of which are based on the drawing press principle. It is possible to test the drawing quality of the raw material on an experimental press using a small die and punch. When there is stock available such as may be obtained from corners that are to be trimmed, tests can be carried out on the stock from which the stampings are to be made. In this case the four corners of the blank can be tested. Such methods may be quite successful in some cases, but it is always well not to base results upon the depth of the draw attained, as material in poor condition may draw well under a moderate load or stress. After the test, the surface should be examined for grain growth. If grain growth occurs, the surface will be roughened to a degree dependent on the increase in grain size. Even moderately large grains may be detected in this way. This roughening of the surface may also be noted in stampings made from stock containing grains larger than normal size or introduced in the preliminary operations. Examination of the material at various stages in the production of a stamping may result in the detection of the source of grain growth, whether it occurs in the raw material or during the manufacturing operations.

Tests of the raw material such as have been outlined are very useful under certain conditions, but their practical application is by no means simple. It is hardly possible to test each individual sheet or strip of stock, and if it were, complete detection could scarcely be attained. Grain growth may occur in spots or in a considerable portion of the sheet stock. The selection of test samples for determining the condition of a shipment of stock may or may not be satisfactory, as the condition of a few sheets does not necessarily indicate the condition of the whole shipment, for the reason that individual sheets may vary widely in their condition. When annealed sheet or strip stock is to be tested, complications may enter due to uneven annealing, which may result in material that is too hard.

While testing methods such as outlined in the preceding paragraph may not draw a hard and fast line between satisfactory and unsatisfactory material, it is possible to apply them in ways that will be valuable commercially or at least so that they will be a definite detection against the acceptance of exceedingly poor stock. The troublesome conditions that may exist in the raw material may be paralleled exactly in the finished or semi-finished parts by faulty handling in the production processes. Grain growth may result through improper control of the annealing. As has been mentioned, it may be possible to control grain growth in some cold-working operations by applying loads that exceed the limits beyond which subsequent annealing operations can possibly have any effect. In the stamping processes, however, this simple method cannot always be applied. Grain growth may be controlled to some extent in simple cases by this method, but it would be very difficult, for instance, in the case of work having a slight bend, or where there is a variation in the gage of the stock. Some apparently minor or unconsidered pressure may also cause trouble.

Grain Growth in Stampings.—How grain growth may occur in a stamping can perhaps be best described by considering the drawing operation on a cup. It is evident that the metal will be drawn to a considerable extent in reducing the diameter of a blank to that of the shell, and that the metal is stressed the least at the bottom of the cup. In this case, it is assumed that the cup is drawn from the blank in one operation. The top or rim is subjected to the greatest stress, the stress decreasing gradually from the top of the cup to the bottom. If the cup is annealed within the critical range already mentioned, for which 1300 degrees F. has been selected as a representative temperature, the grain growth will be as follows: The largest grains will occur near the bottom where the stress is the least and decrease in size toward the top, becoming practically normal before this point is reached.

In such simple cases, it is possible to so control the stresses set up in different parts of the shell that troublesome grain growth will be eliminated. However, this may necessitate several drawing operations in place of one, in order to obtain the necessary uniform distribution of the stresses in the cup previous to annealing. The worst conditions frequently result from annealing after the first or second operation, even though the material is drawn but a small amount. It is evident that with few exceptions successive press operations should be carried on without annealing until it becomes absolutely necessary.

Peculiar results are often obtained by a slight variation in the methods of drawing and annealing. Take, for example, two plants making the same part and using the same part and using the same steel. It will often be found that one plant may carry on the processes to the finished product without annealing or at least with a minimum number of annealing operations, while in the other plant the work may be annealed between each press operation, and yet entirely satisfactory results are not obtained in the latter plant. It is easy for such a variation in results to arise, if, in the case of the second plant, the work is annealed within the critical range after one of the first drawing operations. The introduction of grain growth in an early annealing operation may make it necessary to increase the number of total annealing operations and may also require an increase in the number of press operations.

If the prevention of grain growth is desired, annealing may be carried on either above or below the critical temperature range. If it is a case of removing grain growth from the work, the annealing must be done at a temperature above the critical range, that is, either above 1435 degrees F. or above 1650 degrees F., according to conditions. For this purpose the temperatures commonly used are 1450 degrees F. and 1700 degrees F. The latter temperature represents the point of complete refining.

In the annealing processes that may be selected to meet the needs of the individual case, accurate temperature control is, of course, necessary. It is, however, one thing to have accurate pyrometers and another thing to insure the heating of each piece to exactly the correct temperature. To a very marked degree, accurate control of the furnace temperature is dependent upon the furnace design and the furnace charging methods. Uniformity is required not only for production results but from the standpoint of economy as well.

Requirements of Annealing Furnaces.—An annealing furnace must not only be capable of maintaining a uniform temperature with an empty hearth, but it must also heat the work uniformly and quickly to the desired temperature. Two general types of furnaces are used for annealing, namely, the over-fired, and the under-fired. The latter type, as a rule, is more easily controlled, more uniform in operation and can usually be operated at a lower cost. This may not be apparent if the cost is considered in terms of fuel consumption per unit of time. Costs, however, should not be figured on such a basis, but upon the production obtained.

The furnace charging methods, as mentioned, also have a considerable effect upon the results. If the furnace is so loaded or charged that a uniform distribution of the heat is prevented, the cost of the operation may be increased to a considerable degree and uniform results be impossible of attainment. When retorts are used for annealing, care must be taken to have them arranged so that each surface will receive as nearly the same amount of heat as possible. The size and shape of the retorts may also have an effect upon the uniformity of the product. When open-fire annealing is practiced, interference with heat distribution may result from loading the furnace too full or from an irregular arrangement of the work. In any case, much time can be lost in waiting for part of the load to reach the desired temperature when a considerable portion is ready to be removed from the furnace. Furthermore, the overheating of part of the work that occurs under the conditions mentioned will naturally result in non-uniformity in the product.

Fuel for Annealing Furnaces.—The fuel available will, of course, influence to some degree the design of the furnace. At present the choice appears to lie betwen coal or coke, gas, and oil, with general conditions in favor of the latter. Electricity is used in some cases, but its cost is usually too high to permit of its general adoption both as regards installation and operation. Gas is perhaps the most satisfactory fuel of the first three mentioned, but its cost may be high and it may not be readily available. Coal and coke have been used to a considerable extent, but present considerable difficulty in handling. The results obtained in the average furnace in which these two fuels are burned can hardly be called uniform. With a natural draft its speed of operation is affected by weather conditions. Oil is probably the best fuel to use, considering the factors of cost, availability, and ease of operation. However, the furnace must be carefully designed if this fuel is to be used. It is particularly necessary that the combustion chambers be of ample height.

In considering the cost of operating an oil furnace, it is well to remember that some of the heavier varieties of oil can be obtained at a comparatively low price and that a considerable saving in operating costs will result if the installation is designed to handle the heavier rather than the lighter grades of oil. The furnace design will be influenced to some degree by the method of annealing adopted, but the general principles of furnace design will be the same for both the open-fire and the retort methods. If the product is required to be free from scale, this determines in a large measure which method of annealing is to be adopted. This factor is of less importance in general production than might be assumed. If annealing is carried on just below the grain growth temperature, practically no scale will be formed. When higher temperatures are required, it is possible, by simple and inexpensive "pickling" methods, to produce work that is sufficiently clean and satisfactory as a commercial product when the open-fire method is used.

Except in cases that have been proved definitely to require retort annealing, the choice should be based largely on the cost. From this standpoint, open-fire annealing will usually have the preference. This is by no means universally true, however, for the reverse may be the case in some instances. Size, shape, weight, conditions of handling, and other similar factors must be taken into consideration. As a rule, the heavier stampings can be open-fire annealed to better advantage and at less cost, particularly if small evenly distributed heats are used which can be handled quickly.

It should not be forgotten, however, that the design of the parts to be made, the design and the condition of the dies and punches, the variation in the gage of the stock, and various other factors must be taken into account. The design of the part may be such that undue strains are introduced which cannot be avoided. Then, again, the press tools may be soft or improperly finished, or the drawing operations may be carried to a point beyond the endurance of the steel. With so many factors involved it may be difficult to determine whether the cause of failure is mechanical or whether it lies in the condition of the steel. If fracture occurs, it is possible to determine the reduction in the thickness of the metal at the fractured point. When this is 50 per cent or more, it may be generally assumed that the condition of the metal is reasonably satisfactory.

Grades of Steel Stock for Press Work.—Bright-rolled strip stock is used in the manufacture of many die-made products. Fractures which sometimes occur in connection with bending, forming, or drawing operations may be due to the use of an improper temper or grade of stock. The different classes of tempers or grades are known as: hard rolled, half hard, medium soft, dead soft, and special dead soft.

Hard-rolled Stock.—This grade of material should not be used for bending, forming or cupping because it will fracture. It is about as hard as a mild steel can be. It blanks and pierces neatly and with crisp sharp edges. Sometimes when it is necessary to have very fine edges to a formed or cupped strip the hard-rolled temper is blanked and then annealed, cupped and drawn, but no attempt should be made to bend or form prior to annealing. A series of tests to determine average figures showed for hard stock a Brinell number of 210; a scleroscope hardness of 34.5; and an Erichsen value of 7.8 millimeters.

Half-hard Stock.—This grade blanks well and will also take a sharp right angle bend across the grain but generally it will be found impossible to make two right angle bends at right angles to each other unless the blanks are punched out diagonally across the grain. Average figures based on a series of tests for half-hard stock showed a Brinell number of 156; a scleroscope hardness of 27.5; and an Erichsen value of 10.1 millimeters.

Medium-soft Stock.—Medium-soft material will take a sharp right angle bend along the grain and a complete 180-degree flat bend across the grain. It may conveniently be used for frameworks which have to be bent into bearing arms at right angles to the main body but in different directions. No sharp right angle bend will fracture this grade. A series of tests on medium-soft stock showed the following average values: Brinell number, 126; scleroscope hardness, 24; Erichsen value, 11 millimeters.

Dead-soft Stock.—This grade will take 180-degree bends in both directions of the rolling grain and it is used for cupping work. This is one of the most used grades for general work. A series of tests on dead-soft stock shows the following averages: Brinell number, 99; scleroscope hardness, 19; Erichsen value, 12 millimeters.

Special Dead-soft Stock.—This is mild steel in its very softest condition and it may be drawn to maximum depth without annealing. Experiment shows that when dead-soft metal is "copperized" i.e., thinly plated with copper, the lubricating action on the dies of the latter metal renders it possible to draw even deeper. This specially soft grade does not blank at all well. Usually this is of no great importance since the tops of such shells as are produced will ordinarily be subjected to a final trimming operation. Nevertheless some firms prefer to start off with a harder material and anneal to suit as they go along. This is all right so long as the furnace is modern and well kept; however, it takes careful handling to reduce the hardness of mild steel to its lowest. A series of tests on special dead-soft stock showed the following averages: Brinell number, 94; scleroscope hardness, 18; Erichsen value, 12.6 millimeters.

Composition.—Bright-rolled strip stock may be classed as a very mild steel which has an extra small percentage of sulphur and phosphorous. Analyses of three different brands showed carbon percentages of 0.07, 0.10, and 0.11; manganese, 0.34, 0.40, and 0.45; silicon, 0.01, 0.02, and 0.03; sulphur, 0.01 and traces; phosphorus, 0.01 in each case.

CHAPTER XIII

DIES FOR DRAWING SHALLOW CUPS OR SHELLS

It is evident that drawing dies should be designed to permit finishing in one stroke of the press, whatever part is to be drawn, whenever this is practicable; and most drawing operations on parts which are shallow or which have little depth in proportion to the diameter, may be completed in one operation. As a general rule, the combination type of die is employed for work of this class, since this type serves to perform the blanking and drawing operations during one stroke of a single-action press. In this chapter, some typical examples of dies for drawing comparatively shallow parts will be illustrated and described.

Combination Die for Can Ends.—The die shown in Fig. 1 is the type used for making the ends for sheet-metal cans used for preserving fruits and various food products. The punch consists of only three parts, the punch head *A*, the knock-out *B*, and the forming block *C*. The punch *A* is made from two pieces welded together, the shank being made from machine steel and the lower or cutting edge from tool steel. The forming block *C* is a one-piece tool-steel forging, and is not hardened. The knock-out *B* is also a one-piece tool-steel forging, not hardened.

The cast-iron bolster plate *D* is recessed to fit the plug *E*, which is hardened and finished by grinding. Plug *E* is made of two pieces welded together. This makes it possible to drill and tap the holes for the assembling screws after the hardening operation has been performed. The shoulder of plug *E* projects about 1/8 inch above the cast-iron bolster *D*, so that the cut-edge die *F* can be centered on this shoulder, with a good tight fit. In plug *E* is fitted the insert *G*, which is another tool-steel forging. The pressure ring *H* is also a tool-steel forging, and is supported by the pressure pins *J*. The cut-edge die *F* is a two-piece forging and is held on the bolster by four 7/16-inch hexagonal cap-screws. This permits the removal of the cut-edge die without taking the complete die from the press.

This die is equipped with the regulation pressure pad used in combination drawing dies. This pressure pad consists

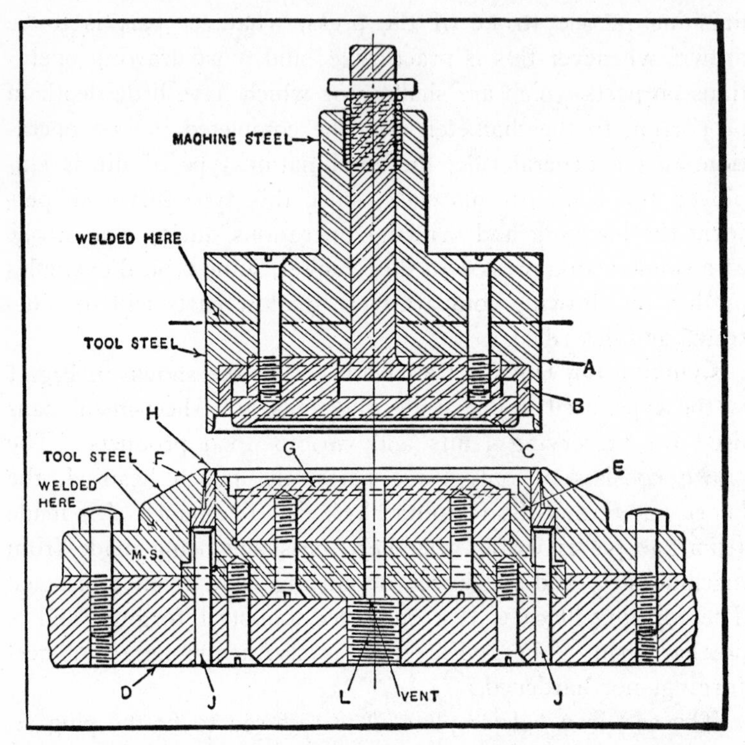

Fig. 1. Punch and Die Designed for Use in the Production of Can Ends

of a rubber pad, of suitable size, held between two cast-iron plates. A nut at the bottom of the pressure pad stud can be adjusted to give any desired pressure that may be required for drawing the shell. This stud is threaded to fit the tapped hole in the bottom of the die at *L*. A hole, drilled through the stud, connects with the air hole or vent in part *G*.

Combination Die for Perforated Can Top.—The shaker can top *A* shown in the upper right-hand corner of Fig. 2 is produced on the combination die shown by the sectional views. While the operations of blanking, forming, shearing, closing, and lettering are all performed at one stroke of this die, it is nevertheless of simple construction.

The die operates as follows: When the punch comes down it cuts out the blank, after which the punch pad forms the contour and draws down the edges of the blank over the die center. As the punch continues downward, the rubber-pads *M* are compressed, so that the piercing punches *J* project through the pad *H* and shear the sprinkler openings. The lower pins *K* are, of course, pushed down when the openings are sheared. Finally, as the punch reaches the end of the stroke, the punch pad and the die center come together solidly on the work, thus bringing the lettering out in sharp relief. As the punch ascends, the lower pins *K* force the lugs in the work back into their respective openings so that they are closed. As the press is inclined, the can tops slide off the die as soon as the punch clears the work. Can tops of the type illustrated are not opened in the usual way, by pushing the lugs down, but by depressing the center of the cover so that the lugs really project outward.

The shoe *C* is made from a cast-iron plate which is machined in the lathe. The recess and the boss for locating the blanking or cutting die *D* and the die center *E* are turned at the same time that the facing operation is performed. This completes the die-shoe with the exception of drilling the hold-down holes and the holes for the clamping studs *F*. The cutting part *D* of the die is made from tool-steel bar stock, which is cut off a little longer than the finished part so that the die can be chucked and the turning operations completed at one setting. The absence of bolt holes in die *D* eliminates to a considerable extent the danger of cracking when the part is hardened. It will be noted that the clamps *B* hold down both the cutting part *D* of the die and the die center *E*. The parts of the die that are finished by grinding are so located in the chuck that all the grinding operations can be performed at one setting, thus insuring the concentricity of the various surfaces.

The holes in the die center *E*, punch *H* and pad *G* are drilled and reamed with the parts assembled, the holes for the punches *J* and pins *K* being located from the center of the die. The contour of the die center *E* and the pad *L*, as well as the punch *H* and pad *N*, are made to fit gages which

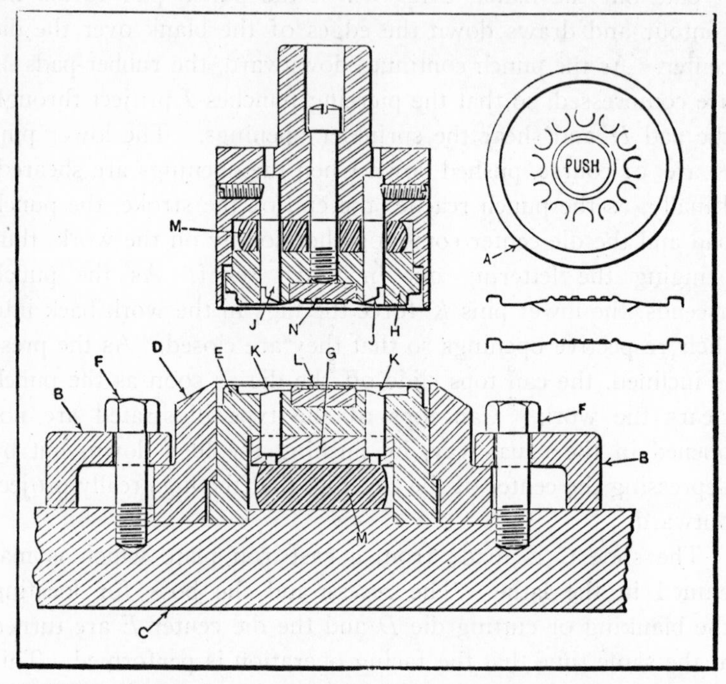

Fig. 2. Combination Die Used in Producing the Can Top Shown at *A*

are stored away for use in making renewals. The punches and the die-pins are made from a standard size of drill rod so that renewals can be quickly made. Rubber pads *M* are used instead of springs, as the movement of the die parts is very short. Lettering pads *N* and *L* are a tight fit in the punch *H* and the die center *E*, respectively.

Combination Die for Can Cover.—Various styles of drawn covers for such articles as tobacco cans, etc., may be produced readily in one power-press operation, provided some type of combination die is used. Fig. 3 illustrates a combination blanking and drawing die employed in the manufacture of the cover shown at the bottom of the illustration, this part being made from 0.011-inch sheetstock, commonly called "tin." In

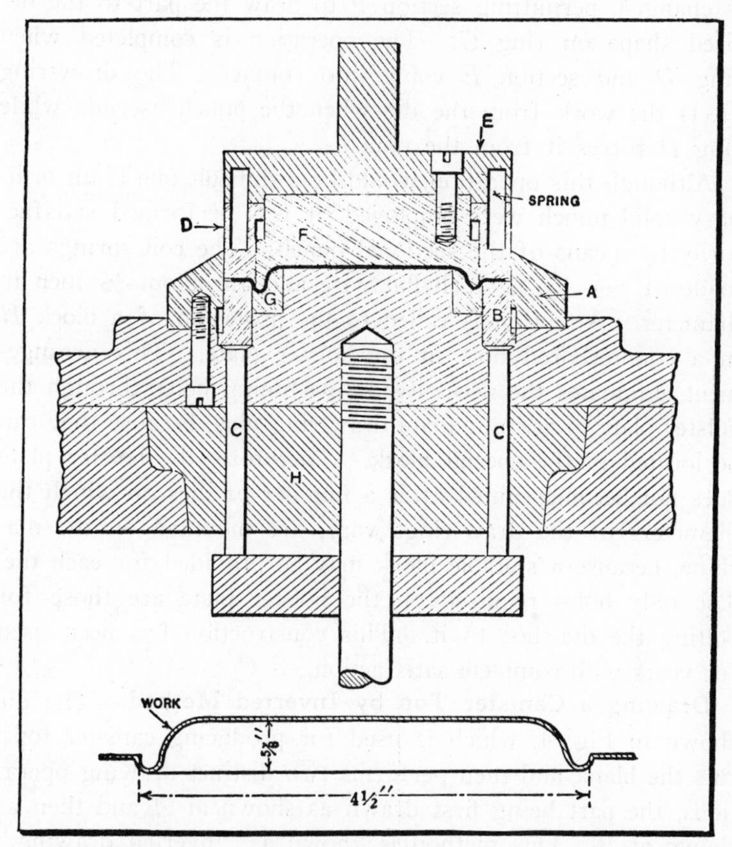

Fig. 3. Combination Blanking and Drawing Die for Making Can Cover Shown

the operation of this die, a strip of metal is placed on die ring *A*, the top of draw-ring *B* being raised to the same level as the cutting edge of ring *A* through the action of the rubber buffer which actuates the block upon which pins *C* rest.

When the punch descends, the face of ring *D* is advanced ahead of the face of section *F* by coil springs placed between the ring and section *E*, and cuts the blank to a diameter of 5⅝ inches as it enters die ring *A*. The draw-ring then holds the blank firmly against the face of ring *D* and retards the movement of the latter, so that the coil springs are compressed and the relation between the faces of ring *D* and section *F* is changed, permitting section *F* to draw the part to the desired shape on ring *G*. The operation is completed when ring *D* and section *E* come into contact. The draw-ring ejects the work from the die when the punch ascends while ring *D* forces it from the punch.

Although this operation would be a difficult one if an ordinary solid punch were employed, it was performed satisfactorily by means of the sectional punch. The coil springs are made of 1/32- by 3/32-inch flat wire and are about ½ inch in diameter. Attention is called to the provision of a block *H* in a counterbored hole in the bolster plate. This arrangement eliminates the necessity of machining holes through the bolster plate to accommodate draw-ring pins, because they can be located in the special block. Therefore, the bolster plate does not become ruined after a number of dies on which the diameters of the draw-rings vary, are mounted on the machine, because a suitable block may be provided for each die. The only holes required on the bolster plate are those for bolting the die-shoe to it. This construction has been used for years with complete satisfaction.

Drawing a Canister Top by Inverted Method.—The die shown in Fig. 4, which is used for producing canister tops, cuts the blank and then performs two distinct drawing operations, the part being first drawn as shown at *A* and then as shown at *B*. This method is known as "inverted drawing." The material used for the part is 0.028-inch tin. Normally, the top of draw-ring *C* is held in the same plane as the top of die-ring *D*, by a stud and rubber buffer arrangement which functions similarly to that on the preceding die. The blank is cut to a diameter of 6½ inches by ring *E* of the punch as the latter enters the opening in ring *D*, after which the draw-ring holds the blank firmly against ring *E* as this member continues to descend, and draws the part on ring *F* of the die to the shape shown at *A*.

As this step is concluded, pad *G* and the spring-actuated ring *H* come in contact with the work and cause it to be drawn to the shape illustrated at *B*, during which time ring *H* is

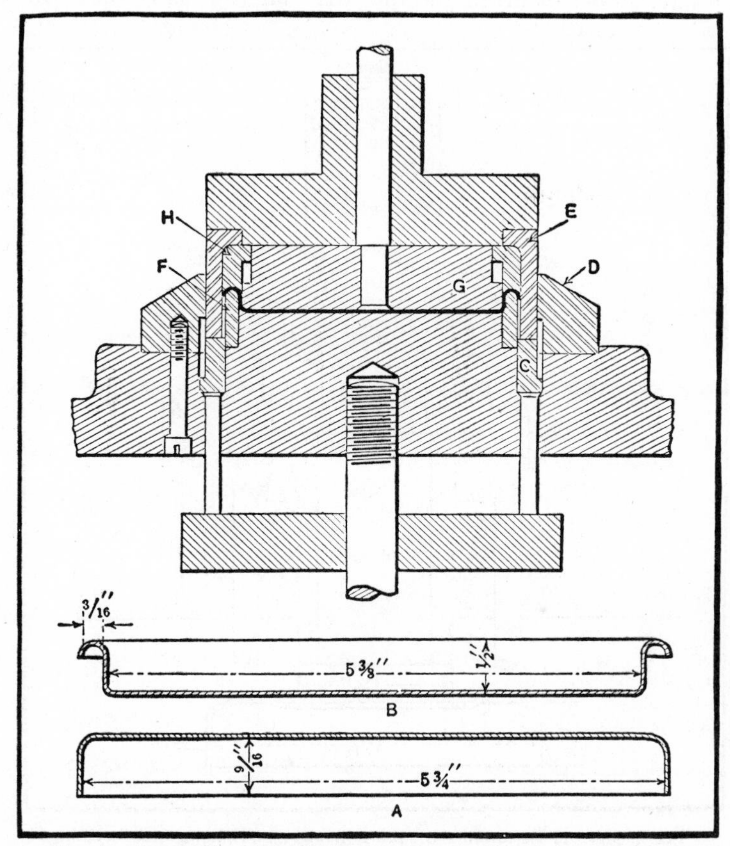

Fig. 4. Combination Die Which Produces a Canister Cover by the Inverted Method of Drawing

retarded so that the springs placed above it (not shown in the illustration) become compressed. By this construction ring *H* functions in the same manner as a draw-ring. Upon the return stroke of the punch, the springs expand and cause ring *H* to eject the work from the punch. Ring *E* is secured to the punch-holder by means of machine screws. As indicated by the view of the work at *A*, the face of ring *E* projects 9/16 inch plus the thickness of the metal beyond pad *G*.

Die Which Blanks, Draws, Punches, and Trims.—An interesting combination die is illustrated in Fig. 5. This die blanks, draws, punches the hole, and trims the lower edge of the part shown beneath the die, the material being 0.035-inch

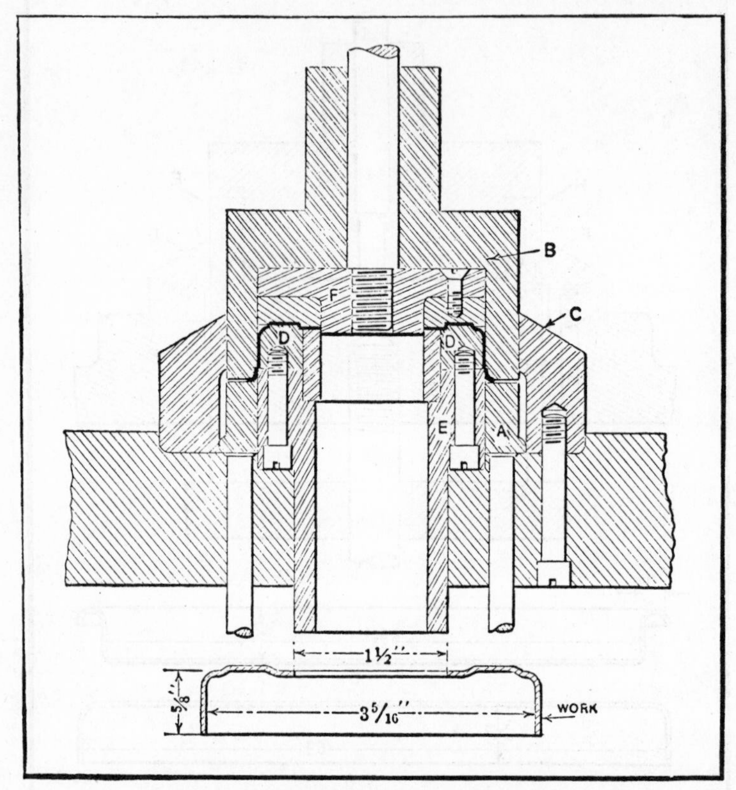

Fig. 5. Die for Performing Blanking, Drawing, Trimming and Punching Operations in a Single Stroke of the Press

cold-rolled steel. Draw-ring *A* of this die serves in the same capacity as those on the dies previously discussed. The blank is cut as punch *B* enters ring *C*, and is drawn upon ring *D* as the punch continues to descend. During the lower portion of this stroke the bottom edge of the work is sheared off as the punch face passes the upper edge of die-sleeve *E* due to the outside diameter of the latter being the same as the internal diameter of the punch. As soon as this trimming step has been completed, section *F* comes in contact with the work and cuts the hole as the stroke of the ram is concluded.

Section *F*, which blanks the hole, enters the die approximately equal to the thickness of the metal. If the section entered the hole much farther, a perfectly round hole would not be obtained. The scrap from the operation falls through the die and an opening in the rubber buffer, which in this case is supported by two studs. Although the trimming step really consists of "pinching" off the metal rather than cutting it, the method has been satisfactory on metal up to 0.065 inch in thickness and is probably practical up to a thickness of 3/32 inch.

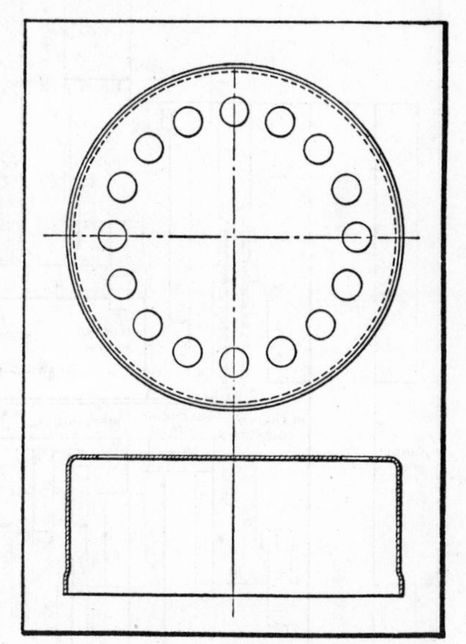
Fig. 6. Automobile Muffler Cup

Combination Blanking, Drawing, Forming and Piercing Die.—The muffler cup, Fig. 6, is finished complete as shown in one operation by means of the combination blanking, drawing, forming and piercing die shown in Fig. 7, in a single-action press. The operation is as follows: When the blanking punch descends, it enters the blanking die, the blank being held firmly by the drawing ring against the bottom of the blanking punch in order to prevent wrinkles in the metal. The pins shown are used to transfer the pressure. As the downward movement continues, the blank is drawn between the bore of the blanking punch and the drawing punch. As it reaches the end of the stroke, the rim is formed between the recess in the blanking punch and the tapered shoulder on the drawing punch; holes are pierced by punches located in the punch-block, as clearly indicated in the illustration. A spring stripper is used on this work and a knock-out is kept in line with the piercing punches by a Whitney key.

Die with Two Drawing Rings.—Two distinct drawing operations on power presses are commonly employed in the production of parts which can be drawn just as satisfactorily in

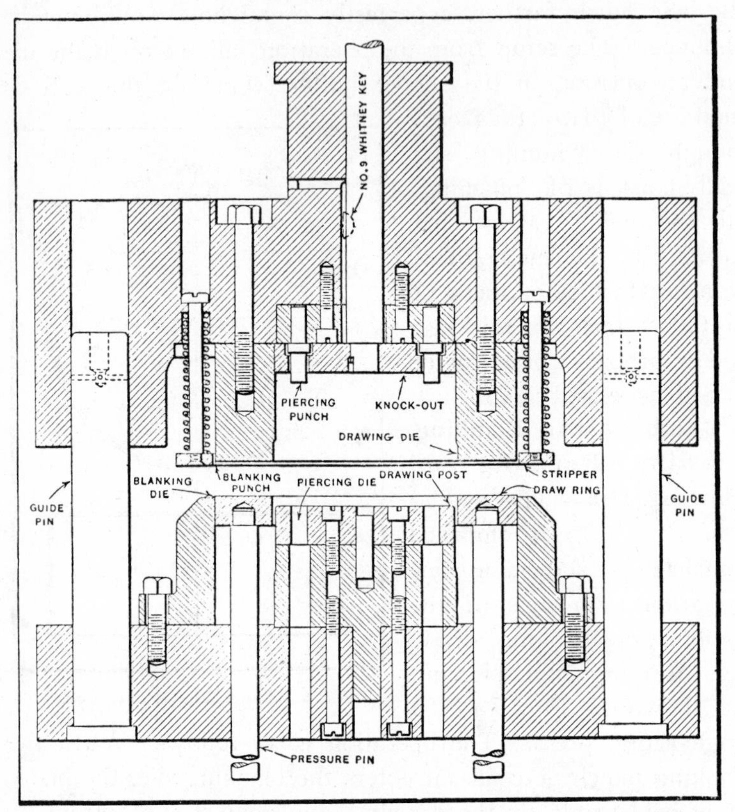

Fig. 7. Combined Blanking, Drawing, Forming and Piercing Die for Automobile Muffler Cups

one operation by means of a punch and die construction similar to that shown in Fig. 8. This punch and die is used for drawing oil-can breasts to the shape and dimensions shown in the lower right-hand corner. The development of a die for producing this part in one operation was difficult because of the shoulder near the open end and the thinness of the metal

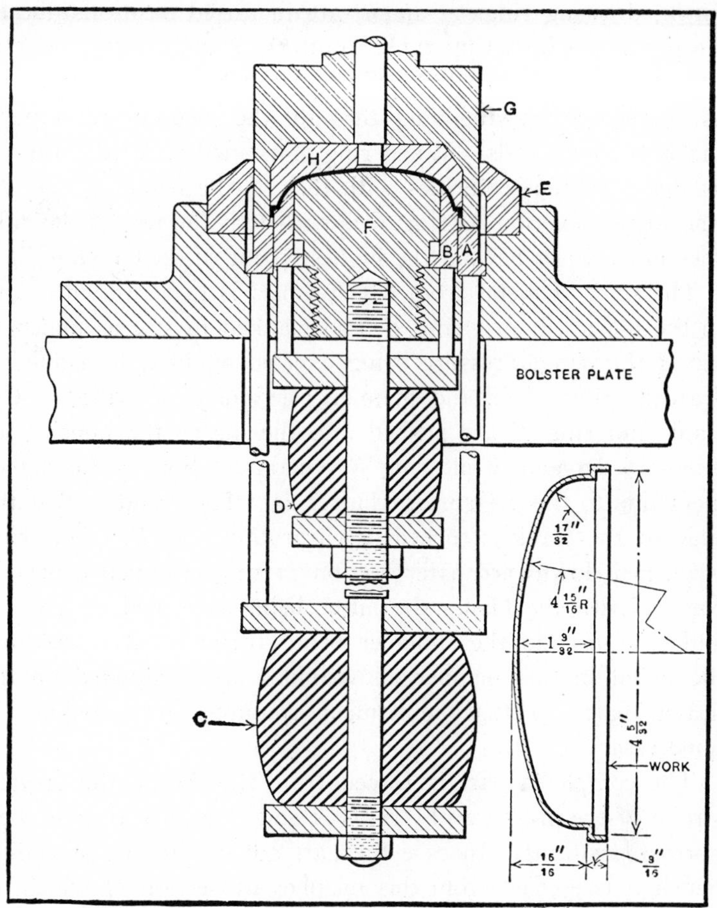

Fig. 8. Punch and Die Construction for Completing in One Operation Parts Generally Produced by Two Dies

from which the part is drawn, this metal being cold-rolled stock, 0.024 inch in thickness. The blank diameter is 5 3/32 inches. The special feature of this die is the provision of two drawing rings, one inside the other, against which upward pressures are exerted by means of two separate rubber buffers.

The illustration shows the relation between the punch and the moving members of the die at the completion of a downward stroke of the press ram. Prior to a descent of the punch, drawing rings *A* and *B* are in raised positions due to the pressure exerted by rubber buffers *C* and *D*, respectively. The pressure of each buffer is transmitted to the bottom of its respective drawing ring through the medium of a plate and two round rods. When ring *A* is in the raised position, its upper surface coincides with that of the blanking ring *E*. The raised position of ring *B* is such that the top of the ring does not project beyond the highest point of center plug *F*.

The strip of metal from which a part is to be drawn is laid on the upper edge of ring *E*, and blanked to size as punch *G* enters this ring, pressure being exerted against the blank by drawing ring *A* in the manner previously described. The blank and ring *A* are pushed into the die as the punch continues to descend, while ring *B* remains stationary for a moment due to the pressure of buffer *D*. The result is that the edge of the blank is turned down around ring *B*. This ring is pushed downward after section *H* of the punch comes in contact with the blank, the latter being stretched on plug *F* and ring *B*, and the shoulder being formed. By stretching the metal in this manner all wrinkles are eliminated on the drawn part, so that subsequent spinning or restriking is unnecessary.

The completed part is forced from the die on the upward stroke of the press ram by rings *A* and *B* as they resume their normal positions. In case the part adheres to the ascending punch it is ejected from this member by section *H* which, in addition to its function of shaping the shell, also serves as a knock-out pad. If the die for making this part were arranged with drawing ring *B* integral with plug *F*, it would be practically impossible to draw a shell without wrinkles. The top edge of ring *B* is rounded, so that the blank is not cut through when it is forced upon the ring.

Dies for Making a Flanged Steel Cover.—The steel cover shown in Fig. 9 is made in two operations from 18-gage hot-rolled steel. To eliminate trimming to length, the cover is made from a developed blank 3 $^{17}/_{32}$ inches in diameter. This is drawn into the cup shown at *A*, on a compound blanking and drawing punch and die, Fig. 10. This cup is then put through an upsetting, piercing, and flanging die, Fig. 11, which produces the cover shown at *B*, Fig. 9. This is a finished article free from burrs.

The blanking and drawing die shown in Fig. 10 produces a shell of uniform depth and height which is essential where no trimming is to be done. The punch-shoe *A* and the die-shoe *B* are made of cast iron and are aligned by steel guide-pins *C* and bronze bushings *D*. The blanking punch *E*, which also acts as a die, is made of hardened tool steel and is set in a counterbored shoe, being held in position by screws *F*. It has a spring knock-out pad *G*, which is actuated by a spring *H*. The blanking die, which is made of tool steel and is hardened

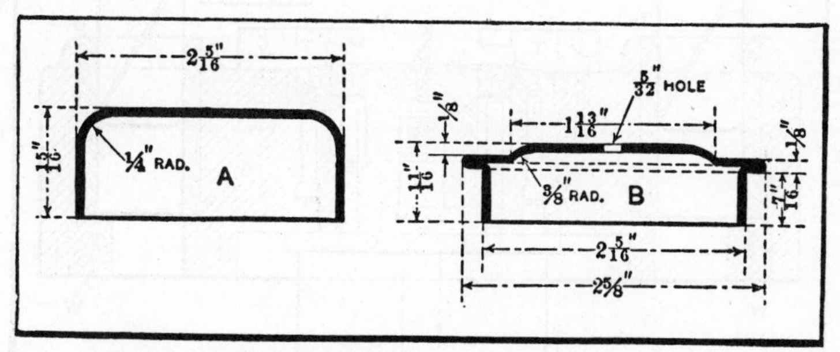

Fig. 9. Cup for Pressed Steel Cover and Finished Cover

and ground with plenty of shear, consists of a ring *I* that is set in die-shoe *B* and is held by screws *J*; *K* is the spacing gage. The forming punch *L* is held in position by a stud bolt *M*, which also holds in place rubber buffer *N* and pressure plates *O* with nut *P*. Rubber buffer *N* must be carefully adjusted when the dies are set up and care must be taken that excessive pressure is not exerted on pressure pad *R*, from the rubber buffer through pins *S*, as this would strain the metal or cause it to break or stretch. The stripper plates *T*, which are held by screws *V*, are made in two pieces and do not completely surround punch *E* while in operation; this is not in accordance with common practice. The top view is shown at *Y–Y*. This stripper is very satisfactory, as it gives the operator a good view and better command of his work. A channel *X* passes

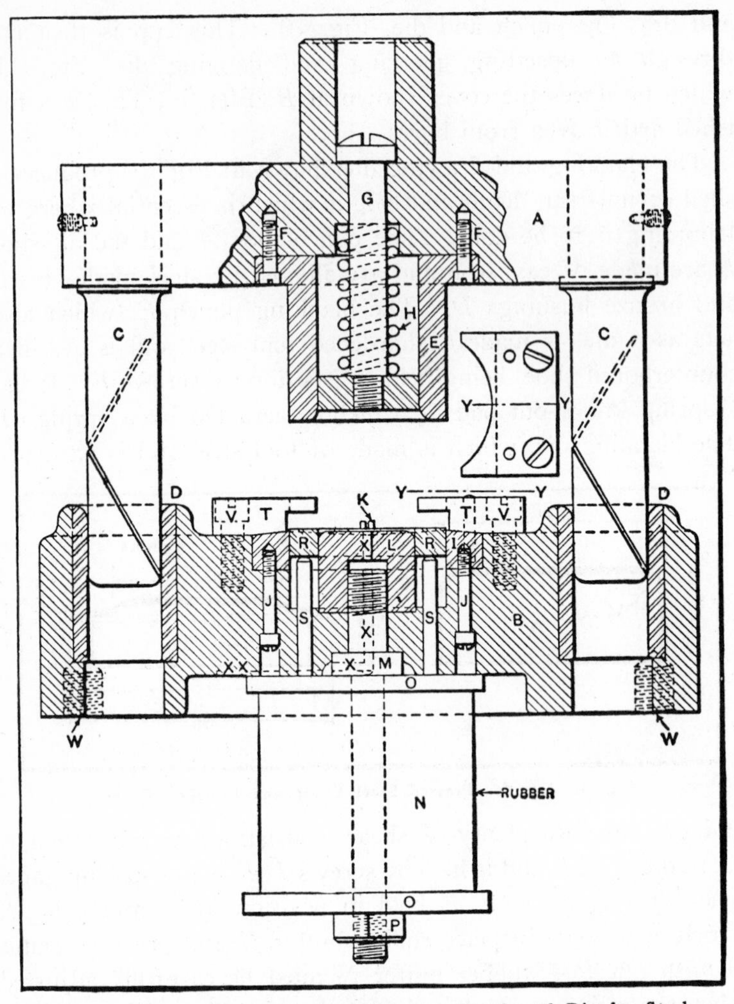

Fig. 10. Compound Blanking and Drawing Punch and Die for Steel Cover

through the forming and drawing punch *L* and the stud bolt, then under the die to the opening *XX*. Its purpose is to eliminate suction while the shell is being stripped from punch *L*, making the stripping easier and causing less wear on the punch. Tapped holes *W* are provided for fastening the die to the bed of the press.

The flanging and piercing punch and die, Fig. 11, is shown

closed with the finished cover in place. The punch *A* is made of machine steel and is counterbored to seat the tool-steel, hardened, working pad *B*, while under pressure. Pad *B* is held in place by screws *C*, which have 1/4-inch clearance beneath their heads, in order to allow the pressure pad 1/4-inch movement. This movement, from springs *F*, releases the shell from the piercing punch *D* when the punch leaves the die on the upward stroke of the ram. The die-shoe *E* is made of cast iron and seats die *G*. The holes for screws *H* are elongated

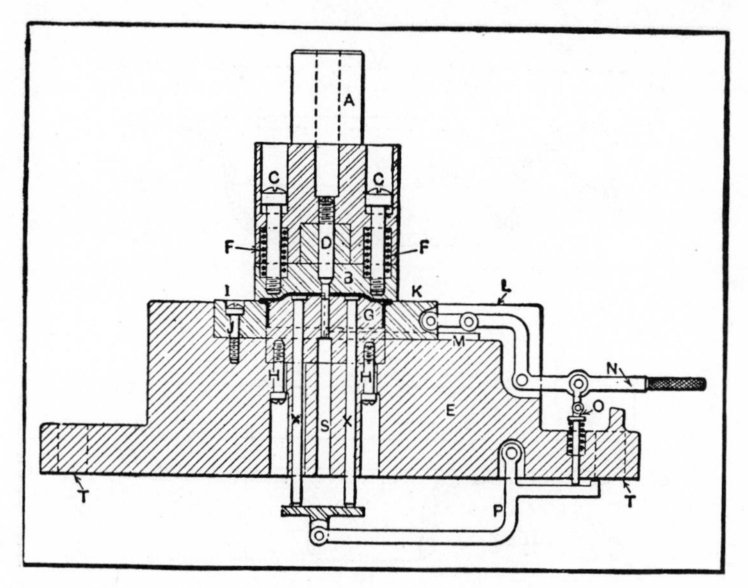

Fig. 11. Upsetting, Flanging, and Piercing Punch and Die

1/16 inch to allow the die a forward motion of 1/16 inch, which is necessary when the die is open to give the proper freedom in placing or removing the shell. The rear flanging section *I* is made of tool steel, hardened and ground and held stationary by screws *J*, while the forward section *K* moves horizontally in channel *L* and bevel gibs *M*. The front section *K* moves forward when the lever *N* is pressed down. At the same time, this lever, through stud *O*, causes lever *P* to raise knock-out pins *X* the proper height to discharge the cover, which is quickly removed and replaced by an unfinished shell. Channel

S is for the discharge of slugs, and holes *T* are for fastening the die to the bed of the press.

Dies for Making a Pressed-steel Ball Retainer.—The pressed steel hub ball retainer illustrated at *B* in Fig. 12 is made of 12-gage cold-rolled steel; it is drawn from a blank 7⅟16 inches in diameter and is finished in two operations. Shell *A* is blanked and drawn in the compound die shown in Fig. 13, and in setting this die it is important to make a careful adjustment in order that just the required pressure may be developed

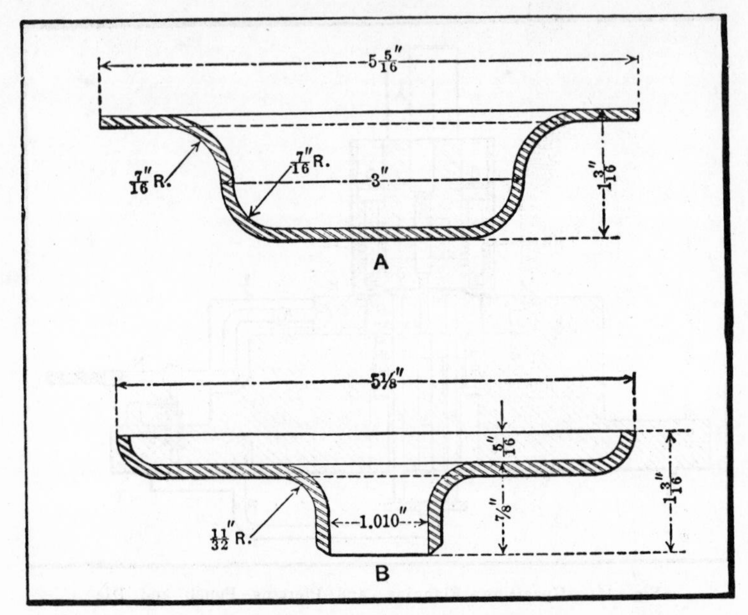

Fig. 12. Shell after First Operation, and Finished Ball Retainer

by the rubber buffer. If this pressure is too great, the diameter of the shell will be increased to such an extent that it will not enter the die shown in Fig. 14, in which the final operation is performed. On the other hand, if the rubber buffer does not exert enough pressure, wrinkles will be formed in the shell, that are likely to develop into cracks.

In blanking and drawing the shell to the form shown at *A* in Fig. 12, it has been found convenient to use an inclinable power press which allows the die to discharge the shell instantly

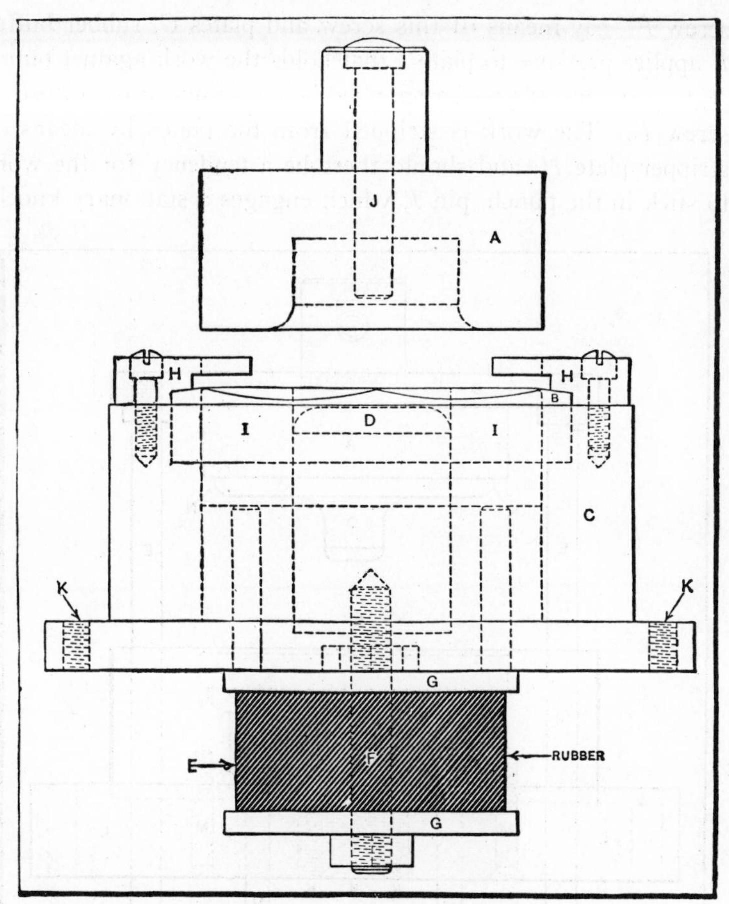

Fig. 13. Compound Blanking and Drawing Die in Which First Operation *A*, Fig. 12, is Performed

so that the press may be operated continuously. When punch *A*, Fig. 13 moves downward, it enters the openings in blanking die *B* and stamps out a blank of the required size. The way in which the blanking die is supported in cast-iron holder *C* will be evident from the illustration. As the downward motion of the punch continues, the blank is carried down into contact with forming punch *D*, which draws it to the shape shown at *A* in Fig. 12.

It will be seen that forming punch *D* fits in a hole bored in die-holder *C*, and that this punch is held down by means of screw *F*. By means of this screw and plates *G*, rubber buffer *E* applies pressure to plate *I* that holds the work against punch *A*, the amount of pressure applied being regulated by adjusting screw *F*. The work is stripped from the punch by means of stripper plate *H*, and should there be a tendency for the work to stick in the punch, pin *J*, which engages a stationary knock-

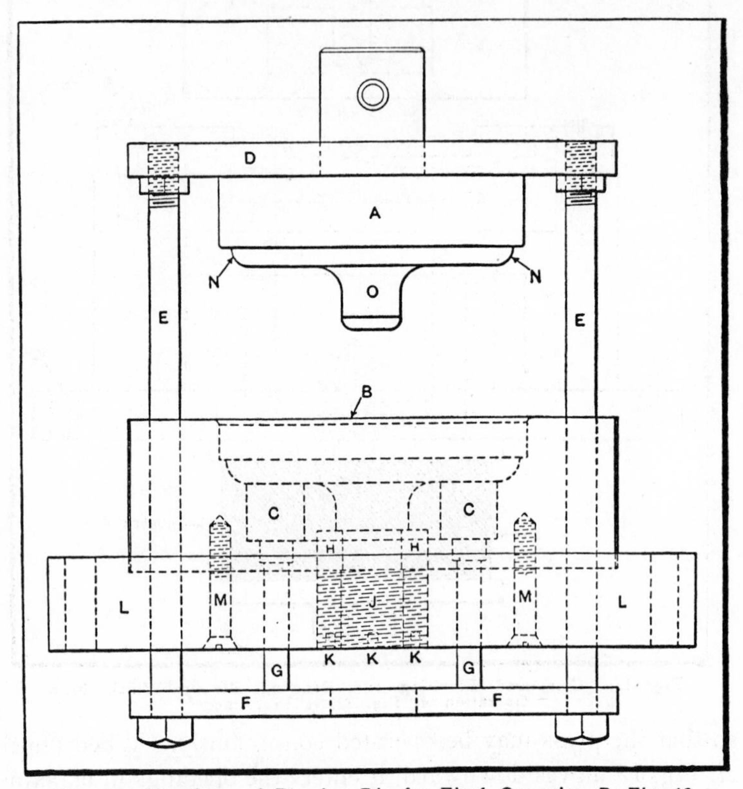

Fig. 14. Drawing and Piercing Die for Final Operation *B*, Fig. 12

out bar bolted to the body of the press, acts as an ejector. It will be evident that tapped holes *K* are for the purpose of securing the die to the bolster on the press.

After the first operation, the work is brought to the condition shown at *A* in Fig. 12, and these shells are next dropped into the forming and punching die, Fig. 14, in which they are drawn to the finished shape *B*, Fig. 12. In Fig. 14, the punch is shown at *A* and the die at *B*. Die *B* is bored out to form a seat for ring *C* which acts as a knock-out to eject the stamping from the die. It will be seen that the punch carries plate *D* which supports knock-out rods *E*; these rods carry plate *F* at their lower ends, and by making a suitable adjustment, plate *F* comes into contact with pins *G* on the up stroke of the ram, thus lifting ring *C* and ejecting the finished stamping from the die.

At the bottom of forming die *B* there is a small hardened steel ring *H* which is bored to fit the pilot on punch *A*. This is the piercing die which provides for punching the hole in the bottom of the stamping. Die *H* is held in place by threaded bushing *J* which is tightened with a spanner wrench fitting into holes *K*. It will be evident that *L* is the die-plate and that the die is secured in place by means of screws *M*.

In performing the final operation in this punch and die, which brings the works to the form shown at *B* in Fig. 12, shell *A* is put in the die upside down, and when the punch descends it turns the shell inside out and punches out the bottom. When the shell starts turning, the flange turns upward and comes into contact with the shoulder *N* on the punch, which forces the stock into the die. Pilot *O* on the punch forms the hub of the retainer and punches out the bottom without stretching the stock. The pilot is 3/16 inch longer than the hub of the retainer, which gives the punch the necessary over-travel to upset the end of the hub and prevent leaving a ragged edge

Drawing Cup Cylindrical on the Outside and Tapering Inside.—The cup shown at the lower part of Fig. 15 in satisfactorily produced on punch presses from steel plate ranging from 3/16 to 1/2 inch in thickness, by means of the type of punch and die shown. Owing to the purpose for which the parts are intended, a high grade of steel is used in the manufacture. Due to this fact, and to the thickness of the metal, a heavy-duty press must be employed for the operation. The die illustrated is of the drawing type, and produces the shell illustrated beneath the die from blanks 3/16 inch thick and 4 inches in diameter, which are cut in a preceding operation. After the drawing operation has been performed, the closed end of the shell is pierced on another machine.

In the operation performed by the punch and die illustrated, the blank is located on the drawing die *A* by means of the gage ring *B*, which serves a double purpose by also securing the drawing die in die-block *C*. The shell is formed as the blank is drawn into die *A* by punch *D*, on the downward stroke. On work like this, surplus metal is provided in the blank, in

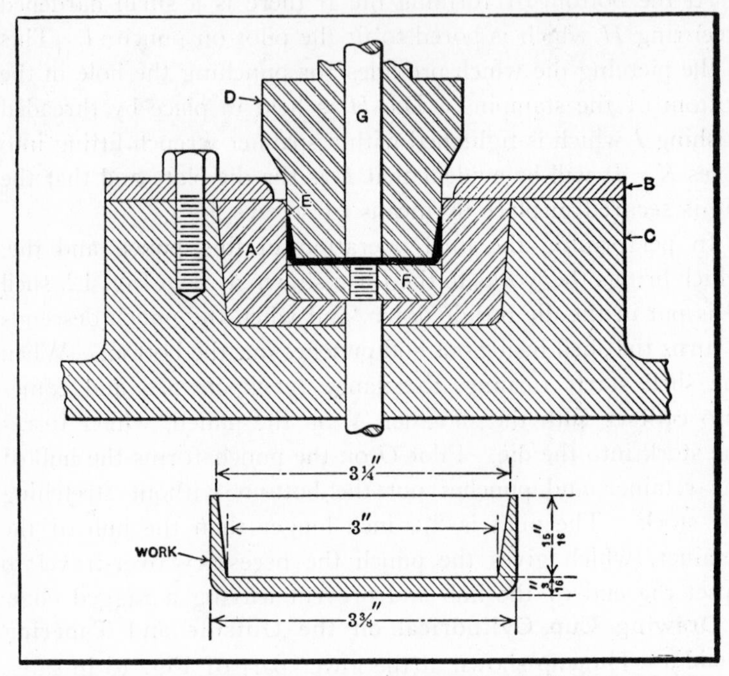

Fig. 15. Die for Drawing Part Shown by Detail View

this case a width of about ⅛ inch being allowed around the entire periphery. This surplus is sheared off by shoulder *E* on punch *D* as the shoulder enters die *A*, at which time sufficient metal has been drawn into the die to produce the shell. The shell is squeezed extra hard toward the end of the stroke, which causes the metal to flow up along the punch about 1/16 inch and insures uniformity and compactness. If the shell remains in the die when the punch is withdrawn, it is ejected by means of the knock-out pad *F*. Rod *G* forces the shell from the punch in case it sticks.

Combination Die for Curled Ring.—Fig. 16 shows a punch and die used for the production of a gasket ring *R* for a combination zinc and cork gasket. This gasket consists of a ring of thin sheet zinc into which is forced, in a later operation, a ring of compressed cork. The die consists of the following parts: The die-holder *A*; the cutting die *B*, which is screwed and doweled to the top of block *A*; the upper stripper ring *C*, which slides freely in a recess in block *A*; the drawing ring *D*, which is screwed to *A*; the inner stripper ring *E*, which slides freely in drawing ring *D*; and the push-rods *F*, which bear against the usual spring and plate below the bolster of the press. The top of the die is covered by a stripper plate (not shown). The punch consists of the punch body *G*, the large cutting and forming punch *H*, the small piercing punch *I*, four stripper-pins *J*, stripper-pin springs *K*, and the pilot *L*, set in the punch *H*.

When the die is in operation, the stock is fed under the stripper by the roll feed of the press, and the punch *I* pierces the central opening of what is later to be the ring that forms the gasket shell. On the next stroke of the press the pilot *L* enters the hole pierced by punch *I* and locates the stock for the cutting punch *H*. After punch *H* has cut the ring for the shell, it carries it down, still guided by pilot *L*, until the ring is grasped between the face of punch *H* and the outer and inner pressure rings *C* and *E*. As the press ram continues downward, the pressure rings *C* and *E* are carried down by the action of the punch, and the stock is drawn over the forming ring *D*, the pressure of rings *C* and *E* preventing wrinkling. On the return stroke of the press, rings *C* and *E* strip the shell from the forming ring *D*, while the stripper pins *J* prevent the shell from sticking in the recess of the forming punch *H*. It is necessary to use the stripper pins *J*, because since the shell surrounds the central portion of punch *H*, there must be some positive means of ejecting it from the groove.

In setting up this set of tools, it was found necessary to

adjust the inner pressure ring E a little tighter than the outer pressure ring C, as the smaller surface of the inner ring allowed the stock to be drawn from under it more readily, which resulted in the inner edge of the shell being lower than the outer edge. This could have been avoided by finding the blank diameter experimentally, but as the job was one on which a

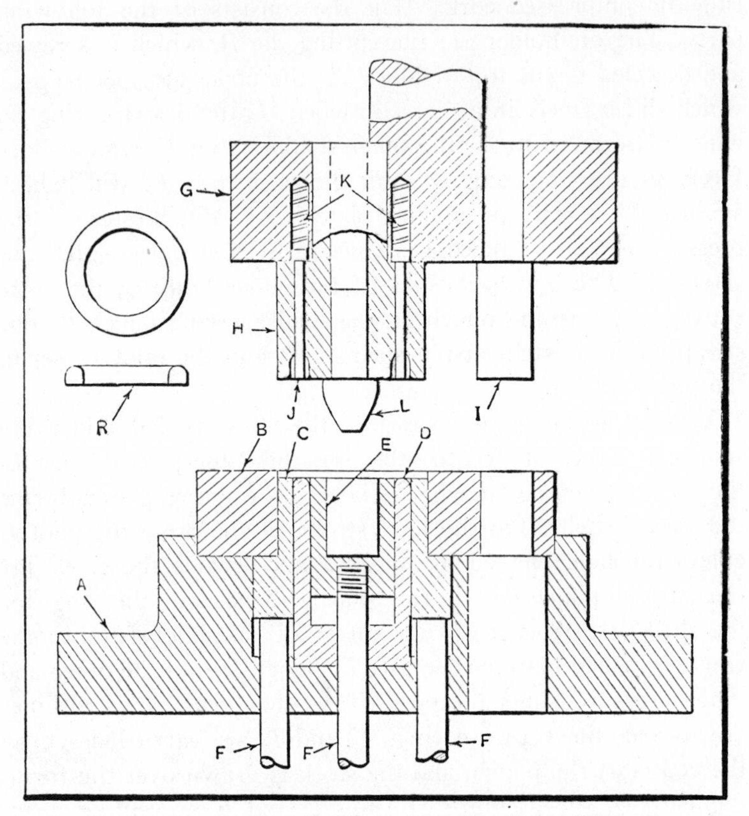

Fig. 16. Die for Blanking and Drawing Gasket Rings

very short time for making the tools had been allowed, it was necessary to compute the diameters of the blank and make up the tools without stopping to find the diameter by the usual methods.

Three sets of these tools were made for gaskets, having inside diameters of 3/4, 1 1/2, and 2 inches respectively, all of which were entirely satisfactory in operation. Owing to the fact that the stock was 0.012 inch soft zinc, the punch *H* was left unhardened, and was sharpened when necessary by peening out the outer edge and shaving it into the die *B*. The edges of the recess in the punch *H* were rounded to a radius of 1/32 inch, to prevent the tearing of the stock in the drawing operation.

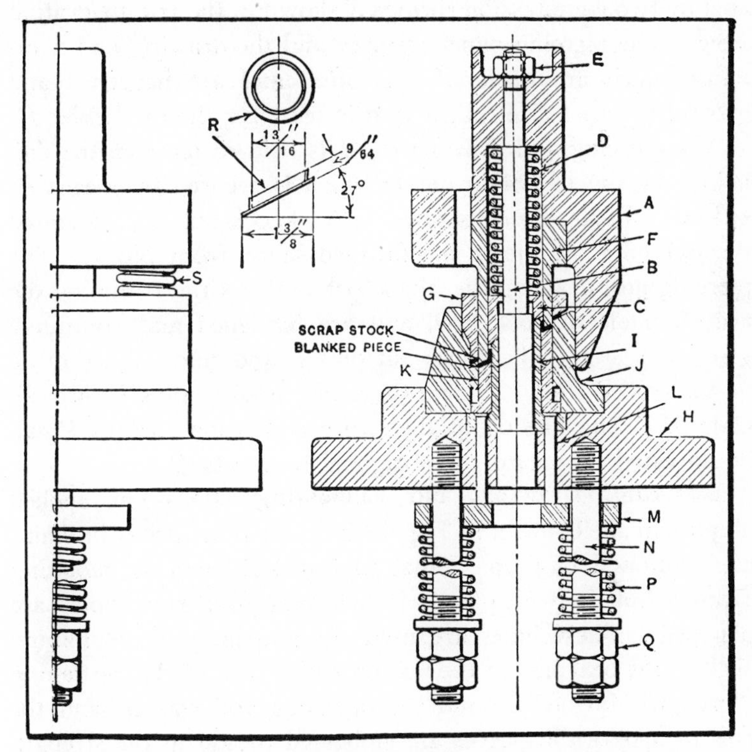

Fig. 17. Combination Die for Piercing, Flanging and Blanking Sheet-metal Collar

Combination Die for Flanged Collar.—The combination die shown in Fig. 17 is designed to pierce, flange, and blank the collar of angular design shown at *R*. This collar, which is of rather an unusual shape, forms part of the gasoline tank of a motorcycle. It is made from strip tin stock, 1 9/16 inches wide and 0.020 inch thick, which is fed through the die at an angle of 27 degrees as indicated by the sectional view of the die.

The punch-holder *A* is made of machine steel and carries the piercing punch *B*, which is fitted with a stripper *C*. The stripper is operated by the compression spring *D*. Punch *B* is held in place by a hexagonal nut *E*. The drawing and trimming punch *F* is screwed into a counterbored hole in punch-holder *A*, and locked in place by a dowel-pin. The stripper *G* is operated by two compression springs *S* shown in the front elevation view. The piercing punch stripper and the drawing and trimming punch are made of tool steel, and are hardened and ground to exact size. Cast iron is used for the die-holder *H*.

The piercing and drawing die *I* is held in place in the die-holder by the trimming die *J*, which is secured by means of ½-inch fillister-head screws. A knock-out *K*, operated through pins *L*, ejects the finished piece from die *J*. The piercing and drawing die, the knock-out and the trimming die are all made of tool steel, and are hardened and accurately ground to size. The knock-out pins *L* and studs *N* are made of cold-rolled steel. Pressure is transmitted to pins *L* through plate *M*. The tension of the two compression springs *P* can be adjusted by means of hexagonal lock-nuts *Q*.

Blanking, Drawing, and Embossing Die.—The spoked aluminum shell shown in Fig. 18 is about four inches in diameter and one inch deep. It has four spokes, or arms, radiating from a hub in which a shaft hole and four rivet holes are punched. These holes are used for attaching the aluminum shell to the bearings of the hub on which it is used. Stiffening "lips" are formed around the openings and spokes, and the ribs or spokes themselves are embossed to add to the strength of the shell. Four rivet holes punched through the rim of the shell serve to attach it to an exterior band.

This shell was made in the following manner and with excellent results: The blanking, drawing, and embossing is done in one operation in a double-action press, using the die shown in Fig. 19. The blank-holder *A* is made of cast iron, and a hardened tool-steel blanking die *D* is fastened to it, which not only acts as a die, but also serves to hold the blank in position while the drawing operation is taking place. *B* is the

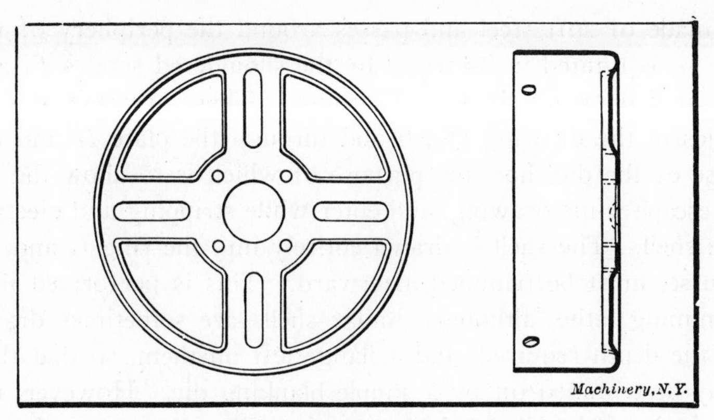

Fig. 18. Aluminum Shell Produced in Dies Illustrated in Figs. 19 to 21 Inclusive

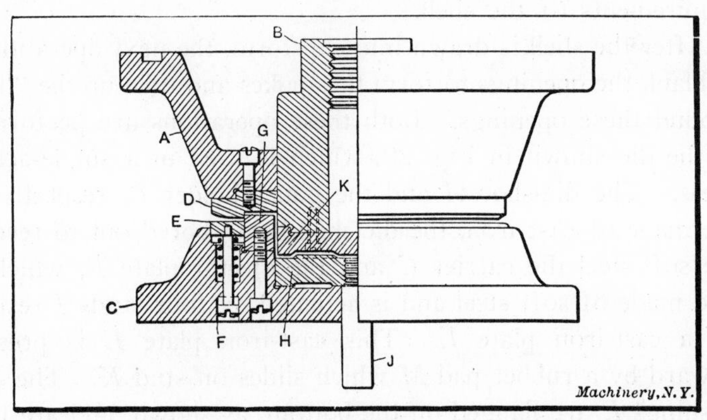

Fig. 19. Combination Blanking, Drawing and Embossing Die for Aluminum Shell

cast-iron drawing punch, to which is attached a hardened steel face *K*. This face *K* contains the embossing recess for the spokes, into which the metal is forced by the embossing punch *H* held to the lower member. The punch *H* also acts as an ejector after the drawing and embossing operations have been completed, and is actuated by the stem *J* and the press knockout mechanism.

The die-shoe *C* is made of cast iron and is bored out to receive the blanking punch *G*, over the inner edge of which the shell is drawn after blanking. The stripper ring *E*, which is made of soft steel and passes around the periphery of the die *G*, is limited in its travel by the shouldered screws *F*, and is acted upon by six helical springs. There are several vent holes in the drawing punch and through the plate *H* and the base of the die-shoe, the purpose of which is to allow the air to escape while drawing, and enter while stripping and ejecting the shell. The shell is drawn entirely into the ring *G* and, of course, must be trimmed afterward. This is performed in a trimming lathe, although similar shells are sometimes drawn to the depth required, and a flange left on them, so that they may be trimmed off by a simple blanking die. However, the method of handling this operation lies entirely with the designer, although it should be governed to some extent by the requirements of the shell.

After the shell is drawn into cup form, the next operation is to blank the openings to form the spokes and turn up the "lips" around these openings. Both these operations are performed in the die shown in Fig. 20, which is used in a single-action press. The die-shoe *A* and the punch-holder *B*, respectively, are made of cast iron, the die-shoe being bored out to receive the soft-steel die carrier *G* and the ejector plate *F*, which is also made of soft steel and is actuated by four studs *J* resting on a cast-iron plate *L*. This cast-iron plate *L* is pressed upward by a rubber pad *M* which slides on stud *K*. The die-bushings *E* are flanged on the bottom, as shown, and are held in the carrier plate in the usual manner. They serve not only as dies for piercing, but also as drawing punches to draw the stiffening "lips" on the shell. The drawing die *C* is held on the punch-holder *B* and carries the piercing punches *D*, which are set ahead of the drawing die so that they will pierce the stock before the die begins to draw the "lips." A stripper ring *H*, actuated by coil springs as shown, is limited in its travel by the drawing die C upon which it comes to rest on the up-stroke of the ram. All the screws and dowel-pins used for holding the various members in their respective holders are omitted for the sake of clearness.

The shell is now ready to have the holes around the rim and

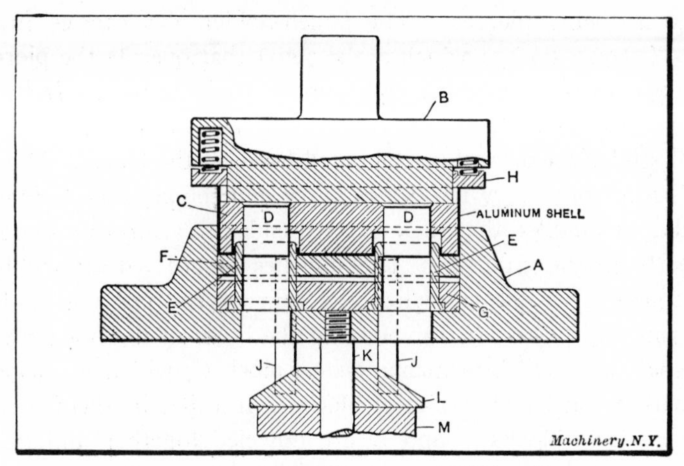

Fig. 20. Combination Piercing and Ribbing Dies

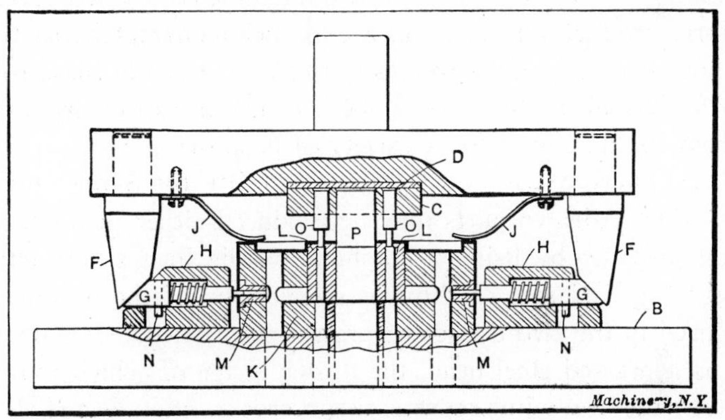

Fig. 21. Die for Piercing Holes in Sides and Bottom of Aluminum Shell Illustrated in Fig. 18

the small holes in the bottom pierced. These operations are done in the die shown in Fig. 21, which is used in a single-action press. A circular disk *B* of cast iron serves as a base for the die, and to it is attached the die-anvil *K*, of soft machine steel. Die-bushings *L* and *M* are driven into the anvil *K* for piercing the holes in the rim and in the bottom of the shell. Recesses are cut in the block *K* to receive the "lips" around the spoke openings. The cast-iron punch-holder carries two flat springs *J*, which serve to hold the shell on the anvil when the holes are being pierced. The punch-holder also carries four studs *F* (only two of which are shown) that operate the piercing punches *G*. These piercing punches *G* fit in blocks *H* held to the die-bolster, and are retained in the blocks *H* by the small studs *N* working in elongated holes in the block. These small studs or pins *N* also serve to prevent the punches *G* from turning around, so that their beveled ends are always presented properly to the studs *F*. The punches *G* are withdrawn by coil springs, as shown, when the ram of the press ascends. The punches *O* and *P*, for piercing the holes in the bottom of the shell, are held in a machine-steel block *C*, which is backed up with a hardened tool-steel block *D* inserted in the punch-holder. The blocks *C* and *D* are doweled together and held to the punch-holder.

Making this aluminum shell in the manner described gives a uniform product, and the tools are of such a character that they are not very costly and are easily repaired. While these tools are of a special character, a number of the features incorporated in them could be used for a variety of purposes.

Double-action Die and Combination Die for Same Operation.—Many drawn parts may be produced either in a double-action press or by using a combination die in a single-action press. Figs. 22 and 23 shows a comparison of the designs of dies used in the two classes of presses mentioned. The drawn part is a pressed steel head, the drawn shape of which is indicated by the heavy line representing a cross-section. It is about 18 inches in diameter and is slightly dished to increase end resistance.

The blanking and drawing die shown in Fig. 22 is used in a double-action press. The blank is cut to the proper diameter as punch *A* enters die *B*. Punch *A* then grips the metal between it and die *B* as punch *C* comes in contact with the blank and pushes it into the die, the drawing being completed when die *D* reaches its lowest position. This die member is also equipped with coil springs which hold it firmly against the work during the descent of punch *C* and raise it at the end of the operation to eject the work from the die. When the punch ascends, die *B* acts as a stripper to pull the work from member *C*. In order to reduce replacement costs and to facilitate grinding, punch *A* and die *B* could be provided with shearing rings made of tool steel, as in the case of the first die described. Block *D* can be made of gray iron, but it is preferable to use a semi-steel casting.

If a double-action press were not available for manufacturing the head, it could be produced in a press of the single-action type equipped with the die illustrated in Fig. 23. In this

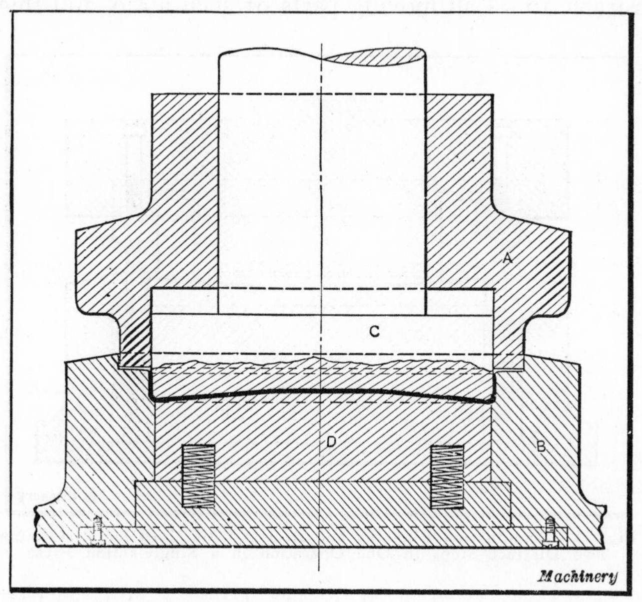

Fig. 22. Construction of Double-action Die Used for Drawing Part for Which Combination Die, Fig. 23, was also Designed

die, the work is drawn with the flange down instead of up, the reverse of the method used in the double-action press. Ejectors are required on both the punch and die of this set. Punch *A* is again, a combination blanking and drawing member, the blank being sheared as the punch enters die *E*, and then drawn by the recess at the center of the punch as the downward stroke of the press ram is completed. Near the end of this operation the center part of the work is stretched slightly. The blanking edge of the punch should be sufficiently in advance of the drawing recess so that the shearing operation will be completed before the drawing is started. Ejectors *B* of the punch are backed up by rubber pads in the die illustrated, but springs could also be used for this purpose.

Block *C* of the die is equipped with an ejector ring *D*, actuated by coil springs. To accommodate this ejector, die-block *E* is under-cut on the inside. A disadvantage of this design is that scale can accumulate in the crevice between ejector *D* and die-block *E* and render the die inoperative. It is desirable to oil all moving parts of such a die, and this is a

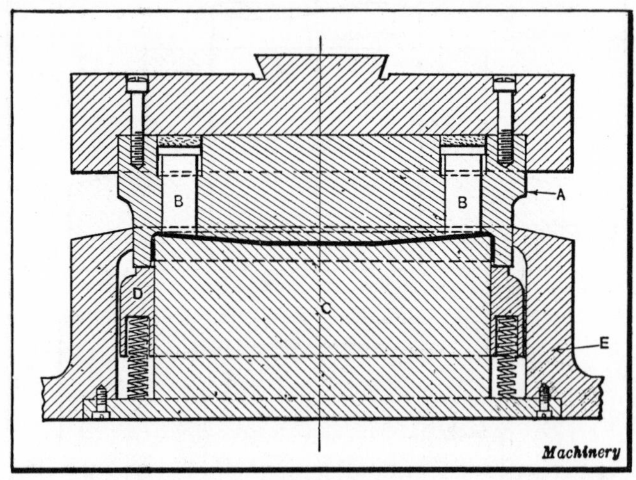

Fig. 23. Combination Blanking and Drawing Die Used for Performing Two Distinct Steps in One Operation in a Single-action Press

factor that increases the scale trouble because oil on scale makes it cling so tenaciously to the metal parts that it cannot be readily blown out by compressed air, even if ports are incorporated in the die for this purpose. In order to remove this scale, it would be necessary to dismantle the die from the machine, and for this reason a double-action press is preferable for this class of work. Of course, the blanking and piercing could be done in one operation prior to the drawing, which would permit the use of a drawing die designed without part *E* so that ejector *D* would be entirely visible and accessible for cleaning without removing the die from the machine.

Die for Comparatively Deep Drawing in a Single-acting Press.—A die for drawing steel cups, such as would usually be made in a double-acting press, is shown in Fig. 24. No double-acting press was available, but only a long-stroke single-acting press of sufficient capacity to do the job. The die was made as follows: On the die *B* were bolted some U-shaped pieces *E* which carried the holding hooks *D*. These hooks *D* could be adjusted to any desired degree of tightness by setting down the pieces *E* with the set-screws provided and then clamp-

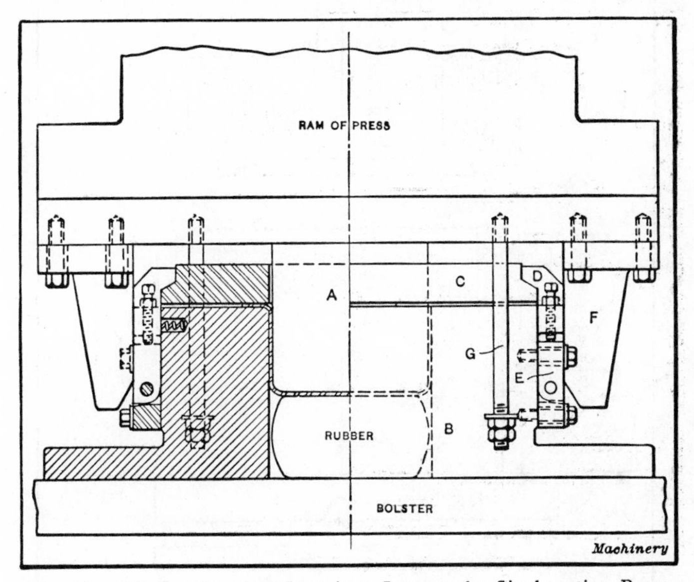

Fig. 24. Die for Drawing Cups in a Long-stroke Single-action Press

ing them securely in place. The blank-holder *C* was suspended on four bolts *G*, and these bolts were adjusted to the proper length so that the blank-holder *C* was laid on the blank early in the stroke; then closing lugs *F* engage the holding hooks *D* and force them in on the beveled ledge of the blank-holder. The lugs *F* then slide along the back of hooks *D* during the remainder of the stroke.

On the up-stroke the closing lugs leave the hooks *D* which are immediately thrown open by springs provided for this purpose. and then the blank-holder *C* is lifted up by the suspension bolts *G*. The formed piece is loosened in the die by the rubber block, or, if necessary, a positive stripper can be provided. At first the closing lugs *F* were made solid with the punch-holder, but after several were broken by dirt or other foreign substances getting under the blank, a new holder was made with the lugs bolted on, so that the bolts would allow the lugs to

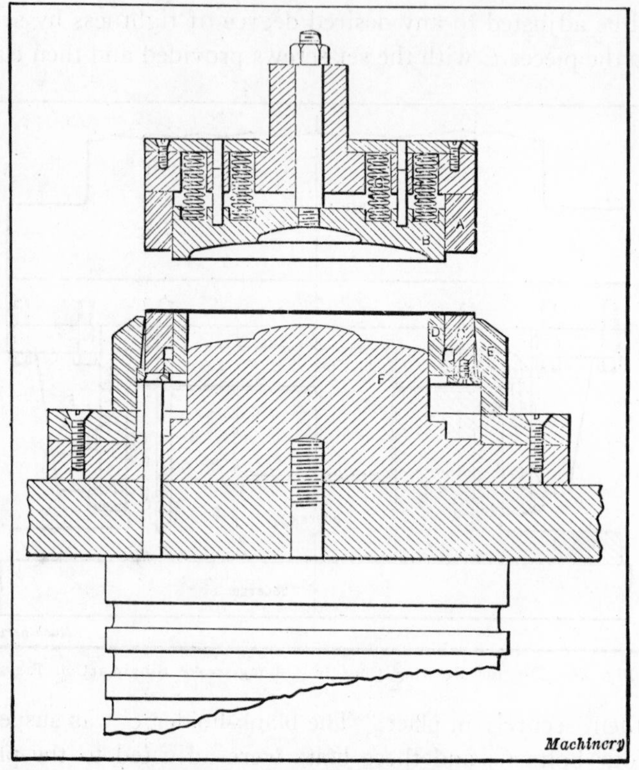

Fig. 25. Double Draw-ring Die

give enough to prevent breakage. This die is more expensive than would be required for a double-acting press, but makes it possible to do the work with the equipment at hand.

Dies Having Double Draw-rings.—The object in using double draw-ring dies is to perform in one operation what usually requires two or three operations. Dies of this type, one of which is shown in various operative positions in Figs. 25, 26, and 27, cut the blank and form two steps in the cover, while the outer and inner draw-rings act as one member. As the die continues downward, the inner draw-ring is stopped by a shoulder on the punch, and the outer draw-ring travels down against the pressure supplied by the air cushion. The latter movement forms another step in the cover. Finally, the sliding center of the die, which is at first supported by the springs,

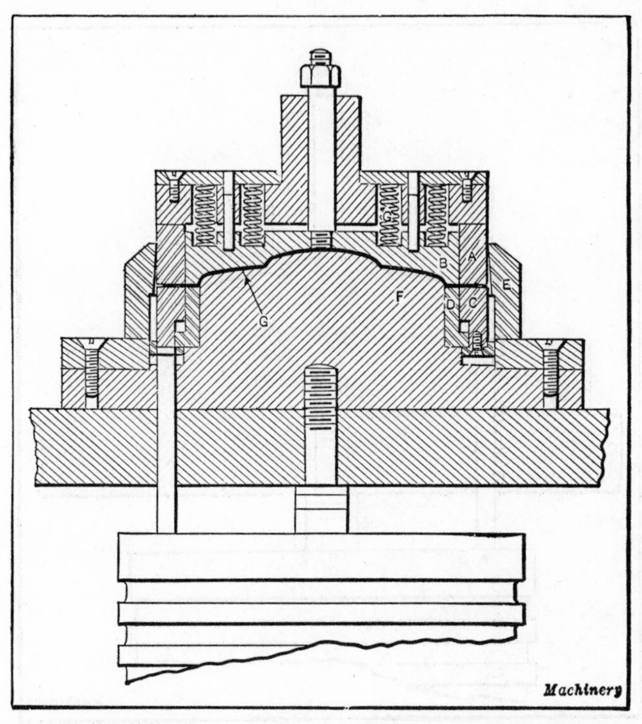

Fig. 26. Die Shown in Fig. 25 with Work partly Formed

comes in contact with the holding member and gives the cover its finished form.

As the pressure-ring descends, the part *B*, Fig. 25, comes in contact with part *D* and compresses the springs *G* until part *A* strikes member *C*. As the die continues downward, the cutting edges of parts *A* and *E* cut the blank from the stock. The blank is forced downward until it reaches the position shown at *G*, Fig. 26, at which time the member *D* is in contact with a shoulder on the punch *F*. The part *C*, or outer draw-ring, is supported by an air cushion which allows it to descend in such a manner that the final step in the cover is formed between the parts *A* and *C*. On the further downward travel of the punch, as shown in Fig. 27, all the springs or cushion-backed members are seated against solid shoulders and sufficient pressure is applied to give the work its final form.

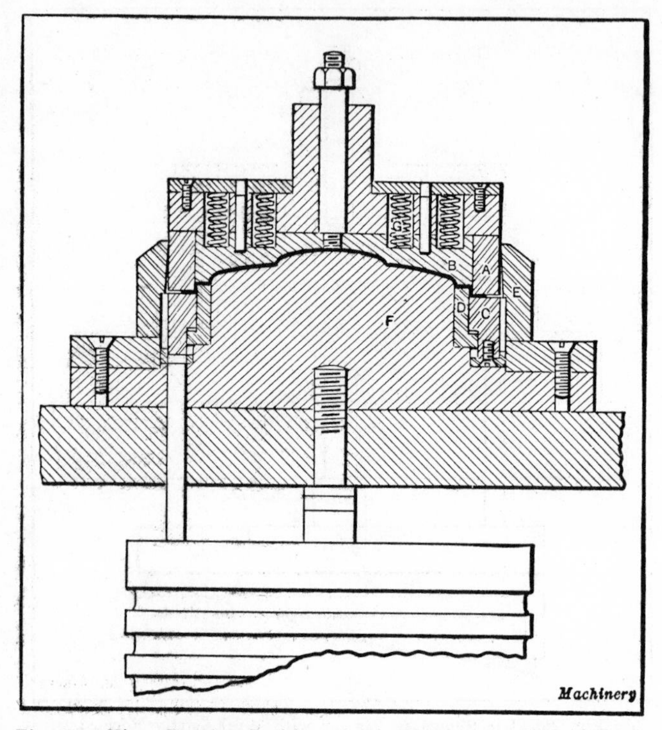

Fig. 27. View Showing Position of Die Members at End of Stroke

Drawn Hubs which Provide Holes for Tapping.—When sheet metal parts are fastened together by means of screws, a tapped hole in one part would not in many instances provide the necessary length of thread. For certain classes of work three or four complete thread turns may be obtained by first piercing a hole through the stock and then drawing a hub, the inside diameter of which is slightly larger than the root diameter of the thread. A hub made in this way ordinarily can have a length equal to about the radius of the hole. Screws or bolts provided with nuts may be preferable, especially for the larger and more expensive stampings which would be spoiled if a tapped hub is stripped of its threads.

Hubs are also formed on some small gears or pinions which are cut from flat stock. These hubs, however, usually are longer than those used merely for tapping and ordinarily are produced in a progressive type of die by a series of drawing operations. The bottom of the drawn hub is blanked out in connection with this series of operations.

CHAPTER XIV

DIES FOR DRAWING DEEP SHELLS

THE drawn parts dealt with in this chapter are so deep in proportion to the diameter that redrawing operations are

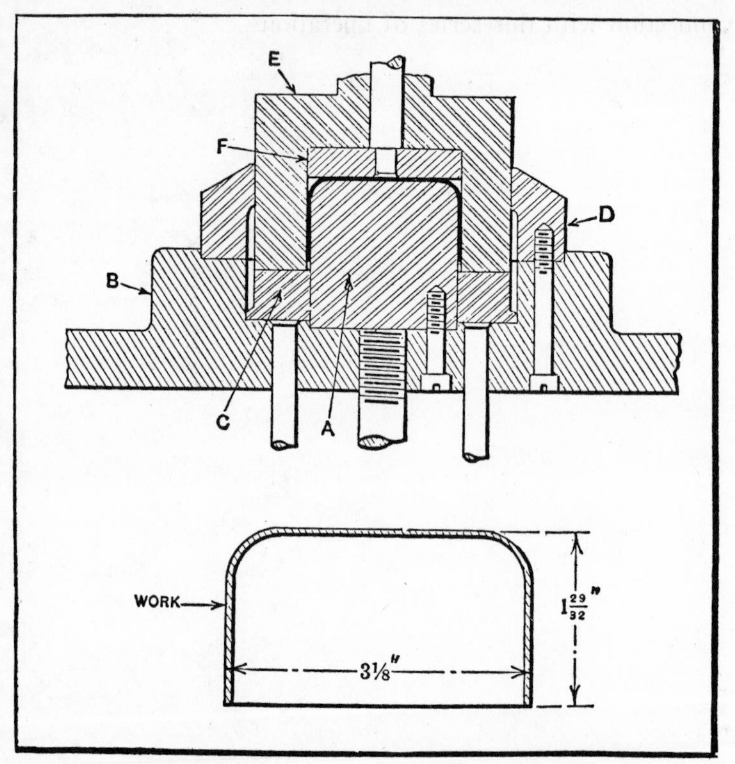

Fig. 1. Blanking and Drawing Die Used for First Operation on Flanged Shell. See also Figs. 2 to 7 Inclusive

necessary in order to obtain the required depth. When two or more drawing operations are essential, the dies should be designed so as to produce the final shape, from a flat blank, by a gradual change of form but without employing more operations than are needed to meet practical requirements. If dies for successive operations are so proportioned as to obtain excessive reductions in diameter or changes in form that are too abrupt, the metal will be over-stressed, if not ruptured. On the contrary, if too many redrawing operations are employed, the cost of production is correspondingly increased.

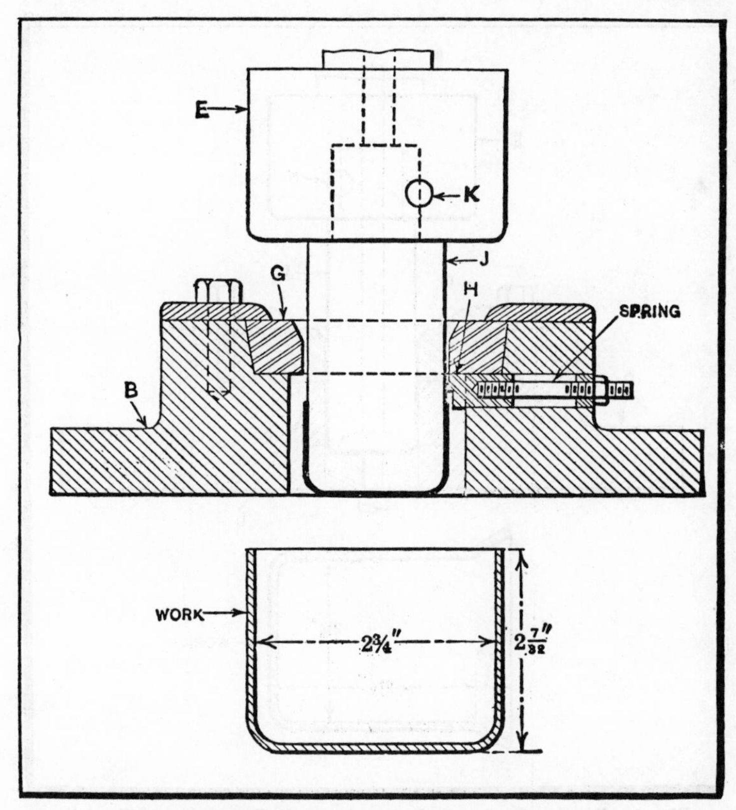

Fig. 2. Die for Reducing the Diameter of the Shell

Somewhere between these extremes there is a safe and efficient course to follow, and determining just where this course lies requires a practical knowledge of drawing die performance. The examples which follow illustrate variety both in regard to drawn products and in the designs of dies constructed to suit various conditions. Most of the drawn parts featured in this chapter are either of cylindrical form or are composed mainly of cylindrical sections. Conical and other special shapes are dealt with in following chapters.

Dies for Flanged Shell Having Two Diameters.—Difficulties encountered in the drawing operations on a steel shell, which is used as a vacuum pot on a certain type of computing

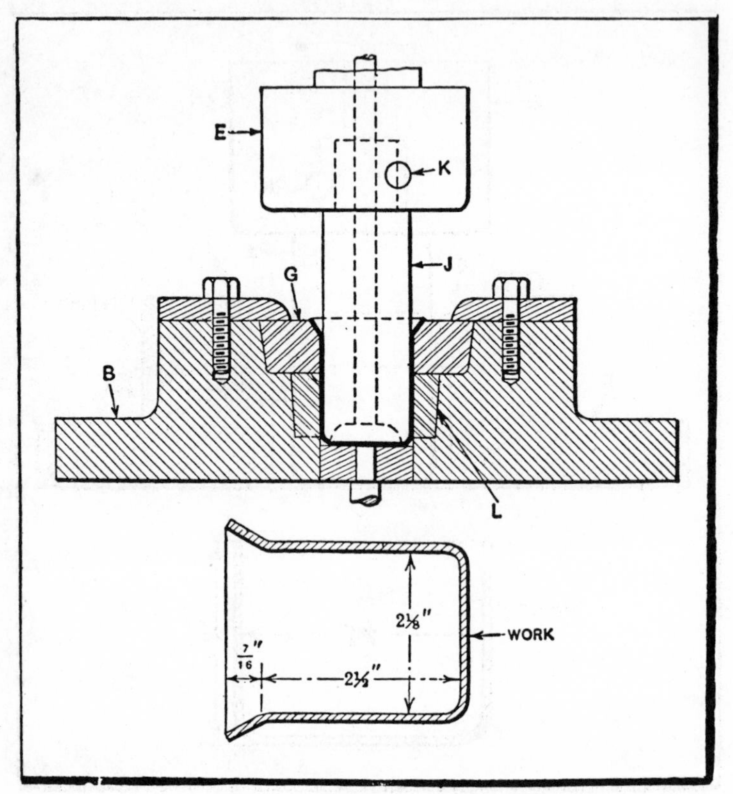

Fig. 3. Die for Further Reducing the Shell Diameter and Partially Forming the Flange

scale, were overcome by using the dies shown in Figs. 1 to 4 inclusive. The illustrations show each die used and the drawn shell as it appears after each operation. All the steel parts employed in the forming and drawing operations are hardened and ground. The corresponding parts of the various dies have the same reference letters throughout the description. The blank of sheet steel from which the shell is drawn is 0.065 inch thick and 5 7/16 inches in diameter.

The die shown in Fig. 1 is a combination die which cuts the blank and performs the first drawing operation. It consists of a forming die *A*, die-block *B*, drawing ring *C*, cutting ring *D*, punch *E*, and shell ejector *F*. The construction of the parts

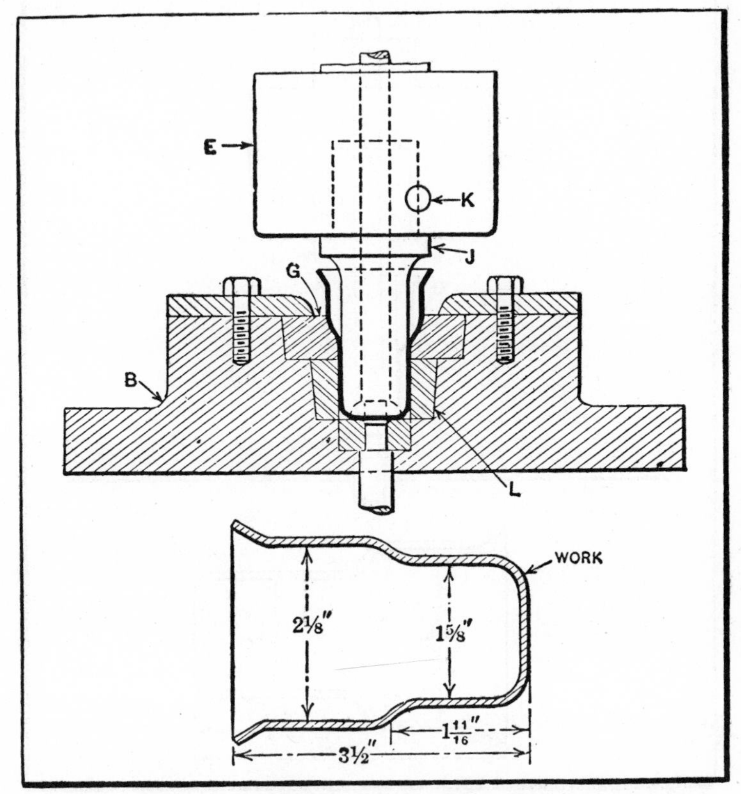

Fig. 4. Die for the Fourth Operation which Elongates the Shell and Forms the Small End

and their method of operation can be readily seen from the illustration, and no further explanation is required.

A plain push-through die, such as shown in Fig. 2, is employed to reduce partially the diameter of the shell. The die ring *G* is carried in the die-block *B* in which it is secured by means of cast-iron straps and cap-screws. An interesting stripping device is used in this die. There are three strippers *H*, which are set radially in pockets or channels, equally spaced underneath die ring *G*, and which engage the end of the shell upon the return stroke of the press and strip the completely drawn shell from the punch. These strippers operate in the

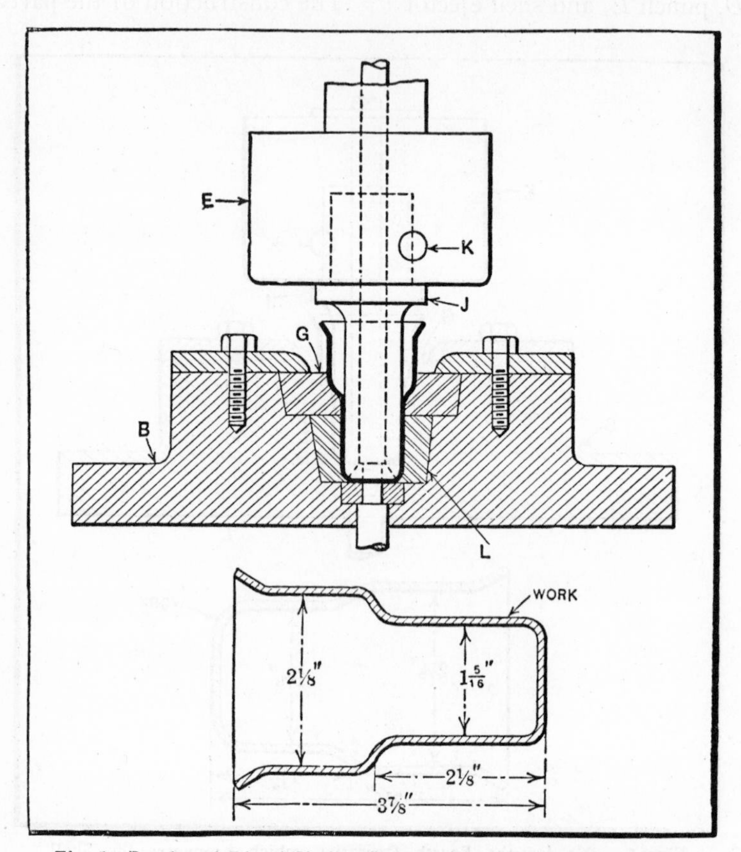

Fig. 5. Punch and Die of Similar Construction to that Shown in Fig 4

following manner: As the punch forces the shell downward, the strippers are pushed radially away from the center of the die, and when the upper end of the shell has passed the strippers, coil springs expand and force the ends of the strippers against punch *J*, so that upon its return stroke the shell is pushed from the punch. This die is so designed that it may be changed to suit various sizes of shells. To make this change, the strippers are adjusted and the punch and the die ring replaced to suit the work being formed. The punch *J* is supported in the machine steel punch-holder *E* by a ⅝-inch pin K, and when it is desired to use a different size punch it

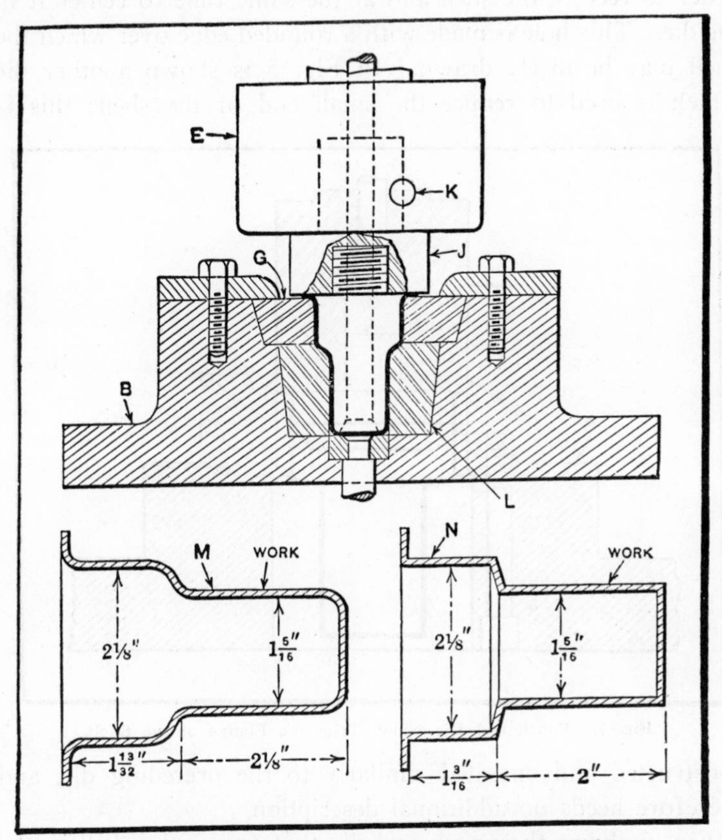

Fig. 6. Die Employed for the Final Forming Operations

is only necessary to remove pin *K* from holder *E*, insert another size punch, and again drive pin *K* into place. The punch-holder *E* has a ¾-inch hole bored in it, which permits the use of a bar for forcing the punch from the holder. This type of punch and holder is used in five of the operations that are employed in the manufacture of this piece.

Fig. 3 shows a punch and die which further reduces the diameter of the shell and also partly forms the flange. Two die rings, *G* and *L*, are used in this die. The die that is shown in Fig. 4 is used for the first operation in forming the small end of the shell. The hole in ring *G* is enlarged on the top in order to receive the shell and at the same time to center it in the die. This hole is made with a rounded edge over which the shell may be nicely drawn. In Fig. 5 is shown another die which is used to reduce the small end of the shell; this is

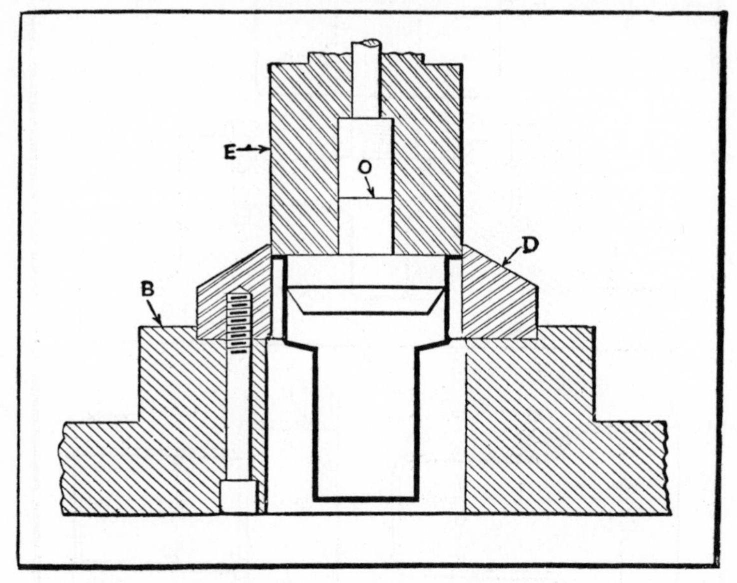

Fig. 7. Punch and Die which Trim the Flange of the Shell

constructed and operated similarly to the preceding die, and therefore needs no additional description.

Fig. 6 shows the punch and die that forms the shell to the shape shown at *M*. By replacing the die rings *G* and *L* with two other die rings (not shown) and by changing the punch *J*, this die is also used to form the shell finally to the shape shown at *N*. It will be noted that the shell *M* is longer than the shell *N*, which allows the metal to be upset a sufficient amount to form the sharp edges, and at the same time does not alter the thickness of the walls of the shell. The die rings *G* and *L* are tapered so as to be a good fit in the die-blocks. This construction reduces the possibility of the dies breaking under unusual strains such as would occur if the operator should put two shells into the die at one time.

The trimming die shown in Fig. 7 trims the flange of the shell. This is a plain blanking die, and has the pilot *O* inserted

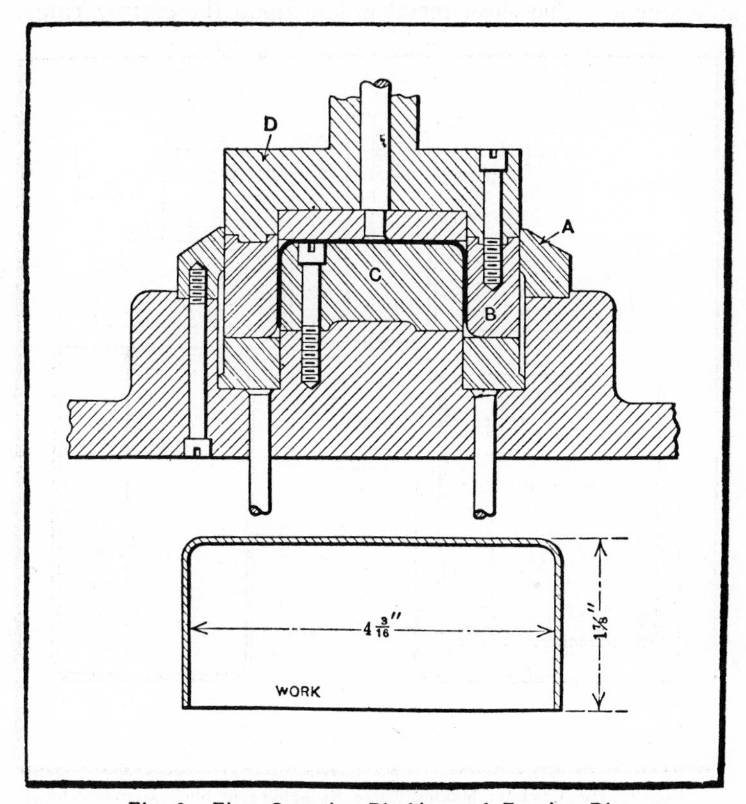

Fig. 8. First Operation Blanking and Forming Die

into the punch to locate the shell properly upon the face of the cutting ring *D* while it is being trimmed. As this pilot is concentric with the outside of the punch, it brings the flange of the shell concentric with the body.

Dies for Oil Filler Cup.—The dies used in the manufacture of an oil filler cup are shown in Figs. 8 to 14, inclusive. Each of the dies is illustrated in the order in which it is used.

and a detail of the shell is shown as it appears after each operation. The shell is made from cold-rolled strip steel 0.065 inch thick, the blank being cut to a diameter of 6¾ inches.

The blank is cut and the first drawing operation performed by the die illustrated in Fig. 8. This die is of a standard type and is used in connection with the usual rubber buffer attachment. The sheet metal is laid upon the cutting ring *A*,

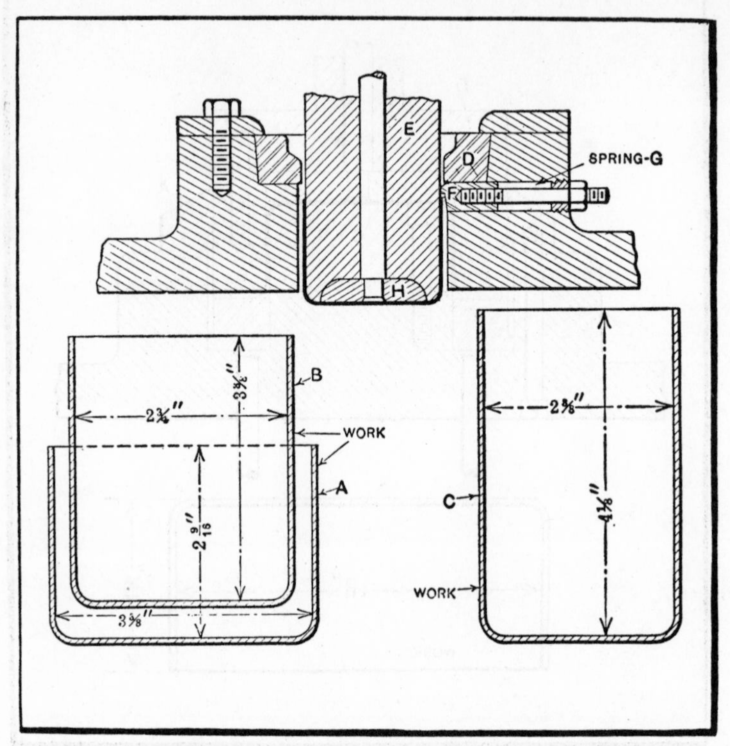

Fig. 9. Die Used for Making Three Reductions in Shell Diameter by Using Punches and Die Rings of Different Sizes

and the blank is cut to the required size as the lower edge of the punch face ring *B* passes the upper edge of ring *A* on the downward stroke of the press ram. The shell is drawn on the forming die *C* as the punch *D* concludes its descent.

The die shown in Fig. 9 is employed to make the three reductions in the diameter of the shell as shown beneath the die. The die as illustrated will produce the shape *A*. In order to reduce the shell to shape *B* after a quantity have been formed as shown at *A*, it is necessary to replace the die ring *D* and punch *E* with ones of suitable dimensions. The punch and die ring are again changed in order to produce the shell as shown at *C*. The upper surface of the die ring *D* is hollowed out to the external diameter of the shell to be operated upon, in

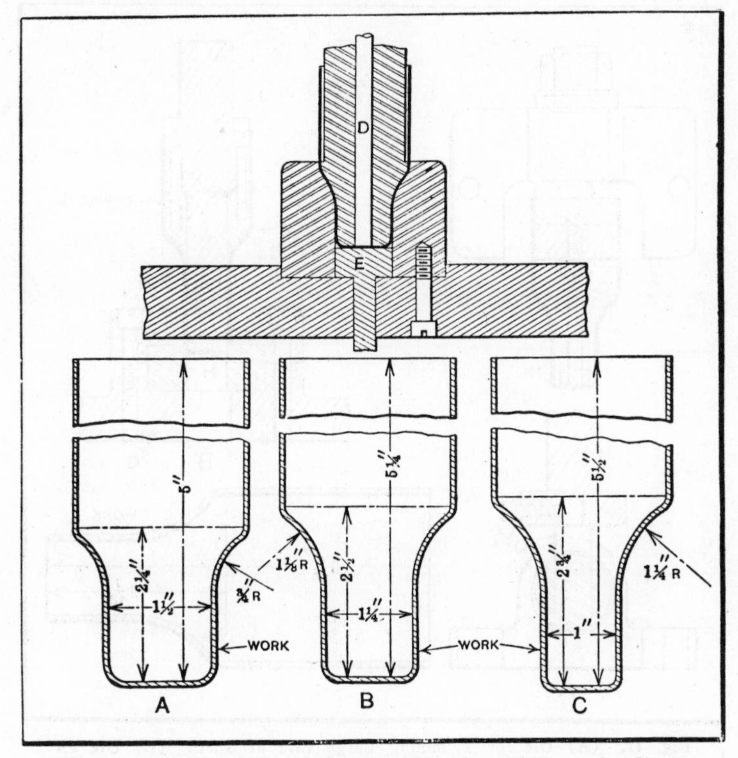

Fig. 10. Type of Die Employed to Draw the Shell to the Shapes Shown

order to locate it properly for the operation. This die is equipped with an automatic stripping device for forcing the shell from punch *E* upon the return stroke of the press. It consists mainly of the stripper *F* and spring *G*. As the shell is forced through the die on the downward stroke of the press ram the stripper is pushed in an outward direction. When the shell reaches the position shown, the stripper is actuated by the spring and forced toward the center of the die so that when the punch makes the return stroke, the end of the stripper keeps the shell from adhering to the punch, and when the punch has been completely withdrawn the shell drops through the die. The knock-out pad *H* is provided for use in case stripper *F* does not function properly.

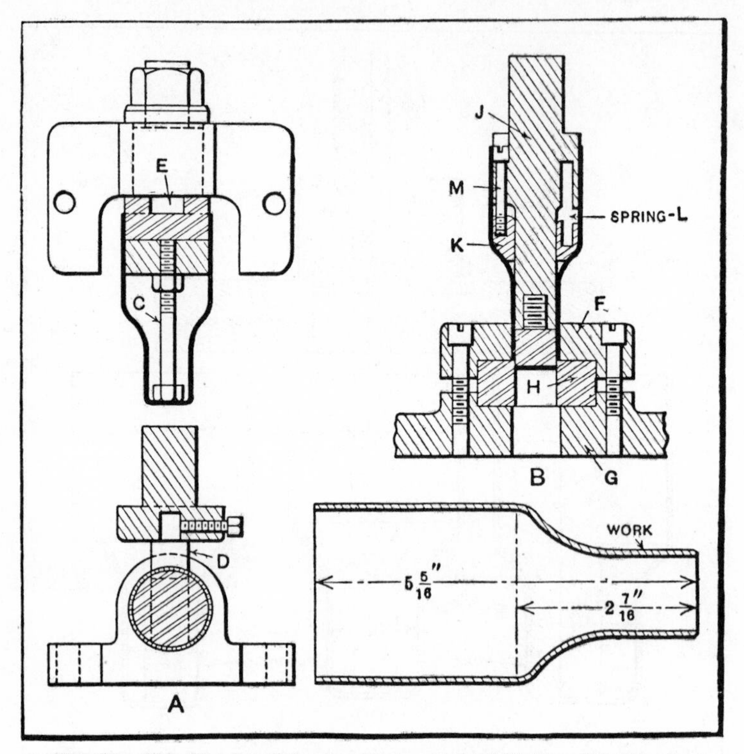

Fig. 11. (A) Die for Trimming Large End of Shell. (B) Die for Punching Hole in Small End

Three dies of the type shown in Fig. 10 are used to draw the shell to the shapes *A*, *B*, and *C*. Knock-out devices *D* and *E* are provided in each case for forcing the shell from the punch and die. These dies complete the drawing operations on the shell. The die illustrated at *A* in Fig. 11 trims the edge of the shell at the large end. The shell is placed on the device as shown, the screw *C* acting as a gage to give the shell the proper length. The end of the shell is trimmed as the cutting tool D descends into slot E, the shell being turned by hand after each stroke of the cutting tool until the entire end has been trimmed. The punch and die shown at B in the same illustration cuts a hole in the small end of the shell. There is sufficient clearance between the ring F and the die-shoe G to permit the cutting ring H to be reground a number of times

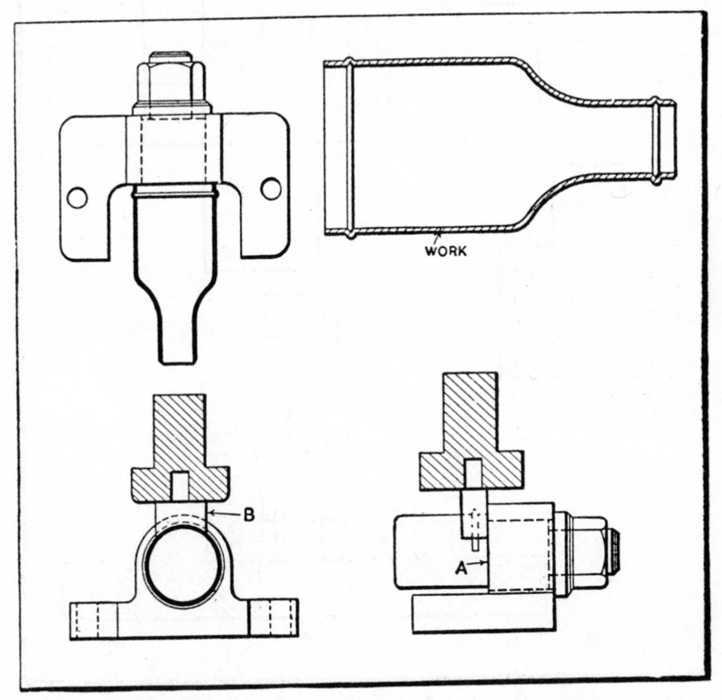

Fig. 12. Die for Forming Beads on Ends of Shell

The punch J is equipped with a novel stripping device consisting of stripper K, which is held in position on punch J by means of screws M, and springs L. The stripper is forced downward on the return stroke of the press ram by the expansion of the springs, thus forcing the shell off the punch.

Fig. 12 shows the die that stamps the bead on the large end of the shell. The method of doing this is very similar to the trimming operation performed by the die shown at A in Fig. 11; that is. the shell is placed in the die with the large end

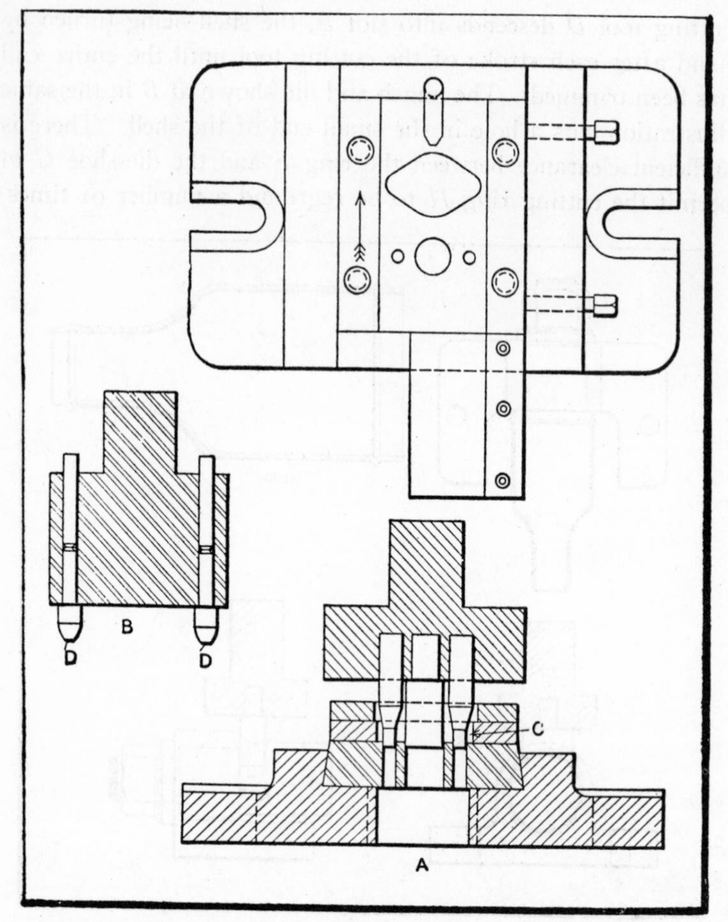

Fig. 13. Combination Piercing and Blanking Die for Producing Foot-plate

against the surface *A*, while the beading tool *B* reciprocates and forms the bead on the shell. The shell is also turned by hand in order to allow it to be beaded around the entire circumference. A die of similar design is employed to produce a bead on the small end of the shell.

The die illustrated in Fig. 13 produces the foot-plate which may be seen attached to the shell in Fig. 14. This part is made from strip metal which is fed through the die opening C in the direction indicated by the arrow in the plan view. Two strokes

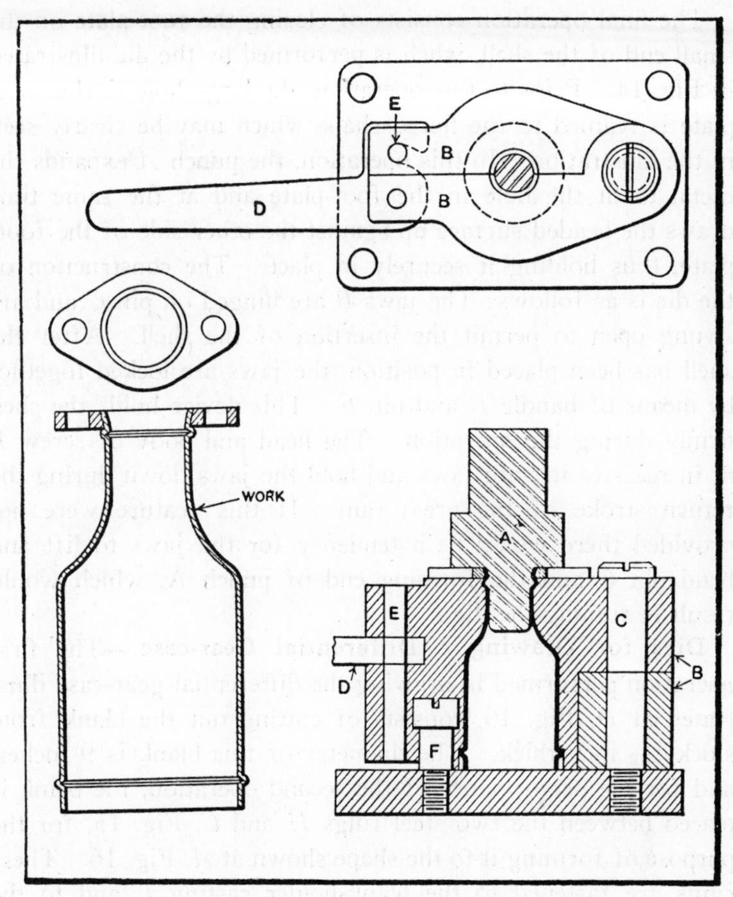

Fig. 14. Die used for Assembling the Shell and Foot-plate

are required to complete one piece, the three holes being punched through on the first stroke, while the blank is cut by the second stroke. It is obvious that after the first operation, a completed piece will be produced with each stroke of the press ram. The construction of the punching tools which pierce the holes in the plate may be clearly seen in the section shown at A, while the enlarged sectional view at *B* shows the tool which cuts the blank. The pilots *D* enter the holes cut in the plate by the first operation to locate the plate for the second operation.

The final operation consists of closing the foot-plate on the small end of the shell, whch is performed by the die illustrated in Fig. 14. Prior to this operation, the large hole in the foot-plate is reamed to the flared shape which may be clearly seen in the illustration. In this operation, the punch *A* expands the metal to fit the hole in the foot-plate and at the same time draws the beaded surface up against the other side of the foot-plate, thus holding it securely in place. The construction of the die is as follows: The jaws *B* are hinged on pin *C* and are swung open to permit the insertion of the shell. After the shell has been placed in position, the jaws are locked together by means of handle *D* and pin *E*. This device holds the shell firmly during the operation. The head and body of screw *F* fit in recesses in both jaws and hold the jaws down during the return stroke of the press ram. If this feature were not provided there would be a tendency for the jaws to lift and bend pin *C* and the forming end of punch A, which would result in ruining the die.

Dies for Drawing a Differential Gear-case.—The first operation performed in drawing the differential gear-case illustrated at *D*, Fig. 16, consists of cutting out the blank from stock 5/32 inch thick. The diameter of this blank is 9 inches, and for the performance of the second operation, the blank is placed between the two steel rings *H* and *C*, Fig. 15, for the purpose of forming it to the shape shown at *A*, Fig. 16. These rings are fastened to the blank-holder casting *L* and to the die-block *B* to which they are fitted by means of annular tongues and grooves, and secured by means of machine screws. The locating ring *R* on the outside of the die ring *C* locates the blank concentrically with the die. In the operation of this die which is of the double-action type, the blank-holder *L* descends before the punch *F* and holds the blank on the surface of the die ring while the punch descends and performs the drawing operation. At the end of the stroke of the press, the punch ascends in advance of the blank-holder so that, if the shell should stick on the punch, the blank-holder ring would strip it from the punch as the latter travels upward through it.

The third operation reduces the shell to the final body diameter as indicated at *B*, Fig. 16. The knock-out *K*, Fig. 15, employed in the punch is set in as shown, thus permitting a larger bearing surface on the bottom of the shell for ejecting it from the punch. For producing heavy shells of large diameter, such as the one shown, this construction is advisable. The die ring *C* is inserted in the die-holder *B* and is held in place by ring *A*, which acts as a gage ring for locating the shell.

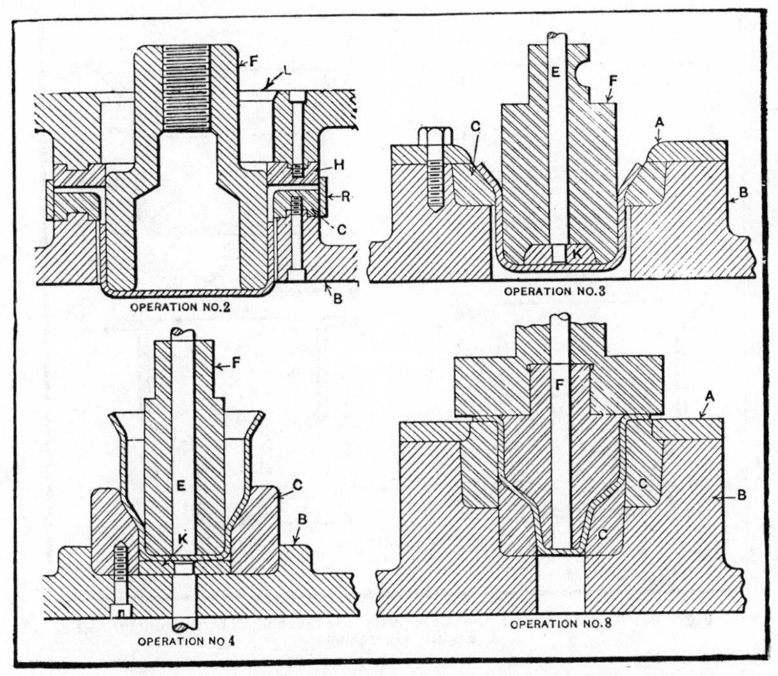

Fig. 15. Some of the Dies used in Drawing the Gear Case Shown in Fig. 16

The die used in performing the fourth operation (see Fig. 15), is provided with two knock-outs *E* and *K*, located as shown in the punch and die, respectively. It will be noted that the punch does not entirely fill the shell, it being necessary for it to enter only the small diameter, as the operation is confined to this end of the shell. The three succeeding operations are not illustrated, for the reason that they consist merely of changing the shape, step by step, and reducing the small end preparatory to performing the final operation.

The shape of the shell after the final or eighth, operation has been completed, is shown at *D*, Fig. 16, and the dies employed are shown in the lower right-hand corner of Fig. 15. The operation consists of flattening the flange and of finishing both the large and small diameters. In this operation, the small end of the shell is reduced 1/32 inch while it is being sized. The

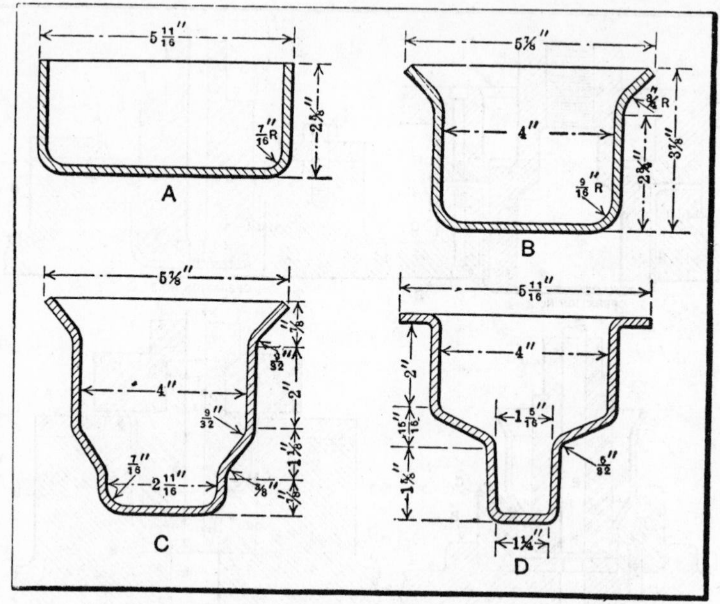

Fig. 16. Appearance of the Case after the Second, Third, Fourth and Eighth Operations

die consists of two steel rings *C*, the smaller of which reduces the small diameter and is located within the larger ring which is employed in the flattening of the flange. This ring is held down by the gage ring *A*. Attention is directed to the fact that the punch-holder is employed to shape the flange against the larger die ring as the press ram completes its downward stroke. The entire arrangement and construction of the dies provides adequate rigidity. Like all other dies of this kind in which heavy work is performed, the holders should be built

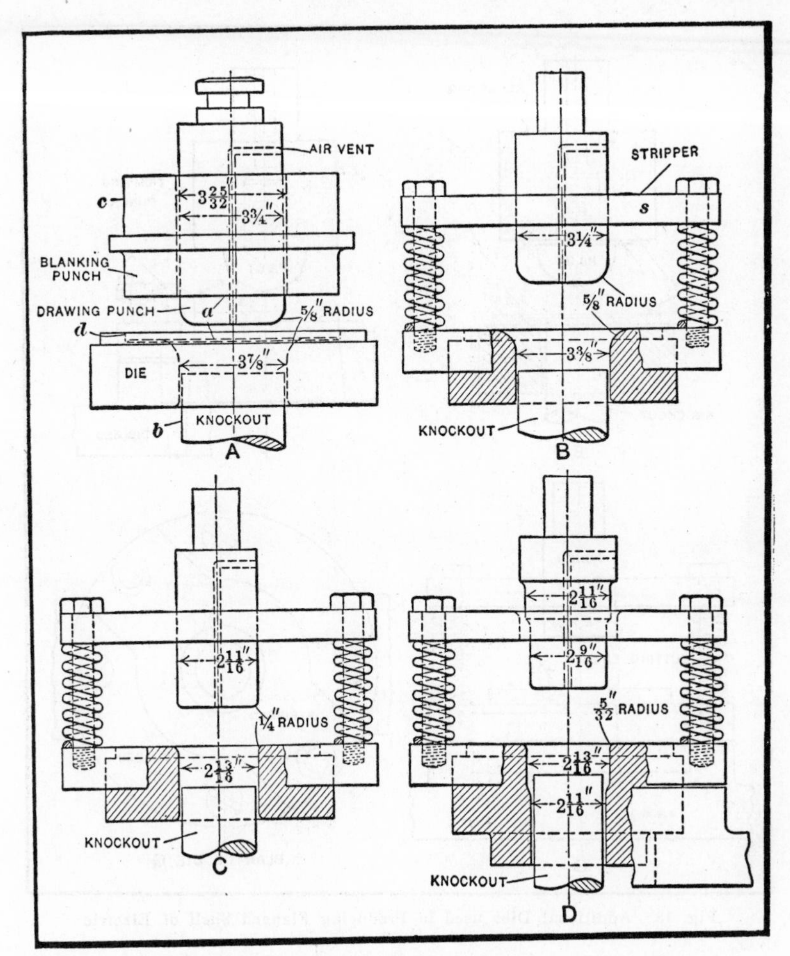

Fig. 17. Dies for Drawing Flanged Shell of Electric Horn

up strongly, so as to withstand the strain exerted upon them during the drawing operation.

The dies used on this job are all hardened and ground to a taper of 1½ degrees and are carefully fitted in the die-blocks. The methods employed in drawing this shell demonstrate the fact that, in drawing flanged shells, the flanges should not be formed first, unless it is absolutely necessary; it is a comparatively easy matter to form the flange after the rest of the shell has been drawn. In some cases, however, it may be

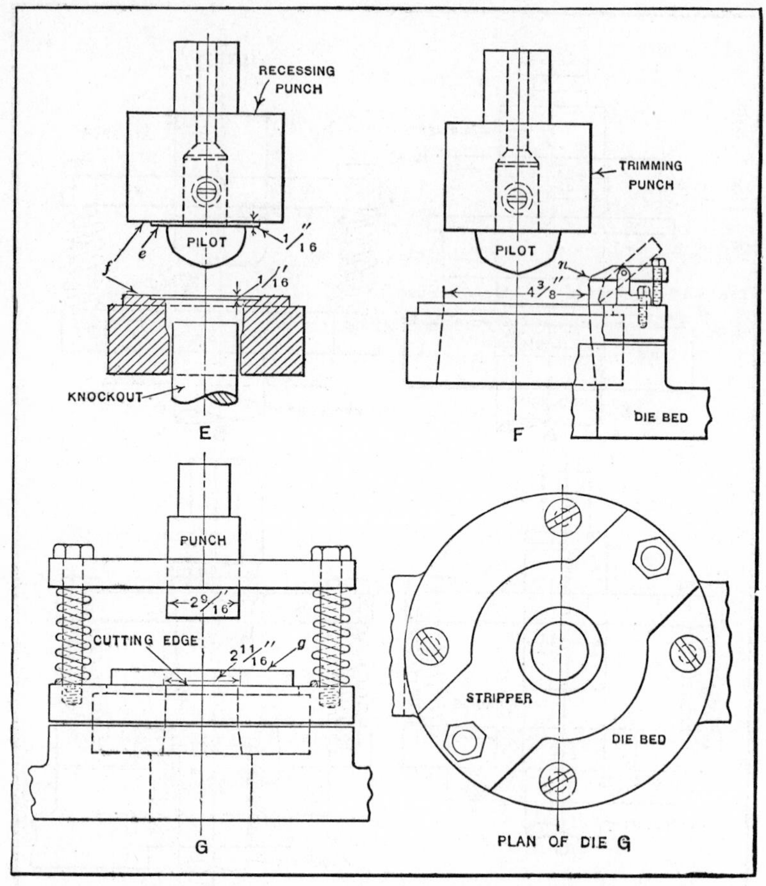

Fig. 18. Additional Dies used in Producing Flanged Shell of Electric Horn

necessary to form the flange first and make all the reductions and drawing operations afterward.

Drawing Flanged Shells for Electric Horns.—Flanged shells for automobile electric horns are drawn by using the dies shown in Figs. 17 and 18. The successive operations from the flat blank to the finished shell are shown in Fig. 19, the order of the reference letters indicating the order of the operations. The dies used are marked with corresponding reference letters, die *A* being used for the first drawing operation *A*, die *B* for the second operation, and so on. The finished shell has a flange 4⅜ inches in diameter with a recessed shoulder 1/16 inch deep. The body of the shell has two diameters of 2 13/16 and 2 11/16 inches, respectively, and it is 3¼ inches long. The shell is made of "three-quarter hard," cold-rolled steel, 1/16 inch thick. The blank diameter was computed by the ordinary method of finding the area of the finished shell in square inches, and then making the blank diameter to correspond to this area. In this case the area is about 43 square inches, which is approximately equal to the area of a circle 7½ inches in diameter. Several circular blanks of this size were cut to be used in making the trial drawing operations.

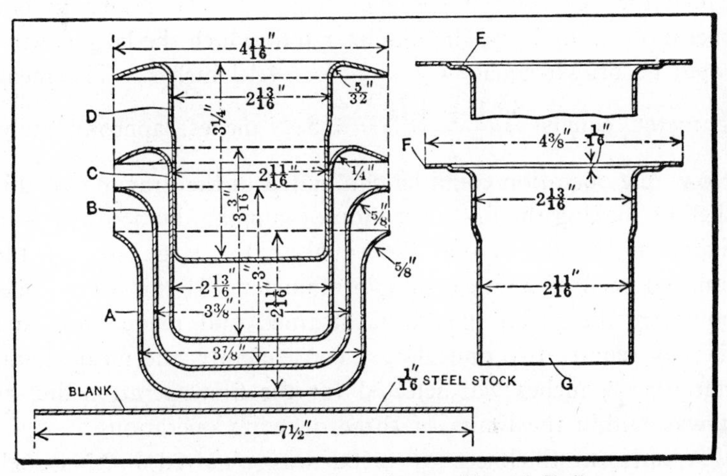

Fig. 19. Successive Operations on Flanged Shell

Establishing the Die Diameters.—In designing dies for the shell illustrated in Fig. 19, the following method of establishing the diameters of the drawing dies was employed: First the diameter of the blank was determined from the area of the finished shell and, as previously mentioned, was found to be 7½ inches, the shell area being about 43 square inches. Now assuming that a flange was not required on this shell, the blank diameter would be 6 9/16 inches. Thus, as the total area of the shell is 43 square inches and the flange area approximately 9 square inches, the area of the shell without a flange equals 43—9=34 square inches, which equals the area of a circle

$6\frac{9}{16}$ inches in diameter. Having these two blank diameters, the respective diameters of plain flangeless cups into which they could be drawn in one operation are determined by multiplying each blank diameter by the constant 0.55. (As explained in Chapter 12 this is a good general rule for determining the diameter of a first-operation or "cupping" die, or, in other words, the diameter to which a flat blank can be drawn in one operation.) The arithmetical mean between these two cup diameters is then determined and the diameter of the first drawing die made equal to this mean diameter. Thus, $6.56 \times 0.55 = 3.61$ inches, which represents the diameter to which the blank for a flangeless cup could be drawn in one operation. Similarly, the diameter into which the larger blank could be drawn equals $7.5 \times 0.55 = 4.12$ inches. The mean diameter equals $\frac{3.61 + 4.12}{2} = 3\frac{7}{8}$ inches, approximately. Now, one operation could be eliminated in the drawing of this shell by making the first-operation or cupping die $3\frac{1}{2}$ inches in diameter and the second die equal to the large size of the finished shell or $2\frac{13}{16}$ inches in diameter. If this were done, however, the metal would be strained and made hard and thereby require two annealings; consequently, the mean diameter of $3\frac{7}{8}$ inches was selected for the first-operation die, as it was within the limits of three drawing operations.

A uniform thickness of metal was required in this shell which necessitated great care in making the drawing corners of the punch and die as round and smooth as possible, in order to insure an even distribution of the metal. The outside surfaces of all dies were turned concentric with the center holes and were made interchangeable in several different die-beds of the type illustrated in Fig. 20. The holding ring which clamps the die to the bed has several tapped holes, as shown by the plan view, for fastening the stripper plates, which will be referred to later.

Determining Exact Blank Diameter by Trial Drawing Operation.—The die for the first operation, by means of which the flat blank is drawn into cup *A*, Fig. 19, is shown at *A*, Fig.

17. A double-action press is used. The blank, after being cut by the blanking punch, is held between surfaces *a* with sufficient pressure to prevent the blank from wrinkling while the drawing punch pushes it through the die to the proper depth, which, in this operation, is 2 11/16 inches, leaving the flange diameter 4 11/16 inches. It should be mentioned that the correctness of this flange diameter was determined by several trial drawing operations, which also showed that a shell of the

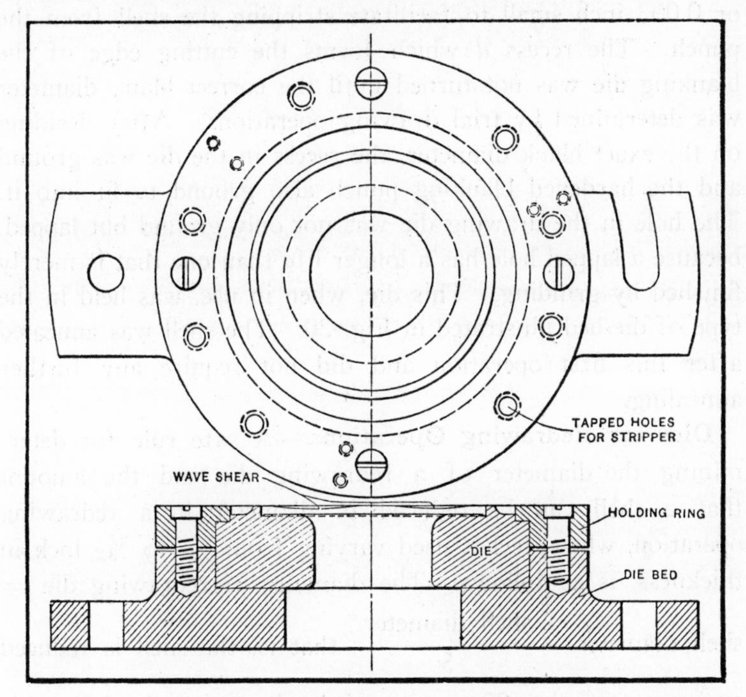

Fig. 20. Drawing Die and Die-bed

required depth could be obtained. The knock-out rod *b*, the upper end of which is shown, is actuated by a cam on the crankshaft and serves to push the shell out of the die. The shank *c* of the blanking punch was turned straight and pressed tightly into the punch block of the press, where it was retained with a set-screw. As the illustration shows, the drawing punch is provided with an air vent to prevent the formation of a partial vacuum between the end of the punch and shell when the latter is being stripped. These air vents are also used on the drawing punches for succeeding operations.

The blanking punch of die *A* is bored 1/32 inch larger in diameter than the drawing punch to prevent any binding between the two. Each drawing punch is 1/8 inch smaller in diameter than the die to allow for the thickness of the stock. All of the punches were ground after hardening and were made slightly tapering, the lower or drawing end being 0.002 or 0.003 inch small to facilitate stripping the shell from the punch. The recess *d* which forms the cutting edge of the blanking die was not turned until the correct blank diameter was determined by trial drawing operations. After deciding on the exact blank diameter, the recess in the die was ground and the hardened blanking punch also ground to fit into it. The hole in the drawing die was not only ground but lapped, because a lapped hole has a longer life than one that is merely finished by grinding. This die, when in use, was held in the type of die-bed illustrated in Fig. 20. The shell was annealed after this first operation and did not require any further annealing.

Dies for Redrawing Operations.—A safe rule for determining the diameter of a redrawing die and the amount that a shell can be reduced in diameter in a redrawing operation, when steel is used varying from 1/32 to 3/32 inch in thickness, is as follows. The diameter of redrawing die = shell diameter $-\frac{\text{shell diameter}}{5}$; that is, the shell is reduced an amount equal to 20 per cent of the diameter. Applying this rule or formula to the cup shown at *A*, Fig. 19, we have $3\frac{7}{8}\text{ inches} - \frac{3\frac{7}{8}}{5} = 3.1$ inches which according to the formula should be the diameter of the die for the second operation; as the diameter of the finished shell is 2 13/16 inches, and as it was not considered practicable to reduce the cup to this dimension, the second-operation die was made 3 3/8 inches, thereby equalizing the work and producing a better shell.

The die for this first redrawing operation is shown at *B*, Fig. 17; it is equipped with a stripper *s*, the shape and position of which is clearly shown by the plan view of die *G* (Fig. 18), the strippers of all the dies being of the same form. As will be seen, the stripper is set at an angle to clear the guides of the press ram. The cup is placed on top of the die under the stripper, the springs shown holding the stripper in its upper position. When redrawing the cup, the punch descends and enters it and then the ram press strikes the stripper, carrying it down while the punch is pushing the cup into the die. On the return or upward stroke of the press, the shell sticks to the punch until the stripper plate strikes the heads of the bolts shown; then the shell is stripped from the punch as the ram continues to ascend to its upper position. The radius on the drawing corners of the punch and drawing die is 5/8 inch and corresponds to the radius on the punch and die shown at *A*. Die *B* produces the cup *B* (Fig. 19) and is used in a single-action press.

The third operation (second redrawing operation) is performed in the die shown at *C* (Fig. 17), which is also used in a single-action press and is similar to die *B*, excepting that it is smaller in diameter. The diameter corresponds to the large size of the finished shell or 2 13/16 inches. According to the formula previously given, the diameter would equal $3\frac{3}{8} - \frac{3\frac{3}{8}}{5} = 2.7$. Therefore the reduction to a diameter of 2 13/16 inches is a little less than the safe maximum, which tends to produce a better shell. As the illustration shows, the radius on the corners of the punch and die is 1/4 inch. When the shell has been drawn in die *C*, the flange is curved down somewhat as illustrated at *C*, Fig. 19, but is flattened by a subsequent operation. By referring to the different shapes corresponding to successive operations, it will be seen that the flange is formed by forcing the surplus metal from the shell body up into the flange.

Shell *C* is next changed to the form indicated at *D* in the die *D*, Fig. 17. This operation simply reduces the lower part of the shell body 1/8 inch in diameter or to the finished size of 2 11/16 inches, and retains the 2 13/16-inch size previously drawn. The next operation is that of forming the recess *E* in the flange, die *E*, Fig. 18, being used for this purpose. The shell is placed in the die and on top of the knockout rod. When the punch descends, the pilot attached to it enters the shell and the knockout rod also descends at the same time. The shoulder *e* on the punch is 1/8 inch smaller in diameter than the recess in the die, and it forms a recess in the flange, while surfaces *f* flatten the remaining part of the flange. When the punch ascends, the knockout rod pushes the shell out of the die. The pilot has a shank which is a light driving fit in the punch and is held by a set-screw.

Trimming and Blanking Dies.—The punch and die for trimming the flange to the required diameter of 4 3/8 inches is shown at *F*, Fig. 18. When the shell is dropped into the die, the flange strikes the ends of three gravity strippers *n* which tilt to allow the shell to pass, as indicated by the dotted lines, and then fall back to the horizontal position. These gravity strippers are adjusted so that the inner ends *n* just clear the punch. When the punch descends, the pilot locates the shell in a central position and then the flange is trimmed. The shell drops through the die, and as the punch ascends the scrap which was trimmed from the flange sticks to it until it is stripped off by the strippers *n*.

The punch and die for the final operation of blanking out the bottom of the shell are shown by the elevation and plan view at *G*. The shell is placed in the ring or "nest" *g* and under the stripper plate. The punch is made long so that the ram of the press will not strike the stripper when it descends, the stripper for this operation simply being held up against the heads of the retaining bolts.

Drawing Shell Having Turned-down Flange.—In the manufacture of a combination piston and cylinder furnished in an air pump used for pumping up automobile tires, the dies shown in Figs. 21 to 26, inclusive, are required. The pump is attached to one of the spark plug holes of an automobile engine while in use. The various dies that are employed in producing this part are illustrated in the order in which they are used, and the dimensions of the shell after each operation are also given on the drawings beneath the illustrations.

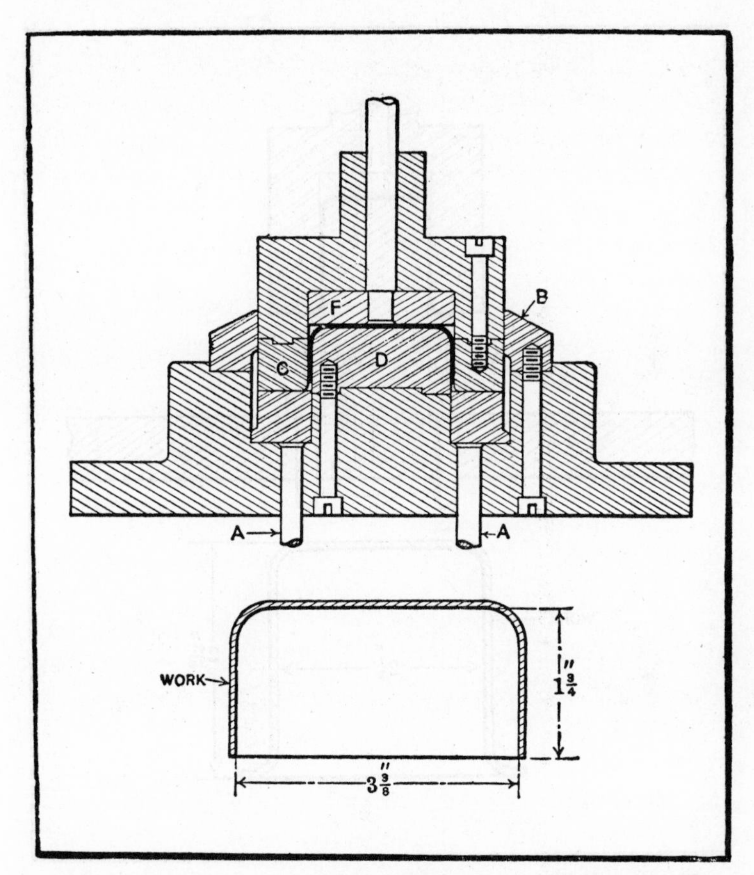

Fig. 21. Combination Blanking and Forming Die for Performing First Operation on Shell

The shell is made from cold-rolled strip steel, 0.065 inch thick, the blank being 5 13/16 inches in diameter. The die shown in Fig. 21 is a combined blanking and drawing die which cuts the blank and performs the first forming operation. This die is of the standard type and is used on a press having the usual rubber buffer attachment and plates for pins

A. The steel strip is laid upon the cutting ring *B*, and as the edge of the punch face ring *C* passes the edge of the cutting ring when the punch descends, the blank is cut to size. As the punch continues its descent, the shell is drawn upon the

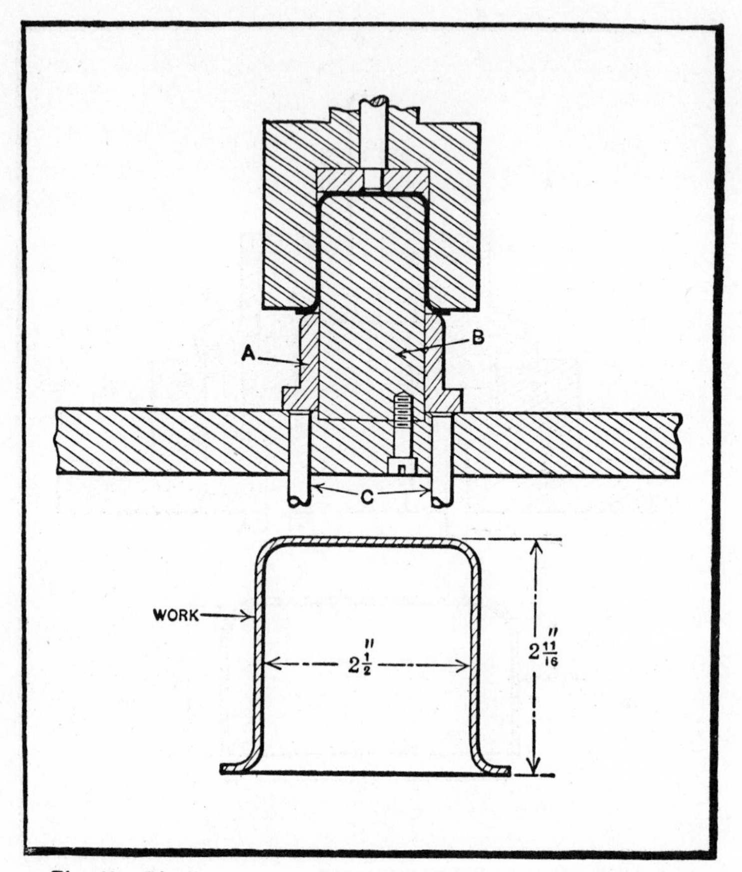

Fig. 22. Die Employed to Reduce the Diameter of the Shell and Start Forming Flange

forming die *D*. The knock-out pad *F* ejects the shell from the punch on the return stroke of the press ram.

A reduction is made in the diameter of the shell by the die illustrated in Fig. 22 which also commences to form the flange. When ring *A* is in the normal position, the upper end of the ring is flush with the upper end of the forming die *B*.

The shell is placed over ring *A*, and as the punch descends, the ring is pushed downward until it reaches the position shown, at which point this operation upon the shell has been completed. The pins *C* push the ring *A* back to its original position upon the return stroke of the press ram and at the same time force

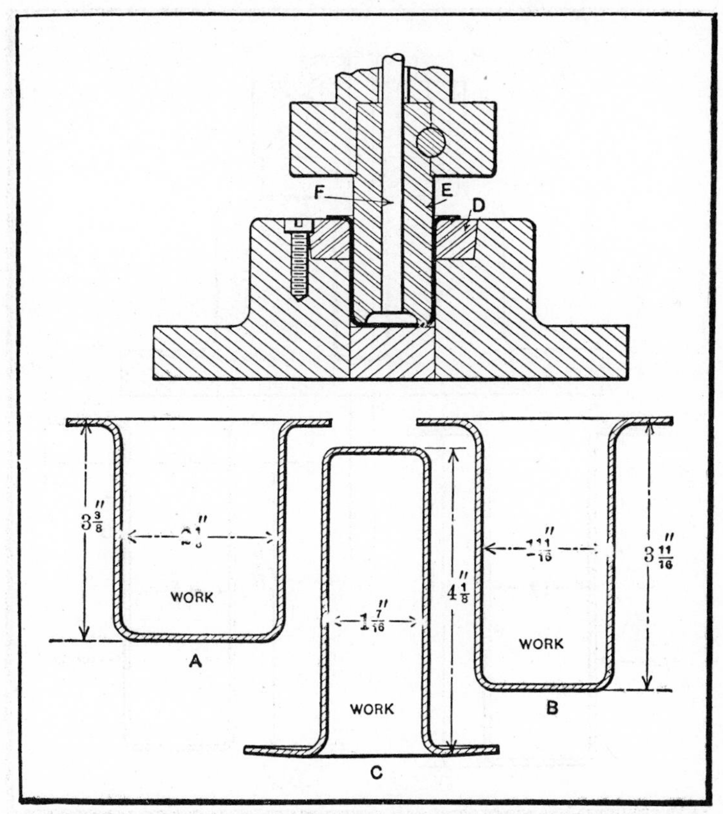

Fig. 23. Type of Die Used to make Three More Reductions of the Diameter of the Shell

the shell from the forming die. Three different sizes of dies of the construction shown in Fig. 23 are used to further the diameter of the shell. The shell is first reduced to the size shown at *A*, then to the size shown at *B*, and finally to the size shown at *C*. In each case the shell is forced into the die only until the flange comes in contact with the forming die *D*. If an attempt were made to draw the shell any deeper, the bottom would be forced out, because the flange cannot be reduced at the same time as the body. The punch E is inserted and held in the press in such a manner that it is not pushed from the press when the rod F forces the shell off the punch.

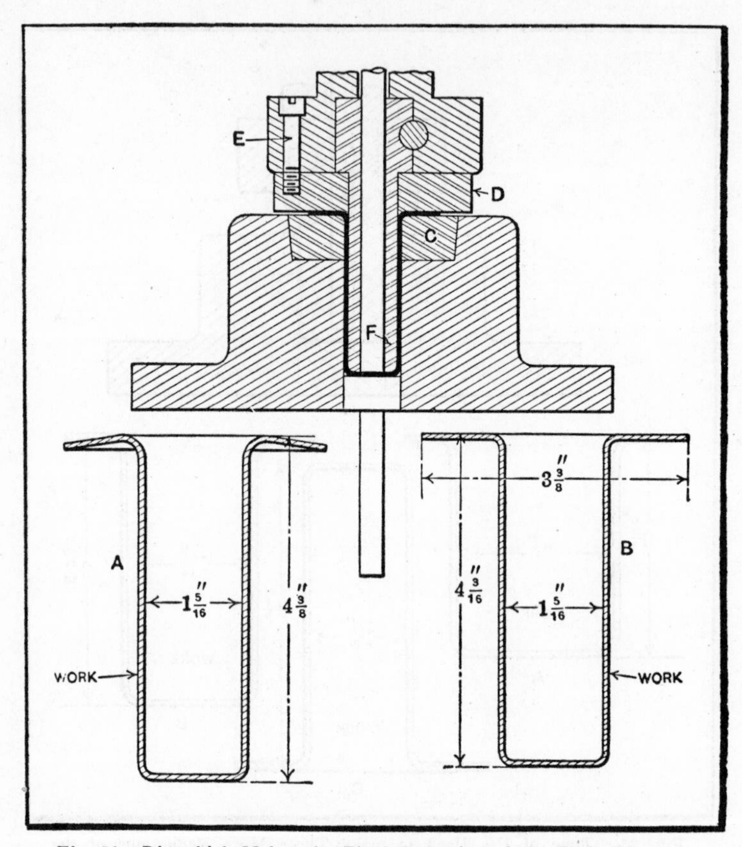

Fig. 24. Die which Makes the Final Reduction of the Shell Diameter and Flattens the Flange

Fig. 24 shows the die that makes the final reduction in the diameter of the shell to the dimensions shown at A, and also flattens the flange as shown at B. Two operations are performed to attain this end. When the shell is being formed to the shape illustrated at A, the ring D and screws E are removed from the punch. As in the preceding dies, the shell is forced into the die only until the flange touches the die-ring *C*. After a certain quantity of shells have been drawn to the shape shown at *A*, the ring *D* is secured in place as shown and a second operation is performed upon the same pieces, flattening the flange as shown at *B*. The die illustrated in Fig. 25

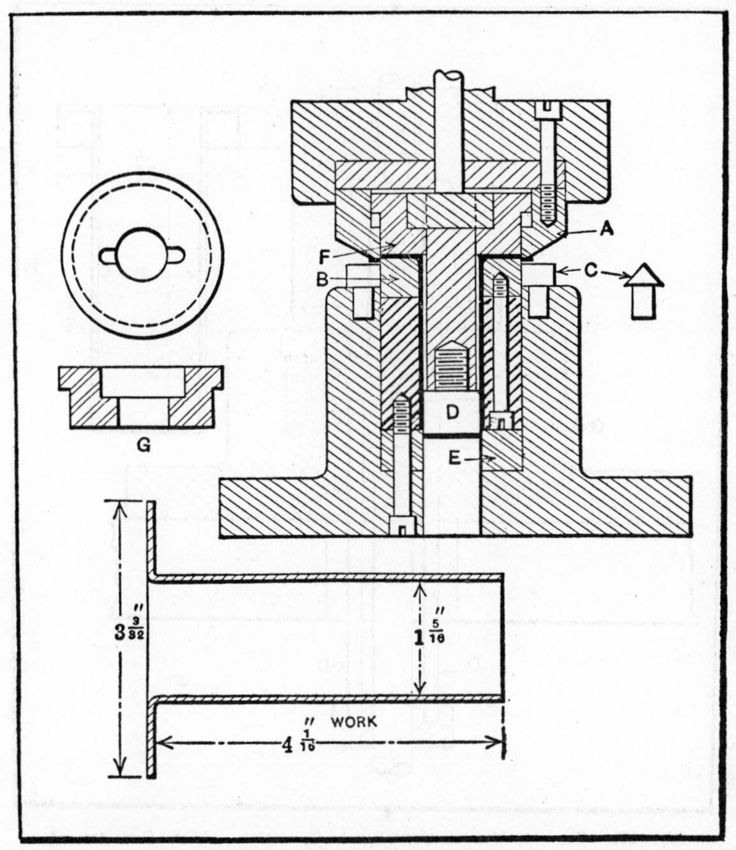

Fig. 25. Method of Trimming the Flange and Cutting the Hole in the End of the Shell

trims the flange of the shell and cuts a hole in the opposite end. The flange is trimmed as the cutting ring *A* passes the edge of ring *B* on the downward stroke of the press ram, the scrap being forced down on the cutter *C* which cuts the scrap into two pieces, permitting it to fall away from the die. The hole is cut in the end of the shell as the face of punch *D* passes the edge of the cutting ring *E*. A detail of the knock-out pad *F* is shown at *G*.

The final operation on the shell consists of turning down the edge of the flange by the die shown in Fig. 26. When ring

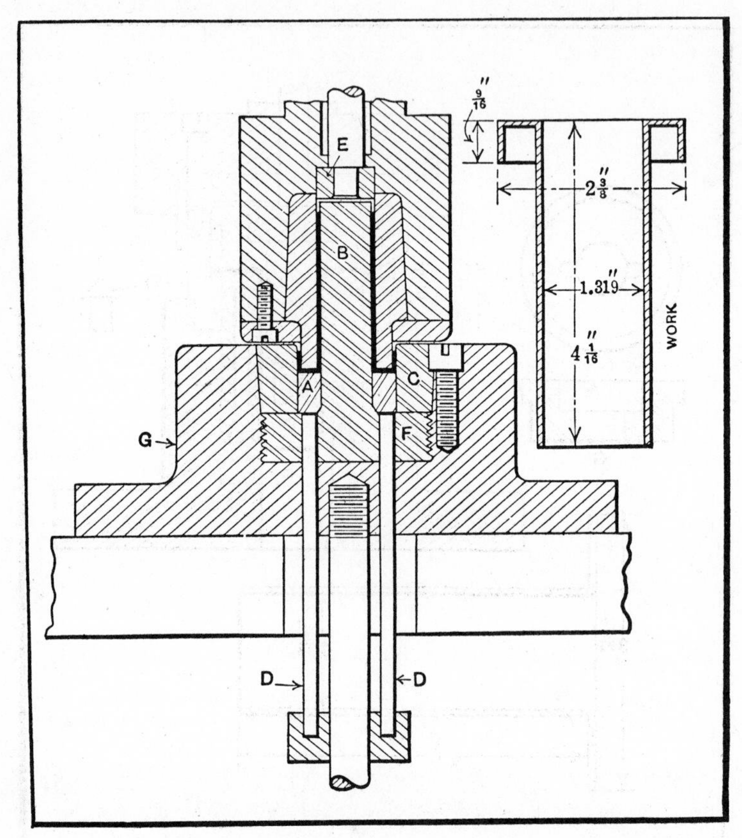

Fig. 26. Die for Performing Final Operation which Consists of Edging Up the Flange

A is in the normal position, the upper face is on a level with the upper surface of the die-ring *C*. The shell is then placed on plug *B* and ring *A* and as the punch descends the edge of the flange is forced back and the face is flattened. The plug *B* is 0.007 inch larger in diameter than the punch *F* in Fig. 24, which makes the final reduction in the shell diameter. This increased size permits the barrel of the shell to be expanded at certain points and upset at other points, thus causing the sides of the barrel to become parallel. After the operation has been performed, the shell is forced from plug *B* by means of the pins *D* which force the ring *A* upward, while the knock-out pad *E* ejects the shell from the punch. The tool-steel plug *F* which is screwed into the die-block *G* serves as a bumping block for ring *A* and as a guide for pins *D*. All parts of the different dies are hardened and ground.

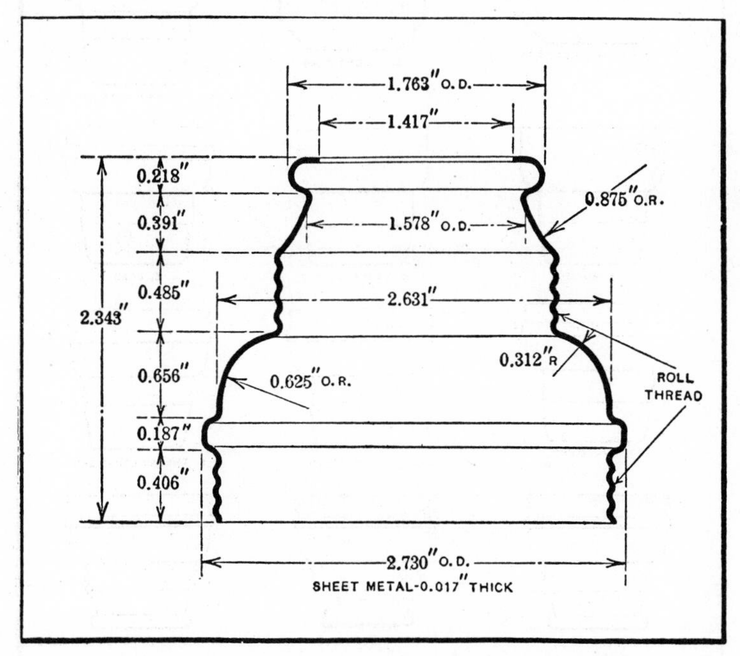

Fig. 27. Dimensioned Illustration of the Finished Shell

Drawing Shell of Irregular Shape.—The drawing of a deep shell depends upon a number of variable factors, and the rules for calculating the flow of metal are empirical. The formulas that have been developed as the result of experimentation pertain chiefly to shells of regular shape. When planning the drawing operations, not only must the amount of reduction in diameter permissible in each succeeding drawing operation be considered, but also the amount that the stock is "ironed" or thinned out while being drawn. This is true because the reduction in gage thickness means greater pressure of the punch against the bottom of the shell; consequently the amount that the shell diameter is reduced in each drawing operation must be lessened when a greater amount of ironing is necessary to avoid overstressing or breaking the shell.

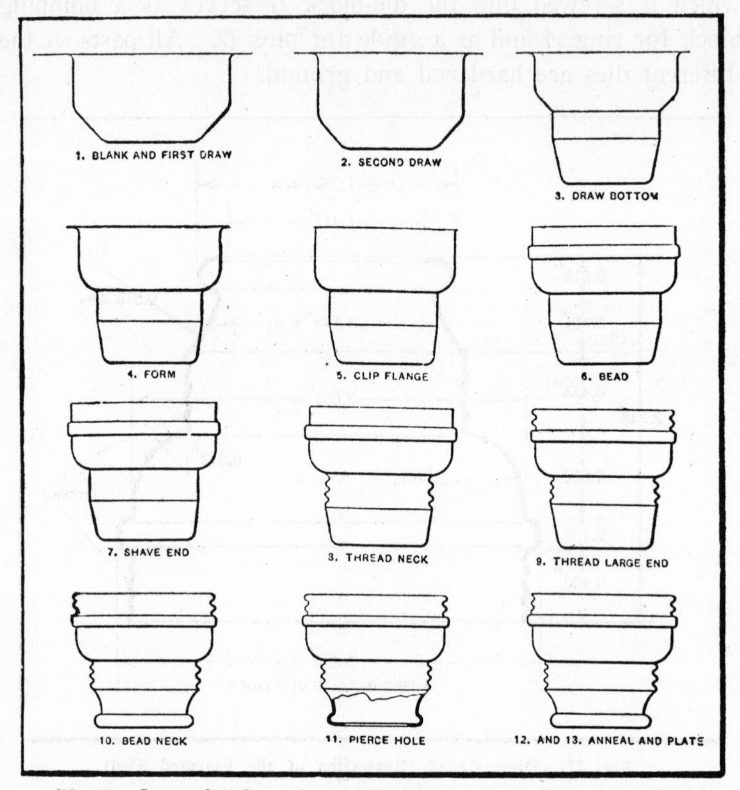

Fig. 28. Successive Operations in Producing a Shell of Irregular Form

In arranging to manufacture an irregularly shaped shell, the rules pertaining to shells of regular shape cannot be applied, except in a general way. In the manufacture of the shell shown in Fig. 27 considerable planning was required on account of this fact. Shells of irregular shape must be carefully studied to determine the probable flow of metal, when planning and designing the tools for use in their production.

Determining Blank Diameter by Weighing Method.— For convenience in following the various steps required in its evolution, an operation sheet, Fig. 28, in addition to a completely dimensioned drawing of the shell, Fig. 27, will be referred to. The shell is made from sheet metal, 0.017 inch thick. The diameter of the blank was determined by weigh-

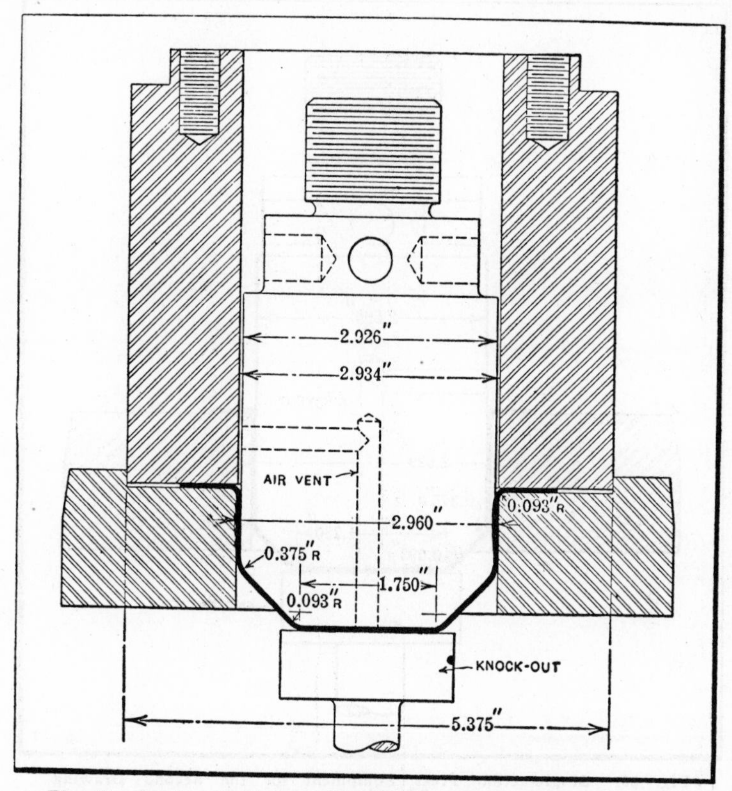

Fig. 29. Punch and Die used for Blanking and First Drawing Operation on Double-action Press

ing a sample, and then, knowing the weight of the sheet metal per square inch, computing the diameter of a piece which would be equal in weight to the sample. The diameter was then increased a certain amount, in this case, 5 per cent, to allow for trimming after the drawing operations were completed. This is necessary on account of the unevenness in the flow of metal due to irregularities in hardness and inaccuracies in setting the dies in relation to the punch. After the size of the blank was decided on, the process of manufacture and the requisite number of operations were determined.

Drawing and Forming Operations.—The punch and die for blanking and for the first drawing operation is shown in

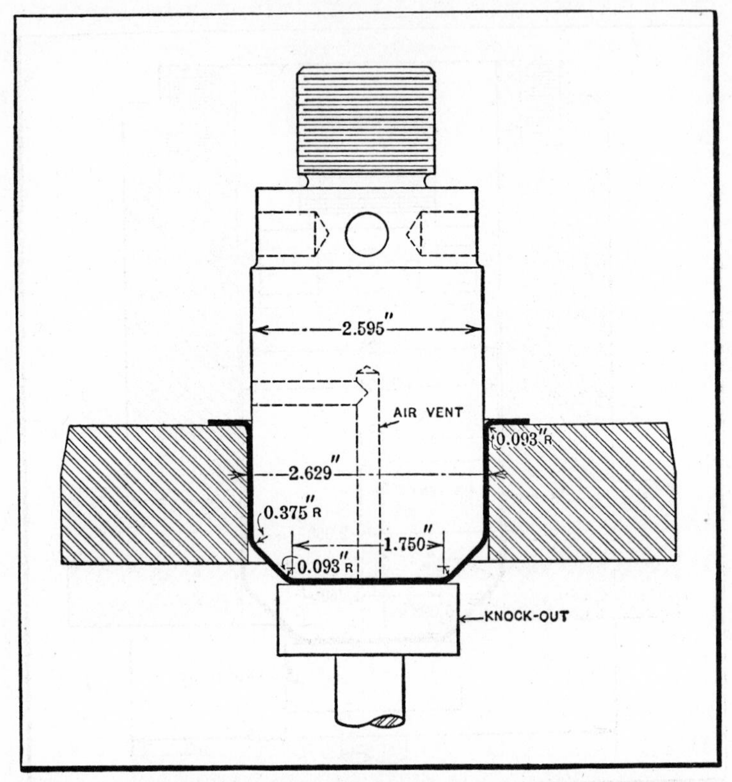

Fig. 30. Single-action Press Equipment for the Second Drawing Operation

Fig. 29. The heavy line illustrates the form of the shell after this first operation. The die is used on a double-action press of standard construction equipped with a knock-out for ejecting the shell from the die. Fig. 30 illustrates the tools used in performing the second operation, which is simply a redrawing operation performed on a single-action press. It will be observed that all dimensions necessary for making the tools that are employed in the forming of the shells are given on the illustrations, and the construction is clearly shown in each case.

Operation 3 is performed with the tools illustrated in Fig. 31, and consists of drawing the bottom of the shell to the shape shown. Attention is called to the fact that the shape

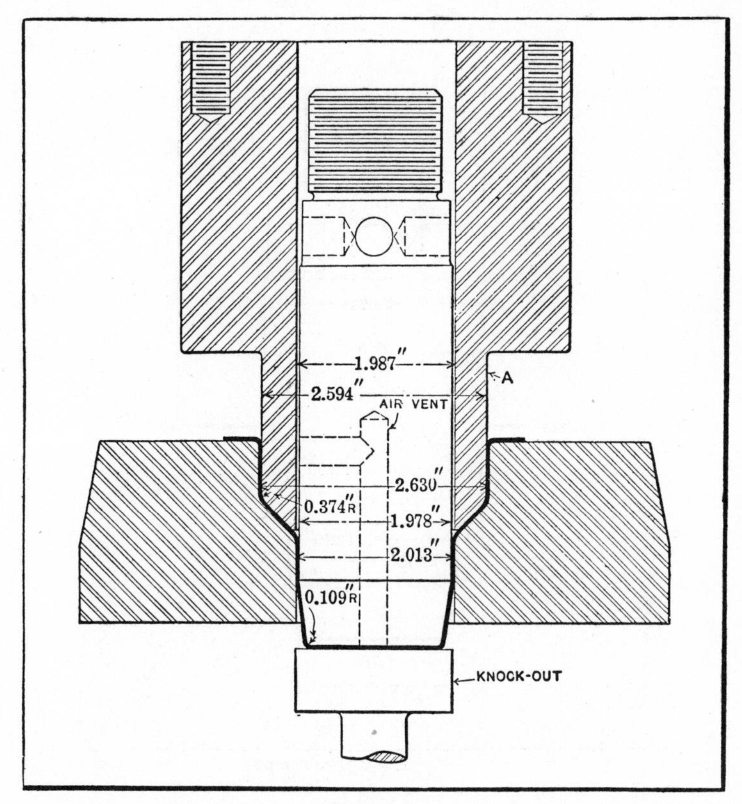

Fig. 31. Third Operation—Drawing the Bottom of the Shell on a Double-action Press

of the shell after Operation 2 is such as to enable it to fit the upper portion of the die used in Operation 3, and that sleeve *A* is so shaped as to hold the work while the plunger draws the bottom of the shell and forms the nose. This operation is also performed on a double-action press, the construction of the tools being similar to those used in the preceding operations as regards knock-outs, air vent, etc. Fig. 32 illustrates the tools used for forming the shell to the shape shown; this equipment contains no features to which attention need be drawn, except that the knock-out is made to bottom in a hole in the die-block so that the small end of the shell will be formed perfectly flat. Operation 5 consists of clipping the flange as

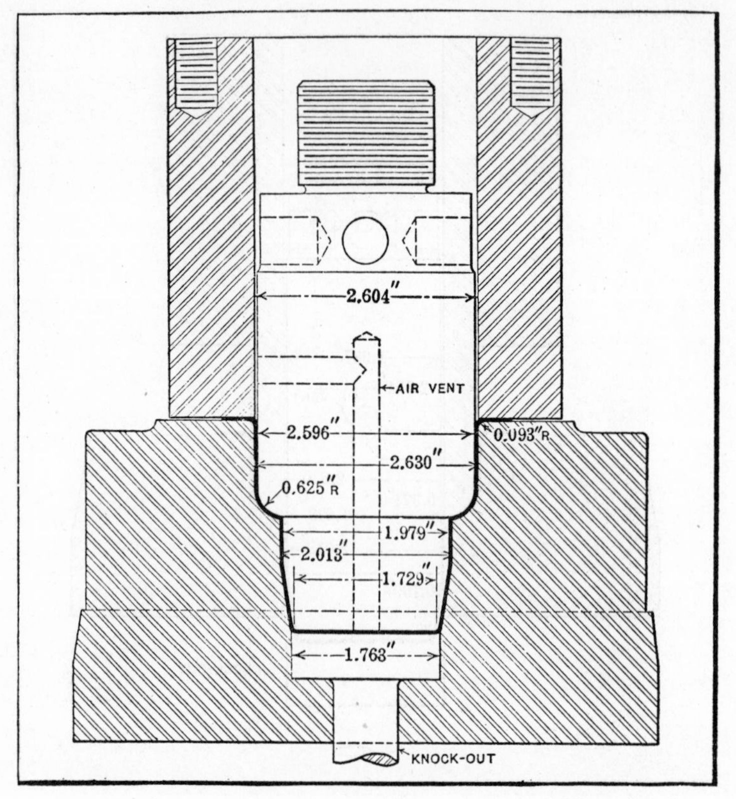

Fig. 32. Forming the Shell to the Shape Shown, and Flattening the Small End

shown in Fig. 33. This is a plain punch and push-through type of die with a hardened steel die ring *A* seated in the die-block. This operation, with the exception of the final piercing operation, completes the press work on the shell and is performed on a single-action press.

As the beading and threading operations are performed by

rolling processes, these operations will not be included. Due to the hardening or ironing that the metal receives during its manufacture, the shell requires annealing several times between the drawing and forming operations; the number required must be found by trial, and must be reduced to a minimum to lessen the cost of the shell.

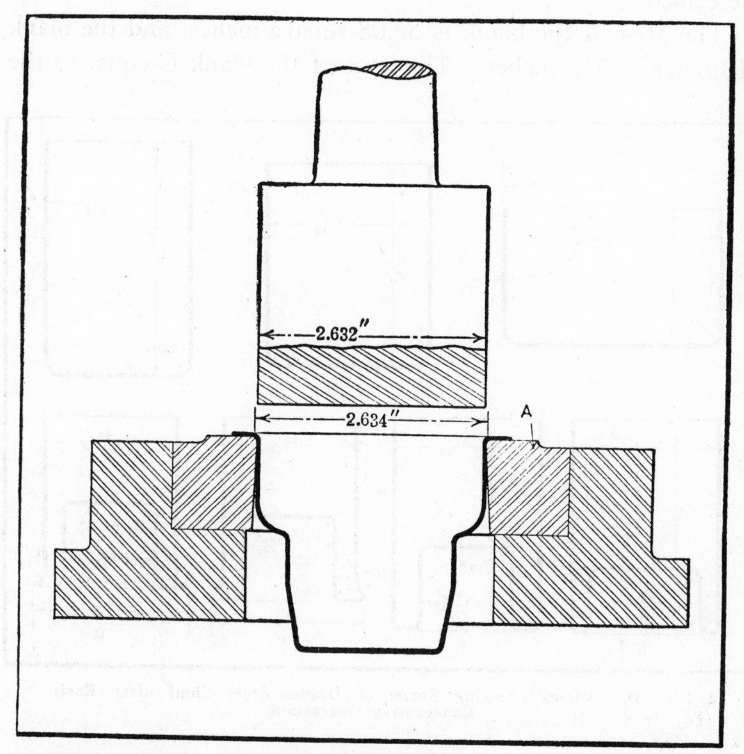

Fig. 33. Clipping the Flange. This Operation is Performed on a Plain Push-through Die

Drawing Double-walled Steel Shells.—The dies to be described are employed in the production of steel shells of the shape and size indicated in the sectional view at *G*, Fig. 34, where each consecutive operation is shown. These shells are used in connection with an auxiliary mechanism of an alternating-current motor, and are generally known as "spring barrel tubes." The dies, arranged in the order in which they are used, are shown in Figs. 35, 36, and 37. Seventeen operations are required in the production of the finished shell. These include blanking, drawing, annealing, trimming, planishing, flanging, forming, perforating, burring, and upsetting. In the following description, however, only the press operations required in blanking, drawing, redrawing and forming are described.

The area of the blank is 55.08 square inches, and the blank diameter is 8 3/8 inches. The area of the blank is equal to the

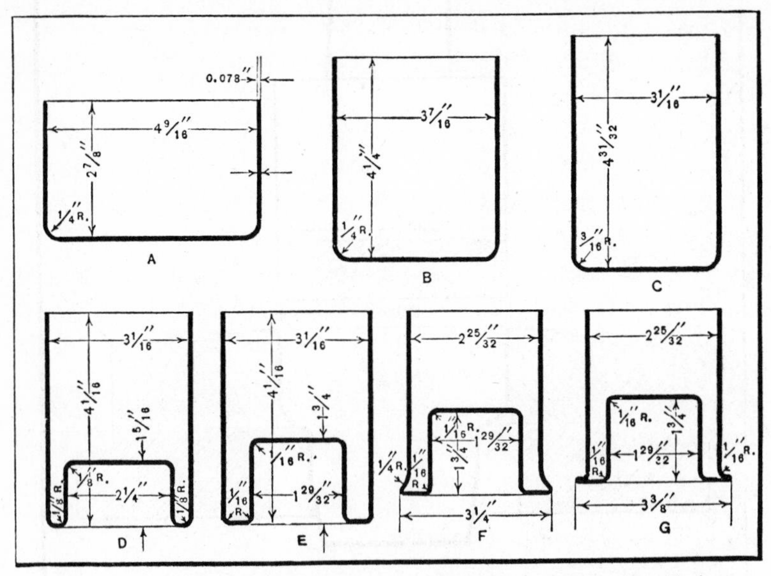

Fig. 34. Views Showing Shape of Drawn Steel Shell after Each Consecutive Operation

area of the inside of the completely drawn shell plus the part trimmed from the end, which has an areal equal to that of a ring 1/4 inch wide with an inside diameter of 3 1/16 inches. The material from which the shell is drawn is cold-rolled steel, 0.078 inch thick. Reference to the detail *A*, Fig. 34, will show that the depth of the shell produced in the blanking and drawing operation does not exceed three-fourths of the diameter, which is in accordance with the practice, where these shells or "spring barrel tubes" are made. If the material is free from flaws, there is no loss due to breakage of the shells in the blanking and drawing operation.

In Fig. 35 are shown the dies used in the first and second operations. The blanking and drawing die for the first operation is set up in a double-acting press, and the upper cutting member *A* is bolted to the ram. After this member has performed the blanking operation, it dwells for a sufficient length of time to hold the blank between its face and the face of the drawing die *B* while the anvil *C*, which is attached to the press plunger, descends and draws the shell. The diameter of the anvil is less than that of the inside of the drawing die by an amount equal to twice the thickness of the metal plus 1/32 inch. This clearance is sufficient to allow the shell to drop from the anvil when it has passed through the die.

Reverse Drawing and Its Advantages.—The die used for the second operation is also operated in a double-acting press. In the second operation, the shell is turned inside out. The lower die *D* (Fig. 35) is cylindrical in form and has an outside diameter equal to the inside diameter of the shell produced in the preceding operation. The inside diameter of die *D* is made equal to the inside diameter of the shell produced in this operation, or 3 7/16 inches, plus twice the thickness of the stock. The top edge of die *D* is rounded to a radius equal to half the wall thickness.

The action of a reverse-drawing die of this type is particularly interesting. When the anvil descends and the drawing action begins, all that part of the shell that is visible moves upward. The metal appears to be climbing up the outside and over the rounded face of die *D* in much the same manner as one would expect of a tubular piece of rubber drawn under the same conditions. When the open end of the shell reaches the rounded end of die *D*, it has a tendency to wrinkle, but is prevented from doing so by the holding member or die ring *E*. If the punch is set to push the shell completely through the upper part of die *D* so that the edges are drawn below the shoulder at *F*, the shell will be drawn off the anvil and fall out through the opening in the die bed. However, it has been

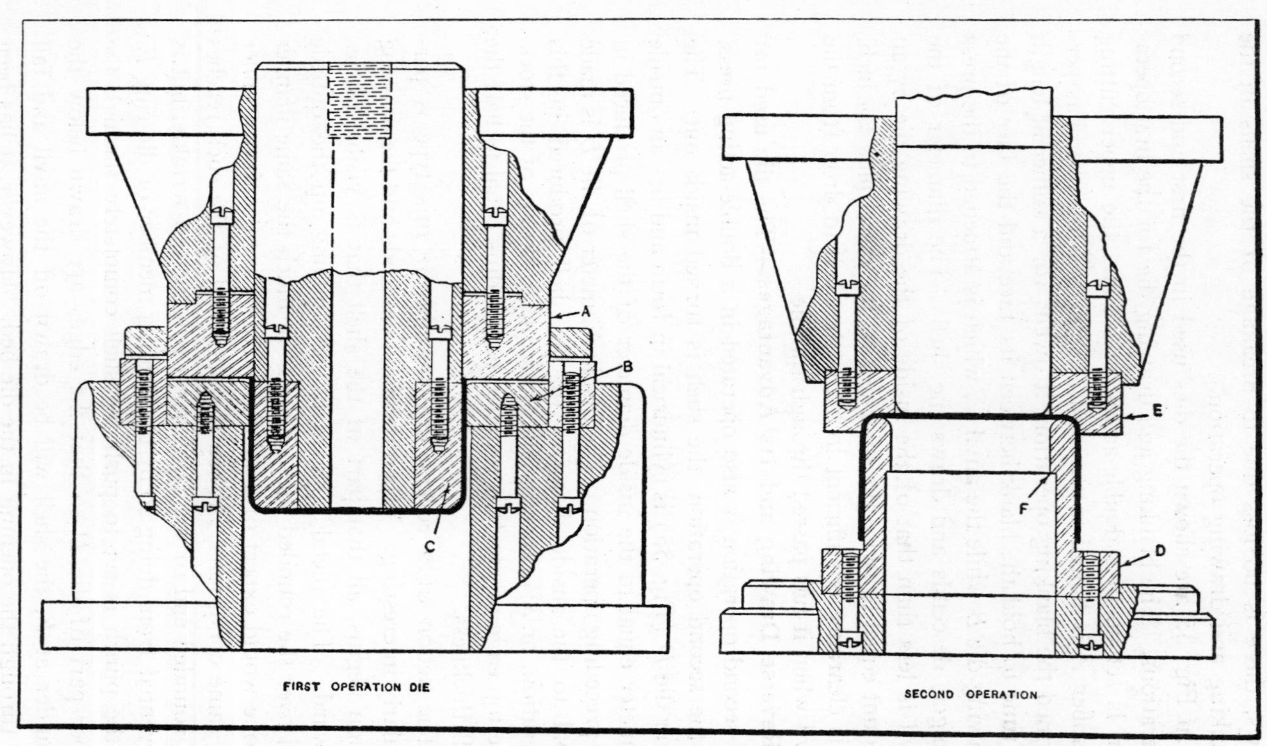

Fig. 35. First-operation Die which Blanks and Draws Shell to Shape shown at *A*, Fig. 34; and Second-operation Die which Turns Shell Inside Out and Draws it to Shape Shown at *B*

found more convenient to set the punch so that the upper end of the shell will not be carried below the shoulder *F*, and thus the shell will be withdrawn from the die as the punch ascends. The shell is then stripped off the punch or anvil by the ring *E*. The operator picks up the finished shell with one hand while placing the next shell on the die with the other.

The advantage of the reverse drawing method over the regular drawing method is that a greater amount of reduction in the diameter can be obtained. The amount of reduction in this case is 25 per cent. In redrawing the shell by the regular method, it is the practice to reduce the diameter not more than 15 per cent. The 25 per cent reduction in diameter is obtained in this case with practically no loss through shell breakage.

The die used for the third drawing operation, which reduces the diameter of the shell to 3⅙ inches, as indicated at *C*, Fig. 34, is shown in Fig. 36. This is a plain drawing die and does not turn the shell inside out, as in the previous operation. The amount of reduction is approximately 10 per cent in this case and the diameter of the shell thus drawn is not reduced further until several other operations have been performed. This die is operated in a single-acting press, and the shell is pushed completely through the die and stripped off the anvil by three spring-actuated strippers, one of which is shown at *F*.

How Double Wall is formed by Reverse Drawing.—In the fourth operation, the bottom of the piece is pressed inward to form the double-walled shell, as shown at *D*, Fig. 34. The die used for this operation, which is shown in Fig. 36, resembles the die used for the second operation. The shell is drawn in the direction that would turn it inside out, but the operation of turning the shell is only partly carried out. The die is operated in a double-acting press. The function of the ram *G* is to strip the shell from the plunger member after the drawing operation. Member *G* is not required to prevent wrinkling in this case, because the drawing is not carried to the point where wrinkling would occur, as in the second operation where the shell is drawn up the outside and over the edge and down inside the lower die. The result of the fourth opera-

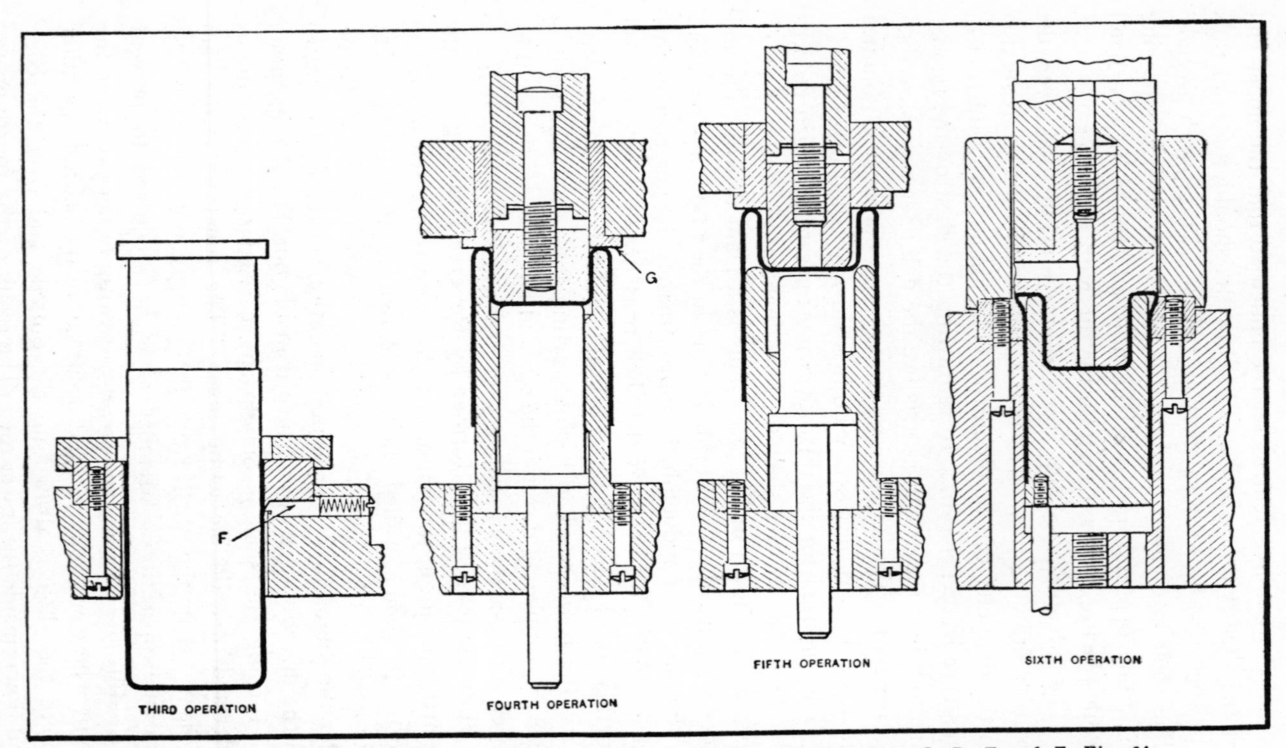

Fig. 36. Dies used in Drawing and Forming Shells to the Shapes Indicated at *C*, *D*, *E* and *F*, Fig. 34

tion is the production of a shell within a shell, or what may be termed a "double-walled" shell. The diameter of the inner shell is 25 per cent less than the diameter of the outer one.

In the fifth operation, the inner shell produced in the preceding operation is acted on, and is treated as though the

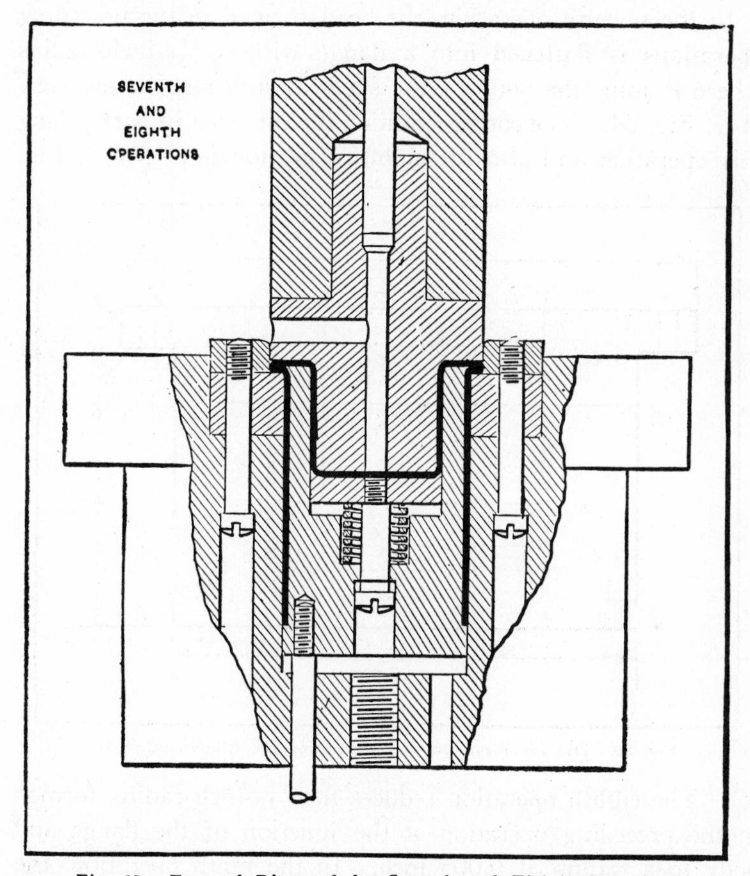

Fig. 37. Type of Die used for Seventh and Eighth Operations

outside shell did not exist. The diameter of the inner shell is reduced approximately 10 per cent in this operation. No drawing action whatever is allowed to take place in the outer shell. The area of all that part of the shell that is inside the 3⅙-inch diameter of the outer shell is not changed in the fourth and fifth operations.

In the sixth operation, the outer shell is reduced in diameter by being forced into a die, open end first. The effect in this case is to produce a head at the solid end, as shown at *F*, Fig. 34. The die used for this operation is shown in the view at the extreme right-hand side of Fig. 36.

In the seventh operation, the head formed in the preceding operations is flattened into a flange with a 1/16-inch radius where it joins the body of the shell, as indicated in the view at *G*, Fig. 34. The construction of the die used in performing this operation and also the eighth operation is shown in Fig.

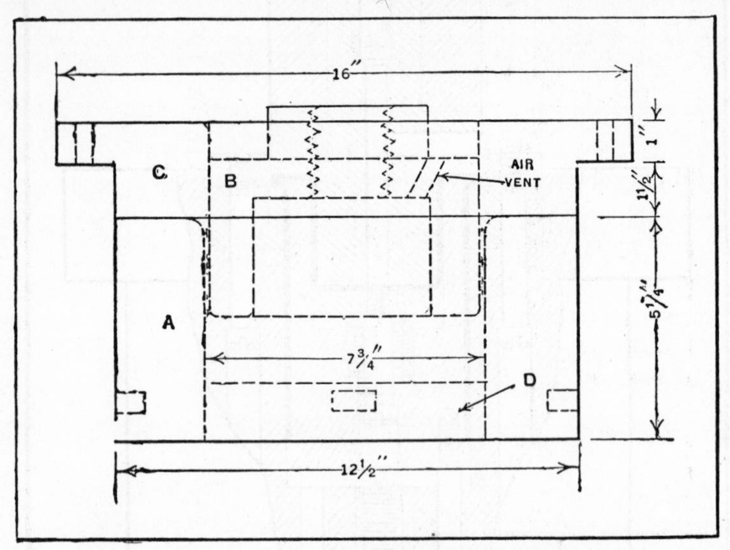

Fig. 38. Die for First Drawing Operation on Aluminum Shell

37. The eighth operation reduces the 1/16-inch radius formed in the preceding operation at the junction of the flange and body to a radius of 0.005 inch. In the ninth operation, the end of the shell is punched out. The shell is annealed after the first and fifth operations.

Reverse Drawing Deep Aluminum Shells.—Among the interesting press operations involved in the manufacture of aluminum cooking utensils is the drawing of deep shells. This can be done satisfactorily by using dies of the type to be described. These particular dies are used in drawing coffee percolators from 18-gage sheet aluminum blanks 12½ inches in diameter.

The first drawing operation is performed on the die shown in Fig. 38, which forms a shell 7¾ inches in diameter by 3½ inches deep. The outside diameter of the die body *A* is the same as the blank diameter, or 12½ inches. The punch *B*, blank-holder *C*, and knock-out pad *D* are of the usual design employed in forming shells in a toggle drawing press.

For the second drawing operation, the shell is turned upside down and placed over the die *E*, Fig. 39. The different members of this die are made of cast iron, the blank-holder and dies of the second and third operations being made from the same pattern. Both of these members are machined to the same outside diameter, which must be a free or loose fit for the shell produced in the first operation. After the shell is placed over die *E*, the punch *G* descends and draws the shell up over the outside of the die and down on the inside, turning the shell inside out. The shell produced in this operation is 6¼ inches in diameter by 5¾ inches deep.

The third operation is performed in the same manner as the second, the shell being again turned inside out by the use of the die shown in Fig. 40. This die is constructed the same as the one used for the second operation except that it is dimensioned to produced a finished shell 4⅞ inches in diameter by 7⅝ inches deep. It has been found that the best results are obtained when the clearance between the punch and the die is 1¼ times the thickness of the metal to be drawn. The radius to which the corners of the dies and blank-holders are finished must also be made to suit the metal being drawn. Decreasing the radius will increase the length of the drawn shell, but with this increase in length there is more danger of shells being spoiled by the breaking away of the metal. In the case of the die shown in Fig. 40, both the inside and outside edges are rounded to a radius of 3/16 inch.

When drawing work of the kind described, the blanks are well greased before being sent to the first drawing die. Trade-marked blanks should be put in the first drawing die with the trademarked side down so that the marking will be on the outside of the finished shell.

Deep Drawing Dies for Double-action Presses.—The deep drawing die shown in Figs. 41 and 42 was developed for use on a double-action press. Under favorable conditions a die of this design will produce a shell in one operation that ordinarily requires two or three operations on the usual type

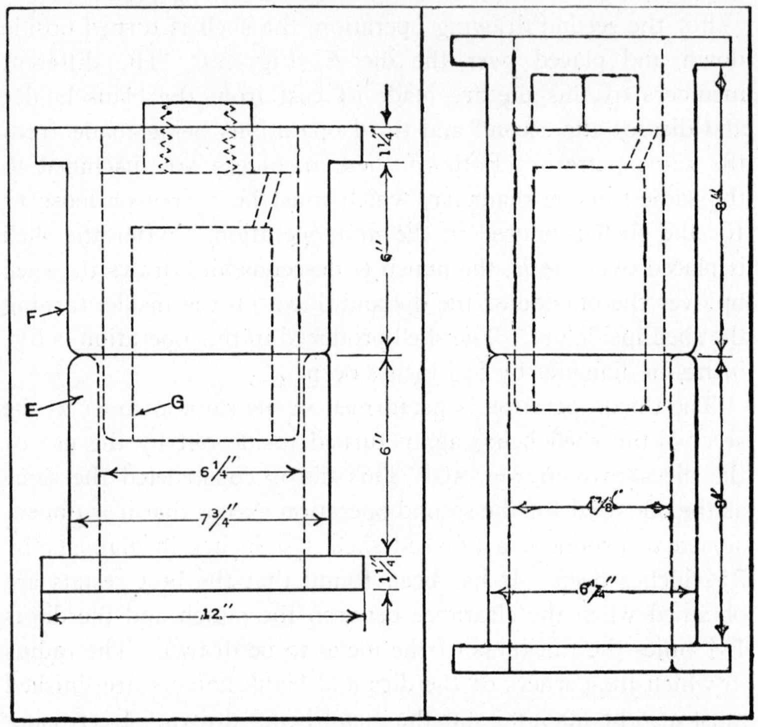

Fig. 39. Reverse Drawing Die for Second Operation

Fig. 40. Reverse Drawing Die for Third Operation

of drawing die. It is also claimed that the shell will have a finer finish, greater accuracy, and will not ordinarily require annealing, unless a spinning operation is to be performed upon it. Dies of this kind are particularly useful in drawing deep tubes, such as are required for pump cylinders, shot shells, or cartridge cases. The closed end of the shell is left comparatively soft, as there is little displacement of the metal; hence the shell can easily be headed to form a cartridge case, shot shell, or other products, without requiring an annealing operation. These dies have been used successfully in drawing deep shells from brass, bronze, steel, and various alloys. The new features incorporated in the die have been patented.

The die-holder *A* has cutting and drawing members similar to those ordinarily used on double-acting presses except that

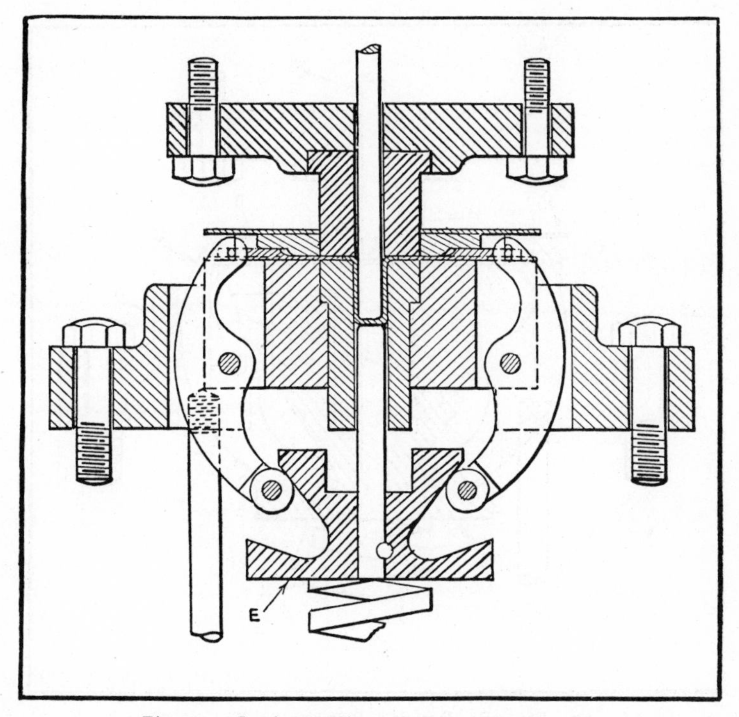

Fig. 41. Sectional View of Deep Drawing Die

a series of radially positioned plungers *B* are provided. A detailed view of one of the plungers is shown at *B*, Fig. 44. These plungers move freely in radial slots, and are connected to rocker arms *C*, which are pivoted in the die-holder. At the lower end of each rocker arm is a roller *D* which normally is in contact with the conical surface of member *E*, Figs. 41 and 42. Although no stock stripper is shown in the illustrations, it is necessary that one be employed, the conventional type being satisfactory for this work. The blank shown at *F*, Fig. 44, which is drawn to form the shell *G* is scalloped, as indicated, in order to facilitate the drawing operation.

When the die is in operation, the blanking punch *H*, Fig. 41, moves downward, cutting the blank to the required size and shape. Upon the continued downward movement of the press ram, the blank is forced down until it rests on the top surface

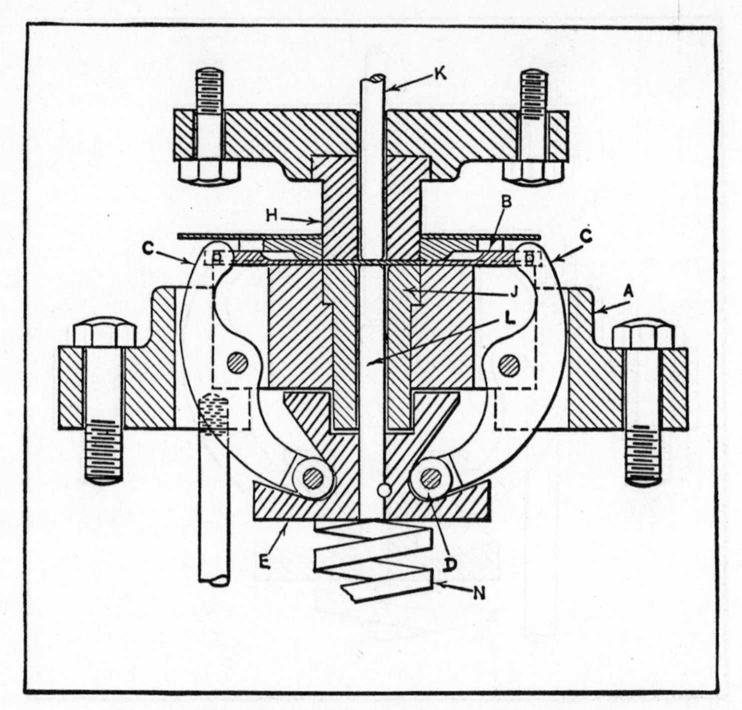

Fig. 42. Die with Drawing Punch near End of Stroke

of the drawing die *J* where it is held with just sufficient pressure to keep it from wrinkling during the drawing operation. The drawing punch *K* begins the drawing operation as soon as the blank has been brought into position on the drawing die.

The ejector *L* is carried downward during the drawing operation, causing the cone-shaped member *E* to force the lower ends of the rocker arms *C* outward, which, in turn, causes the plungers *B* to exert an inward pressure on the edge

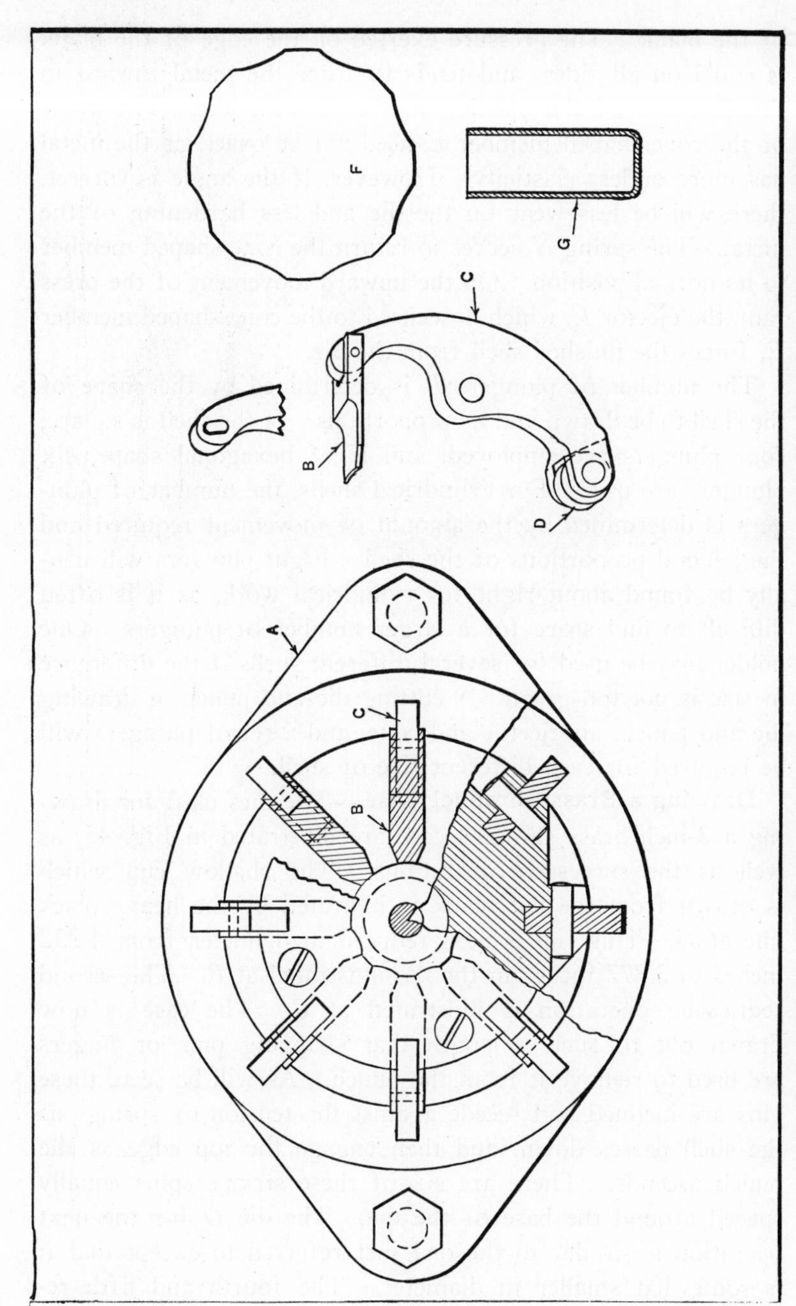

Fig. 43. Plan View of Die shown in Fig. 41

Fig. 44 Parts of Die, Shell, and Blank

of the blank. The pressure exerted on the edge of the blank is equal on all sides, and tends to force the metal inward in the direction of the opening in the drawing die. The angle of the cone-shaped member *E* need not be exact, as the metal has more or less elasticity. However, if the angle is correct, there will be less wear on the die and less hardening of the metal. The spring *N* serves to return the cone-shaped member to its normal position. On the upward movement of the press ram, the ejector *L*, which is secured to the cone-shaped member *E*, forces the finished shell from the die.

The number of plungers *B* is determined by the shape of the shell to be drawn and its proportions. If the shell is square, four plungers are employed, and if of hexagonal shape, six plungers are used. For cylindrical shells, the number of plungers is determined by the amount of movement required and the general proportions of the shell. Eight plungers will usually be found about right for cylindrical work, as it is often difficult to find space for a larger number of plungers. One holder may be used for several different shells if the difference in size is not too great. A cutting die and punch, a drawing die and punch, an ejector and cone, and a set of plungers will be required for each different size of shell.

Drawing a Brass Shrapnel Case.—The dies used for drawing a 3-inch brass shrapnel case are illustrated in Fig. 45, as well as the successive operations. The shallow cup which is drawn from the flat blank is indicated by the heavy black line at *A*. This cup is next reduced in diameter from 4.232 inches to 3.877 inches in the die illustrated at *B*. The second redrawing operation is illustrated at *C*. The case is now drawn out to such a length that stripping pins or fingers are used to remove it from the punch. As will be seen, these pins are inclined and recede against the tension of springs as the shell passes down, and then engage the top edge as the punch ascends. There are six of these stripper pins equally spaced around the base of the die. The die *D* for the next operation is similar to the one just referred to except that it is somewhat smaller in diameter. The fourth and fifth re-

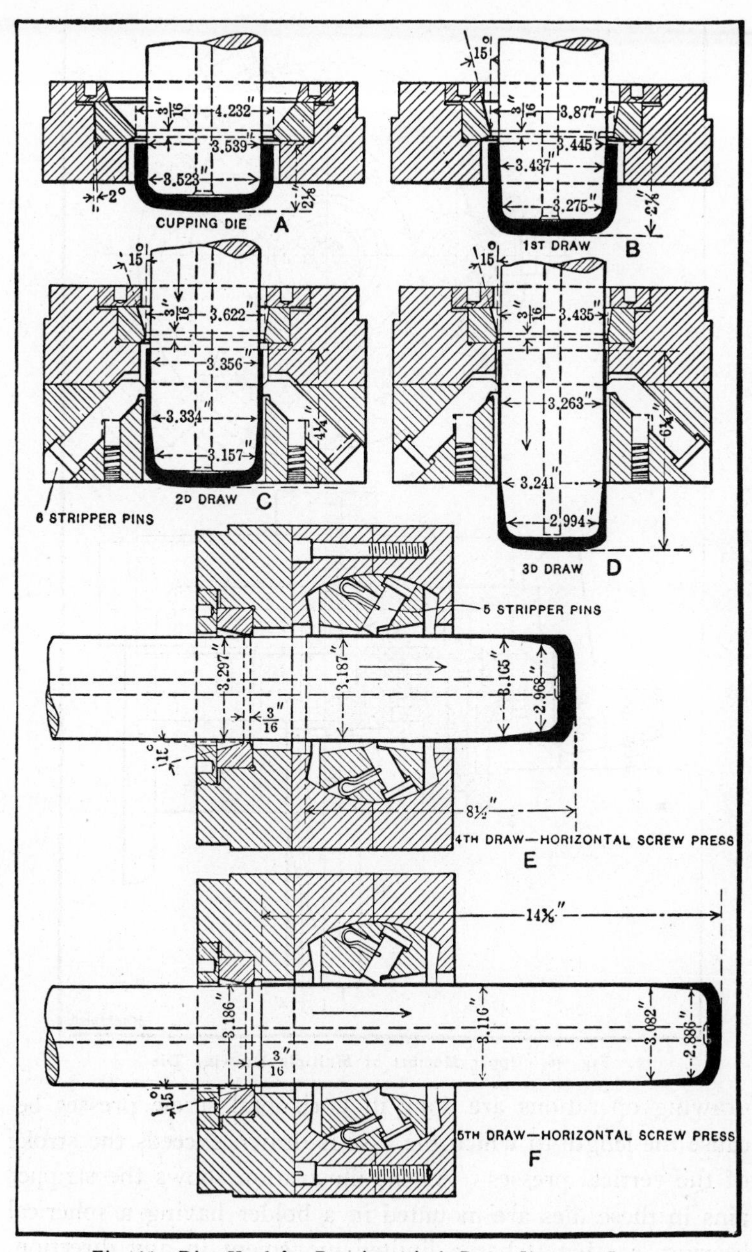

Fig. 45. Dies Used for Drawing 3-inch Brass Shrapnel Cases

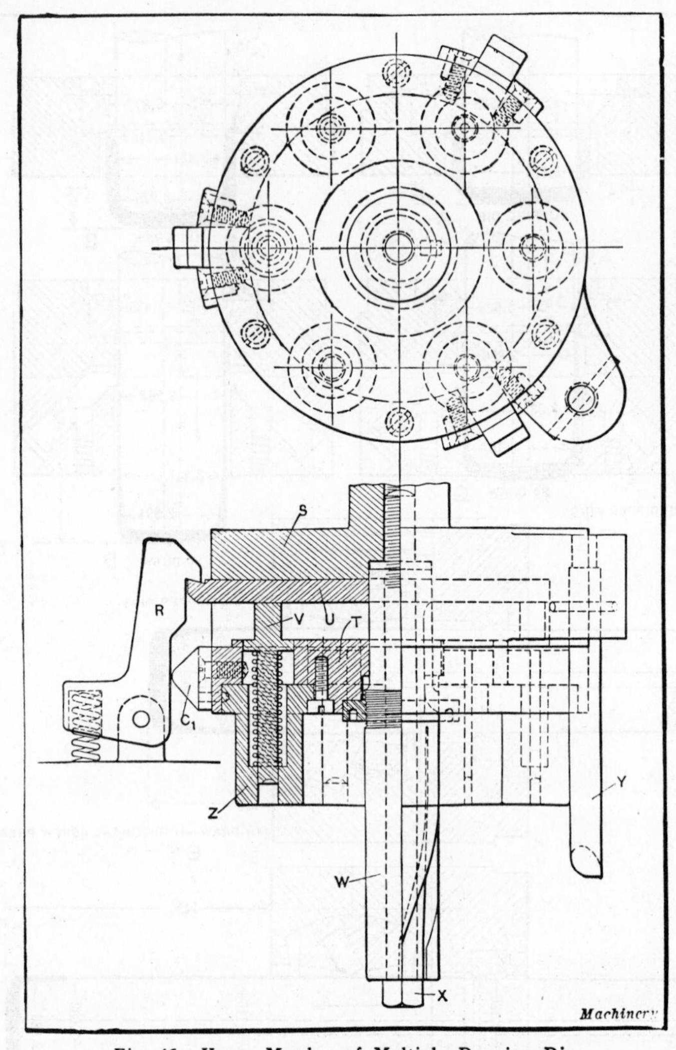

Fig. 46. Upper Member of Multiple Drawing Die

drawing operations are done in horizontal screw presses because the length to which the case is drawn exceeds the stroke of the vertical presses. As the illustration shows the stripper pins in these dies are mounted in a holder having a spherical bearing, so that it has a limited movement in any direction. As the result of this universal movement, the stripper pins automatically adjust themselves to conform to any unevenness of the edge of the drawn case; consequently, a practically uniform pressure is exerted upon the case when it is being moved from the punch. The case is annealed after every drawing operation and it is reduced to an outside diameter of 3.186 inches, and lengthened to 14⅜ inches. All of the punches are tapered on the end in order to secure thicker walls near the end, as indicated by the illustrations.

Multiple Drawing Die of Indexing Type.—The upper and lower members of a multiple drawing die for performing six drawing operations at one stroke of the press are shown in Figs. 46 and 47. The lower member, Fig. 47, contains the punches and is equipped with an automatic indexing mechanism which serves to carry the work around so that it is acted upon by the six punches and dies which successively reduce the size of the drawn part. Inasmuch as all of the punches and dies operate simultaneously, evidently a drawn piece is produced at each stroke of the press. Eight operations are required to complete the drawn part and their successive order is indicated in Fig. 48. The first operation is done in a compound blanking and drawing die equipped with a roll feed; the six operations following are performed in the automatic indexing die, which is shown in the accompanying illustration, and the eighth or final operation, which consists of turning down a flange and leveling the bottom, is done in another separate die.

The automatic indexing die has a shoe *A* which rests on the bolster of the press and serves to hold six equally-spaced drawing punches *B* and their respective stripping collars *C*. These stripping collars are held in place by retaining ring *D* which also provides a bearing for pawl carrier *E*. This carrier is hardened and ground and has attached to it a pawl *F* (see plan view) and also two hardened pins *G* which engage spiral grooves formed in extension *W* of the upper member (see Fig. 46). The pawl *F* is normally held outward by spring *H* and engages hardened teeth *J* inserted in plate *I*. These teeth take the end-thrust of pawl *F* as the latter, with

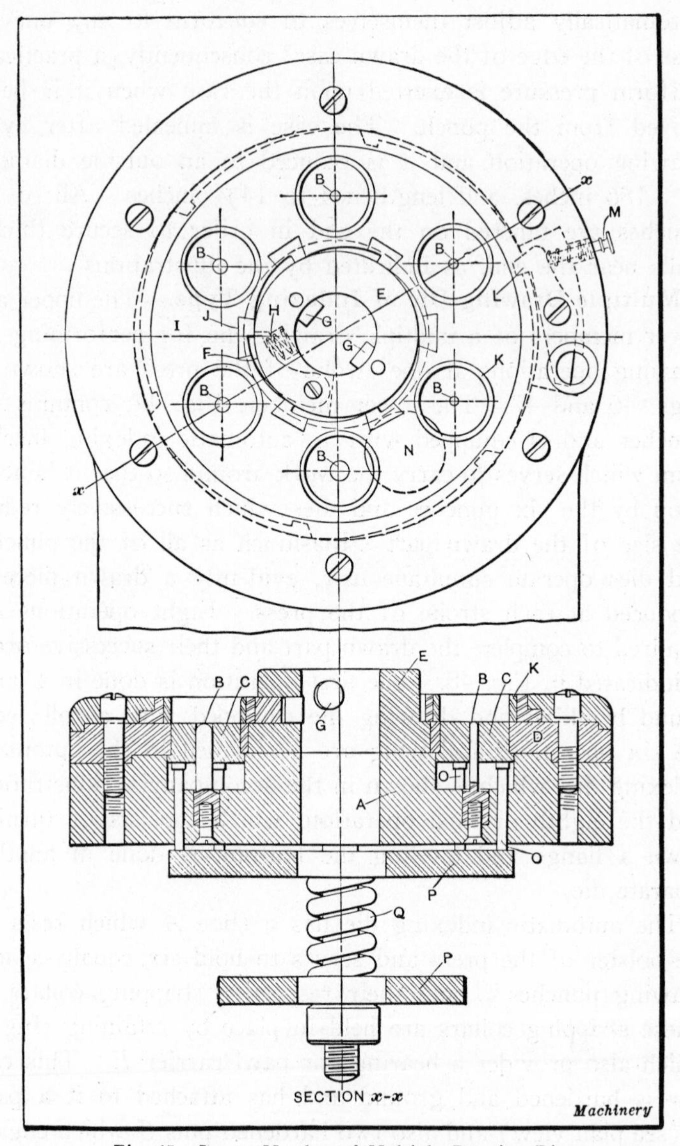

Fig. 47. Lower Member of Multiple Drawing Die

plate *E*, is revolved when the press ram ascends. Plate *I*, which is the index plate, has six holes into which are pressed the hardened bushings *K*. On the periphery of this plate there are six slots which are engaged by the end of locating lever *L* which serves to hold the plate firmly in position and locate the work accurately relative to the drawing dies. The thumb-nut *M* connecting with lever *L* is used for disengaging the lever when it is desired to turn the index plate by hand, in case it is necessary to remove the drawn parts.

During one revolution of plate *I* each of the six holes passes over the clearance hole *N*, which is just beyond the final drawing die, thus allowing the drawn part to drop out of the die and into a box beneath the press. The stripping collars *C* for the punches are actuated by three springs *Q* that are located on a circle underneath plate *P* and are held in position by three studs. These springs normally hold plate *P* upward and also collars *C*, by means of pins *O*.

The steel plate *T* (Fig. 46) is held to punch-holder *S* by screws and serves as the holder for the six drawing dies *Z*. Between holder *S* and plate *T* a space is cored out to receive stripper plate *U* which rests upon the strippers *V*. (The action of this plate will be referred to later.) The driver *W* has two spiral grooves milled into it which engage pins *G* (see Fig. 47) and operate the pawl carrier as previously mentioned. The bolt *X* provides adjustment for this driver. The hardened rod *Y* serves to release the locating lever *L* on the lower member so that index plate *I* may be revolved.

The operation of the dies is as follows: When the upper member descends, the successive drawing operations on the six parts are performed (assuming that the die is completely loaded) and at the same time plate *E* and index pawl *F* are turned backward into engagement with the next tooth *J* on plate *I* preparatory to indexing. The rod *Y* also engages the end of locating lever *L* and withdraws it from the index plate. When the upper member ascends the drawn parts are stripped from the punches and dies, and plate *E*, with index pawl *F*, is turned forward, thus indexing the six drawn pieces from one die to the next by the rotation of index plate *I*. When lever *L* is released by the upward movement of rod *Y* it drops into a notch and accurately locates and locks the index plate in position. This cycle of movements is repeated for each stroke of the press.

In designing this die, one of the points which had to be considered very carefully was to secure a rapid and positive stripping action for the dies in the upper members; in fact, the drawn parts have to be stripped from the dies as soon as the press slide starts upwards so that the work will not be disarranged by being carried up out of the index plate. This positive stripping action was effected by means of plate *U* in conjunction with three levers or pawls *R*. These levers are pivoted to the lower member and as the upper member de-

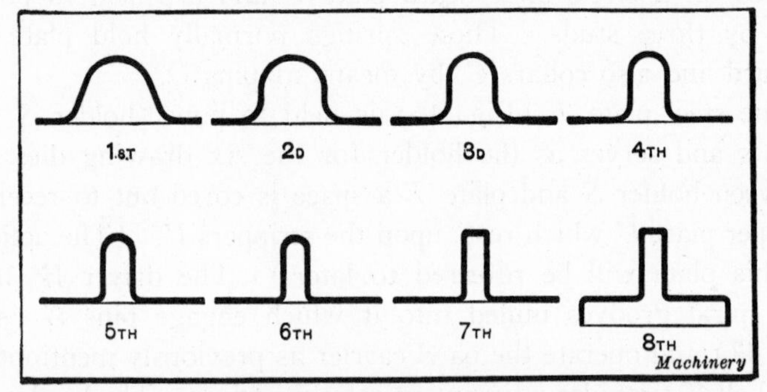

Fig. 48. Successive Drawing Operations, Six of which are done in a Multiple Die of Automatic Indexing Type

scends they are forced outwards by three cams C_1. At the end of the downward movement, levers *R* are in engagement with plate *U*, as the illustration, Fig. 46, indicates. When the slide begins to ascend, plate *U* and the strippers *V* are held stationary while the dies *Z* move upward, thus ejecting the drawn parts. When the cam surface on lever *R* is engaged by cam C_1, it is forced outward, thus releasing plate *U*. In this way the strippers are actuated at the beginning of the upward stroke so that the drawn parts are pushed from the dies without leaving the index plate. As the slide continues to ascend the index plate is revolved into position for the next drawing operation.

CHAPTER XV

DIES FOR DRAWING SHELLS HAVING WIDE FLANGES

WHEN a shell is being drawn, the strains to which the metal is subjected in connection with a given diameter reduction, may be affected decidedly by the shape of the shell. For example, when drawing shells having flanges which are wide in proportion to the shell diameter, there may be difficulty (which would not occur otherwise) due to over-stressing the metal, unless approved methods of drawing flanged shells are employed. It is evident that a flangeless shell of given diameter and depth will require less pressure for drawing than a flanged shell of equal diameter and depth, assuming that each is drawn in the same die from a flat blank. This difference in pressure is due to the fact that a larger blank must be used for the flanged shell and, consequently, more pressure is required for changing the shape of this larger blank.

In preceding chapters, a number of dies for drawing flanged shells have been illustrated and described but without particular comment as to the methods of drawing flanged parts, especially when the flanges are wide in proportion to the diameter of the shell body. This subject will now be discussed, as it is of importance in connection with the design of certain classes of drawing dies. After explaining the general methods of drawing flanged shells, some examples of dies for producing shells having comparatively wide flanges will be presented.

Two Methods of Forming Flanges on Drawn Shells.— Two methods of drawing a flanged shell which requires more than one operation will be described. The method that is commonly employed is first to draw the blank into a flanged cup and then reduce the size of both the cup and flange by

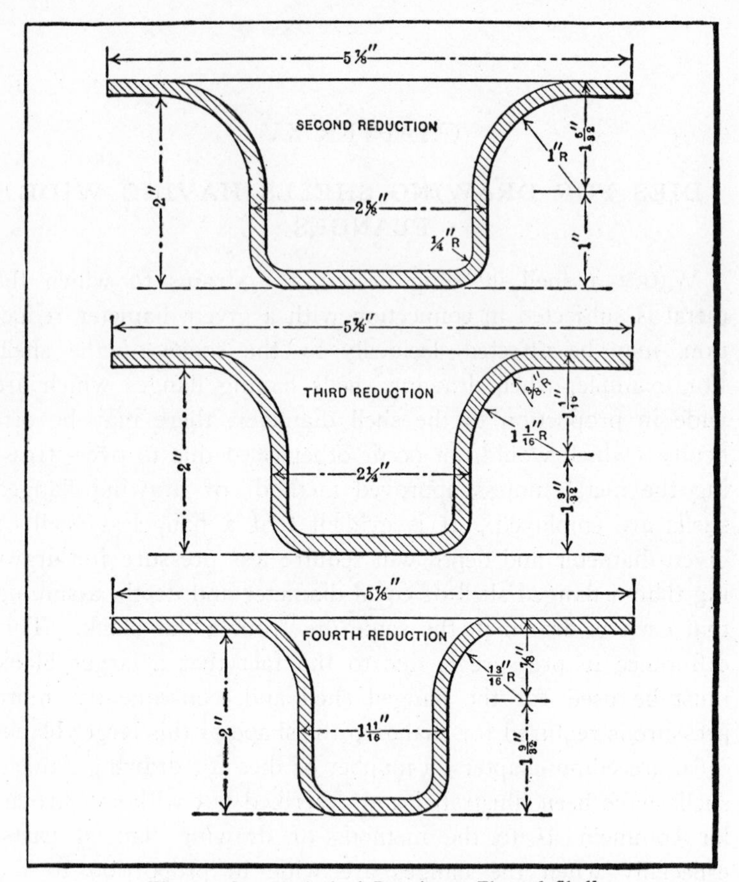

Fig. 1. One Method of Drawing a Flanged Shell

means of successive redrawing operations until the required dimensions are obtained. When this method is employed, the width of the flange remains approximately the same, but the flange is reduced in diameter for each successive redrawing operation, the metal being drawn into the body of the cup or shell. The other method differs from the one just referred to in that the outside diameter of the flange remains about the same for all the drawing operations but the width is increased for each successive operation because some of the surplus metal obtained when reducing the body diameter is forced up into the flange. Thus, as the diameter of the shell body is decreased, some of the metal flows up into the flange which is thereby increased in width as illustrated in Fig. 1. The stroke of the press must be so adjusted that the drawing punch will not descend far enough to pull in the flange, thus reducing the original diameter. This second method makes it possible to secure a greater reduction in diameter of the shell body in one drawing operation, and a greater length of cup in the first operation, which reduces the strain on the metal in succeeding operations; therefore the second method ordinarily is preferable when the flange diameter is large in proportion to the diameter of the shell.

When the flange and shell body are both reduced, the flange width remaining about the same, the metal is subjected to a greater strain and more stretching, and, consequently, is made harder and more brittle, thereby necessitating several annealing operations. This additional strain upon the metal is due to the fact that a flat flange is reduced in size for each operation and must be drawn into the body of the shell. On the other hand, when the flange is gradually enlarged by pushing the metal up into it from the shell body, the stress on the metal is less. Even though the same number of press operations may be required with one method as with the other, the second one referred to is often preferable, not only because it reduces the number of annealings necessary but also because it enables cheaper dies to be used and gives a more uniform thickness of metal in the finished part.

When designing dies for forming a flange by pushing the metal up into the flange, it is advisable to have as large a radius on the drawing edge of the first die as possible, the radius on dies for succeeding operations being reduced when necessary, thus forcing the surplus metal into the flange.

Example of Flanged-shell Drawing.—A wheel hub for a small automobile will be used as the first example of flanged-shell drawing. Nine dies were required to complete this part which was drawn from hot-rolled strip steel, $5/32$ inch thick.

The first operation, which consisted of cutting the blank to a diameter of 7 inches, was performed by a blanking die of standard construction, and is not illustrated. The first drawing operation on the shell was performed by the double-action type of die shown in Fig. 2, which was used in connection with a double-action press. Prior to operating, the punch *A* and the blank-holder *B* are in a raised position, with the lower face of the punch somewhat higher than the lower face of

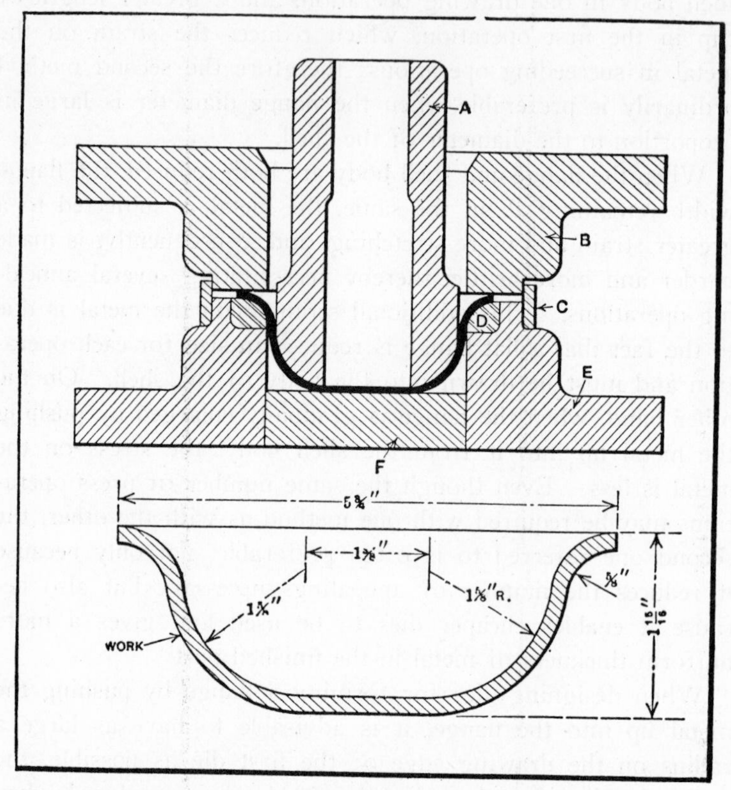

Fig. 2. Double-action Die which Performs the First Drawing Operation on Flanged Shell

the blank-holder. The blank is placed within the gaging ring *C* and rests on the forming ring *D* and the die-block *E*. On the downward stroke of the press ram, the blank-holder descends until it comes in contact with the blank, in which position it remains and holds the blank while the punch continues to descend and draw the shell as shown. By this arrangement, pressure is applied on the blank by the blank-holder during the drawing operation. On the return stroke of the press ram, the punch is raised from the die, somewhat in advance of the blank-holder, and thus the blank-holder prevents the shell from adhering to the punch. The knock-out pad *F* is provided for ejecting the shell from the die. The punch and blank-holder are both made of cast iron.

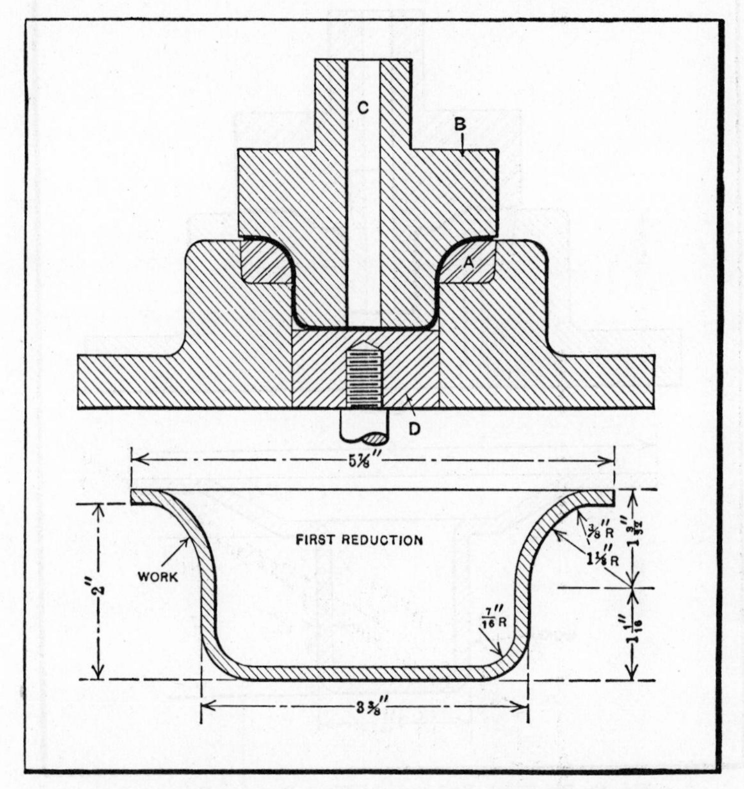

Fig. 3. Type of Die Used for Reducing the Body Diameter

The die illustrated in Fig. 3 is employed to make the first reduction in the diameter of the shell and to continue the formation of the flange. The shell is placed on the forming ring *A* and as punch *B* descends it is drawn to the shape illustrated. The punch is equipped with a knock-out rod which operates in the hole *C* and which forces the shell from the punch after the operation has been performed. The knock-out pad *D* is provided for ejecting the shell from the die. The punch *B* is made of cast iron. Similarly constructed dies are used to make the second, third, and fourth reductions in the diameter of the shell and to continue the development of the flange. Fig. 1 shows the shell as it appears after each

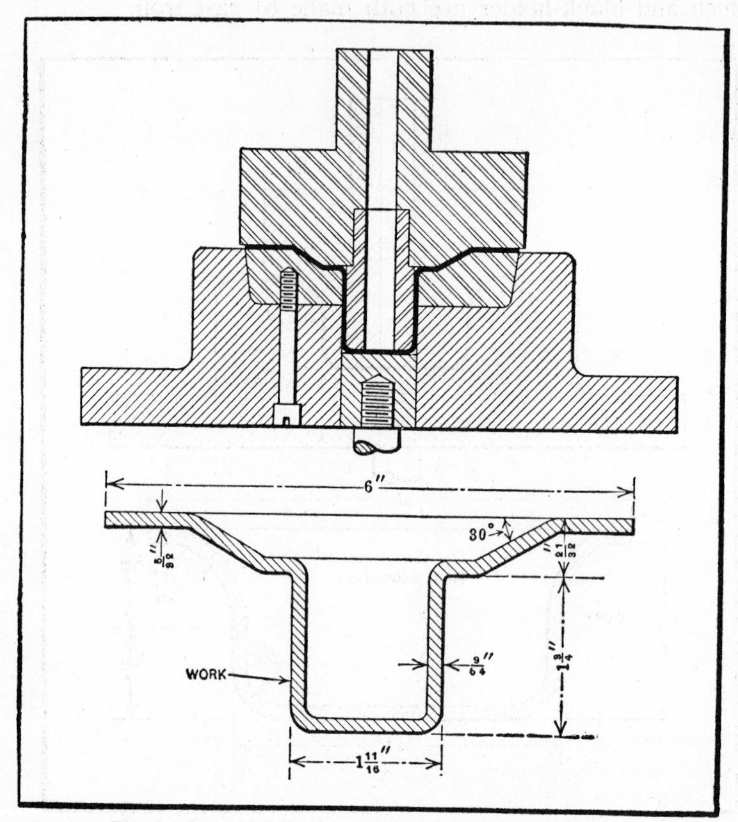

Fig. 4. Die which Performs the Final Drawing Operation

of these operations. It should be noted that, in the first reducing operation, the shell was drawn to an over-all depth of 2⁵⁄₃₂ inches and the flange formed to a diameter of 5⅞ inches. As these dimensions are maintained during the successive reducing operations, it is obvious that as the diameter of the body is decreased, more metal is formed in the flange. It will be noted that the metal which connects the flange to the body is, in each case, formed to a large radius. By this method of gradually forming the flange by several operations, comparatively large flanges can be produced readily on similar work.

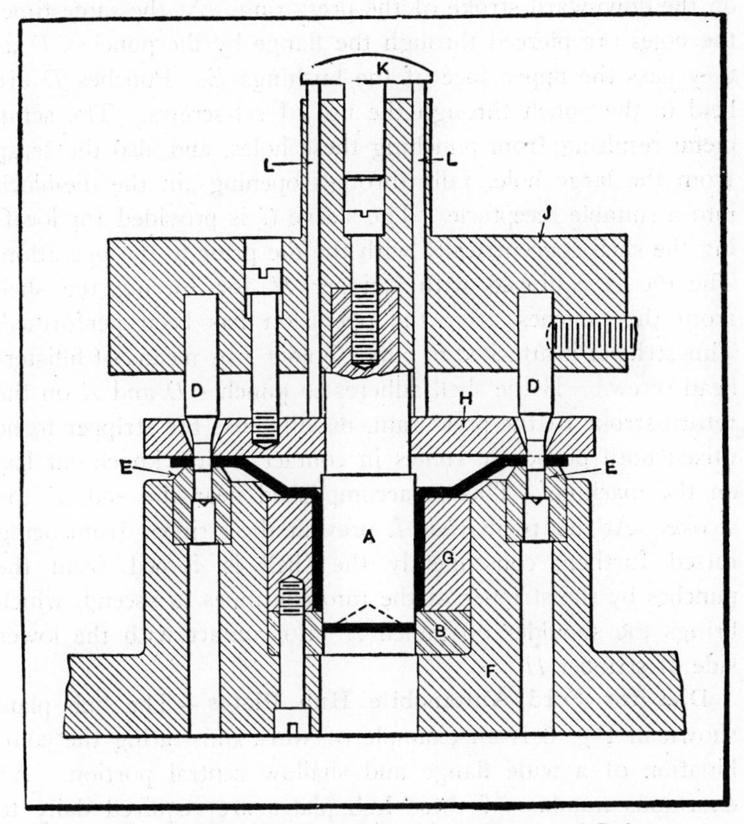

Fig. 5. Die which Cuts Holes in the Flange and Body

The final drawing operation is performed by the die illustrated in Fig. 4. In this operation, part of the flange is formed to an angle of 30 degrees, a portion of the body is straightened, and the diameter of the flange is increased slightly. The next operation consists of trimming the flange to the desired diameter, for which purpose a plain blanking die is employed which is equipped with a device for locating the shell in the die preparatory to the operation.

The work is completed by the die shown in Fig. 5. In this operation, a hole is cut in the end of the shell and six holes are pierced through the flange. The hole is cut in the body as punch *A* passes the upper edge of cutting ring *B* on the downward stroke of the press ram. At the same time, the holes are pierced through the flange by the punches *D* as they pass the upper face of the bushings *E*. Punches *D* are held in the punch through the use of set-screws. The scrap metal resulting from punching these holes, and also the scrap from the large hole, falls through openings in the die-block into a suitable receptacle. The sleeve *G* is provided for locating the shell concentrically with the die prior to the operation. The die is equipped with stripper *H* for forcing the shell from the punches after the operation has been performed. This stripper is attached to punch-holder *J* by means of fillister-head screws. If the shell adheres to punches *D* and *A* on the return stroke of the press ram, it will cause the stripper to be raised until pusher *K* comes in contact with a knock-out bar on the machine. This is accomplished near the end of the stroke. At this point rods *L* prevent the stripper from being raised further; consequently the shell is forced from the punches by the stripper as the ram continues to ascend, which brings the shoulder on punch *A* into contact with the lower side of stripper *H*.

Dies for Ford Automobile Hub Plates.—The hub plate shown in Fig. 6 is an example of work illustrating the combination of a wide flange and shallow central portion. An enormous number of these hub plates are required daily to meet the needs of the assembling departments in the Ford automobile shops. It will be noted that several dimensions must be within specified limits. One manufacturer of these parts produces them on power presses in three operations, and two of the dies used for this purpose are described in the following: The first operation consists of cutting the blank to the outside diameter of the finished part, and is performed on a press equipped with a blanking die of standard construction.

The second operation on the plate consists of piercing a hole ¾ inch in diameter through the center of the blank, drawing the hub, and rounding one edge of the flange. The punch and die used in this operation is illustrated in Fig. 7. A noteworthy feature of the operation is that the diameter of the flange remains the same as that of the original blank, the hub being drawn from the metal between the inner portion

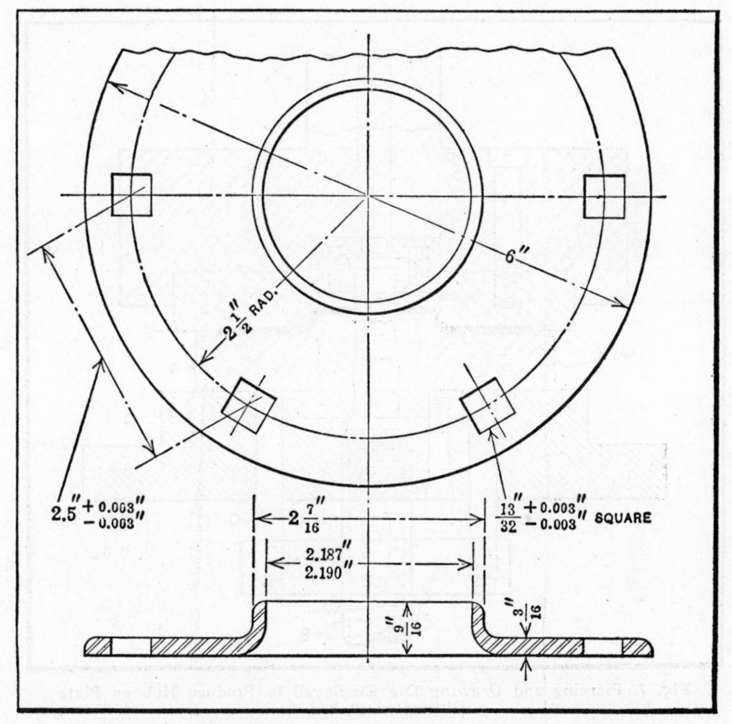

Fig. 6. Hub Plate of Type Used on Ford Automobile

of the flange and the hole pierced through the blank. As a result, it will be seen that the thickness of the metal forming the hub is considerably less than the thickness of the flange. The hole is punched through the blank prior to drawing the hub, the purpose of the hole being to permit the metal to be drawn more easily near the center of the part without changing the diameter of the flange.

In Fig. 7 the punch is shown in the position occupied at the end of a downward stroke. Prior to an operation, the blank is placed on the draw-ring *A*, which is raised by means of spring *B* and four pins *C* to a position in which its upper face is in alignment with the top surface of the punch *D*. The blank is located in the proper position on the ring by means of a slight recess in the upper face of the ring, which is of the same diameter as the blank. On the downward

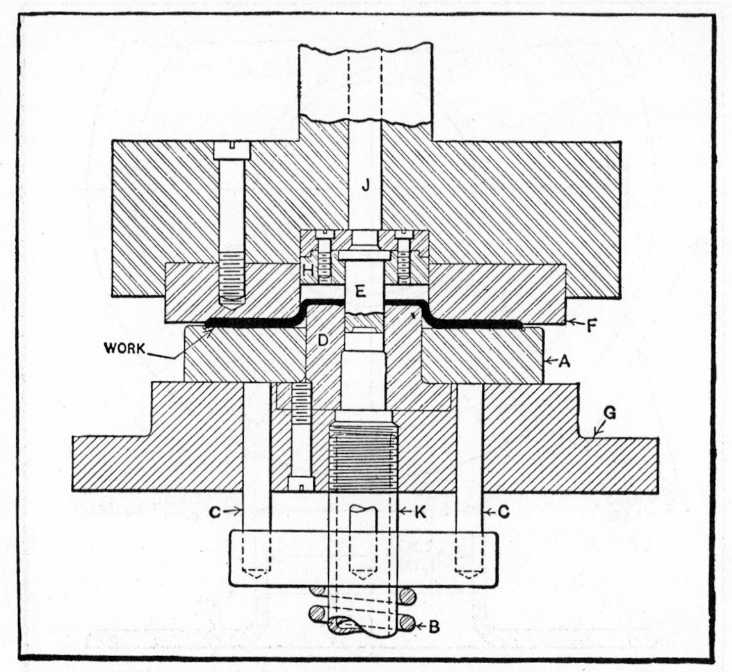

Fig. 7. Piercing and Drawing Die Employed to Produce Hub on Plate Illustrated in Fig. 6

stroke of the press ram, the piercing punch *E* comes in contact with the blank, and while it is being forced through the blank the forming punch *F* holds the plate against draw-ring *A*, thus insuring that the diameter of the blank will remain unchanged while the hub is being drawn. The upper edge of the flange is rounded by punch *F* as the draw-ring comes in contact with die-block *G* at the end of the stroke.

On the upward stroke of the ram, the blank is stripped

from punch *F* by block *H*, to which punch *E* is attached, block *H* being actuated by knock-out rod *J*. The latter is forced down by coming in contact with a cross-bar in the ram. It will be noted that spring *B* is mounted on a tube *K* instead of on a solid rod as is the customary practice. The slugs produced by punch *E* in punching the hole through the plate drop through this tube, and are thus ejected from the die. The press that performs the operation is inclined so that the finished pieces may slide on a conveyor, which carries them to the machine for the next operation.

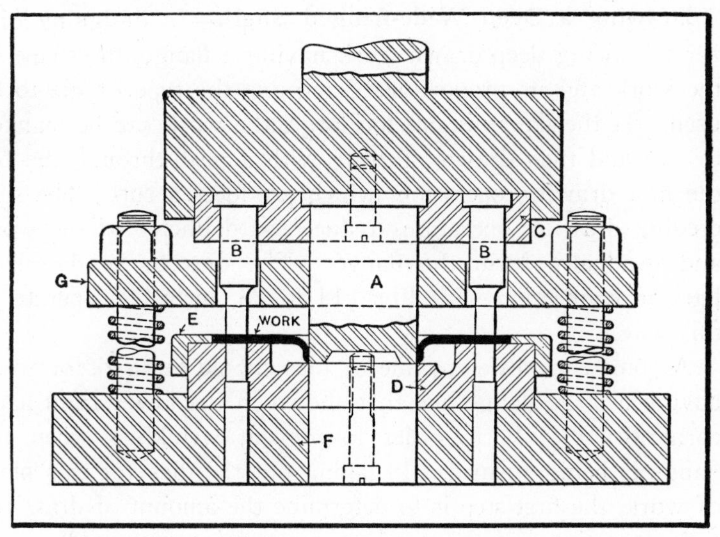

Fig. 8. Punch and Die used to Punch the Large Hole in the Hub and the Six Square Flange Holes

In the third and final operation on the plate, the large hole is punched through the hub and the six square holes pierced through the flange. The punch and die employed in this operation is illustrated in Fig. 8. It will be seen that punches *A* and *B* are held to the punch proper by plate *C*, which is attached to the punch by means of fillister-head machine screws. Proper location of the blank in the die is obtained by the use of ring *E*. Punch *A* is of such length that, on the downward stroke of the ram, it finishes cutting through the hub just as punches *B* come in contact with the flange. This arrangement reduces the force of the blow on the blank, which would be very great if all the punches came in contact with the work simultaneously, and is a principle that should be adhered to in the design of all heavy piercing dies. It will be seen that holes are provided through the die-blocks *D* and *F* to permit the scrap to fall through the die. The finished part is forced from the punches on the return stroke by stripper plate *G*. Dies to be used similarly to those described should be of generous proportions and so constructed that they can be easily reground or repaired.

Drawing a Deep Wide-flanged Shell.—In designing dies for producing deep drawn work having a flange, the shape of the work and its proportions determine the type of die to be used. If the flange is not too large, the work can be blanked to size and then drawn, starting with a push-through die for the first drawing operation, which produces a cup. The succeeding drawing operations reduce the diameter of the work and gradually form the flange. The dies to be described later in connection with Figs. 14 to 23, inclusive, operate in this way.

A somewhat different line of dies should be used for work having a large flange like that shown in the lower right-hand corner of Fig. 9, in order to prevent wrinkling when the flange is being formed. In laying out the dies for this piece of work, the first step is to determine the amount of draw for each operation and the number of operations required.

The approximate size of the blank is first determined, and as the final size of the work is a known factor it is then possible to lay out the blank size and the finished work on paper. The various drawing operations can next be planned and the shape of the work after each operation sketched in accordingly. This naturally requires knowledge of drawing practice based on experience. Each piece of work to be drawn requires a separate lay-out and the method of procedure is naturally based on the equipment available. For instance, it is necessary to know whether a single- or double-action press is to be used and what the capacity of the press is in tons. Definite knowledge of the material to be drawn is perhaps the most important factor, because the amount of drawing to be accomplished in each operation is governed partly by the nature of the material. Some materials draw very readily, while others have poor drawing qualities.

The lay-outs of the dies required for drawing the piece of work shown in Fig. 9 are illustrated in Figs. 10 to 13. These illustrations are not intended to be actual working drawings but merely to show the best general design dictated by ex-

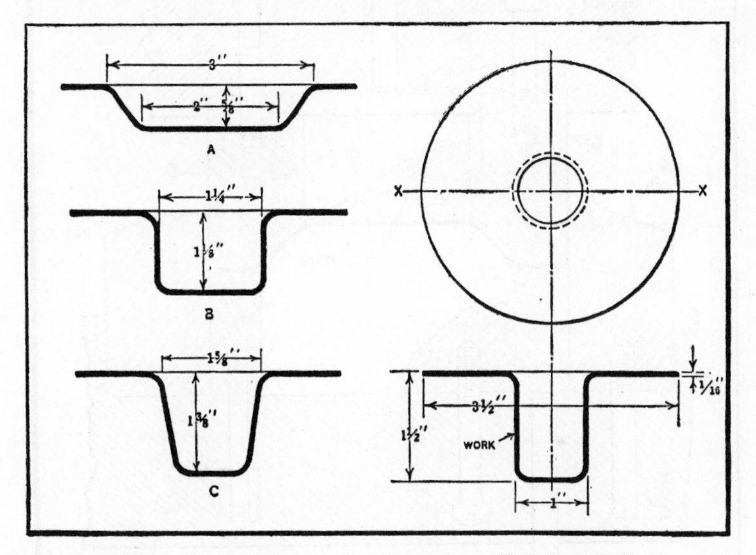

Fig. 9. Successive Steps in Drawing a Wide-flanged Shell

perience and modern practice. They are, however, similar to dies which have been successful in practice.

The sequence of the drawing operations for this work is shown in Fig. 9. The dimensions of the finished piece of work are shown in the sectional view in the lower right-hand corner, while the shape of the work after each of the first three drawing operations is shown at *A*, *B*, and *C*, respectively. The dimensions given show the amount of draw in each operation. The fourth drawing operation brings the shell to the desired diameter and length. A certain amount of stock is allowed for a final trimming operation, as it is apparent that on deep drawn work the outside diameter of the flange would not be uniform but would have an irregular edge that requires trimming.

The die for the blanking and first drawing operation is shown in Fig. 10. The die *A* and punch *B* blank the work to the correct diameter on the downward stroke of the press

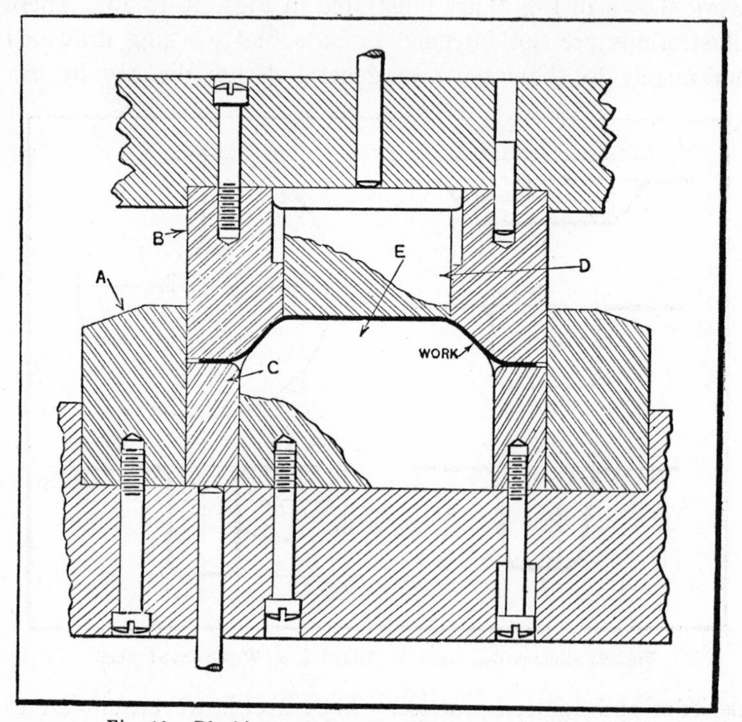

Fig. 10. Blanking and Drawing Die for First Operation

and form it to the shape shown by the heavy black line. The work is held securely against the punch by a pressure-ring *C* while the forming is being done, thus preventing wrinkling. Pressure is also exerted on the stock by a pressure-plate *D* acting against block *E*. As the punch is withdrawn, the work is ejected by the pressure-ring *C*, in case it should tend to stick on the forming block *E*. When it sticks to punch *B* it is stripped by the pressure-plate *D*. If it were desired to

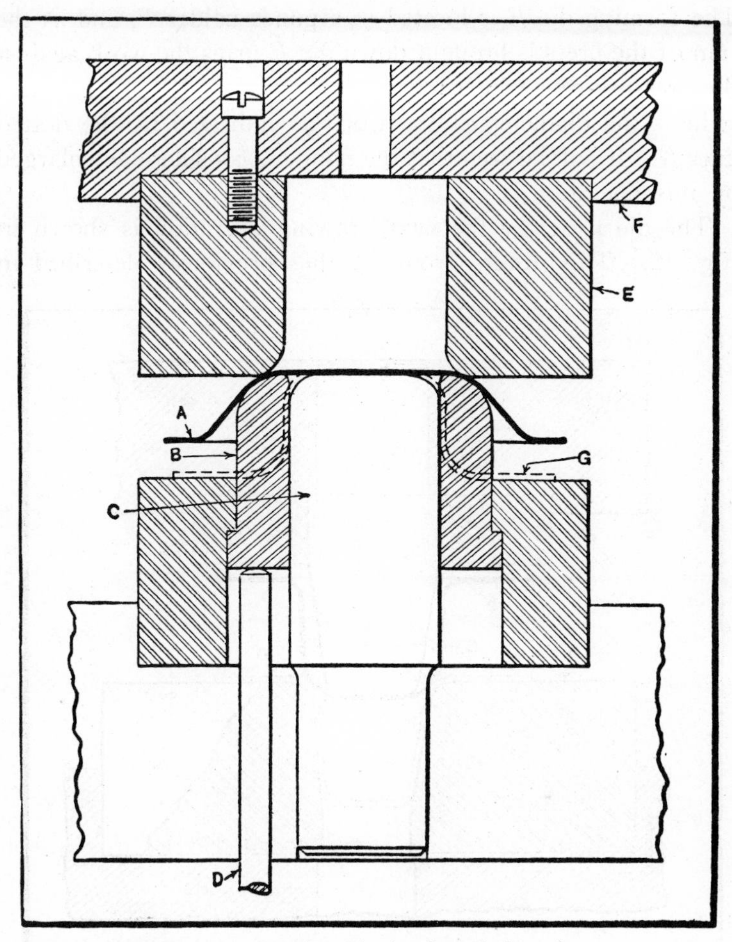

Fig. 11. Drawing Die for Second Operation

blank the work to size in a previous operation, the die would be of similar construction except that the work would then be located in a nest on the die-block *A*.

The die for the second operation, shown in Fig. 11, differs somewhat in principle from the one just described. The work *A* is located on a pressure-ring *B*, which is a sliding fit on the forming punch *C*. Spring pressure is applied to ring *B* through the pressure-pins *D*, which are connected with heavy coil springs or with a rubber cushion under the bolster plate.

The forming die E is located in a punch-holder F, and as the ram of the press is brought down die E grips the work against the pressure-ring which moves downward under pressure and reduces the diameter of the work as indicated by the dotted lines G. It will be seen that the flange is considerably enlarged by this operation.

The die used for the next drawing operation is shown in Fig. 12. This differs from the dies previously described in

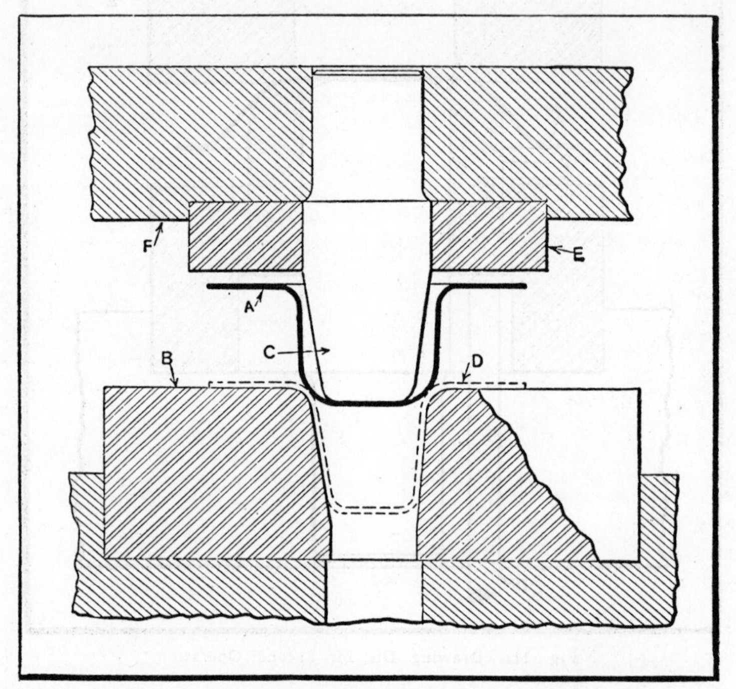

Fig. 12. Die for Fourth Operation on Deep-drawn Shell

that its action is more that of sizing than drawing. The work A is located on the top of die B. The punch C fits down into the work and forces it into the hole in the die, stretching out the drawn part, as shown by the dotted lines at D. As the punch reaches the end of its stroke the flange is flattened out between die B and plate E, which is located in punch-holder F.

The final drawing operation is simple, and is performed by a die of the same type as that shown in Fig. 12. After the work has been completely drawn, the flange is trimmed to the required diameter by the die shown in Fig. 13. The work *A* is located in the block *B*, which serves as a punch for trimming the flange. The punch-holder is provided with a die *C* which trims the work to size on the downward stroke of the press. A pressure-plate *D* holds the work firmly while the trimming is being accomplished. On the upward stroke, stripper *E* strips the flash *F* from the punch.

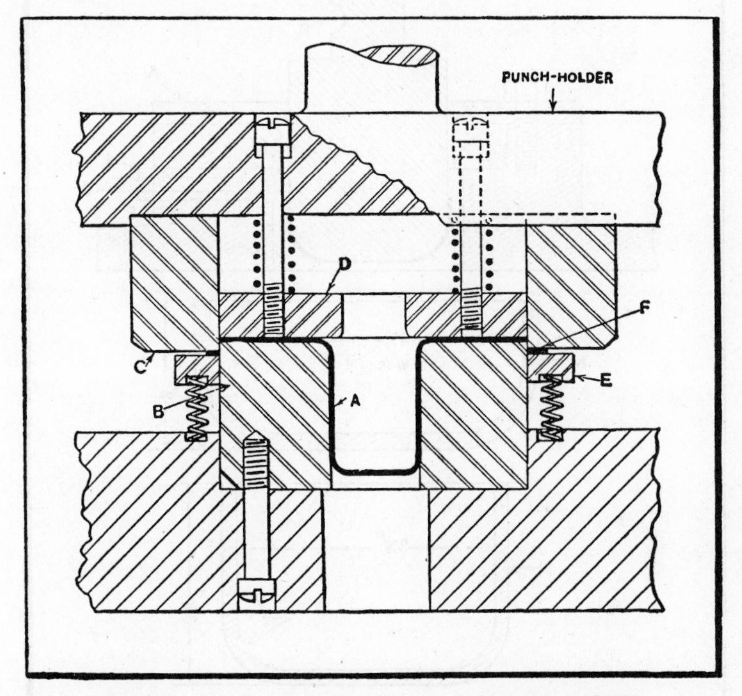

Fig. 13. Die for Trimming Flange of Deep-drawn Shell

Dies for Double-flanged Shell.—Steel shells having a flange at each end are usually manufactured with difficulty, but by the use of proper methods and equipment, such work can be readily produced. The set of dies employed in drawing a shell of this type, and the methods followed will be described. The various dies are shown in the order in which they are used, and the dimensions of the shell after each operation, are also given. The shell is drawn from 3/16-inch thick, hot-rolled strip steel. The first operation is performed in a blanking die of standard type, in which the blank is cut to a diameter of 7 inches.

The first and second drawing operations are performed on the plain push-through die shown in Fig. 14. The illustration shows the die equipped for performing the first of these opera-

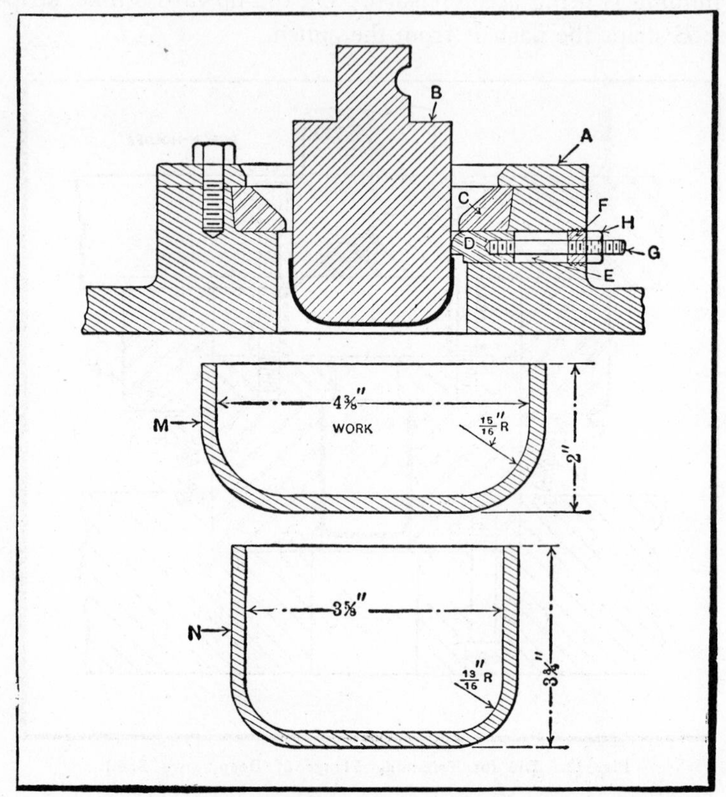

Fig. 14. Type of Push-through Die for the First Two Drawing Operations on Double-flanged Shell

tions, which forms the shell to the shape shown at *M*. The steel blank is placed in the hole of the gaging ring *A*, by which means it is located concentrically with the die. As punch *B* descends on the downward stroke of the press ram, the blank is drawn through the die ring *C* in the shape illustrated. The shell is forced from the punch on the return stroke of the press ram by means of three stripping devices which extend radially from the die. One of these devices can be clearly seen in the illustration; it consists of the stripper *D*, an expansion coil spring which operates in space E, the threaded plug *F*, the stud *G*, and the nut *H*. As the shell is pushed through the die ring, stripper *D* is forced radially outward when the work

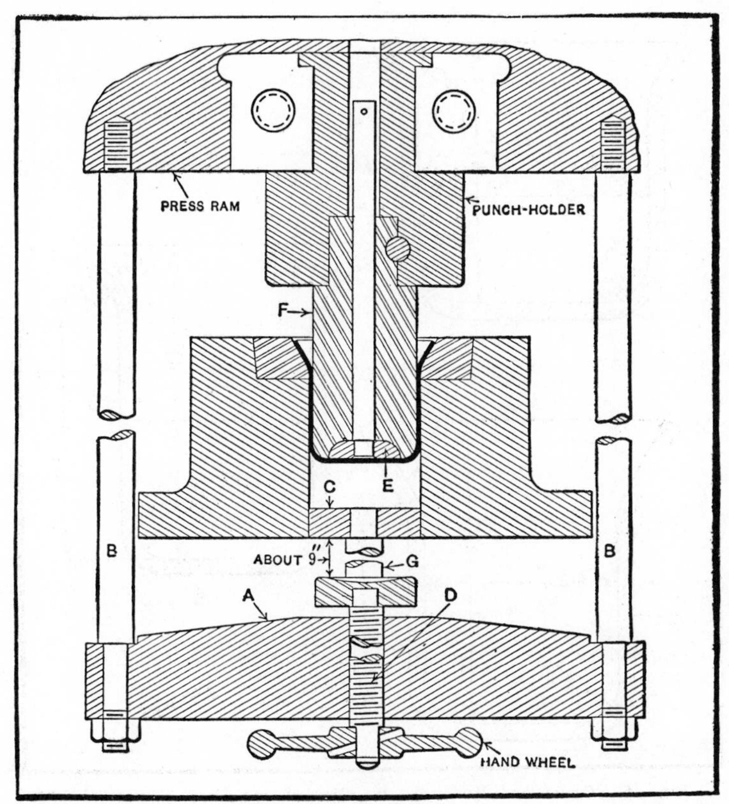

Fig. 15. Die used in Reducing the Shell Diameter and Partly Forming One Flange

comes in contact with it. When the shell has reached the position illustrated, the stripper is forced toward the center of the die by the action of the spring in space *E*, in which position it forces the shell from the punch on the return stroke. The shell then drops through the opening in the die-block into a receptable beneath. The second drawing operation, which brings the shell to the shape shown at *N*, is accomplished by replacing punch *B* and die ring *C* with similar parts having proper dimensions for this operation, and then proceeding as before.

Forming Flange on Plain Shell.—The plain cup or shell shown in Fig. 14 is subjected to several redrawing operations

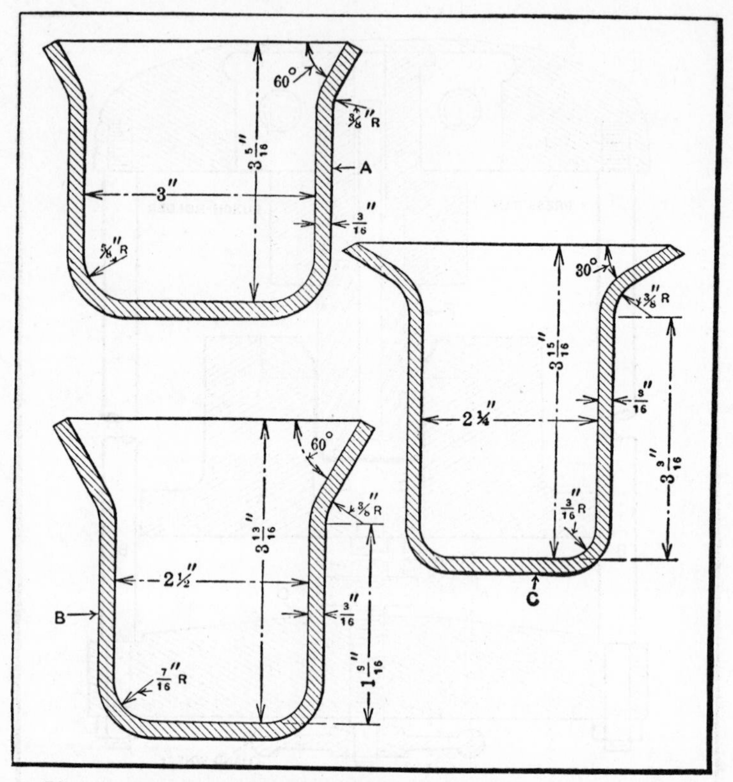

Fig. 16. Operations Performed by Dies of the Type Illustrated in Fig. 15

which serve to reduce the diameter and form flanges on each end. Fig. 15 shows the construction of the die employed in further reducing the diameter of the shell and partly forming the flange, as shown at *A* in Fig. 16, while two similarly constructed dies form the shells to the shapes shown at *B* and *C*. By referring to Fig. 15, it will be noted that the illustration shows a device for ejecting the shell from the die. The knock-out bar *A* is attached to the press ram by rods *B*, so that on the return stroke of the ram, the bar is pulled upward by the rods, thus raising the pad *C* by means of the adjusting screw *D* and rod *G*, and causing the shell to be ejected from the die. The adjusting screw *D* permits the pad *C* to be adjusted vertically

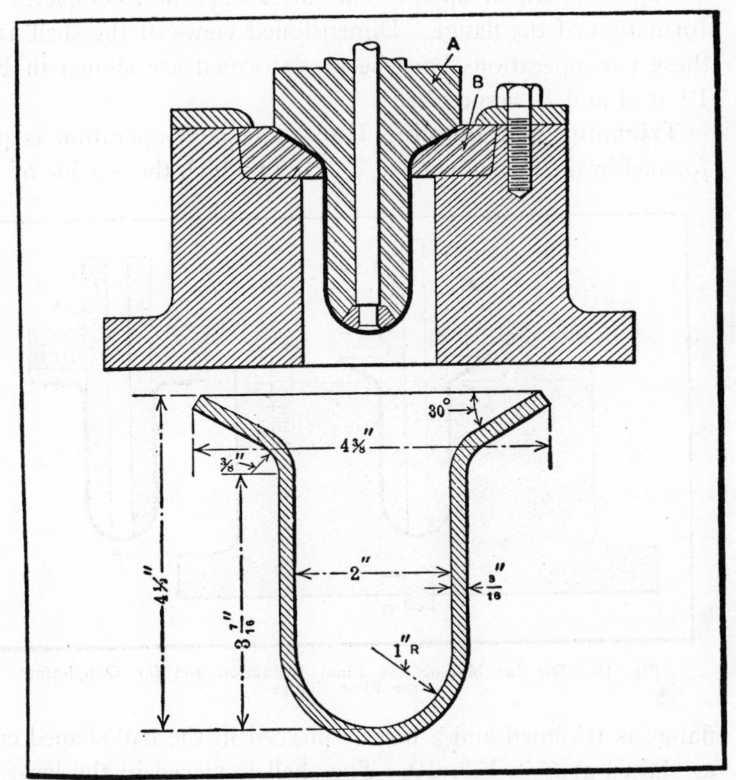

Fig. 17. Die which Reduces Shell Diameter and Forms End

to the proper position in the die. A knock-out *E* is provided for forcing the shell from the punch *F*.

The die illustrated in Fig. 17 makes another reduction in the shell diameter and, in addition, produces a ball-shaped end on the closed end of the shell. By having an end of this type, it is possible to keep the metal at that part of the shell approximately the same thickness during the drawing operations. By replacing punch *A* and the forming ring *B* with suitable parts, as shown at *O* and *P* in Fig. 18, the same die is used in performing the next two operations. In the operation illustrated at *O*, the final reduction is made on the diameter of the shell. After a quantity of shells has gone through this operation, collar *C* is placed on the punch, as at *P*, and the same shells are again operated upon. The latter operation completes the formation of the flange. Dimensioned views of the shell after these two operations have been performed are shown in Fig. 19 at *A* and *B*, respectively

Trimming and Piercing Die.—The next operation is performed in the die shown in Fig. 20, in which the outside of the

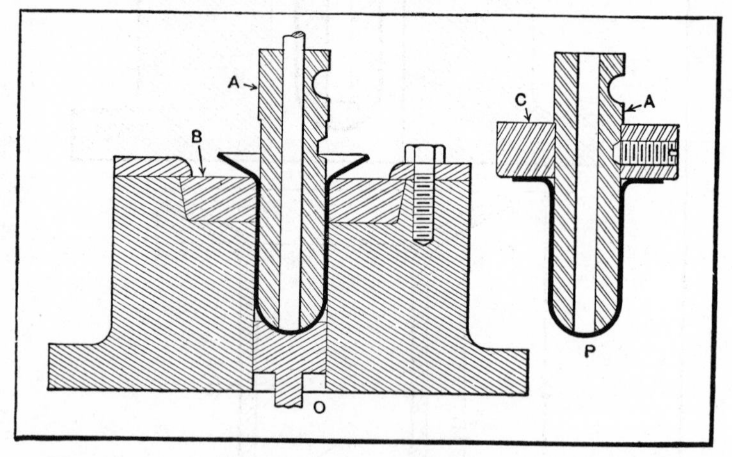

Fig. 18. Die for Making the Final Reduction and for Completing the First Flange

flange is trimmed and a hole is pierced in the ball-shaped end, as shown at *C* in Fig. 19. The shell is placed in the locating sleeve *A*, which holds it concentric with the die. The hole is pierced in the shell by punch *B* on the downward stroke of the press ram, and the flange is trimmed at the same time by the cutting ring *C*. The scrap from the hole falls through an opening in the die. A knock-out device, of which parts *D*, *E*, and *F* are illustrated, is provided for ejecting the shell from the cutting ring on the return stroke of the press ram. The part *E* operates in a slot in punch-holder *K*. It will be noted that at the conclusion of this operation on the shell, the scrap

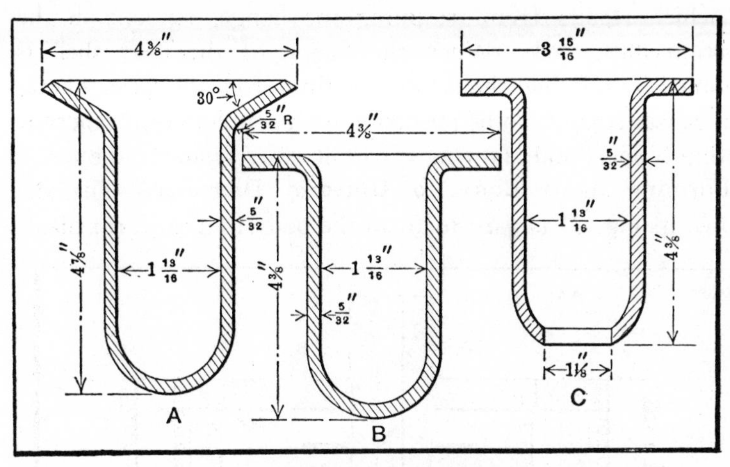

Fig. 19. Appearance of Work after Each of the Operations Performed by the Dies shown in Figs. 18 and 20

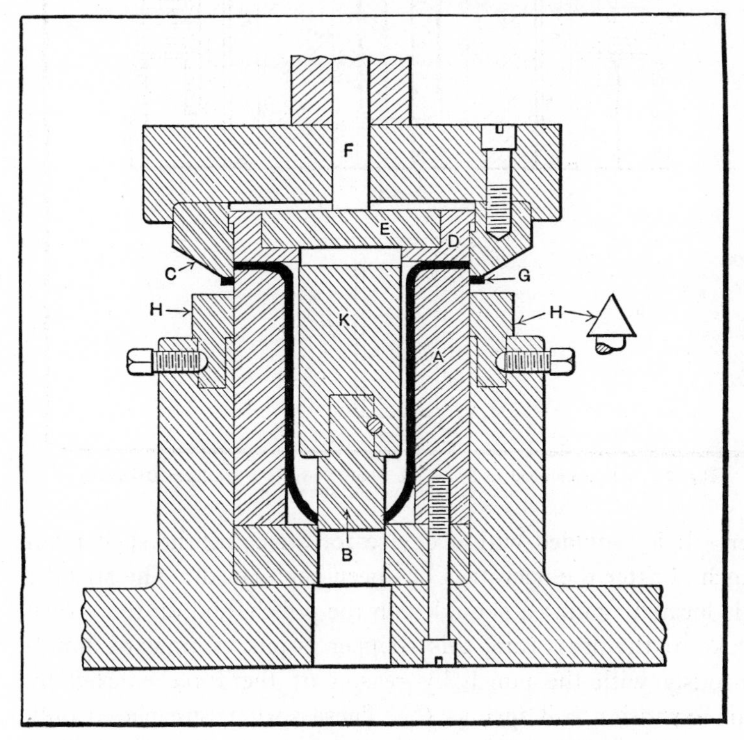

Fig. 20. Die Used for Cutting Hole in Small End of Shell and for Trimming Flange

G, which results from trimming the flange, remains in the position illustrated. When the flange of the next shell is trimmed by this die, the scrap resulting from the latter operation causes scrap *G* to be pushed down upon cutters *H*, thereby cutting it apart and allowing it to fall away from the die.

Forming Shell Body to Uniform Diameter.—The die shown in Fig. 21 is used to form the body to a uniform diameter.

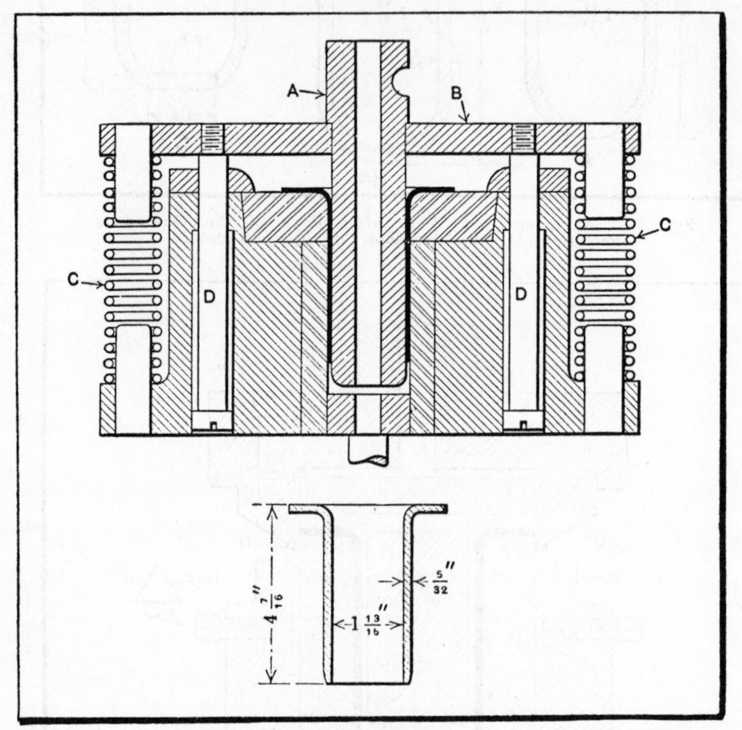

Fig. 21. Die Employed to Form the Shell Body to a Uniform Diameter and to Dimensions Shown

eter. It is provided with a device for stripping the shell from punch *A* after the operation has been performed. The stripper *B* is located against a shoulder on the punch, and on the return stroke of the press ram, this stripper is pushed upward simultaneously with the punch by reason of the force exerted by four expansion coil springs *C*. These springs are placed only on two sides of the die, so as to permit the insertion and withdrawal of the shell. The distance that the stripper rises is governed by the heads on the screws *D* and the depth of the hole in which they operate. After the stripper has reached its maximum height, the shell is forced from the punch as the latter continues to ascend. The stripper is raised sufficiently to enable the shell to be removed from the die and to permit another one to be placed in position. The operator uses a forked imple-

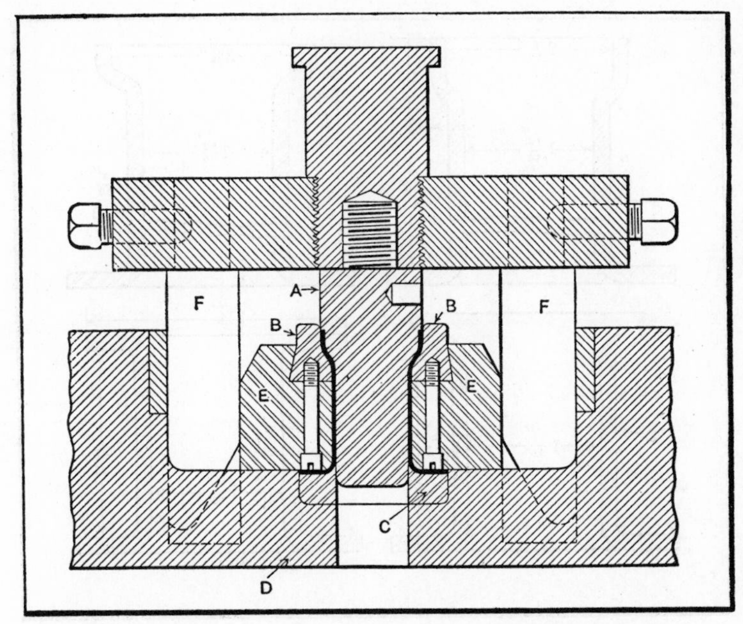

Fig. 22. Die Used to Form the Second Flange on the Shell as shown in Fig. 23

ment to remove the shell so that it is unnecessary for him to insert his hand between the stripper and the die. The distance between the prongs on this tool is sufficient to permit them to go around the body of the shell, so that it can be easily removed.

Forming the Second Flange.—The die shown in Fig. 22 is employed to perform the four final operations, which consist of forming the second flange on the shell. These different operations are accomplished by replacing punch *A* and forming dies *B* with similar parts having suitable dimensions. The appearance of the shell after each successive operation is shown in Fig. 23, at *A*, *B*, *C*, and *D*, respectively. Fig. 22 shows the die equipped for forming the shell to the shape shown at *A*, Fig. 23. The locating center *C*, which fits in a recess in the die-block *D*, locates the shell concentrically with the punch. Two forming dies *B* are secured to two sliding jaws *E* which are provided with expansion coil springs that are not illustrated. Prior to the operation, punch *A* and cams or pushers *F*

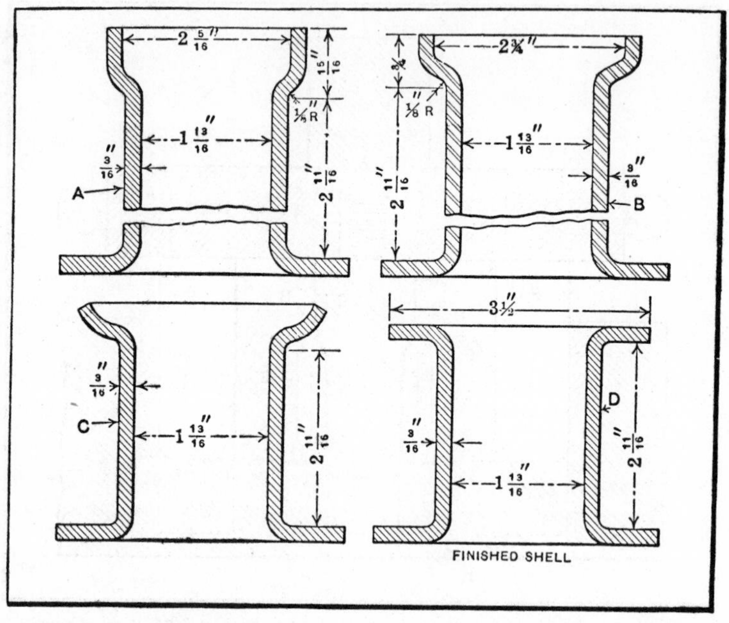

Fig. 23. Successive Operations in Producing Second Flange on Shell

are raised out of the die and the jaws *E* and dies *B* are forced away from the center of the die by the action of these springs. When the jaws and dies are in the position just described, the shell can be placed on the locating center; then as the punch descends, the jaws and dies are closed around the shell in the position shown, by reason of the pushers *F* bearing against the jaws as the pushers descend simultaneously with the punch. These jaws and dies are completely closed around the shell before the punch has descended far enough to commence the forming action. After a quantity of shells has been produced, as shown at *A*, Fig. 23, the punch and die are changed, as previously stated, in order to bring the shell to the shape shown at *B*. This same procedure is followed for producing the shapes *C* and *D*.

Forming a Flanged Ring in One Operation.—The die illustrated in Fig. 24 produces flanged rings of the type shown beneath the die, in a single operation of the punch press. The operation consists of blanking the sheet metal from which the flanged ring is manufactured, punching a hole through the center of the blank, and drawing the flange to the desired shape. The illustration shows the die and the flanged ring at the completion of an operation. The material from which this ring is made is 1/8 inch thick, the outside diameter of the blank being 8 3/8 inches.

When punch *A* is withdrawn from the die at the end of an operation, drawing ring *B* is also raised until its upper surface coincides with that of the inner die ring *C*. This is accomplished by means of pins *D* which are actuated by a rubber buffer of the common type. The sheet-metal strip from which the blank is to be cut is laid on the upper surface of the outer die ring *E*, preparatory to the performance of an operation. Then as punch *A* descends on the downward stroke of the press ram, the blank is cut to size when the bottom edge of punch *A* passes the cutting edge of die ring *E*. The upper surface of die ring *C* is 1/8 inch, or the thickness of the blank, beneath the upper surface of die ring E, so that at the end of the first step in the operation, the blank rests on the top surface of die ring *C* and drawing ring *B*. The large hole is cut in the center of the blank by the central punch part *F* as the punch continues to descend, and since the bottom surface of part *F* is in the same plane as that of punch *A*, this punching step commences immediately upon the completion of the blanking.

The ring is drawn to the desired shape around die *C* as punch *A* continues to descend, pushing drawing ring *B* downward at the same time. The pressure between the drawing ring and the punch is sufficient to draw the blank from between die ring *C* and stripper *G*. This stripper is held on the top surface of die ring *C* on the return stroke of the press ram, by means of several expansion coil springs *H* contained in punch *A*, until the lower surface of punch *A* passes the upper surface of die ring *C*. When this occurs, the heads of the fillister-head machine screws *I* come in contact with the bottom of the counterbored holes in which they are contained and thus cause the stripper to be raised as the punch completes its return stroke.

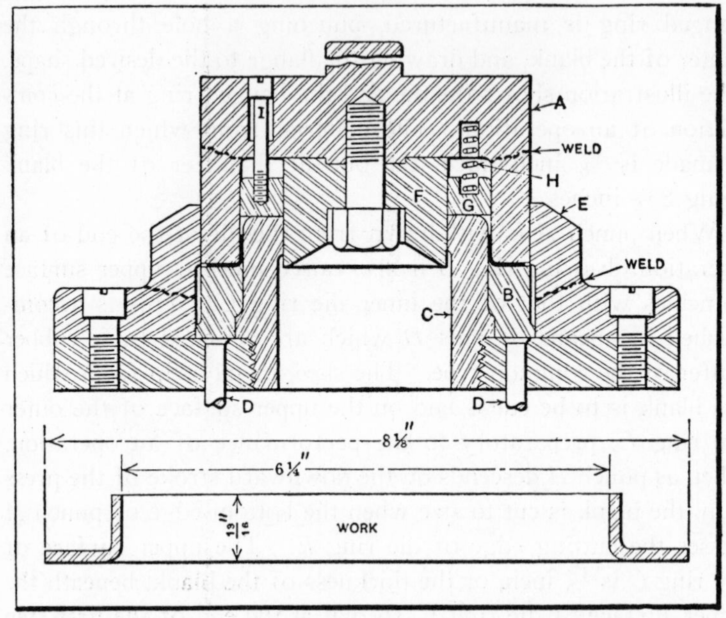

Fig. 24. Die in which Flanged Ring Shown is Produced During One Stroke of Press

The ring is prevented from adhering to the punch as it is raised by coming in contact with the stripper. Drawing ring *B* is returned to its normal position as the punch and stripper ascend, and thus ejects the flange from the die.

In order to effect economy and facilitate machining, the lower portion of punch *A* was made of tool steel while the upper portion was made of machine steel. These two parts are welded together at the point indicated by the heavy dotted lines. The die ring *E* was also made of two materials, the upper portion being tool steel.

CHAPTER XVI

DRAWING DIES FOR CONICAL OR TAPERING FORMS

IN DRAWING tapering or conical shapes, it is often necessary to employ methods which differ considerably from those utilized for producing shells of cylindrical form. The taper of the shell and its depth in proportion to the diameter are two essential points which must be taken into account, their importance varying for different classes of work. In some cases it is practicable to form a shallow tapering part from a flat blank in one operation, whereas other tapering or conical shapes can be obtained only after one or more preliminary operations. Sometimes a cup of cylindrical form is first drawn from a flat blank, and this cup is afterward redrawn in order to obtain a shape which will provide just enough stock, properly distributed, to permit forming the taper part in the final operation. The shape given to the shell by these preliminary operations must be governed in each case by the shape of the finished product and by the method of drawing. The shape, to begin with, may be cylindrical as mentioned, or the shell may taper somewhat and possibly have corners of rather large radius with a surplus of metal at certain points to permit obtaining the required shape by an easy, natural process during the final operation. Judgment and experience are required in determining where to provide surplus metal and how much should be allowed, because an excessive amount which cannot be distributed properly will cause trouble. On the other hand, insufficient metal may result in over-stressing the shell and possibly cause breakage. Determining the number of drawing operations as well as the shape of each die is another important factor, as in the case of cylindrical shells. Attempts to draw conical shapes directly from a flat blank sometimes result in the formation of wrinkles or in rupturing the metal before the shell is completely formed. A careful study of the methods which have proved successful in practice will indicate in a general way, at least, the possibilities and limitations in connection with taper drawing operations. The dies described in this chapter are for drawing shells having depths up to approximately one half the diameter at the large end of the shell. In

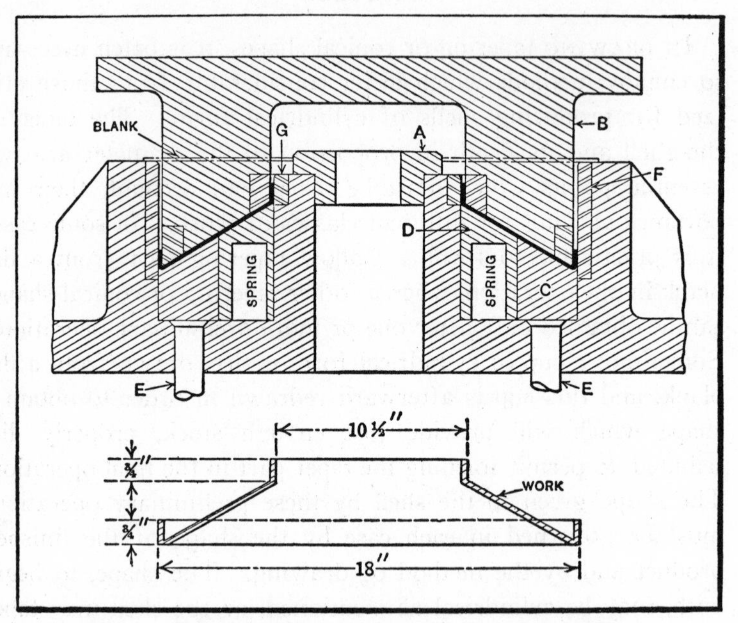

Fig. 1. Punch and Die for Drawing Conical Part Shown

the following chapter, the drawing of deeper shells will be considered.

Die for Drawing Flanged Conical Rings.—The punch and die used for drawing the flanged conical rings which form the sides of a certain type of blower fan are shown in Fig. 1. An idea of the size and shape of the rings may be obtained by referring to the drawing shown beneath the die; the material from which these rings are made is 0.065 inch thick. Two operations are required before the blank is ready for the drawing operation; the first is performed on a plain blanking die which shears the blank to the correct outside diameter. In the second operation, a hole is cut in the center of the blank, the diameter of this hole being the same as the diameter of plug *A* on the die. This permits the blank to be placed on the die as indicated by the dot-and-dash lines, and insures its proper location.

It will be noted that the illustration shows the relative positions of punch *B* and the movable parts of the die, at the time that the shaping of the work is completed. Prior to an operation, the punch is in position above the die, and rings *C* and *D* are also in a raised position. Ring *C* is raised by pins *E* which are actuated by a rubber buffer, while ring *D* is raised by means of compression coil springs. The blank is then placed on the die as previously mentioned, and is forced into the die as the punch descends, the flange on the outside of the ring being formed from the metal that extends past the punch when the latter first comes in contact with the blank. This flange is held between the punch and die ring *F* as the punch continues to descend and, as the inner flange is similarly held, the remainder of the blank is forced to the desired shape. Ring *C* exerts pressure against the work during part of the downward stroke and so assists in preventing the outside flange from being drawn between the tapered surfaces of the punch and the die ring *C*.

The work is ejected from the die on the upward stroke of the punch by rings *C* and *D* as they are raised in the manner previously described. All the working surfaces of the punch and die are made from tool steel, and are hardened and ground. The outer circumference of the drawing ring *F* is ground to a taper of ½ degree, the surface of the hole, however, being ground straight. This ring is a press fit in the die-block, and after it is forced into place, the inside surface is again ground to size. Ring *G* is also a press fit on the die-block, while the two inserted rings on the punch are a similar fit on that member. The performance of this punch and die has been entirely satisfactory.

Blanking, Drawing and Trimming Die.—In producing drawn sheet-metal parts that have to be trimmed or clipped, it is customary to blank and form the part in one operation and trim the drawn part in a separate operation. The punch and die shown in Fig. 2 was designed to eliminate the second operation, so that only one operation is required to blank, draw, and clip the part.

A double-action press of standard make, with a knock-out for ejecting the shell after the operation is performed, is em-

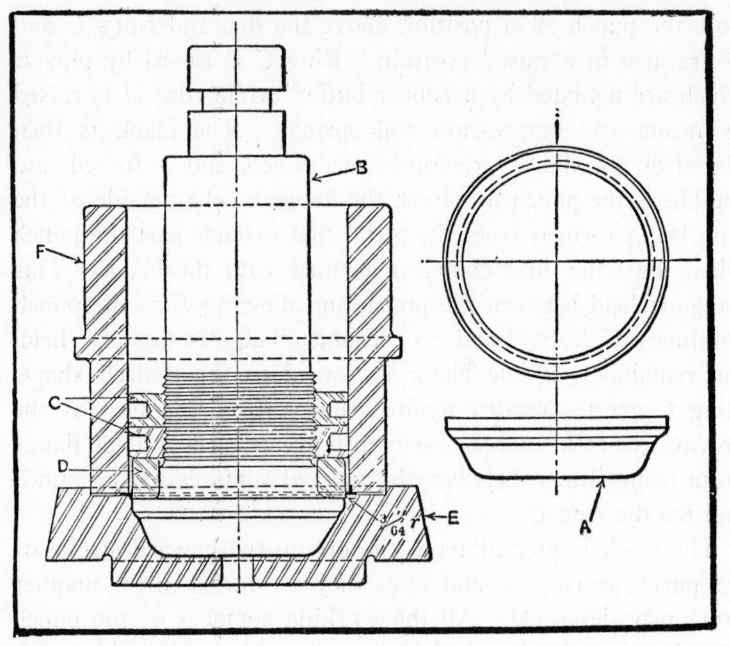

Fig. 2. Blanking, Drawing and Trimming Die Used in Double-action Press

ployed. The shell shown at *A* is of sheet brass, 0.015 inch thick, and the blank diameter is 4.625 inches. The view at the right shows the shell after having been blanked, formed, and clipped. By referring to the illustration of the die it will be seen that the drawing punch *B* is threaded at the lower end, and that two check-nuts *C* hold the clipping ring *D* in place. The clipping ring should be 0.0015 inch smaller than the mouth of die *E*. In this instance, ring *D* and die *E* measure 3.4355 inches and 3.437 inches, respectively. To insure a good running fit, the blanking punch *F* should be bored to a slightly larger diameter than the check-nuts *C* which, in turn, should be from 1/64 to 1/32 inch larger than the clipping ring. The clipping ring is thus saved from unnecessary wear.

The radius at the mouth of die *E* is given as 3/64 inch, in this case, but it could be made as large as 1/4 inch, if necessary, or as small as 1/64 inch, depending on which would work to the best advantage. In assembling the tools, clipping ring *D* should be so set that it will have trimmed the shell by the time that drawing punch *B* has reached its lowest position in die *E*, or within a distance from the bottom of the die recess equal to the thickness of the metal being formed, which in this instance is 0.015 inch. Some toolmakers call this the "pinch-off" method of clipping.

Dies of this type can be used satisfactorily on both sheet brass and steel. The wear on the tools is no greater than that on tools used to perform the same work in two separate operations. All the parts of the punches and dies are made of tool steel except the lock-nuts *C*, which are of machine steel.

Dies for Making a Roller Bearing Cage.—The making of a roller bearing cage from sheet metal in the punch press involves some unusual methods in press working. This particular roller bearing cage is made from 0.032-inch bright strip steel and is completed in seven operations. This cage comprises an inner and outer section, drawn up into cone shape and perforated so that it forms, when assembled, the retainer for the tapered rollers. The cage must be made accurately and the slots through which the rollers project must be very evenly spaced. This cage is entirely completed in the punch press. As the tools for making the outer and inner members of the cage are identical in construction, only those for making the outer member will be illustrated and described.

Trimming Die.—The dies for performing the blanking and cupping operations are of the inverted combination type and form the cups shown at *B* and *F*, Fig. 3. Before performing the subsequent operations on the outer and inner cage, it is necessary to trim the outer edge or flange of the cup. This is accomplished with the punch and die shown in section in Fig. 4. Both die and punch in this case are composite forgings; that is, the top part of the trimming die *A* is of high-carbon steel, whereas the lower part of the die ring is of wrought iron. It will also be noticed that the top edge of the die is sheared, which assists greatly in the ease of trimming this blank. The shear is about 1/32 inch deep, and the lands about 1/2 to 5/8 inch wide. Four lands are provided on this die. This is an extremely fast cutting punch and die and also a die that is easy to keep sharp and in repair. Two hook gages regulate the position of the blank approximately, and the exact

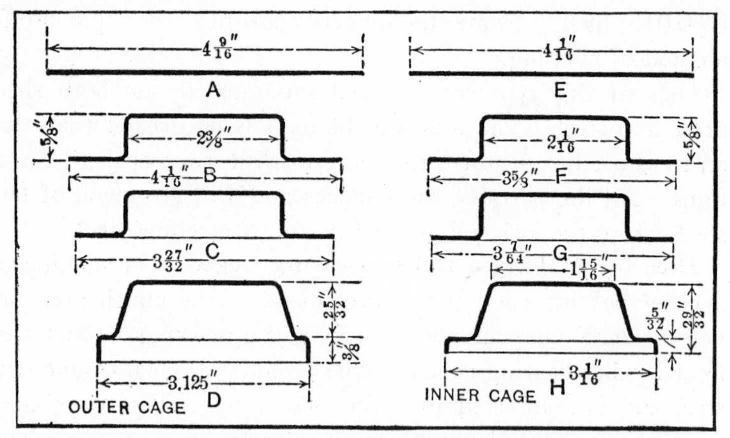

Fig. 3. Sequence of Operations on Inner and Outer Members of Roller Bearing Cage

position is determined by the spring pad *C* on the bottom of the punch. The cutters *D* shown on the sides of the punch are worthy of note, these being two in number. As the shells are trimmed, the scrap is forced up around the punch and is gradually cut into two pieces which separates it and allows it to drop clear of the die. These knives are of crucible steel, hardened. The lower part of the trimming die is soft steel, whereas the upper part is high-carbon tool steel. The spring pad *C* is held down by means of a spring surrounding the knockout punch *E*, which is operated by a bar passing through the ram of the press. The two shearing blades are backed up by the punch body, and are held in place by cap-screws; otherwise the construction of this die is comparatively simple. The results of the trimming operation just described are shown diagrammatically at *C* and *G* in Fig. 3.

Final Drawing and Forming Operations.—The die and punch for performing the final drawing and forming operations on the inner and outer cages is shown in Fig. 5. This punch and die not only sets the taper on the main body of the inner and outer cages, but also edges up the flange. This com-

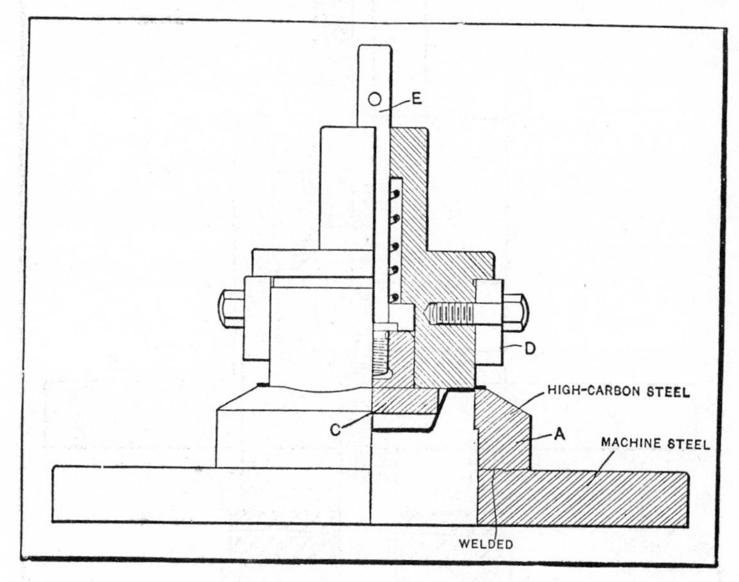

Fig. 4. Trimming Punch and Die

bination of the two operations is not generally considered good practice, but in the present case it worked out very well and has saved an extra operation, without sacrificing either speed or ease of upkeep of the tool. The pressure ring *A* operates on a rubber pressure pad located beneath the bed of the machine in the regular combination die manner. Die-shoe *B* holds the forming punch *C* which is surrounded by the pressure ring *A*, the latter being operated by a rubber pad beneath the press acting on four ½-inch by 4¾-inch spring pins. The forming part of the punch is held to the lower member of the die by the screw indicated. The outer member *E* of the forming punch is a composite forging, the shank being of machine steel and the lower member of tool steel, while the inner member is a tool steel forging machined out to the shape of the finished pieces. Screwed to the inner forming pad *F* is a knock-out plunger *G* which is operated by a rod passing through

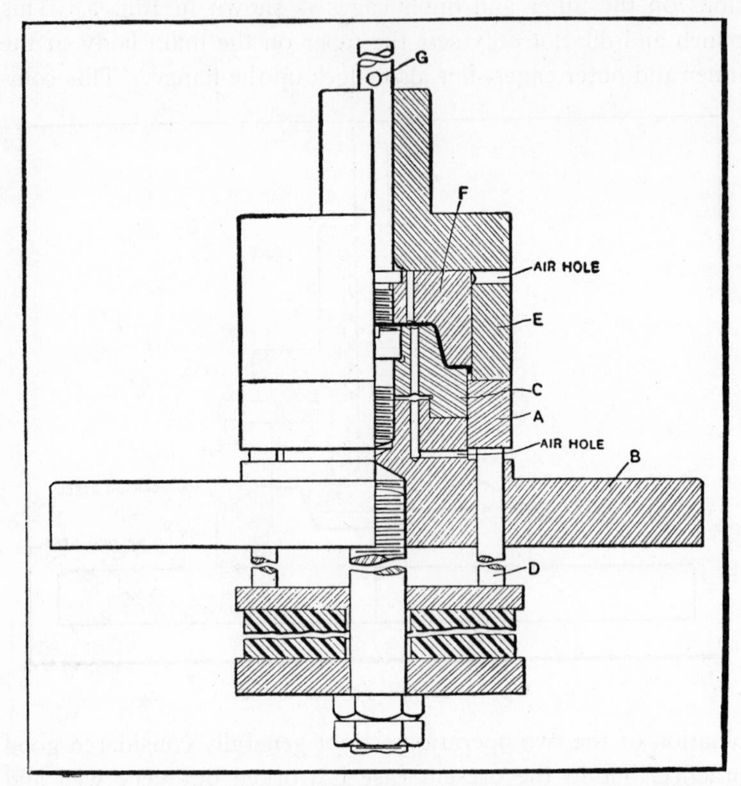

Fig. 5. Final Drawing and Forming Die for Roller Bearing Cage

the ram of the punch press. It will also be noticed in this case that particular attention has been given to the provision of air holes to prevent the work from being distorted and to facilitate the operation of the tools. The result of this operation on the outer and inner cages is shown at *D* and *H* in Fig. 3. Following the forming of the outer and inner cages is a series of piercing operations which will not be described.

After the cages have been completed, the inner cage is dropped into the outer one, the proper number of rolls are put in place, and then the top or outer part of the cage is wired down to prevent the rolls from coming out. This wiring is done by dropping the assembled cage into a recess in a block on the bolster plate of a light press and using a punch which has a recess in its face shaped exactly like the curve that it is desired

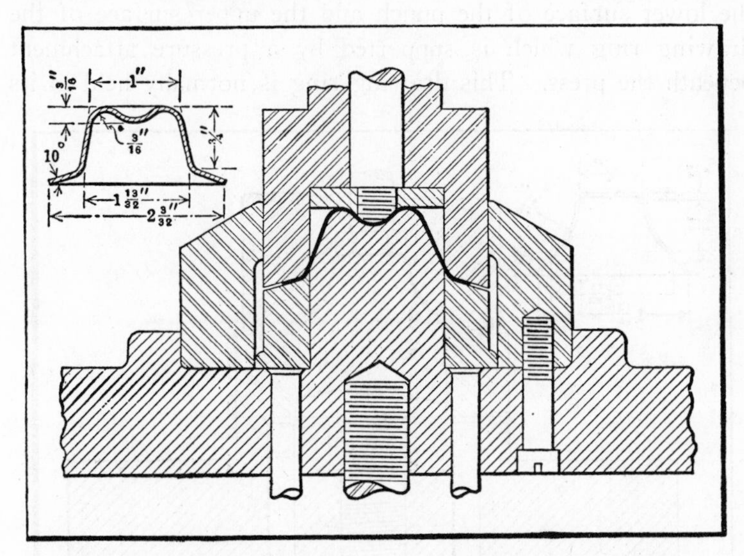

Fig. 6. Die used for Preliminary Drawing Operation on Conical Part

to produce. The operation is very simple, and this finishes the work on the cages.

Conical Shells Requiring Two Operations.—An example of conical shell drawing which involves two operations is shown in Figs. 6 and 7. First, the die shown in Fig. 6 is used to form a shell which is so shaped that surplus metal is provided where it will be required for the final operation. This preliminary shape is shown in the upper left-hand corner of the illustration. The finishing die and the shape of the completed shell are shown in Fig. 7. This final shape should be compared with the half-drawn shell shown in Fig. 6, in order to observe the relation between the preliminary and the final forms.

In the first-operation die, the bottom of the shell is indented to provide the surplus metal required for forming the right-angle turns at the corner of the finished shell (see Fig. 7), although there is some stretching of the metal in connection with this drawing operation. When the die is at work, the blank is first cut as the combination blanking and drawing punch descends. After the blank is severed, it is held between the lower surface of the punch and the upper surface of the drawing ring which is supported by a pressure attachment beneath the press. This drawing ring is normally held in its

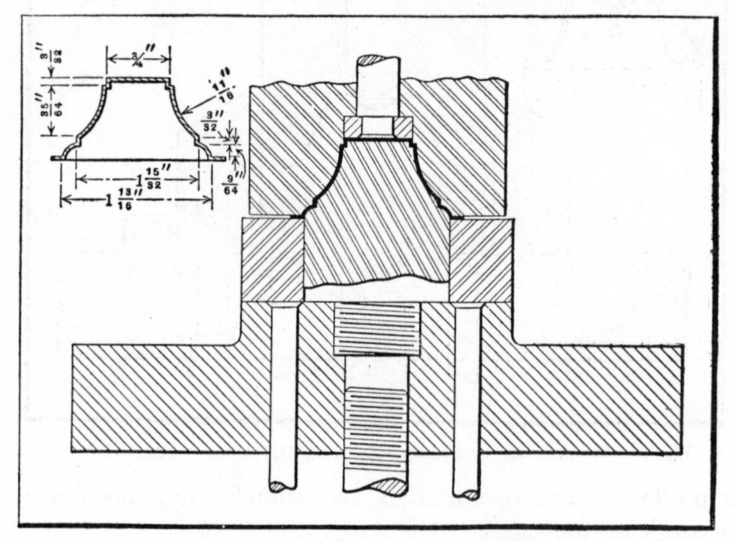

Fig. 7. Die for Final Operation on Conical Part

upper position until forced downward by the punch. As the punch descends and grips the outer edge of the blank, the drawing ring moves downward against the pressure of the attachment and the blank is drawn over the central forming die. A former plate, attached to the central part of the punch, then forces the bottom of the shell down into the cavity of the forming die, which completes the preliminary drawing operation.

Reference to Fig. 7 will show that the finishing die also has a drawing ring supported by pins extending down to the pressure attachment. When this ring is in its normal or upper position, the outer flange of the half-drawn shell rests upon it, as this shell is large enough to clear the upper part of the forming die. When the forming punch descends, the flange of the shell is soon gripped between the lower surface of the punch and that of the drawing ring, thus holding the shell

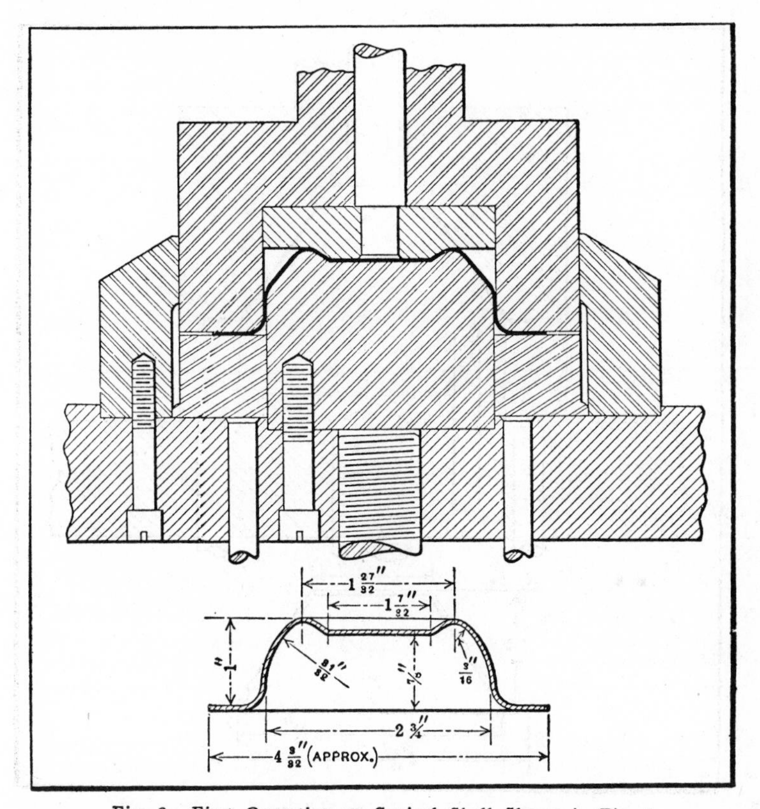

Fig. 8. First Operation on Conical Shell Shown in Fig. 9

securely as the metal is forced to conform to the shape of the punch and die as the result of a stretching, bending, and drawing action. The blank from which the shell is drawn is 2⅝ inches in diameter, and is made of cold-rolled sheet steel, 0.022 inch thick.

Another set of dies which operates on the same principle as the dies already mentioned, is shown in Figs. 8 and 9. These dies are used in the production of a conical shaped shell for cream separators. It is imperative that these taper shells be drawn without wrinkles or drawing marks of any kind, and their tapered surfaces must be perfectly straight. These cream separator shells are made from cold-rolled sheet steel, 0.019 inch thick, the diameter of the blank being 4⅞ inches. The

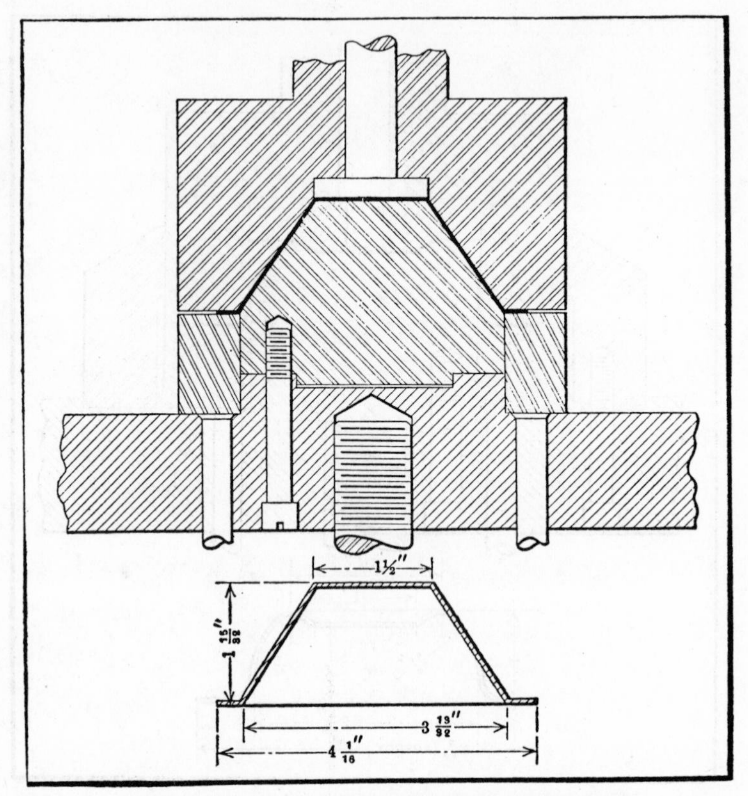

Fig. 9. Die in which the Conical Shell is Completed

sectional views of the shells obtained from each die are dimensioned so that the relative shapes of the half-drawn and finished shells may be studied carefully.

Dies for Automobile Muffler Housings.—The dies used to make the two shells which form the housing for a certain type of automobile muffler are shown in Figs. 10 to 15 inclusive. The illustrations also show the housing or shell as it appears after each operation. The corresponding parts of the various dies have the same reference letters throughout the description. The functions of the various die parts that are shown in Fig. 10 will be described, but only those features of the other dies which are incorporated for the purpose of performing some special operation will be described. The blanks from which

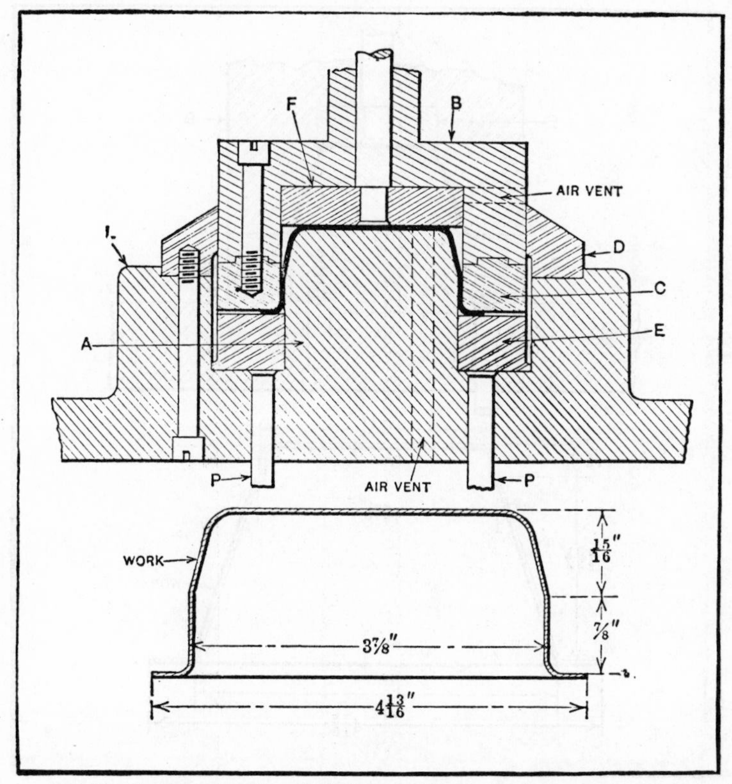

Fig. 10. Combination Die which Cuts the Blank and Performs the First Drawing Operation

the housings are made are sheet steel, 0.0375 inch thick and 6¾ inches in diameter.

The combination die shown in Fig. 10 forms the shell to the shape shown in the lower part of the illustration. The taper on this shell is started at the very beginning of the forming operation. The design of the die provides for employing the familiar punch press construction, with rubber buffer attachment and supporting plates for pins *P*. The forming die *A* is an integral part of the cast-iron holder, the construction being found very efficient for a preliminary operation of this kind. The punch *B* is also made of cast iron and has a tool-steel ring *C* fitted to its bottom face. The cutting ring *D* is

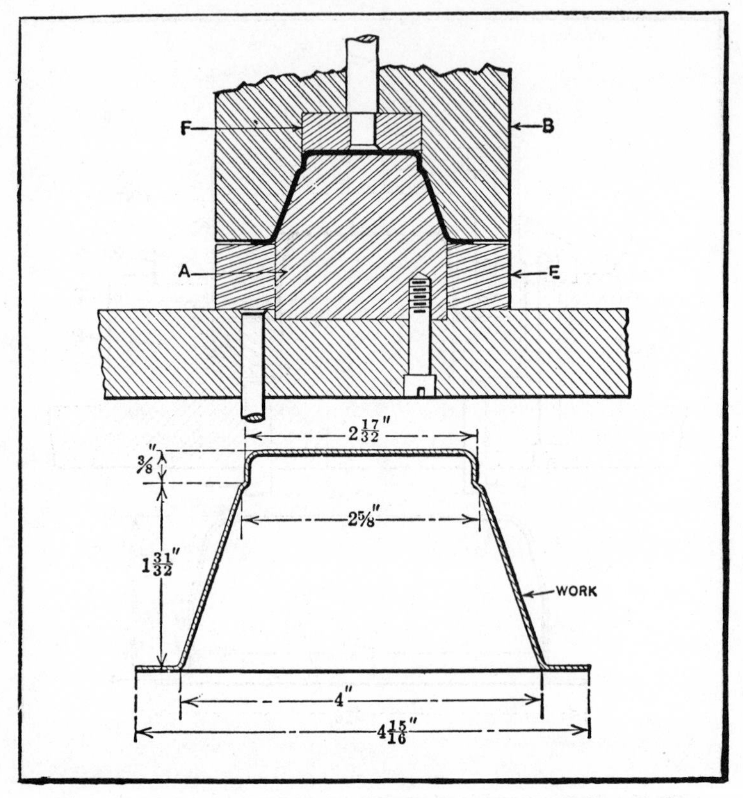

Fig. 11. Die for Forming the Tapered Part of the Shell and the Small End

inserted in a recess in the cast-iron die-holder L. The flange of the shell is formed and held firmly between the ring *C* and the drawing ring *E* at the completion of the drawing operation. Knock-out pad *F* is used to eject the shell from punch *B* upon the upward stroke of the press.

The die illustrated in Fig. 11 forms the main or tapered part of the shell and also forms the small end of the shell preparatory to performing the next operation. In its normal position, the ring *E* is raised on the buffer-plate pins sufficiently to allow the flange of the shell to rest upon its top surface, and when in this position the shell is concentric with the forming die *A*. The rubber buffers are screwed up fairly tight during this

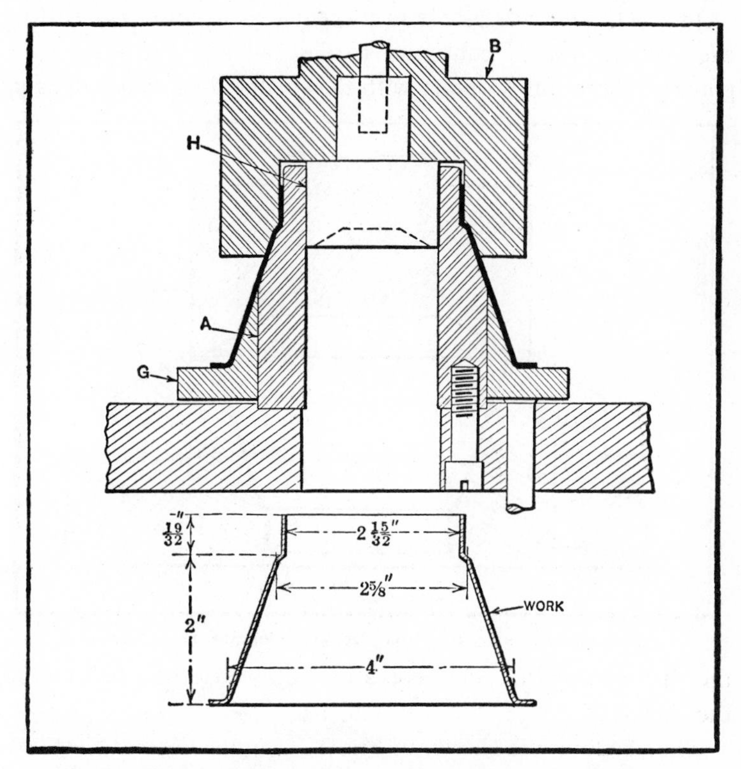

Fig. 12. Hole and Flange Die which Cuts a Hole in the Small End of the Shell and Turns up the Edge

operation so that when punch *B* descends, the gripping action on the flange will hold the shell securely between punch *B* and the ring *E*, and the shell will not be distorted or changed during the operation of the press. The top part of the shell becomes contracted and the lower part expanded to the shape of the forming die as the punch completes its descent. This method has proved very satisfactory for these tapered shells.

The die shown in Fig. 12 is known as a hole and flange die. The forming die *A* has a cutting edge on its inside diameter. The locating ring *G* conforms to the taper of the shell, and is so shaped as to furnish a seat for the flange, the shell thus being located concentrically with the punch. In operation, the cutting punch *H* comes in contact with the shell a trifle ahead of punch B, and cuts a hole in its center as it passes the cutting edge of *A*. As *H* continues to descend into the hole in *A*, punch *B* comes into contact with the shell and turns or edges up

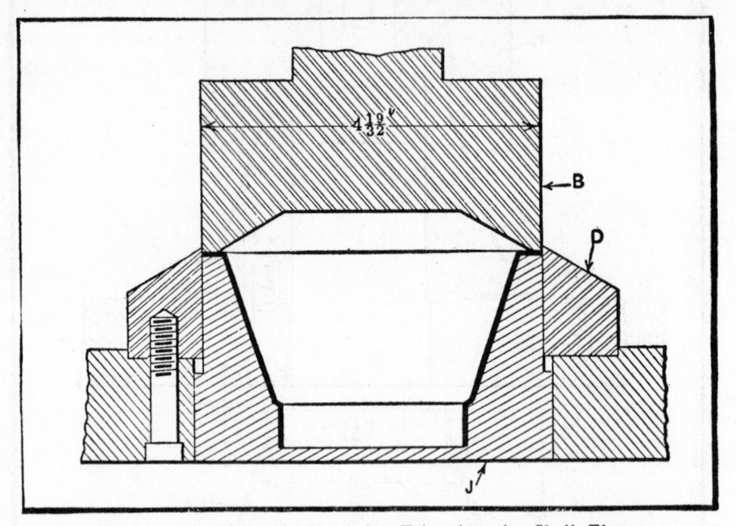

Fig. 13. Blanking Die Used for Trimming the Shell Flange

the shell as shown. This operation completes the small end of the shell.

The blanking die shown in Fig. 13 operates on a rubber buffer, the same as the combination die shown in Fig. 10, and is used for trimming the flange of the shell concentric with the shell itself, which is very essential in work of this type. The pad *J* holds the work and locates it properly in relation to the cutting edge of punch B, and also lifts the shell out of the die on the return stroke of the press. It will be noted that there is a space provided between the lower surface of the cutting ring *D* and the pad, which allows sufficient movement of the pad to permit the shell to be readily removed from it.

There is another die used in making the muffler housing which is not illustrated, but which is similar in construction to the one shown in Fig. 13. This die is employed to trim the shell flange on one half of the housing 1/4 inch smaller in diameter, the purpose of which will be apparent later. Fig. 14 shows a die that turns or edges up the flange on the other half of the housing. The ring *K* is recessed at *R* to suit the diameter of the flange, thus locating the shell properly. The punch *B* descends upon the shell and edges up the flange by pushing it

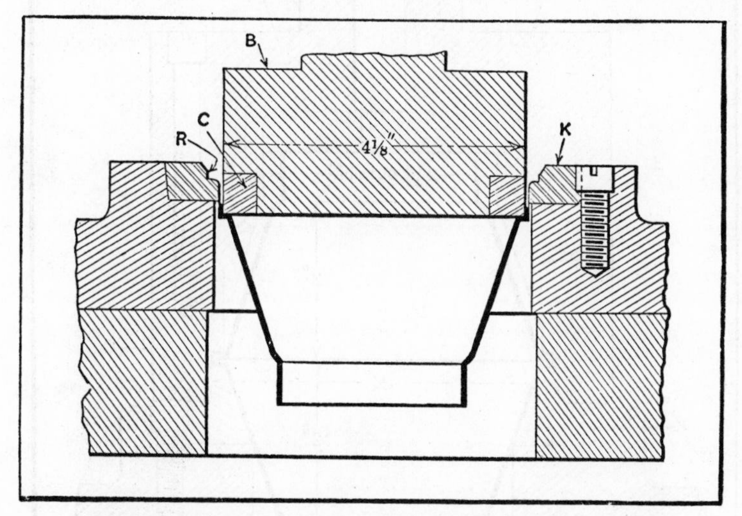

Fig. 14. Push-through Die for Turning up the Shell Flange

clear through ring *K*, after which the shell drops off the punch and through a hole in the die.

In the operation illustrated in Fig. 15, one of the shells, which has had the diameter of its flange trimmed 1/4 inch smaller than shown in Fig. 13, is placed within the turned-up flange of the other shell which is placed in holder *L*. This die is a plain closing die which is employed to fold the edge on the lower shell over the flange of the upper shell to produce the complete muffler housing. The cast-iron punch *B* has a tool-steel ring or face *C* attached as shown, and is also equipped with a knock-out pad *F*. The tool-steel ring *K* is inserted in the holder *L*, both rings *C* and *K* being hardened and ground to their proper shapes. Dies of this type work very well if properly made, the correct method being to make the inside diameter of ring *C* where it comes in contact with *K*, the same as the inside diameter of the ring *K* in Fig. 14, and the ring *K* in Fig. 15 should be made to fit ring *C* very closely.

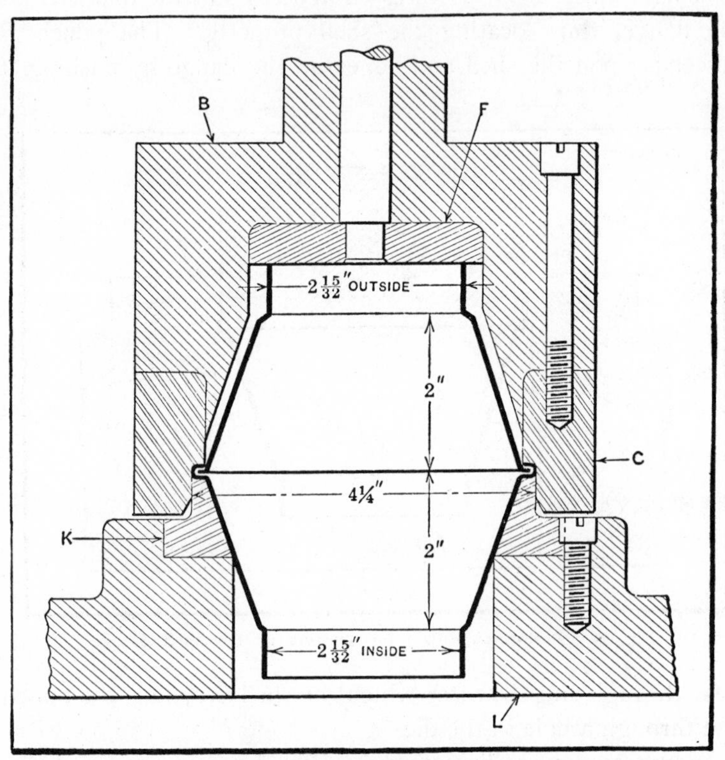

Fig. 15. Closing Die which Locks the Two Shells Together, Producing a Complete Muffler Housing

Dies for Automobile Service Brake Covers.—Six press operations are required in the manufacture of a service brake cover for a certain type of automobile. Four of the operations are performed on machines equipped with punches and dies of standard construction, but the remaining two require punches and dies of unusual design. The appearance of the shell after the performance of each operation is shown in Figs. 16 and

17, in which the reference letters indicate the procedure of the successive operations. These illustrations give the dimensions of those portions of the shell that are changed in any of the operations, while the drawing of the completed shell, shown at *F*, Fig. 17, is fully dimensioned. The blank required for the production of this part is cut from cold-rolled stock 0.065 inch thick, and is 8¾ inches in diameter.

Blanking, Drawing, and Trimming Operations.—The first operation consists of cutting the blank to the diameter stated,

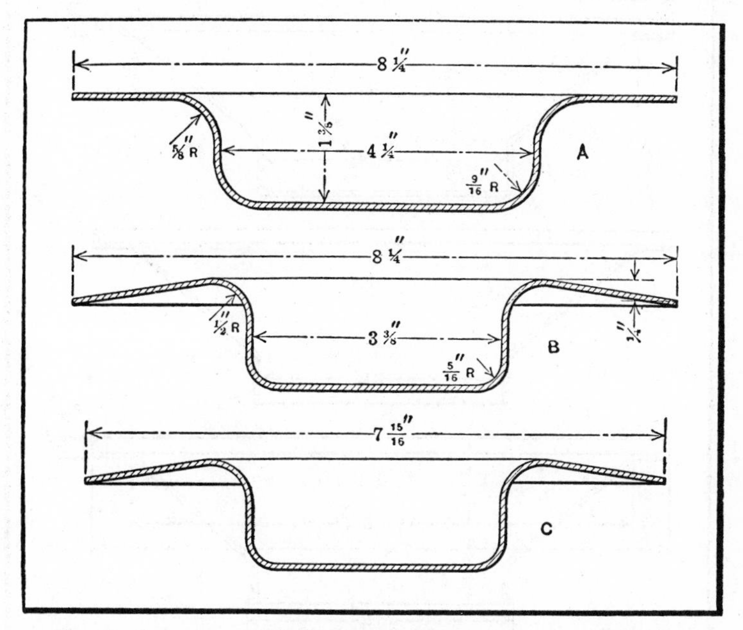

Fig. 16. Appearance of Shell After Blanking and Drawing, Redrawing, and Trimming Operations

and then drawing it to the shape and dimensions shown at *A*, Fig. 16. The machine used for this operation is equipped with a combination blanking and drawing die. In the second operation, the dome of the shell is redrawn to a smaller diameter and the flange is bent back as shown at *B*. This shaping is accomplished by means of a drawing die, the punch and die being cut away suitably to permit the flange to be bent. The third operation is performed on a press equipped with a trimming die, and consists of cutting the edge of the flange to the diameter indicated at *C*.

Forming Punch and Die.—The fourth operation consists of forming the shell to a conical shape, edging up the flange, and making a further reduction in the diameter of the small end. The appearance of the shell at the completion of this operation is shown at *D*, Fig. 17. It will be noted that the flange, conical

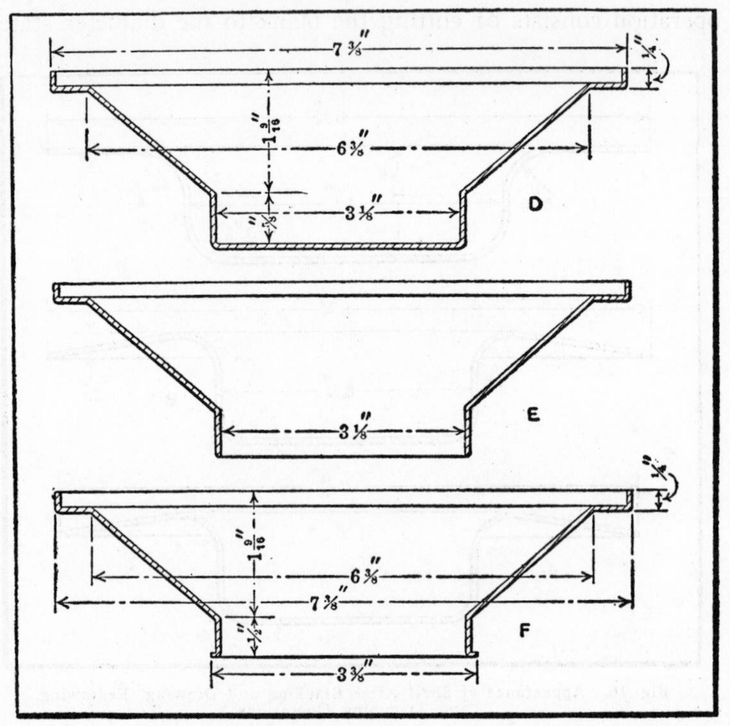

Fig. 17. Shell after Forming, Blanking and Edging Operations have been Performed

portion, and diameter of the cylindrical portion at the small end, reach their final stage in this operation and remain unchanged during the succeeding ones. The punch and die used in forming the shell as mentioned may be seen in Fig. 18, in which the punch is shown in the position it holds at the completion of the downward stroke of the press ram.

When the punch is withdrawn from the die, on the return

stroke of the ram, rings *A* and *B* and part *C* are raised by springs, thus causing the finished shell to be ejected from the die. Rings *A* and B are then used in locating another unfinished shell in the die, preparatory to the next descent of the punch. Ring *B* is raised until a shoulder on the ring comes in contact with the under side of ring *D*, by means of coil springs placed in holes in base *E* which are arranged in a circle

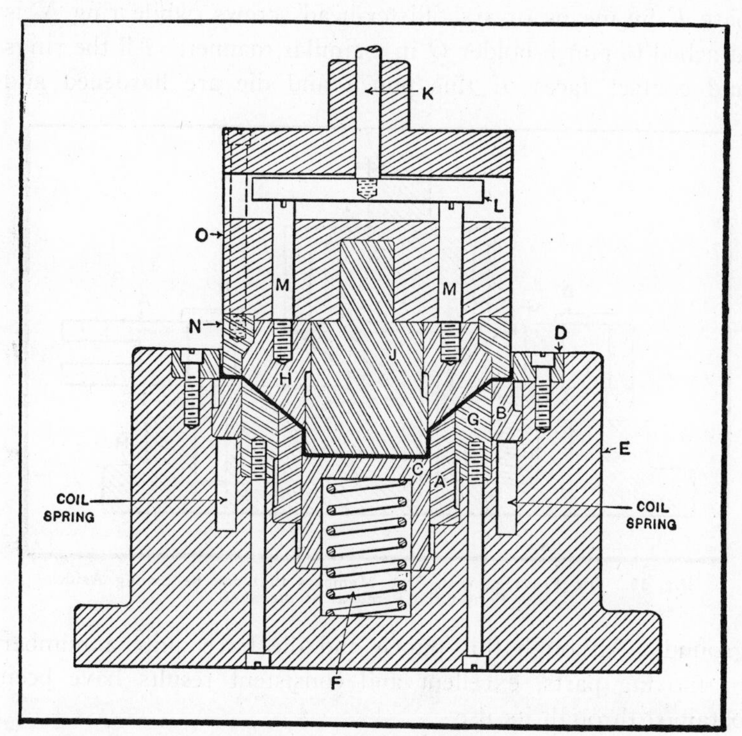

Fig. 18. Construction of Punch and Die Employed in Forming the Shell as Shown at *D*, Fig. 17

beneath ring *B*. Ring *A* and part *C* are raised by coil spring *F* which raises part *C* until a shoulder on the latter comes in contact with the lower surface of ring *A*, after which the two parts are raised together until the shoulder on ring *G* prevents ring *A* from rising further.

The shell is forced from the punch on the return stroke of the press ram by means of a mechanism which lowers ring

H on punch *J* until the shoulders on the ring and the punch come in contact with each other. The mechanism that actuates ring *H* consists of knock-out rod *K* which forces bar *L* and pins *M* downward. The latter are screwed into the upper side of ring *H*. The method of arranging ring *H* on punch *J* insures the maintenance of the proper relation between the two parts. The stationary die rings *D* and *G* are each secured to base *E* by means of six fillister-head screws, while ring *N* is attached to punch-holder *O* in a similar manner. All the rings and contact faces of this punch and die are hardened and

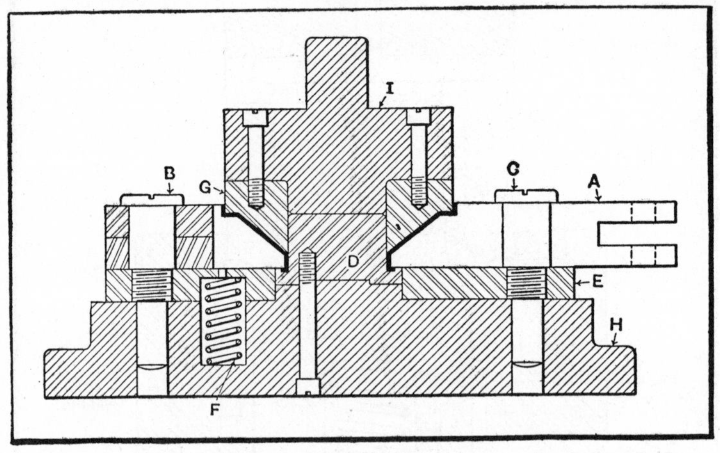

Fig. 19. Die Provided with Two Members that can be Swung Aside to Permit the Removal of the Shell

ground. Although this punch and die have quite a number of moving parts, excellent and consistent results have been obtained through its use.

Die Formed of Pivoted Sections.—In the fifth operation, a hole is cut through the small end of the shell as shown at *E*, Fig. 17, a standard type of blanking die being used for this purpose. The next and final operation on the shell consists of bending back the edge formed by cutting the hole, as indicated at *F*. The punch and die used in performing this sixth operation is illustrated in Fig. 19, in which the punch is shown in its position at the end of the downward stroke. This die is of unusual construction, the part which supports the shell during the operation being made of two sections, one of which is shown at *A*. These sections pivot on pin *B*, and when closed together form an opening of the same size and shape as the outside of the shell after the preceding operation. The purpose of constructing the die in this manner is to permit the removal of the shell from the die after the edge on the small end has been bent back, this removal being readily accomplished after the die sections have been drawn apart. The function of pin *C* is to keep the ends of the die sections tight against plate *E* after they have been closed. The sections are retained in the closed position by suitable means which connect the jaw-like ends.

When the punch is withdrawn from the die, three compression coil springs *F* force plate *E*, and consequently the die sections, upward about 3/16 inch. This is enough to permit the shell to be placed in the closed die sections without the lower edge of the shell touching the bending groove on the die part *D*. The pressure of the springs is sufficient to hold the shell close against face *G* of the punch when the punch descends into the die. This insures that the shape of the body of the shell will remain unchanged as the shell is pushed down on part *D* and the edge is bent back. Part *D* is tapered slightly to allow the shell to be easily removed after the die sections are opened. Die-block *H* and punch-holder *I* are made of cast iron, all the remaining parts being made of tool steel.

CHAPTER XVII

DEEP DRAWING OPERATIONS ON CONICAL-SHAPED PARTS

SOME unusually interesting drawing operations are employed for producing tapering or conical-shaped shells which have considerable depth in proportion to the diameter. This chapter deals with operations on shells having depths exceeding one half the diameter at the large end. While all of these shells, according to the chapter heading, have been classed as conical or tapering, some of the forms included are either "stepped," or combinations of cylindrical and tapering surfaces.

Dies for Automobile Rear Axle Housings.—The drawing and forming dies employed in the manufacture of rear axle housings for a certain type of automobile have been selected as the first example of conical drawing. These dies have worked very satisfactorily, having produced thousands of these housings. By the methods followed in the production of this part, various taper shells can be readily produced which, as a rule, are difficult to manufacture. Each illustration shows one of the dies and a dimensioned drawing of the housing or shell as it appears after having been operated upon by that particular die. The description of the dies is given in the order in which they are used. The first operation consists of cutting a blank 14 inches in diameter from sheet steel, $\frac{5}{32}$ inch thick. This operation is performed on a plain blanking die, which is of standard construction and is therefore not illustrated.

The first shaping operation on the rear axle housing is performed by the double-action drawing die illustrated in Fig. 1, which is used on a double-action press. This die produces a shallow cup of cylindrical shape, from which the conical-shaped housing is formed in succeeding dies. In the operation of this die, blank-holder *B*, which has a hardened and ground steel ring *C* on its lower face, descends and exerts pressure on the blank that has previously been placed on the hardened and ground steel die ring *E*, which is mounted on the die-block *D*. Then punch *A* descends and forces the blank into the cavity of the die, thus drawing it to the desired shape.

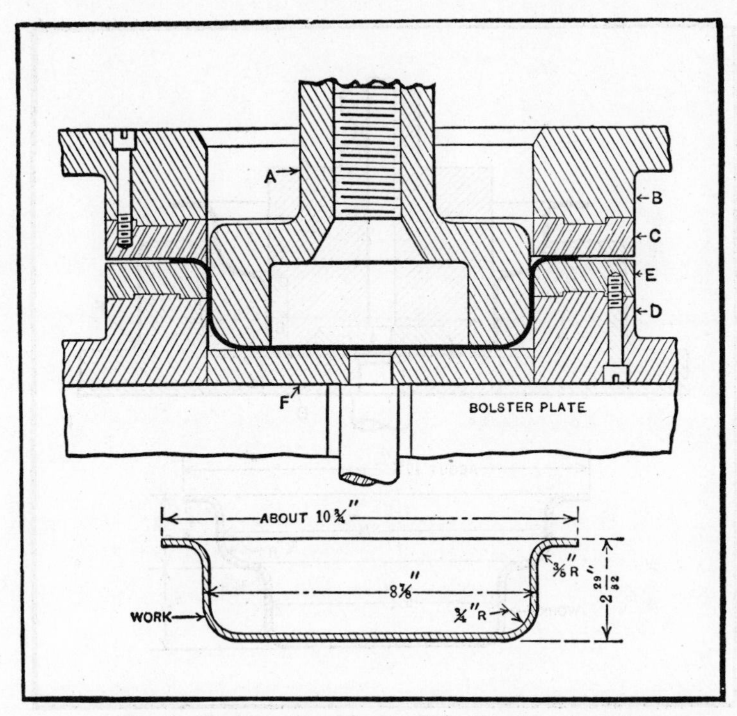

Fig. 1. Double-action Die for First Drawing Operation

Punch *A* is an iron casting, cored out at the center in order to make it lighter. By this means a closer-grained metal is obtained than would be possible if the punch were cast solid, so that this type of punch has proved more satisfactory in several ways than a solid one. Rings *C* and *E* are ground on both sides to eliminate all tendency of spring in the blank-holder or die-block. In dies of this kind the faces of these rings should be ground flat unless the metal is of such thickness that the exposed surface of the rings must taper toward the center of the die in order to permit the metal of the blank to thicken as the diameter is reduced. The machine screws which secure these rings to their respective holders are staggered in circles concentric with the hole in each ring; this tends to eliminate spring in the blank-holder and die-block. The die is equipped with a knock-out pad *F* for removing

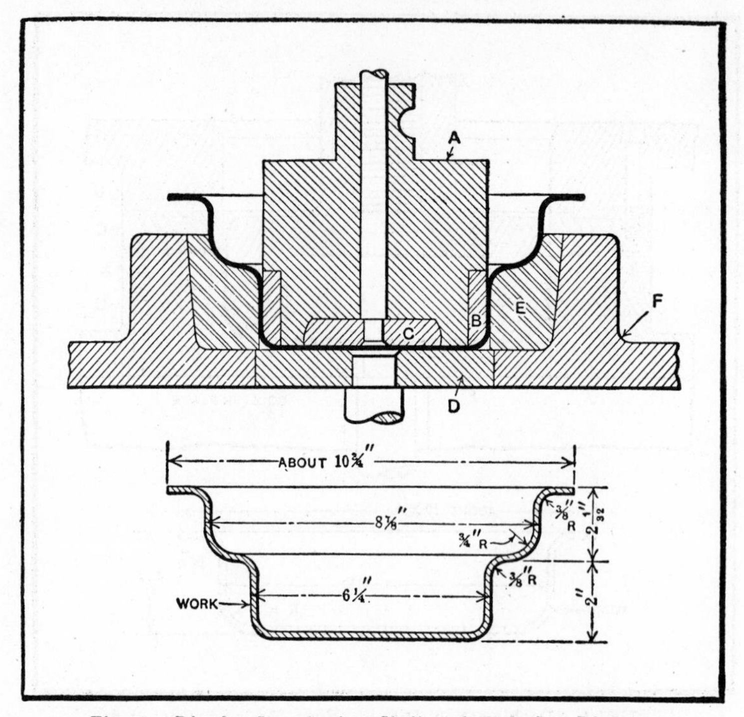

Fig. 2. Die for Lengthening Shell and Reducing Diameter

the shell from the die after the punch has ascended, while the blank-holder serves as a stripper for forcing the shell from the punch on the return stroke of the press ram.

Reducing the Cylindrical Cup to a Stepped Form.—The die illustrated in Fig. 2 is employed to lengthen the shell and reduce the diameter of the closed end. The shell as produced in the preceding operation is placed in the recess of die ring *E*, the contour of which is similar to that of the bottom of the shell, so that the shell is correctly located for this operation. As punch *A* descends, the closed end is drawn to the dimensions given, while the portion of the shell remaining in the recess of the die ring at the completion of the operation, assumes approximately the same shape as the recess. Punch

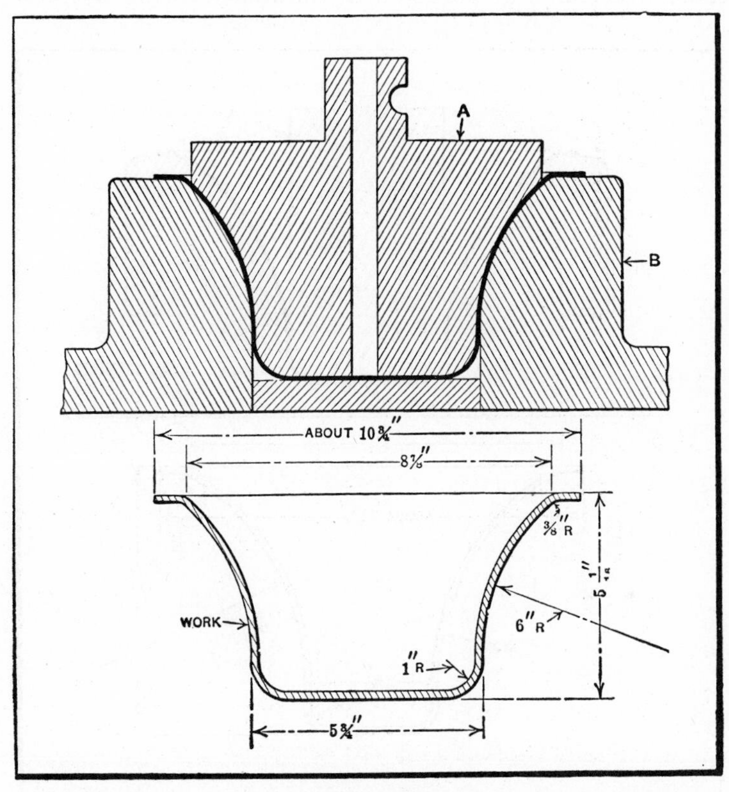

Fig. 3. Forming Die which Reshapes the Shell Body Without Changing the Flange Diameter

A is also made of cast iron, but a hardened and ground steel ring *B* is provided for contact with the shell. This ring is pressed on the punch. The punch is also furnished with a knock-out pad *C*, which forces the shell from the punch on the return stroke of the press ram, while knock-out pad *D* removes the shell from the die. Die ring *E* is hardened and ground, and its circumferential surface has a taper of 1.5 degrees. It is secured in die-holder *F* by means of bolts.

Changing Body of Shell to Tapering Concave Form.— The forming die illustrated in Fig. 3 reduces the diameter of the body of the shell although the diameter of the flange remains the same as produced in the first drawing operation.

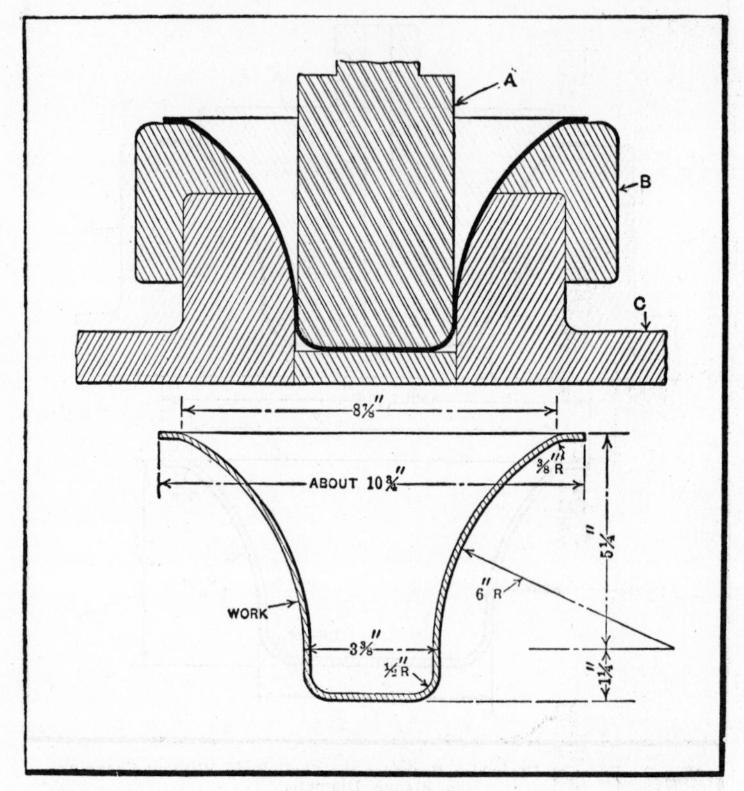

Fig. 4. Drawing Die Used to Still Further Reduce the Shell Diameter and Increase the Length

In this operation, punch *A* forces the shell into die *B* until the flange of the shell comes in contact with the upper surface of the die. The punch and die are both made of cast iron and are equipped with devices for removing the shell from each respective part after the performance of the operation.

Fig. 4 illustrates a die that is used to reduce the shell body diameter still further, at the same time increasing the length. At the beginning of the operation, die ring *B* is in a raised position relative to die-block *C*, which permits it to locate the shell properly for the operation. The raising of the die ring is accomplished by means of springs and bolts, which are not shown in the illustration. During this operation the shell and die ring are pulled down by punch *A* as it descends, until the inner surface of the die ring comes in contact with the upper surface of the die-block as shown in the illustration, at which time the shell has been drawn to the desired shape. The die is provided with a knock-out pad for forcing the shell from the die after the performance of the operation. There is no tendency for the shell to adhere to the punch in this operation, and for this reason no knock-out device has been provided for the punch.

Die Used in Final Operation on Conical Shell.—The final drawing operation on the shell is performed by the die illustrated in Fig. 5. In this operation the main body of the shell is drawn to a taper, the surface of the body adjacent to the closed end is straightened, and seven pockets are formed close to the flange. Punch *A* is made of cast iron, but pieces *B*, *C*, and *D* which come in contact with the shell are hardened and ground steel pieces, secured to the punch. By constructing the punch in this manner, the hardening and grinding of the various parts were greatly facilitated. It will be noticed that the die is constructed in a similar manner, the die-block *H* being an iron casting, and parts *F* and *G*, which are inserted in it, being hardened and ground steel pieces. The pockets are formed in the shell by means of seven hardened and ground steel pieces *E*, inserted in die ring *F*. By having these pieces made separate from ring *F*, the manufacture of the die was a more simple proposition, and as these pieces wear more rapidly than the remaining die parts, they can be readily replaced when necessary. Both the punch and die are provided with knock-out devices for removing the shell from the respective parts after the operation has been performed. The illustration shows the flange diameter reduced to 10½ inches, but this is performed in a later operation on a trimming die which is not illustrated.

Two more operations are performed on the shell before the part is finally completed. The first of these consists of punching holes around the flange, which is done by a piercing die of standard construction. The final operation consists

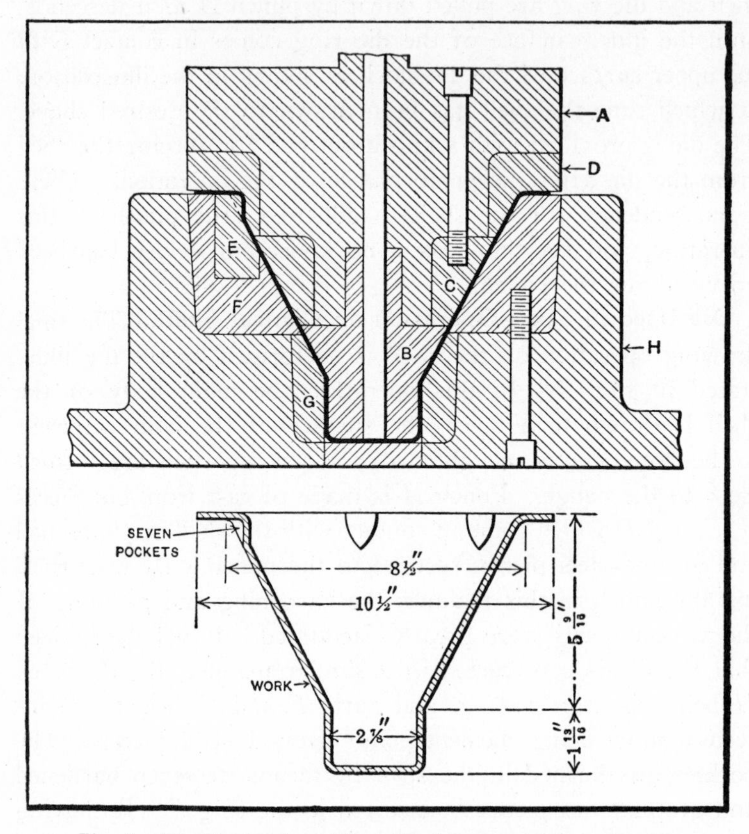

Fig. 5. Die Employed in Final Shaping Operation on Housing

of cutting a hole in the closed end of the shell to permit the housing to be fitted over the axle tube of the automobile. Neither of these dies is illustrated.

Drawing a Tapered Steel Shell.—Difficulty is usually experienced in drawing tapered steel shells such as shown at *A* in Fig. 6. In drawing this particular shell, five sets of tools were required, the first of which is the combination blanking and forming die shown in Fig. 6. The material of which these shells are made is No. 20 U. S. gage steel plate stock, 0.0375 inch thick. The blank is $5\frac{13}{16}$ inches in diameter and is drawn in the first operation to the shape shown at *B*. The

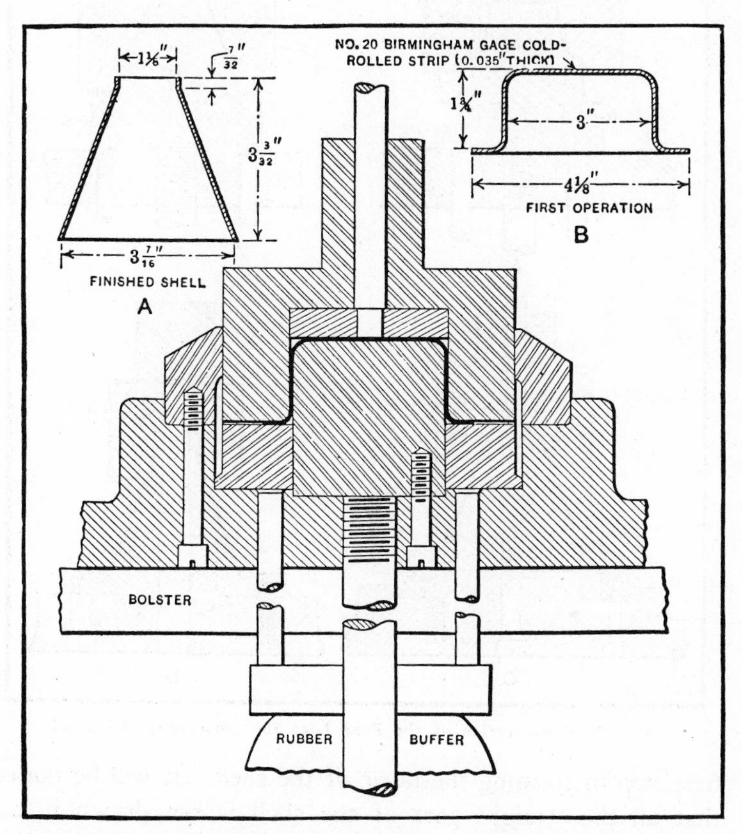

Fig. 6. Combination Blanking and Forming Die used for First Drawing Operation *B* on Shell Shown at *A*

details of the punch and die are clearly shown in the illustration and the construction and operation should need no detailed explanation. It will be noted that the familiar rubber block construction is employed as a buffer for the drawing ring.

The second operation is shown in Fig. 7 at *A*, which is the

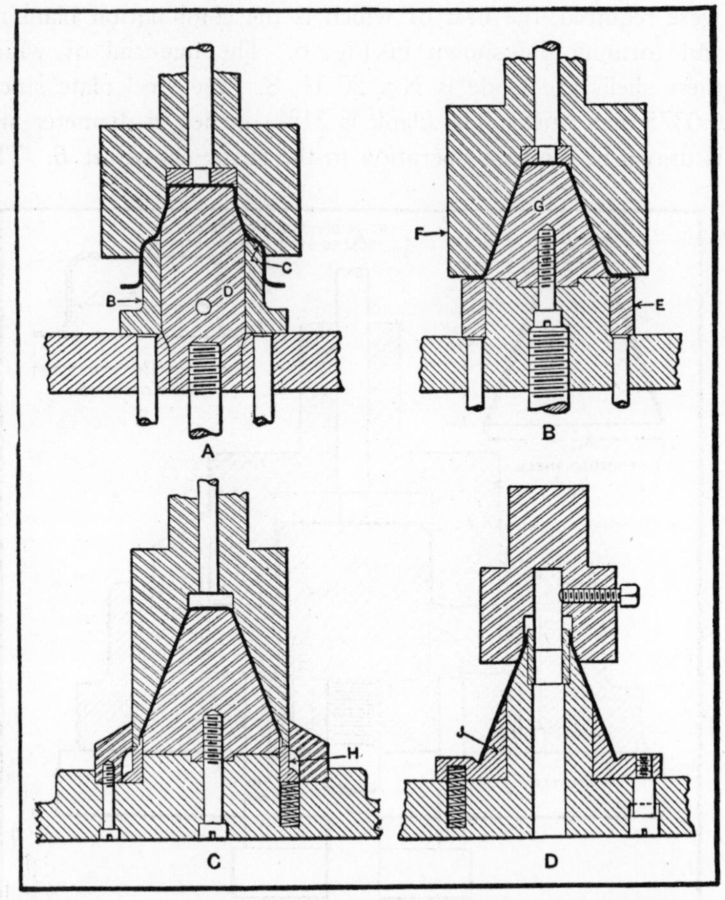

Fig. 7. Construction of the Four Dies for Completing the Shell

first step in forming the taper of the shell. It will be noticed that all the straight part of the shell is not drawn in and that a flange is left for subsequent locating purposes. This flange is cut off in a later operation. The die has a rubber buffer similar to that shown in Fig. 6, the attachment screw and also the drawing pins being shown. The outside diameter of the drawing ring *B* is made the same as the inside diameter of the shell formed in the first operation, or 3 inches. The shell is thus positively located on the ring and its shape maintained while the drawing is taking place over the corner of the ring at *C*. Drawing the shell when held in this manner prevents it from being upset and also keeps the metal normal. It will be noted that a part of the shell at the top is also drawn straight so as to insure greater concentricity. The center part of this die *D* is a pressed fit in the die-holder.

The third drawing operation is performed in the die shown at *B* (Fig. 7) and consists of stretching the taper on the shell. The flange of the shell is held firmly between the drawing ring *E* and the punch *F*, the drawing ring being supported by rubber buffers which are adjusted sufficiently to hold the shell. The same rubber supports as used on the previous dies may also be used on this die. The drawing ring *E* is raised sufficiently by the rubber so that when the shell is placed on the die it locates itself on the cone *G*, while the flange rests on the drawing ring. The trimming and edging die for finishing the large or open end of the shell is shown at *C*. The drawing ring *H* is spring-supported, being used merely to strip the finished work from the die after the flange has been trimmed. In this punch, as well as in the previous punches, it will be noticed that a knock-out rod is provided for ejecting the shells when they become lodged in the punch. The final operation is performed in a die known as a hole and flange die, shown at *D*. Its construction is quite simple and should require little explanation. Ring *J* locates the work while the hole is being punched and the small end formed, and by means of its spring support it also ejects the work after the operation.

Dies for Seamless Water Pails.—The seven punch press operations required in the manufacture of a seamless water pail and the dies used in the performance of each operation will now be described. The first of these operations is a blanking operation; the next four are drawing operations in which the pail or shell is drawn to the desired shape; the sixth operation consists of trimming a flange formed on the open end of the shell; and the final operation consists of bending this flange around a wire to form the rim of the pail. In order to permit the construction and operation of the drawing dies and curling or wiring die to be thoroughly understood, illustrations of these dies are presented. A dimensioned drawing of the work as it appears after each drawing operation is shown beneath the die. The blanking and trimming dies employed in the production of this part are of standard construction and for this reason are not illustrated. The metal from which the shell is produced is sheet steel, 0.028 inch thick, of

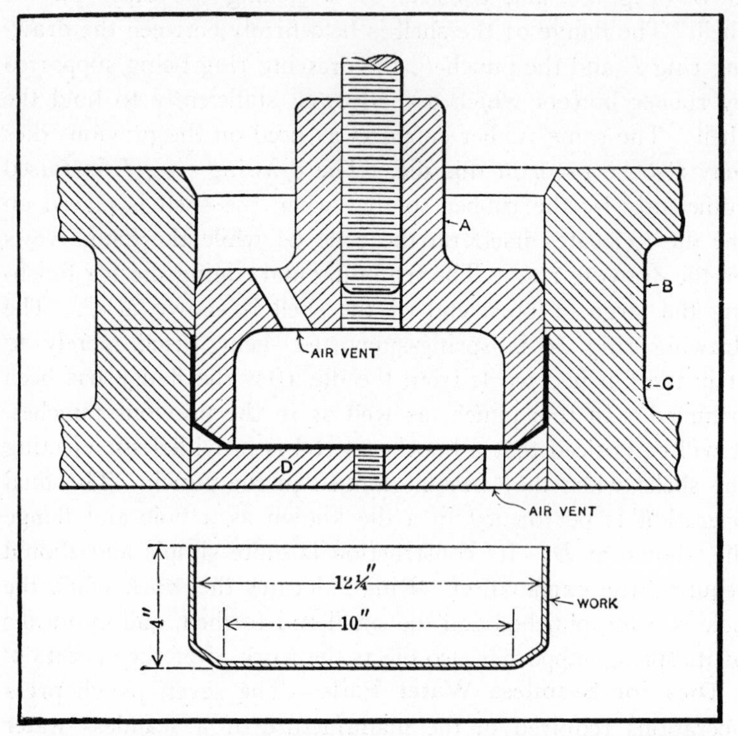

Fig. 8. Double-action Drawing Die for First Operation on Seamless Pail

a deep drawing quality, the blank being cut to a diameter of 18¼ inches in the blanking operation.

First Drawing Operation on the Shell.—The die used in the first drawing operation on the shell is illustrated in Fig. 8. This is a double-action die which is used in connection with a double-action press and consists essentially of punch *A*, blank-holder *B*, die-block *C*, and knock-out pad *D*, all of these parts being made of cast iron. Prior to an operation with this die, a blank is placed on the upper surface of die-block *C*. Then on the downward movement of the press ram, blank-holder *B* descends slightly in advance of punch *A* until it exerts a certain pressure on the blank, at which time its descent is stopped by means of the operating mechanism of the press. The blank is drawn to the desired cup shape by punch *A* as it continues to descend after the blank-holder has been stopped, drawing the blank from betwen the blank-holder and die-block into the opening in the die-block. On the return stroke of the ram, the shell is forced from the punch by coming in contact with the bottom surface of the blank-holder which overhangs the die opening. Knock-out pad *D* is provided for ejecting the shell from die-block *C*.

It will be noted that punch *A* is cored out for the purpose of lightening it. An air vent is provided in both the punch and knock-out pad to permit the ready escape of air when the punch and shell descend into the die. This is an important requisite on dies of this type. Mention has already been made of the fact that the various parts are made of cast iron; this material is satisfactory for dies which produce light metal parts of comparatively large dimensions.

Successive Reducing Operations Performed with Double-action Dies.—The double-action die used in the second drawing operation in which the diameter of the shell is reduced, consequently increasing its length, is shown in Fig. 9. Punch-holder *A*, blank-holder *B*, die-block *C* and knock-out pad *D* are all made of cast iron. The die-block, however, is provided with an inserted ring *E* made of chilled cast iron. In the operation of this die the shell is seated on the tapered surface of the die ring *E*, which is ground to suit the bottom of the shell as formed in the preceding operation. On the downward movement of the press, blank-holder *B* descends into the shell and exerts a pressure on the inside of the taper surface on the bottom of the shell, at which point its downward movement is ended. The shell is then drawn to the dimensions shown, by punch *A* as it continues to descend, drawing the shell from between the blank-holder and the die ring. The means provided for the escape of air and for the removal of the shell from the punch and die are similar to those on the die previously described.

Fig. 10 shows the die employed for the performance of the next operation, which consists of making another reduction in the shell diameter and at the same time increasing its length. The open end of the shell is bell-mouthed in this operation

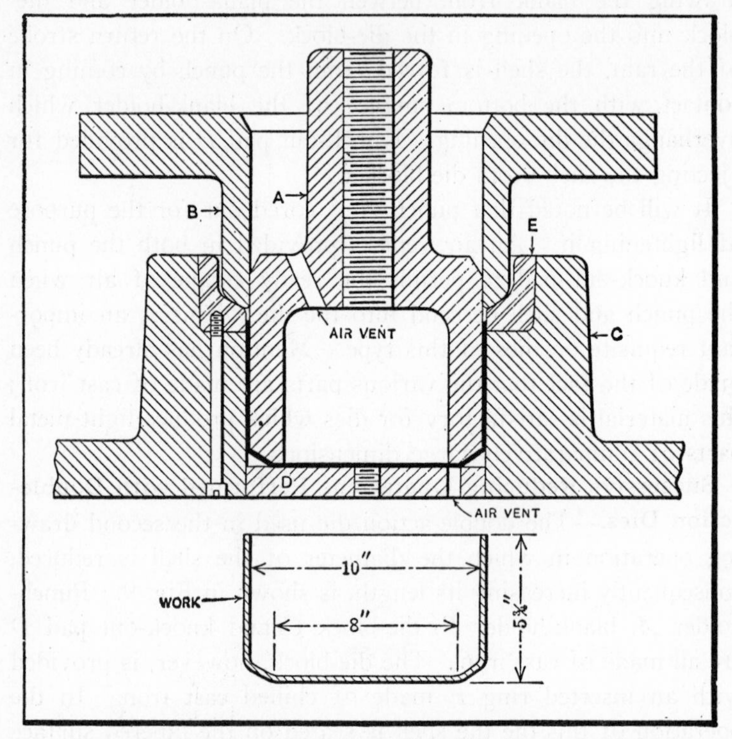

Fig. 9. Drawing Die used to Reduce the Shell Diameter and Increase the Length

to facilitate the forming of a flange in the succeeding operation. This die is also of the double-action type, and as its construction and operation are very similar to that of the die shown in Fig. 9, a more detailed description is unnecessary.

Drawing Shell Body to Taper Form.—The double-action die illustrated in Fig. 11 is used for the fourth drawing operation in which the body of the shell is drawn to a taper while the bell-mouthed opening is flattened to form a flange. As in the dies previously described, punch *A*, blank-holder *B*, die-block *C* and knock-out pad *D* are made of cast iron. In preparing for this operation, the outside surface of the bell-mouthed portion of the shell formed in the preceding operation

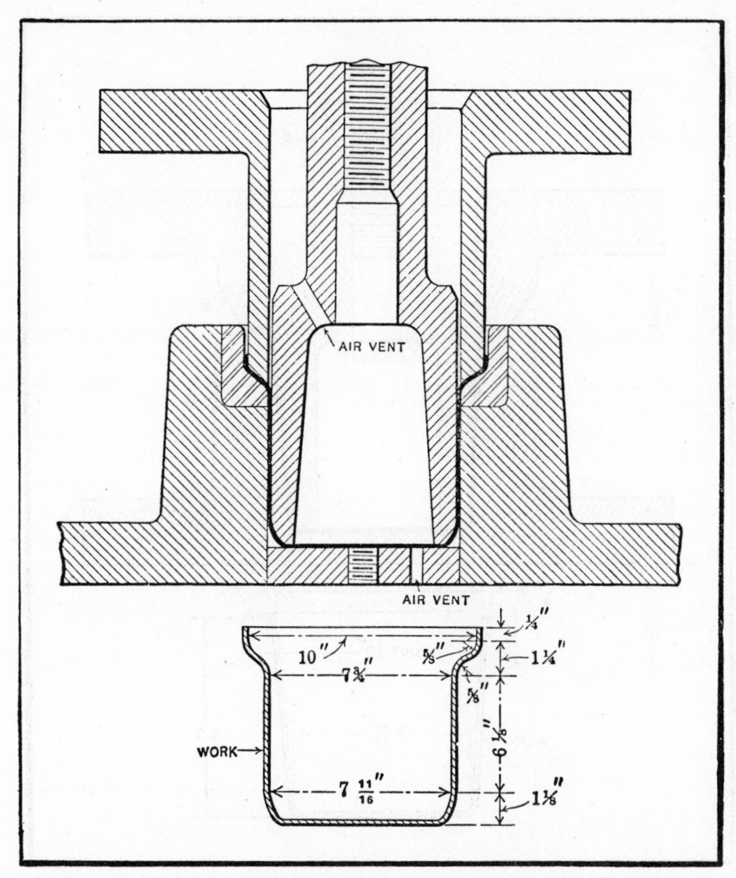

Fig. 10. Operation in which the Shell Diameter is Further Reduced while the Open End is Bell-mouthed

is seated on the top surface of die-block *C*, the body of the shell projecting into the die opening. It will be noted that the end of blank-holder *B* is beveled to permit its ready entry into the shell opening when the blank-holder descends on the downward stroke of the press. The shell is pressed firmly on die-block *C* by blank-holder *B*, while the punch *A* descends and draws the shell to shape, the flange being formed by means of the flat bottom surface of the blank-holder. The removal of the work from the punch and die, after the completion of the operation, is effected in the same manner as on the dies

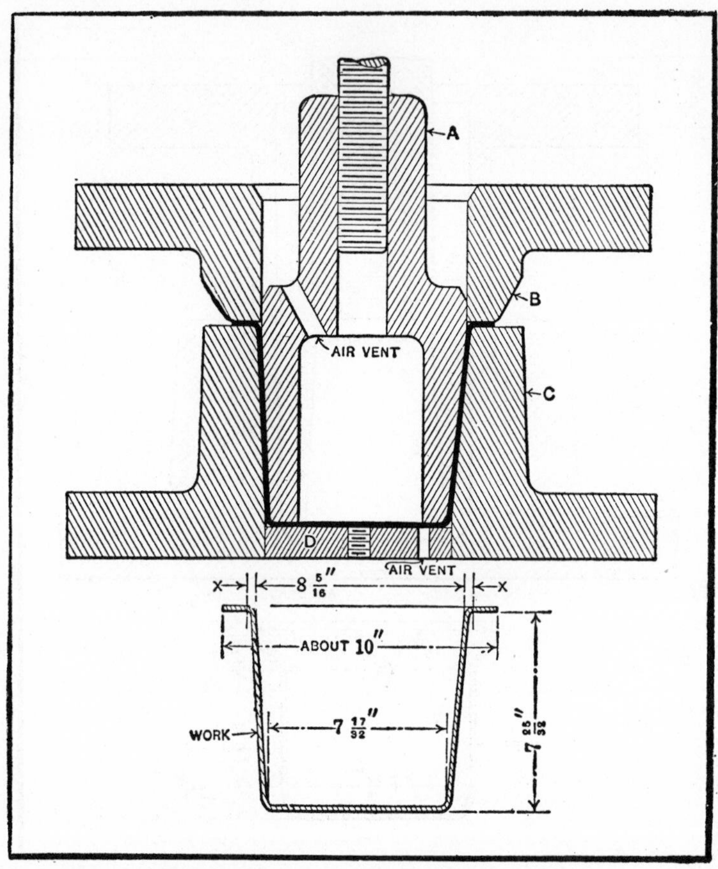

Fig. 11. Final Drawing Operation in which the Body of the Shell is Tapered and a Flange is Formed on the Open End

previously described. The sixth operation consists of trimming the flange of the shell close up to the rounded corner at the open end as indicated by lines *X* in the detail drawing of the work. The construction of the trimming die used in this operation is not illustrated.

Die Employed in Wiring Operation on Pail.—The final press operation on the pail consists of forming a depression in the bottom surface and curling the edge of the open end over a wire placed around the outside of the pail. The die used for accomplishing these results is shown in Fig. 12. It will be noted that the punch is built up of a number of parts consisting mainly of punch-holder *A*, curling ring *B*, nose-piece *C*, disk *D*, rubber buffer *E*, and fillister-head screw *F*. When

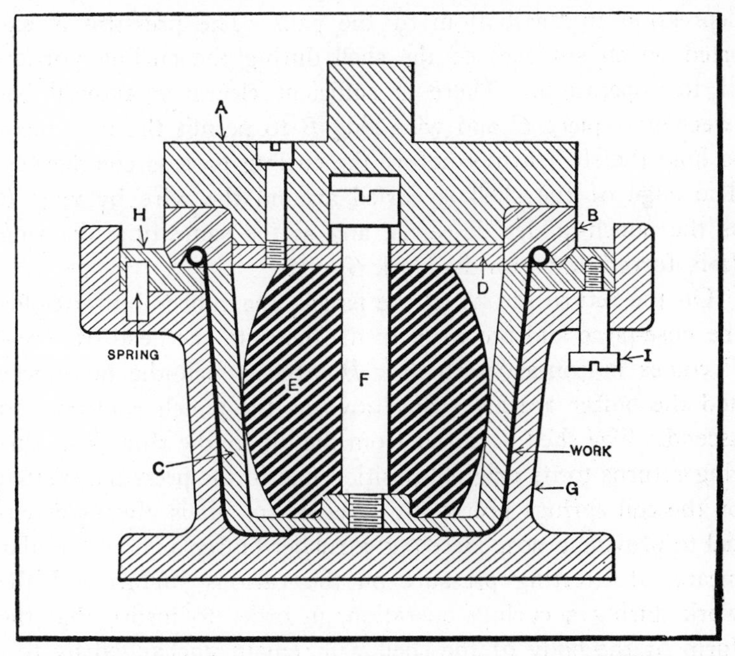

Fig. 12. Die used to Curl the Edge of the Shell Around a Wire

the punch is lifted from the die there is a clearance between curling ring *B* and the upper surface of nose-piece *C* equal to the clearance shown between the head of screw *F* and disk *D*. Die-block *G* is provided with die ring *H* which is in a raised position prior to the descent of the punch, the purpose being to hold up the wire, around which the edge of the pail is to be curled, when ring *B* is engaged in this curling process. Die ring *H* is raised to this position by means of several coil springs placed between the die-block and the die ring, the height of the position being determined by the head of screw *I* coming in contact with the die-block.

Prior to the performance of an operation in this die, the wire around which the edge of the pail is to be curled, is laid upon the die ring *H*, and the shell is inserted through the wire into the die. On the downward movement of the press ram, nose-piece *C* enters the die, and the pressure exerted by the rubber buffer *E* between the nose-piece and disk *D*, causes a depression in the bottom of the pail. The pressure is exerted on all surfaces of the shell during the curling portion of the operation. There is sufficient clearance allowed between nose-piece *C* and wire ring *B* to permit the nose-piece to hold the shell firmly before the curling process commences. The edge of the shell is curled around the wire by ring *B* as the punch-holder descends, and at the same time die ring *H* is forced down on die-block *G*.

On the return stroke of the punch, the rubber buffer holds the nose-piece and the work in the die until the head of screw *F* comes in contact with disk *D*, after which the nose-piece and the buffer are also withdrawn as the punch continues to ascend. The shell is raised from the die by die ring *H* as this ring returns to its original position due to the pressure exerted by the coil springs previously referred to. It is always essential to provide a nose-piece and a rubber buffer or other similar means of exerting pressure on the various surfaces of the work during a curling operation, in order to insure that the form of the body of the shell will remain unchanged by this operation.

Drawing a Deep Conical Shell.—The production of the conical-shaped part shown at *K*, Fig. 13, required eleven operations as shown, as this is an unusually difficult example of conical drawing. This tapering part is the rear cap or tail-piece of incendiary bombs manufactured in large quantities for the United States Government during the war. This piece was first made by cutting out the blank on a power press, then rolling it into a conical shape, and finally welding the

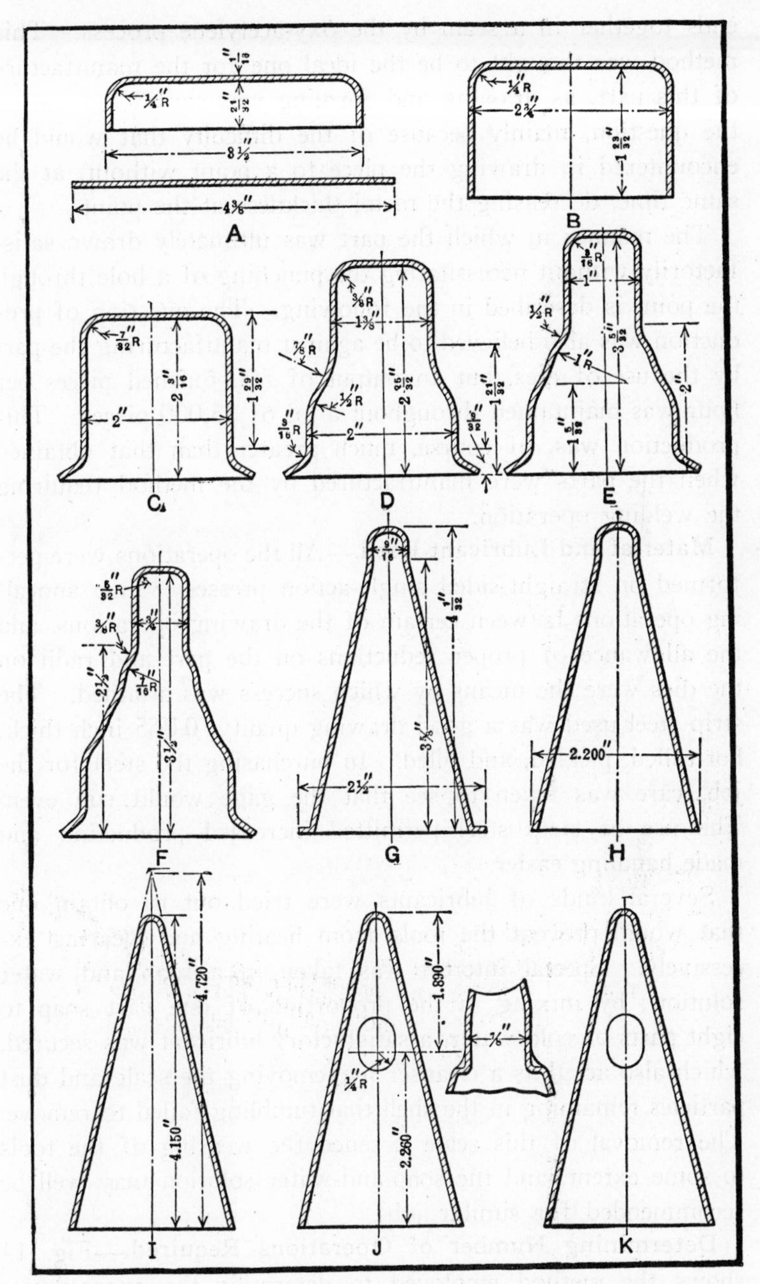

Fig. 13. Successive Operations on Deep Conical Shell

ends together in a seam by the oxy-acetylene process. This method was thought to be the ideal one for the manufacture of this part, as drawing and forming was considered out of the question, mainly because of the difficulty that would be encountered in drawing the piece to a point without, at the same time, decreasing the metal thickness at the point.

The manner in which the part was ultimately drawn satisfactorily without necessitating the punching of a hole through the point is described in the following. The question of production was also believed to be against manufacturing the part by the use of dies, but an output of 500 finished pieces per hour was maintained throughout a lot of 35,000 pieces. This production was, of course, much greater than that obtained when the parts were manufactured by the method requiring the welding operation.

Material and Lubricant Used.—All the operations were performed on straight-sided single-action presses. Two annealing operations between certain of the drawing operations, and the allowance of proper reductions on the part and radii on the dies were the means by which success was attained. The strip steel used was a good drawing quality, 0.065 inch thick, hot-rolled, pickled, and oiled. In purchasing the steel for the job, care was taken to see that the gage would run even. The use of strip steel permitted increased production and made handling easier.

Several kinds of lubricants were tried out to obtain one that would prevent the tools from heating and wearing excessively. Special interest was taken in a soap and water solution; by mixing in the proportion of one part soap to eight parts of cold water, a satisfactory lubricant was secured, which also acted as a cleanser by removing the scale and dust particles remaining in the shell that tumbling failed to remove. The removal of this scale lessened the wearing of the tools to some extent, and the soap-and-water solution may well be recommended for similar jobs.

Determining Number of Operations Required.—Fig. 14 shows the method employed to determine the approximate

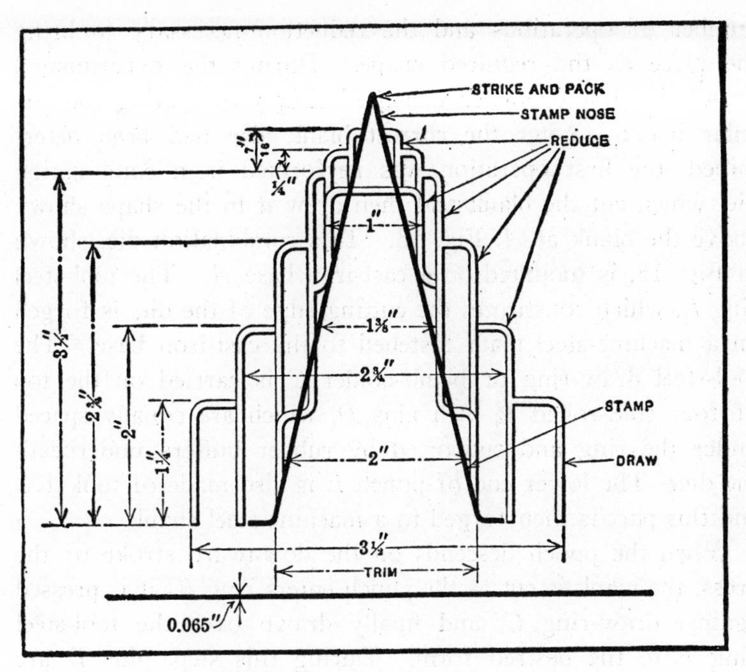

Fig. 14. Lay-out made to Determine Approximate Number of Operations for Drawing Deep Conical Shell

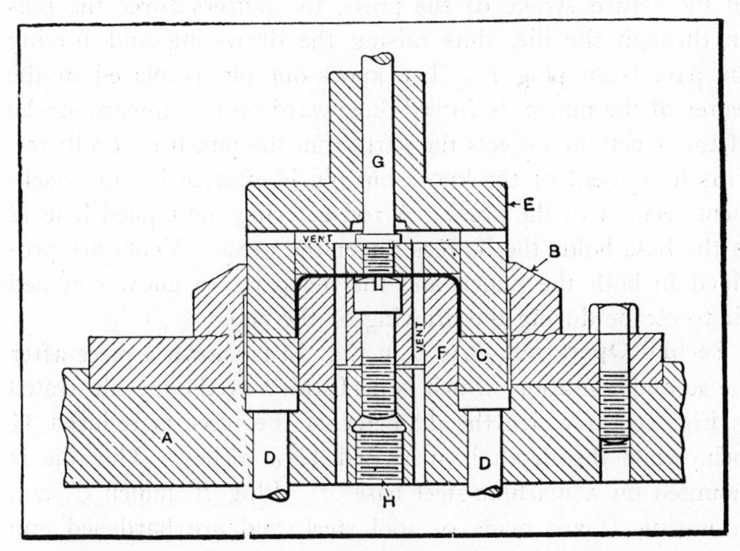

Fig. 15. Combination Die which Cuts the Blank and Performs the First Drawing Operation

number of operations and the reduction necessary to bring the piece to the required shape. During the experimental stages the first operation consisted simply of cutting the circular blank. After the correct blank size had been determined, the first operation was performed in a combination die, which cut the blank and then drew it to the shape shown above the blank at *A*, Fig. 13. This combination die, shown in Fig. 15, is mounted on a cast-iron base *A*. The tool-steel ring *B*, which constitutes the cutting edge of the die, is forged on a machine-steel plate fastened to the cast-iron base. The tool-steel draw-ring or blank-holder *C* is carried on the top of four cold-rolled 3/4-inch pins *D*, which are equally spaced under the ring and supported by rubber buffers underneath the die. The lower end of punch *E* is also made of tool steel and this part is then forged to a machine-steel shank.

When the punch descends on the downward stroke of the press, the blank is cut as the punch enters ring *B*; it is pressed against draw-ring *C*, and finally drawn over the tool-steel plug *F* to the desired form. During this step, pins *D* are forced down on the rubber buffers previously referred to, and on the return stroke of the press, the buffers force the pins up through the die, thus raising the draw-ring and forcing the part from plug *F*. The knock-out pin *G* placed in the center of the punch, is forced downward on the upward stroke of the punch, and ejects the part from the punch if it adheres. This movement of the knock-out pin is effected by an attachment secured to the press. A rod entering the tapped hole *H* in the base holds the buffers under the press. Vents are provided in both the punch and the die parts to allow confined air to escape during the drawing of the cup.

Second Operation.—At *B* in Fig. 13 is shown a piece after the second operation, which is performed by the die illustrated in Fig. 16, in which the diameter of the piece is reduced 3/4 inch, while the depth is increased 1 1/16 inches. This die is mounted on a machine-steel base *A*. Plug *B*, punch *C*, and draw-ring *D* are made of tool steel, and are hardened and ground. Vents are again provided in the plug and punch to allow confined air to escape from under the descending cup, thus avoiding bulging and wrinkling of the piece. The draw-ring is supported by pins mounted on a rubber buffer, which strip the work from plug *B*. A knock-out device is also provided in the punch.

Successive Reducing Operations on the Shell.—Prior to the third operation the parts are dipped into a solution consisting of one part of muriatic acid to five parts of water. This loosens the scale which forms on the surface of the steel

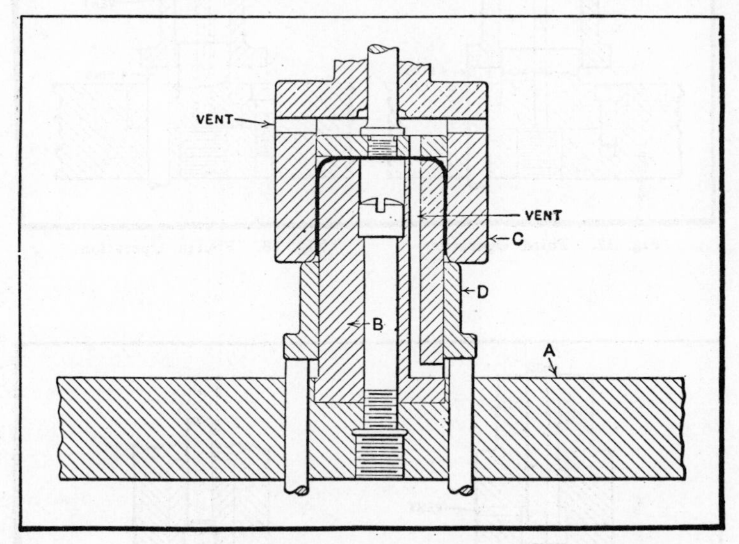

Fig. 16. Second Operation in which the Diameter of Part is Decreased and Length Increased

during the subsequent process of annealing. The parts are then annealed by heating them to a cherry-red. It is an easy matter to remove the loose scale by tumbling, this removal being essential in prolonging the life of the wearing parts of the die. The annealing process releases all internal strains set up in the work during the first two drawing operations and prepares the piece for further drawing. The third operation is performed on a press equipped with the die illustrated in Fig. 17 which draws the part to the shape shown at *C*, Fig. 13. A reduction of 3/4 inch is made in the diameter during this

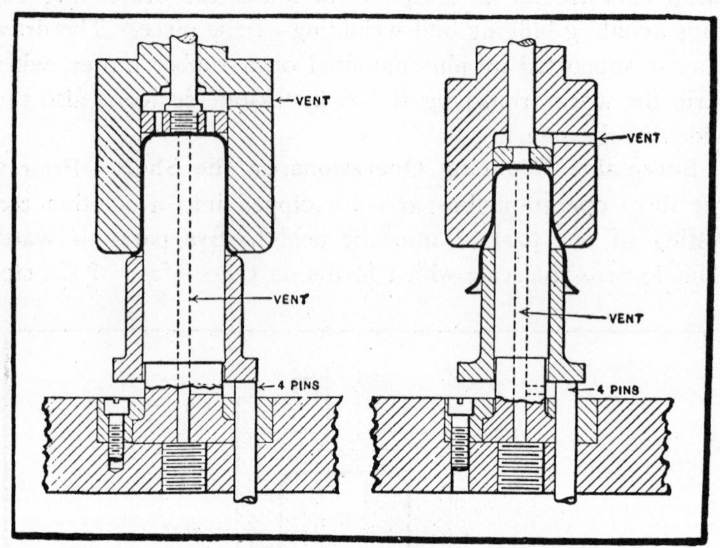

Fig. 17. Third Operation

Fig. 18. Fourth Operation

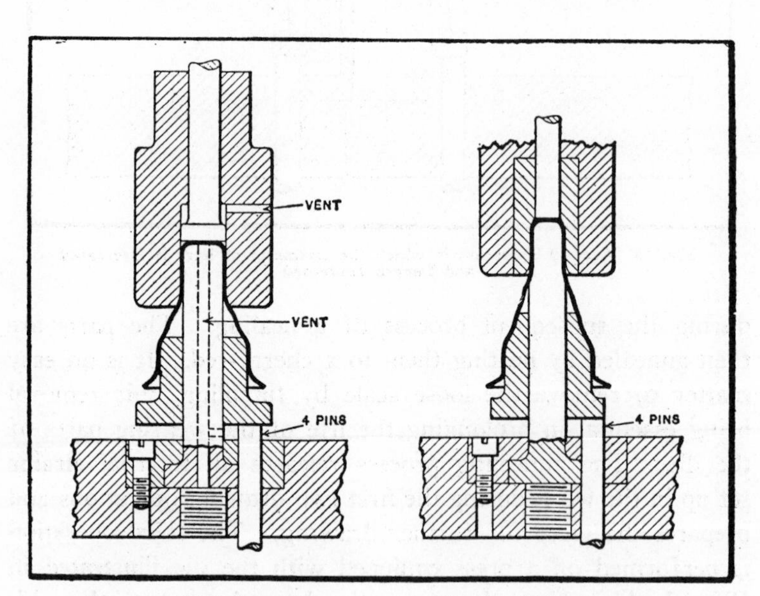

Fig. 19. Fifth Operation

Fig. 20. Sixth Operation

operation, and the depth is increased $\frac{15}{32}$ inch. The base of the part is now the proper size for the final drawing, and is held at this diameter during the next three operations. This die is practically like the one preceding it, in construction and operation.

Fig. 13 at *D* shows the piece after it has been put through the fourth operation, which is performed by the die shown in Fig. 18. In this operation the diameter of the nose is reduced $\frac{5}{8}$ inch, while the length of the part is increased $\frac{19}{32}$ inch. The construction of this die is similar to the preceding ones. The next reducing operation produces the shape shown at *E*, Fig. 13, the die employed being illustrated in Fig. 19. The diameter of the nose is decreased $\frac{3}{8}$ inch, while the depth of the shell is increased $\frac{3}{8}$ inch. By keeping the increase in depth in the correct proportion to the decrease in diameter, the tendency to stretch the material is almost entirely overcome, and the desired thickness of the part is maintained.

The last of the reducing operations brings the piece to the shape shown at *F*, Fig. 13. The die used is shown in Fig. 20. It will be seen that it is quite similar to the dies previously described. The stampings are again annealed, before this operation. By means of the two annealing operations the part is produced satisfactorily with a minimum of breaking and tearing. The piece was given several other annealings during the experimental stage, but these were omitted during production without any undesirable effects.

Tapering the Cone and Forming the Flange.—The seventh operation tapers the sides of the cone, reduces the diameter of the nose, and forms a flat flange at the face, as shown at *G* in Fig. 13. This is done on a press equipped with the die illustrated in Fig. 21. The previous annealing operations have relieved all internal strains in the metal and have somewhat softened it so that the production of a cone with uniform sides is possible. A rather interesting feature of this die is the construction of the plug upon which the part is shaped; this is made of two tool-steel pieces *A* and *B*. The plug was formerly made of one piece, but considerable trouble was experienced with this construction, because of the fact that the plug would wear away rapidly about one inch from the top so that an annular depression was formed. Several different kinds of steel, tempered to various degrees of hardness were experimented with, but with little success. However, the problem was satisfactorily solved by the construction illustrated. Plug *A* is fastened to plug *B* by a screw that fits in a hole running through the center of plug *B*. When the upper plug becomes so worn that the work does not pass inspection, it is removed and another fastened in place. A supply of these

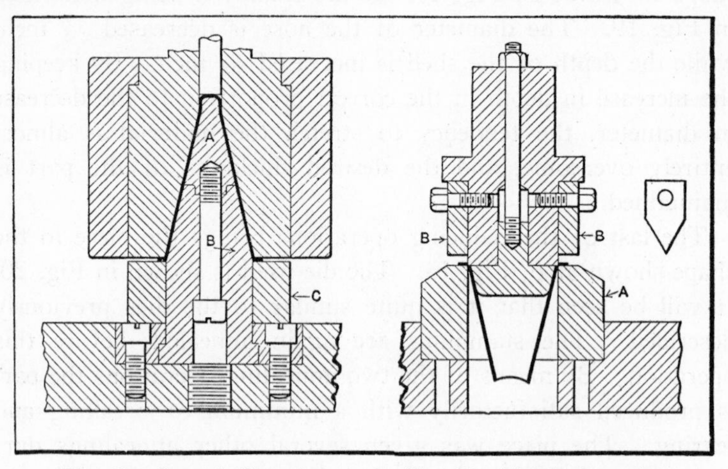

Fig. 21. Seventh Operation Fig. 22. Eighth Operation

tips is made up and kept on hand so that the production of the part is not greatly interfered with when substitution is necessary. Draw-ring C is supported on pins (not illustrated), which are used in connection with rubber buffers, as on the dies previously described.

The eighth operation is performed on a press equipped with the die shown in Fig. 22, which trims the part as shown at *H*, Fig. 13. The flat flange produced during the previous operation permits the cone to rest evenly in an inverted position on the top surface of the trimming die *A*. Two cutters *B* are fastened on opposite sides of the punch above the trimming edge, for the purpose of cutting in two the trimmed-off scrap rings which accumulate around the punch. Holes are drilled in the base beneath die-part *A* to facilitate the removal of the part.

Final Punch Press Operations on the Conical Shell.—The ninth operation is performed by means of the die illustrated in Fig. 23, which forms the part to the shape shown at *I*, Fig. 13. In the preceding drawing operation enough material was left straight at the nose of the part so that it could be squeezed to shape from the outside rather than from the inside. This

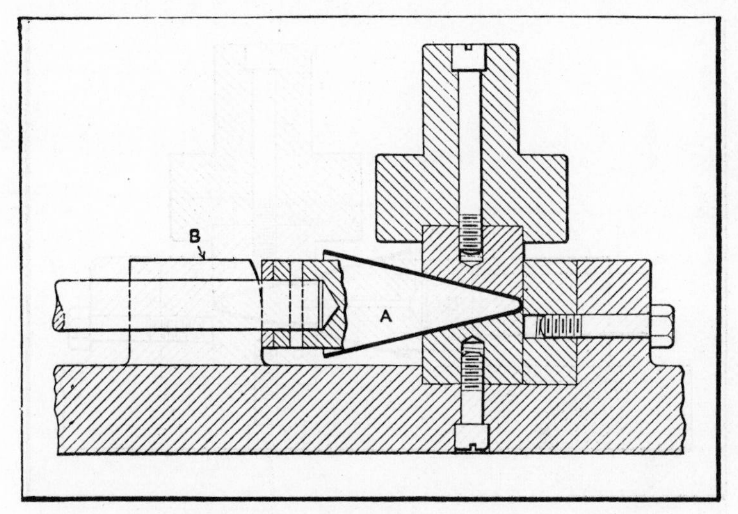

Fig. 23. Die Employed to Form Point on End of Conical Shell

method was adopted because of the trouble which results from the other method of drawing; the piece invariably ruptures at the point and is entirely unsatisfactory. It will be seen that this die holds the part in a horizontal position. The punch-holder and base of the die are made of cast iron, while the remaining parts with which the work comes in contact are made of tool steel.

The work is placed over the tool-steel piece *A*, which is shaped like a cone and acts as a plug. A 1-inch cold-rolled bar attached to the plug serves as a handle, by means of which the operator places the plug and work in the lower half of the die. The plug is prevented from being forced from the die as the punch comes in contact with the work, by means of two lugs *B*. In this operation, as the upper half of the die descends with the ram, it presses the work on the plug. Four strokes of the press are required to complete the operation, the plug being given a quarter-turn after each stroke. A slight jar against the side of the part is sufficient to loosen it from the plug in order to effect its removal.

The tenth operation embosses two flats on opposite sides of the cone, as shown in Fig. 13 at *J*, the die employed for

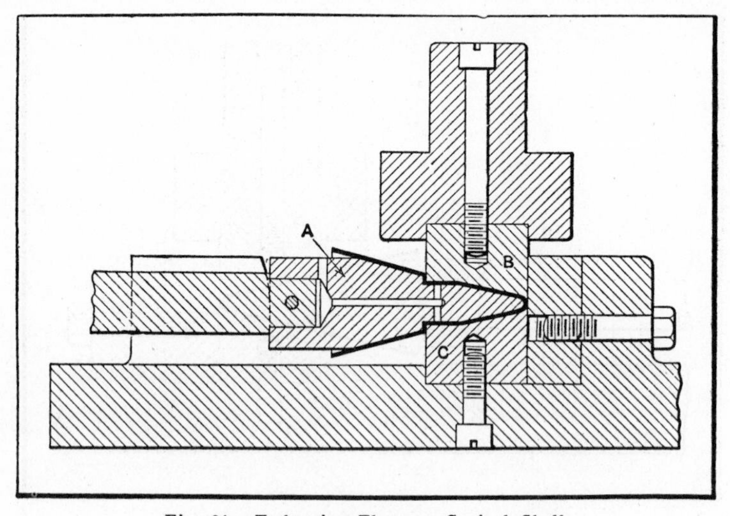

Fig. 24. Embossing Flats on Conical Shell

this purpose being illustrated in Fig. 24. As in the preceding operation, the part is held in a horizontal position on a tool-steel plug *A*. The punch-holder and the die in this case also are made of cast iron, while the parts which come in contact with the work are made of tool steel. The handle of the plug is a cold-rolled 1¾-inch square steel bar. In addition to its use in placing work in the die, the handle provides a gage for insuring that the plug will be so placed in the die that the embosses will be made directly on the axis of the work. Both embosses are made at one stroke of the press, parts *B* and *C* of the punch and die, respectively, being similar. The part is easily removed from plug *A* by jarring it slightly against the bolster plate of the press.

The final punch-press operation on the part strikes and packs the base as shown at *K*, Fig. 13, this shape being identical to that shown at *J*. The operation is performed to smooth out any wrinkles that may be left by the previous reductions, and brings the piece to the exact desired size. The die used is shown in Fig. 25. The base and punch-holder are made of cast iron, while the parts which come in contact with the work

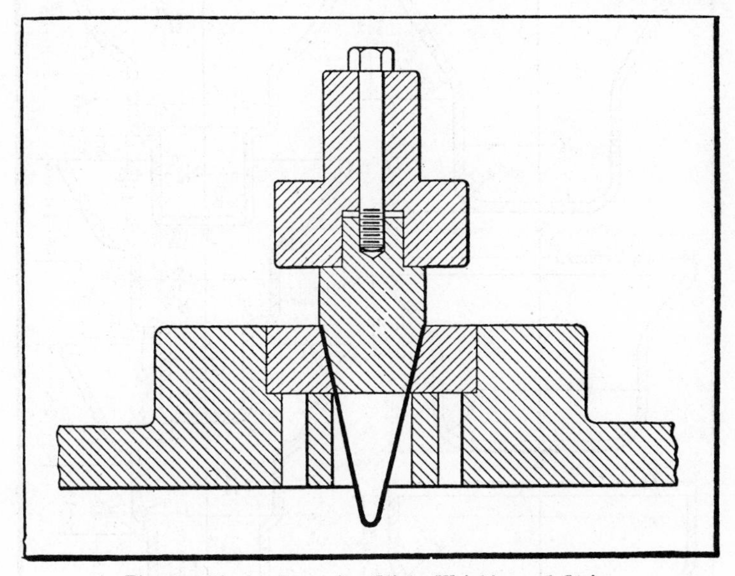

Fig 25. Die for Removing Slight Wrinkles and Sizing

are made of tool steel, as in some of the dies previously described. This makes a construction which is, in general, equal to an all-steel die, and has the advantage that the material and labor costs are less.

An idea of the accuracy required in the parts produced by the dies here described, can be readily obtained by considering the method of gaging. The gage is in the form of a taper plug which extends into the shell 1½ inches, approximately. At the large end of this plug there is a flange and a line is scribed 0.011 inch from this flange. It was necessary for the end of the part, when the latter was slipped over the gage, to come between this line and the base. The parts were so consistently accurate that only a few failed to pass inspection.

Dies for Drawing a Universal Joint Cover.—Some of the more interesting dies used in forming the step-shaped universal joint cover shown at *D* in Fig. 26, will now be described. The shell is drawn from metal 0.166 inch thick, the blank being 8

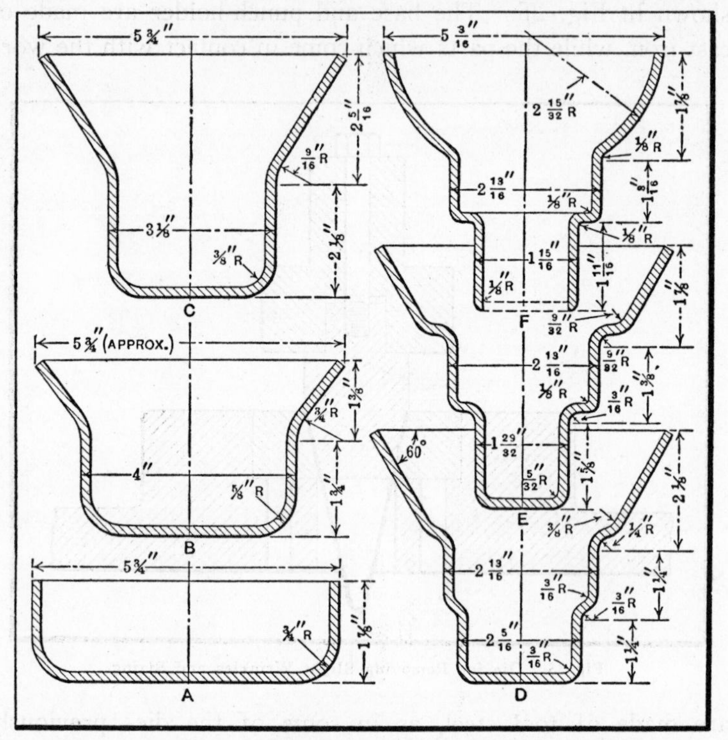

Fig. 26. Various Stages in the Drawing and Forming Processes on a Universal Joint Cover

inches in diameter. The die employed in the blanking operation is of simple construction and does not require special description. The second operation on the shell is performed by a push-through die shown (see upper illustration in Fig. 27). The blank is located on the die by means of the gage ring *A* which is attached to the die-block *B* and holds the drawing ring or die *C* in place. The drawing ring has a 30-degree angle and a liberally rounded corner over which the shell is drawn. There are three radial holes *D* in the die-block, which hold spring-actuated strippers so that when the punch ascends after having formed the shell as shown, the strippers will operate and prevent the shell from adhering to the punch. The punch is also provided with a knock-out which operates in hole *E*, but in this particular die the knock-out is not necessary, as the shell is stripped from the punch by means of the spring-actuated device previously mentioned. The dies used in the third and fourth operations are not illustrated, since their general construction is similar to that of the die employed in performing the fifth operation. Reference to Fig. 26 will show at *B* and *C* the shape of the shell after each of these operations.

The fifth operation, besides further reducing the body of the shell, also starts a small reduction on the end, as shown at *D*. The die shown at the center of Fig. 27, which is employed for this operation, is of the same construction as the other dies used in the forming operations, except that on account of the tapered end of the shell a gage ring is not required to locate it in the die. A knock-out is provided in the punch at *E* and also one in the die at *K*. The sixth operation consists of further reducing the small end of the shell, and the dies employed are of similar design to those previously described. The shape of the shell after this operation is shown at *E*, Fig. 26. It will be noticed in all of these reducing operations that the 5¾-inch diameter at the flared end of the cover has been maintained.

The finish-forming die shown at the bottom of Fig. 27 is used in the seventh operation to expand the small end of the shell slightly and at the same time to form the bell-shaped flange to the dimensions shown at *F*, Fig. 26. This die consists of two separate die rings *C*, Fig. 27, the lower one of which is used for forming the straight part and the other for making the bell shape. The latter ring holds the lower ring in place and, in turn, is secured by means of gage ring *A* and machine screws, as shown. Both dies are carefully fitted in the cast-iron holder *B*, which should be of rather heavy con-

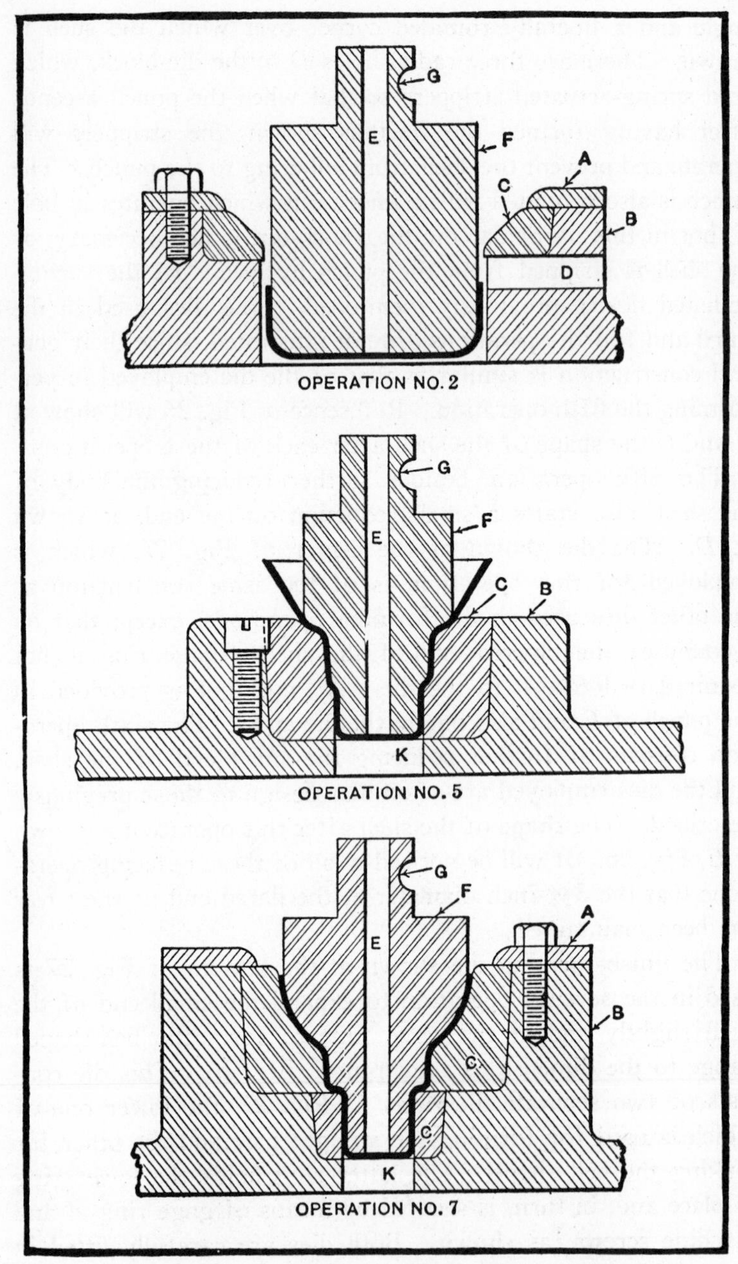

Fig. 27. Dies for Drawing the Shell Shown in Fig. 26

struction on account of the considerable amount of force exerted on these tools. This will permit the die rings to be made comparatively light. The final operation on this shell consists of cutting out the bottom as indicated by the dotted lines at *F*, Fig. 26. This completes the forming of the shell, which must now be machined out in the small diameter before being ready for assembling.

It should be stated generally that in drawing shells of this kind, it is good practice to keep the radii of the corners over which the metal is drawn quite large on both die and punch as this will prevent drawing thin places in the shell. In the dies illustrated, a 1½-degree taper has been allowed for fitting the die rings into the die-block. All the die should be hardened and ground at these angles and then carefully fitted in place. The punches are secured in the holder by means of a pin passing through the holder as indicated at *G* in Fig. 27. This provides a simple way of replacing punches without removing the holder from the press. In those dies where a knock-out is provided, as at *K*, the familiar type of rubber buffer attachment is employed in drawing the shape.

Drawing a Deep Shell having Cylindrical and Conical Sections.—The drawing of a steel shell requiring the use of five sets of drawing and forming tools is illustrated in Figs. 28 to 32, inclusive. The illustrations show the dies and the shell as it appears after each successive operation. The metal used in making the shell is cold-rolled strip steel, 0.035 inch thick, and the blank is 5¹³⁄₁₆ inches in diameter. All parts of the dies are hardened and ground. It will be noted that corresponding parts of the different dies have the same reference letters throughout the description. The functions of the various parts of the die shown in Fig. 28 will be described, but only those features of the other dies that are radically different will be mentioned.

The combination die shown in Fig. 28, cuts the blank and draws it to the shape shown. This is a standard type of die and is designed for use on a press having the ordinary rubber buffet attachment and plate for pins *P*. The forming die *A*

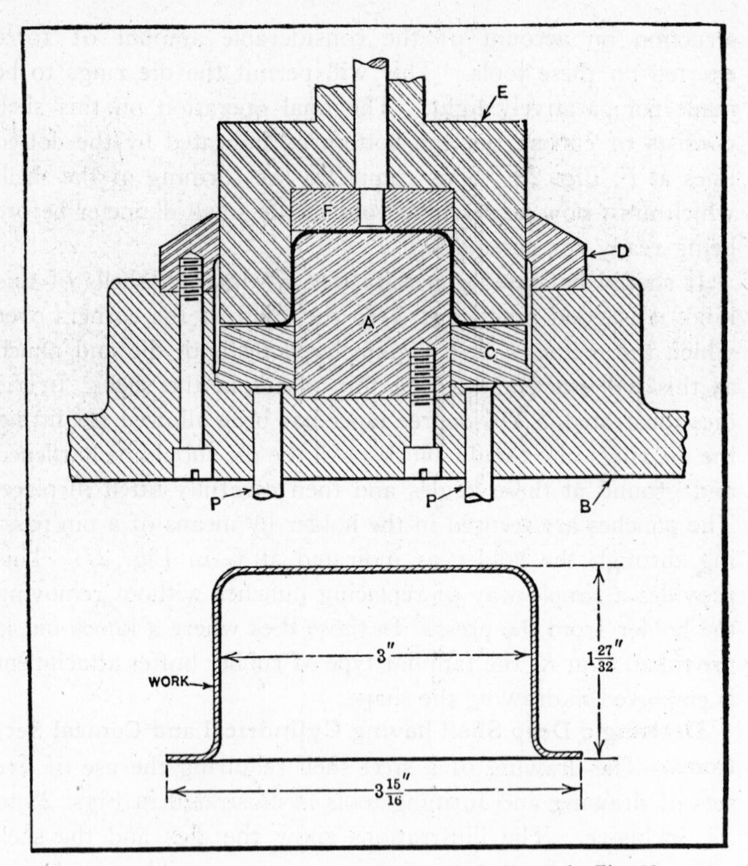

Fig. 28. First Drawing Operation on Shell Shown in Fig. 32

is secured to the cast-iron die block *B* by three small screws and is recessed into the die-block to insure concentricity with the remaining die parts. The drawing ring *C* is the part upon which the flange of the shell is formed. The steel blank is laid upon the cutting ring *D*, and as the punch *E* descends past the cutting edge of ring *D*, the blank is cut to the required size; as the punch continues to descend, the shell is drawn to the shape that is shown. The knock-out pad *F* ejects the shell from the punch on the return stroke of the press. The faces of the punch and of the drawing ring between which the flange of the shell is held, are ground parallel, which enables the shell to be seated evenly on the drawing ring.

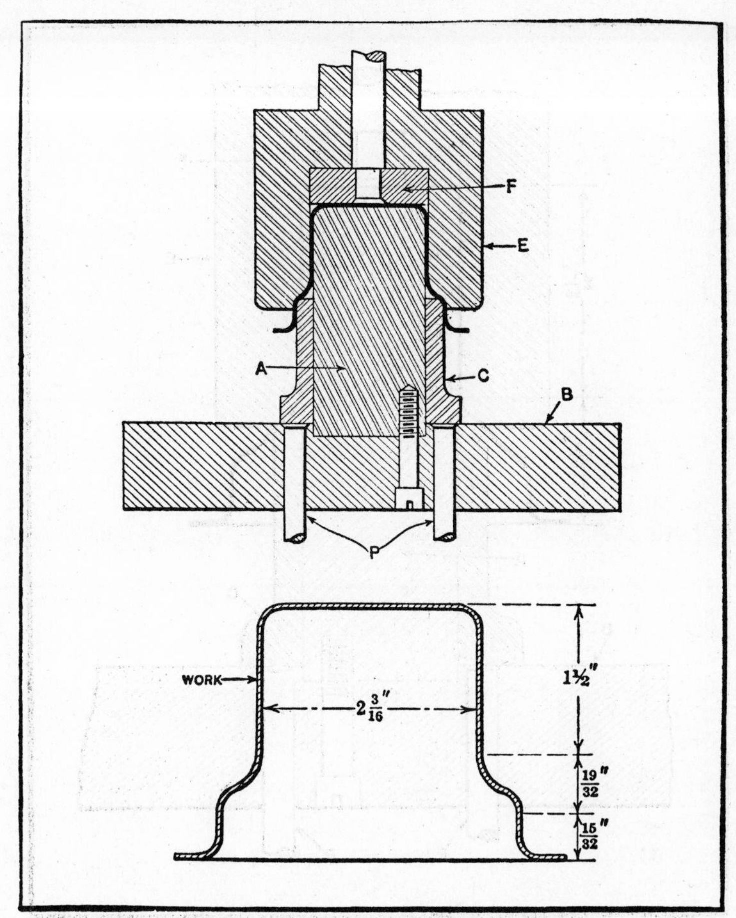

Fig. 29. Die Used in Reshaping the Shell

The die shown in Fig. 29 is used to reshape the shell as indicated in the illustration. The drawing ring *C* is made so that it fits the inside of the shell, and the end is rounded, which permits the metal to be readily reshaped; also, the end of the opening in the punch *E* is correspondingly shaped for the same purpose. Fig. 30 shows a die that is also employed to reshape the shell by reducing the small end, the construction being similar to that of the die shown in Fig. 29.

The die used for redrawing the small end of the shell, and for forming the flared part as well as the large diameter, is

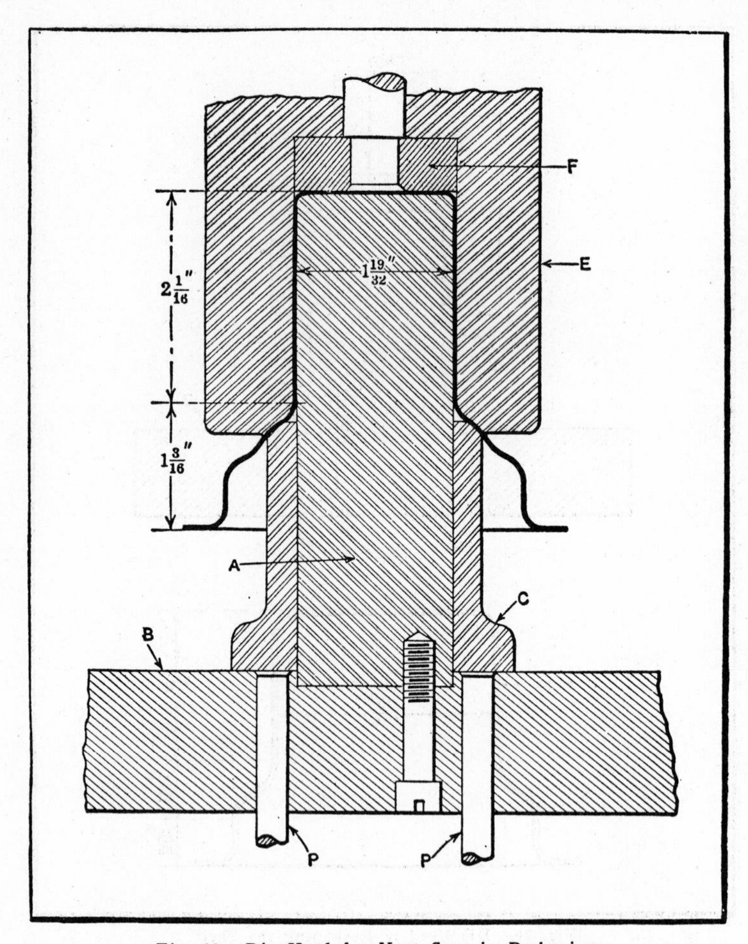

Fig. 30. Die Used for Next Step in Reshaping

illustrated in Fig. 31. The drawing ring *C* serves a double purpose: First, by reason of its being raised to a certain height by means of springs, it acts as a gage for locating the shell in the die *A*, previous to the forming operation; and second, after being pushed down against the top surface of the die by the action of the press, it serves as a die in which the large diameter of the shell is formed. In this operation, the flange on the shell is flattened out between the ring *C* and the punch *E*, thus preparing the shell for the final operation on this end.

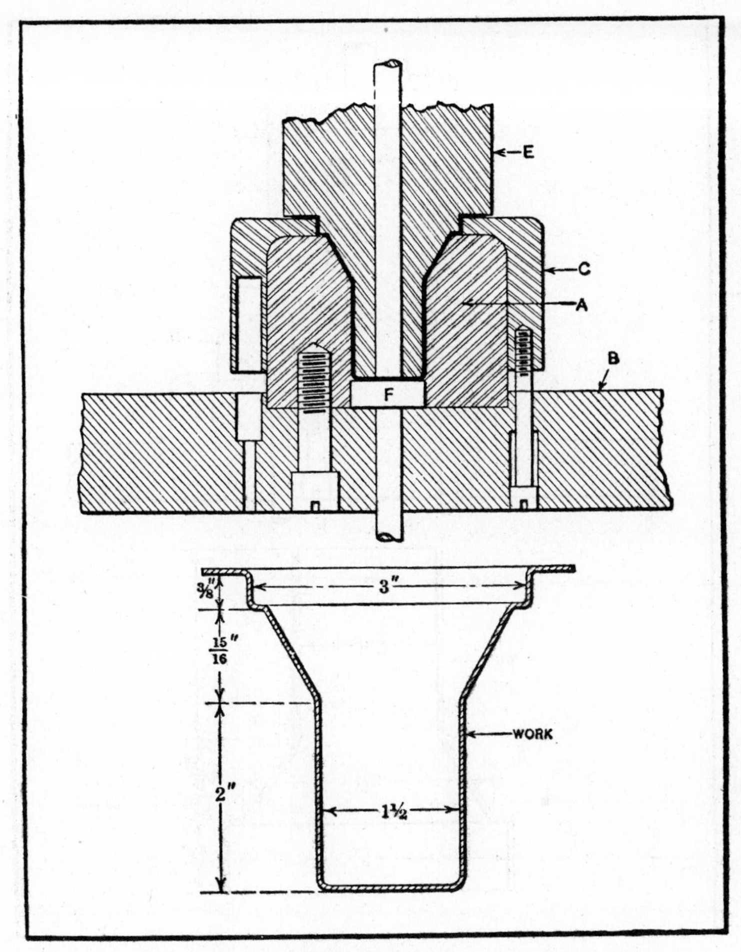

Fig. 31. Die that Redraws the Small End of the Shell and Forms the Flared End

The die that completes the work on the shell is shown in Fig. 32. Both the forming die *A* and the cutting ring *D* fit into recesses in the die-block *B*. A small cutting die *G* is secured on the top of die *A* as shown. In this operation, as the face of punch *E* descends past the cutting edge on ring *D*, the flange of the shell is trimmed, and as the press completes its downward stroke, the shell is formed as shown and the bottom of the shell is pushed out by die *G*. This is possible

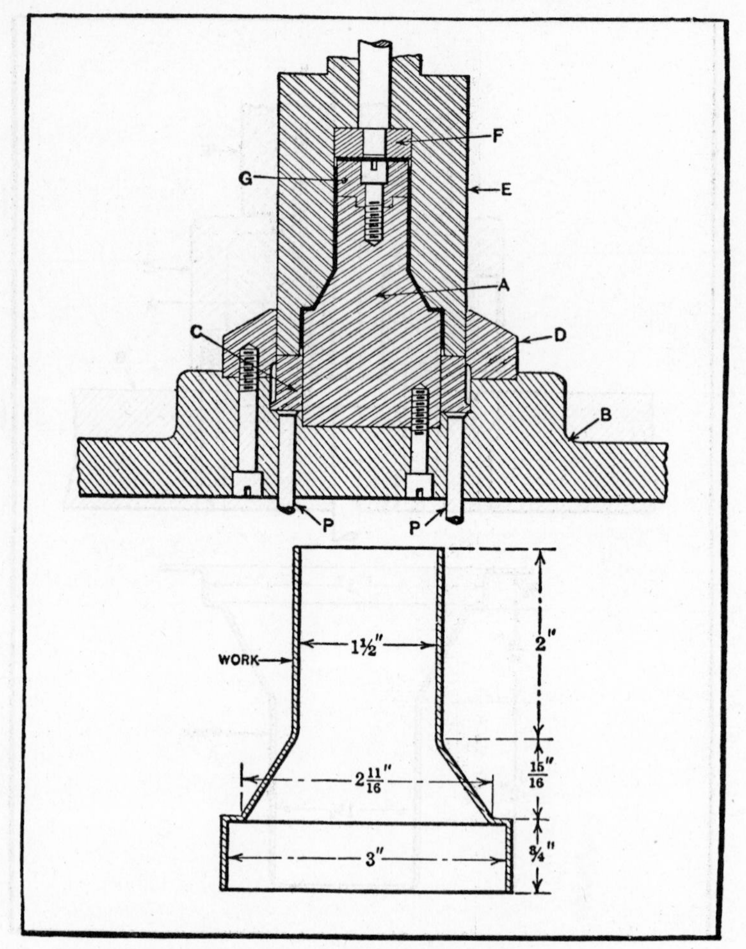

Fig. 32. Die that Cuts out the End of the Shell and Performs the Final Forming Operation

because the cutting edge of die *G*, when the punch is in this position, extends ⅟16 inch higher than the end of the long cylindrical part of the shell. The knock-out pad *F* forces the shell out of the punch on the upward stroke of the machine.

Drawing of Large Tapered Shell.—In Fig. 33 is shown the lay-out for a large tapered shell, which, when completed forms a familiar type of water pail. The heavy outline represents the completed shell. The method of drawing the shell

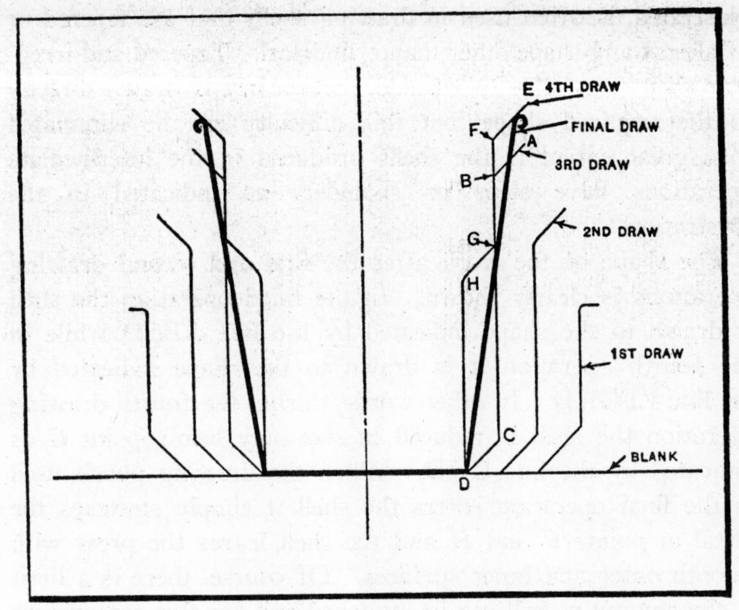

Fig. 33. Evolution of Tapered Shell such as Used for Water Pails

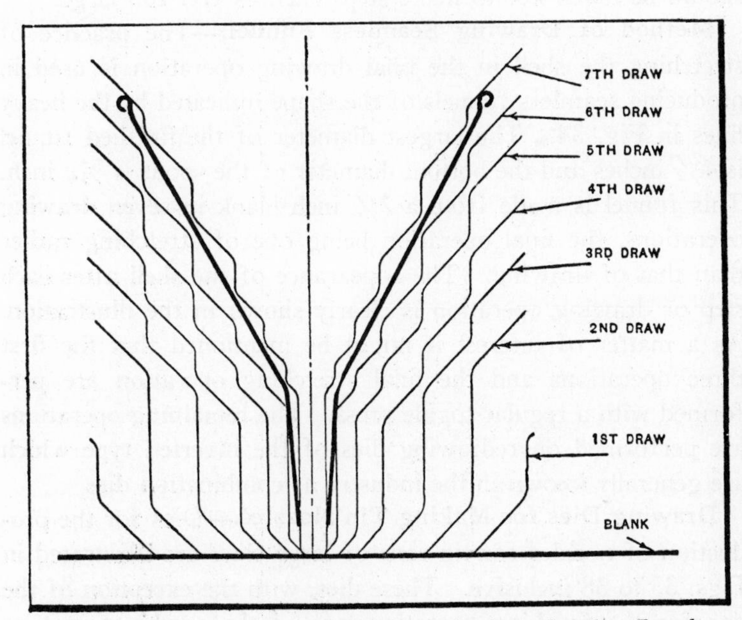

Fig. 34. Diagram Illustrating Method of Drawing a Seamless Funnel

illustrated, is often used in drawing shells that are tapered or of almost any shape other than cylindrical. Tapered and irregular shells are liable to wrinkle, particularly if drawn directly to the required shape, but this difficulty can be eliminated to a great extent if the shells produced in the intermediate operations have steps or shoulders as indicated in the illustration.

The shape of the work after the first and second drawing operations is clearly shown. In the third operation the shell is drawn to the shape indicated by the line ABCD while in the fourth operation it is drawn to the shape indicated by the line EFGHD. In other words, during the fourth drawing operation the shell is reduced in size only below point *G* as indicated by the line GHD. When the drawing punch used in the final operation enters the shell it simply stretches the metal at points *F* and *H* and the shell leaves the press with smooth outer and inner surfaces. Of course, there is a limit to the amount a shell can be stretched and for this reason care should be taken not to make steps such as GH too large.

Method of Drawing Seamless Funnel.—The practice of stretching the shell in the final drawing operation is used in producing seamless funnels of the shape indicated by the heavy lines in Fig. 34. The largest diameter of the finished funnel is 4½ inches and the bottom diameter of the spout is 5/16 inch. This funnel is made from a 7½ inch blank in seven drawing operations, the final operation being one of stretching rather than that of drawing. The appearance of the shell after each step or drawing operation is clearly shown in the illustration. As a matter of interest it might be mentioned that the first three operations and the final stretching operation are performed with a regular toggle press. The remaining operations are performed on redrawing dies of the inverted type which are generally known in the industry as combination dies.

Drawing Dies for Making Tin Nozzles.—Dies for the production of nozzles for tin cans of large sizes are illustrated in Figs. 35 to 38 inclusive. These dies, with the exception of the one for the finishing operation, are of the combination type and, therefore, used in single-action presses. The die for the first operation is shown in Fig. 35 and is composed of the following principal parts: A bolster plate *A*; a blanking die *B*; a drawing punch *C*; and a pressure ring or blank-holder *D* which rests upon three pins connecting with the rubber pressure attachment *P* for regulating the pressure while drawing the shell. The combination blanking punch and drawing die *G* is fitted on its outside to blanking die *B*, whereas, the inside diameter equals the diameter of the drawing punch *C* plus

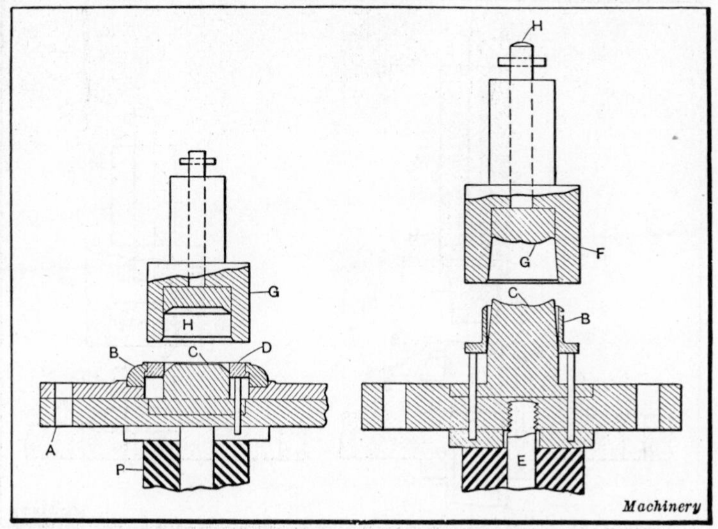

Fig. 35. First-operation Die for Can Nozzles

Fig. 36. Redrawing Die for Can Nozzles

twice the thickness of the stock. The forming pad *H* within the punch is made to fit the top of the drawing punch for forming the top of the shell at the end of the stroke. As will be seen, this part also serves as a knockout for the drawn shells. This die is operated by a press of the inclinable type. The punch, as it comes into contact with the blanking die *B*, cuts the blank which is then held by pressure ring *D* against the end of die *G*; as the die descends, the blank is drawn over the drawing punch *C* and when it moves upward the stem of the knockout comes into contact with a bar in the press, thus pushing the pad *H* down and forcing the shell out. The form produced in this die is illustrated at *A*, in Fig. 39.

The die for the second operation is shown in Fig. 36. The center block or drawing punch *C* of this die is tapered, and the die *F* is also bored out to a corresponding taper. The pad *G* in the die is of a peculiar shape, as will be noticed; the reason for this shape will be explained later. The shell is placed on the drawing ring *B* and the die, as it descends, draws it down and compresses it to the shape of the punch *C*.

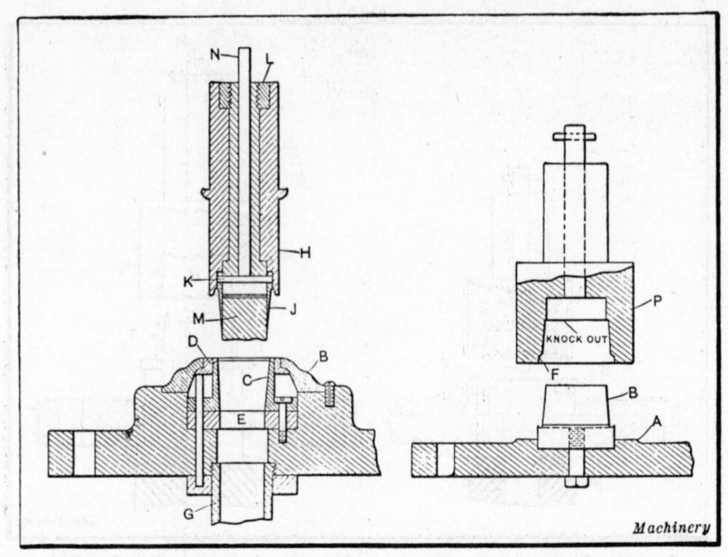

Fig. 37. Die for Third Operation on Can Nozzles

Fig. 38. Die for Finishing Can Nozzles

The shell, which now resembles the form shown at *B*, Fig. 39, is knocked out on the up-stroke by the engagement of stem *H* with the knock-out bar, the same as in the first operation.

The die for the third operation, which really consists of three operations, is illustrated in Fig. 37. The principal parts are the trimming die *B*; the center block *C*; the drawing ring *D*; the lower die *E*; and the tube *G*, through which the bottom of the nozzle passes after being punched out. Incidentally, these bottoms are used for roofing shells for fastening tar paper in place on roofs, etc., so that two articles are made at once.

Inasmuch as these blanked out ends are to be utilized in this way, they are formed by pad *G* (Fig. 36) in the second operation. The die for the third operation is also used in an inclined press. As the punch *M* descends, it cuts out the bottom and at the same time punch *H* trims the flange. As the downward movement continues, the shell is pressed over the edge of center block *C*. When the punch moves upward the knockout bar comes in contact with stem *N*, thus forcing the cross-pin *K* and stripper *J* down and ejecting the nozzle, which is now shaped as illustrated at *C*, Fig. 39.

The die for the fourth and finishing operation is illustrated in Fig. 38. This is of simple form and yet much depends upon it, because the nozzles all have to be of uniform size on the finished edge in order to receive a sealing cap, which, when

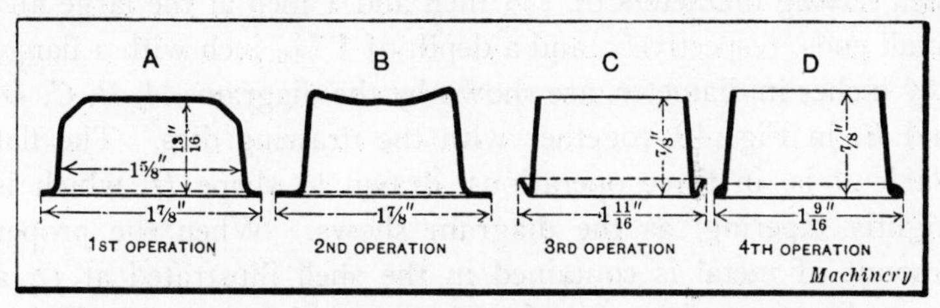

Fig. 39. Successive Operations Performed in Dies Illustrated in Figs. 35 to 38 Inclusive

closed, must be water-tight. The die has a bolster plate *A*; a punch-block *B* of tool steel, hardened and tempered; and a die *P* which is also hardened and tempered and ground out to fit a gage. In the operation of the die, the nozzle is slipped over the punch-block *B*; as the die descends, the recess at *F* engages the edge which was partially curled over in the preceding die, thus completing the curling operation and pressing it to the shape illustrated at *D*, **Fig.** 39. As the die rises, the shell is ejected by an automatic knockout of the usual form.

Drawing a Flanged and Tapered Shell.—When drawing tapered shells with flanges, the requirements for the construction of the dies and the method of forming the shells are different than when drawing cylindrical shells, especially if the taper of the finished shell is large in comparison with the height and diameter. The blank should first be drawn into a cylindrical shape or one having a slight taper, the area being equal to that of the metal required in the finished shell. When trouble is experienced in drawing tapered shells, it is almost invariably caused by an attempt on the part of the diemaker to produce a "steep" taper in the first operation, or to draw a tapered shell directly from the flat blank. If this practice is followed, the shell may either split at the bottom or waves and wrinkles are formed which cannot be removed. Another frequent cause of trouble is due to a surplus of metal in the shell with the result that it cannot be disturbed in the finishing operation or be returned to the flange from which it was drawn.

The successive operations in producing a flanged, tapered shell having diameters of 1⅜ inch and 1 inch at the large and small ends, respectively, and a depth of 1 7/16 inch with a flange 2⅜ inches in diameter, are shown by the diagrams *A*, *B*, *C*, *D*, and *E*, in Fig. 40, together with the drawing dies. The flat blank *A* is, in three operations, drawn to shape *D*, which is slightly tapering, as the diagram shows. When the proper amount of metal is contained in the shell illustrated at *D*, a succeeding operation of re-forming—not drawing or reducing through friction—will shape the cylindrical shell to the desired taper, as indicated at *E*. The reason for this practice of keeping the shell cylindrical (or nearly so) until the last operation, is that in drawing a cylindrical shell or one that is slightly tapering, the metal is confined at all times during the process of drawing, between the die and punch surfaces, making the formation of wrinkles impossible and the flow of metal equal and constant during the entire operation. When the depth to be drawn is quite shallow, as compared with the depth of the shell diameter, even steep tapers can sometimes be drawn in one operation. In general, however, taper parts having a diameter at the bottom which is small in proportion to the extreme diameter of the flange, are difficult to draw, because of the formation of wrinkles and also because of the small area at the end of the drawing punch (in comparison with the

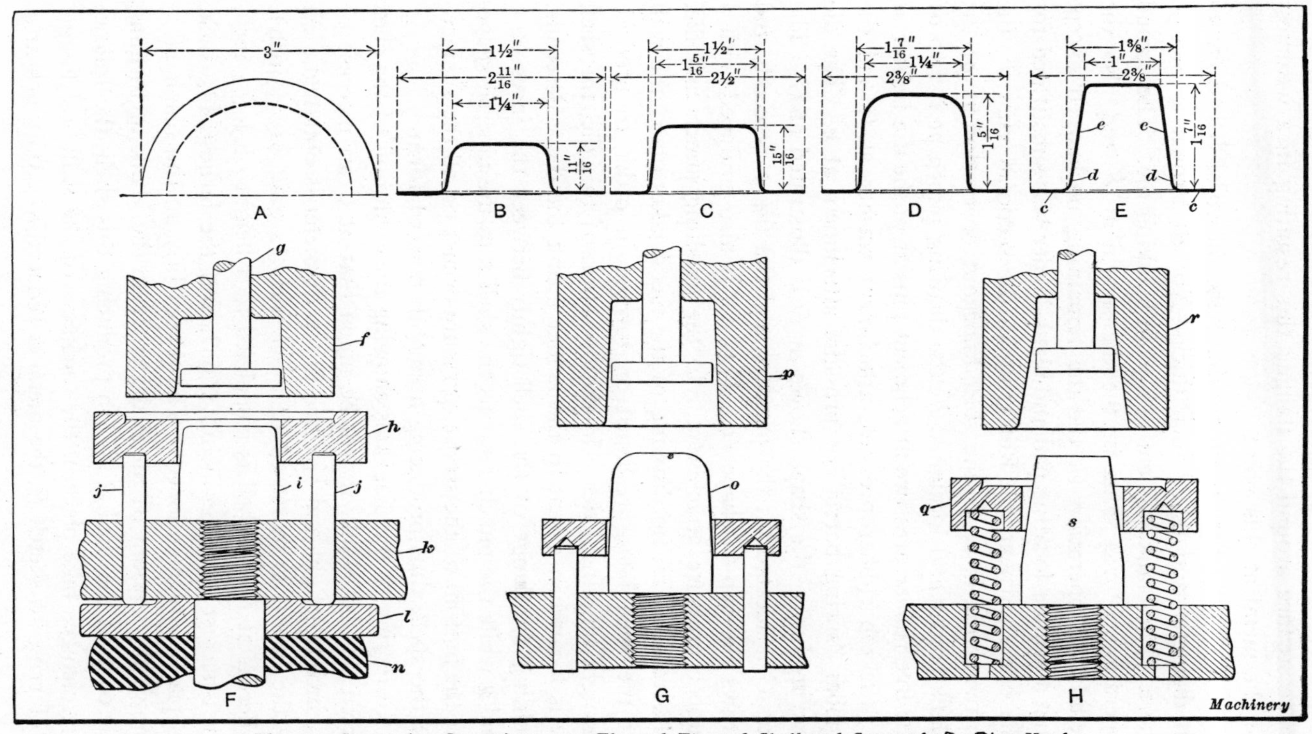

Fig. 40. Successive Operations on a Flanged Tapered Shell and Some of the Dies Used

large surface around the flange) this resulting in a weakness of the metal at this point.

The blank *A* for producing the shape shown at *E* is 3 inches in diameter and 0.032 inch thick—No. 20 Brown & Sharpe gage. The blank was cut in a plain blanking die. The second operation *B* was done in the die shown at *F* and also the redrawing operation *C*, the die remaining unchanged except that a thinner locating pad and blank-holder was substituted for the one shown at *h*. Referring to the sectional view *F*, the drawing die is at *f*; the shell knockout or ejector at *g*; the blank-holder and locater at *h*; the drawing punch at *i*; two of the five rubber pressure attachment pins at *j*; the die bolster at *k*; the top rubber pressure attachment washer at *l*; and the rubber "spring barrel" or pressure attachment at *n*. The die for producing the shape shown at *D* is illustrated at *G*. The cup *C* is located on the punch *o* and the die *p* descends and draws the cup to shape *D*. This die is also equipped with a rubber pressure attachment. In the finishing punch and die, illustrated at *H*, no drawing of the metal takes place, the wall of the shell being reshaped or formed in order to produce straight tapering sides. In the operation of this die, the shell *D* is located in a seat in the holder *q* and the die *r* descends, holding the flange of the shell tightly between the faces of *q* and *r* while the punch *s* forms the shell into the tapered shape. At the bottom of the stroke, pressure occurs on all the surfaces of the shell, thus producing a smooth tapered form.

Referring to the diagrams showing the evolution of the shell from the flat blank, it will be noted that at *C* an increase of 1/4 inch in height and 1/16 inch in top diameter is obtained. At *D* the height is increased to 1 5/16 inch (a gain of 3/8 inch), whereas at *E* the shell is completed to a height of 1 7/16 inch, the smallest diameter being 1 inch and the largest 1 3/8 inch, as previously mentioned. The dotted line on the blank at *A* shows the amount of metal drawn from the blank in forming the cone of the shell at *E*. In producing this shell, the following changes take place in the thickness of the wall and flange. Referring to sketch *E*, the metal is reduced to 0.030 inch at *c*, to 0.022 inch at *d*, to 0.018 inch at *e*, and to 0.021 inch on the end or bottom of the shell.

It was necessary to anneal the shell after the first and third operations. To secure satisfactory results, annealing has to be done without producing a surface scale because the scale would impair the smoothness and accuracy of the finished product. Thin lard oil was used as a lubricant during the first two operations and then the shells were run dry and clean during the last two operations. None of the shells were fractured, and the tools shown in the illustration produced a large quantity. The drawing pads, punches, and rubber buffer pins used in the dies *F* and *G* were made of steel and the other parts of cast iron. For the finishing die *H*, steel was used throughout for the working parts and the pad and die surfaces were hardened and lapped. When drawing taper shells of the type referred to, in which a uniform thickness of metal throughout the wall of the shell is not necessary, a slight lack of metal in the cup next to the last operation is preferable, because the finishing tool can then stretch the metal so as to produce a smooth, true surface.

Successive Operations on Coffee Pot Cover.—The various steps in drawing and forming a coffee pot cover are shown in Fig. 41. The drawing operations are indicated by heavy lines, and the remaining finishing operations by lighter lines. All the work on this cover (except spinning the neck) was performed by combination dies. It will be noticed that the bevel at *A* is maintained until the fifth drawing operation, so that the metal will not be distorted to any great extent in forming the concentric bulges.

Drawing Tapering Shell of Concave Form.—Fig. 42 shows the successive drawing operations on a shell used in making fan bases and Figs. 43 and 44 show the dies used. The first operation in producing the fan stand consists of blanking and drawing. In making the first draw on a cylindrical shell, it is usual to limit the height of the draw to three-fourths the diameter. The largest section of the work above the flange in this case has a diameter of 4 9/16 inches. It is obvious that the

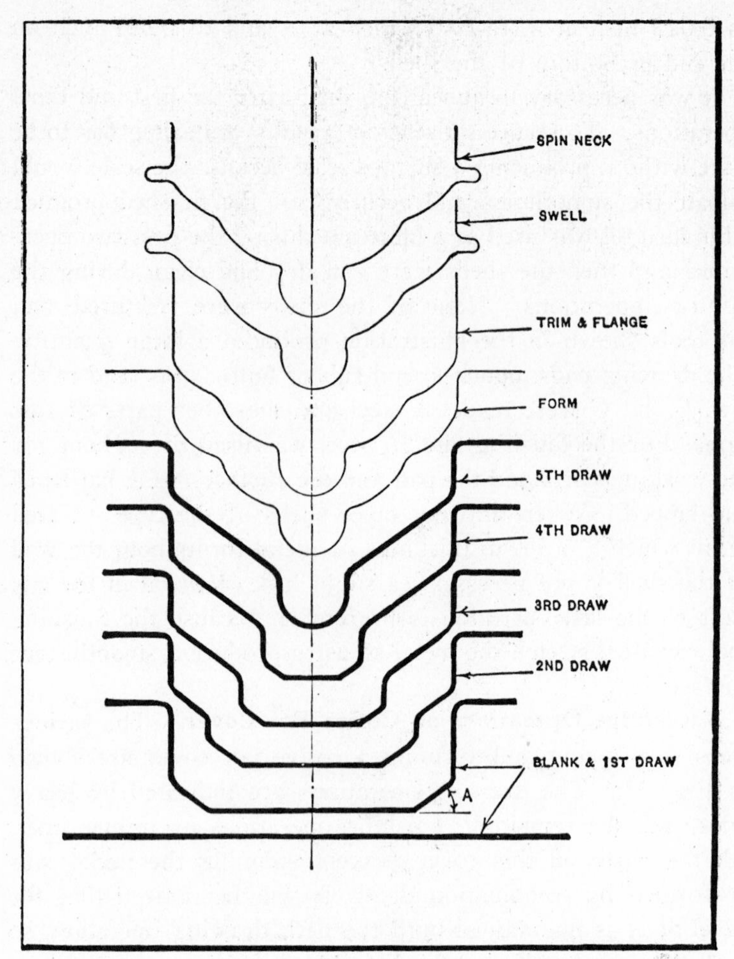

Fig. 41. Diagrams Showing Successive Steps in the Formation of a Coffee Pot Cover

blank which in this case is 9.22 inches in diameter can be readily drawn to a depth of 2.24 inches. Since this is the only operation in which the flanged section of the work is subjected to a drawing action, the drawn part beyond the flange should have an area equal to the area of all the remaining sections to be drawn in the succeeding operations.

In the first drawing operation, the cylindrical part, which is 4 $\frac{9}{16}$ inches in diameter, is finished, and in each subsequent

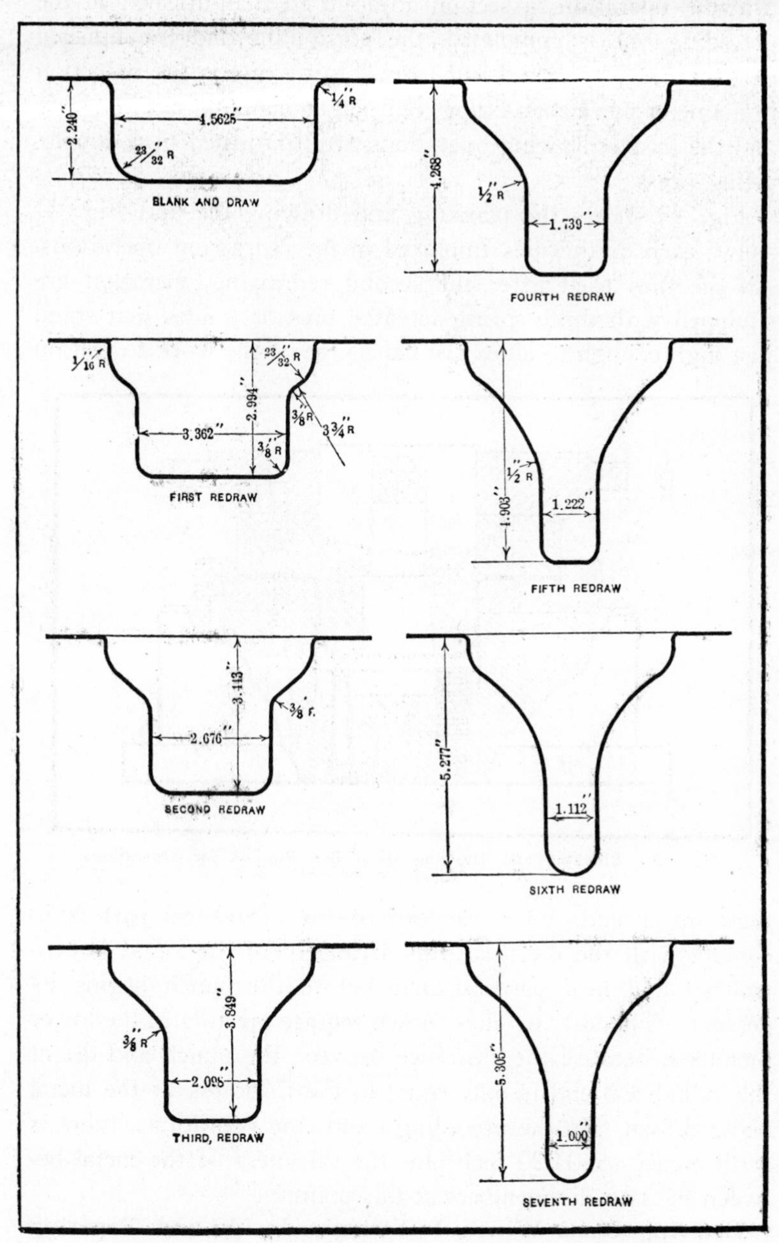

Fig. 42. Sequence of Operations on Tapering Concave Shell

drawing operation, a section adjacent to that finished in the preceding one is completed, the portion beyond the finished part retaining its cylindrical form. In no case is the reduction in diameter more than 20 per cent. The blanking and drawing and the first redrawing operations are performed in a double-acting press.

Fig. 43 shows the blanking and drawing die and Fig. 44 shows each of the dies employed in the redrawing operations. All the dies used after the second redrawing operation are equipped with three spring-actuated pins or guides that stand just high enough to allow the flat flange of the work to rest on

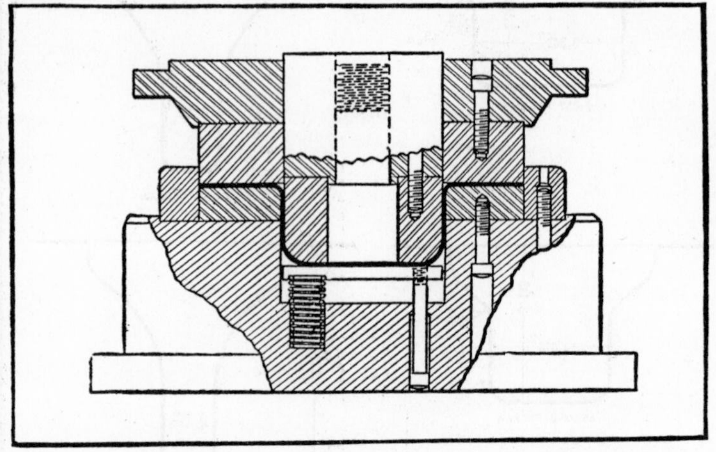

Fig. 43. Blanking and Drawing Die. See Fig. 44 for Operations Which Follow

their upper ends when the end of the cylindrical part is in contact with the die. By this arrangement the stand is centralized and held perpendicular before the punch begins its descent. The last two dies shown require ejectors in the lower members, because the clearance between the punch and die at the cylindrical end is only equal to the thickness of the metal being drawn. In the preceding redrawing operations, there is a difference of 0.020 inch plus the thickness of the metal between the two die members at this point.

Drawing Shell Which Is Straight Inside and Tapering Outside.—The die shown in Fig. 45 is used for drawing shells

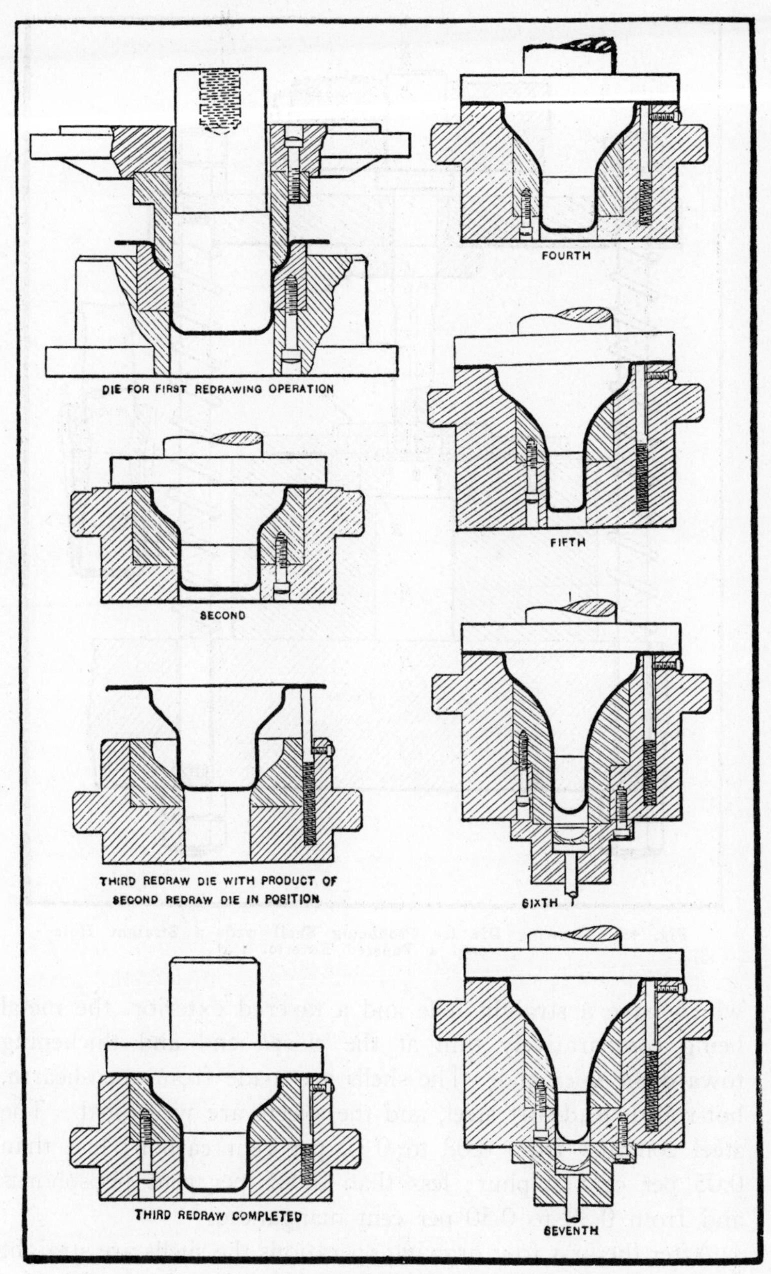

Fig. 44. Successive Redrawing Dies Used for Operations Shown in Fig. 42

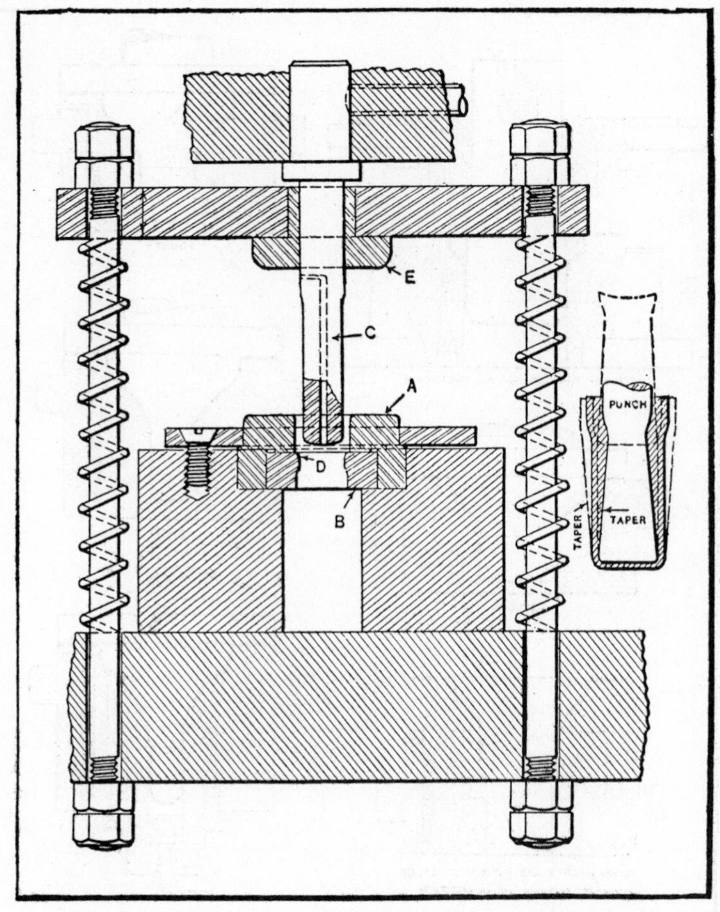

Fig. 45. Drawing Die for Producing Shell with a Straight Hole and a Tapered Exterior

which have a straight hole and a tapered exterior, the metal being comparatively thin at the closed end and thickening toward the open end. The shells are made from open-hearth, hot-rolled dead-soft steel, and the sheets are well oiled. The steel contains from 0.08 to 0.12 per cent carbon; less than 0.05 per cent sulphur; less than 0.045 per cent phosphorus and from 0.30 to 0.50 per cent manganese.

After the first four drawing operations the shells are straight on both the interior and exterior, but from then on the thinning of the stock at the closed end and the tapering commences. The illustration shows the punch and die used in the seventh operation. This design is typical of all others used in this plant for producing a straight hole and a tapered outside surface. Any long-stroke single-action press is suitable for the job.

The die *A*, which is held in the die-block by a ring, is designed with liberal drawing radii on the central hole, and machined out underneath to receive a drawing ring *B*. The design of this drawing ring, in combination with the rounded punch which has a reverse taper at *C*, makes it possible to produce a tapered shell with a straight hole. The metal is drawn over the annular ring *D*, formed on the inside of the drawing ring *B*. To facilitate the drawing of the metal, the pressure is applied at only one point between the punch and the die ring.

As the punch draws the shell, the radial pressure on the metal decreases in proportion to the decrease in the diameter of the punch, so that the metal is thicker around the reduced diameter of the punch. During the upward stroke of the press ram this thicker metal is expanded by the punch, practically filling the hole in die *A*. The exaggerated sketch at the right shows, in section, the shape of the shell before the punch starts to ascend. At this point the overhead stripper plate has brought the bushing *E* into contact with the end of the shell, so that on the upward stroke of the ram the shell is stripped from the punch.

Before being stripped, the shell is securely held on the punch by its reverse inside taper, as the sketch shows, but in stripping, the large end of the punch expands the metal as it is withdrawn, thereby transferring the inside taper to the outside and reversing it, leaving a straight cylindrical hole. In the enlarged sketch, the punch and shell are shown by the dotted outline as this expansion is completed. The liberally curved drawing edges on these tools, the venting of the punch, and the generous lubrication of the metal are all factors in producing a smooth shell of uniformly tapering section.

CHAPTER XVIII

DRAWING DIES FOR SPHERICAL AND OVAL SHAPES

IN SOME lines of manufacture it is necessary to produce die-made parts having spherical or possibly oval surfaces. The metal balls for ball floats, or parts which must have a spherical seat for accommodating some ball-shaped member, are examples of spherical work. The methods and dies employed for changing a flat blank into a shell of spherical form vary in different plants, the same as for other classes of work, because the designs not only depend upon local requirements but are influenced to some extent by individual opinions and experiences. In this chapter a number of designs will be included which have proved satisfactory for the classes of work described. These designs, with more or less modification, may also be utilized for other operations involving the same general principles in metal drawing.

Dies for Hemispherical Shells.—Hemispherical shells for making ball floats may be made in two operations by using the dies shown in Figs. 1 and 2. Fig. 1 shows the die for the first operation and also the shape of shell it produces. This half-drawn shell is given a spherical shape by means of the die shown in Fig. 2. These dies have proved very effective for this particular operation.

The shell is made from a 7 3/16-inch diameter blank of sheet copper, 0.007 inch thick, and its position in the die is shown in heavy lines. By referring to the dimensioned drawing of the shell (Fig. 1) it will be seen that it is drawn straight for about 1/2 inch, and then is formed to a radius of 2 1/4 inches. It will be seen that the finished shell, Fig. 2, has a radius of 2 1/2 inches, so that by first drawing the shell to the smaller radius, provision is made for stretching the metal to the finished size. In dies of this type it is necessary to provide full round corners in every part of the shell so that during the stretching operation, no drawing marks will be in evidence on the shell.

The combination die in Fig. 1 and the finishing die in Fig. 2 are of similar construction, and their method of operation is identical. The principal parts of the die shown in Fig. 1 are the forming plug *E* which is made of cast iron, the drawing ring

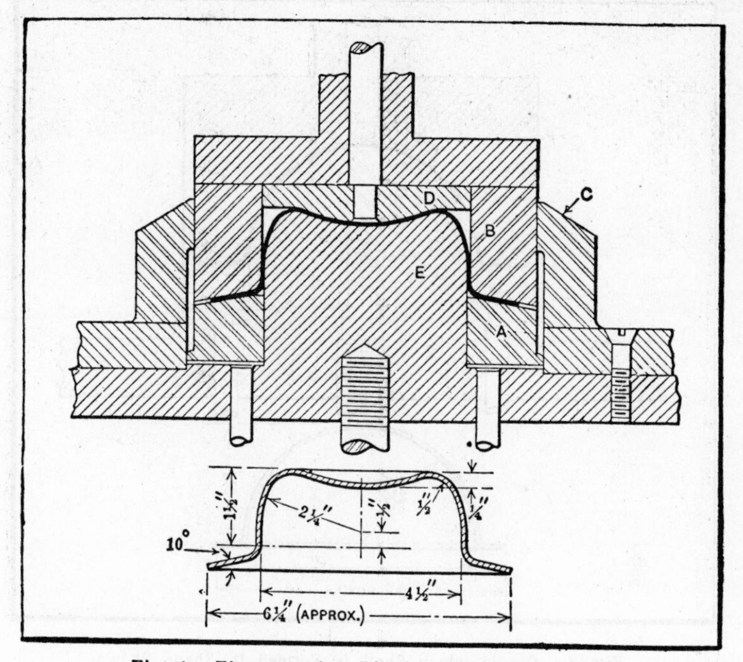

Fig. 1. First-operation Die for Hemispherical Shell

A, the die *B*, and the blanking die *C*. The last three parts are made of tool steel, and are hardened and ground. The drawing operation is accomplished by forcing ring *A* downward, drawing the blank over the plug *E* against the pressure exerted by a rubber buffer attachment of familiar construction. The drawing die *B* is welded to a wrought-iron holder, which is an economical construction. A machine steel former *D* is attached to the die for producing the concave part of the shell. It will be noted that the blanking die *C* is also a two-piece construction, the tool-steel and wrought-iron parts being welded together.

When die *A* (Fig. 2) which is made of tool steel with a wrought-iron upper portion, is in its raised position, the shell on which the first operation has been performed, is placed on the tool-steel die ring *B*, the concave part of the shell fitting over the convex part of the punch *C*. Since the shell is ½ inch smaller in diameter than the finished part, it is evident that

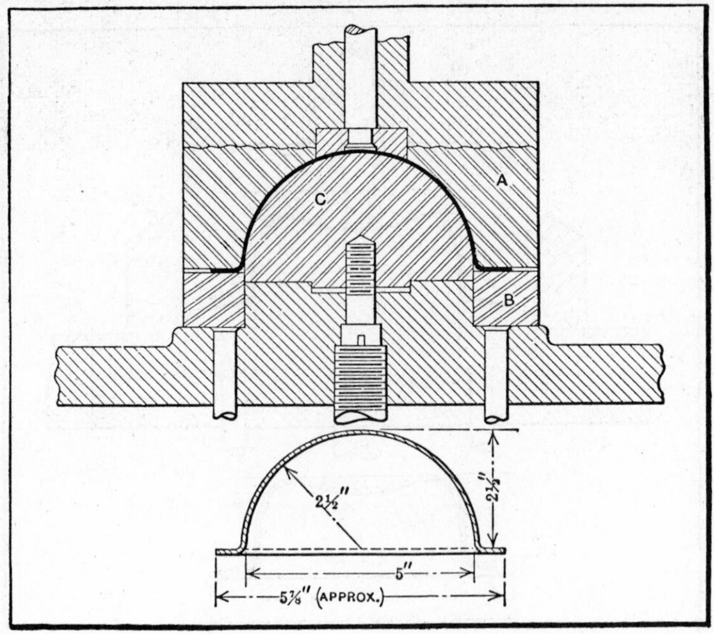

Fig. 2. Die in which Shell is Formed to Shape Shown

die *A* can pass over the shell in this position, so that the surfaces of the die and of the die ring can grip the flange under the pressure exerted by a rubber buffer attachment, and hold the shell securely. As the die continues to descend, forcing the die ring downward, the shell is simply stretched over the tool-steel punch on which it rests. Not only is the shell stretched, but its diameter is also expanded, and it is this combination that enables a smooth shell, free from wrinkles, to be produced. After this drawing and expanding operation has been completed, the edges of the shell are trimmed, and the two halves closed together, thereby completing the copper float.

There does not appear to be any hard and fast rule governing the difference in diameter between the first-operation shell and the finished product, although it has been found by experience gained in making several balls by this method, that from 3/8 to 1/2 inch is a fairly close approximation. This amount, of course, depends upon the size of the shell; if the diameter is less than 3 1/2 inches it is probable that the amount of expansion would be about 3/8 inch, whereas, for a 2-inch diameter shell it would not be advisable to allow more than 1/4 inch. The

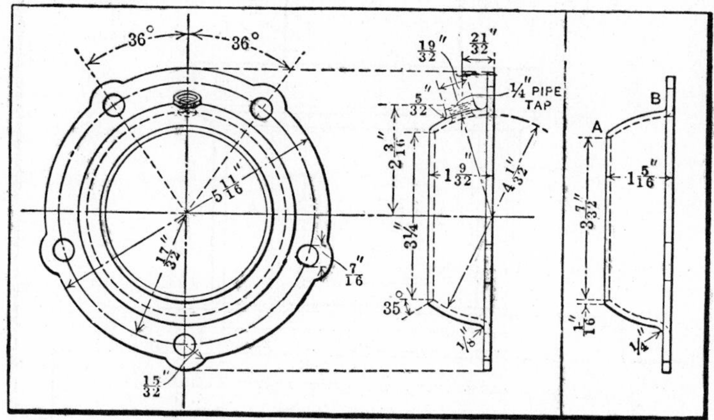

Fig. 3. Universal Ball Cover—View to Right Shows Result of First Operation

principal consideration, however, is to make sure that the die can pass down well over the shell and securely hold it by the flange before the expanding and stretching starts.

Press-work on a Universal Joint Cover.—The universal joint cover illustrated in Fig. 3 is one of two parts of a gasoline motor transmission. This part is made of 5/32-inch hot-rolled steel and is finished under the punch press in three operations. It must be of uniform strength at all points, and for this reason great care must be exercised in performing the press-work in order to avoid stretching the metal in a way that would lead to the rejection of the work when it reaches the inspection department.

Fig. 4 shows the punch and die used for performing the first operation. Referring to this illustration, it will be seen that *A* is the drawing punch which is made of machine steel and provided with a high-speed steel point *B* which can be readily replaced when necessary. The blanking punch is shown at *C* and this punch also acts as a blank-holder while the draw-

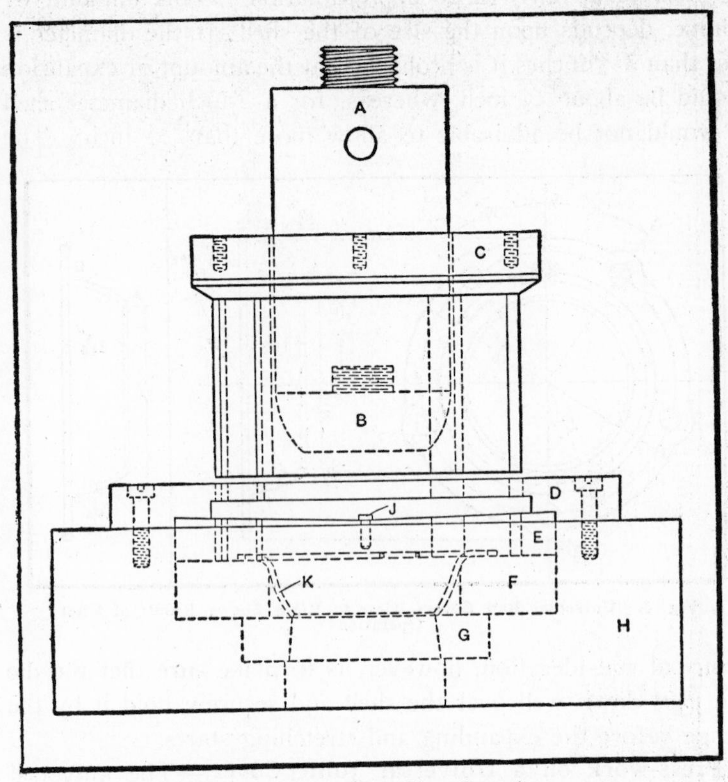

Fig. 4. Die used for First Operation

ing operation is in progress. The stripper provided to strip the steel from the blanking punch is shown at *D*. It will be evident that *E* is the blanking die and *F* the drawing die, while the piercing die employed to remove the bottom of the stamping is shown at *G*. These three dies are of the ring type; the drawing die is made of high-speed steel, while the blanking die *E* and piercing die *G* are made of carbon tool steel. The three ring dies described in the foregoing are held in the cast-iron die-holder *H*, as shown.

The height of the drawing die must be maintained constant in order to insure the proper depth of the stamping. The gage pin *J* is provided to space the blanks properly. The way in which the bottom of the stamping is pierced is somewhat unusual. For this purpose, the punch must be set, so that it does not touch the sharp edges of the piercing die *G*, and at the same time close enough so that it will force out the bottom of the stamping. To avoid damage to the die, care must be exercised in setting up the tools, and after they are set up with all bolts and nuts properly tightened, there is seldom any need to make further adjustment. Literally speaking, the punch and die does not cut out the bottom of the stamping *K*, but rather crushes it out part way and then the bottom breaks away. The edge is clean and even all around and it is inclined at an angle of about 20 degrees which makes it easier to finish the third operation, that is, finishing the edge to the required angle of 35 degrees.

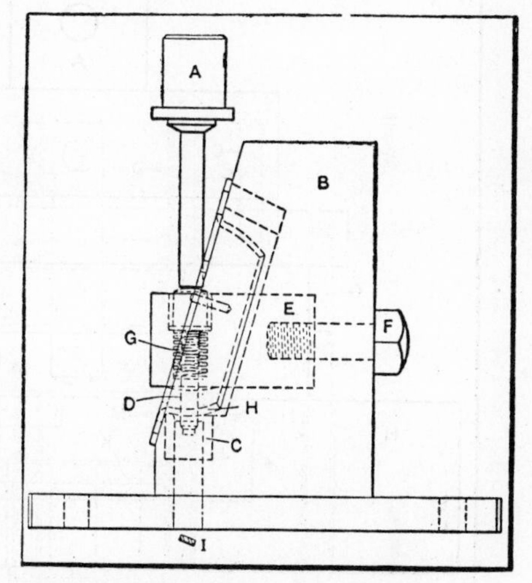

Fig. 5. Die for Piercing 5/16-inch Hole and Drawing up a Boss Around it

The second operation combines two ordinary operations, viz., piercing a 5/16-inch hole and drawing out the boss at the same time. The thickness of the steel makes it possible for the 5/16-inch punch to go through without drawing the work to any appreciable extent, and when the shoulder on this punch comes into contact with the work, it draws the steel down into the die to form the required boss. In Fig. 5, which shows the punch and die used for this operation, the punch is shown at *A* and the die or bushing holder at *B*. The die-holder *B* serves the additional purpose of a gage which locates the work in the desired position, and the piercing and drawing die *C* is mounted in the holder *B*. The piercing and drawing punch *D* is seated in and guided by the extension block *E*, which, it will be seen, is held in place in the holder *B* by means of the cap-screw *F*. The spring *G* is employed to draw the punch back when it has reached the end of its stroke. The stamping

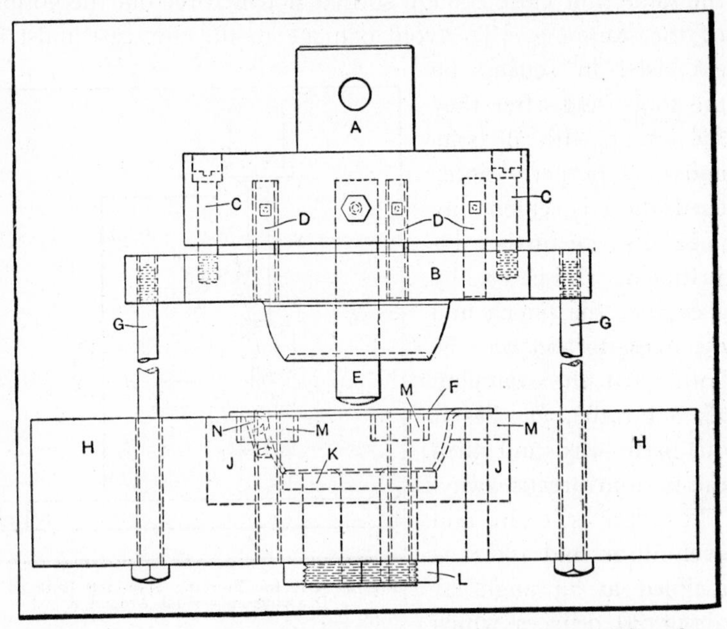

Fig. 6. Die for Piercing Holes in Flange, Beveling Bottom Edge of Shell and Truing up Work

is shown at *H*, and *I* illustrates the slug of metal which has been pierced from the wall of the stamping previous to drawing the boss.

The third operation provides for reducing the ¼-inch radius at the flange to ⅛ inch, and also flattening the flange to correct for any distortion which may take place in piercing the shell and drawing up the boss. The die for this operation also pierces five 7/16-inch holes in the flange and bevels off the bottom of the stamping—which was left rough from the piercing operation—to the required angle of 35 degrees. In Fig. 6, it will be seen that *A* is the punch which has the flattening stripper plate *B* attached to it by means of the screws *C*. The punches for piercing the five 7/16-inch holes in the flange are shown at *D*, and the punch is provided with a central guide pin *E* to preserve the required alignment. The stripper plate *B* has a motion of 1/4 inch to provide for stripping the finished stamping *F* from the piercing punches *D*, the stripper being actuated by the stripper rods *G* which are properly adjusted in relation to the die-holder *H*. This die-holder is made of cast iron and supports the die *J* which is provided with a central plug or punch *K* that forms the 35-degree beveled edge at the bottom of the stamping. The bevel punch *K* is held in place by means of the nut *L* which engages the bottom of the die-block. The piercing dies *M* are dovetailed into the die *J* and can be easily replaced when necessary. It will be seen that clearance for the boss on the stamping is provided in the die at *N*, and this space also acts as a locating point in placing the stampings in the die.

A set of templets should be made for the punches and dies when they are new, so that the proper form of the tools is not lost as the result of wear. The occasional use of the templets enables both the punches and dies to be reground when necessary to preserve the required shape. For instance, it is important for the radii of curvature on both the punch and die used for performing the first operation on this job, to be held quite close to the original dimensions in order to obtain uniform stampings. To allow these radii to change from their original lengths through wear would naturally result in changing the dimensions of the stampings as well as their extreme diameters.

Another Joint Cover of Spherical Form.—The universal joint cover or "boot" shown at *H*, Fig. 7, is deeper in proportion to its diameter than the one shown in Fig. 3, and dies of different design are used. Twelve operations performed on straight-sided single-action punch presses equipped with dies of a number of different designs, were employed in the quantity production of this part. Pressure was provided against the

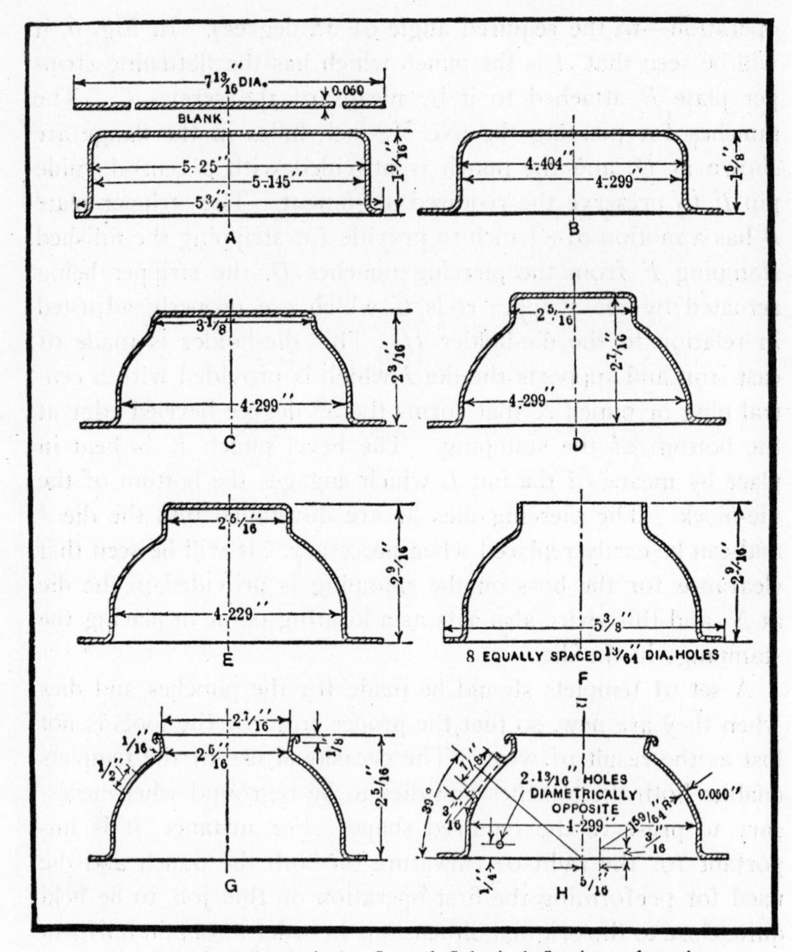

Fig. 7. Dimensions of the Cup of Spherical Section, after the Performance of Successive Operations

work during all the drawing operations by means of rubber buffers, and all the drawing dies were so designed with the proper radii and drawing depth that no annealing of the work was necessary in order to obtain a product of good quality. The material used in the manufacture of the joint boot was 0.050-inch thick one-pass blue annealed hot-rolled sheet steel, of a good drawing quality, sheared into strips 8 inches in width.

Combination Blanking and Drawing Die.—The first operation on the part consists of cutting the blank and drawing it to the dimensions shown at *A*, Fig. 7. This is accomplished by means of the combination blanking and drawing die illustrated in Fig. 8, in which the various movable members are shown in the positions occupied at the conclusion of the downward stroke of punch *A*. When the latter is in the raised position, the top of draw-ring *B* is in the same plane as the top of die ring *C*, due to the action of the rubber buffers on which the lower ends of pins *D* rest during the entire cycle.

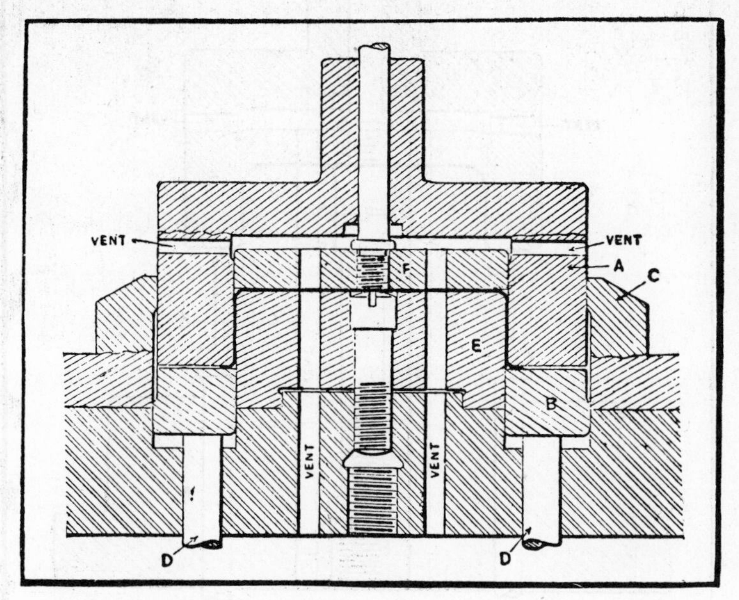

Fig. 8. Blanking and Drawing Die which Performs the First Operation

After a strip of steel has been placed over the die and the press has been tripped, the descending punch cuts out a circular blank $7\frac{13}{16}$ inches in diameter as it enters die ring *C*. The blank is held firmly between the faces of the punch and the draw-ring, and as the punch continues to descend and pushes the draw-ring with it, the work is drawn on plug *E* to the desired dimensions. When the punch ascends, the compressed buffers expand and cause the draw-ring to follow the punch, thus stripping the shell from plug *E*. The result is that the shell remains in the punch, but at the completion of the return stroke, the knock-out *F* is forced down so that the shell is pushed out of the punch, falling on top of the die.

The cutting edge of ring *C* is made of tool steel, hardened and ground, and is forged to a machine-steel base. The latter is mounted on a cast-iron shoe by means of four machine screws. Punch *A* has a machine-steel shank with a tool-steel

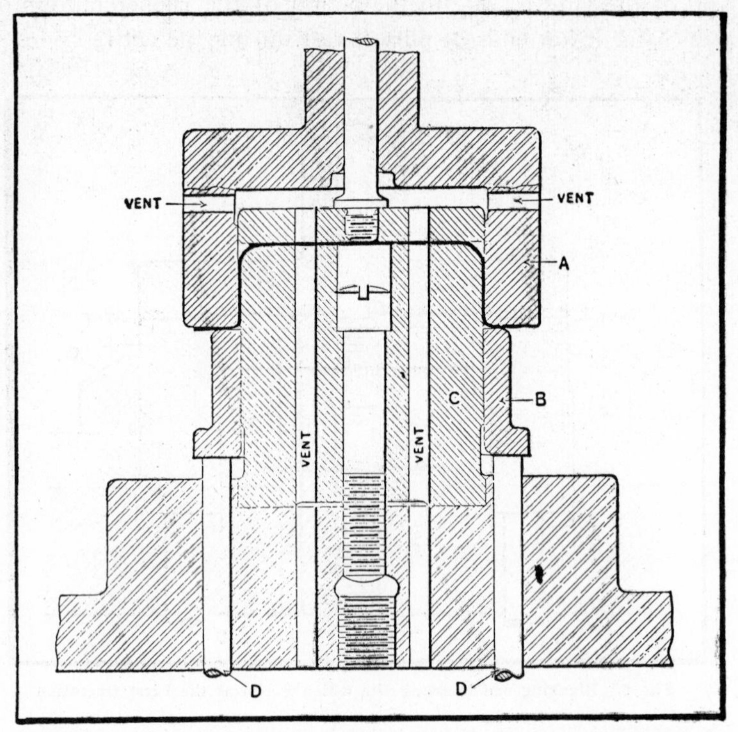

Fig. 9. Redrawing Die, which Increases the Depth and Decreases the Diameter of the Body

cutting face forged to it. This construction gives a strongly built die of economical design. Vent holes are provided in the die plug and the die shoe to permit the escape of air confined under the work as the punch descends, while vents in the punch and knock-out device permit the escape of air confined between the part and these members.

Dies for Redrawing Operations.—The appearance of the part after the second operation is illustrated at *B*, Fig. 7. This operation increased the depth, decreased the diameter of the body, and flattened the flange. The die used for this work is shown in Fig. 9. Prior to the descent of die *A*, the top of draw-ring *B* is raised to the same level as the top of plug *C* by an arrangement similar to that used on the preceding die. The work is then slipped over the draw-ring, and as the die

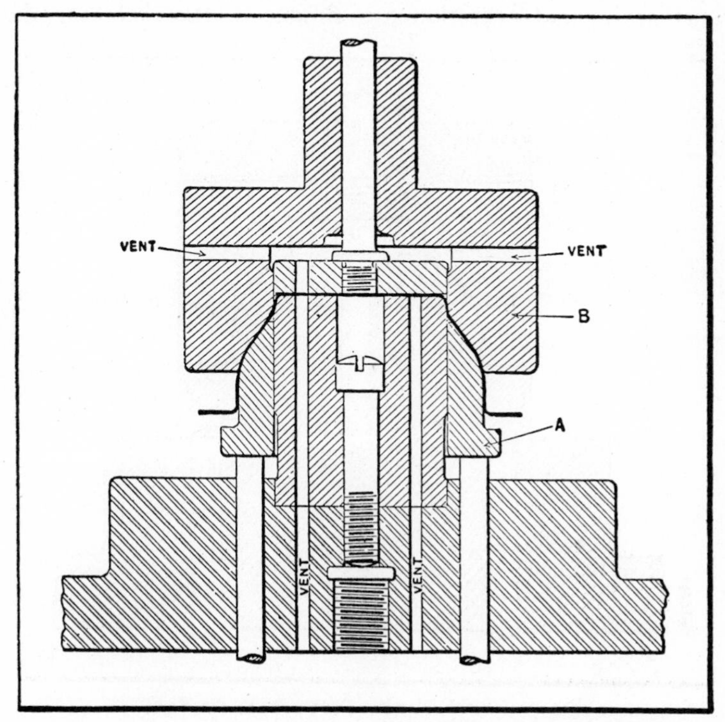

Fig. 10. Second Redrawing Die, which Decreases the Diameter of the Body at the Closed End

descends the metal is drawn from between the faces of the die and the draw-ring, on plug *C*. The outside diameter of the draw-ring is such that the part obtained from the preceding operation fits the draw-ring fairly close. The part is stripped from the plug at the completion of the operation by the rising draw-ring, and from the die by a knock-out device, the same as on the preceding die. This die is also provided with a tool-steel face, and the draw-ring and die plug are made of tool steel.

The third operation produces the shape shown at *C*, Fig. 7, the depth having been increased 9/16 inch, while the diameter of the body near the open end and the diameter of the flange remain the same as before. The die employed in this operation is shown in Fig. 10, from which it will be seen that the construction and operation are similar to the preceding die.

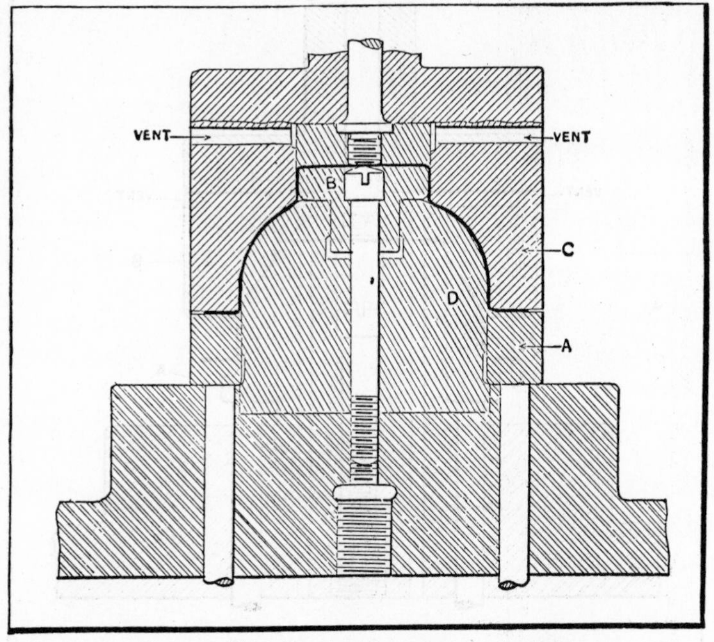

Fig. 11. Final Forming Operation on the Body

The work is placed on the raised draw-ring *A* and drawn to size as the descending die *B* pushes the draw-ring down. One difference between this die and the previous one, however, is that the die is made entirely of tool steel; this is a more economical construction because of the small size of the die, than a tool-steel ring forged to a wrought-iron or machine-steel shank.

The fourth operation consists of drawing the closed end of the shell still further, the depth being increased 1/4 inch and the diameter at the closed end, decreased 13/16 inch, as shown at *D*, Fig. 7. The dimensions of the open end, however, were not altered. This operation was performed by a die of the same general type as the one shown in Fig. 10.

The fifth operation completes the series of redrawing operations and brings the body of the shell to the shape shown at *E*, Fig. 7. The depth of the part is increased 1/8 inch by changing the rounded body slightly, the diameters of the closed and open ends remaining unchanged. This operation is performed by the die shown in Fig. 11, which functions similarly to those previously described; the draw-ring *A* is actuated by pins resting on rubber buffers, and the part is formed to the contour of plugs *B* and *D* by the descending die *C*. The latter has a wrought-iron shank with a tool-steel face forged to it. The base of the die is made of cast iron, and the tool-steel plugs *B* and *D* are secured to it by means of a long machine screw. The draw-ring is made of tool steel.

Die for Trimming the Flange.—In the sixth operation the flange is trimmed to the diameter shown at *F*, Fig. 7, the die illustrated in Fig. 12 being employed for the purpose. It will be seen that the part is placed in an inverted position in the die, with the body extending into the die opening, the part being supported by the flange. The latter is trimmed as the cutting edge of punch *A* enters the die opening. Two small knives *B* are attached on opposite sides of the punch for the purpose of severing the rings of scrap which accumulate around the punch. Each stroke of the press adds another trimmed off ring to the lower end of the punch, and at the same time cuts the previously trimmed ring next to knives *B*.

The shell is centered by means of gages placed in the die, and by the machine-steel plug *C* which enters the work before the punch comes in contact with the flange, thus locating the body centrally in relation to the punch and die centers. Plug C is pressed downward by a coil spring in the punch, which is compressed as the punch descends after the plug has entered the work. The die consists of a wrought-iron base, on which is forged a tool-steel ring that forms the cutting edge of the die. This cutting edge has four high points ground equidistant around the top, while the cutting edge of the punch is flat. This arrangement produces a gradual shearing action when the punch enters the die, and facilitates the trimming operation.

Piercing Die.—In the seventh operation eight holes are pierced around the flange of the shell, as shown at *F*, Fig. 7. The die used for this purpose is illustrated in Fig. 13, from which it will be seen that the work is again placed in an inverted position. The holes are punched through the flange as punches

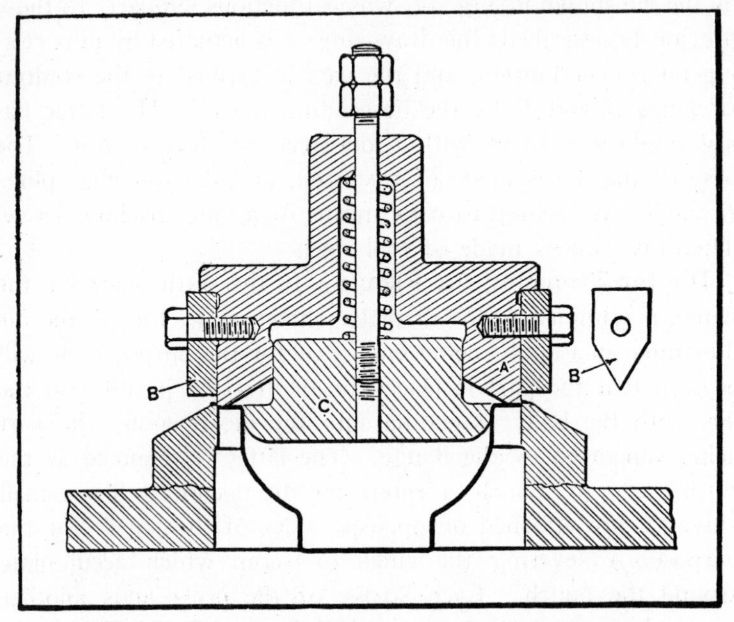

Fig. 12. Trimming the Flange to the Required Diameter

A descend on the work and enter corresponding holes in die ring *B*, the slugs falling through the die into a receptacle beneath. After the operation, there is a tendency for the work to adhere to the punches and so be carried out of the die on the upward stroke of the ram. To prevent such an occurrence, a machine-steel stripper plate *C* is provided. This stripper is held in place by means of a standard knock-out rod, and at the end of the upward stroke, the knock-out arrangement forces the stripper down and ejects the work from the punches.

The construction of this die is very simple, the punch-holder being made of cast iron, and the piercing punches attached to it by means of set-screws placed at an angle of 2 degrees with the horizontal. The punches are made of tool steel, hardened and ground. Die ring *B* is also made of tool steel, while the base is an iron casting.

Cutting and Wiring the Small End.—In the eighth operation, a hole 2 5/16 inches in diameter is cut through the closed end of the shell, as shown at *F*, Fig. 7, preparatory to wiring

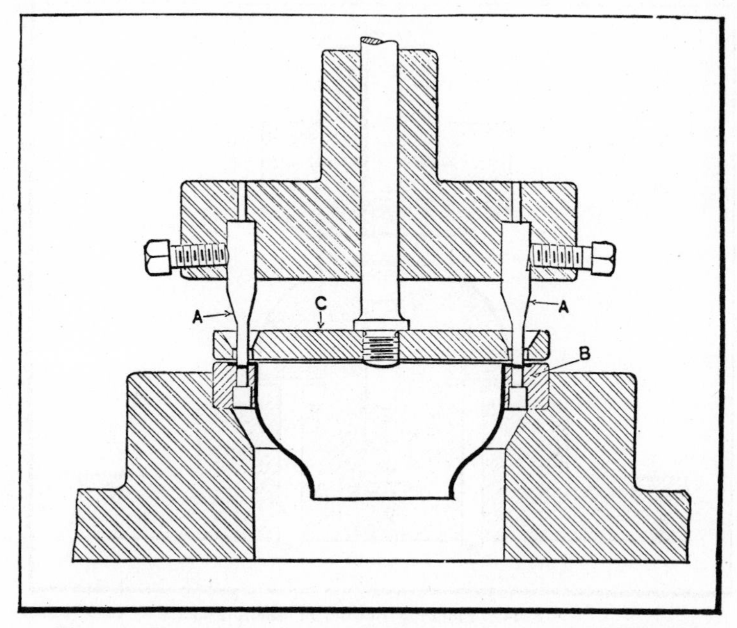

Fig. 13. Piercing Eight Holes Spaced Equally Around the Flange

it. Fig. 14 shows the die employed for this operation. Ring *A* is normally in a raised position, due to the action of the rubber buffers supporting the pins on which the ring die rests. The work is slipped over this ring, and as die *B* descends, it forces the work and ring downward. When the work has reached the top of the tool-steel plug *C*, the top is sheared off by the action of the die as it continues to push the work along the plug. Ring *A* follows the die on the return stroke, and strips the work from the plug, while the usual knock-out device is provided for ejecting the slug from the die opening. The die is made of tool steel, and ring *A* around plug *C* is made of machine steel.

Spreading and Wiring the Small End.—The die for the ninth operation does two things—it spreads or tapers the small end and rolls over or wires the edge, as shown at *G*, Fig. 7. The die used in this operation is illustrated in Fig. 15. The part is placed over the machine-steel plug *A*, and as the tool-steel punch *B* comes in contact with the work, the wall of the

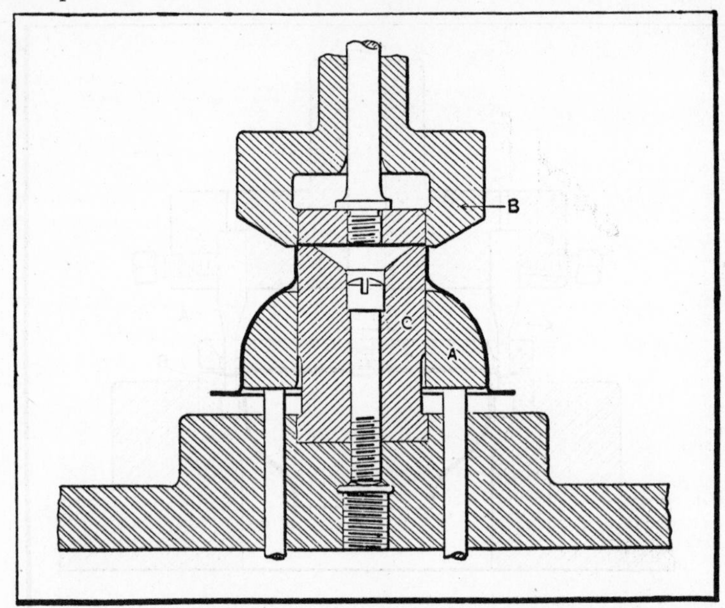

Fig. 14. Blanking Bottom of Small End

opening is spread or tapered to an included angle of 15 degrees. As the punch continues to descend, the edge of the shell is rolled over, this operation completing the small end of the work.

Piercing Hole.—In the tenth operation, a ½-inch hole is cut in the body of the shell, as shown at *G*, Fig. 7, by means of the die shown at the left in Fig. 16. It will be seen that the work is slipped over the machine-steel plug *A*, which is secured to the cast-iron base by means of a machine-steel ring and machine screws. The work is properly located for the opera-

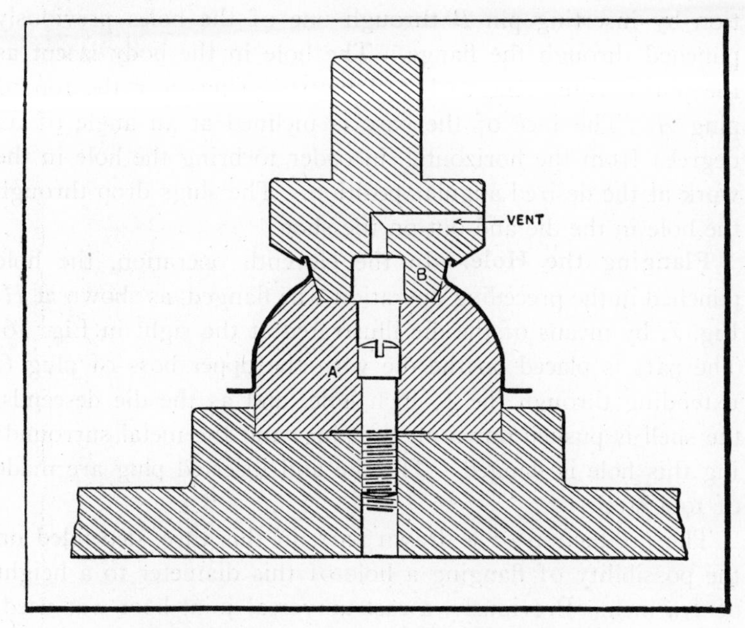

Fig. 15. Tapering and Wiring the Small End

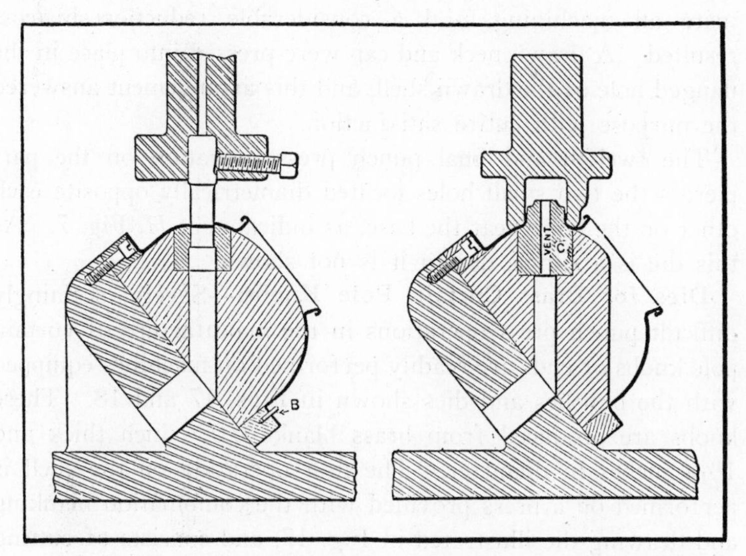

Fig. 16. Punching a Hole through the Body and Flanging the Hole

tion by inserting pin *B* through one of the holes previously punched through the flange. The hole in the body is cut as the punch enters the tool-steel inserted ring near the top of plug *A*. The face of the base is inclined at an angle of 39 degrees from the horizontal, in order to bring the hole in the work at the desired angular position. The slugs drop through the hole in the die and out on the shoe.

Flanging the Hole.—In the eleventh operation, the hole punched in the preceding operation was flanged, as shown at *H*, Fig. 7, by means of the die illustrated at the right in Fig. 16. The part is placed on the die with the upper boss of plug *C* extending through the ½-inch hole, and as the die descends, the shell is pushed down on the plug, and the metal surrounding this hole is flanged. The die and inserted plug are made of tool steel.

The production of a drawn part, in this case, depended on the possibility of flanging a hole of this diameter to a height of 3/16 inch. Previously, a cast universal joint boot was used, the opening in the body being cored, machined and tapped. By replacing the casting by a drawn part, it was possible to eliminate all machining, and a considerable reduction in cost resulted. A drawn neck and cap were pressed into place in the flanged hole of the drawn shell, and this arrangement answered the purpose with entire satisfaction.

The twelfth and final punch press operation on the part pierces the two small holes located diametrically opposite each other on the body near the base, as indicated at *H*, Fig. 7. As this die is a simple design it is not shown.

Dies for Brass Curtain Pole Knobs.—Several seemingly difficult punch press operations in the manufacture of curtain pole knobs or ends are readily performed on machines equipped with the punches and dies shown in Figs. 17 and 18. These knobs are produced from brass blanks 0.026 inch thick and 1 9/16 inches in diameter. The first operation on the shell is performed on a press provided with the combination blanking and drawing die illustrated in Fig. 17, and consists of cutting the blank to the proper size and then drawing it to the shape and dimensions shown in the upper right-hand part of the illustration. The drawing of the shell to this extent in only one operation is helped materially by having the top ball-shaped.

The illustration shows the relation of punch *A* to the die at the end of the downward stroke of the press ram. Prior to the descent of the punch, the blank-holder *B* is raised by means of three pins *C* until the upper surface of the blank-holder coincides with the cutting edge of the blanking die *D*. Pins *C* are actuated by a rubber buffer located beneath the die-block

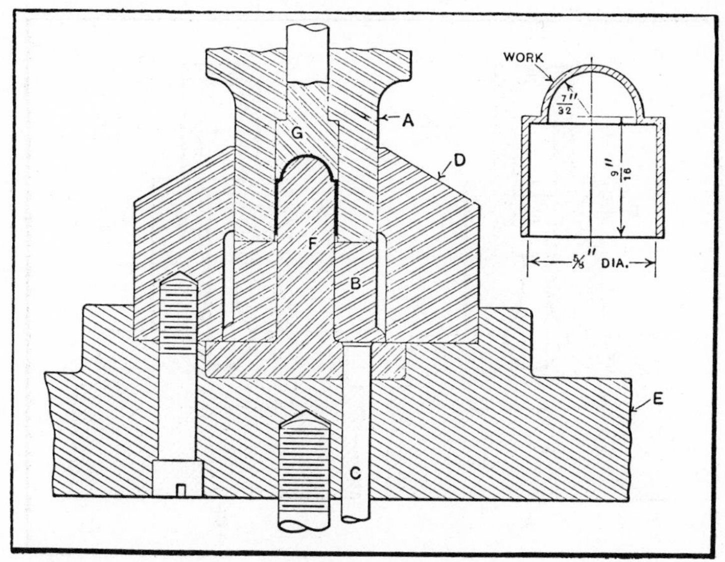

Fig. 17. Combination Blanking and Drawing Die which Produces in One Operation the Part Shown

E. Thus, when the punch descends after the brass stock has been laid across the top of the blanking die, the blank is cut as the punch enters the die, and is at the same time held firmly between the faces of the punch and the blank-holder. The latter condition prevents the formation of wrinkles when the blank is drawn upon the drawing plug *F*, which occurs as the punch and the blank-holder continue to descend. The shoulder on the upper end of the shell is produced near the end of the stroke by the knock-out *G* in punch A. The shell is ejected from the die by the blank-holder as the latter is raised by pins

C when the punch is withdrawn. In case the shell remains in the punch, it is removed by the knock-out *G* previously referred to.

The next two operations form the neck on the open end and complete the punch press work on the shell. These operations are performed on a machine having two plungers. The punch shown at *A* in Fig. 18 is attached to the end of one plunger, the punch shown at *B* in the same illustration being attached to the end of the other plunger. Only one die is provided on

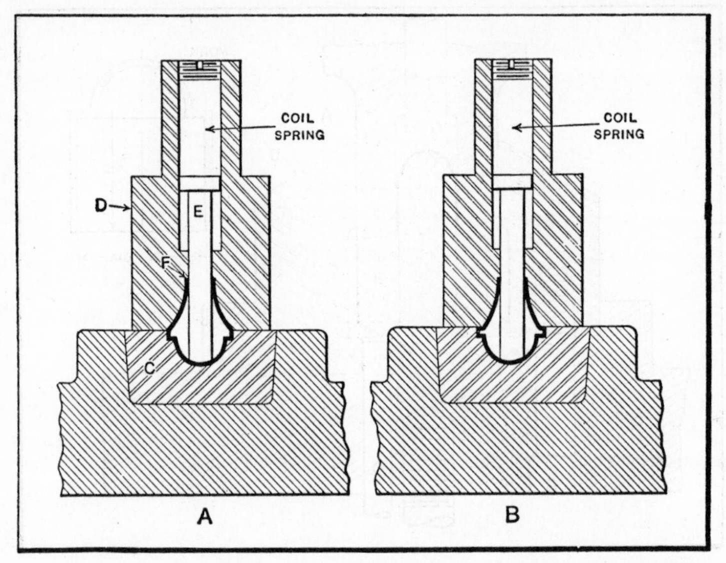

Fig. 18. Forming Neck on Open End of Shell on Double-plunger Press

the machine, although one is shown under each punch in the illustration, arrangements being made so that this die can be swung under the second punch after the neck of the shell has been partially formed by the first. As the edge of the open end of the shell is quite regular after the preceding operation no trimming is necessary on this end preparatory to these final forming operations.

The die is first placed in position beneath the punch shown at *A*, after which the shell is seated in the die part *C*, by means of the ball-shaped end and the shoulder on this end. Then when punch *D* descends, spring pin *E* enters the shell and exerts pressure on the ball-shaped end. As the punch continues to descend, the open end of the shell is closed to the contour of the opening in the punch until the edge of the metal reaches shoulder *F*, the spring pin *E* causing the hole to be made to the proper size. The shell is ejected from the punch on the return stroke by the spring pin, as this pin is momentarily kept from rising with the punch by the coil spring placed above it.

The next step is to swing the die and shell beneath the punch shown at *B*. In the operation performed by this punch, the diameter of the large portion of the neck is reduced a trifle, so that a shoulder is formed on this side. The operation of this punch is similar to that of the punch shown at *A*. In the design of punches and dies of the type just described, care must be taken to see that the shoulder in the punch which the edge of the shell touches at the end of the operation, is located properly, and that the pin which regulates the size of the hole is of the correct diameter.

Tank Sections having Spherical Bottoms.—The dies to be described are for drawing the two sections of the gasoline tank shown at *A*, Fig. 19. The sections are each 12 inches in diameter and about 13 inches long, the over-all length of the assembled tank being 24 inches. The sections are made from No. 18 gage sheet steel, and each one is provided with a bead near the open end. The two parts are assembled by simply telescoping the bead of one section over the bead of the other, and then welding the two sections together. In planning the dies for any part, the drawing die should be made before the blanking die, because it is next to impossible to determine the exact diameter that a blank should be, prior to forming and drawing the actual pieces. In the case of comparatively deep draws, such as these tank sections, the work will always be longer at some points than at others, necessitating a trimming operation before it is completed; hence, the blank is usually made slightly larger in diameter than is required theoretically.

Each tank section could be completed, with the exception of the beading, in two drawing operations performed in single-action presses. However, the operations would be more in the forming than in the drawing class, and the work would be more or less wrinkled. The first operation would consist of producing the part to the shape illustrated at *B*, and in the second operation, the part would be produced as shown at *C*. In redrawing to the shape shown at *C*, the diameter would be reduced about 6 inches and the length increased at the same time to the desired dimension.

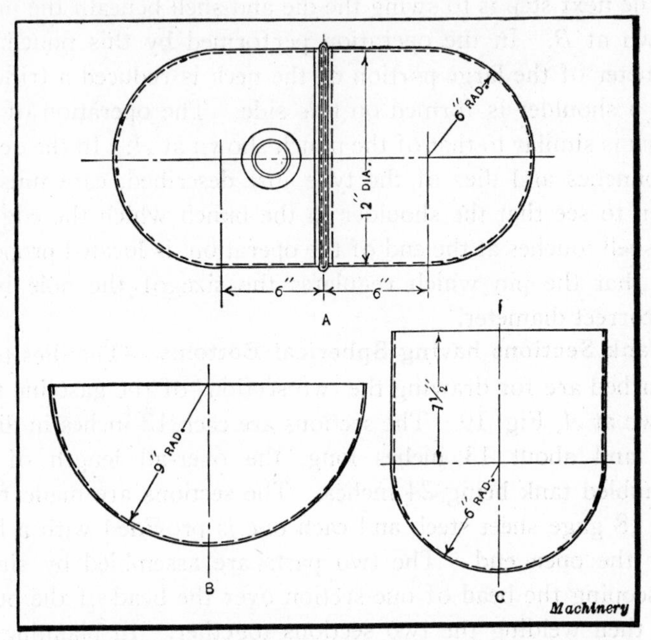

Fig. 19. (A) Gasoline Tank Composed of Two Sheet-steel Sections; (B and C) Steps in the Manufacture of the Tank Sections when Single-action Dies are Used

In drawing many parts, the thickness of the metal in the walls is decreased during one operation, but in such cases, the diameter of the part is not changed in subsequent operations. When the thickness is decreased, a die equipped with a blank-holder must be used. A single-action press may be equipped with a spring blank-holder for such an operation, but when a double-action press is used, the blank-holder is actuated by a ram separate from that which moves the punch.

Even if the tank sections were produced to the shape illustrated at *B* in a double-action die, and to the shape illustrated at *C* in a single-action die, there would be wrinkles along the edge of the part that might make it difficult to obtain a tight tank when welding the sections together. Therefore, in planning the dies for producing these sections, it was decided to use two double-action dies and a third single action die.

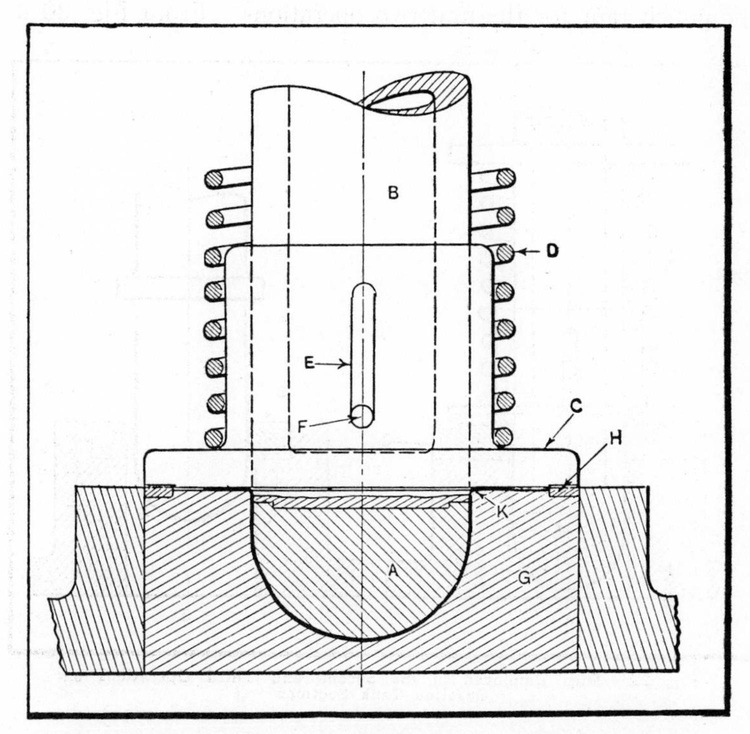

Fig. 20. Die Equipped with a Blank-holder, which is Used in the First Drawing Operation Performed on the Tank Sections Illustrated at *A* in Fig. 19

The first operation consists of drawing the part to the shape illustrated by the heavy line in Fig. 20, the difference between this shape and that shown at *B*, Fig. 19, being that a flange is left on the part so that it may be gripped by the blank-holder in the second operation. The second operation .brings the section to the shape illustrated at *C*, Fig. 19, and almost to the exact size; the third operation is performed simply to size the shell accurately. This method of drawing the piece leaves it smooth, free from wrinkles, and uniform in thickness throughout. The blank-holders of the first two dies grip the stock with a pressure that prevents any tendency of the stock to wrinkle.

As no double-action press was available for making the tank sections, it was necessary to provide a blank-holder on the punch ram for the first two operations. From Fig. 20 it

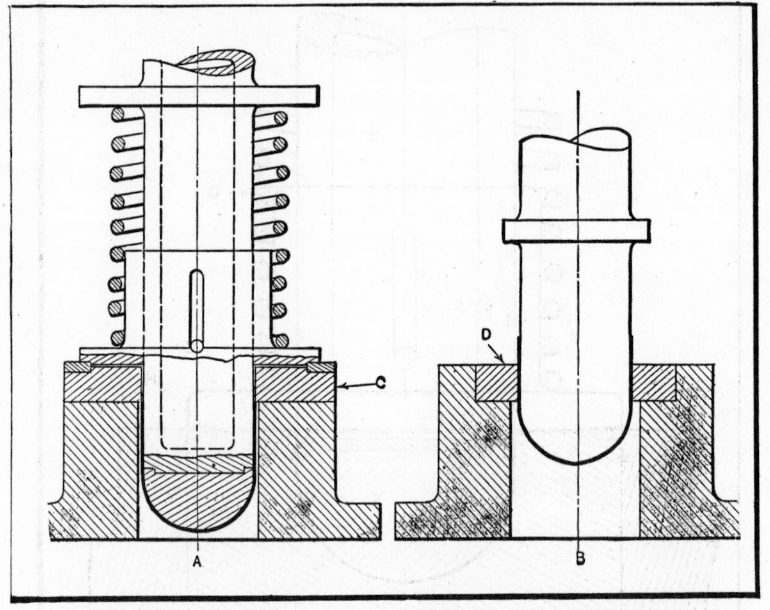

Fig. 21. Dies Employed in the Second and Third Operations on Gasoline Tank Sections

will be seen that the punch of the equipment used in the first operation has a spherical bottom *A*, formed to suit the shape desired in the end of the tank sections. However, the punch is slightly larger in diameter than the finished piece. Piece *A* is attached to a shank *B*, the upper end of which is fastened to the ram of the press. Surrounding the shank is a blank-holder *C*, and between the blank-holder and the upper collar on the punch, there is a heavy coil spring *D*.

When the press ram descends, the blank-holder first comes

in contact with the work, and exerts an increasing pressure on it until the punch travels a distance equal to slot *E*, relative to the blank-holder; during this movement the work is drawn to the shape outlined. The travel of the punch relative to the blank-holder is limited by pin *F*, attached to the shank, which slides in slot *E* of the blank-holder. Die *G* is equipped with a ring gage *H*, by means of which the blank is seated properly in the die. Edge *K* is rounded slightly, so that the stock will not be sheared as it drawn over this edge. The operation is stopped before the stock is entirely withdrawn from between the blank-holder and the die, in order that a flange may be left that can be gripped by the blank-holder in the second operation.

The die used in the second operation is shown at *A*. Fig. 21. The only difference between this design and that shown in Fig. 20 is in the construction of the die and die-block, the punch parts being the same. In this case, the work is pushed clear through the die, and stripped from the punch by the lower edge of die *C* on the return stroke of the ram.

The third and final operation is performed with the single-action die shown at *B*, which brings the tank sections to size within close limits. However, there is sufficient spring in the metal to expand the part enough after it passes through die *D* so that it will be stripped from the punch by the lower edge of the die upon the return stroke of the press ram.

Drawing Spherical Covers.—A punch and die for drawing spherical covers to the full depth in one operation without leaving a wrinkle, and finishing four at a time, are shown in Figs. 22, 23, and 24. The shape of the drawn part is indicated by the heavy line in Fig. 24. As is well known, it is difficult to draw a shell to this shape in one operation by the use of a standard double-action die, because the stock tends to wrinkle and tear, making it necessary to remove the wrinkles by another operation. To enable this work to be done in one operation a triple-acting die for use in a double-acting press was designed. Fig. 22 shows the relative positions of the punch, pressure ring, and blank-holder, just before the drawing op-

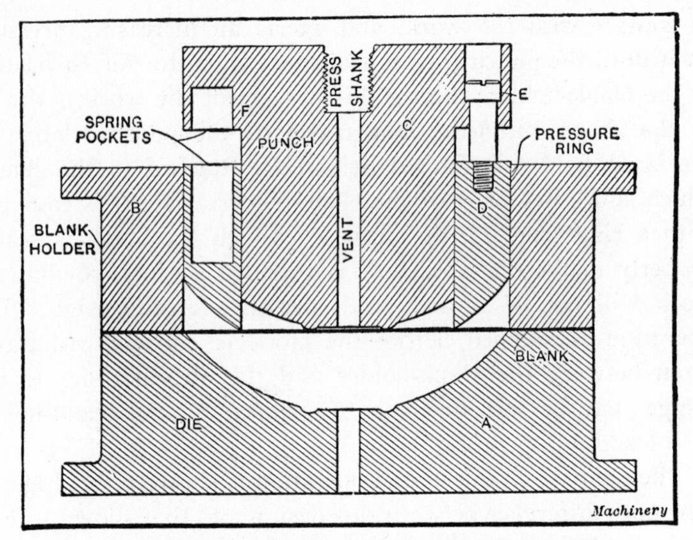

Fig. 22. Triple-action Die for Drawing Spherical-shaped Covers

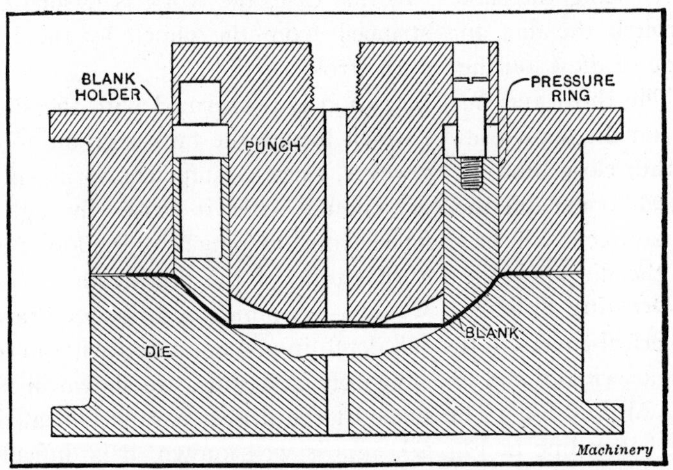

Fig. 23. View Showing First Stage of Spherical Cover Drawing Operation

eration begins. The action is as follows: After the four blanks have been placed in position on the top face of die *A*, blank-holder *B* descends until it holds the blanks firmly against the die face. The pressure ring *D* (which is backed up by heavy springs that are strong enough to form the first drawing operation) then descends to the position indicated in Fig. 23. This pressure ring then acts as an inner blank-holder while the punch descends to the bottom of the die, thus forming the central part of the blank, as indicated in Fig. 24. The action of this die was perfect and no defective shells were produced, the drawing being easy and uniform.

The die is made of cast iron and provided with a vent hole, as shown, through which the ejector operates. The drawing faces of both the die and blank-holder conform to the size of the blank. The blank-holder is of the regulation double-action type and is made of cast iron. Both the die and blank-

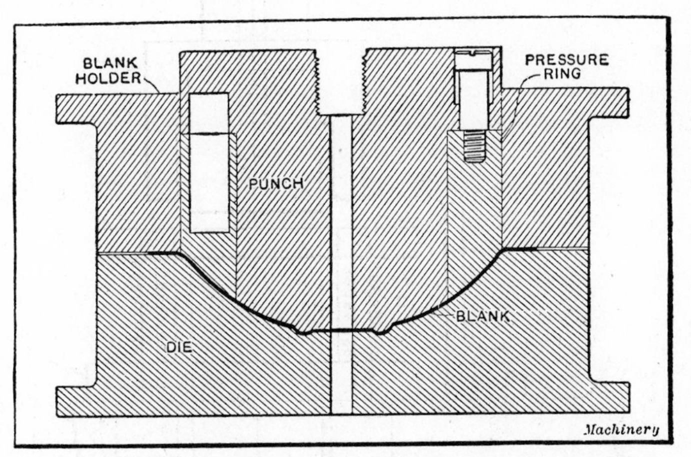

Fig. 24. Relative Positions of Punch, Die and Pressure Ring when Spherical Covers are Drawn

holder are secured to the press by means of a clamping flange. The pressure ring is held in position by several screws *E* between which are the pockets which contain the heavy spiral springs. These covers are of a large size, ranging from 15 to 22 inches in diameter.

Die for Blanking and Flanging Oval Holes.—The die shown in Fig. 25 was built to pierce an oval hole in the body of an aluminum tea-kettle and draw a flange around the edge of the hole. The spout is welded to the body over the flanged hole. The flange, which is about 1/8 inch high and fits inside the spout, serves to locate the spout on the body shell. The die *A* is of hardened tool steel and is secured to the "horn" *F* of the press by dowels and machine screws. The stripper plate *B* is a sliding fit over the die, and is held in place by four screws. The springs placed over these screws serve to push the plate *B* upward after the piercing and flanging operation,

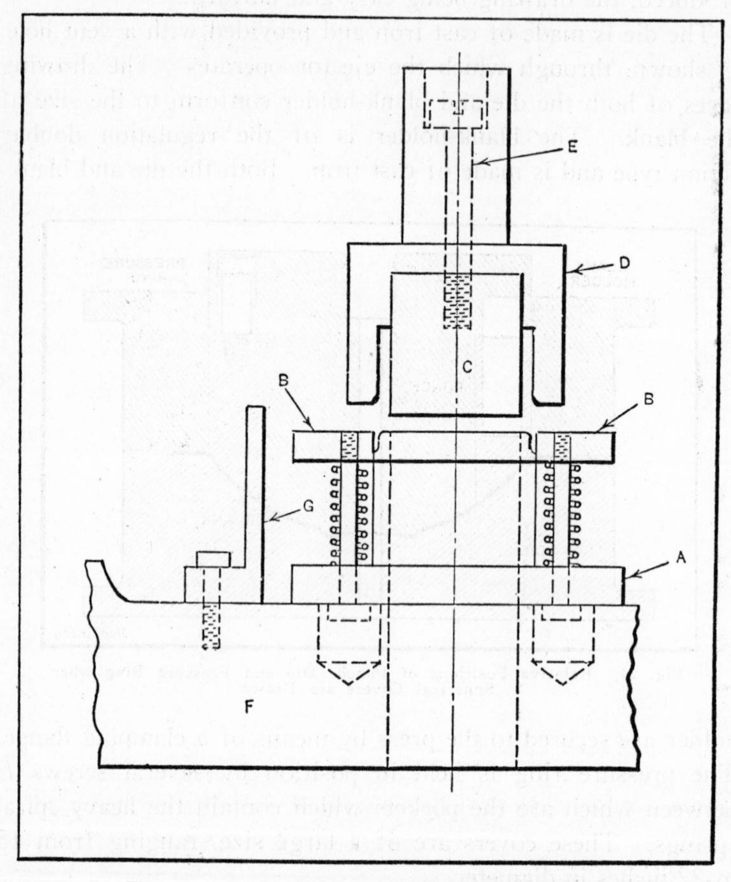

Fig. 25. Die for Piercing and Flanging Oval Hole

and thus strip the work from the die member. The piercing punch *C* is held in the forming punch *D* by the screw *E*. The scrap punched out by the central punch *C* passes through the die *A* and the horn *F*. Gage *G* serves to locate the shell on the die.

Friction Pad for Drawing Die.—The combination blanking and drawing die shown in Fig. 26 is used on a single-action press to produce small shells of the shape shown at *A*. Considerable trouble was experienced in drawing these shells until the friction pressure-pad *C* was incorporated in the die. Be-

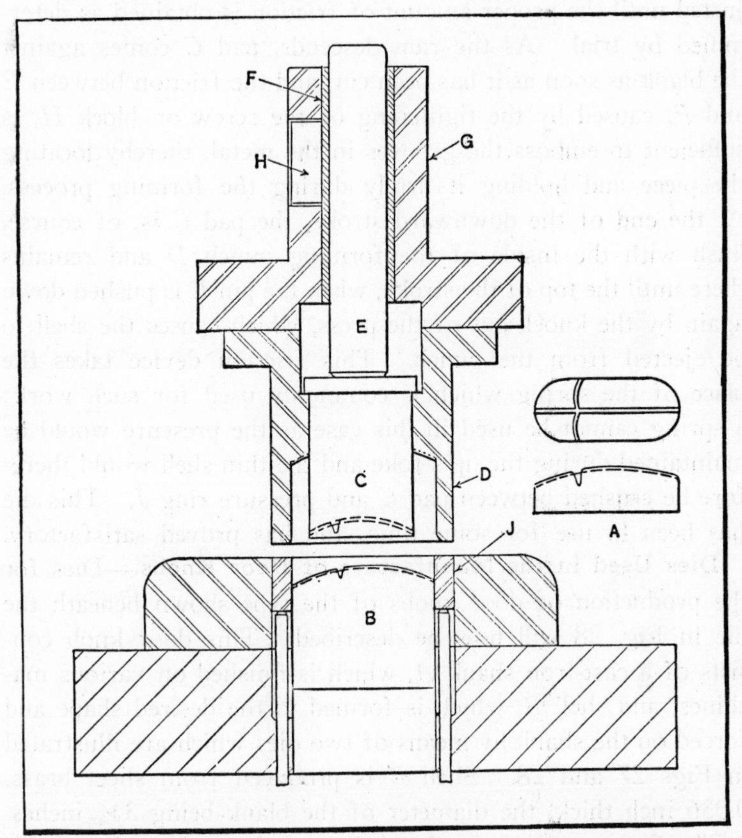

Fig. 26. Combination Blanking and Drawing Die for Producing Shells of Shape Shown at *A*

fore the pressure-pad was used, many pieces were spoiled from the slipping of the blank on the forming punch *B* during the drawing operation. The friction pad *C*, which entirely eliminated this trouble, is fitted in the combination blanking and forming punch *D* as shown. The hardened tool-steel pin *E*, in contact with pad *C*, is fitted in a hard fiber collar *F* which is held tightly in holder *G*. A tool-steel block *H* is set in a slot in punch-holder *G* so that it is located under a heavy set-screw in the ram of the press.

When the die is in operation, the set-screw in the press ram is screwed up fairly tight against block *H*. It should be adjusted until the proper amount of friction is obtained as determined by trial. As the ram descends, pad *C* comes against the blank as soon as it has been cut, and the friction between *E* and *F*, caused by the tightening of the screw on block *H*, is sufficient to emboss the grooves in the metal, thereby locating the piece and holding it firmly during the forming process. At the end of the downward stroke, the pad *C* is, of course, flush with the inside of the forming punch *D* and remains there until the top of the stroke, when the pin *E* is pushed down again by the knock-out of the press, which causes the shell to be ejected from the punch. This friction device takes the place of the spring which is commonly used for such work; a spring cannot be used in this case as the pressure would be maintained during the up stroke and the thin shell would therefore be crushed between pad *C* and pressure ring *J*. This die has been in use for some time, and has proved satisfactory.

Dies Used in the Manufacture of Door Knobs.—Dies for the production of door knobs of the type shown beneath the die in Fig. 28 will now be described. This door knob consists of a cast-iron shank *A*, which is finished on various machines, and shell *B*, which is formed to the desired shape and forced on the shank by means of two dies which are illustrated in Figs 27 and 28. Shell *B* is produced from sheet brass, 0.036 inch thick, the diameter of the blank being 3¾ inches.

The first operation on the shell is performed by the combination blanking and drawing die shown in Fig. 27; this illustration shows the positions of the various moving parts at the completion of the downward stroke of the punch press ram. Prior to the downward stroke, punch *A* is in a position above the die, and drawing ring *B* is also in a raised position, its upper surface being in the same plane as the upper surface of die ring *C*. This is accomplished by means of pins *D*, which are actuated by a rubber buffer of standard design. The brass strip from which the blank is cut is placed on the upper surface of the die ring C, and is blanked to the proper size by punch A as it passes the cutting edge of the die ring on the downward stroke. The shell is then drawn to the proper shape by the forming die E as the punch continues to descend, forcing

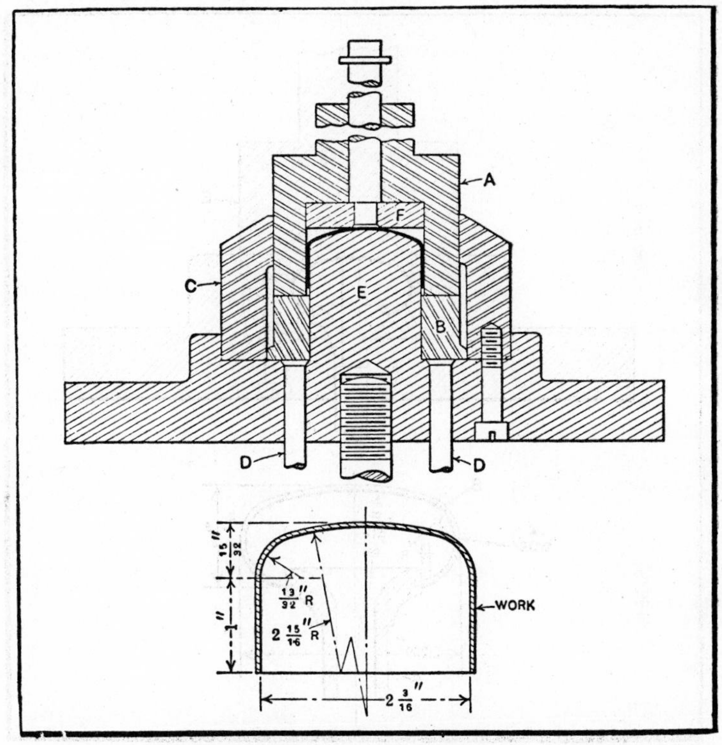

Fig. 27. Combination Blanking and Drawing Die used in First Operation on Door Knob Shell

drawing ring B downward at the same time. The pressure between the punch and the drawing ring is sufficient to prevent wrinkles from being formed on the shell in this operation. A knock-out device F is provided to force the shell from the punch when the punch is raised from the die. The removal of the shell from the die is easily effected by drawing ring B when it is raised to its normal position by pins D.

The second and final operation on the door knob is performed by the die illustrated in Fig. 28. At the beginning of this operation, rod *C* is in a raised position, and shank *A* and the shell produced in the first operation are placed on it. The position of rod *C* is such that when the shell is placed on it, the lower portion of the shell extends into the die ring *D*.

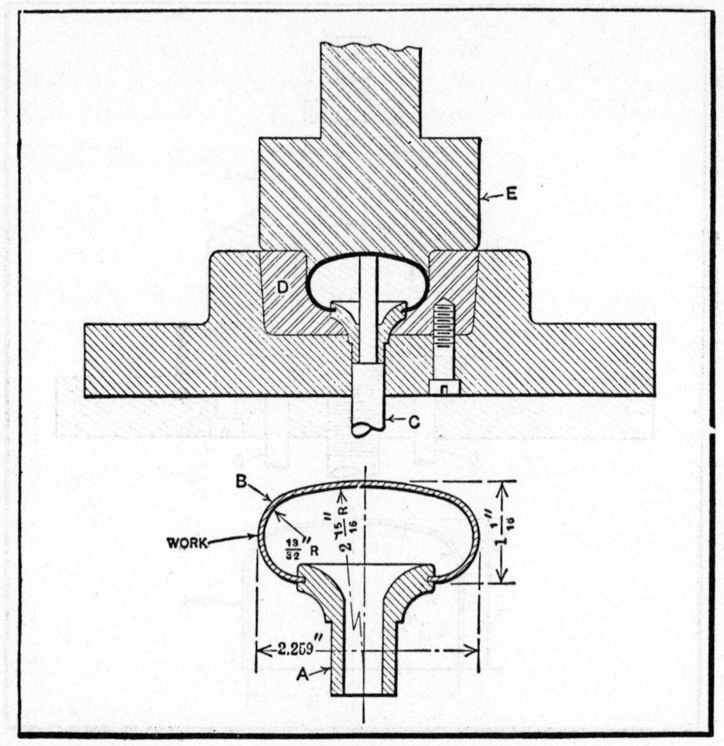

Fig. 28. Die in which Door Knob Shell is given Required Shape and is Assembled on the Shank

It is evident that as punch *E* descends on the downward stroke, the work and rod *C* are forced downward. This movement causes the lower portion of the shell to be rounded to the same shape as die ring *D*, and forces the edge of the shell into a corresponding groove on the periphery of the largest portion of the shank. When rod *C* is returned to its original position, the completed door knob is removed from the die.

CHAPTER XIX

DRAWING SQUARE AND RECTANGULAR SHAPES

WHEN making dies for drawing square or rectangular and square shapes, the first thing to consider is the form of the part to be drawn. This point is often overlooked by the designer, as all he may have in mind is to produce a box of a certain size. Therefore, he may specify a radius of 1/8 inch at the corner of the box when the radius could just as well be 1/2 inch, and perhaps the radius at the lower corner or edge could also be larger than is specified. This matter of corner and edge radius is important and may greatly affect the drawing operation. The kind of metal to be used should also be considered. It is often more profitable to make small parts of brass than of steel because there is less wear on the dies and fewer spoiled parts. When steel is necessary and the depth of the draw exceeds one-half the width of the box, a "deep drawing" steel should be used. A deep drawing steel which has proved satisfactory contains from 0.08 to 0.18 per cent carbon (preferably about 0.10 to 0.12 per cent); about 0.35 per cent manganese, with the percentage of phosphorus and sulphur less than 0.03 per cent.

It is advisable to be on the safe side when deciding what thickness of metal to use; that is, it is preferable to use a little extra metal and have ample strength at the lower edge of the box, where the greatest strain from drawing occurs, than to use a metal that is barely strong enough to withstand the drawing operation. This is especially true if the part must be drawn to considerable depth. When using brass and aluminum, the cost of the material is an important factor and it is common practice to begin with stock, say, 1/32 inch thick; this original thickness is retained in the first draw but is reduced in each succeeding draw so that, when the box is finished, the sides will be considerably thinner than the bottom. With this method, less metal may be used or, in other words, a smaller blank than if the box were made of uniform thickness. The reduction of thickness at each draw should not exceed 0.0025 inch on a side. Thinning the sides in this way is not considered practicable when using steel, owing to the comparative cheapness of steel and the increase in wear on the dies which would result from "ironing" or thinning the stock.

Dies for Rectangular Drawing.—Dies of the combination and double-action types are used for drawing rectangular and square shapes and, in some cases, special designs are employed, particularly if the part must be drawn to considerable depth and only a single-acting press is available. The principal difficulty connected with using a single-acting press is in the arrangement of the blank-holder or pressure-pad on the die. A common method is to attach the drawing die to the ram of the press and support the punch below; the pressure-pad extends around the punch and rests upon pins which pass through the press bed and bear against a plate which is backed up by a rubber buffer or spring pressure attachment that can be adjusted to give the pressure required. This arrangement is satisfactory for many classes of work, but when drawing comparatively deep parts it is objectionable if the blank-holder pressure increases as the die descends, for if this pressure is sufficient for the beginning of the drawing operation, it will be excessive at the end of the downward stroke. This defect is sometimes remedied by using extra long springs or buffers or a special compensating attachment.

For deep drawing, when a single-acting press is to be used, a die equipped with a pressure-pad of the type shown in Fig. 1 is preferred by some diemakers. The die and die-shoe rest upon the bolster of the press and into the latter are screwed two shoulder studs *S* having coarse threads onto which are fitted the handled nuts *N*. These nuts serve to hold down the pressure pad which is pivoted on one of the studs and slotted to receive the other so that it can be swung out of the way. (See plan view.) The underside of the pad is faced with a hardened tool-steel plate about ¼ inch thick. When using the die, the pressure-pad is swung out, the blank placed in position and then the pad is swung back and tightened by nuts *N*. After a few parts have been drawn, the operator will be able to determine how much these nuts should be tightened to prevent wrinkling. The heavier and more rigid the studs and pad are the less tightening is necessary, because the object is simply to confine the metal before it goes into the die so that wrinkling will be impossible. This form of die has proved

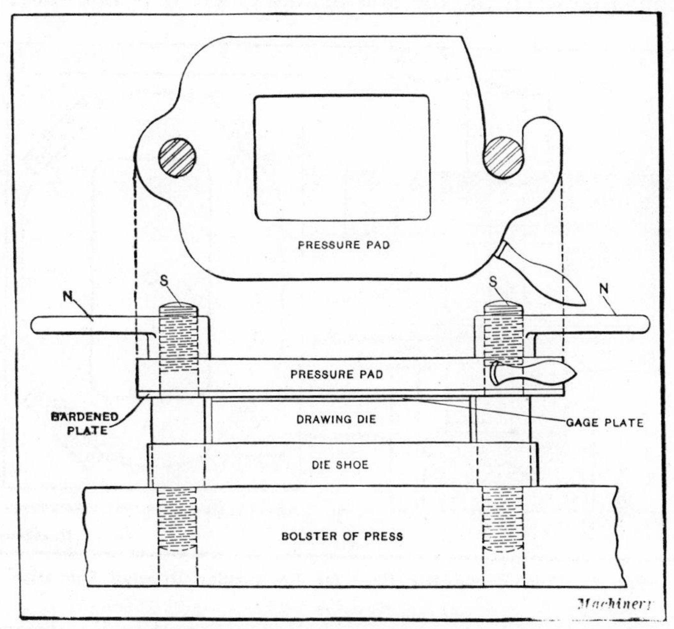

Fig. 1. Rectangular Drawing Die Equipped with Hand-operated Blank-holder for Use in Single-action Press

satisfactory and it is similar in effect to the action of the double-acting press.

Combination Die for Deep Rectangular Drawing.—In order to avoid the use of a compensating attachment, a combination die has been used, that is especially adapted for comparatively deep drawing operations and is simple in construction. A rectangular case which is drawn in one operation, is an example of the work done in this die. The stock is aluminum, 0.050 inch thick, and the case is 4¼ inches wide, 8⁹⁄₁₆ inches long and is drawn to a depth of 2¹³⁄₁₆ inches. In order to draw to this depth in one operation in a combination die and avoid the excessive increase in blank-holder pressure, four steel pressure strips *A* were attached to the blank-holder near the corners of the blank, as indicated in Fig. 2, which shows a detailed view of the die. These strips are the same thickness as the stock and they are engaged by the die during the drawing operation. The result is that while the blank is confined between the die and blank-holder, it is not subjected

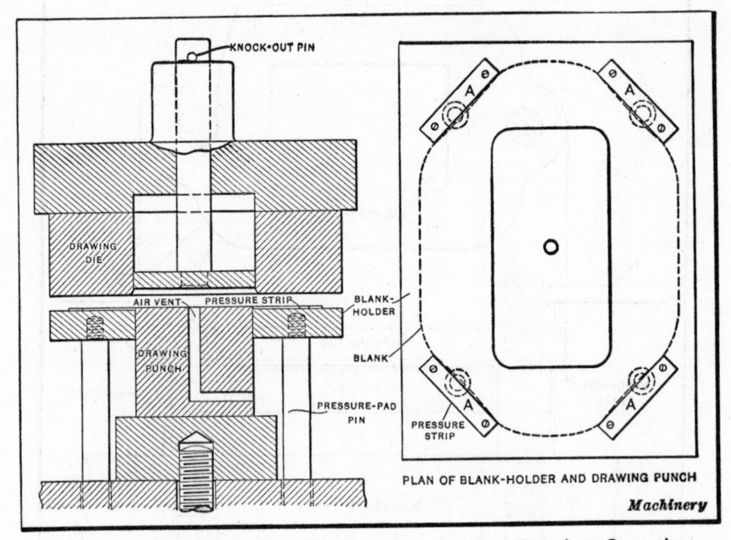

Fig. 2. Combination Die Used for Rectangular Drawing Operation

to an appreciable increase in pressure as the die descends, because the steel strips hold the die in a fixed position relative to the blank-holder. By this simple method, the increase in pressure resulting from the compression of the drawing rubber is not transmitted to the blank; the latter is merely confined between the flat surfaces of the die and blank-holder which are positively held a fixed distance apart. As the plan view to the right shows, the four pressure strips are so located on the blank-holder as to form a "nest" for the blank.

The use of these pressure strips or distance pieces between

the die and blank-holder not only simplifies the construction of the die but, in this particular instance, enables the required depth of 2 13/16 inches to be drawn in one operation. At first, experiments were made with pressure strips 0.012 inch thicker than the aluminum stock. While the results were fairly satisfactory, there was slight wrinkling. When strips of the same thickness as the stock were used, however, the aluminum cases were drawn without difficulty, and are a fine example of rectangular drawing. The radius of the corners of the case is 13/16 inch, whereas the radius at the bottom, on the inside, is 3/32 inch, which, of course, corresponds to the radius of the

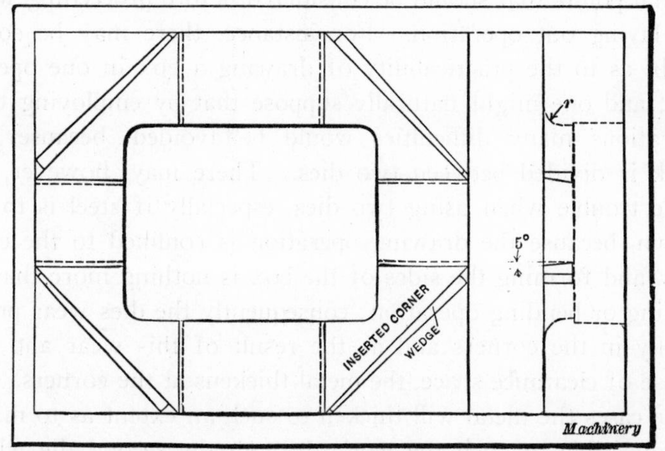

Fig. 3. Rectangular Drawing Die Provided with Inserted Corner Pieces

drawing punch. The drawing edge of the die has a radius of 1/4 inch, or five times the stock thickness. Located within the drawing die, there is a knockout which is operated by a crossbar in the usual manner, at the upper end of the stroke. The drawing punch is provided with an air vent hole in the center to prevent the formation of a partial vacuum under the case when the latter is being stripped from the punch. The blanks are cut out in a separate blanking die.

A die equipped with inserted corner pieces is shown in Fig. 3. This form is sometimes used when a large number of steel parts have to be drawn. This construction allows the corners to be replaced when worn and they can be made much harder than if they were a part of a solid die. This design also permits the use of expensive steel, such as high-speed steel, for these corner pieces. This form of die is not recommended for small work. The particular die illustrated was designed for drawing steel parts 6 by 8 inches in size and it has outworn several sets of corner pieces.

Laying Out Rectangular Dies.—After having carefully considered the design of the part to be drawn and the material from which it is to be made, the next step is that of laying out the die or dies, as the case may be. There are several fundamental points that should be considered before proceeding with the laying out operation. For instance, there may be some doubt as to the practicability of drawing a box in one operation, and one might naturally suppose that by employing two operations many difficulties would be avoided, because the work is divided between two dies. There may, however, be more trouble when using two dies, especially if steel is to be drawn, because the drawing operation is confined to the corners, and forming the sides of the box is nothing more than a folding or bending operation; consequently the dies wear principally in the corners and as the result of this wear and increase of clearance space, the metal thickens at the corners. In some cases the metal will thicken to such an extent as to make it impossible to push the work through the second die when two are employed, without rupturing the box at the corners. Moreover, when there are two operations, annealing may be required between the draws, and if this is done in an open fire oxidation takes place which would require a pickling operation to free the part from scale. Even though a closed furnace is used, the parts should be washed to free them from grit as otherwise the die would be lapped out very quickly. If there is any doubt as to whether a part should be drawn in one die or two, it is advisable to first make the finishing die and attempt to produce the part in one operation. If this trial draw shows that one die is not practicable, then the first-operation die can be made.

Corner Clearance.—The amount of clearance at the corners is another important point. By allowing a little more than the thickness of the metal between the punch and die at the corners, the pressure required for drawing is considerably reduced. For instance, if stock 0.0625 inch thick were being used, a space of about 0.067 inch should be left at the corners; this clearance is advisable for a one-operation die and also for the final die of a series. The top surface of a first-operation die should be perfectly flat and smooth. If this surface is ground the grinding marks should be polished out as otherwise the pressure of the blank-holder will tend to hold certain parts of the blank more than others, causing an uneven draw. The corners of a rectangular shaped punch and die should be very hard, because most of the wear is in the corners. Care should be taken that the metal does not thicken up perceptibly during any one draw if others are to follow, but it is advisable to allow the corners to thicken slightly if there is only one operation or during the final operation of a series.

Radius of Drawing Edge.—The radius of the drawing edge should be uniform and the surface smooth. The edge radius of the first drawing die (assuming that more than one operation is required) is the most important. Theoretically, this radius should be as large as possible but it is restricted for the reason that the larger the drawing radius the sooner the blank is released from under the blank-holder or pressure-pad, and if this release occurs too soon, the metal will wrinkle; if wrinkling occurs, a fractured corner is liable to be the result. It is also important to make the corner radius as large as possible. When the corner radius does not exceed 3/4 inch, the radius of the drawing edge of the first die should be about the same as the corner radius, whereas for a corner radius exceeding 3/4 inch, a drawing edge radius of 3/4 inch should be retained.

Determining Number of Drawing Operations.—When laying out rectangular dies, naturally one of the first things to consider is the number of operations required to complete the box or whatever part is to be drawn. The number of operations is governed by several factors such, for instance, as the quality of material, its thickness, the corner radius and also the radius at the bottom edge of the drawn part. In some cases, this lower edge can be rounded considerably, whereas in others it must be nearly square; obviously, when the corner is sharp a fracture at this point is more liable to occur owing to the pull of the drawing punch. Because of these variable conditions no definite rule can be given for determining the number of operations, although the following information will serve as a general guide.

When drawing brass, it is safe to assume that the part can be drawn to a depth equal to six times the corner radius. Suppose a box is to be drawn that is 5 inches wide, 6 inches long and 3 inches deep, and that the corner radius is ½ inch, and the lower edge rounded to about ¼ inch radius. By applying the foregoing rule we find that this can be done in one operation; thus, the depth equals six times the corner radius, or $6 \times \frac{1}{2} = 3$ inches. If the corners were of ¼-inch radius, then two operations would be required. The larger the radius the greater the depth which can be obtained in the first draw. However, when the corner radius exceeds about ½ inch, the maximum depth should be somewhat less than six times the corner radius. A general idea of the maximum depths for corners of given radii may be obtained from the following figures taken from actual practice: With a radius of 3/32 to 3/16 inch, depth of draw, 1 inch; radius 3/16 to ⅜ inch, depth, 1½ inch; radius ⅜ to ¼ inch, depth, 2 inches; radius ½ to ¾ inch, depth, 3 inches.

Corner Radius.—When two dies are required the first die should have a corner radius equal to about five times the corner radius of the finished part. The relation between the corners of the first and second dies is indicated by the diagram *A*, Fig. 4. As will be seen they are not laid off from the same center but so that there will be enough surface *x* between the two corners to provide a drawing edge. The reason for selecting such a large corner radius for the first die is that when these large corners are reduced to the smaller radius in the second die, a large part of this compressed metal is forced out into the sides of the box. Now if the first die were laid out as indicated at *B* or from the same center as the second die, there would be a comparatively large reduction at the corner and, consequently, the metal would be more compressed and the drawing operation made much more difficult, because, as previously mentioned, the drawing action is confined to the corners when drawing rectangular work. Sometimes dies are made as indicated at *B* but the reduction necessary in the second operation is liable to result in fracturing the metal. The radius of the first die should be laid out from a center that

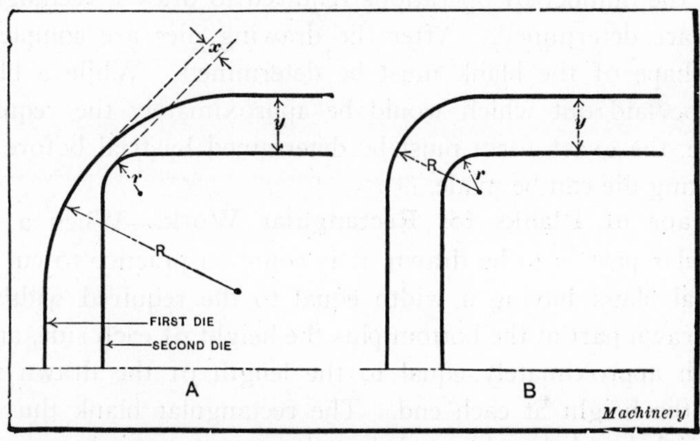

Fig. 4. Diagrams Showing Relation Between the Corners of First- and Second-operation Dies for Square or Rectangular Work

will leave a surface *x* (see sketch *A*) about 1/8 inch wide, although this width should be varied somewhat, depending upon the size of the die.

Amount of Reduction in Re-drawing.—The amount *y* that a rectangular part can be reduced between draws depends upon the corner radius and diminishes as the corner radius becomes smaller. For instance, a box with corners of 1/8-inch radius could not be reduced as much as one with corners of 3/8-inch radius. To obtain the total amount of reduction or 2 *y*, multiply the corner radius required for the drawn box by 3; then add the product to the width and length, thus obtaining the width and length of the preceding die. This rule should only be applied when the corner radius is less than ½ inch. For all radii above ½ inch, simply multiply the constant 0.5 by 3 in order to obtain the total reduction. Suppose a box is to be drawn that is 5 inches wide, 6 inches long, ⅛-inch corner radius, and we desire to establish the size of the first-operation die. By applying the rule just given, we have $\frac{1}{8} \times 3 + 5 = 5\frac{3}{8}$ inches, and $\frac{1}{8} \times 3 + 6 = 6\frac{3}{8}$ inches. Therefore, the die should be made 5⅜ inches by 6⅜ inches. As previously mentioned, the corner radius for the first-operation die should be about four times the corner radius of the finished part; hence the radius in this case would equal $\frac{1}{8} \times 4 = \frac{1}{2}$ inch. In this way, the number of operations required to draw a rectangular part are determined. After the drawing dies are completed, the shape of the blank must be determined. While a blank can be laid out which would be approximately the required shape, the exact form must be determined by trial before the blanking die can be made.

Shape of Blanks for Rectangular Work.—When a rectangular part is to be drawn, it is common practice to cut out a trial blank having a width equal to the required width of the drawn part at the bottom plus the height of each side, and a length approximately equal to the length of the drawn part plus the height at each end. The rectangular blank thus obtained is beveled and rounded at the corners until by repeated trial "draws" the correct shape is obtained. The simple method to be described will make it possible to secure the required blank shape in a more direct and accurate way. It is not claimed that the dimensions obtained will be absolutely correct or close enough for the final dimensions of the blanking punch. This method will, however, enable the diemaker to determine quickly the approximate shape for the blank, and the results will be sufficiently accurate to eliminate many trial drawing operations, thus saving considerable time.

When laying out a blank by this method, first draw a plan view of the finished shell or lines representing the shape of the work at the bottom, the corners being given the required radius, as shown by the diagram *A*, Fig. 5. Next draw the sides and ends, making the length L and the width W equal to the length and width of the drawn part minus twice the radius r at the corners. We now have a blank which would produce a rectangular piece without corners. To provide just the right amount of material for the corners is the chief problem, which may readily be solved. The first step is to find what blank diameter would be required to draw a cylindrical shell having a radius r. This diameter can be obtained by the well-known formula $D = \sqrt{d^2 + 4\,dh}$, in which D = blank diameter; d = diameter of drawn shell; and h = height of shell. This formula may be expressed as a rule as follows: Multiply the diameter of the finished shell by the height; then multiply the product by 4, and add the result to the square of the finished shell diameter. The square root of the sum thus obtained equals the blank diameter. After determining the diameter D, scribe arcs at each corner having a radius R equal to one-half of diameter D. The outline of the blank for the rectangular part is then obtained by drawing curved lines between the ends and the sides, as indicated by the illustration. These curves should touch the arcs R. The exact shape of the curve depends somewhat upon the proportions of the drawn part but it can readily be determined by drawing a few trial blanks and making whatever changes may be necessary to secure a more even edge along the top of the drawn part.

It will be noted that the width x at the corner is considerably less than the width or height h at the side and, at first thought, one not experienced in rectangular drawing might naturally suppose that there would be insufficient metal at the corner. It must be remembered, however, that the stock in passing through the die tends to fold and wrinkle at the corners; but as there is insufficient space between the punch and die to prevent wrinkling, the metal is packed up or upset and is forced upward, thus increasing the height of the corner so that the upper edge is about the same height as the sides and end. If the drawn part is quite narrow in proportion to the length, the dimensions h_1 at the ends of the blank should be slightly less than the height required for the work, because the metal tends to stretch more at the ends, thus increasing the height.

After laying out the trial blank, as described in the foregoing, and trimming or cutting the edge to conform with the outline obtained, the shape of the blank should be transferred to another piece of the same stock. The trial blank is then drawn and the outline showing its shape prior to the drawing operation serves as a record and enables the diemaker to see

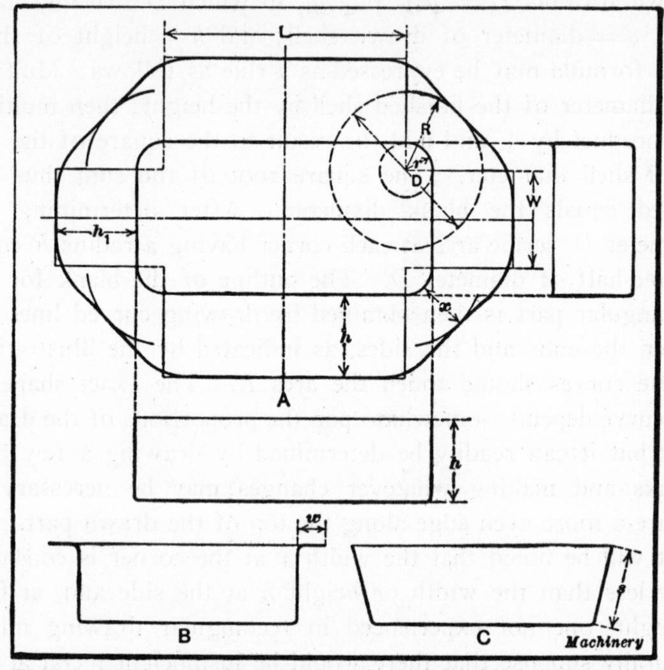

Fig. 5. Diagram Illustrating Method of Determining Approximate Shape of Blanks for Drawn Rectangular Parts

what changes in the outline should be made in order to secure a more even edge along the top of the drawn rectangular part. When a blank of the correct shape is obtained, it is used in laying out the blanking die. Of course, if the part must be drawn quite deeply, it is not feasible to secure an even edge along the top and the usual practice is to finish this edge by the use of trimming shears or a separate trimming die.

When determining the size of the blank for an irregular or

rectangular shape, it is good practice to begin by making the blank a little smaller than what is expected to be the required size. Then if fracturing occurs, it is very evident that a larger blank cannot be used, whereas if the blank is oversize a fracture may occur, thus leading to the conclusion that the draw is not practicable, although a proper sized blank might be drawn without difficulty.

When laying out the blank, it is often advisable not to attempt to secure a shape that will form corners that are level with the sides of the drawn part but rather a form of blank that will produce corners that are a little higher than the sides. This is desirable because the wear on the die is at the corners and when wear occurs the metal will thicken and then the drawn part will be low at the corners provided that no allowance were made on the blank.

Blanks for Rectangular Flanged Shells.—When a flange is to be left on a drawn rectangular part, the shape of the blank may be determined in practically the same way as described in the foregoing, except that the width of the flange must be considered. Referring to Fig. 5, the dimensions h and h_1 on the flat blank are made equal to the height of the drawn part plus the width w of the flange (see sketch B); whereas, the radius R at the corners should be established from the formula for a shell of radius r, having a flange corresponding to the width required. The blank diameter for a cylindrical shell having a flange can be determined by the formula $D = \sqrt{d_2^2 + 4\,d_1 h}$, in which D = blank diameter; d_1 = diameter of the drawn shell; d_2 = diameter measured across the flange; and h = height of shell. After determining diameter D and the corresponding radius R, the outline of the blank is drawn the same as for a rectangular shape without the flange.

Blank for Rectangular Tapering Shell.—If a rectangular part is to have tapering or slanting sides, the dimensions h and h_1 (see plan view A, Fig. 5) should be made equal to the slant height s or the height measured along the slanting surface as indicated by the diagram C. To determine the blank radius R at the corners, find the blank diameter for a tapering shell corresponding to the size of the corners. This diameter $D = \sqrt{d_1^2 + 2s(d_1 + d_2)}$, in which D = blank diameter; d_1 = diameter of drawn shell at bottom; d_2 = diameter at top; and s = slant height. The radius R is made equal to ½ D and then the outline of the blank is drawn as previously described for a plain rectangular part. If the work should have slanting sides and a flange, the width of the flange should, of course, be added to the slant height and radius R established from the formula for a flanged tapering shell. This formula is as follows: $D = \sqrt{d_1^2 + 2s(d_1 + d_2) + d_3 - d_2^2}$, in which D = blank diameter; d_1 = diameter of drawn shell at bottom; d_2 = diameter at top; d_3 = diameter across flange; and s = slant height.

Blanks for Oval or Elliptical Shapes.—The establishing of blanks for drawn parts of elliptical or oval shapes requires a little more time than laying out the blanks for rectangular shells. In order to determine the outline of the blank for an elliptical shell, first lay out an ellipse of the same size as the bottom of the drawn part, as shown in Fig. 6. Then draw a rectangle *a-b-d-c* and a diagonal line *a–d*. Next draw from corner *b* a line *b–g* perpendicular to *a–d*; the intersection of line *b–g* with the center-line *x–x* locates center *D*, and the intersection with center-line *y–y* locates center *C*. Now determine what blank radius *R* would be required for a plain cylindrical shell of radius *C–a* and height *h*; then draw arcs having a radius *R* corresponding to the blank radius, from the centers *C* and C_1. In a similar manner, determine the blank radius *r* for a plain cylindrical shell of radius *D–d* and height *h*. Then draw an arc having a radius *r* and also an arc r_1 at the opposite end. We now have the major or longer axis *L* and the minor or shorter axis *W* of the elliptical blank. The ellipse representing the outline of the blank is then drawn through points located by the well-known method, which is partially illustrated by the dotted lines. The method is briefly as follows: Two circles are first described with *c* as a center and *W* and *L* as diameters. A number of radial lines are then drawn from center *c*, and from the points at which these lines intersect with the inner and outer circles, horizontal and vertical lines are drawn as shown. The intersections of these horizontal and vertical lines are points on the curve of the ellipse which is then traced through these points and represents the required outline for the blank. If an elliptical part is to have a flange, the blank radii *R* and *r* are found for round shells having a flange of whatever width may be required. The ellipse is then constructed the same as described in the foregoing. Similarly, if a blank for an elliptical part having slanting sides is required,

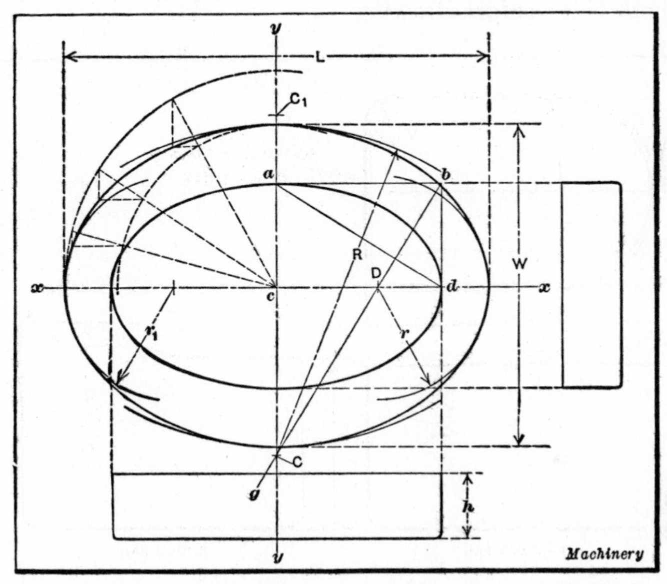

Fig. 6. Method of Determining Approximate Shape of Blanks for Work of Elliptical Shape

the blank radii *R* and *r* are found for tapering shells by the formula previously given.

By following the methods described in this chapter, anyone engaged in this work should be able to lay out in a comparatively short time a blank which will have approximately the correct shape. Of course, it is impossible to lay out a blank which will give an absolutely even edge along the top of the drawn part, because the shape will be varied more or less by the surface condition of the dies and the physical properties of the metal being drawn.

Drawing Pan Which Has Circular and Square Ends.—The possibility of deep-drawing brass shells of irregular shape in one operation is illustrated by the brass pan shown in Fig. 7. The depth is $2\frac{13}{16}$ inches. The material is soft-drawn brass, $\frac{1}{32}$ inch thick, the corner radii being $\frac{19}{32}$ inch and $1\frac{11}{16}$ inches, respectively, and the bottom radii $\frac{9}{32}$ inch. The drawing was accomplished on a double-stroke press. A good quality of lard oil about the consistency of medium motor oil was used as a lubricant, and each blank was coated with this oil on both sides before drawing.

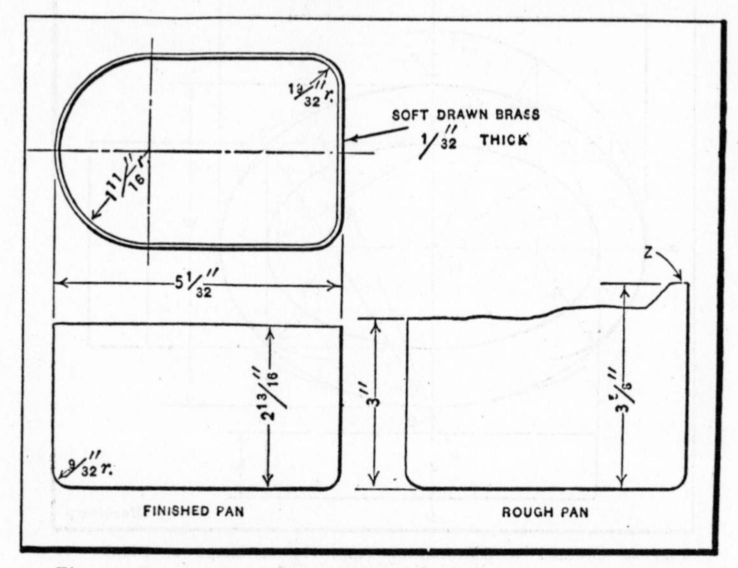

Fig. 7. Pan which is Drawn in one Operation on a Double-action Press

The blank outline is shown in Fig. 8. The first pan off the press was only about 1 inch in depth, and it could be plainly seen where the metal was pinched. The die was made with a $\frac{3}{16}$-inch radius at *S*, Fig. 9, and the opening was made 0.010 inch larger than the outside dimensions of the shell. After the first trials, the radius *S* was increased to $\frac{1}{4}$ inch. This made the over-all dimensions 0.050 inch large at the top of the die. The original 0.010 inch full dimension was kept for $\frac{1}{4}$ inch up from the bottom of the die at *W* with a slight taper extending to the ¼-inch radius at *S*. These changes gave a freer draw, and after the contour of the blank had been changed to that shown in Fig. 8 the depth of the drawn shell was found to be 3 inches.

An odd point worth noting is the corners *Z*, Fig. 7, which has considerable excess of metal. The natural remedy for this would be to remove the metal at these points on the blank out-

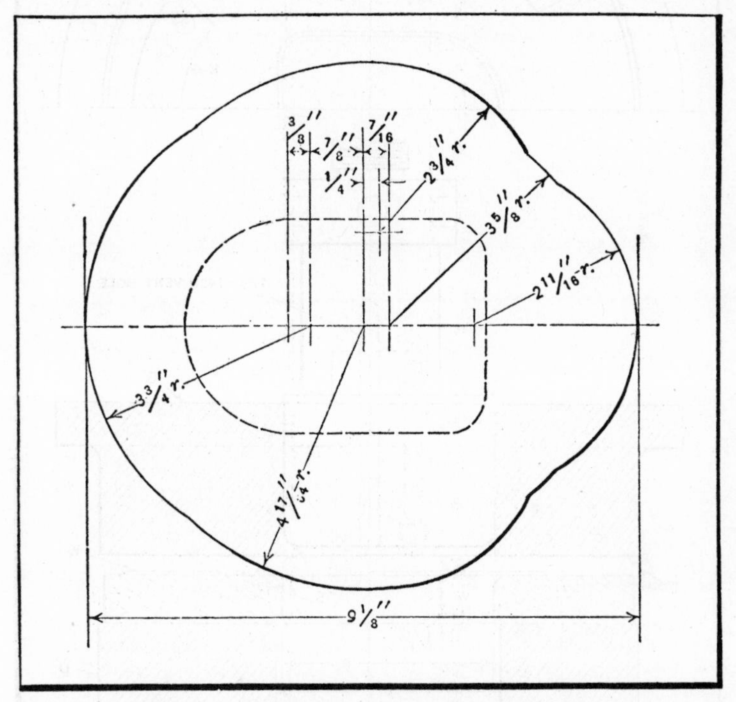

Fig. 8. Blank Outline for Pan Shown in Fig. 7

line, but this proved unsatisfactory, as the metal would tear about 1½ inches from the bottom of the pan in being drawn. The blank outline as shown in Fig. 8 was therefore retained. The blank-holder and die base *B* and *D*, Fig. 9, were made of cast iron, from the same pattern. The surfaces *F* were scraped and stoned to a mirror finish. Much attention was given to this point, as a small scratch or crevice would mar the work considerably. Dimension *M* was made ¼ inch greater over-

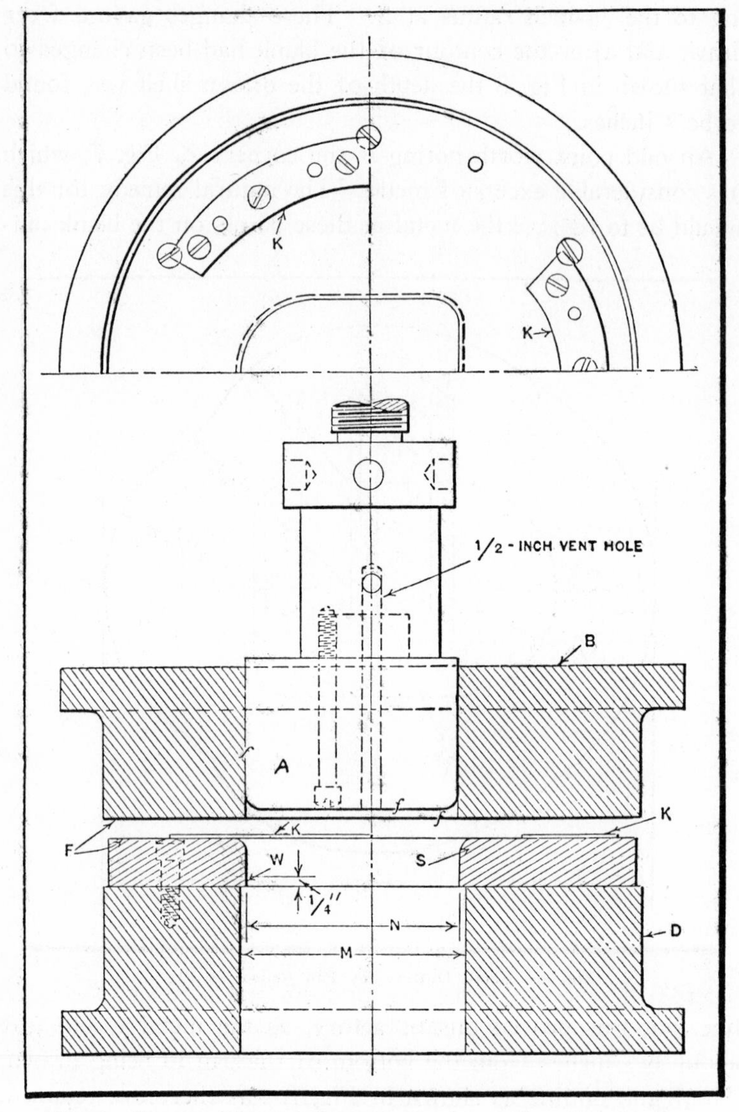

Fig. 9. Drawing Die used in the Production of Pans like the One Shown in Fig. 7

all than *N* to allow the drawn pans to drop through the die base more freely.

The die was made of hot-rolled steel and pack-hardened.

It was fastened to the die base with screws and dowel-pins. The punch *A* was made of cold-rolled steel and pack-hardened. It conforms to the inside dimensions of the pan, and was screwed and dowelled to a stud fitted to the press ram. The gage-plates *K* are located on the die as shown, and are made of cold-rolled steel, 1/32 inch thick. In conclusion, it may be interesting to note how the pan was trimmed. A quick-operating chuck was designed for a hand-operated turret lathe and the pan was faced to the required size with a tool held in the cross-slide. The production on this job averaged seventy pans per hour.

Dies for Producing a Square Part.—A number of interesting dies are used in manufacturing the bottom of a square coffee-grinder and in assembling this part to the body of the grinder. The square shape makes the operations more difficult than if the part were round. No. 20 gage material is used for this part, which is about 4 inches square and 3/4 inch deep when completed. The blanking die has no unusual features in its design, and for that reason is not illustrated.

The blank is taken to a press equipped with draw-pins, a rubber buffer, and the plain drawing die illustrated in Fig. 10, on which it is drawn to the shape of the heavy full line, both the flange and raised portion being square and having rounded corners. The die-block is made of cast iron, and has a hardened and ground tool-steel part *A* by means of which the blank is pressed against the punch face while it is drawn, part *A* being actuated by the draw-pins and the rubber buffer. The punch is also an iron casting, and has hardened and ground inserted facings *B*. After an operation is completed, the work is forced from the punch by the knock-out rod and pad *C* at its lower end. The work, of course, is forced from the die, in the event that it adheres to the latter, through the functioning of the rubber buffer and the draw-pins.

In the next operation the piece is beaded in the die shown in Fig. 11. Block *A* is of an outside diameter that permits the work to be slipped over it. Then, when the punch descends to the lowest point of its stroke, the major portion of the raised section of the part is inverted by face *B*, as indicated by the heavy line. If the flange on the work were not so long, it would be possible to accomplish this and the preceding operation at the same time. The die-block and punch are made of cast iron, while faces *A* and *B* are made of tool steel, and are hardened and also ground accurately to the form required.

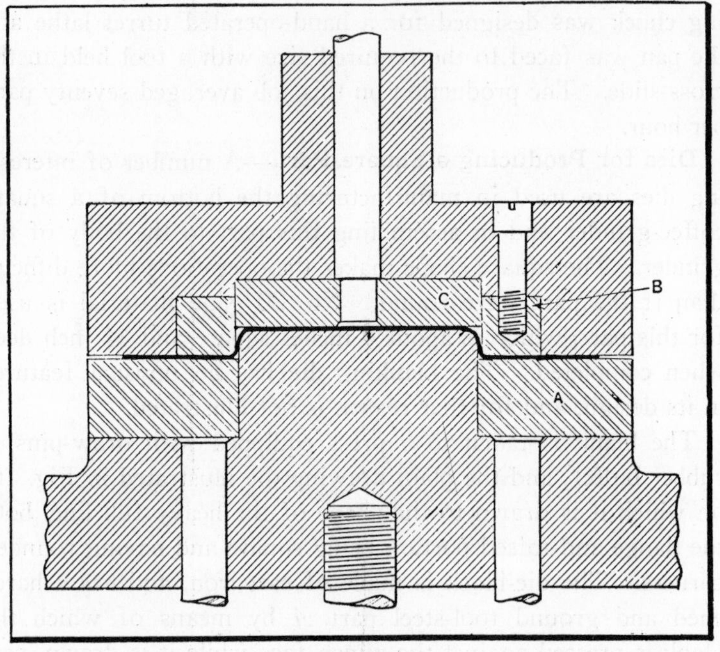

Fig. 10. Preliminary Drawing Operation on the Bottom of a Metal Coffee-grinder

Forming and Trimming Operations on Square Part.—The next step in the production of the bottom of the coffee-grinder is performed on a press equipped with the die shown in Fig. 12. This die is also used in connection with a rubber buffer and draw-pins. The die-block is made of cast iron, and provided with hardened and ground tool steel parts *A*, *B*, and *C*. The punch is also made of cast iron, and has tool-steel parts *D*, *E*, and *F*. Prior to the descent of the punch, part *C* is in a raised position, its upper surface being in alignment with the top surface of parts *A* and *B*. Then as the punch descends, the blank is held securely between the face of the punch and the die part *C*, and is drawn to the shape illustrated. Knock-out *F* advances slightly ahead of the other punch members, owing to the action of the rubber pad, and thus serves to hold the blank on die part *A*.

The work is forced from the punch at the completion of the operation through the action of the knock-out *F*, and it is lifted

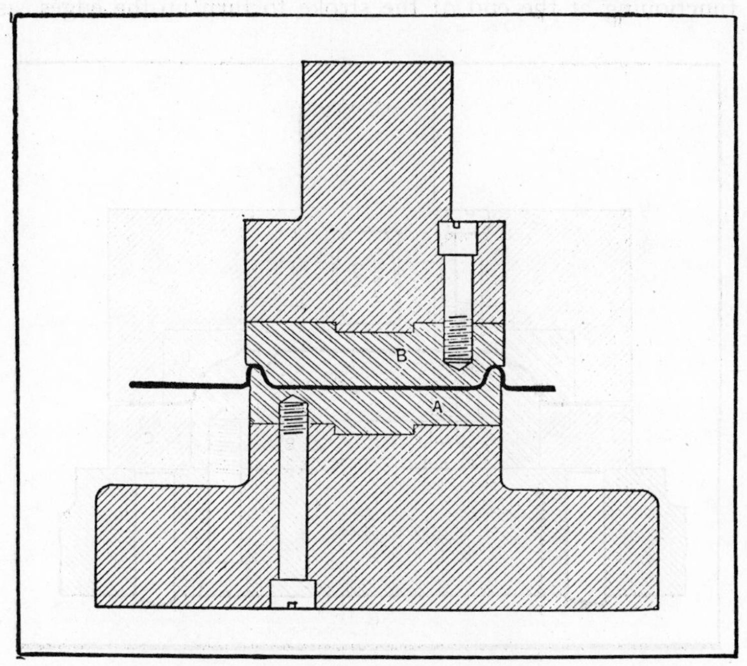

Fig. 11. Operation in which the Raised Portion of the Bottom of the Coffee-grinder is Inverted

from the die members as the draw-pins again raise part C to its normal position. If one die part were used, instead of parts *A* and *B*, it would be necessary to mill a recess in the face to form the inverted bead. The double construction makes the parts far easier to machine, and thus results in a considerable saving in time and money. In addition, member *A* can be replaced as it becomes worn without requiring replacement of part *B*.

The die equipment illustrated in Fig. 13 is employed for

trimming the flange and at the same time slightly turning up the edges all around to facilitate a succeeding operation. Punch *A* is made of tool steel, and there is a sheet *B* of tool steel fastened to its face by means of machine screws. These screws pass through accurate holes in the sheet, and serve to hold it in the correct position relative to the die. The work is trimmed as punch *A* passes the top edge of die member *C*, sheet *B* functioning at the end of the stroke to turn up the edges, as

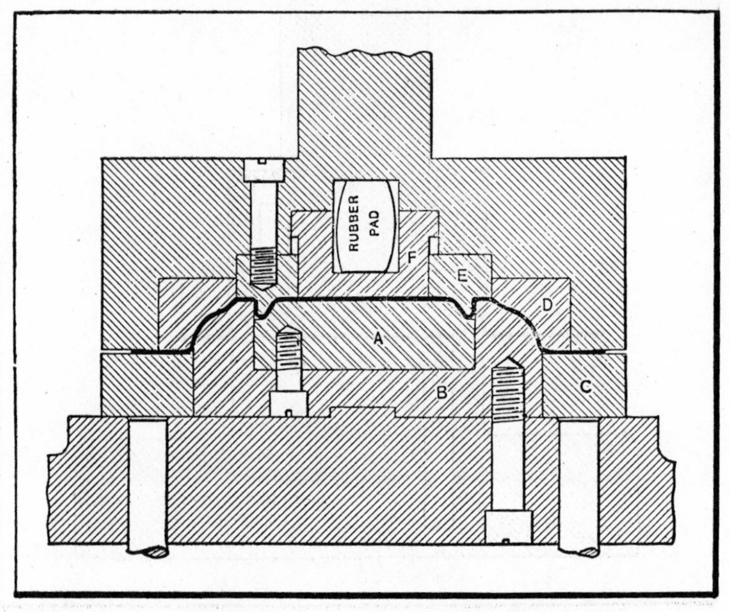

Fig. 12. Forming Punch and Die of Unusual Construction Necessitated by the Square Shape of the Work

already mentioned. The work is properly located for the operation by die part *D*, which is machined to suit the contour of the work.

Part *D* is raised somewhat at the time the punch comes in contact with it through the action of coil springs placed in counterbored holes in its lower side. It is forced downward as the punch descends, and when the punch rises on the return stroke of the ram, it is again lifted by the coil springs. By means of this construction the work is forced from the die.

Part *D* is made of cast iron, and has a tool-steel plate *E* set on each of its four sides. The upper section of die member *C* is made of tool steel, and the lower part of wrought iron, the two parts being welded together. Plate *F* is inserted in the bottom of die member *C* to hold the part *D* and its springs in the die.

Bending Back and Curling the Flange.—The next operation, which consists in bending back the flange, is performed

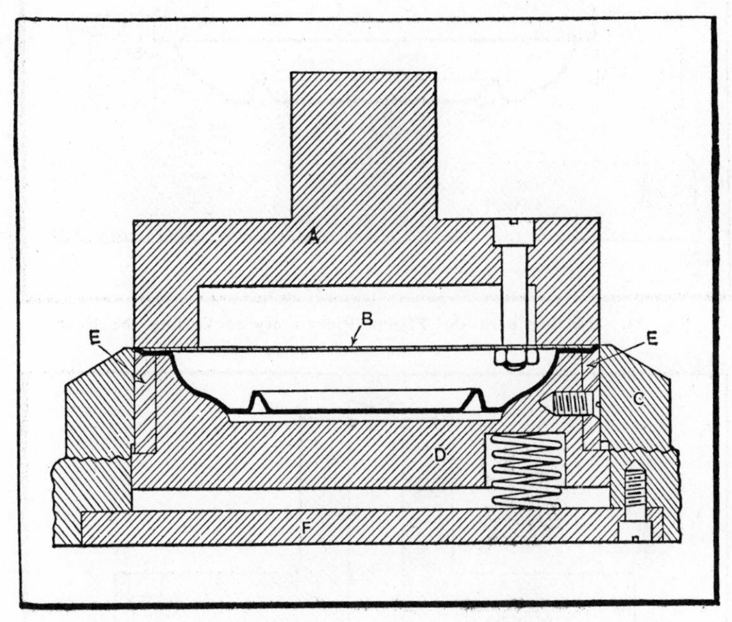

Fig. 13. Die for Trimming the Flange of the Work and Slightly Curling Up the Edges

with the die illustrated in Fig. 14. It will be seen that this die is designed along the same lines as the one just described. The work is placed in die member *A*, which, previous to the descent of the punch, is held in a raised position by the coil springs shown, its top edge being in a line with the top of die-block *C* and the inserted pieces *D*. Part *A* is made of cast iron, while punch *B* is made of tool steel and hollowed out to reduce its weight.

The final operation on the piece prior to assembling consists

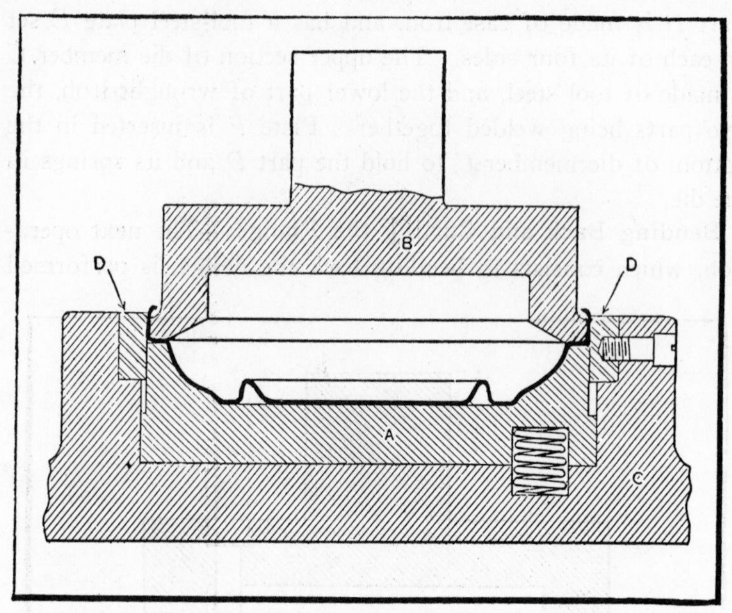

Fig. 14. Bending back the Flange Preparatory to Curling the Edge

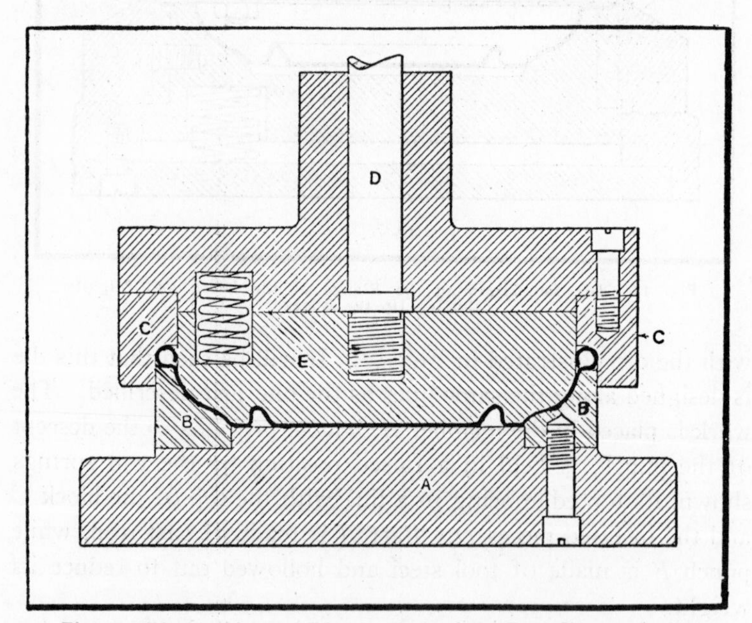

Fig. 15. Die in which the Edge on Each of the Four Sides is Curled

of curling or wiring the lower edge. This is accomplished by means of the punch and die shown in Fig. 15. The work is correctly located in the die by the four tool-steel pieces *B*, which are attached to the die-block *A*. When the punch descends, knock-out E, which is advanced ahead of the other punch members by the action of several coil springs between it and the punch proper, is the first to come in contact with the work. At this point knock-out *E* remains stationary while the other punch parts continue to descend, thus exerting an increasing pressure on the work as the coil springs are compressed, and holding the work in a fixed position.

The edge of the work is curled as parts *C* on the punch slide over parts *B* on the die. It will be obvious that there must be an accurate fit between parts *B* and *C*. This curling operation is considerably facilitated by the fact that the edge of the work is slightly curved in the previous operation. On the return stroke of the punch, knock-out *E* remains stationary as parts *C* slide from parts *B*, and thus holds the work in the die, from which it can be readily removed as the punch reaches the end of its upward stroke. Should the operation of the knock-out fail to remove the work from the punch members, it is forced out when rod *D* is operated at the end of the stroke.

Die for Assembling the Parts.—The assembly of the bottom to the body of the grinder is performed by means of the punch and die shown in Fig. 16; this illustration shows a section through the punch and die members, and a plan view of the die. It will be apparent that the body of the grinder is first placed on the upright die member *A*, after which jaws *B*, which swivel on pin *C*, are brought together and locked by lever *D*. The body is approximately 4 inches square. The bottom of the grinder is then seated on die parts *E*, which are attached to the top of the jaws.

Two different punches are used with this die, the second of which is shown. The first punch is solid and has an angular face that begins bending the edge of the bottom at *G*, so that it can be completely bent around the flange of the grinder body by means of the second punch, shown in the illustration. Member *F* is provided with rubber pads *H* to advance it ahead of the punch proper and the face attached to the punch.

Trimming Drawn Rectangular Parts.—After a square or rectangular part is drawn, it is necessary to trim the edges unless the depth of the draw is comparatively small, as in the case of can or box covers, etc. There are several ways of trimming the edges in a punch press. If the box is square it can be placed on a fixture of the type shown in Fig. 17 and be trimmed by cutting the four sides successively, the work being indexed

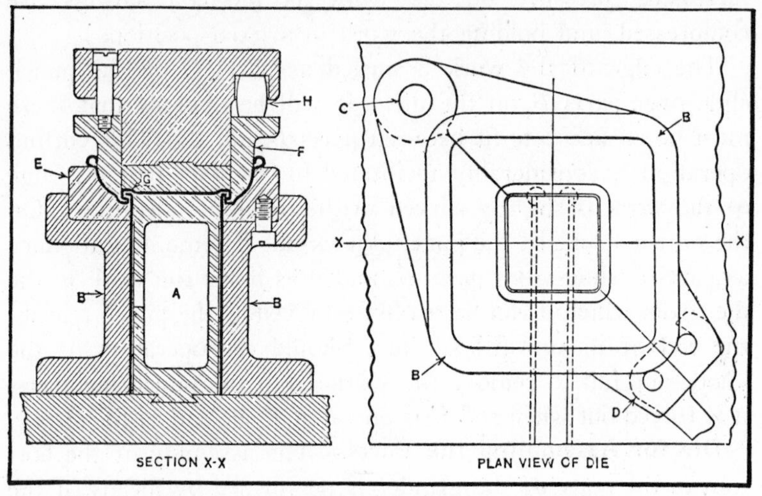

Fig. 16. Hinged Die Employed in Assembling the Bottom to the Grinder Body

by turning spindle *B*. Each cut should overlap the other by a small margin to insure a smooth even edge. The spindle *B* is a running fit in the main casting *A* and holds the hardened tool-steel knife *C*. The dotted lines show the position of the box to be trimmed. As shown, a tapered wedge *D* which slides in under the lower side of the box serves to locate it and also to take the downward thrust of the cut. The blade or knife *E*, which is attached to the ram of the press, may be ground square across the end or at a slight angle on the cutting face; a slight amount of angle or rake is desirable when trimming thick stock. If the part to be trimmed is rectangular, the length of the knife should be equal to the length of the longest side of the box

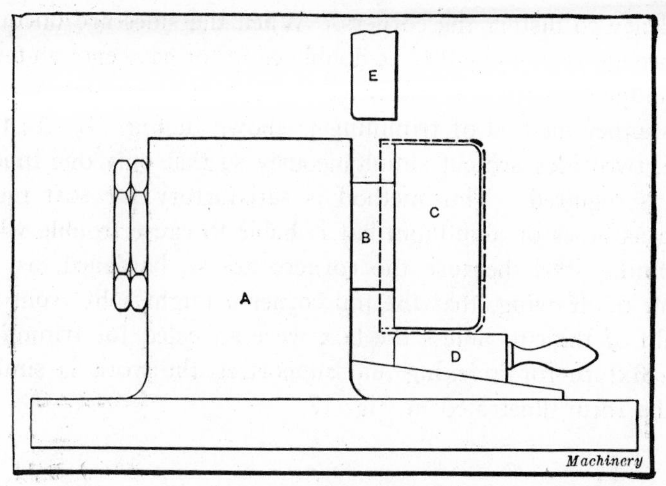

Fig. 17. Fixture for Trimming Edges of Drawn Parts

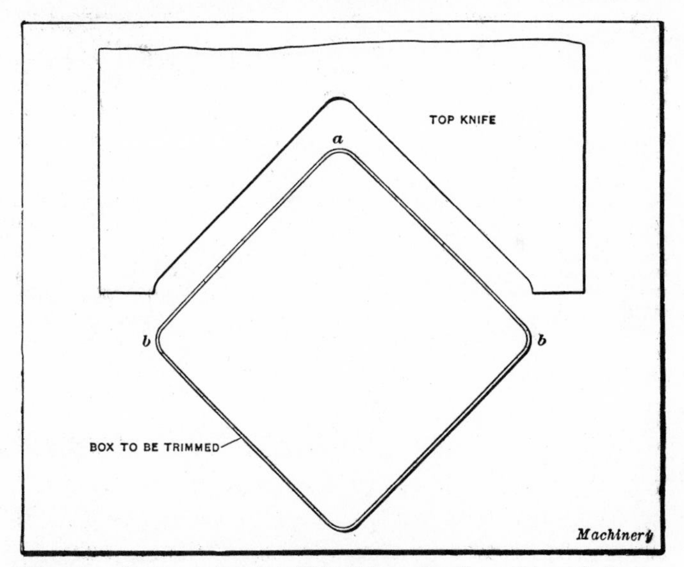

Fig. 18. Form of Punch which Trims the Two Sides of Drawn Boxes Simultaneously

minus the radius of one of the corners. For instance, a box 5 by 6 inches having a ½ inch corner radius should be trimmed with a knife 5½ inches long. The two long sides should be cut first because if the short sides were cut first, there would be a tendency to distort the corners. When the sides are unequal, the wedge *D* should either be double-ended or have enough taper to compensate for the difference in the box dimensions.

Another method of trimming is shown in Fig. 18. In this case, two sides are cut simultaneously so that only one indexing is required. This method is satisfactory for soft metal such as brass or aluminum but is liable to cause trouble when trimming steel, because the corners are so hardened, as the result of drawing, that the top corner *a* might split from the strain of the cut, unless the box were annealed for trimming. The fixture for indexing and supporting the work is similar to the form illustrated in Fig. 17.

CHAPTER XIX A

THE USE OF RUBBER IN CONJUNCTION WITH PRESS TOOLS

When using rubber in conjunction with press tools, advantage is taken of a property which it possesses in common with fluids, namely, its ability to flow. If a quantity of rubber is placed in a cylinder and pressure is brought bear upon it by applying a force to the ram, any such force must set up a resultant reaction on every surface with which the rubber comes into contact. This fluid quality is augmented in the case of rubber by the additional property of cohesion, a factor which plays a vital part in the working of materials with the aid of rubber and dies.

Experiments tend to show that, provided a press capable of exerting up to at least two tons pressure per square inch over the whole area of the rubber is available, a fairly soft rubber with a good elastic property is an ideal medium for the majority of applications, and can be used with satisfactory results for such operations as punching and shearing, in addition to bending and flanging.

Cohesion of Rubber an Important Factor.—The fact that rubber possesses the property of cohesion is one of the main reasons why it has proved suitable for press work. Referring to Fig. 1, at *W* is shown a cylindrical vessel, partially filled with a fluid and placed on a rigid bed. A piece of sheet metal is attached to a forming block, which, in turn, is secured to a plunger. If the plunger is depressed, as seen at *X*, the fluid immediately surrounds the suspended plate, and in consequence, any applied pressure on the plunger has no effect on the plate, because the forces are neutralized, as shown by the arrows. On the other hand, if the fluid is replaced by rubber, as at *Y* and *Z*, a similar movement of the plunger will result in the distortion of the plate, due to cohesion or resistance to free flow.

The cohesion property of rubber, however, has its limits, and great care must be taken in the design of tools not to expect too much of the material; in other words, every assistance should be given to the rubber to enable it to maintain its form unbroken and so preserve its life. Furthermore, in the case of cutting and shearing, the severed edge of the work will tend to have a burred appearance unless specially designed tools are used.

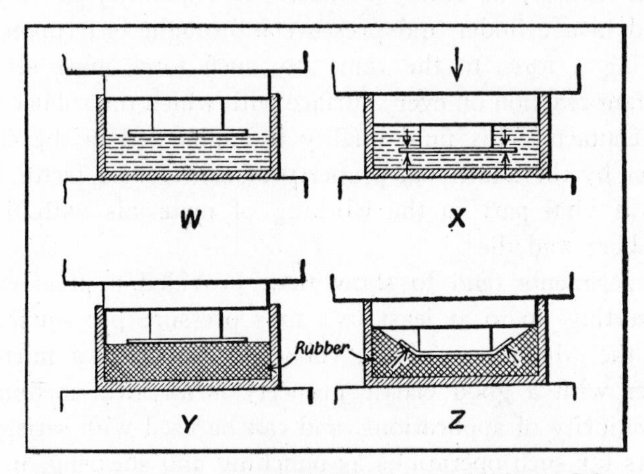

Fig. 1. Diagrams Contrasting the Behavior of a Liquid and Rubber under Pressure

Effect of Incorrectly Designed Forming Tool.—The diagrams, Fig. 2, show the reactions on the rubber when a wrongly designed forming tool is used. A lip about 3/16 inch wide is to be bent on a fairly heavy piece of sheet metal to form a flange. This bend may be considered one of the most difficult to obtain with rubber as the bending agent, excluding, of course, forms having curved contours. The required form of flange is shown in dotted outline at *y*. The forming block illustrated is unsuitable for the job, as no consideration has been given to the mass of rubber which will come into action at the point *x*. This mass will descend in a bulbous form (as shown by lower left-hand diagram) before any considerable pressure has been exerted. In this view are indicated the reactions after the initial pressure has been applied. The pressure exerted by the rubber has effect in all directions, as shown by the arrows. It will be observed that the force indicated by the arrow *d* is acting in opposition to the lip *x*. Before exerting sufficient pressure to effect any further deformation of the lip *x*, the rubber around the arrow *d* has taken the line of least resistance and traveled past the lip until it made contact with the forming block as shown by the upper central diagram.

On the application of further pressure, an increase in the distortion of the lip *x* is to be expected, and, at the same

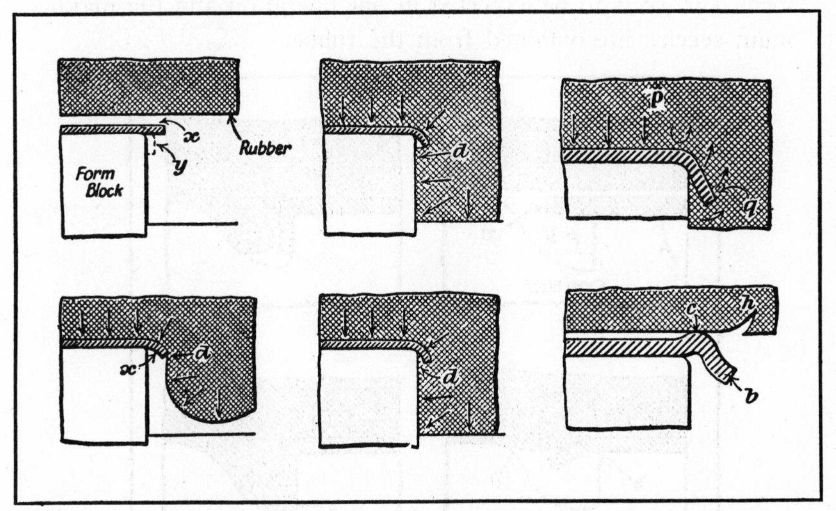

Fig. 2. Stages in the Bending of a Narrow Lip, Using Rubber with Unsuitably Designed Tools

time, the rubber which came into contact with the forming block has spread out and taken up a position under the lip. (See lower central diagram.) After this has occurred, no amount of pressure can have any effect on the lip, and, in consequence, the bend is only partially completed.

A further complication is introduced when pressure on the rubber is relieved. Owing to the fact that, when under pressure, the mass is greater in the region marked *q* (upper right-hand diagram), the reaction of the rubber in that area will, on release of the pressure, be faster than that of the rubber mass about *p*. This difference in reactions gives rise to a variation of flow, as shown by the arrows, and explains the distorted shape of the work as shown by the lower right-hand diagram. The variation in the immediate reaction of the rubber causes the rise at *c*. The faster flowing rubber, trapped beneath the lip *b*, has tended to lift the lip while the main body of the work was still held down. Furthermore, tears and cuts in the rubber will result from the same causes, as shown at *h*. For small flanges, recourse must be had to means whereby the cohesive properties are aided, if fully formed work is to be expected in one operation and the maximum service life obtained from the rubber.

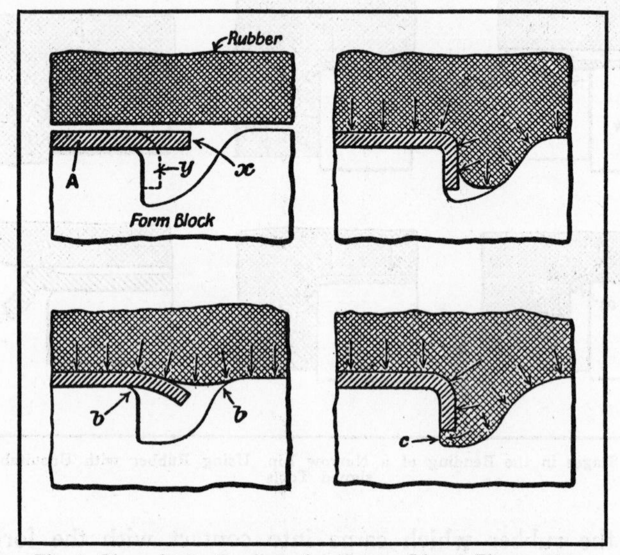

Fig. 3. Stages in the Bending of a Narrow Lip or Flange, Using Rubber with Suitably Designed Tools

Effect of Correctly Designed Forming Tool.—The diagrams, Fig. 3, show the reactions of the rubber and consequent effect on the metal when the tool is designed to overcome the difficulties described in connection with the previous example. A piece of sheet metal *A* is to be bent from the position *x* to that at *y*. The forming block has been made to conform more closely to the desired bend and a shoulder is provided to counteract the mass descent of rubber in the region where bending is to take place.

Pressure applied as shown by the arrows will cause a more or less even bulge between the points *b* (lower diagram at left). It will be observed that the sharp edge of the metal leaves the surface of the rubber. The upper diagram at right shows that the rubber pad has, through continued pressure, bulged still further and the work is practically completed, although the edge of the metal is still clear of the rubber.

The pressure has been fully applied in lower diagram at right. No cutting of the rubber occurs, due to the fact that in filling the gap *c*, the rubber has what may be described as a rolling motion about the edge of the metal.

Use of Rubber for Shearing Operations.—Bearing in mind the essential factor that brought about the application of rubber to press work, namely, the way in which rubber makes it possible to dispense with costly and accurate toolmaking and setting, it is advisable at this point to consider the important operation of punching and shearing. While a considerable saving in toolmaking is thus achieved in connection with bending and similar operations, a still greater saving may be expected where cutting and stamping are to be performed, and more especially in the case of irregular contours. These operations, when carried out by the usual methods, call for tools of the highest precision, while great care is necessary and much time must consequently be spent on setting up and maintenance.

Where both cutting and forming are to be done in one operation, the precision factor in tool construction becomes even more important. Quite complicated and intricate structures are frequently involved, and in most cases considerable experimental and try-out work becomes necessary.

In general, the principle of bringing into action stresses to overcome the shear strength of the work can be applied when using rubber. Assume an arrangement such as is shown in Fig. 4. A piece of sheet metal is laid on a sharp-edged tool *B*, which rests on the solid bed of the press. The result

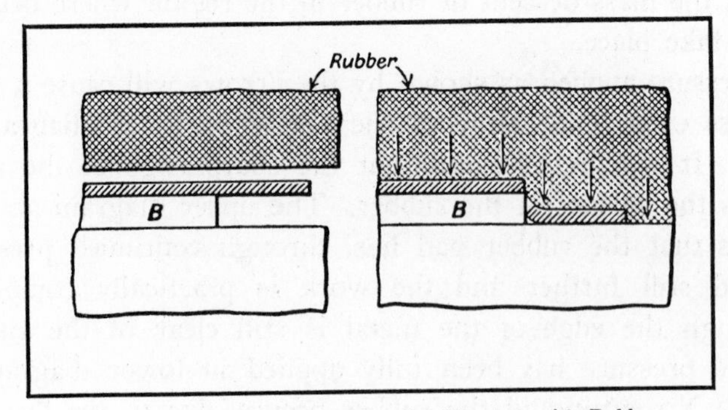

Fig. 4. A Simple Arrangement for Shearing with Rubber

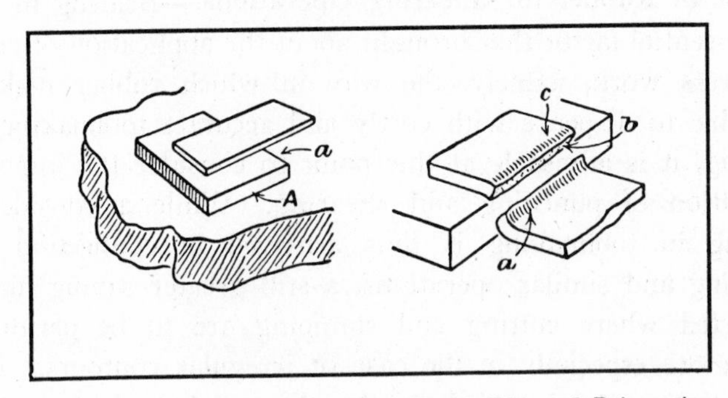

Fig. 5. This arrangement Produces a Rough Edge and Deformation as shown by Diagram at Right

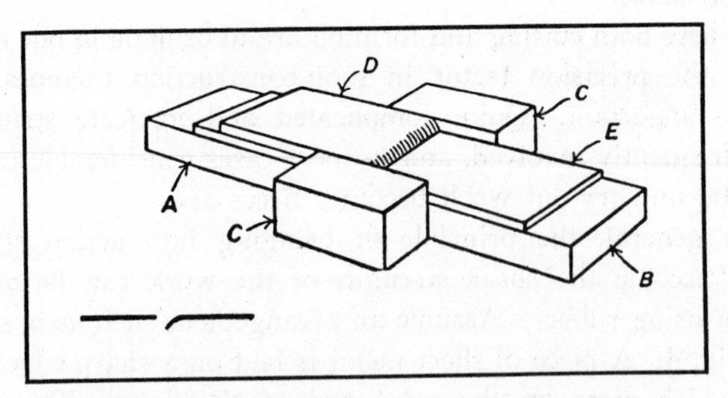

Fig. 6. This Arrangement Produces a Clean Sheared Edge

shown by the diagram at the right will be obtained if pressure of a magnitude greater than the shear strength of the plate is applied. No matter how spongy or soft the rubber may be, provided that it is trapped, pressure can be exerted until the rubber mass attains a density comparable with that of the work. An advantage is that rubber readily adapts itself to any irregularities in the shape of the work and serves, at once, as a clamp and as an active agent. The rubber, moreover, has less tendency to cause damage in the way of bruising or scoring than metal or wood.

In practice, however, the arrangement shown in Fig. 4 is not suitable for blanking when a well finished edge is desired. This was proved by the following test. A piece of sheet-metal strip was arranged as shown in Fig. 5, resting on a block *A*, the edge *a* of which was ground to a sharp square corner. The block was placed on the bed of the press and pressure applied. The result is shown by the right-hand diagram. It will be seen that considerable distortion had taken place around the region of the edge *a* before collapse occurred, due to the fact that the strip tried to conform to the contour formed by the block and the press bed. When the breakage of the metal did occur, it was due to tension rather than shear, and, in consequence, the edge *b* was very rough. In addition, the upper surface *c* had a burred appearance, because the edge of the block had acted as a fulcrum when the pressure was first applied.

To correct these faults, the arrangement shown in Fig. 6 was tried. Blocks *A* and *B* were reduced in width to correspond with strip *E* and were placed on the bed of the press, together with two more blocks *C*, one on each side. These latter blocks act as barriers to prevent any rubber passing beneath the strip. In addition, a steel pressure pad *D* was placed on top of the strip to overcome distortion. Pressure was then applied and a clean cut was obtained.

These experiments showed that, apart from a case where only a few pieces of a particular shape are required, it is not sufficient to use a cutting templet only, as the time wasted in cleaning up ragged edges is considerable, and it is necessary to use an outer form as well. Consider the case where it is desired to cut twelve pieces of sheet metal to the shape shown in Fig. 7. It would be quite sufficient to make a sharp edged templet out of 10- or 12-gage steel and use it as a blanking tool. If, however, one thousand pieces were required, it would be preferable to use a tool of similar design to that shown.

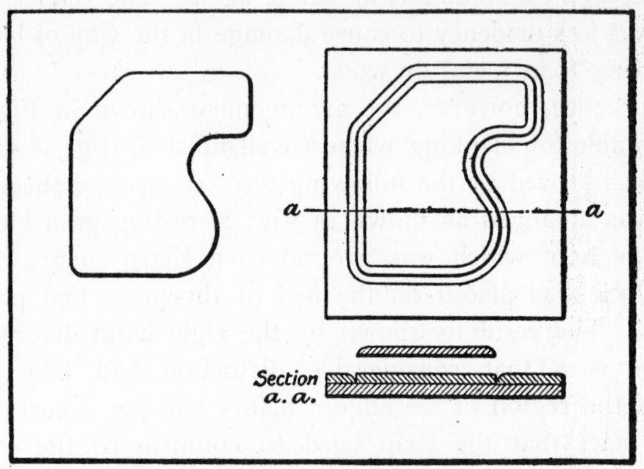

Fig. 7. Blank to be Produced and Tool Required to Produce the Blank with Clean Edges

Advantages of Rubber for Piercing.—In blanking or piercing on an ordinary power press, it is only necessary to calculate the energy requirements to overcome the shear resistance of the metal to be worked, that is, strength of material × area to be sheared. From this formula, sufficient information can be derived as to the size of press needed, allowances being made for shock and other factors. This calculation could not be applied in determining the capacity of press needed for rubber press work, since the work is completed in a very brief portion of the press stroke in the one case, whereas continuous pressure is the vital factor in the other.

With the ordinary blanking or piercing tool, the whole of the energy available can be concentrated at the point where work is to be done. With the rubber pressing process, however, due to the nature of the medium employed, the pressure must be built up until it is sufficient to overcome the resistance offered by the work. This pressure, moreover, cannot be applied at a given point, but must necessarily be exerted over the whole area with which the rubber comes into contact.

Assume that a clean hole, 1 inch in length by ⅛ inch wide, is to be punched in a duralumin sheet 0.022 inch thick. The area of metal to be sheared in this instance is found to be 0.05 square inch, and assuming the shear strength of duralumin to be 15 tons per square inch, it will be necessary to apply a force of over 0.75 ton. There is, however, an area of only 0.125 square inch on which to operate, so that a pressure of 6 tons per square inch is required to bring about the desired collapse of the material. This is an example of a job that is quite simple on an ordinary press but impractical on a press utilizing rubber. It was chosen to emphasize the consideration that must in all cases be given to small details before decisions are reached as to whether a job is suitable for production by rubber pressing and the methods which are to be employed.

It may be noted that a press capable of exerting a pressure of 2 tons per square inch would not have quite sufficient capacity to punch out a clean hole with a diameter of ⅝ inch in a duralumin sheet 0.022 inch thick. Emphasis has been laid on the word "clean," because where circumstances permit, it is possible to pierce a smaller hole in the same material, provided there is no objection to a ragged edge. Fig. 8 illustrates this point.

Assume that it is desired to punch a hole ½ inch in diameter in a piece of duralumin 0.022 inch thick. In a correct set-up for clean shear, as shown at *X* (left-hand diagram), the effective pressure area (denoted by arrows at *Y*) is 0.197 square inch. To pierce the hole, a pressure of 2.6 tons per square inch would be needed. On the other hand, a set-up such as shown at *X* (central diagram) would, for the same size hole, give an effective pressure area (see arrows at *Y*) of about 0.6 square inch, and a pressure of only 0.86 ton per square inch would be sufficient to cause the collapse shown.

At this point, reference may be made to the subject of effective, or working, areas. It will be seen that the arrows denoting pressure are placed immediately above the unsupported portions of the work. In calculating the pressure required to accomplish any cutting operation, all reckonings must be based on the area of unsupported metal, an area dependent on (a) the type of cut desired, that is, clean or rough, and (b) the gage and nature of the metal being worked. In using a press with a rubber pad and applying a pressure of 2 tons per square inch, the area may, for practical purposes, be taken as being equal to that of a strip varying from 1/8 to 3/8 inch in width along the line of the cut. The

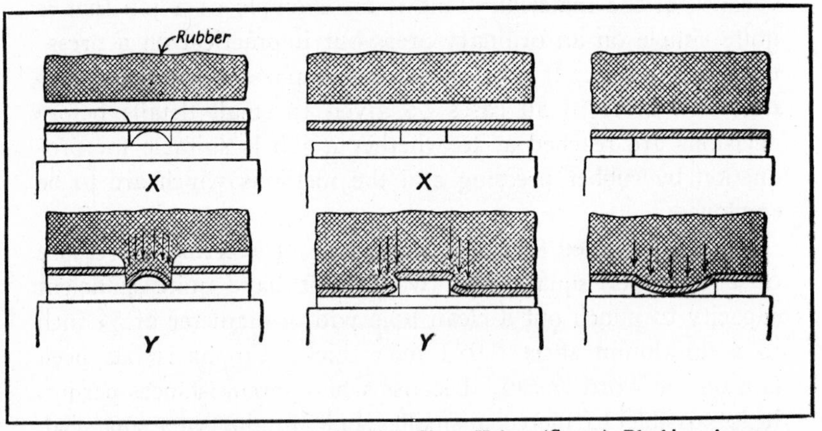

Fig. 8. (Left) Arrangement for Blanking Clean Holes. (Center) Blanking Arrangement Giving a Larger Effective Pressure Area, but Resulting in Rough Edges. (Right) Set-up for Blanking which will Result in Torn Edges

temptation to gain extra effective working area may give rise to the situation illustrated by the right-hand diagram. This is a set-up to be avoided, since tearing will be the outcome. The heavier the gage of the metal to be worked, the greater is the effective area available, as there is less tendency for the metal to become bent or distorted.

Use of Rubber for Bending and Flanging.—In piercing flanged holes, clean-cut edges are essential; otherwise cracks and splits may be expected to develop. When properly used, the rubber process is ideal for producing flanged holes. Consider the set-up shown in Fig. 9, in which a flanged hole is required in the plate *A*. The hole is located by the pin *B*, which also serves to retain the pressure pad *C* in position. It will be seen that the recess, which leaves unsupported enough metal to furnish a sufficient effective area, has solid walls that serve a dual purpose. They not only act as boundaries to confine the effective area within suitable limits, but serve at the same time as formers to receive the cut metal. The effective area is indicated by the arrows. A pressure of one ton per square inch would be sufficient to produce a flanged 9/16-inch hole by this method in a sheet of duralumin 0.022 inch thick.

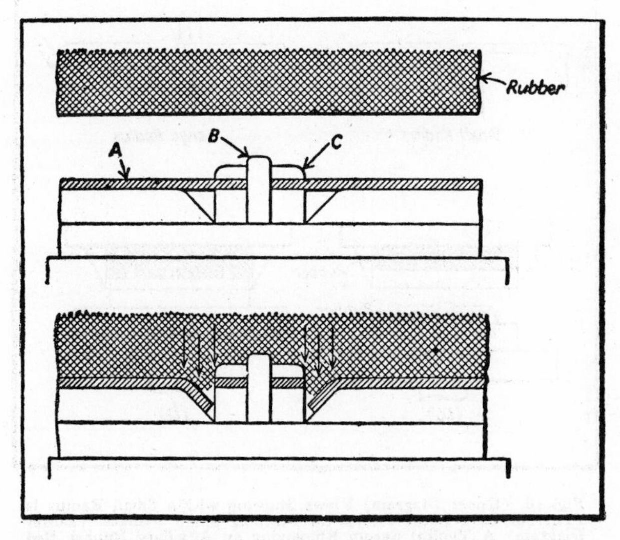

Fig. 9. Set-up for Piercing a Flanged Hole and Result Obtained

Bending or Forming Small Flanges or Lip Formations.—The production of small bends and turnovers may be regarded as among the most difficult rubber forming operations. In many cases, turnovers can only be effected by the application of a pressure which, although it could be obtained by reducing the area of the rubber bed, would have a very harmful effect on the structure of the metal itself, due to crushing. It is advisable that, for small turnovers, the bend radii should be as small as possible. This is necessary in order to maintain, as long as possible, a reasonable effective working area, as shown by the upper diagrams, Fig. 10. As a general rule, flanges and lips should be at least equivalent to three times the gage of the metal being worked on, and, as already stated, bend radii should be kept to a minimum.

Flanges and Bends in Opposite Directions.—Up to this point, attention has been confined to cases in which all work done has been accomplished by the metal giving way to the

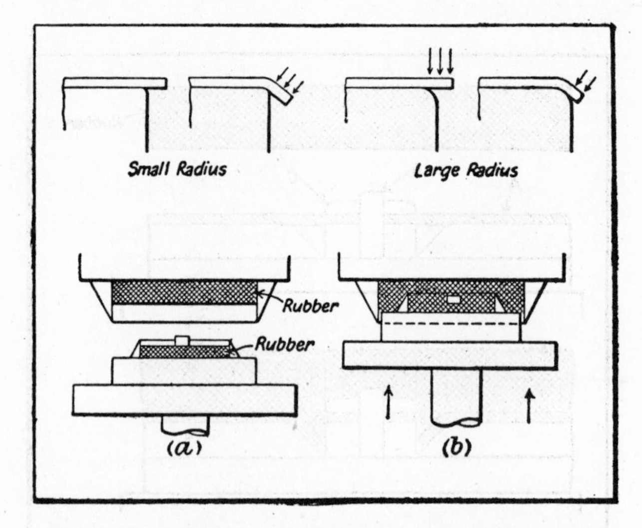

Fig. 10. (Upper Diagram) Views Showing why a Small Radius is Preferable to a Large Radius for Forming Small Flanges. (Lower Diagram) A Typical Set-up Employing an Auxiliary Rubber Bed

natural flow of the rubber mass. In many instances, however, parts are so designed that there is no alternative to forming flanges and lips in opposite directions. This calls for directional effort immediately opposed to that of the mass of rubber. Such work may be done in two ways. First, it may be carried out in two or more operations, the portions already finished in the first stage being shielded from further pressing action while the subsequent stage or stages are being completed. Second, it may be executed in one operation by the use of an auxiliary rubber bed.

The secondary rubber bed can be set up as shown by the lower diagrams, Fig. 10, and provides virtually a double rubber mass. By carefully screening or shielding the work done by each individual mass, simultaneous cutting and flanging of a part in opposite directions becomes a relatively simple matter.

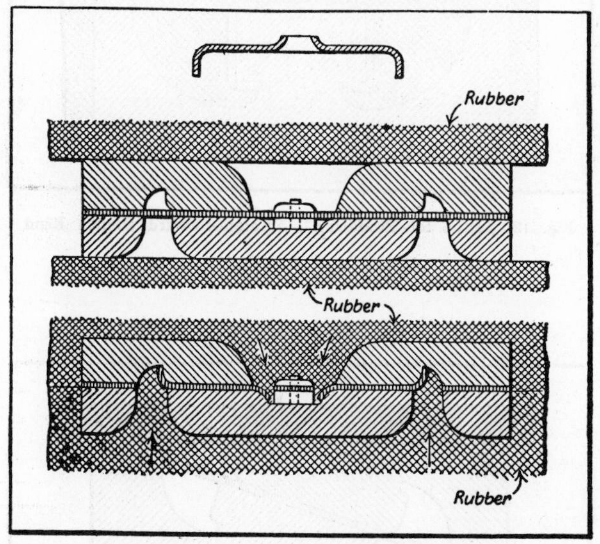

Fig. 11. Sectional View of Part that Requires Flanging in Two Directions and Set-up for Producing the Part Shown

Consider, for example, the metal fitting, a sectional view of which is shown at the top of Fig. 11. This calls for a small flanged hole and two lips at the outside edges which must be formed in a direction opposite to the flange around the hole. It would be advisable in this case to complete the job in one operation with the aid of a set-up such as shown in section by the lower diagrams. It should be noted that combined cutting and flanging operations are only advisable where the flanges or turnovers are relatively small, as in this instance.

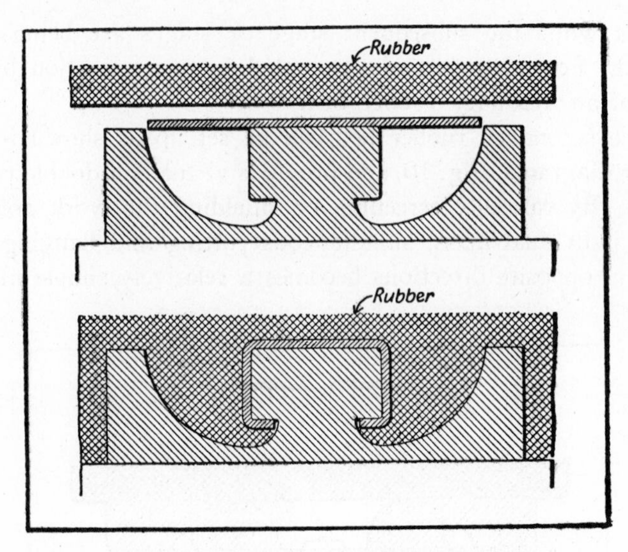

Fig. 12. Set-up for Producing a Straight-forward Double Bend

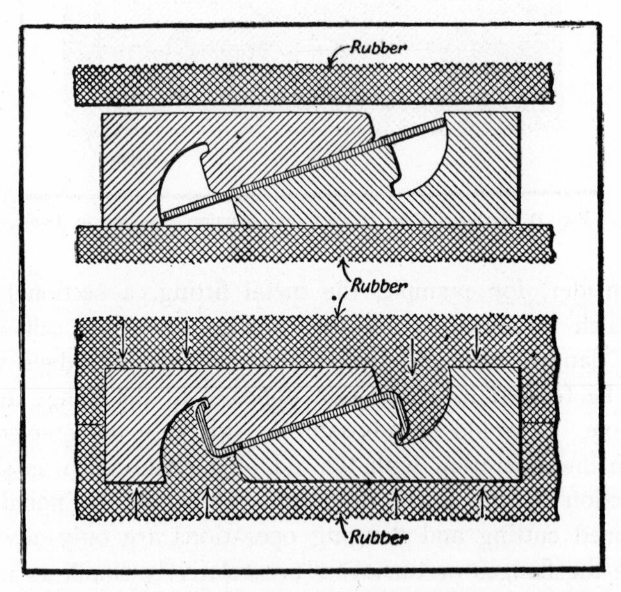

Fig. 13. Set-up of Rubber Press for Double Flanging in Opposite Directions

Double flanging operations present no special difficulties, provided care is taken in the design of the outer barriers of the forming tools. Typical designs are shown in Figs. 12 and 13. The first of these shows a straightforward double bend, while Fig. 13 shows a lay-out for double flanging in opposite directions.

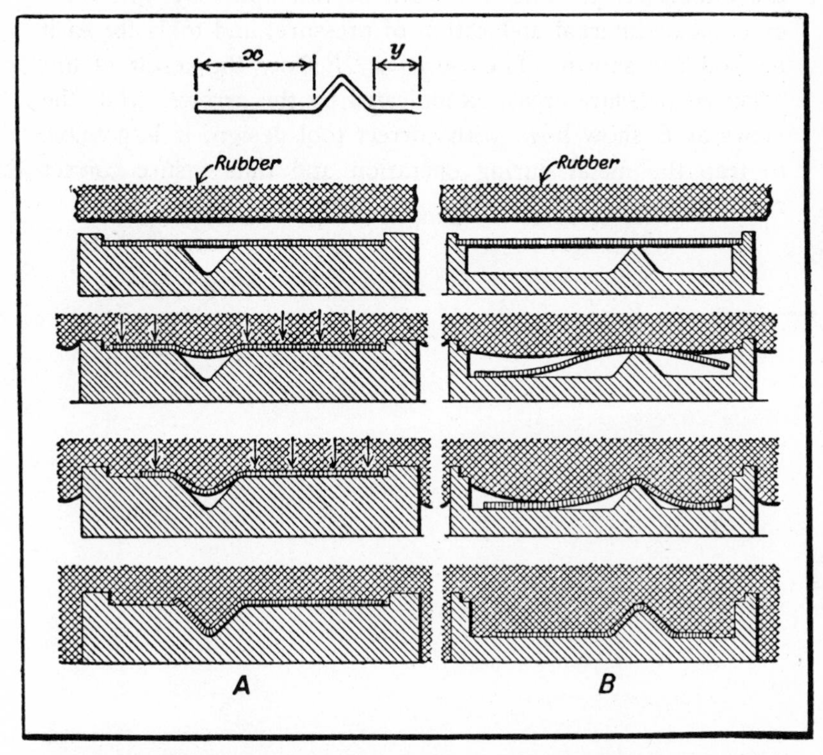

Fig. 14. (A) The Part shown Requiring a V-bend Cannot be Produced Satisfactorily by Internal Pressure. (B) The Required Result can be Readily Obtained by External Pressure

External versus Internal Forming Operations.—It is advisable, in the design of tools for forming, to arrange for the bending operations called for to be accomplished by forming over a projection rather than into a recess. This is advisable for two reasons. First, external bending tends to eliminate waste of effort in overcoming the friction experienced in internal forming, and facilitates the production of consistently accurate forms. Second, less effort is needed in general for external bends than for internal forming.

To illustrate the first point, consider the production of the metal detail shown in section at the top of Fig. 14. The dimension x in this example may be taken as three times the dimension y. The work can be attempted by either the external or internal application of pressure, and tools for each method are shown. The views at *A* show the result of unbalanced pressure areas, as indicated by the arrows, while the views at *B* show how, with correct tool design, it is possible to trap the metal during operation and thus insure correct registration.

CHAPTER XX

EXPANDING DIES OF RUBBER AND HYDRAULIC TYPES

IF THE lower section of a sheet metal shell or cup-shaped part must be enlarged or "swelled" so that the diameter exceeds that of the top, as in producing a metal water pitcher or any similar product, it is evident that an ordinary drawing die cannot be used for this expanding operation. There are three general methods of forming parts that must be expanded or swelled out. The most common method is by using a rubber-ended punch or pad which is expanded in order to enlarge a cup or shell previously drawn to cylindrical shape. The shell is placed in a die having a cavity corresponding to the enlarged form required and as the punch descends a rubber pad beneath it expands, thus forcing the shell out into the die cavity. A two-part die, or one divided through the center, is used so that the die sections can be separated for removing the shell after it has been expanded. A second method of enlarging drawn parts is to use a steel punch of the expanding segment type. This construction, however, is comparatively expensive and is liable to leave marks or ridges on the work, but it may have the advantage of durability as the expanding rubber pads may have to be renewed quite frequently. A third method of expanding shells is by placing the previously drawn shell into a special die so arranged that hydraulic pressure can be applied to the inside of the shell, thus forcing it out into the die cavity. Specific examples of these different methods will now be described.

Rubber Pad Attached to the Punch for Expanding Bottom of Aluminum Shell.—A die for swelling the bottom of an aluminum coffee percolator, to give it a larger heating surface and improve its appearance, is shown in Fig. 1. It consists essentially of a split die member having a forming cavity, and a punch member with a rubber pad secured to its lower end. When the rubber pad hits the bottom of the shell, it is squeezed out, causing the shell to fill the cavity in the die.

The baseplate *D* has a 15-degree dovetail slot machined on its top surface to receive the split members *A* and *B* of the die. Compression coil springs located in holes at each side of the die cavity force slide *A* outward when cam *C* is swung around, thus opening the die so that the shell can be removed. The pin *F*, which holds the rubber swelling member *G* to the end of punch *E*, is retained in the latter member by a cross-

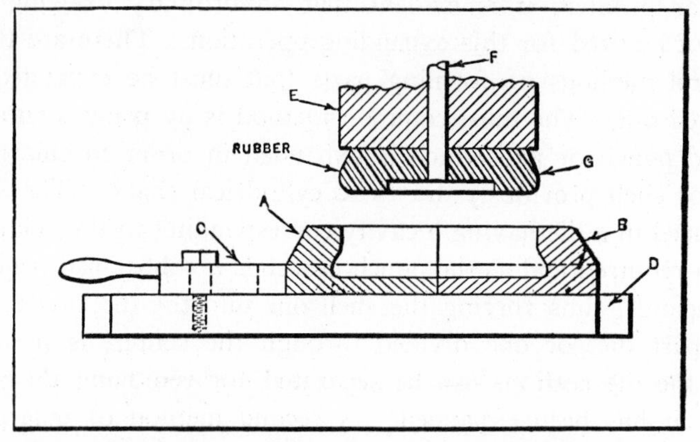

Fig. 1. Section through Split Die and Rubber Expanding Punch

pin in its upper end, which slides in a slot cut in punch *E*. In making this die, the baseplate was first planed to size, after which the two halves *A* and *B* of the die were pressed in the dovetail slot. The whole assembly was then secured to the faceplate of a lathe and the cavity formed. The member *A* was then relieved equally on both sides to give a close sliding fit in the dovetail slot.

In operation, a shell is placed in the cavity of the closed die and the press tripped, causing the punch to descend. The punch *E* forces the member *G* against the bottom of the shell, causing the rubber to expand and force the shell out into the cavity of the die. On the up stroke, the pressure on the rubber member *G* is released, allowing it to regain its original form while being withdrawn from the shell. The die is then opened and the swelled shell removed.

Expanding a Bowl by Inserting beneath Punch a Detached Rubber Pad.—A cream separator bowl made from No. 18 gage sheet steel, cut into squares of about 24 inches, is shown in Fig. 2. This part is made to the shape illustrated so as to avoid splashing when pouring milk into it. Especially interesting drawing dies are required to produce this shape. The first and second operations consist of blanking and drawing the bowl to approximately the required depth, with straight sides. Any stresses set up in these operations are neutralized by an annealing process, after which, in the third operation, the bottom is rounded and the part drawn accurately to depth.

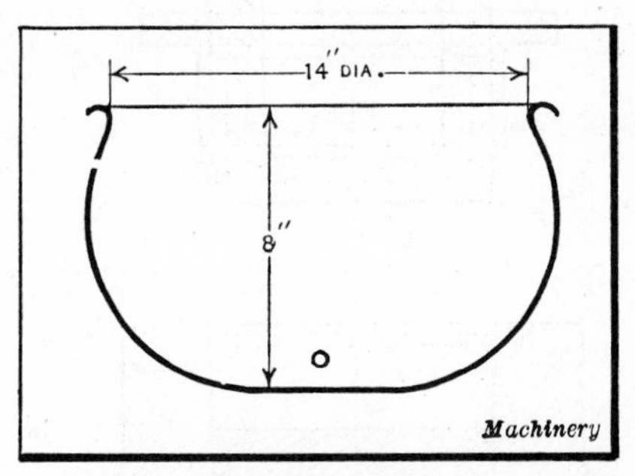

Fig. 2. Outline of Bowl for a Cream Separator

The punch and die employed in the third operation are shown at *A* in Fig. 3, from which it will be seen that the equipment is of the double-action type. The punch is equipped with a blank-holder *C*, which grips the blank against die-ring *D* as punch *E* pushes it into the die. This punch is of considerable size, and so in order to reduce the cost of replacements to the minimum, it is provided with a sleeve *F* that actually does the drawing. Only this sleeve need be replaced when the punch becomes too worn to draw satisfactory work. Sleeve *F* is preferably made of low-carbon tool steel, machined roughly to size, carburized, hardened, and then ground accurately. Ring *D* is simply held in the die-block by machine screws, the lower corners of the ring being rounded off to prevent a shearing action on the work. A knock-out pin is provided in the die-block for lifting the ring, when this is necessary. When there are no facilities for carburizing, a water-hardening tool steel may be employed for sleeve *F* and ring *D* in place of a low-carbon steel.

In the fourth operation, use is made of the die set shown at *B*. The diameters of the different parts in this set approximate those of the set illustrated at *A*; however, the punch is equipped with a bottom *G* that is rounded to the contour desired in the bottom of the work, and die part *H* is shaped to correspond. The diameter and depth of the work are brought to the finished size within close limits in this redrawing operation. In this case the punch nose is made quickly replaceable, as considerable wear is experienced on this part. A ring *J* is provided

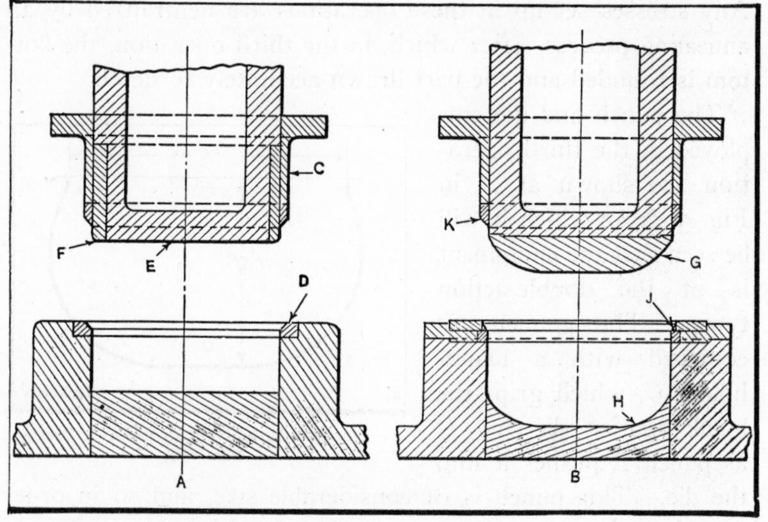

Fig. 3. Construction of the Redrawing Dies used in the Third and Fourth Operations on a Separator Bowl

on the die-block for trimming the shell, and the punch is equipped with a combination flange-holder and trimmer *K*.

The next operation, which consists of bulging out the work to the shape shown in Fig. 2 is performed by means of the die set illustrated at *A*, Fig. 4. After the work has been placed in the die, a circular rubber block, which fits fairly close to the straight sides of the work, is laid in it. This block is compressed by the punch when the ram descends, and as it spreads sidewise it expands the work to the desired shape. The operation could, of course, be performed hydraulically, but by the method explained, the use of water is entirely dispensed with and the operation has proved altogether satisfactory.

In this punch and die set, the die pieces *C* and *D* are made in two parts so as to permit removal of the work after it has been bulged. The halves of ring *D* are fastened to those of ring *C*, and the two units are matched together by pin *E*, which is inserted through block *F*. A flange-holder *G* is provided on the punch, and the bottom of the punch itself is square, the edges being rounded so as not to cut the rubber. On the return of the ram, the rubber regains its former shape, and can

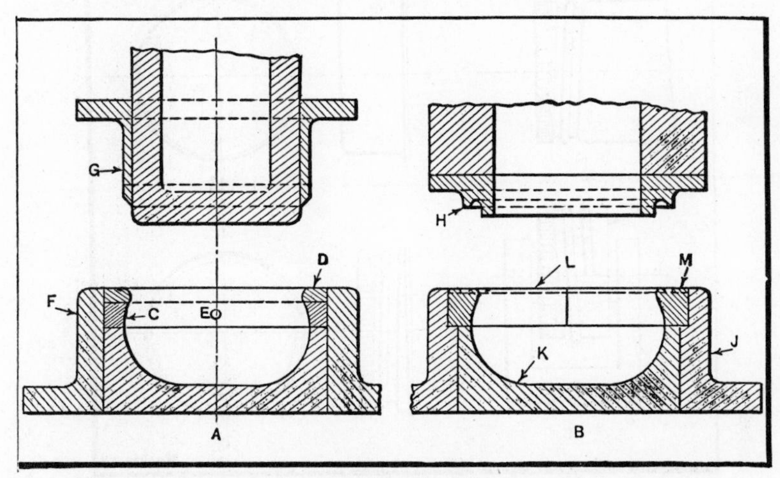

Fig. 4. Bulging, Curling and Trimming Die Sets used in Producing a Separator Bowl

thus be easily removed from the work. Pin *E* is then withdrawn and the work taken out with the upper portions of the die. These die portions are next removed from the work and placed in the die for shaping the next piece.

The next operation consists of curling and trimming the top edge of the separator bowl by means of the die shown at *B*. It is possible to perform this operation in a single-action press, since no flange-holder is required. The punch is equipped with a curling ring *H*, on which there is a short extension that reaches into the work and thus controls the inside diameter. The lower half *K* of the die into which the work is seated for the operation is secured in block *J*. The forming ring *L* is made in halves, which are placed around the work under the flange before putting the work in the die. On the descent of the ram, ring *H* engages the flange and curls it as desired. Ring *M* is also made in halves, which are secured to those of ring *L* for trimming the flange of the work when the edge on the curling ring passes the top of block *J*. Some manufacturers make such bowls from aluminum, others from

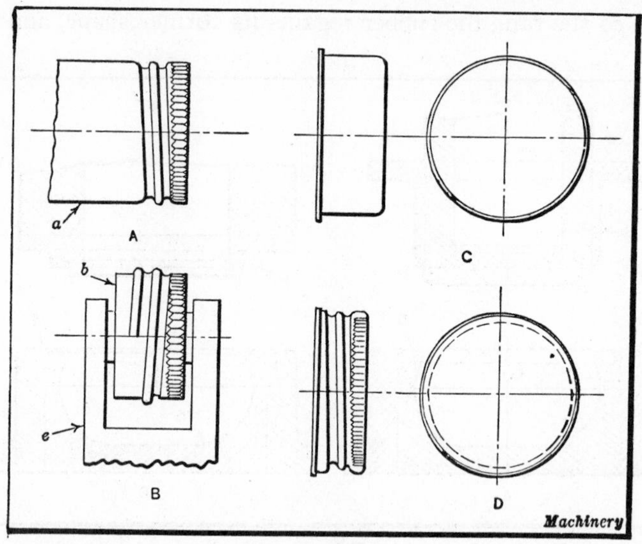

Fig. 5. (A) and (B) Thread-rolling Tools; (C) Metal Shell; (D) Shell C after Thread is Rolled

copper, and still others from sheet steel, which is later nickel-plated. A faucet is soldered in the pierced hole shown in Fig. 2.

Making Threaded Bottle Caps by Drawing and Thread Rolling.—The mucilage bottle cap shown at *D*, Fig. 5, is a typical example of threaded work. Two methods of making the cap will be described. The first consists of producing the shell *C* in one stroke of the machine and forming the threads in another stroke. The second method consists of producing the cap, including the curling of the edge, under a die, and then rolling the threads and knurling the edge by means of a rolling operation.

The die shown in Fig. 6 is used in drawing and curling the edge of the shell. The blank is held by a blank-holder *A* which is provided with a shear edge at *H*. This permits the blank to be cut from the sheet stock and drawn at one stroke of the press. The ring blanking die is shown at *B*. The stock is blanked out and then held against the top surface of the die *C* while the punch *D* forms it into a shallow cup and at the end of the stroke curls the edge. The turning of the edge is accomplished by the curling recess *R* in the punch, and the corresponding recess and rib on the die *C*. A cylinder of steel *E* which just fits the bored hole in die *C*, rests on a rubber

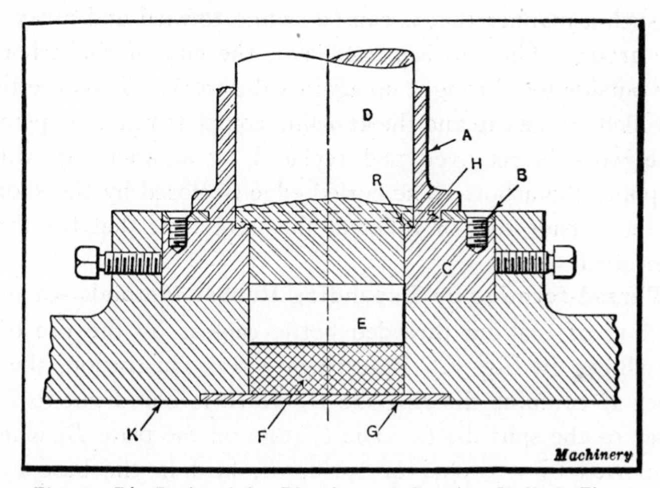

Fig. 6. Die Designed for Blanking and Forming Shell *C*, Fig. 5

cushion *F* and is held in the lower die by the plate *G*. This cylinder constitutes a stripper which forces the work out of the lower die while the stock is being removed from the punch. Die *C* is held in a die-holder *K*, which is secured to the table of the press.

The next operation is to produce the threads in the cap, complete the curling operation, and form the knurling. Rolling is one method by which this can be done. The rolling tools required are shown at *A* and *B*, Fig. 5. A right hand thread of the pitch required on the cap is turned on one end of the tool-steel arbor *a*. The outside diameter of the threaded portion must be smaller than the inside diameter of the cap by an amount equal to twice the depth of the thread in order that the cap can be removed after rolling. The end of this arbor has a series of serrations that conform with the knurled section of the cap.

A left-hand thread is cut on the roller *b* which is mounted in the holder *e*. The threaded roller *b* is made the same diameter as the arbor plus the thickness of the stock to be worked. The outer end is also serrated to match the arbor. The arbor *a* and the roller *b* are both hardened. The arbor is held in a lathe chuck and the rolling tool is mounted on the cross-slide in such a manner that it can be swung toward and away from the arbor. The cap is placed over the end of the arbor and the outside tool brought up against the work. Thus the thread is rolled on the cap and the knurling completed in one operation. The work is removed and replaced by another cap without stopping the arbor. The curled edge is closed by the shoulder of the outside tool or roller at the same time that the threads are rolled.

Thread-forming by Expanding Rubber Method.—A second method of making threaded bottle caps is by the use of the die shown in Fig. 7. Referring to this illustration, the base block *A* contains the ring die *B*, which is bored out to fit the taper of the split die *C*. Die *C* rests on the plate *D*, which is supported by a rubber or spring *E*, held in the base by the plate *F*. The punch is shown at *G*, and the stock-holder at *H*. The purpose of the spring or rubber pad *E* is to raise the work above the surface of ring *B* to facilitate its removal from the die. Die *C* is provided with threads and serrations that conform with those required on the cap.

In operating the press, the work is placed in die *C* and the halves brought together. A smaller rubber cylinder is then placed within the cap. As the ram moves downward, the holder *H* comes in contact with die *C*, forcing it down on its seat by compressing the rubber pad *E*. Further movement of the ram causes the rubber cylinder within the cap to be expanded by the plunger *G*, which forces the metal into the threads of die *C*. The removal of the work is readily accomplished, since die *C* opens when raised above the surface of ring *B*. Several rubber cylinders are kept at hand, and as the work is removed, a new shell is placed in the die without waiting to remove the rubber from the one just threaded.

Without some means of holding the split die *C* when it reaches the upper position and opens, considerable time would be lost in placing the work and die together for the next operation. This is accomplished by providing ring *B* with two

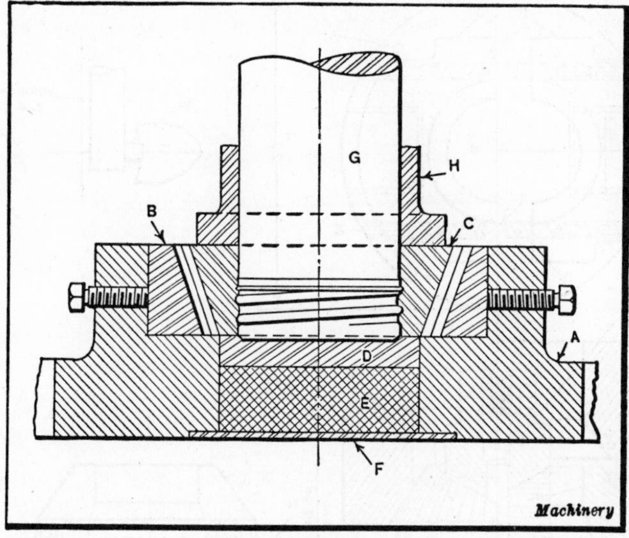

Fig. 7. Thread-forming Die Designed to Form the Threads on Cap Shown at *D*, Fig. 5

T-slots and the halves of die *C* with corresponding slides. These T-slots are located diametrically opposite each other, and are not shown in the illustration. As die *C* is raised, it automatically opens sufficiently to allow the work to be removed.

The work is set in the die and centered by the depression in the plate *D*. Die *C* must be slightly higher than the height of the cap in order to provide for a sufficient volume of rubber to expand into the first thread of the cap, but not so high that it will expand over the surface of this die. The curled edge of the cap is closed by the expansion of the rubber around the top, and at the same time is slightly expanded at this point, making it easier to start the cap on the bottle or other object on which it is to be used. Any lettering on the surface of the cap is produced by having plate *D* suitably engraved.

Rubber-expanding Die for Water Pitcher.—The die illustrated in Fig. 8 was designed and used in producing the water

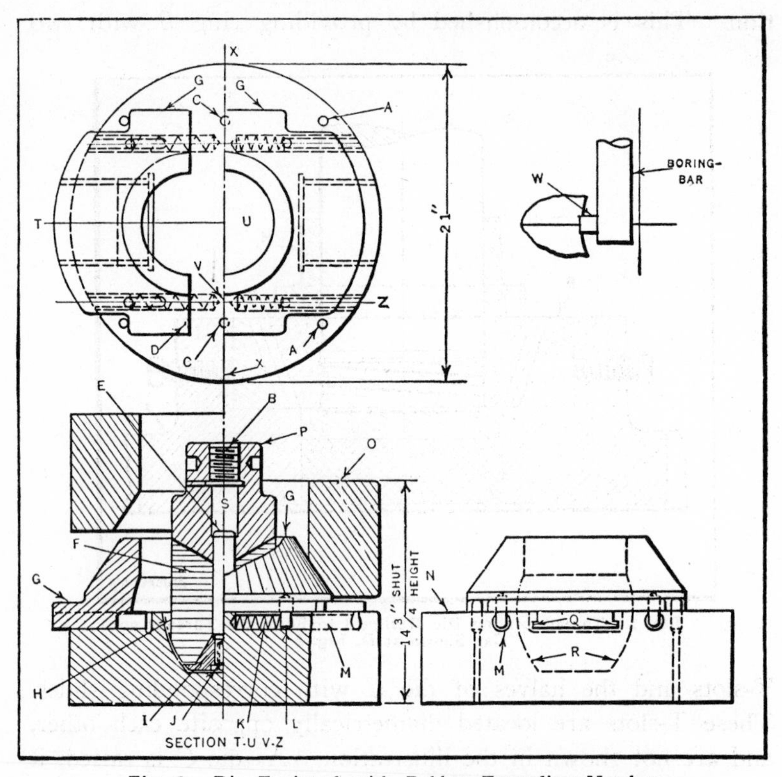

Fig. 8. Die Equipped with Rubber Expanding Member

pitcher body shown in Fig. 9. At *B* is shown the outline of the shell as it comes from the final drawing die, while at *C* is shown the shell as it comes from the die shown in Fig. 8. The final shape *A* is obtained by a spinning operation. The three principal parts of this die are the base *N*, the slides *G*, and the closing ring *O*. These parts are all made of semi-steel castings. The die members *G* slide in T-slots *Q* in the base *N*, being forced inward when the closing ring *O* descends. Any misalignment of members *G* is straightened out when they come in contact with the heavy dowel-pins *C*. When closed, the cavity formed in the three parts has the shape required for the shell. On both sides of the base, one-inch holes *M* are drilled, and slots ¾ inch wide are cut to meet these holes. The springs *K*, located in the drilled holes, press against the pins *L* and force the slides open when the closing ring *O* ascends.

The punch consists of a cast-iron holder *P* in which slides a stud *E*. This stud carries the rubber expanded *F* and the bottom plate *I*. The four parts are held together by means

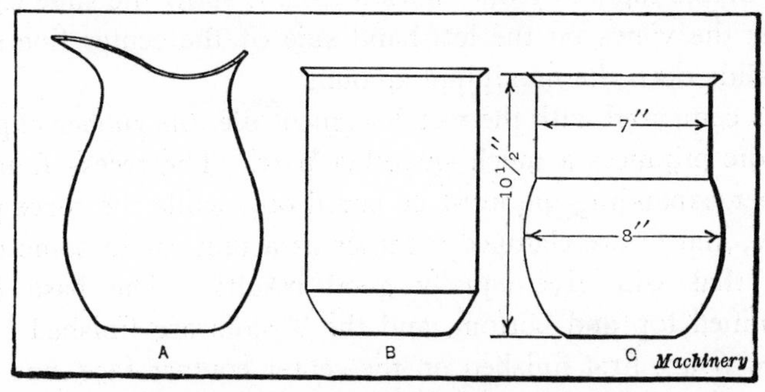

Fig. 9. Steps in Production of Metal Pitcher

of the screw *J*. The large size of this die made it necessary to install it in a toggle press. The punch-holder was, therefore, tapped at *B* to fit the threaded end of the punch ram. Although not shown in the illustration, castings *N* and *O* are cored out, pockets being formed in this manner to receive the ends of the straps used to clamp them in place. The base *N* was fastened to the bed of the press, and the closing ring *O* to the blank-holder slide.

When the punch and blank-holder slide are at the top of the stroke, a shell is inserted in the die. The rounded pocket in the die makes the operation of centering the work very simple. When the press is started, the blank-holder slide comes down ahead of the punch and closes the slides of the die so that they form a continuous recess with the cavity in the base. The punch soon follows, entering the shell and passes down until stopped by the bottom of the cavity in base *N*. The continued downward movement causes the rubber *F*, which is caught between the conical surface of the punch-holder *P* and the bottom plate *I*, to expand. The pressure spreads the rubber at the point of least resistance, which, in this case, is at *H*. The expanding rubber forces the metal shell outward until it fills the cavity at *H*.

On the up stroke, the punch is withdrawn first, after which the ring *O* follows. Springs *K* push slides *G* back until they are stopped by pins *A*. The die is then opened wide enough to allow the expanded shell to be removed. The right-hand side of the top and front views in Fig. 8 show the slide closed, while the views on the left-hand side of the center line show the slide open the maximum amount.

As compared with the metal segment die, the rubber expanding die produces a much smoother part. The recess *R* in the rubber expanding die must be bored out, while the three parts *G*, *N*, and *O* are clamped together as a unit, or in some other way that will give equally good results. The base *N* is machined top and bottom, and the T-slots are finished. The slides *G* are first finished on the center contact face, and then clamped or held together while the other faces are finished and fitted to the slots in the base *N*.

The next operation is that of drilling and reaming the holes for the dowels *C*. The center line *X—X* is drawn through the dowel holes and the slides are set up; first one is placed with its face against the line *X—X*, after which the other is placed in contact with the first one. While the three parts are thus held together, the holes are transferred to the slides from the bottom member. The slides are then removed from the base, clamped together again, and the half-holes *D* drilled and reamed to size.

The next step is to turn the taper on the slides. This can be performed best in the boring mill, with the slides in place on the top of the base *N*. Care should be taken to true up the work so that the contact line of the slides is exactly on the center line. The ring *O*, which is finished complete, is next put on top of the slides, the whole assembly clamped down, and the recess *R* bored out.

The large size of the die made it possible to bore out the whole spherical cavity without removing the clamps. Templets were used to obtain the required shape. When the bore or cavity is smaller, the machining problem is more complicated, but it is usually possible to obtain a good job. It is a good plan to use a very broad tool, shaped like the one shown at *W* in the view in the upper right-hand corner of Fig. 8, for finishing the cavity at the joint to the required diameter. The two halves can then be removed and the spherical surface in each part machined from the large end, using the finished surface as a truing or locating point for the cavity templet.

The punch does not require any special care in its construction. The stud *E* is a sliding fit in the holder. Space *S* must be long enough to allow the stud to slide upward when the rubber is compressed. The bottom plate *I* should be keyed to the stud in order to prevent the screw *J* from becoming loose. Rubber can be machined by various methods, but grinding seems to be the quickest way to form the expanding member to the required shape. Care should be taken to have the rubber under a slight pressure for grinding. When the pressure is released, the rubber cylinder will shrink in the middle, so that it will be less likely to become caught on the shell to be expanded.

One objection to the rubber expander type of die is that the rubber wears out quickly. The continuous compression and contraction, together with oil or other foreign matter found in the shells, causes the rubber to deteriorate. A few weeks' experience in the operation of a die of this kind will show approximately how long the rubber expanded will last. When this has been determined, it is only necessary to have an expander on hand to replace the worn one the minute any signs of failure appear.

It may be of interest to note here that a steel segment

expanding die was first designed for the work handled by the die shown in Fig. 8. The best that could be done in making up the steel segment type of die was to use twenty sections or segments. As the die is required to expand the work from a diameter of 7 inches to a diameter of 8 inches, it is necessary that the metal on the circumference be stretched approximately 3.1416 inches. When the metal segment die was fully expanded, the spaces between the segments were 0.157 inch wide. While these spaces are not much wider than those between the segments of the die shown in Fig. 9, the long spherical surface of the work produced had the appearance of a barrel in which the staves had dried out.

Although the steel segment die was a large, expensive device, it had to be scrapped. The rubber expanding die which was then designed and built produced smooth water pitchers. As previously mentioned, the expanded shell illustrated at *C* is formed to the final shape shown at *A* by a spinning operation. The metal in the section having a diameter of 7 inches is spun out a sufficient amount to permit the lip to be formed at the top edge, as shown.

Expanding Die of Steel-segment Type.—In Fig. 10 is shown a steel expanding die used in bulging out the upper part of a can cover. The expanding is done by a set of segments *E* that are forced outward by a conical central plug *N*. The right-hand side of the illustration shows the punch member at the bottom of the stroke, with the work completed, while the left-hand side shows the die as it appears just before the expanding operation begins. At *C* is shown the drawn shell, which has been trimmed to the proper length ready for the expanding operation.

The die ring *M* is made to fit over the outside of the drawn shell, and at the lower portion there is a step *J*. The ring *M* and the plug *N* are held in the die-shoe by means of the fillister-head screws *I* and *K*. In the space between the die ring and the plug *N* is located the pressure-ring *L*, which is actuated by four pressure pins *H*. The sectors *E* are held together by means of a spiral spring *F* encircling them in a groove, as

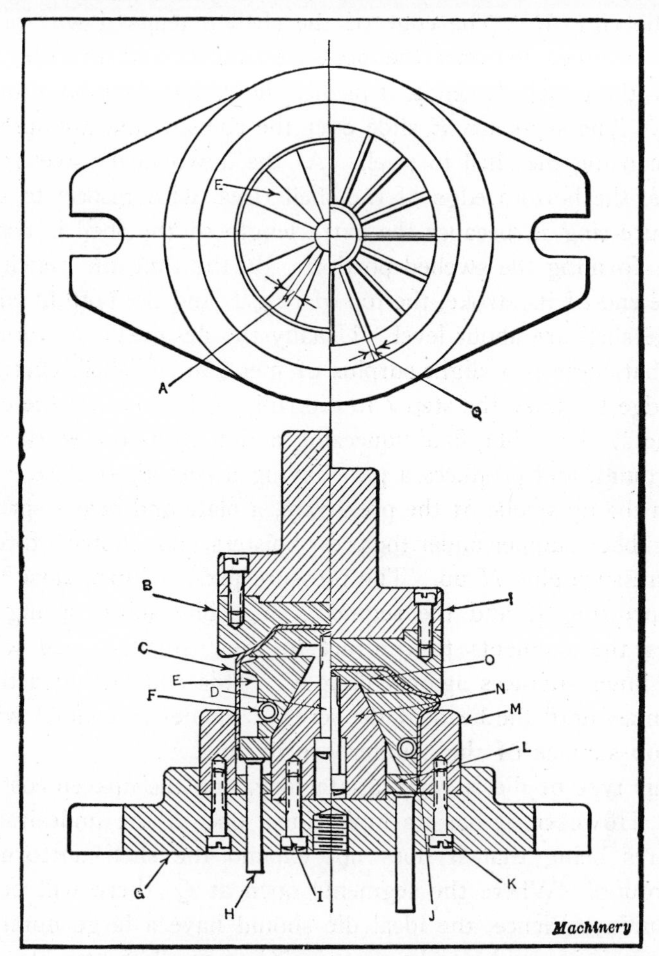

Fig. 10. Steel Segment Type of Expanding Die

indicated. The spring is made endless by screwing the ends together and then soldering. The whole assembly is held together by means of a cap *O* and a screw *D*.

When the upper part of the shell is flat or convex, the punch pad *B*, under the punch-holder *P*, need be only a flat plate. The particular shape of the shell shown in the die, however, necessitated the use of a pad *B* formed to fit the contour of the shell.

The shell is placed over the contracted segments *E* and inside the die ring *M*. The edge of the shell extends down for a short distance between the pressure-ring *L* and the die *M*. When the punch descends, it pushes the whole assembly downward. The segments *E* slide over the cone *N* and are spread out, causing the shell to swell. As the downward travel continues, the bottom edge of the shell rises, with respect to the pressure-ring *L*, because the extra length of the shell is taken up in forming the swelled portion. By the time the punch is at the end of its stroke, the top of ring *L* and the bottom edge of the shell are about level. Usually the design is so worked out that there is a slight surplus of metal in the shell, causing the edge to strike the step *J* in die ring *M* just before the end of the stroke. The final squeezing action irons the work out all around, and produces a part having a smooth surface.

On the up stroke of the press ram, a plate and heavy spring or a rubber bumper under the press bolsters (not shown) forces the pressure pins *H* up. The pressure pins, in turn, raise the pressure-ring *L* and the segments *E*. The spiral spring *F* causes the segments to contract to their smallest size with their inner surfaces against plug *N*. This contracting action continues until the head of the screw *D* comes in contact with the top surface of the counterbore in plug *N*.

This type of die is very satisfactory, and the upkeep cost is low. However, it has its limitations, one of the undesirable features being that it does not expand the shell uniformly all around. Where the segments open at *Q*, there will be a flat surface; hence, the ideal die should have a large number of segments in order to have spaces *Q* as small as possible.

If we attempt to use a large number of segments, however, another difficulty is encountered. When the number of segments is increased, the inner surfaces will necessarily be very thin, and, of course, there is a minimum allowable bearing surface for the segments. Thus, care must be taken in determining upon the number of segments to be used. The diameter of the shell expanded in the die shown is $3\frac{27}{32}$ inches before expanding and $4\frac{1}{2}$ inches after expanding, which gives a difference of $\frac{21}{32}$ inch in the diameter. This means that the metal at the circumference of the shell must be stretched 2.0617 inches. By using sixteen segments, the slots would be 2.0617 $\div$ 16 = 0.129 inch wide. This also gave for the smallest width A a dimension of 7/32 inch, which proved ample for the purpose.

Another feature that must be carefully considered in designing an expanding die of the type shown is the angle of the cone center. An acute angle will mean a long travel and require long moving members. The die will then become very tall, necessitating the use of a large press, while an angle that will permit the use of a short or stubby cone will result in cutting away much of the metal on the taper side of the segment behind the spiral spring, leaving that part very weak. In the die referred to, the angle is 23 degrees on the side. This angle has proved satisfactory, giving an expansion of 21/64 inch on the side, with a vertical movement of the ram of slightly over 3/4 inch.

Hydraulic Method of Forming Shells.—In the manufacture of many sheet-metal parts, operations such as bending, forming, and expanding can be performed economically by the hydraulic "bulging" method. With the method to be described first, the work is placed in a die, which is usually split, and water under a pressure varying from 600 to 1200 pounds per square inch is admitted from either a hydraulic accumulator or a force pump. A force pump is generally sufficient for the purpose, and gives a ready means of varying the fluid pressure; the initial cost is also low. In the case of hollow work, the water under pressure is admitted directly into the work itself, so that in this respect it differs from the older method of hydraulic bulging, in which the quantity of water is measured, put into the receptacle to be bulged, and the operation performed under a power press.

With the improved method, a power press is not required, and the construction of the dies is so simple that their first cost is much less than when the combined mechanical and hydraulic operation is employed. Furthermore, the method of operation does not depend for its success upon the watchfulness of the operator in measuring the fluid. It is merely necessary to start the work in the lower half of the dies, clamp the top half in position, admit the water under pressure from a suitable water cock and drain the water off after the piece has been formed. Another advantage of the process is the rapidity with which the water pressure forms the article to the desired shape, the time required being not more than one-sixth that taken by the other method.

Pressures Required for Hydraulic Method.—The finish produced by this bulging method is quite free from tool marks, and all bends are of full section throughout. An important point to be considered is the water pressure, which must be governed by the thickness of the metal and its physical characteristics. A safe pressure to use at first is about 700 pounds per square inch for annealed brass 0.020 inch thick, increasing this to approximately 1200 pounds per square inch for a thickness of 0.060 inch. If the pressure is excessive, it may burst the end of the shell, and so it is advisable to increase the pressure gradually until the desired results are obtained. An operation such as bending a tube requires more pressure than a simple expanding operation, since, in bending, the tube must be forced around a curved recess in the die. In an operation of this kind plenty of thin oil should be used to facilitate the movement of the work in this recess.

General Arrangement of the Dies.—A typical arrangement of the dies used for bending is shown in Fig. 11. The lower die is fixed to a T-slotted table, and the upper half is clamped to it by means of a handwheel-operated screw passing through a bridge iron which is attached to the table. Instead of a handwheel for manual operation, it is entirely practicable to arrange a hydraulically operated plunger in the bridge as a clamp for the dies. In such an installation, a three-way cock may be employed first to admit pressure to the clamping plunger and then to admit the water to the dies and drain it from the dies.

The tube shown in the die, has a diameter of 0.68 inch and is drawn from a blank of sheet brass, 4.125 inches in diameter and 0.044 inch thick. The end of this tube is bent to a U-shape by hydraulic pressure, in the die illustrated. From what has previously been said it will be understood that the dies are made in halves, the upper half *A* being clamped by means of the handwheel *B*, and a rigid support for the clamping screw is provided by the substantial bridge construction. The upper and lower members of the die are aligned by means of dowel-pins and during the operation they are opened just enough to permit the work to be placed in position. The plan

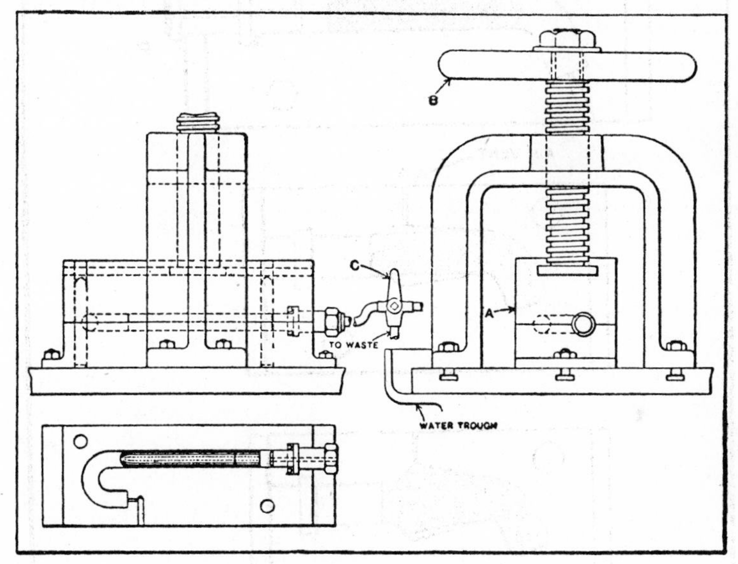

Fig. 11. Dies for Making a U-Shaped Bend, and Fixture in Which the Dies are Clamped While Under Pressure

view shows the position of the tube in the lower die prior to the bending operation. The water is admitted to the dies by means of a flexible connection to the pump or accumulator, and is controlled by the two-way cock *C*. A pressure of 1200 pounds per square inch is employed, and the water, when admitted, enters the shell and forces it around the bend, producing a shell with a square end and with a surface that is entirely free from wrinkles. In the end of the recess in the die is a channel leading to an air vent, which is an essential detail in the construction of dies of this type.

After the operation has been completed the two-way cock is turned around to its second position, which shuts off the source of supply and permits the water in the shell to pass into the waste pipe. The contacting surfaces of the two die members are carefully lapped, and as a result, only a very

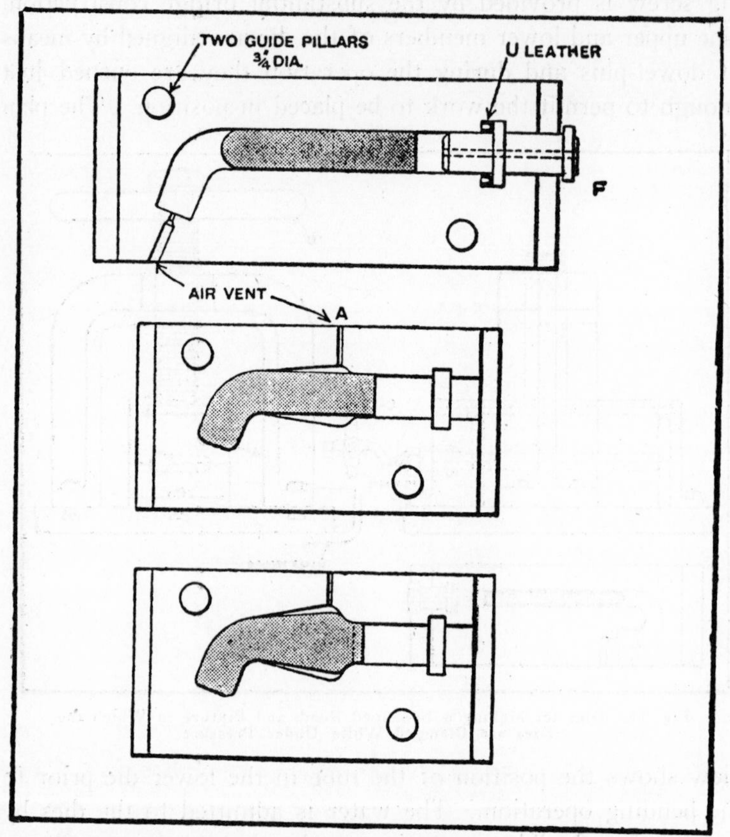

Fig. 12. Dies Used for Bending and Bulging a Gramophone Horn Elbow. Only the Lower Halves of the Dies are shown

slight line is produced at the parting. Lubrication of the tube and interior of the die is very important.

Bending and Bulging Operations.—A good example of possibilities of this method of metal-forming is shown in Fig. 12 since both hydraulic bending and bulging operations are employed. The shell is drawn from a blank of brass,

6 5/16 inches in diameter and 0.050 inch thick, and five drawing and annealing operations are performed before the shell (indicated by the shaded area in the upper view) is produced. The drawing operations are performed in dies of familiar construction. The first bend is performed hydraulically, the lower half of the bending die being shown in the upper view. These dies are of similar construction to those used in the previous bending operation, and the method of clamping and operation are essentially the same. A pressure of 1200 pounds per square inch is used to produce the bend. The shell is then annealed preparatory to expanding. This operation is performed with the same type of bench fixture that is shown in Fig. 11, but the bulging dies are not of the same construction. Two bulging operations are performed. The lower members of both sets of dies are shown in the lower part of Fig. 12. The second expanding operation, which is preceded by annealing, is necessary to finish the shell to the required shape. Both expanding dies are of the same type and it is necessary to provide a small air vent *A* at the bulged section. The bulged end of the tube is then trimmed to length, after which the small end is cut off and a bead spun on the stem.

Bulging Automobile Side-lamp Shells.—The drawn shell shown by the dot-and-dash lines of Fig. 13 is made from 0.025-inch thick sheet brass, and two bulging operations are required. After the necessary annealing and trimming operations, the die shown is used to produce an oval shape by direct hydraulic pressure. These dies are made in halves and are operated on a bench fixture of the type illustrated in Fig. 11. A water pressure of 800 pounds per square inch is employed, which may be furnished either by a hydraulic accumulator or a force pump. It is important to note that an annealing operation was necessary before this bulging operation, since otherwise the hard shell produced in drawing would cause the work to be split under the strain of bulging.

It is not practicable to perform the next forming operation hydraulically. This operation consists of expanding the mouth of the shell, and if an attempt were made to use water pressure a space would have to be left around the shell for the water to force the metal into. The result would be that water would be admitted to both sides of the shell, and no expanding action would result. With this method of hydraulic forming the water must be confined to the interior and not be allowed to fill spaces that are intended for the forming operation. The operation of expanding the mouth of this shell is performed on a power press, with split dies arranged to hinge and clamp by means of a cam.

The final forming operation, in which two bosses on the lamp case are produced, is a typical example of the sort of

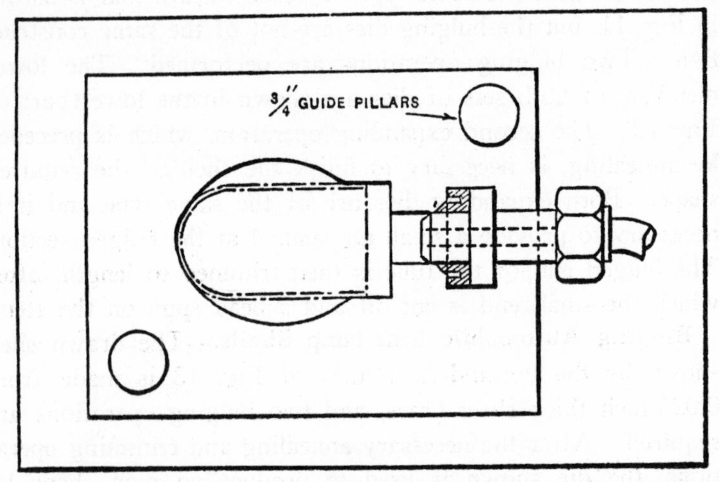

Fig. 13. Plan View of Die Used for Bulging Shell of Automobile Side-lamp

work that can be performed by hydraulic bulging without difficulty and without a great expenditure for tools. The dies for this operation are similar to those shown in Fig. 13 except that they contain recesses to produce the bosses. One boss recess is let into the bottom half of the die and the other is partly in each die member. The same construction of dowel-pins for aligning the die members, flexible connections, and two-way cock are used as employed in other bulging and forming operations previously described. The pressure employed in this operation is 800 pounds per square inch.

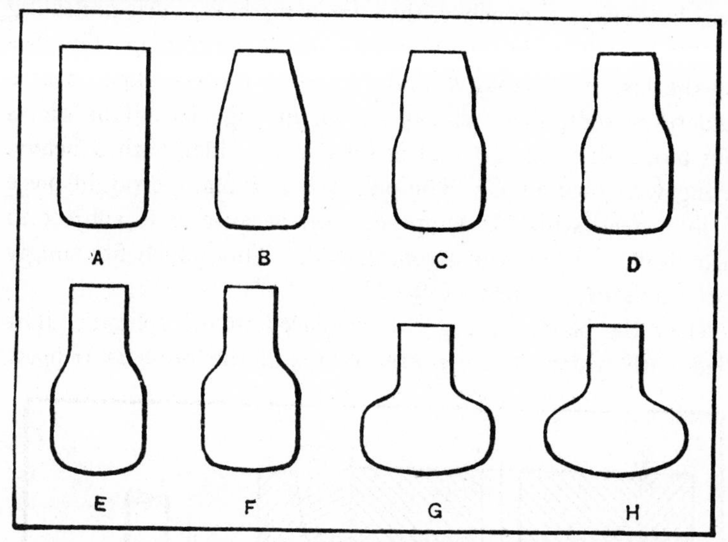

Fig. 14. Successive Steps in Making One-piece Brass Door Knob

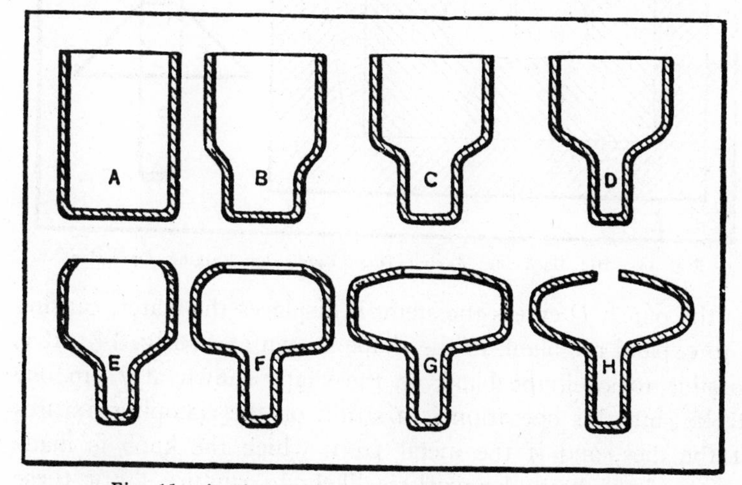

Fig. 15. Another Method of Making Brass Door Knobs

Making a One-Piece Brass Door Knob.—Two ways of making a one-piece, pressed, brass door knob are illustrated in Figs. 14 and 15. The shell *A*, Fig. 14, used in connection with the method to be described first, is a simple job of drawing, and it is produced in dies of the usual type. The next five blanks *B*, *C*, *D*, *E* and *F* are made with simple tapering dies, but using a punch with a tapering bore. An annealing operation is necessary between each press operation. The dies for the last two blanks *G* and *H* are of the type known as a fluid or water punch; one is shown in Fig. 16. This die is split along the line *AB* and is held in a holder with a heavy, strong wedge clamp *C*. The punch *D* is a plain, straight piece of tool steel, which is tempered, not because it is subject to wear, but to stiffen and strengthen it. This punch fits snugly in the hole in the stem of the blank.

After the blank *F*, Fig. 14, is placed in the split die, it is filled with water (some prefer oil) and the press is tripped.

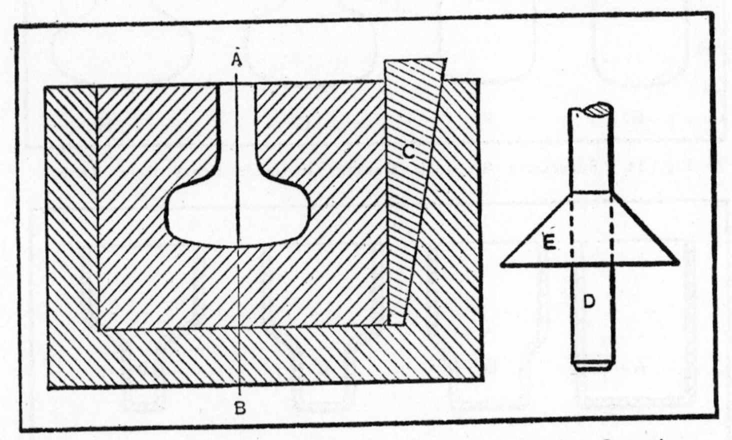

Fig. 16. Die Used for Making Door Knobs by Bulging Operation

As the punch *D* enters the stem, it displaces the water, causing it to expand the blank to the shape shown at *G*, Fig. 14. It is possible to swell the blank to the shape shown at *H* in one stroke; but this operation is a strain on the clamping fixtures of the dies, and if the metal from which the knob is made is not of the best, the work is likely to rupture. For these reasons blank *F* is pressed into the form *H* in two stages, between which the work is annealed. The operations in both these stages, are the same.

As the punch descends in the work, some of the fluid is forced out; and as it is under heavy pressure and passes through a small opening, it is likely to be thrown some distance from the press. This trouble and the work of filling each blank are partly avoided by setting the die in a pan that is deep enough to keep the work and die submerged in the fluid. The fluid on the surface retards the upward flow of the water from the work, but does not entirely stop its being thrown about, so a thin brass guard *E*, Fig. 16, is fastened to the punch.

The second method of making one-piece, drawn door knobs (shown in Fig. 15) is somewhat similar to that described, but the reduction in diameter is on the closed end of the blank. This reduction is continued until the desired size for the shank of the knob has been obtained. Afterward the open end is gradually closed in. It is possible to close the end almost entirely, but it is sometimes left open about 5/8 inch and then turned in the lathe to fit an embossed button, which is soldered or screwed in place.

CHAPTER XXI

DIES FOR SPECIAL OPERATIONS

THE dies included in this chapter are miscellaneous types, many of which are not used in the average plant as generally as those described previously. Some of the designs illustrated, however, are used extensively in certain branches of sheet-metal manufacture.

Forming Rivets and Dowels on Die-made Parts.—The cost of manufacturing various light sheet-metal parts often can be reduced greatly by forming in a die and integral with the work, projections which take the place of rivets. This general plan has been utilized quite extensively in the electrical and other industries for permanently assembling light parts. The diagram Fig. 1 illustrates how these projections or rivets are formed in a die. As the illustration shows, the punch is pushed about half way through the metal; this causes the metal to flow into the die, thereby producing a projecting rivet as shown at *A*. The punch is slightly tapered and the diameter at the end is about 1/32 inch larger than the diameter of the hole in the die in which the rivet is formed. It will be understood that this difference in diameter prevents the metal from being completely sheared off in the sheet.

This method may be described as a partial punching operation, as a punch penetrates about one-half the stock thickness and forces the boss into a pocket in the die which controls the diameter and compresses the metal, thus forming a stronger projection than would be obtained otherwise. The length h Fig. 2, of the dowel or boss should not exceed one-half of the dowel diameter d and h should not exceed one-half of the stock thickness t. This is a practical rule which may be applied either to steel or non-ferrous metals, such as brass.

This same method may also be utilized to form dowel-pins

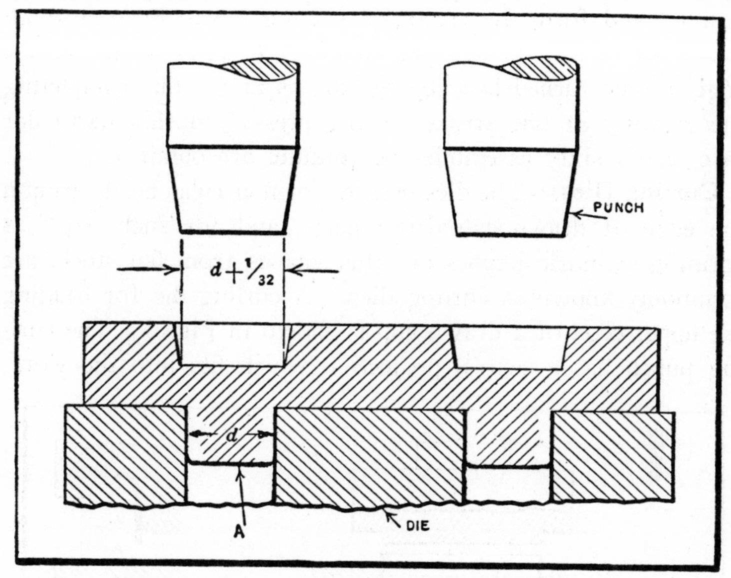

Fig. 1. Method of Producing Projections on Sheet-metal Parts, which may be Used as Rivets

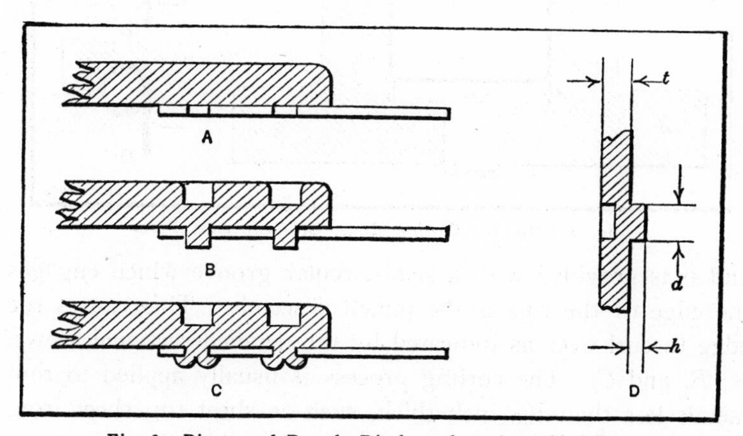

Fig. 2. Rivets and Dowels Die-formed on Assembled Part

such as are required in some cases to insure the accurate location of parts relative to each other.

Diagrams *A*, *B* and *C* Fig. 2, illustrate how a steel spring is cold riveted to the heavier section. Plain round punches descend and form the rivets by forcing metal down through the holes in the spring (see diagram *B*); the metal at the edge is then turned back by the die as at *C*, thus completing the riveting at one stroke of the press. In this particular case, about sixty assemblies per minute are obtained.

Curling Dies.—The dies used to form circular beads around the edge of drawn cylindrical parts, and for such work as forming cylindrical tubes or other shapes from flat stock, are commonly known as curling dies. A curling die for beading the upper edge of a drawn cup is shown in Fig. 3. The curling punch has a central projection which fits into the work,

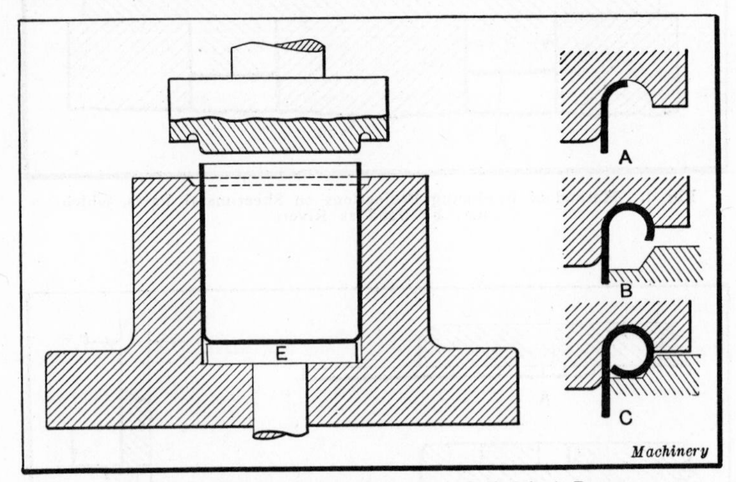

Fig. 3. Die for Curling Edges of Cylindrical Parts

and it is provided with a semi-circular groove which engages the edge of the cup as the punch descends. This causes the edge to curl over as indicated by the detailed sectional views, *A*, *B*, and *C*. The curling process is usually applied to thin metals less than 1/32 inch thick, such as sheet tin, sheet iron, and sometimes brass or copper. Some curling dies are equipped with an ejector or "knockout" *E*, especially if the work is of such a shape that it cannot readily be removed by hand.

The diameter of the bead that can be formed in a curling die must not be too large in proportion to the diameter of the work, and is ordinarily not over $\frac{3}{16}$ inch for tin plate and sheet iron. This limitation as to diameter is due to the fact that, as the edge is forced outward by the curling punch, the circumference increases and the metal is stretched; hence, if the diameter of the bead is too large, this excessive stretching of the material causes it to crack in a radial direction at numerous points around the edge. If the metal is well annealed, naturally a comparatively large bead can be formed. Curling dies, especially when used for forming a bead or curl around a wire at the edge of tin-ware, etc., are commonly referred to as wiring dies. Some wiring dies are practically the same

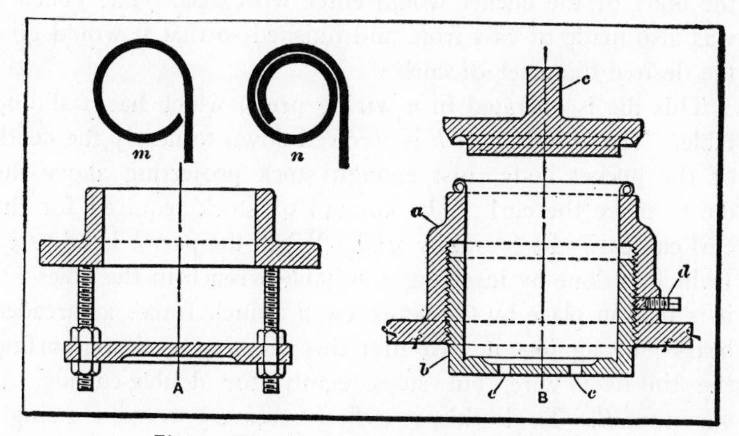

Fig. 4. Dies for Curling the Rims of Buckets

as the one just described, excepting that the die has a floating spring-supported ring upon which the wire ring rests. As the punch descends, the curl is formed around the wire, enclosing it. Curling or wiring dies for tapering parts such as milk pans, etc., have a curling punch which is composed of six or eight segments instead of being solid, so that it can contract when entering the tapered part.

Curling Dies for Tin Buckets.—In Fig. 4 are shown two adjustable curling dies, such as are used for the curling, or "false wiring," of straight tin buckets. Dies of this style can be used for curling the rims of buckets of various depths, by adjusting the bottom of the die to the depth of the bucket to be curled. The die shown at *A* is an old design, and it was somewhat difficult to properly adjust the bottom of this die, as one side was very apt to be a little higher than the other, which caused trouble. Because of this trouble in connection with the adjustment, a new die was made, as shown at *B*. The cast iron body *a* was faced off as indicated by the finishing marks *f*, and a thread cut on the inside as shown. The part *b* was then threaded to fit *a*, and these two parts were screwed together. They were then clamped to the faceplate of a lathe, and set by the finished surfaces *f* of *a*. The hole on the inside was then bored, and it was given 1/64 inch taper, so that the body of the bucket would enter with ease. The punch *c* was also made of cast iron, and finished so that it would give the desired diameter of curl.

This die is operated in a wiring press, which has a sliding table. The bottom part *b* is screwed down to nearly the depth of the bucket body, just enough stock projecting above the die to make the curl. The amount of stock required for the curl can easily be found by trial. When the part *b* is adjusted (which is done by inserting a suitable wrench in the holes *e*), it is held in place by the set-screw *d*, which forces a threaded brass plug against it. At first this die was used for curling the tin over wire, but subsequently for double-curling, as shown at *B*. To do this, it is first necessary to make a single curl, as shown at *m*, then screw the part *b* in about 1/4 inch, and repeat the curling operation, thus obtaining a double curl as at *n*. Much time is saved by curling buckets in this way, and they are almost as strong as when wire is used.

Curling Dies for Small Brass Covers.—Three forms of curling or "wiring" dies are shown in Fig. 5. These were designed for curling the edges of brass covers, but on account of the smallness of the wire in proportion to the thickness of the metal, considerable trouble was experienced before securing a die that would do the work properly. The brass was 0.018 inch thick, and the wiring was 0.075 inch in diameter. The covers were first drawn to the right shape and length in single-action combination dies. Then a die of the design illustrated at *A* was made, but it was not a success, as the covers appeared as shown in the enlarged section. The metal, instead of curling at the top, curled back at the point *a*, forming an inner shoulder. To overcome this difficulty, the punch was bored out, as shown at *B*, and a spring pressure-pad inserted to prevent the bottom buckling. While this undesirable feature was eliminated, buckling occurred in the side at the unprotected section, between the pad and the punch, as shown at *b* in the enlarged section. This, however, gave a clue to the proper solution of the problem, which was to bore out the body of the punch still larger and insert a pressure-pad equal in size to the full diameter of the inside of the cover, as shown by the right-hand view *C*.

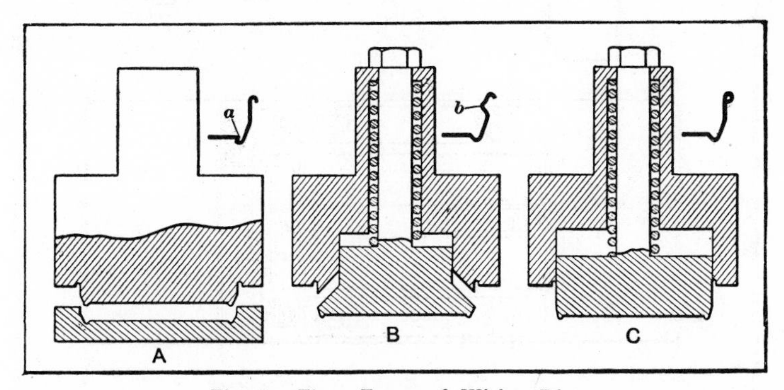

Fig. 5. Three Forms of Wiring Dies

Curling Dies for Hinges.—The dies used for making hinges are about as numerous in design and vary as much as the hinges themselves. They range from small punches and dies for blanking and curling in separate operations, to the complicated automatic machines and press attachments for producing the hinge complete with the two parts and pin assembled. The exact design of the die for making a hinge or, in fact, any other difficult piece of work cannot, of course, be determined arbitrarily but must be governed by conditions. In any case, a die should be so designed that its first cost is not out of proportion to the amount saved by its use. The two dies shown in Figs. 6 and 7 are for curling both parts of the same style of hinge and are simply two differently designed tools for doing the same kind of work. This hinge is shown in the upper right-hand corner of Fig. 6. The ratio of production between the two dies was about 5 to 7 in favor of the die shown in Fig. 7. This difference in output was noted while they were being used at different times in the same press and

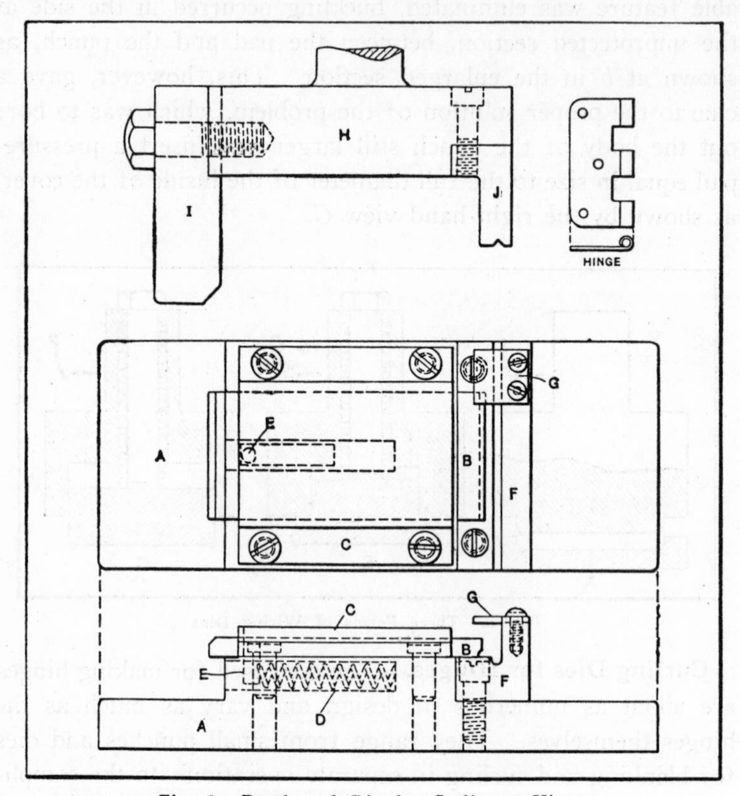

Fig. 6. Punch and Die for Curling a Hinge

by the same operator, the press being run at as high a speed as is consistent with good practice.

The die shown in Fig. 6 consists of a holder or body *A* of cast iron; a slide *B* of tool steel (hardened, and finished by grinding); a cast-iron cap *C* secured to the body *A* by four screws and holding in place slide *B*, permitting it to have a free lateral movement; a spiral spring *D* for moving the slide outward on the upward stroke of the press, by pressure against pin *E*; a tool-steel die *F* which curls the blank, thus forming the hinge joint; and a gage *G* for locating blanks and preventing the operator from pushing them too far back into the die. The punch consists of a holder *H*, a punch *J*, and a cam *I*. The working face of this cam is polished and made as hard as possible; it engages the angular end of slide *B*. The punch *J*

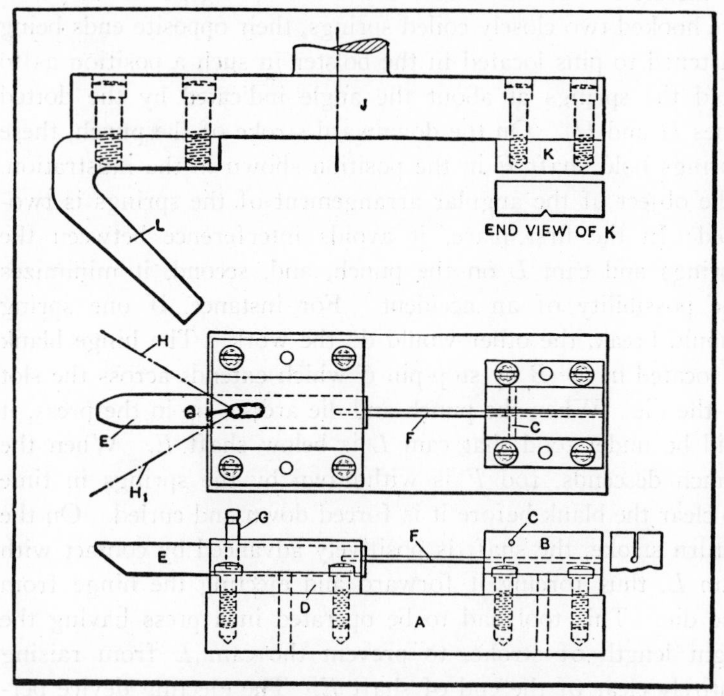

Fig. 7. Hinged Curling Die with Automatic Ejector

has a small V-shaped groove planed in its lower face and engages the upper edge of the hinge blanks. When the die is in operation, the blank is placed between the inner end of slide *B* and the die *F*. When the punch descends, it forces the slide firmly but lightly against the side of the blank and the continued downward movement causes the lower edge to curl around in the circular pocket formed by the parts *B* and *F*. On the upward stroke, the slide *B* is pulled out to the limit of its movement by spring *D*, thus permitting the finished hinge to be removed and a new blank inserted.

The second die, illustrated in Fig. 7, has a cast-iron base *A* to which die *B* is attached. At the rear of die *B* there is a bracket *D* in which the sliding shaft *E* is mounted. Inserted in the forward end of this shaft is a piece of drill rod *F*, the outer end of which is hardened and fits into the hole in the die *B*. Driven into shaft *E* is a spring post *G* to which are hooked two closely coiled springs, their opposite ends being fastened to pins located in the bolster in such a position as to hold the springs at about the angle indicated by the dotted lines *H* and H_1. On the downward stroke of the punch, these springs hold shaft *E* in the position shown in the illustration. The object of the angular arrangement of the springs is two-fold: In the first place, it avoids interference between the springs and cam *L* on the punch, and, second, it minimizes the possibility of an accident. For instance, if one spring should break, the other would do the work. The hinge blank is located in die *B* by stop-pin *C* which extends across the slot in the die. When the punch and die are set up in the press, it will be understood that cam *L* is below shaft *E*. When the punch descends, rod *F* is withdrawn by the springs in time to clear the blank before it is forced down and curled. On the return stroke, the shaft is positively advanced by contact with cam *L*, thus forcing it forward and ejecting the hinge from the die. This tool had to be operated in a press having the right length of stroke, to prevent the cam *L* from raising entirely clear of the end of shaft *E*. The ejecting device permitted a continuous feeding of the blanks to the die, thus increasing the output, as previously mentioned.

Although these dies are simple in design, there are several points which should be observed when constructing them. To insure accurate and uniform production, the parts which curl the metal must be accurately made and smoothly finished. The curved surfaces should also be as hard as possible because there is considerable wear at this point, owing to the friction of the curling operation. When setting the die, it should be carefully aligned with a punch so that when the V-groove on the lower side of the punch engages the upper edge of the blank, the latter will be held in line with the slot in the die, as otherwise the blanks will have a tendency to buckle. The stroke of the press should be carefully adjusted so that the punch descends just far enough to complete the curl, and no more. If it descends too far, the work will jam the die so that it cannot readily be removed. It is also essential that a lubricant be used on the blanks to eliminate unnecessary friction in the curling operation. When using a die of the type shown in Fig. 7, it is important to use blanks that have no burrs on them, because the opening in the die to receive the blank should be only about 0.003 inch wider than the thickness of the stock.

Curling Die for Typewriter Part.—The punch and die illustrated in Fig. 8 completely forms the curl in the forked lever shown in the upper illustration and also in position in the die at *P*. This piece is known as the "ribbon-reverse weighted lever" of a typewriter. It is the usual practice in most cases to form the curl of such a piece in two or three operations. The first operation usually starts the bend, and the curl is finished in the second or third operation by being formed around an arbor. However, in the present case the eye is completely formed in one stroke of the press in a vertical-acting punch and die.

To the base *Y* of the die are attached the other working parts, the principal one being the clamp or jaw *G*. This jaw is provided with a nest for holding the piece to be operated upon. It rocks on the shaft *E*, the ends of which turn in hardened and ground bushings *F*, which are provided to protect the base from excessive wear. The bushings are provided with oil holes as indicated. The jaw is not fitted tightly to the shaft, in order to facilitate its assembly in the die, but is fastened to it by two small set-screws *H*. This feature allows the jaw to be adjusted at exactly the correct angle, and also permits of easy and quick dismounting in case of repairs.

When the press starts its downward movement, the pin *I* bears against the lug *J* on one end of the jaw *G*, causing the

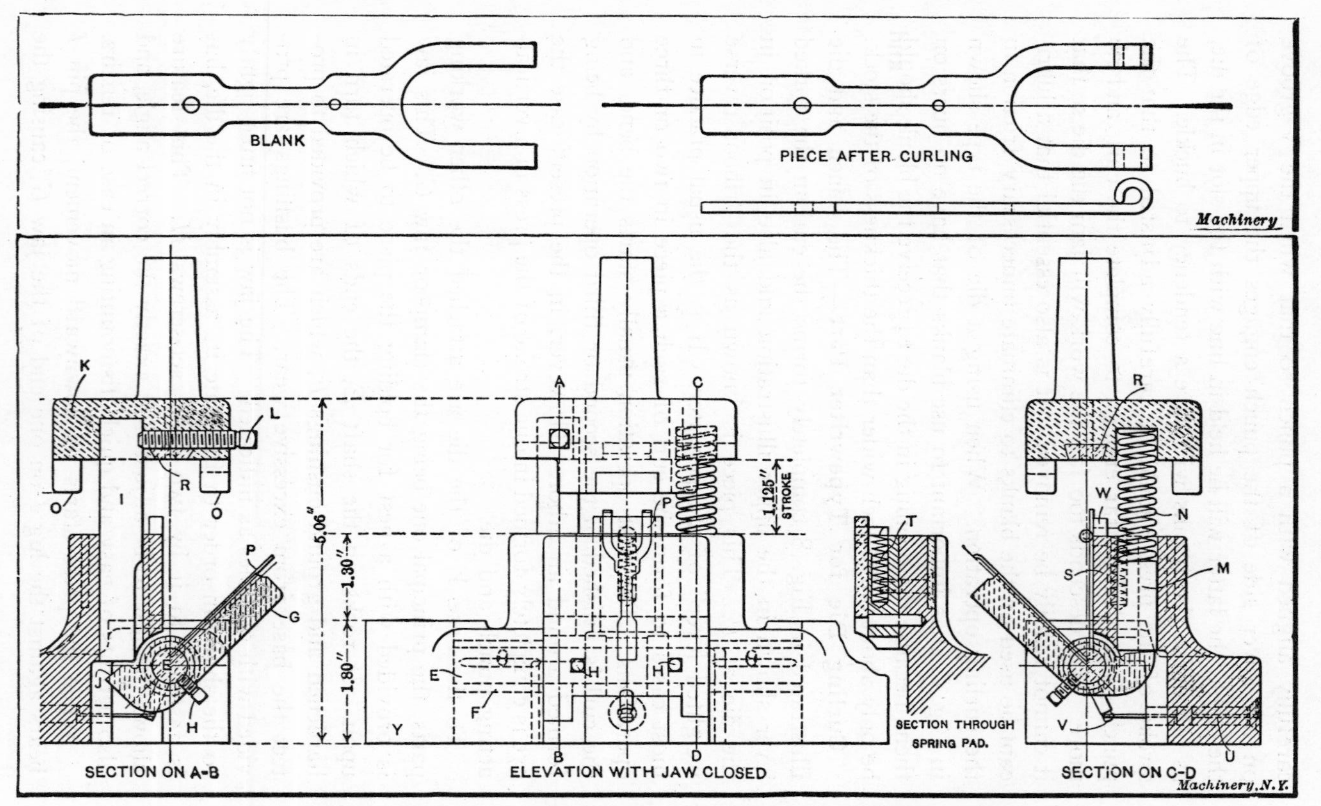

Fig. 8. Curling Die for Typewriter Part shown in Upper Illustration

latter to swing up into a vertical position. The pin *I* is secured in the tool-steel plunger *K* by the set-screw *L*. At the opposite side of the plunger, and bearing against an opposite lug of the jaw *G* is a short plunger *M* actuated by spring *N*. This plunger is provided for equalizing the pressure on *G* and for preventing excessive torsional or twisting strain.

A further downward movement of the ram causes the ears *O* on the plunger to engage and bear against the front or outside of the jaw and the rear of the base, thus holding the jaw securely in the upright position and preventing it from springing back. A hardened and ground bearing plate of tool steel is provided in the rear of the base, where it engages lug *O*, to prevent excessive wear. The grooved former *R* next comes in contact with the top of the work and starts the curl, which is finished at the end of the stroke. The supporting pad *W* is depressed in the meantime, sliding in the block *S*. On the up-stroke of the press the pad is returned to its normal position by the spring shown at *T*. The jaw is released by the raising of the pin *I* and falls back by gravity into the position shown to the left. It is aided in falling back by the spring *U*, secured to the back of the base and to the stud *V* at the bottom of the jaw.

Progressive Die with Adjustable Punches.—The difference between turning out a really satisfactory product and one that will just pass inspection is often a matter of adjustment, as provided for in the design of the die. One of the principal objects in designing the die to be described, was to provide means for adjusting independently, the forming punches which advance from the sides and form small eyes on the edges of the work.

This die is designed to take flat steel sheared to the required width and in standard lengths of about 14 feet. The first punch and die at *A*, Fig. 9, trims notches in both sides of the strip, the second die at *B* bends down the edges of the remaining prongs, while the curling punches at *C* complete the curling of the eyes, as indicated at *a*, Fig. 11. A short length of the work is notched and formed at each stroke of the press

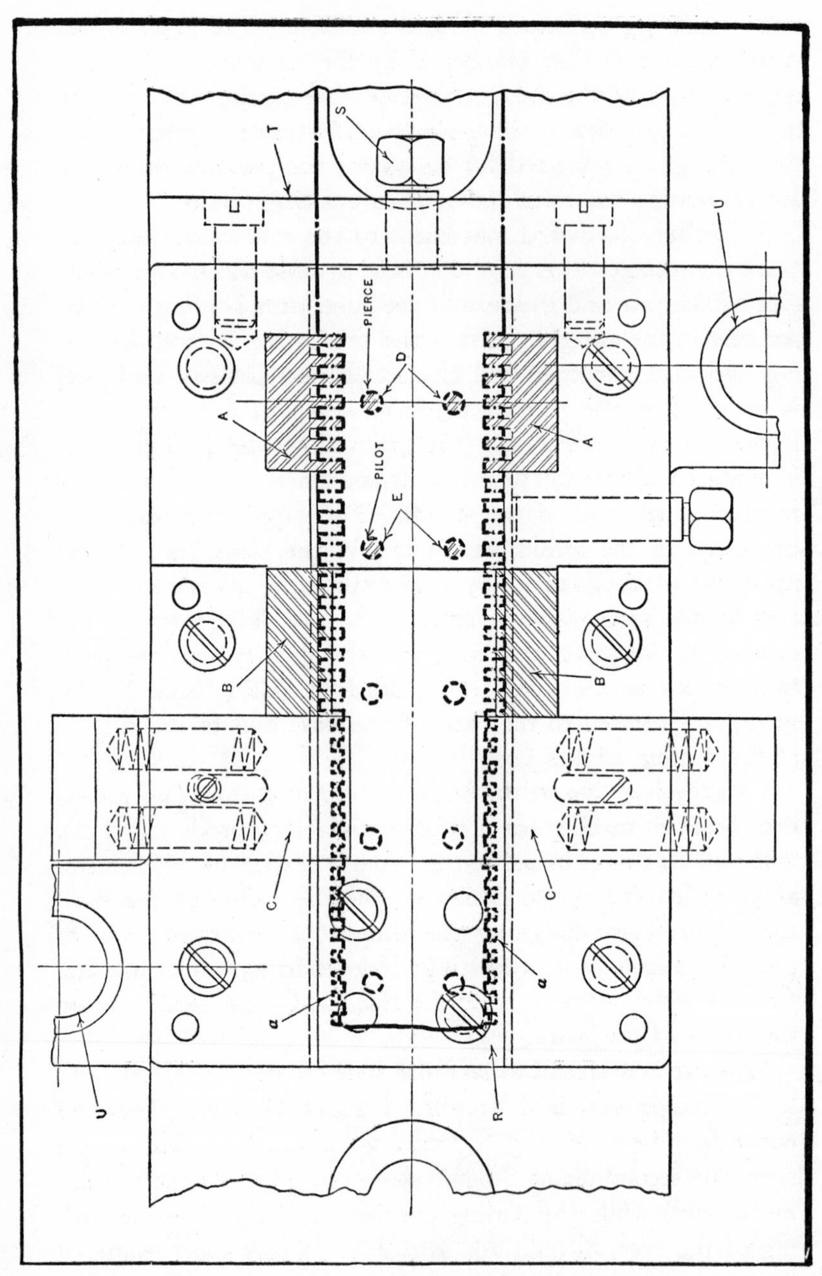

Fig. 9. Plan View of Die with Side-forming Punches

and the stock is fed forward the proper distance after each stroke by means of a roll feed of the usual type. Two punches at *D*, Fig. 9, pierce holes in the work at each stroke, and the pilot pins *E* enter these holes after the work has been advanced to bring the holes under the pins. The work is thus accurately located after the feeding movement.

A cross-section through the trimming dies *A*, Fig. 9, is shown in the view at *X*, Fig. 10. The notching punches shear against the die-block *D*, and the round punches *E*, passing into holes in the die-block, pierce the holes in the work. While the punching operation is being performed, the block *F* is

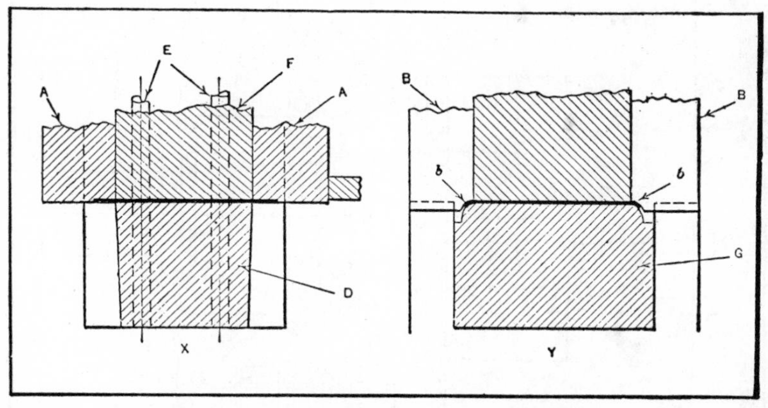

Fig. 10. Cross-section Through Punches and Dies

held in spring contact with the work so the latter will be stripped from the punches as they ascend.

At *Y* is shown a section of the first forming die which turns down the ends of the prongs *b* on the work. The punches *B* form the prongs over the formed block *G*, and in both the trimming and forming units the punches are backed up by a solid wall in the die so that there can be no tendency for them to spring away from the work.

At the next station in the die the eyes on the work are curled completely by dies *C*, shown in Fig. 9 and in the cross-section view, Fig. 11. In this end view, Fig. 11, the die is broken away to show the forming slide construction. The

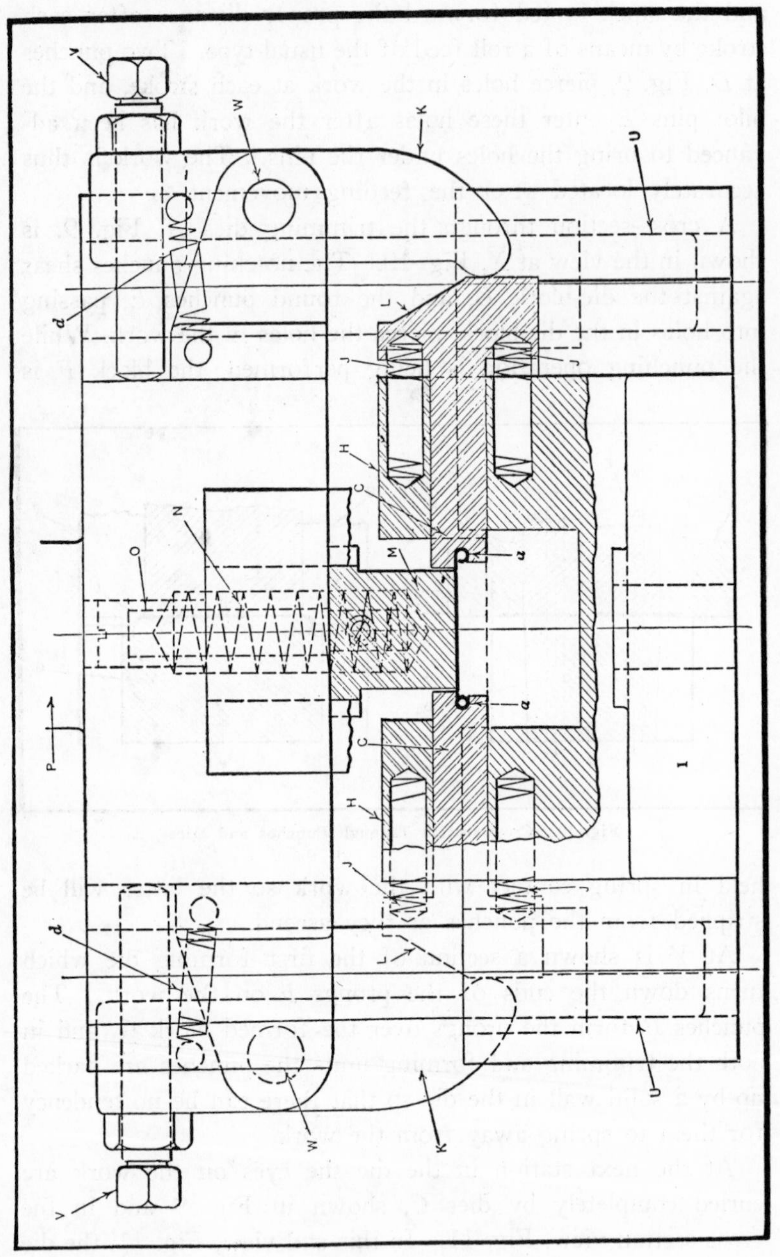

Fig. 11. End Elevation, Showing Section of Side-forming Punches

side punches *C* are mounted in blocks *H* which are attached by means of screws and dowels to the upper surface of the die-holder *I*. The punches *C* have springs *J* inserted in them which tend to hold the punches back from the position shown and clear of the work, so that the only time they are in the forward position shown, is at the bottom of the stroke when levers *K* have forced them in by coming in contact with the beveled surfaces *L* as the levers *K* descend with the punch-holder. This action of forcing the slides in causes the eyes on the work to be curled to shape. As the curl for the eyes is started at the previous station by punches *B*, Figs. 9 and 10, the curling operation is easily accomplished.

Spring block *M*, Fig. 11, which is forced down by a series of heavy springs *N*, holds down the work and strips it from the punches, the spring block being prevented from coming out of the die by screws *O*. The block *R*, Fig. 9, is fastened to the left-hand end of the die-block by screws and dowels. The various sections of the die are forced against this block by a screw *S* in plate *T* which is attached to the end of the die-bed. Pillar pins and bushings at *U* serve to keep the punch member properly aligned with the lower die member. The punch and the die-holder are attached to the press members in the usual manner.

Adjustment of the levers *K*, Fig. 11, so that the eyes on the work at *a* are properly closed, is effected by adjusting screws *V*, which cause the levers to swing on pivot studs *W*. This adjustment varies the movements of the slide punches *C*. The levers *K* are held in brackets attached by machine screws to the sides of the punch-holder. The springs *d* serve to hold the screws *V* of levers *K* in contact with the punch-holder so that the levers will not be jarred out of place by the action of the punch.

Contracting Punch for Hot-drawing Die.—While there appears to be little available information on the subject of hot press-work, much has been published on cold-drawn work in sheet metals up to 1/8 inch thick. The conditions in handling cold-drawn and hot-press work are by no means similar.

In the latter case, the heating of the work introduces expansion and contraction, which does not occur in the cold-drawing operations. This obviously affects over-all sizes, particularly on large size pressings. Again, in hot-press work, the dimensions of the finished pieces are further affected by delays in stripping the work from the punch, for it is obvious that if the pieces leave the punch at different heats, there will be a variation in the permanent "sets" or in the size of the pieces.

In using a single-action press, the difficulty of stripping becomes a serious problem for the die designer, especially when mass production is required. The devices for stripping cold-drawn work from the punch usually comprises some form of spring action, although compressed air is sometimes used. Neither of these methods, however, are practical for hot-press work, where the grip on the punch is augmented by the shrinkage of the pressed part. To overcome this condition, large and powerful springs would be necessary, and it is not always convenient to make or procure these.

Under some conditions, stripping can be effected without the aid of spring or pneumatic power by employing the principle shown in Fig. 12. This design is simple in construction and operation and is capable of a variety of applications to hot press-work, although its advantages depend to some extent on the form of the work. The parts made with this particular die are triangular-shaped body brackets of the design shown in the reduced scale view at *W*.

A half-section view of the punch member of the die, as fitted to the top stationary head of the press, is shown in the lower view. The two false jaws *A* and *B*, made of machine steel, are machined to fit the inclined surfaces of the punch member *C*. The jaws *A* and *B* are held in contact with the inclined surfaces of the punch by screws *D* and pins *E*. The elongated slot at *F* permits the jaws to slide down on the inclined surface for a distance of 3/4 inch. This movement reduces the over-all dimension *L* 1/4 inch or more, depending upon the degree of taper on the sliding jaws and the length of the slots *F*. The bracket is thus immediately released by the contracting punch member, and is held in the bottom die by the spring-actuated plungers *G*.

Trimming Die for Small Forgings.—Fig. 13 shows a trimming die for removing the fin or flash from cycle free-wheel ring forgings in one operation. This die has a cast-steel bolster *A* into the top of which is screwed the hardened external trimming ring *B*. Two fillister-head screws *C* are inserted in ring *B* to prevent it from working loose. The die

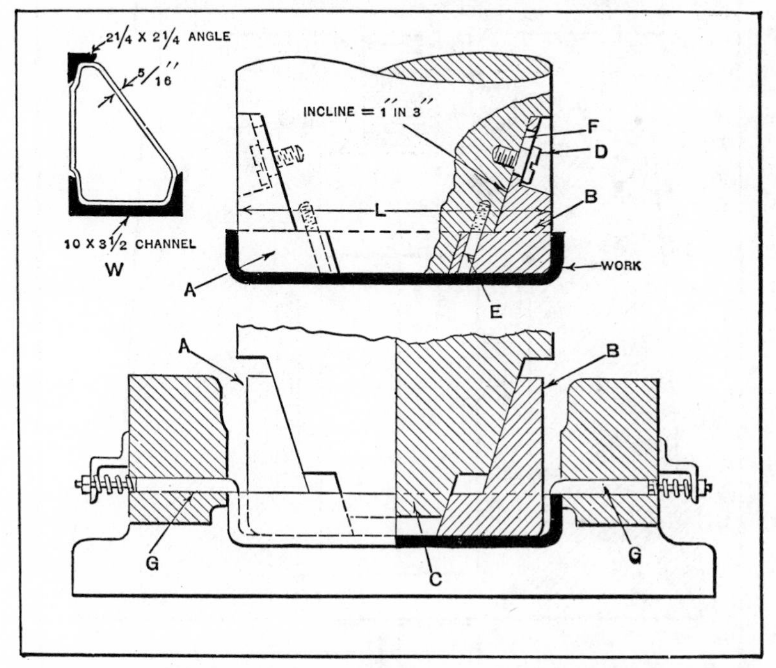

Fig. 12. Contracting Punch for Hot-drawing Die

D, which is made of special punch steel, serves an an extractor and also forms the ring for punching out the center part *S* of the forging. On the up stroke the spring *E* actuates die *D*, causing the forging *T* to be extracted from ring *B*. The center punch *F* is also made of special punch steel and is hardened and ground. This member forms a center which locates the sliding punch *G*. There is a shoulder on the outside diameter of punch *G*, on which flange *H* rests. It is

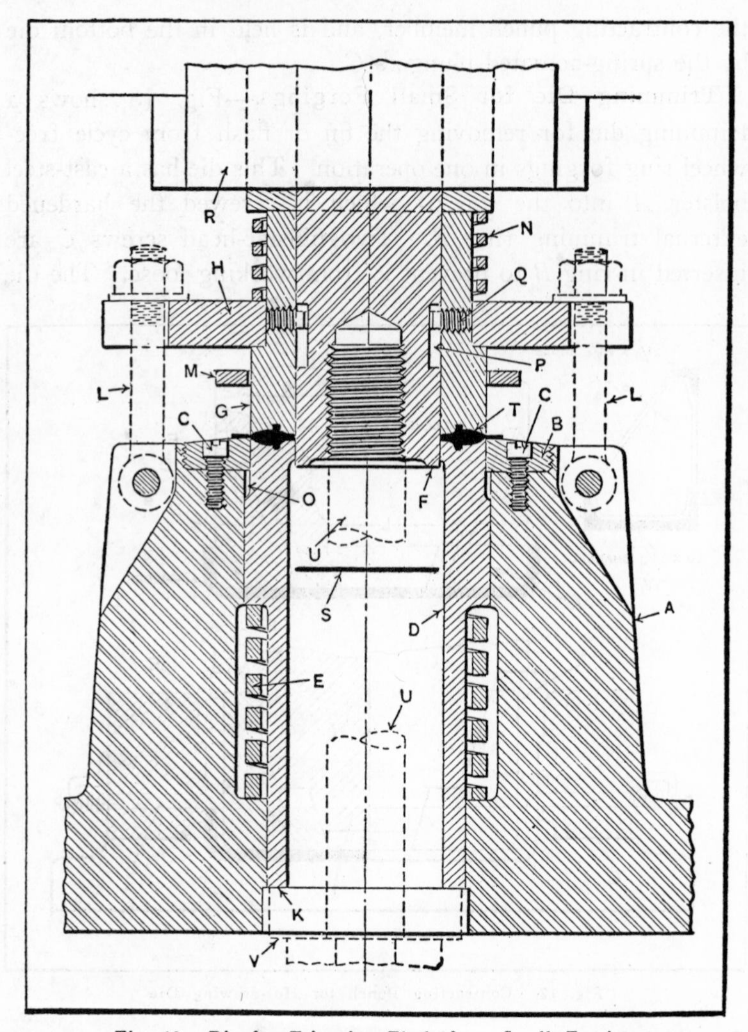

Fig. 13. Die for Trimming Flash from Small Forgings

necessary to provide a stripper M for the outer flash. Spring N acts on punch G through flange H.

The operation of the tool is very simple, and it is well adapted for use on a single-acting press. Referring to the illustration, it will be noted that the center of the forging has just been punched and that the fin is falling through the hole in die D. As the ram of the press continues its downward stroke, punch *G* will clip the outer part of the forging. On the return of ram *R*, stripper *M* removes the fin from punch *G*. Die *D*, actuated by spring *E*, follows the up stroke of the press until the shoulder at *O* strikes the bottom of the trimming ring *B*. Ram *R* continues its upward stroke carrying with it punch *F*.

Punch *G*, through the action of spring *N*, will remain down until punch *F* has moved upward a sufficient distance to bring the bottom of the slot *P* into contact with the screw *Q*. This enables ram *R* to open the dies so that the finished forging can be taken out. It should be noted that punch *G* and die *D* are both formed at the ends to fit the forging. This is necessary to prevent any distortion of the forging, which is of very light weight and is required to be kept within close limits of accuracy, only 1/32 inch being allowed for finishing. Center punch *F* is threaded for an extractor bolt *U* (shown in dotted lines) on which is placed a mild steel washer *V*, which rests on the end of punch *D* at point *K* when the bolt is employed to release the dies. It will be noticed in the illustration that two swinging bolts *L*, shown by dotted lines, are fitted into slots cast into bolster *A*. When the dies become worn, they occasionally stick in ring *B*. The extractor bolt is then screwed into the punch *F* from beneath the press table. The bolt thus clamps the parts *R, F, G*, and *D* together as one piece. The dies are then released by turning the flywheel by hand. To release a forging in case it becomes stuck on punch *F*, it is only necessary to swing the bolts *L* into slots cut in flange *H* so that the punch can be readily withdrawn.

Riveting Die.—The riveting die illustrated in Fig. 14 is used for attaching ears to tin pails. The cylindrical horn *A* is attached to the power press, extending out horizontally so that the pail may rest on it while the ears are being riveted in place. The pail is abutted against the spring gage block *B* as shown in the illustration, and the ear *C* laid on it in the proper position for riveting. The rivets *D* are set in suitable depressions in the horn, these depressions being formed by special long screws which do not extend quite to the circum-

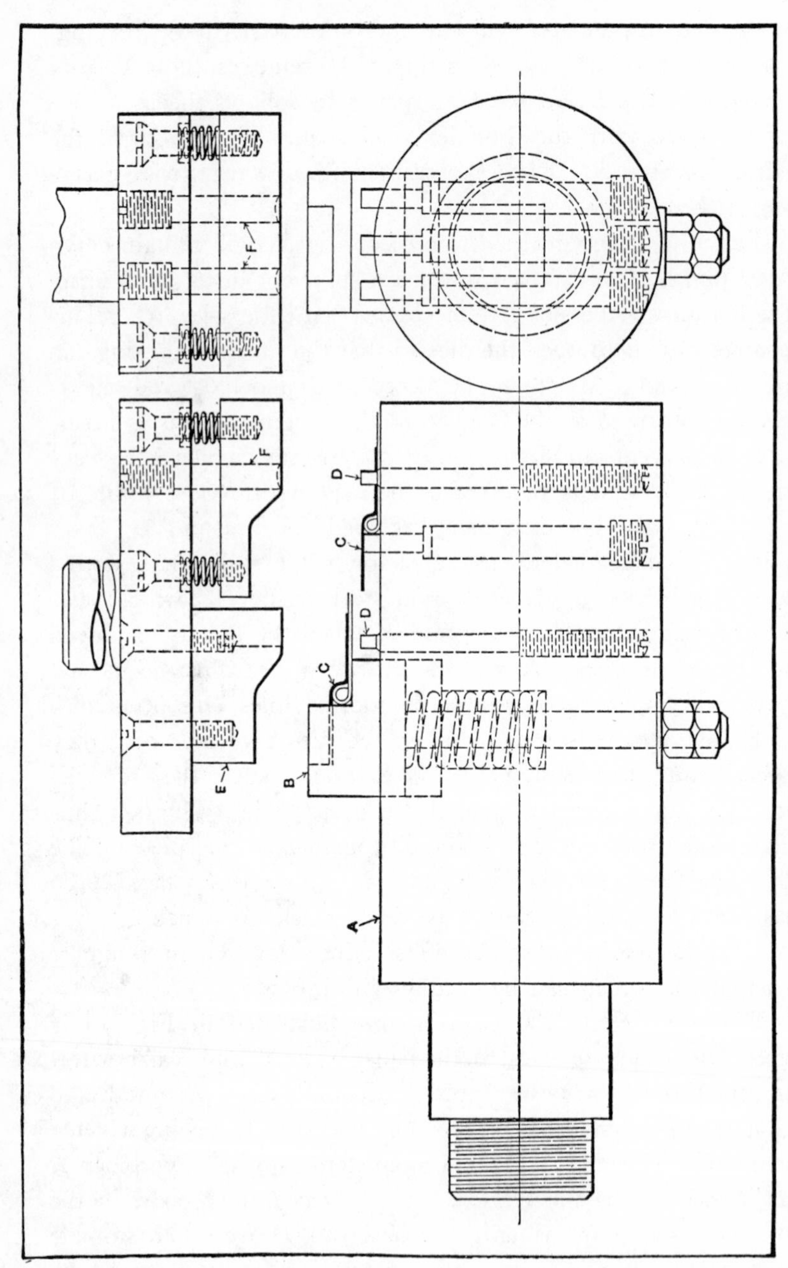

Fig. 14. Die Used on Power Press for Riveting Ears to Pails

ference on the horn. To permit the depth of depressions to be maintained regardless of wear produced in the riveting operation, it is merely necessary to adjust the screws to the proper depth. The upper member carries a punch-block *E* which, on the descent of the press ram, forces the gage-block and the work which it supports down until the rivets have pierced the pail and ear. The second position of the pail, with the ear partly assembled, is shown near the end of the horn. The ear is supported by spring pins during the riveting operation which takes place with the work located in the second position. The riveting punches *F* are protected by a spring-

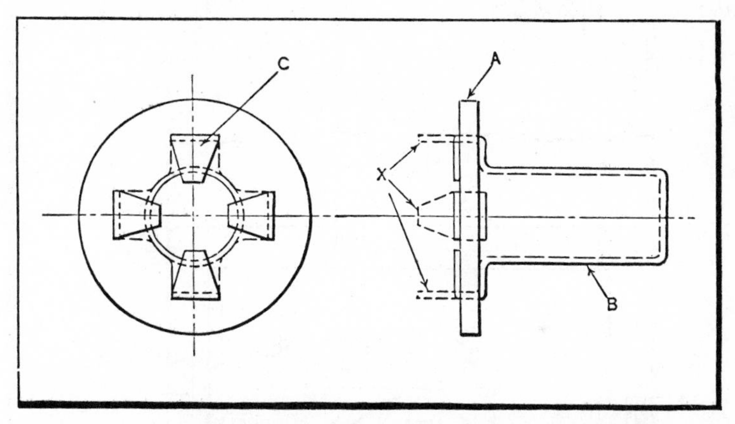

Fig. 15. Part Assembled by Means of the Punch and Die shown in Figs. 16 and 17

backed guard block which, when the press ram descends and the rivet is set down, rests on the ear and acts as a shock absorber. Work of this kind is usually done on a regular horning press that is arranged especially for the performance of rivet-setting operations of this nature, but such a press is not required when dies constructed according to the general design illustrated are employed.

Four-slide Assembling Die.—In order to manufacture the part shown in Fig. 15 on an economical basis, it was necessary to design a quick-acting tool for assembling the ring *A* on the drawn brass sleeve *B*. In assembling these parts, the four prongs on sleeve *B* are passed through notches in the ring *A*

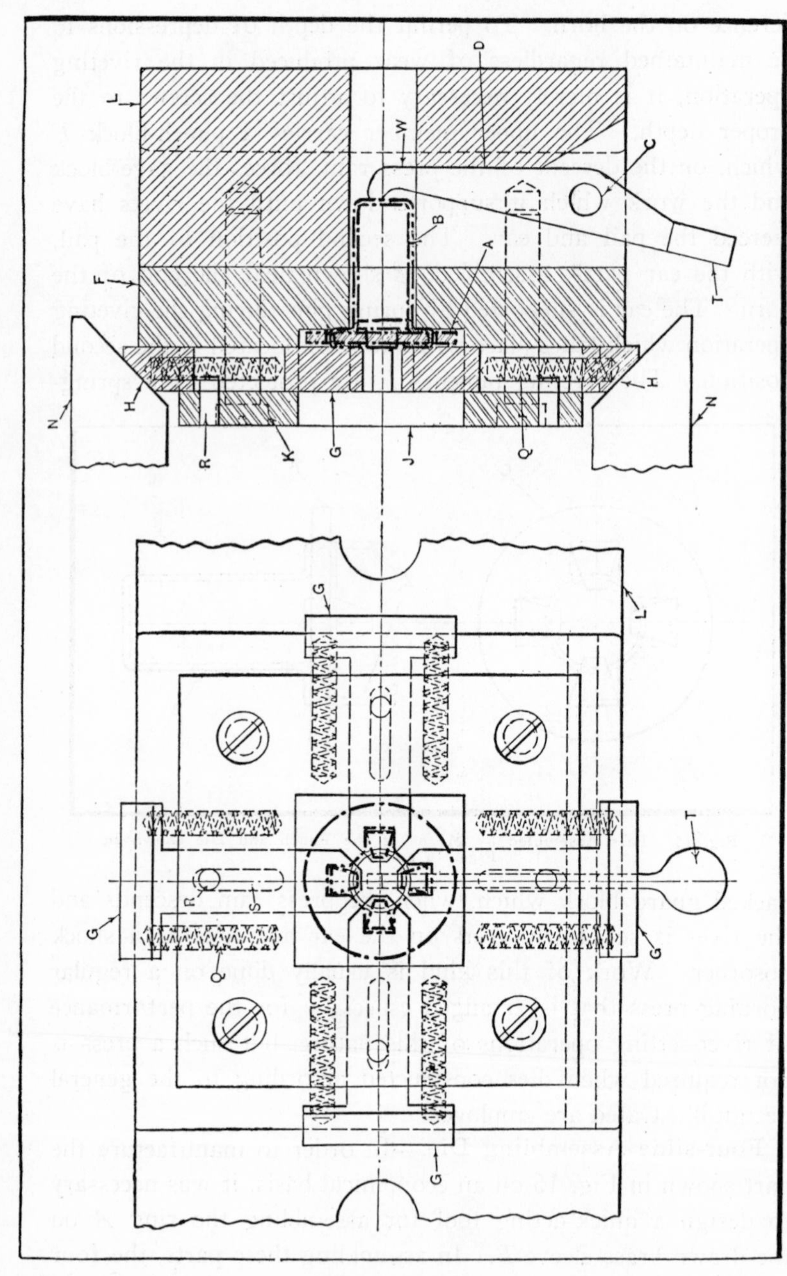

Fig. 16. Die Used in Connection with the Punch shown in Fig. 17 for Assembling Parts shown in Fig. 15

and then bent over into the position shown by the full lines at *C*. The dotted lines at *X* show the position of the prongs before being bent over. This assembling operation was satisfactorily accomplished on a punch press equipped with the die and punch shown in Figs. 16 and 17.

The sleeve or stem *B* of the work is put in a hole in the die, with the closed end resting against the lever *W*, which is pivoted at *C* and prevented from being further depressed by the surface *D*. The sleeve *B* is put in place with the ring *A* over the prongs, the ring resting in the recess in the steel block

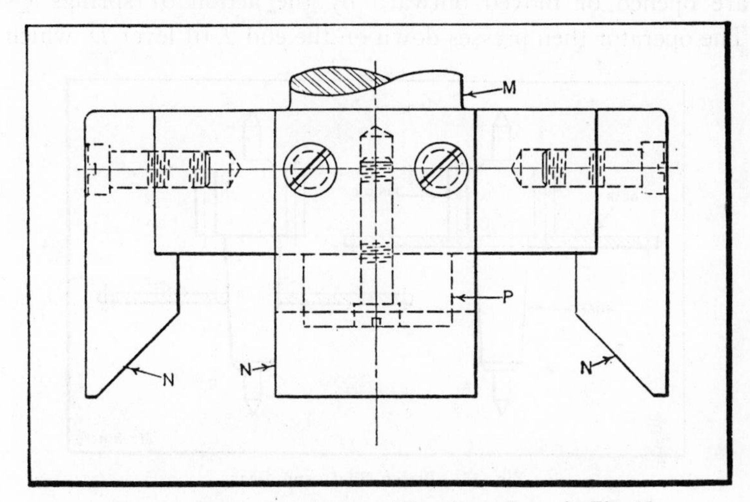

Fig. 17. Punch Used in Assembling Parts shown in Fig. 15

F. In block *F* are four slides *G* which have beveled ends at *H*. These slides are retained in the slots by plate *J*, which is held in place by screws *K* passing through block *F* and entering the base *L*.

The four beveled plungers *N* of the punch (Fig. 17) are attached to the holder *M*, and the steel ring *P* is attached to the center of holder *M*. Springs *Q*, Fig. 16, normally hold slides *G* back about ½ inch from the position in which they are shown so that the stem *B* of the work with the ring *A* in place may be put in the die. The size of the opening in the die is controlled by pins *R*, which enter elongated slots *S* in the slides and limit the outward movement of the slides. As the punch descends, the beveled plungers *N* come in contact with the beveled surfaces *H* on the slides *G*, thereby driving them into the position shown. This action forces the four prongs of the work over, so they clinch the stem on the ring.

A slight amount of play or looseness is allowed in the slides. The disk *P*, Fig. 17, which is attached to the punch strikes the top surfaces of the slides *G*, thus pressing the prongs of sleeve *B* more tightly against the ring *A*. As the punch ascends after completing this operation, the slides *G* are opened or moved outward by the action of springs *Q*. The operator then presses down on the end *T* of lever *D*, which

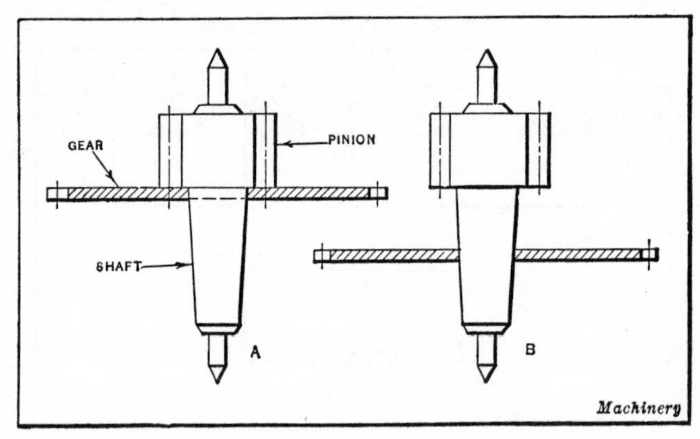

Fig. 18. Pinion Shaft and Gear

pivots about *C* and thereby raises the work so that it can be removed from the die and a new piece put in place. As the end *D* of the ejecting lever is much longer than the opposite end, its greater weight has a tendency to hold the lever in the position shown, so that it does not interfere with the insertion of the work in the die.

Fixture and Die for Assembling Instrument Gear and Shaft.—In order to maintain accuracy in assembling instrument gears on their pinion shafts, as shown at *A*, Fig. 18, it was found necessary to employ the assembling fixture shown in Fig. 19. This fixture drives the pinion shaft from the position shown at *B*, Fig. 18, down through the hole in the gear

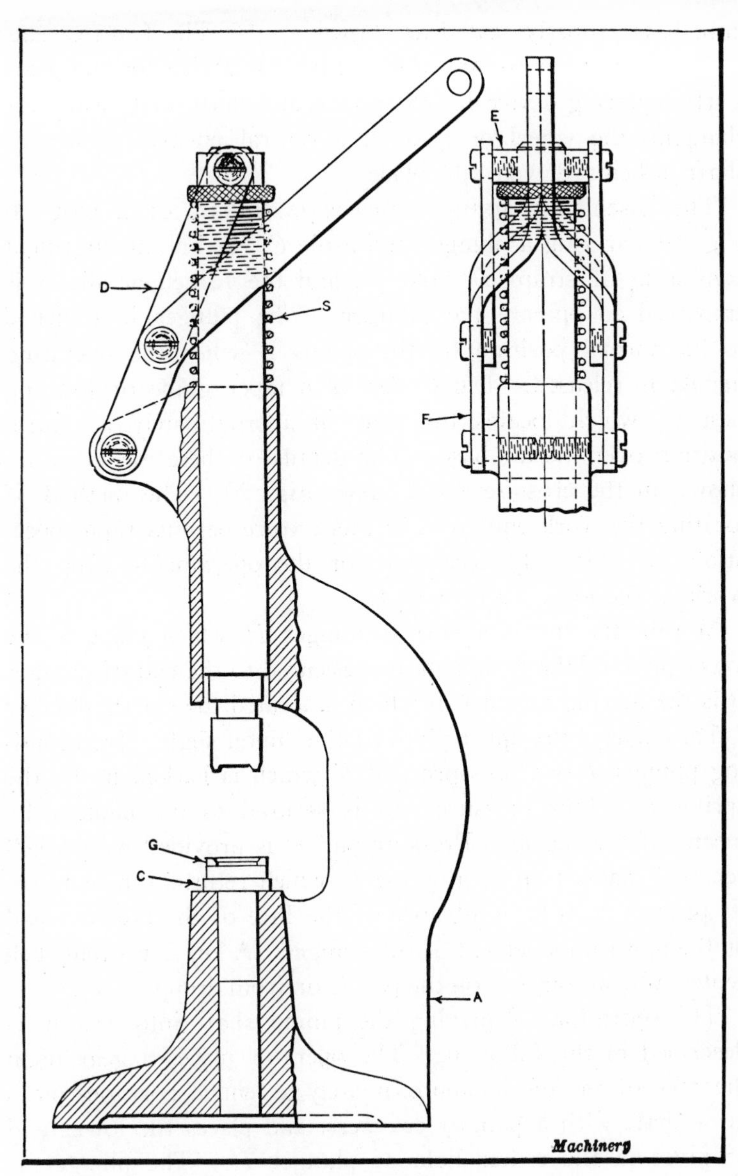

Fig. 19. Fixture for Assembling Shaft and Gear shown in Fig. 18

until it is properly seated as shown at *A*. The features embodied in this fixture are a self-centering device for the gear, a self-centering device for the pinion and shaft, and means for clamping the wheel or gear in a central position while the shaft is being driven into place.

The assembling fixture consists essentially of a base *A*, Fig. 19, carrying a plunger and a die *C*. A link arrangement consisting of straps *D*, yoke *E*, and the forked handle *F* is employed to operate the plunger. The plunger is returned to its normal position by the spring *S* when the operating handle is released. Die *C* carries a taper guide or locating nest *G*, which locates the gear in approximately a central position over the die base. The details of these members are shown in the cross-sectional view, Fig. 20. The method of locating the work employed in this fixture permits rapid operation, as it is only necessary for the operator to drop the work in the loose-fitting nest *G*.

Within the die is a spring plunger *H* which engages the lower pivot of the pinion shaft. Secured to the end of plunger *B* is the driving punch *I* in which is located the spring plunger *J* that engages the upper pivot of the pinion shaft. Surrounding plunger *J* is a pressure pad *K* which is backed up by the spring *L*. This pressure pad is secured to the plunger by means of the cap *M*. Pressure pad *K* is provided with a bell center *N* backed up by a spring *O* which returns the center to its position a little in advance of the face of the pressure pad on the upward movement of the plunger. A key *T* prevents bell center *N* from turning on the pad *K* or from dropping off.

The operation of driving the pinion shaft into a gear is described in the following: The operator places a gear upon the face of the die in approximately a central position, picks up a shaft with a pair of tweezers, and places the lower end or pivot in the center hole of plunger *H*. The plunger is then lowered until the upper pivot of the pinion shaft engages the plunger *J*. When the operating members of the fixture are in this position, the shaft is held in a vertical position and in true alignment with the center of the die.

Upon removing the tweezers and continuing the downward stroke of the plunger, the gear is engaged at its outer edge by the bell center, which, backed up by the light spring *O* to prevent injury to the work, is drawn to a central position on the die. The face of the pressure pad *K*, which is backed up by a heavy spring *L*, clamps the gear in its true central position on the face of the die before the driving punch engages the shoulder on the pinion shaft. During the last part of the downward movement, the punch *I* comes in contact with the shoulder on the pinion shaft and drives the latter member down until the pinion is in contact with the gear. The handle is then released and the plunger returns to the position shown in Fig. 19, after which the assembled pinion and gear are removed from the die member.

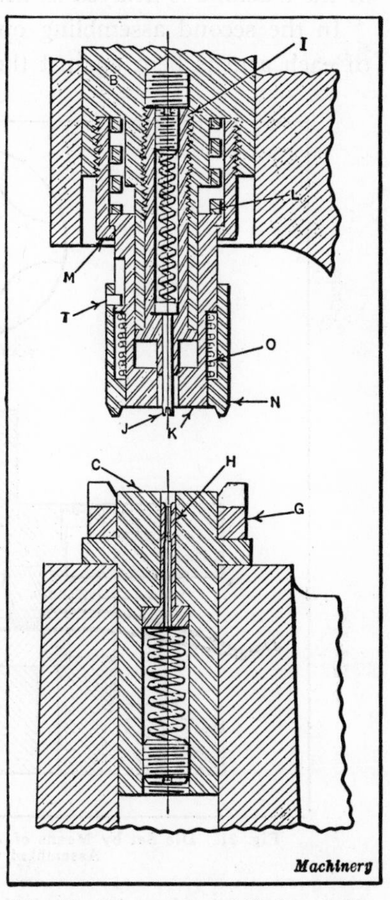

Fig. 20. Cross-section of Shaft and Gear Assembling Dies

Clinching Steering Wheel Arms to Hub.—The four arms of a steering wheel are clinched to the hub by two sets of dies. The first of these sets is shown in Fig. 21. A hub with four arms loosely assembled is placed on die-block *A*, which is cut away as illustrated in the plan view to accommodate the arms. Then on the downward stroke of the ram, the punch bends down the upper edge of each arm over the upturned flange edges of the hub, locking the arms securely on the hub. A knock-out pad *C* is provided to eject the work from the punch, and guide posts keep the punch and die members aligned. Hubs are delivered to the press in which this operation is performed, with the arms loosely assembled on them, so that the operation of the machine is delayed as little as possible.

In the second assembling operation, the bottom inner edge of each arm is bent against the inside of the hub proper, and

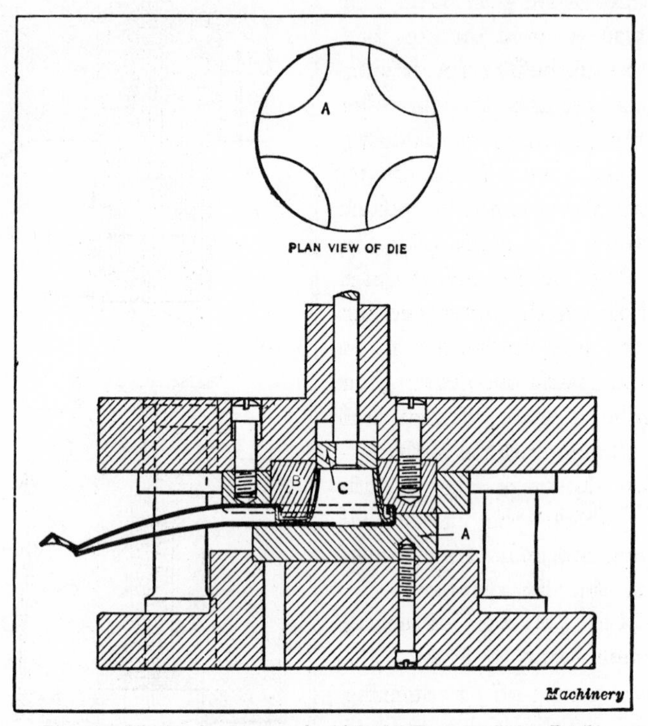

Fig. 21. Die Set by Means of which the Four Arms are Partly Assembled to the Hub

the outer end of each arm is bent back, as illustrated in Fig. 22. The outer end of the arms is later fastened by wood screws to the wooden steering wheel, and is not finish-shaped until this time, so as to insure uniformity in the different arms and facilitate assembling the wheels. For this operation, the hub is seated on die plug *A*, with the outer end of each arm lying on a block *B* which occupies a raised position at the beginning of an operation due to the action of two coil springs located beneath it. On the downward stroke of the press ram, the bottom inner edge of the arms is forced against the inside of the hub, as mentioned, when punch *C* pushes the work down on plug *A*. Simultaneously, the outer end of each arm is bent back as punch *D* forces it on die-block *E*. Stripper plate *F* is actuated by coil springs to eject the work from the punch

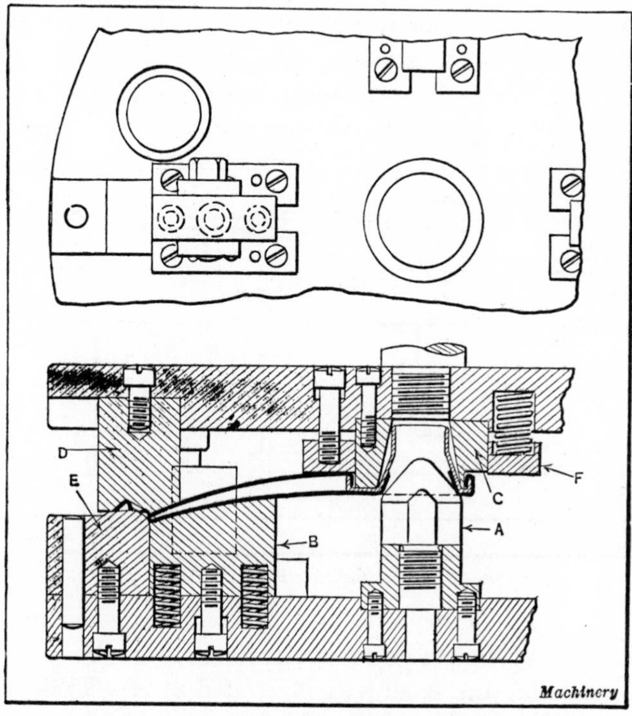

Fig. 22. Second Die by Means of which the Assembling of the Arms to the Hub is Completed

on the return stroke of the ram. Guide posts are also furnished for this set of dies. This operation is the last one performed on power presses, the next step being the casting of the hub center; the alloy used and the equipment employed in casting the center will be described in the following.

The alloy center is cast in the hub, to form a rigid bearing for the steering rod of the automobile. This alloy is a composition of aluminum, copper, and zinc. It is not important that the alloy be especially strong, because the hub stamping gives the necessary strength to the spider, but the alloy should be hard enough to obviate crushing when the nut and washer of the steering rod are clamped on it.

Swaging Dies.—Swaging dies are a type in which parts are formed to the required shape by compressing the metal so that the impressions in the punch and die faces are reproduced upon the work; in other words, instead of shaping the metal by cutting, bending, or drawing, it is formed by compression. The pressure required for swaging is relatively high because it must be sufficient to cause the metal to flow into the punch

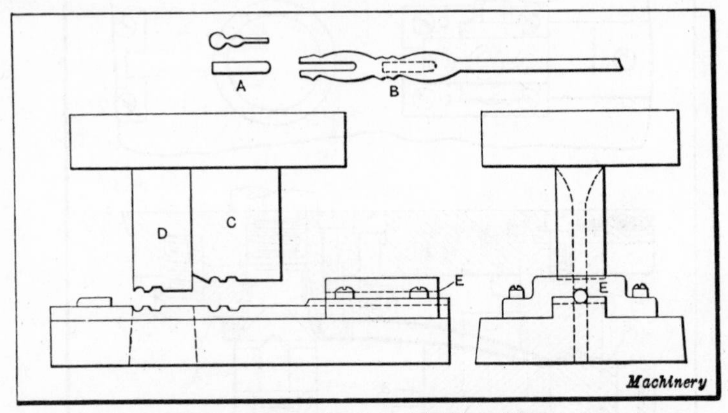

Fig. 23. Swaging and Blanking Die

and die cavities or depressions. A combined swaging and blanking die of simple form is shown in Fig. 23, which is used for making the small part illustrated at *A*. These parts are formed by feeding an annealed brass wire through the die, swaging to the required form, and then blanking it. At *B* is shown the end of the wire after the swaging and blanking punches have done their work. The swaging punch is illustrated at *C*, while *D* is the punch which cuts and forces the blank through the die. The wire is fed through a hole in guide *E* which keeps it in proper alignment with the working faces of both die and punch. The dotted lines shown on the swaged end at *B* indicate where the next piece *A* will be cut

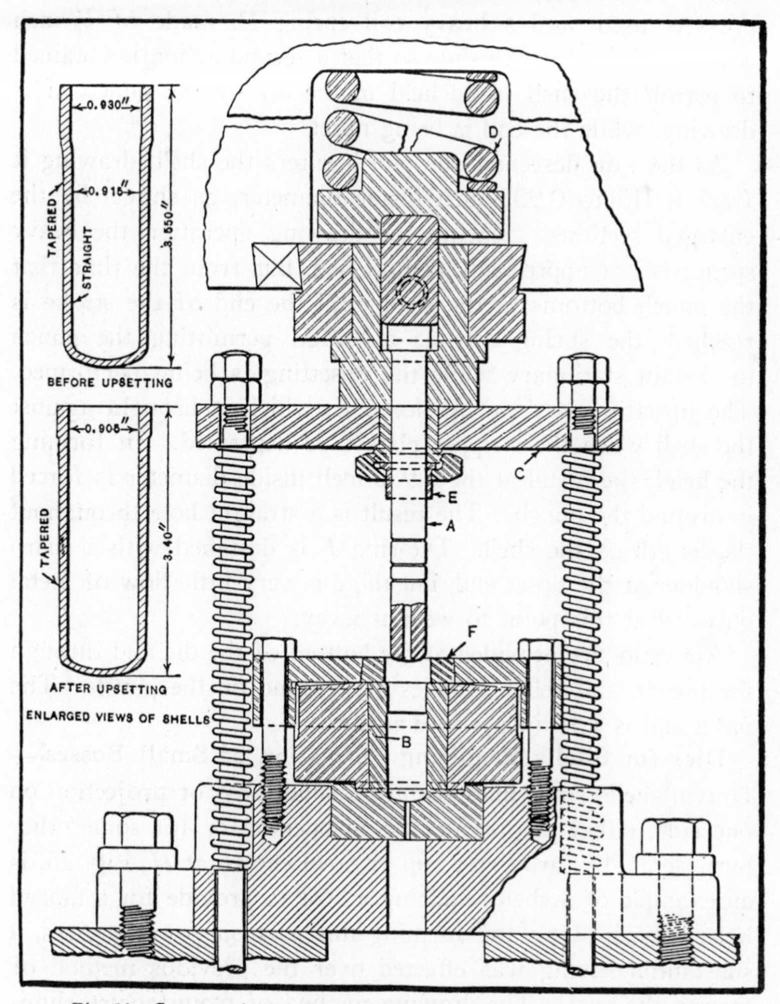

Fig. 24. Cross-section of Upsetting Die, showing its Special Application to the Power Press

from the stock by the blanking punch *D*. A stripper (not shown) removes the scrap from the blanking punch. The pieces after coming from the die are tumbled to remove all fins, and then drilled.

Upsetting End of Drawn Shell.—The die shown in Fig. 24 is used to upset the open end of a drawn shell. This upset end later is squared and threaded. A long-stroke single-action press is used, and a heavy coil spring *D*, made of ⅞-inch wire, is inserted in the slide so that a second action is obtained to permit the shell to be held in the die by the punch after drawing, while the end is being upset.

As the ram descends, the punch enters the shell, drawing it from 0.915 to 0.905 inch inside diameter, as shown by the enlarged sections. During the drawing operation the heavy spring is not appreciably compressed, but from the time that the punch bottoms in the shell until the end of the stroke is reached, the spring acts as a buffer, permitting the punch to remain stationary while the upsetting is being performed. The upsetting is done by sleeve *E*, which is brought against the shell when the stripper plate *C* is depressed. In forming the head, the metal at the 0.930-inch inside diameter is forced in around the punch. The result is a straight hole throughout the length of the shell. Die-ring *F* is designed with a sharp shoulder at the upset end, but there is very little flow of metal outward at this point to wear it away.

Air vents are provided at the bottom of the die and through the punch, and relief grooves are ground on the punch. The upset end is 1.16 inches in diameter.

Dies for Shells Requiring Formation of Small Bosses.— Drawn shells sometimes require a small boss or projection on one side, either to provide for an opening or for some other purpose. The carburetor cup or bowl shown at *H*, Fig. 25, is an example of a shell requiring a boss to provide for a tapped hole. By drawing and forming this part on power presses, a substantial saving was effected over the previous method of casting the part. The drawing method of manufacture eliminated all cleaning and machining necessary when a casting was used. In addition, tolerances on the various dimensions were actually decreased, because it was possible to secure more accurate work and at a lower cost than when the part was cast. The appearance and dimensions of the part after each of the operations are shown in Fig. 25. One apparent obstacle to the successful drawing and forming of the part was the fact that a metal thickness sufficient to permit the drilling and

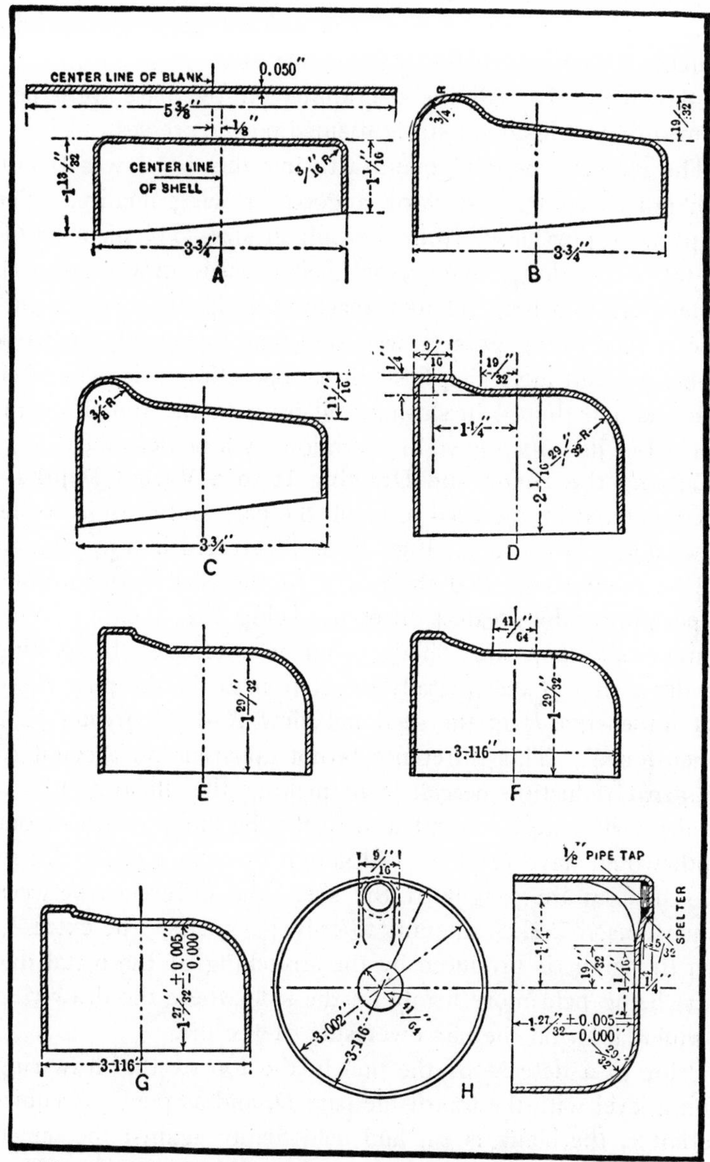

Fig. 25. Successive Operations on a Shell Which Requires the Formation of a Small Boss on One Side

tapping of a hole for a standard 1/8-inch pipe was required at the bottom of the boss. This difficulty was successfully overcome, however, by filling the inside of the boss with spelter as shown at *H*. All the operations on the part were performed on single-action straight-sided power presses.

The material used in manufacturing this bowl was 0.050-inch hot-rolled strip steel of a good drawing quality. The strips were purchased from the mill in sizes 5 5/8 inches wide by 60 inches long, and before being used, they were well coated with slushing oil in a machine designed for this purpose. This oiling process was sufficient to permit the work to be put through the first three operations; it was then annealed and dipped in slushing oil prior to the fourth operation. The dies for the eight operations will be described.

Cutting the Blank and Drawing It to a Varied Depth.—The combination die used to blank the part and draw it to the dimensions shown at *A*, Fig. 25, is illustrated in Fig. 26. It will be readily seen that the height of the shell varies around its periphery, the greatest difference being 11/32 inch, at points diametrically opposite. This result was effected by placing the draw-ring *A* eccentrically in relation to the die plug *B*, so that dimension *R* in the sectional view *X–Y* is greater than dimension *S*. This difference is not apparent on account of the great reduction necessary in making the illustration. If the draw-ring were concentric with the die plug, a shell of one depth would have resulted. Although there is a difference of 11/32 inch in the height of the shell, the difference between dimensions *R* and *S* amounts to only 7/32 inch. The extra 1/8 inch of height is produced by the stretching of the metal due to its being held more firmly on the side where the draw-ring is wider, than on the narrower side of the die.

Prior to a descent of the punch, the top of the draw-ring is on a level with the top of die part *D*, and as punch *E* enters the latter, the blank is cut and held firmly against the punch by the draw-ring during the remainder of the operation. Pins *C* are pushed down on the rubber buffers supporting them, and on the ascent of the punch these buffers expand, forcing the draw-ring to follow the punch upward and thus stripping the shell from plug *B*. At the end of the upward stroke, the knock-out device *F* forces the shell from the punch, and as the shell falls on the top of the die, it is removed by the operator. Die part *D* consists of a machine steel base on which is forged

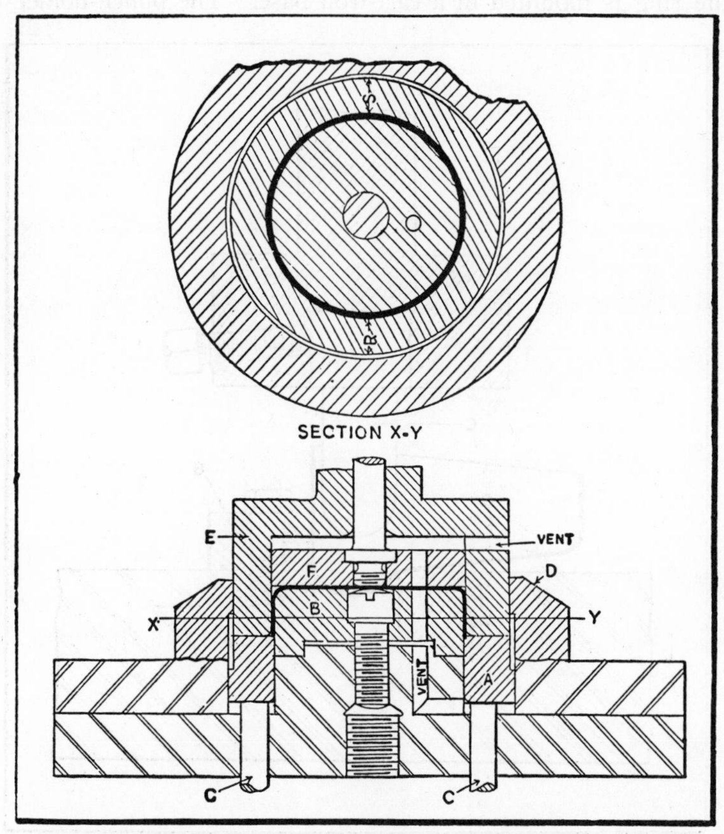

Fig. 26. Combination Die with Eccentric Draw-ring for Varying Depth of Shell

a ring of tool steel. Punch *E* and plug *B* are also made of tool steel. Vents are provided in the punch and die to allow confined air to escape when the punch descends. With this die a production of about 4000 pieces per day was maintained.

Forming the Boss on the Shell.—The second operation was an embossing one, a boss at the bottom of the bowl being made to the dimensions shown at *B*, Fig. 25. The construction of the die for this operation is shown in Fig. 27. The work is placed over the hole in the tool-steel ring *A* of the die, being located properly by means of stop-gage *B*, which is curved on the inside to correspond with the periphery of the shell. The die ring is mounted in a cast-iron base. The punch-holder is

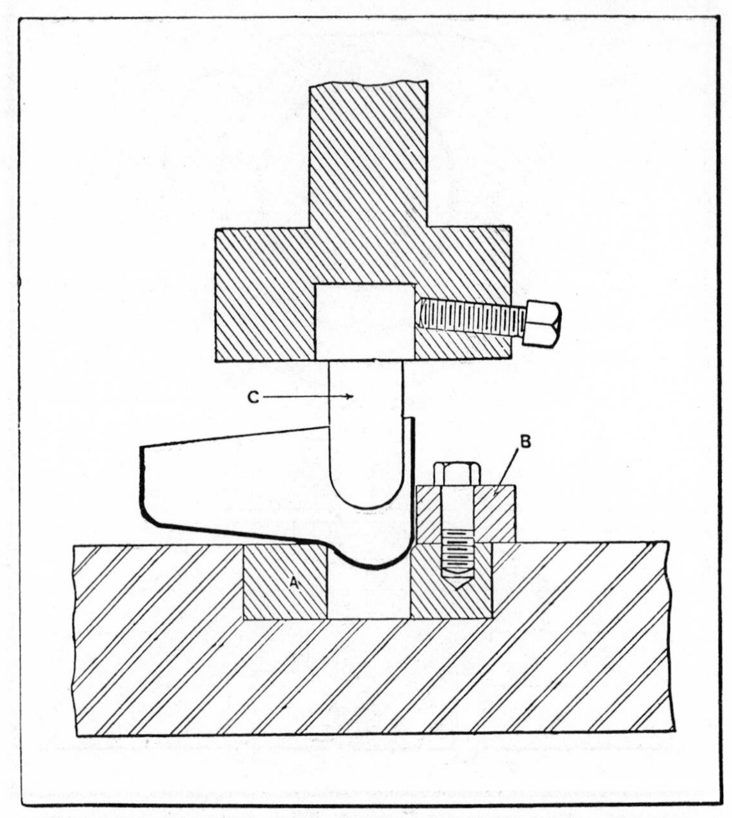

Fig. 27. First Embossing Operation on Shell at Place Where Boss is to be formed

also made of cast iron and is carried in stock. Punch *C* is made of tool steel, so that all parts of the die which actually come in contact with the shell during the forming operation are made of tool steel. The punch is held in the holder by means of a set-screw inclined at an angle of about 2 degrees from the horizontal, which is a simple but satisfactory arrangement for keeping such a member in place. The production on this die was about 6000 pieces per day.

The die for the next operation is shown in Fig. 28; this die increases the depth of the boss, and forms it to a smaller inside radius, as shown at *C*, Fig. 25. The construction of the die is very similar to the one for the preceding operation, with

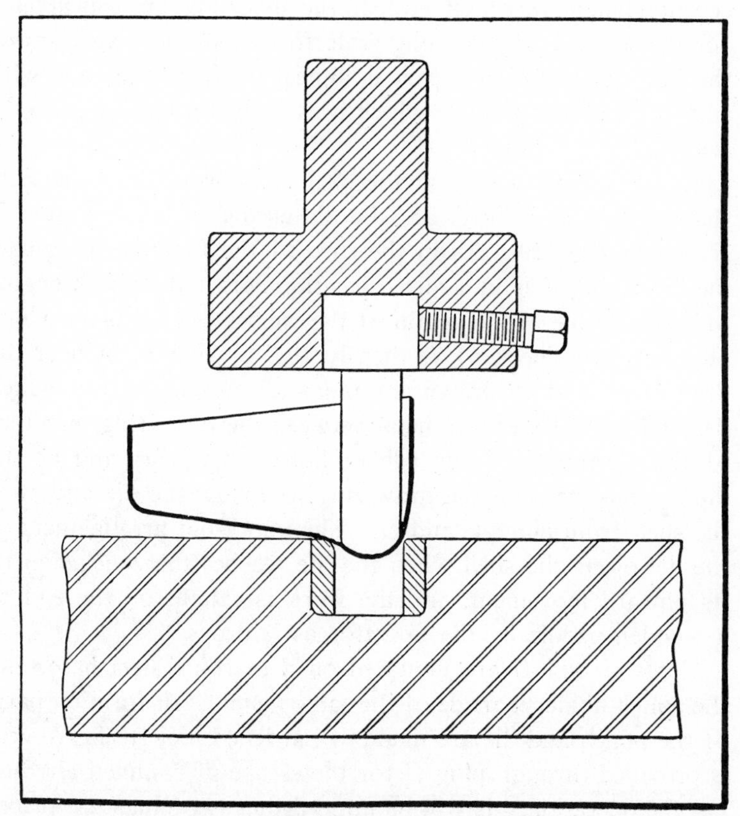

Fig. 28. Second Embossing Operation

the exception that a stop-gage is not required. The shell is placed with the boss in the opening of the die ring and the die ring serves as a stop gage. The shell is held in place during this operation by the operator, who holds it at a point diametrically opposite the boss. The punch and die ring are made of tool steel, and the die base and punch-holder of cast iron.

With this die the production per day is about 6000 pieces.

Final Drawing Operation.—Prior to the fourth operation, it was necessary to anneal the shell thoroughly. The shell was heated to a cherry red, and the annealing was performed in a gas furnace after the shell had been dipped in a solution of one part of muriatic acid to five parts of water. This solution had no direct effect upon the annealing, but was applied for the purpose of loosening scale formed by the oxidation of the hot steel. When a part is annealed after being wet with such a solution, the scale which invariably forms can easily be removed by tumbling.

In the fourth operation the shell was brought to the final shape shown at *D*, Fig. 25; the die used for this operation is shown in Fig. 29. As in the case of the first die described, the draw-ring *A* is in a raised position before the punch begins to descend, due to the action of the rubber buffers upon which pins *B* rest. The work is then located by slipping it over the draw-ring, and is drawn on plugs *C* and *D* as the punch descends and draws the metal between the draw-ring and face of the die-ring *E*. The rubber buffers again expand as the die ascends, causing the draw-ring to follow the die and strip the shell from plugs *C* and *D*. The knock-out arrangement in the die ejects the shell when the die reaches the conclusion of its upward movement, and the work is caught on the end of a wooden paddle by the operator as it drops.

Plugs *C* and *D* are mounted on a machine steel base, and the punch-holder is made of the same metal. All forming parts of the punch and die are made of hardened tool steel. A vent is provided through plug *C* for the escape of confined air during the operation. It will be noticed that two plugs are placed in the die; one of these flattens the top of the boss, while the other flattens the closed end of the shell at the center. The view of the completed shell at *H*, Fig. 25, shows that a flat space of 1 1/16 inches in diameter is required at this point.

This specification caused some difficulty when the dies for this operation were first tried out, the trouble being that the metal at the bottom of the boss became several thousandths of an inch thinner than at the center of the closed end. While this condition had been anticipated, the exact thickness at the two points had not been estimated correctly. The result was that the bottom of the boss was not entirely flat. However, this condition was quickly remedied by grinding down the shoulder of the small plug placed in the die above the boss, and

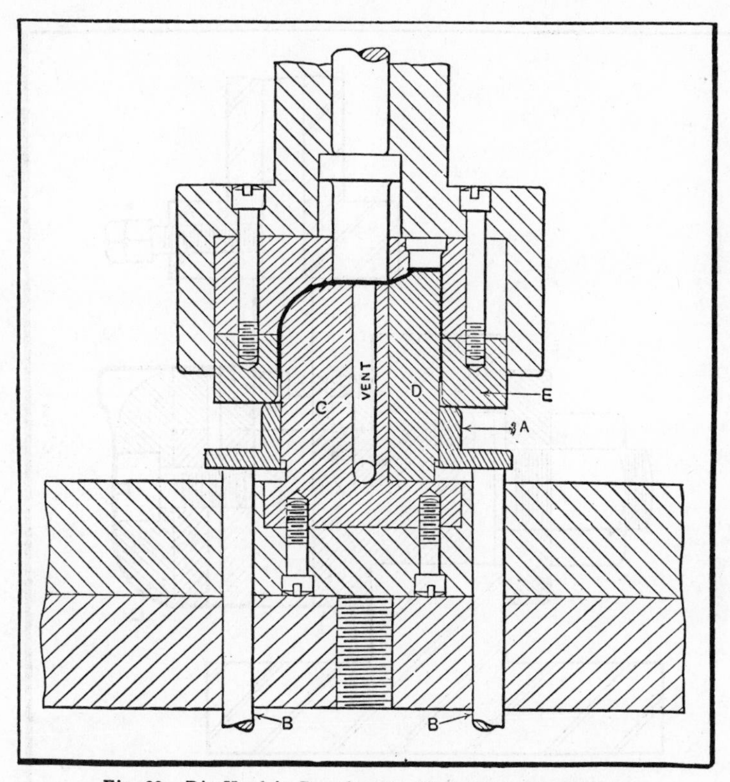

Fig. 29. Die Used in Drawing the Shell to the Final Shape

thus lowering the plug several thousandths of an inch. The thickness at the center of the closed end and at the bottom of the boss as the shell was finally produced differed from 0.003 to 0.004 inch, the bottom of the boss being the thinner. The production of this part averaged 5000 pieces per day.

Rough-trimming, Piercing, and Sizing Dies.—The fifth operation consisted of roughly trimming the open end of the shell, thus reducing its height to the dimension given at *E*, Fig. 25. This operation was accomplished by the die illustrated in Fig. 30. The base of this die and plug *A* are made of machine steel, but the plug is fitted with a hardened tool-steel block *B* which serves as a cutting edge. End *C* of the plug is also made of machine steel. Punch *D* is a hardened tool-steel

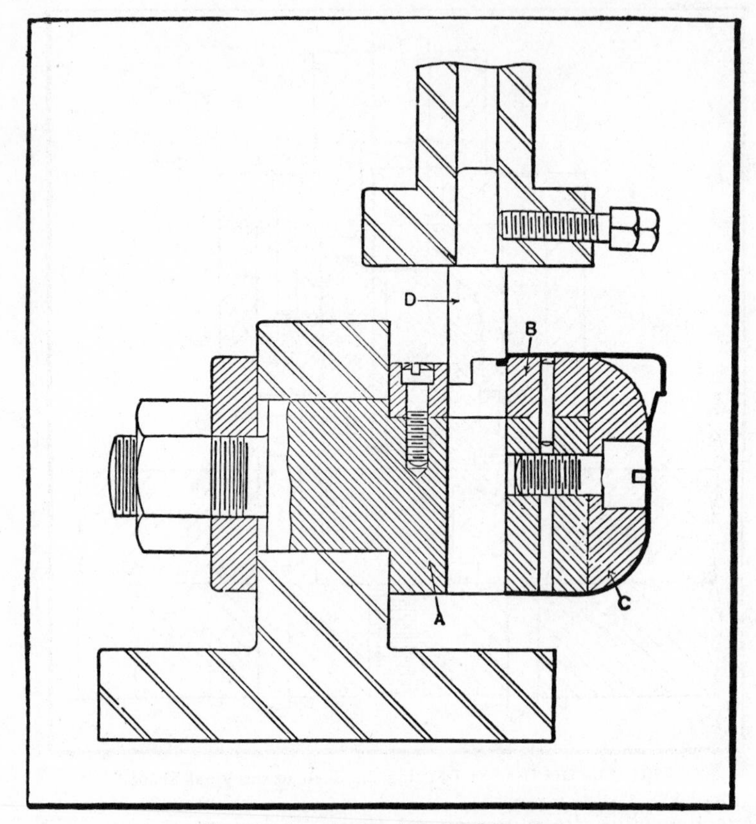

Fig. 30. Rough-trimming the Open End

piece, held in a machine-steel punch-holder of standard construction. In this operation, the shell is slipped over the plug and turned slowly by the operator while the punch is kept moving up and down, until the entire periphery of the shell has been trimmed. A production of about 2500 pieces was obtained with this die. A far more efficient die for this sort of operation is a type known as the "Brehm," which is provided with cams that give it a rotary motion around its perpendicular axis. The expense of a die of this design, however, did not warrant its use in the production of the limited number of shells made.

The sixth operation sized the open end of the shell to the dimension shown at *F*, Fig. 25. This was found necessary,

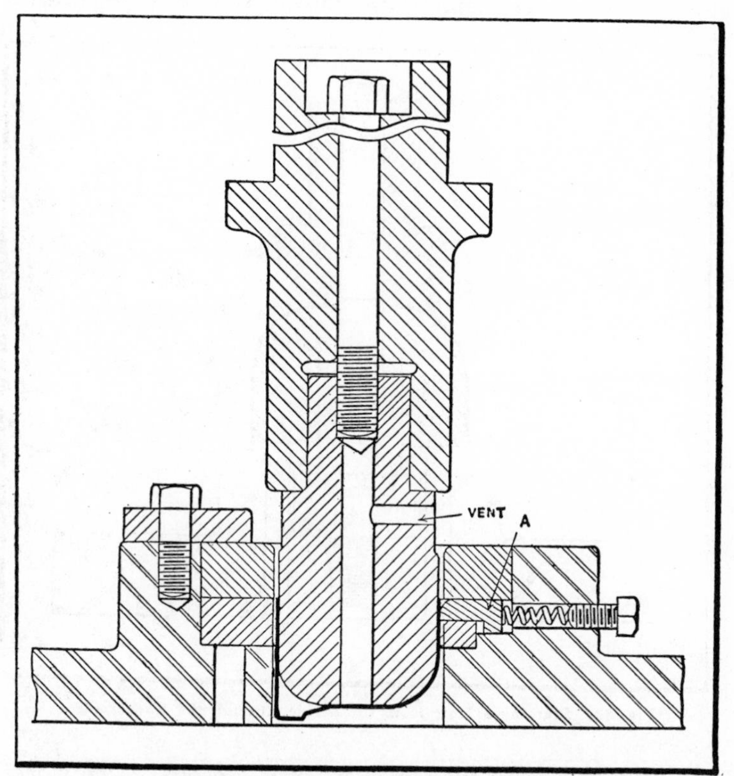

Fig. 31. Push-tnrough Die used in Sizing the Open End of Shell

because, while the final drawing operation brought the top of the shell to size, it did not bring the open end to the proper dimension. The operation was performed on the push-through die shown in Fig. 31. This die is so constructed that the shell will pass through the die and not stick to the punch upon its upward stroke. The stripping of the shell is accomplished by means of three spring-plungers *A* which protrude into the opening of the die when the punch is in a raised position. These plungers are beveled at the top so that they are forced back flush with the internal surface of the die as the shell is pushed against them on the downward stroke of the punch. However, the pressures of the springs hold them against the outside of the shell, and as the open end passes them, the plungers are forced against the punch, thus enabling them to

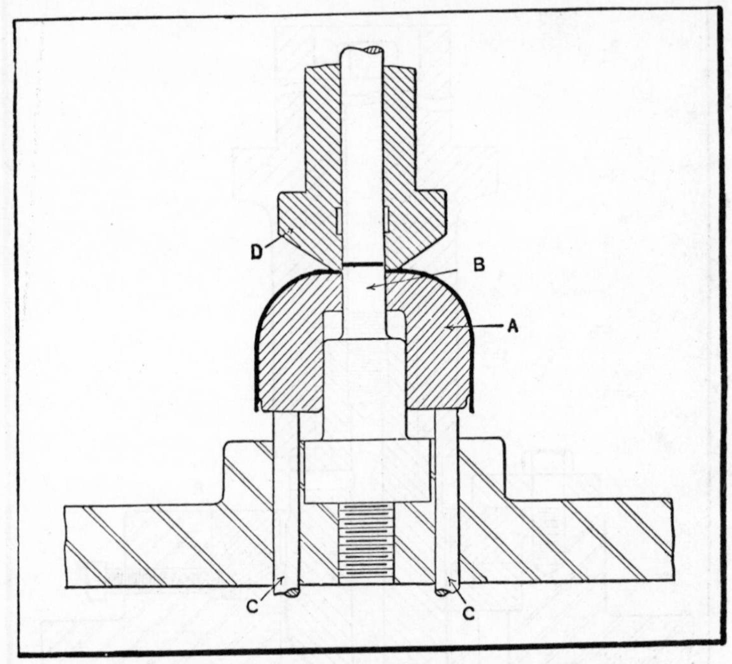

Fig. 32. Piercing a Hole from the Inside through the End of the Shell

strip the shell from the punch when it ascends. The work is forced through the die by the next shell being sized. It will be seen that this punch is also provided with a vent. The die is mounted on a cast-iron circular base, and all parts coming in contact with the work are made of tool steel. A production of about 5000 pieces per day was obtained.

The diameter of the hole punched at the center of the closed end of the shell is indicated at *F*, Fig. 25. and this operation is done by the piercing die shown in Fig. 32. It will be noted that the hole is pierced from the inside rather than from the outside. This method made it easy to dispose of the slugs punched from the shell, and permitted a simpler construction. The work is slipped over the machine-steel work-holder *A*, the top surface of which is on a level with the top of the tool-steel punch *B* when the die is in the raised position, due to the action of pins *C*, which rest on rubber buffers. The hole is punched through the part as the tool-steel die *D* descends and forces the work and holder *A* downward while punch B remains stationary. Each slug is knocked out of the die at the end of the return stroke by the knock-out rod at the center of the die. The production was about 5000 pieces per day.

Final Operations.—The shell was finish-trimmed to the height indicated at *G*, Fig. 25, in an operation performed on a small screw machine. The height of the shell was measured from the inside, and it will be seen that a tolerance of only 0.005 inch was allowed. If it had not been for the close limits, the shell could have been satisfactorily trimmed on a press equipped with a die similar to that used in the rough-trimming operation previously mentioned. A chuck was made especially for this finish-trimming operation. This was the slowest operation of the series, but the production per day was about 900 pieces.

The spelter shown in the view of the shell at *H*, Fig. 25, was, as previously mentioned, placed in the bottom of the boss to give the latter sufficient thickness to permit the drilling and tapping of a hole to accommodate a pipe. The spelter was bought in rods 3/8 inch in diameter and 30 inches in length, and in order to cut the rod into small pieces of the proper size to fill the boss, the die shown in Fig. 33 was employed. The rod is fed through the tool-steel support *A* until it strikes the end of set-screw *B*, which serves as a stop-gage. The press is then tripped, and the descending punch *C* shears the spelter to the proper size.

The method used to fuse the spelter in the boss was simple, yet quite effective. The shell was placed on a small furnace with the open end upward and the boss projecting through the top of the furnace into the flames. The work was kept in this position until the boss reached a red heat. A piece of spelter and a small amount of powdered borax were then placed in the boss and melted and fused in the steel shell. The latter when cooled was placed in a jig and a hole drilled through the boss. This operation was performed

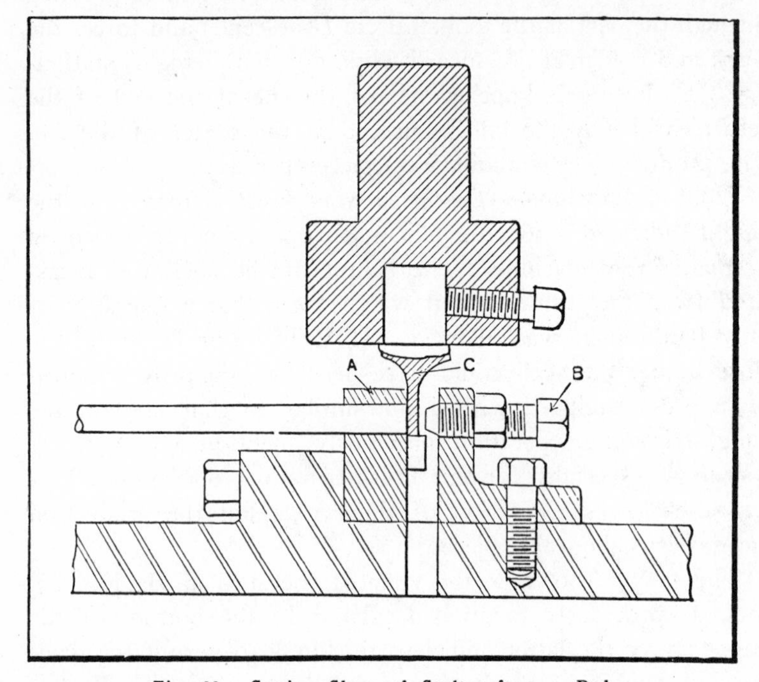

Fig. 33. Cutting Slugs of Spelter from a Rod

from the inside in order to prevent any danger of the spelter becoming loosened. The hole was finally tapped.

Another Drawing Operation Requiring Formation of a Boss on the Shell.—The manufacture of a muffler cap of unusual shape which is used on a certain type of motorcycle, requires seven drawing and forming dies, as shown in Figs. 34 to 40 inclusive. A view showing the appearance and dimensions of the work after each operation will be found beneath the die used to produce that particular shape. The

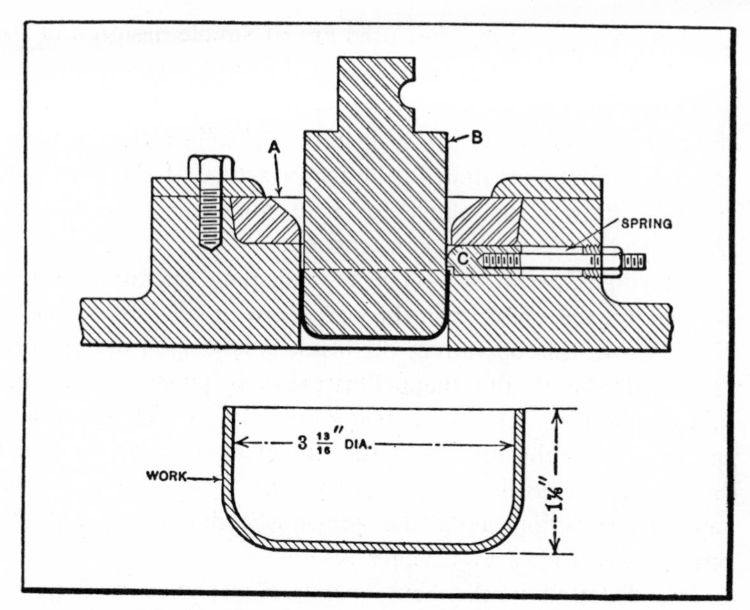

Fig. 34. First Operation on Shell shown in Fig. 40

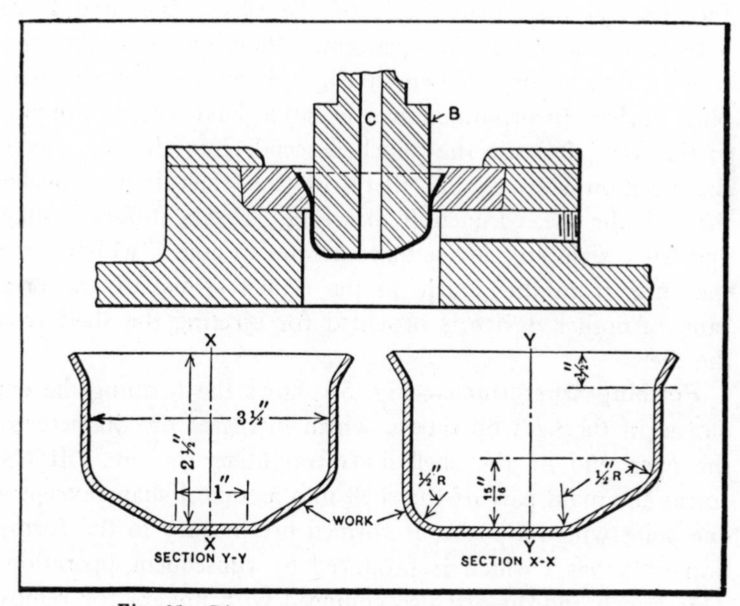

Fig. 35. Die used for the Second Drawing Operation

blanking and trimming dies used are of simple design and for this reason are not illustrated. All the steel parts of the dies are hardened and ground. The sheet steel blank from which the part is produced is 3/32 inch thick and 6 3/16 inches in diameter. The first operation in the manufacture of this part consists of cutting the blank to these dimensions on a plain blanking die of standard construction.

Drawing Operations.—The first shaping operation is performed by the plain push-through drawing die illustrated in Fig. 34. In this operation, the blank is laid upon the die ring *A* and drawn to the shape illustrated as punch *B* descends into the die ring. Three stripping fingers *C*, which are equally spaced around the die, force the drawn shell from the punch on the return stroke of the press ram. This die is of the same construction as a die previously illustrated and described (see Fig. 2 of Chapter XIV).

The die used in the next operation is shown in Fig. 35. It reduces the diameter of the shell, forms a slanting surface around the greater part of the closed end, and leaves a tapering flange on the open end. This die is of the same construction as that shown in Fig. 34, except that the stripping devices incorporated in the latter have been eliminated in this case, because the punch descends into the die only to the position shown, and therefore the shell is not pushed through the die. Punch *B*, however, is of a different shape and has a stripping device that operates in hole *C* which forces the shell from the punch on the return stroke of the press ram. Another device is provided for ejecting the shell from the die.

Forming Operations.—Fig. 36 shows the forming die employed in the next operation, which increases the diameter of the open end of the shell and straightens its rim. It also forms the main part of the shell into a conical shape except at one point where a pocket is formed preparatory to the formation of a boss, which is produced by subsequent operations. This punch and die are also equipped with fingers for removing the shell after the performance of the operation.

The forming die shown in Fig. 37 is used to produce the boss just mentioned, on the conical portion of the shell. Gage *A* is provided to locate the shell properly prior to the operation. No device is required to remove the shell from either the punch or the die in this case, as the shape of the shell readily permits its removal without the employment of a special device.

The forming die which is employed to perform the next operation is illustrated in Fig. 38. The results of this opera-

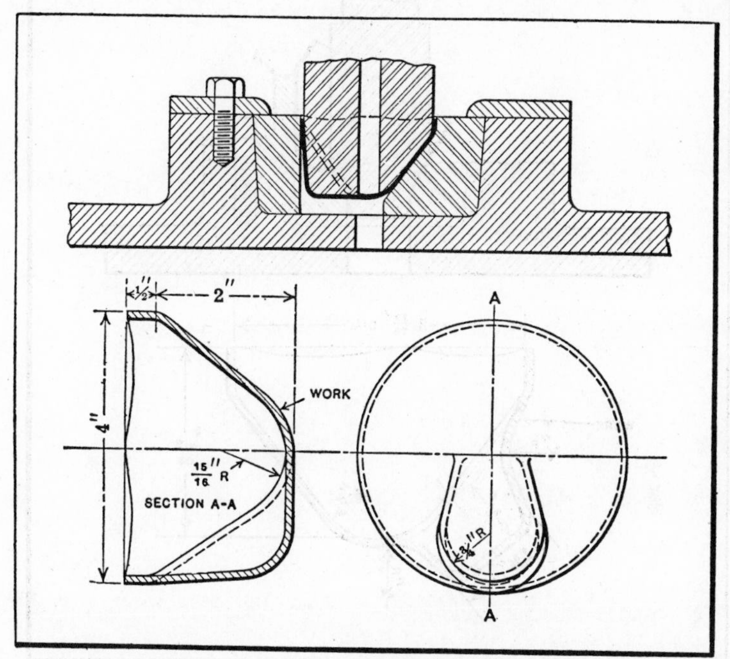

Fig. 36. Die which Forms a Pocket Preparatory to Formation of Boss

tion are a lengthening of the conical portion of the shell and a flattening of its end, and a decrease in the angle between the center lines of the shell and the boss. The diameter and depth of the boss are also decreased, which serves to increase the thickness of the shell at this point. By this means, the thickness of the metal can be kept approximately uniform throughout the entire shell.

The forming die shown in Fig. 39 performs the final forming operation on all parts of the shell except the boss and part of the surface adjacent to it. It straightens the rim at the open end of the shell to a uniform depth of ⅝ inch and finishes the conical shaped part. Both the punch and the die are equipped with devices for removing the shell.

Fig. 40 shows the die used for the final shaping operation on the shell. It increases the depth of the boss and also

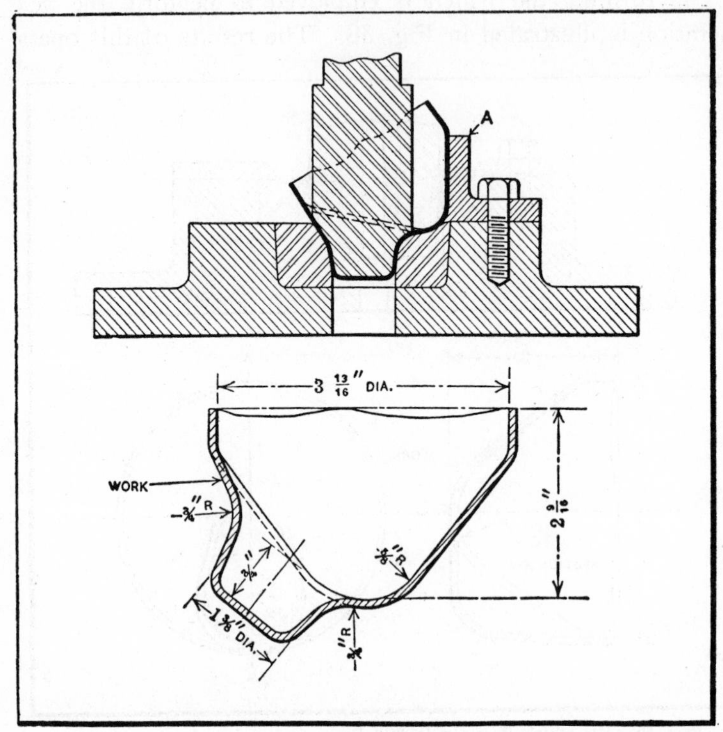

Fig. 37. Punch and Die which Produces a Boss on the Conical Surface of the Shell

straightens its sides and the slanting surface which connects part of the boss with the rim of the shell. This punch and die is also equipped with devices to effect the removal of the shell from these parts after the operation. It will be noticed that during the various operations, the edge of the rim on the open end of the shell becomes quite irregular, it being very difficult to prevent this from happening on the class of work being dealt with. In order to remove this iregular edge, the shell is operated upon by a trimming die or shear, after the last forming operation. The final operation on the shell consists in punching a small hole through the center of the boss.

Embossing Dies.—An embossing die is used to form raised letters or an ornamental design, in relief, upon the surface of the work. An embossing die differs from a forming die in

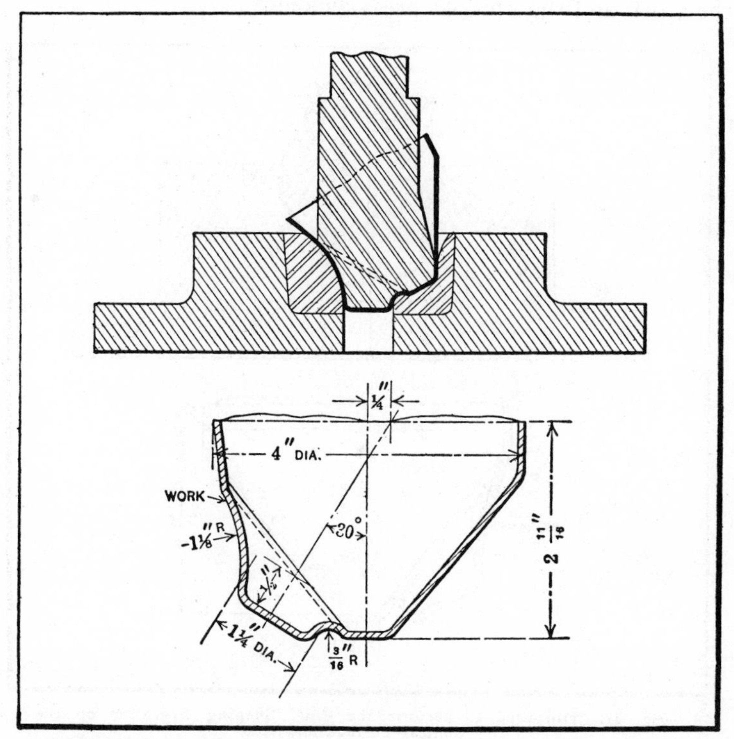

Fig. 38. Forming Die Employed to Lengthen the Conical Surface and Flatten its End

that the projections or designs made by it are comparatively small or shallow, and usually in the nature of relief work upon a surface, whereas a forming die gives the required shape to the work. The formation of lettered inscriptions, symbols, and decorative designs on all kinds of sheet-metal boxes and cans is done by embossing dies. A simple form of embossing die is one used for producing the circular ridges on the heads of tin cans, etc. Such a die would have one or more annual grooves and the punch would have annular ridges of corresponding size for forcing the metal into the die grooves. Embossing is commonly done in a die designed to cut, draw, and emboss the blank in one operation. An embossing die of this kind may be either a combination, a double-action, or a triple-action type, depending upon the nature of the work and the kind of press available.

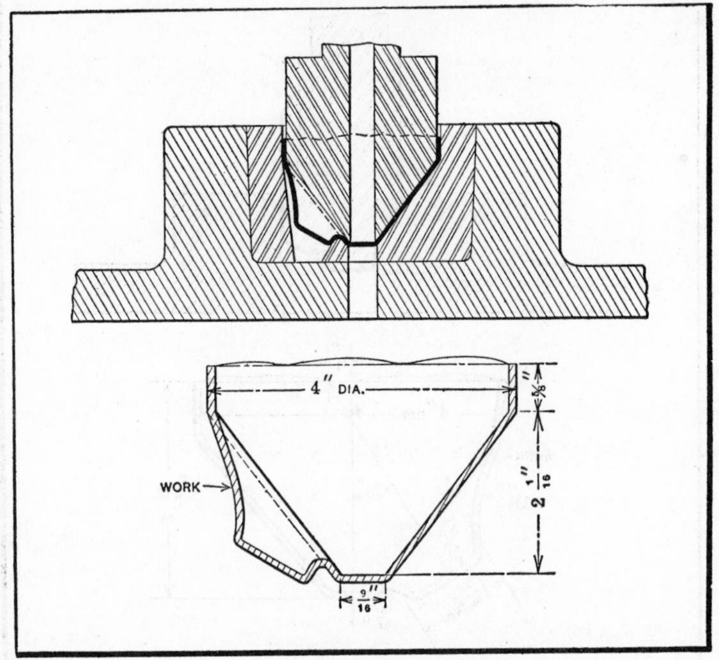

Fig. 39. Die used to perform the Final Shaping Operation on the Conical Surface and Rim

Embossing dies differ from coining dies in that the latter generally have different designs on the upper and lower dies. An embossing dies is one having the same design on both the upper and lower dies, one being the reverse of the other; that is, the lower may have the depressed design and the upper the raised design.

There is a local stretching and compressing of the metal in all embossing operations. The amount of stretching and compressing depends upon the dimensions of the design and the amount it extends above or below the surface. Occasionally the design must be worked over from an experimental stage until a piece can be produced without tearing the metal or causing excessive wrinkling at some points. The difficulties may occasionally be eliminated by the selection of a slightly tougher material or other changes in the material specifica-

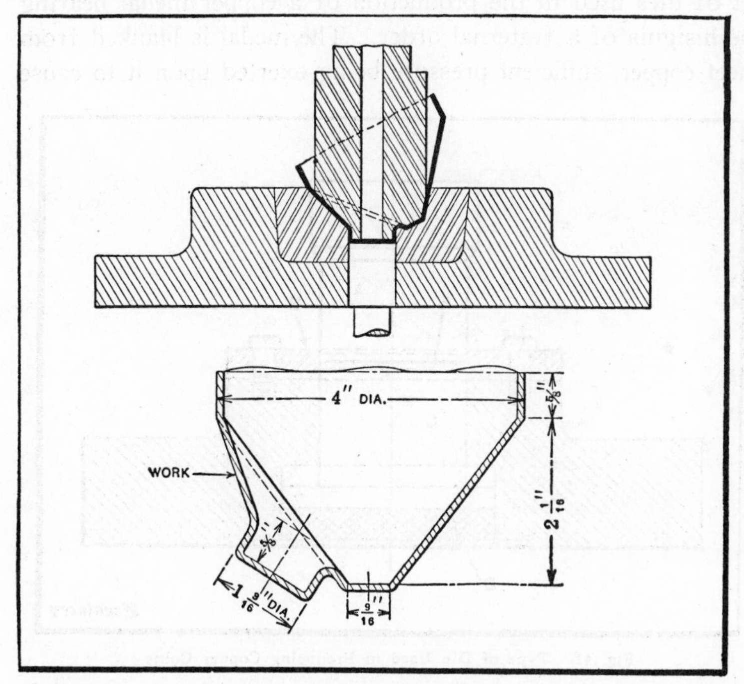

Fig. 40. Final Shaping Operation on the Shell which Completes the Formation of the Boss

tions. Practically every problem has its own limitations, and the design must be considered with respect to the material available. Sharp corners and angles must be avoided. as far as possible, which makes it extremely difficult to produce Gothic designs, except where the flow of material is entirely in one direction; that is, where there is no combination ot stretching and compressing.

The working surface of the dies will affect the results in

a material way. For example, in some work one die surface must be left soft and in others, both surfaces may be hardened. The degree of hardness of the surface may be varied in order to eliminate some of the difficulties. Dies for the production of an accurate design are best worked out experimentally.

Coining Die for Copper Medal.—In Fig. 41 is shown a set of dies used in the production of a copper medal bearing the insignia of a fraternal order. The medal is blanked from sheet copper, sufficient pressure being exerted upon it to cause

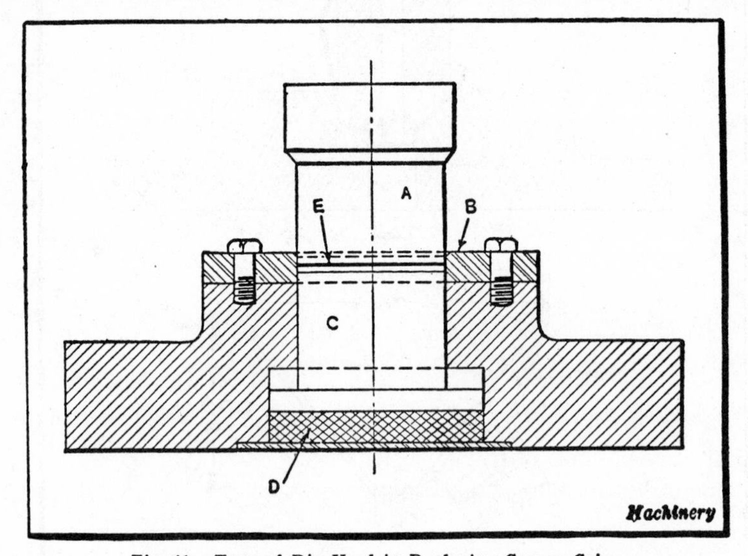

Fig. 41. Type of Die Used in Producing Copper Coins

the metal to flow into the various depressions in the punch face and die face. The punch face contains the reverse of the medal face and the die contains the reverse of the medal back. That is, wherever a raised portion appears on the coin, there is a corresponding depression on the die.

Brittle metals cannot be coined cold with any degree of success. The metal must be ductile and flow readily. The coining of badges, medals, and emblems is done by the cold process. When a thickened rim is desired, the coin cannot be blanked in the coining operation. In this case, the blanks are first cut from the sheet, and then rolled between grooved jaws in order to form a rounded and thickened rim. The edge of the coin may be knurled or left plain. If knurled, the dies must also have the knurled design so that the metal can be forced into the recesses.

The die shown consists of three pieces, namely, the punch, or upper die *A*, the collar *B*, and the lower die *C*. The lower die rests on a spring or rubber cushion *D* and its travel is limited, so that it serves as an ejector of the finished work. Collar *B* is slightly beveled to facilitate centering the work in the die. If the work is blanked out at the same time it is coined, the edge of the collar is left straight to form a shear. The upper die member then serves as a punch as well as a die.

The press used is of the single-acting, adjustable ram type, and the space *E* between the upper and the lower dies is the exact thickness of the finished coin. The advantage of doing this work on an adjustable press is that the pressure exerted on the work may be readily adjusted to take care of variation in the metal. If the pressure is too great, the coin will come out of the die with a fin running up between the die and the collar. In case the edge of the work is to be rounded, this will not be objectionable, except from the standpoint of material used.

Knuckle-joint Embossing or Coining Presses.—Knuckle-joint power presses are used extensively for embossing coins, medallions. and other intricate forms, as well as for lettering or embossing that requires a large amount of pressure for a comparatively short time. Because of their use for this class of work these presses are often termed "coining" presses. There is a demand for many different sizes, and consequently these machines are built in over-all heights of from 5 to 20 feet, weighing from 6000 to 150,000 pounds. The smaller sizes are not geared, while the largest are double-geared and are reinforced with vertical tie-rods shrunk in place to insure strength and rigidity.

While an enormous pressure is exerted by the knuckle joint

embossing press, this pressure is unlike an equal force obtained from the impact of fast-acting machines, such as drop-hammers and other types of power presses. In comparison with other power presses the knuckle-joint press gives a force similar to a squeeze, as distinguished from a sharp blow. It is this slow increasing pressure that distinguishes the knuckle-joint press from other types. Such a pressure enables the metal to flow under the force of the punch, and fine intricate

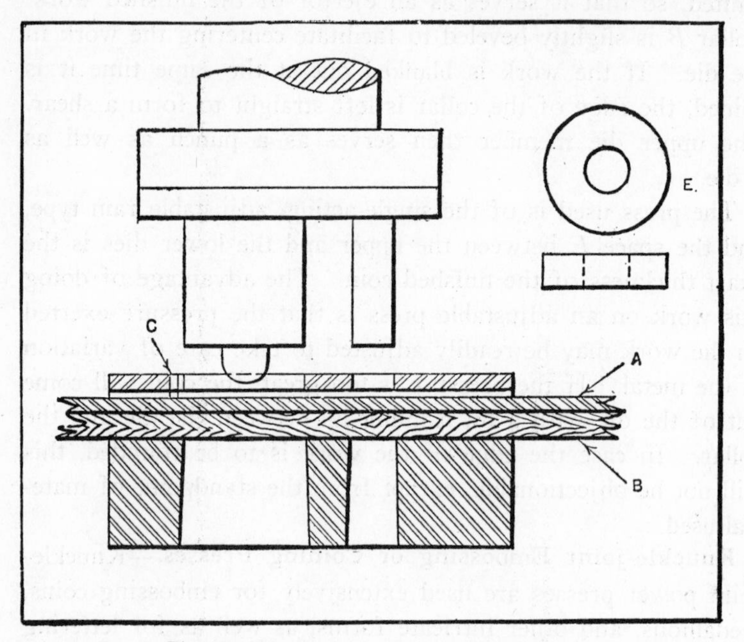

Fig. 42. Die Used for Cutting Felt Washers

embossing is possible. An equal pressure in the form of a sharp blow would not give the metal the same opportunity to enter the delicate markings of the die, and for this reason a slower pressure is essential. It allows the metal to form over sharp edges and into curves, where a quicker-acting force would cause it to crack and tear.

Cutting Felt Washers in a Die.—In a large automobile plant it was necessary to cut a lot of felt washers $\frac{1}{4}$ inch thick, like the one shown at *E*, Fig. 42. There was a die in the shop like the one shown in the illustration, which had been used to cut metal washers of the same size as the felt washers, and an attempt was made to use this die for cutting out the felt washers. However, it was impossible to obtain washers with clean cut edges by employing the die in the usual manner.

After various methods had been tried, a toolmaker of considerable experience suggested that 1/16-inch thick sheet metal *A* be placed on top of the felt *B*, and stamp the steel and the felt together. This method proved satisfactory. In order to use this equipment, however, it was necessary to remove the stop-pin from the die and place it in the stripper plate, as shown at *C*. As the steel washers are used regularly in the assembly department, no waste of material results from this practice.

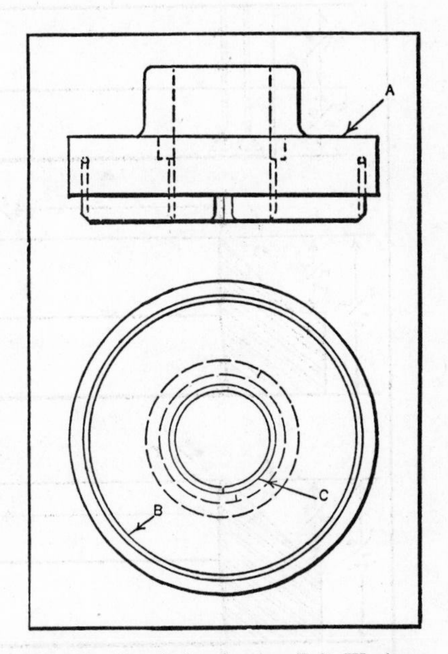

Fig. 43. Punch for Cutting Felt Washers

The die shown in Fig. 43 is used for cutting felt washers, which are 1/2 inch thick, 4 inches in diameter, and have a central hole 1 1/2 inches in diameter. The light punch press was fitted with hard maple facings, so that with the ram in its lowest position, there was a clearance of 2 1/2 inches. The die shown in the illustration was improvised from a 2-inch thick disk *A* formed from a 5-inch bar of round steel, and two experimental cutter blades *B* and *C* made from saw steel 5/64 inch thick. The saw steel cutters were made to fit into grooves in the face of the disk. The inner cutter for the 1 1/2-inch hole was made to bottom against a shoulder in the clearance hole, which extended around the disk, while the outer or 4 inch cutter was made to be held in place with blind set-screws.

Through an error, the slot in the disk was cut ⅛ inch too deep, so that when the cutter was fitted in place, it projected only ⅜ inch instead of ½ inch, the thickness of the felt pad. It was found that this was an advantage, as the compression of the felt within the die assisted in producing a cleaner cut.

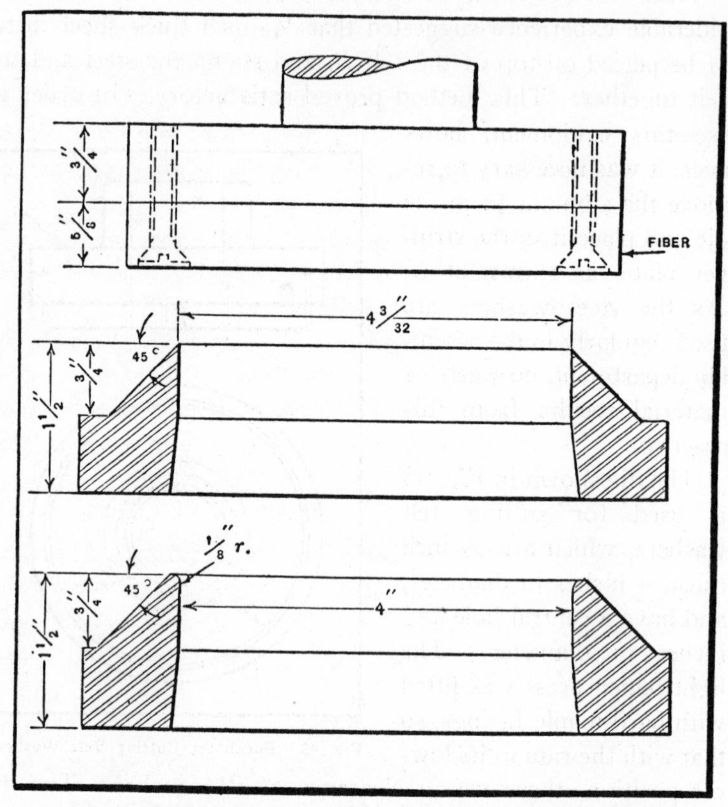

Fig. 44. Punch and Dies Used in Blanking and Sizing Fiber

After the die had been in use for a few hours, a small piece broke away from one end of the large cutter, and as the washers were urgently needed, the broken end was ground smooth, leaving a gap between the ends of the cutter of about ¼ inch. This gap also proved advantageous as the washers, being cut all around except for the ¼-inch gap were held in pad formation. The washers could be more readily handled in this pad form than as individual pieces, as the assemblers could, in one snip of a pair of tin shears, cut off the washers as they were required.

The die, as described, remained in service until over 5000 washers had been produced, and the maple facings on the punch press withstood their hard usage satisfactorily. An ordinary piece of wrapping twine, soaked in shellac, was forced into the groove of the die ahead of the larger cutter, and served as a resistance pad for the knife, distributing the stress uniformly around the groove and yet cushioning the thin metal blade sufficiently to prevent it from being broken under the jar or shock of the press strokes.

Die for Blanking Fiber.—The die equipment shown in Fig. 44 proved successful in cutting or blanking pieces 4 inches square from hard black fiber sheets 5/8 inch thick. Two dies are used. The first one is 3/32 inch larger than the finished blank size and it is used to cut the blank. The die for finishing does not have cutting edges, but an upper edge radius of 1/8 inch and smooth sides which compress the edges, thus reducing the blank to the required size and leaving a smooth finish.

It will be noted that the punch has a flat fiber facing secured to it by means of flat-head machine screws. The punch does not enter the die, but presses the stock down on the cutting edge until the blank is severed from the sheet stock. The blank, thus produced, has rough uneven edges and was slightly over size. By passing the blank through the die shown in the lower view of the illustration these defects were remedied, and a good smooth blank of the required size obtained. When using these dies, the fiber sheets were heated to a temperature of about 160 degrees F.

Die for Piercing Four Holes Simultaneously.— The automatic die with opposed inward-sliding punch units shown in Figs. 45 and 46, is designed for piercing four holes simultaneously in the flanges of a long sheet-metal, box-shaped member which is fed along intermittently between the punch units. The punch units are withdrawn automatically from

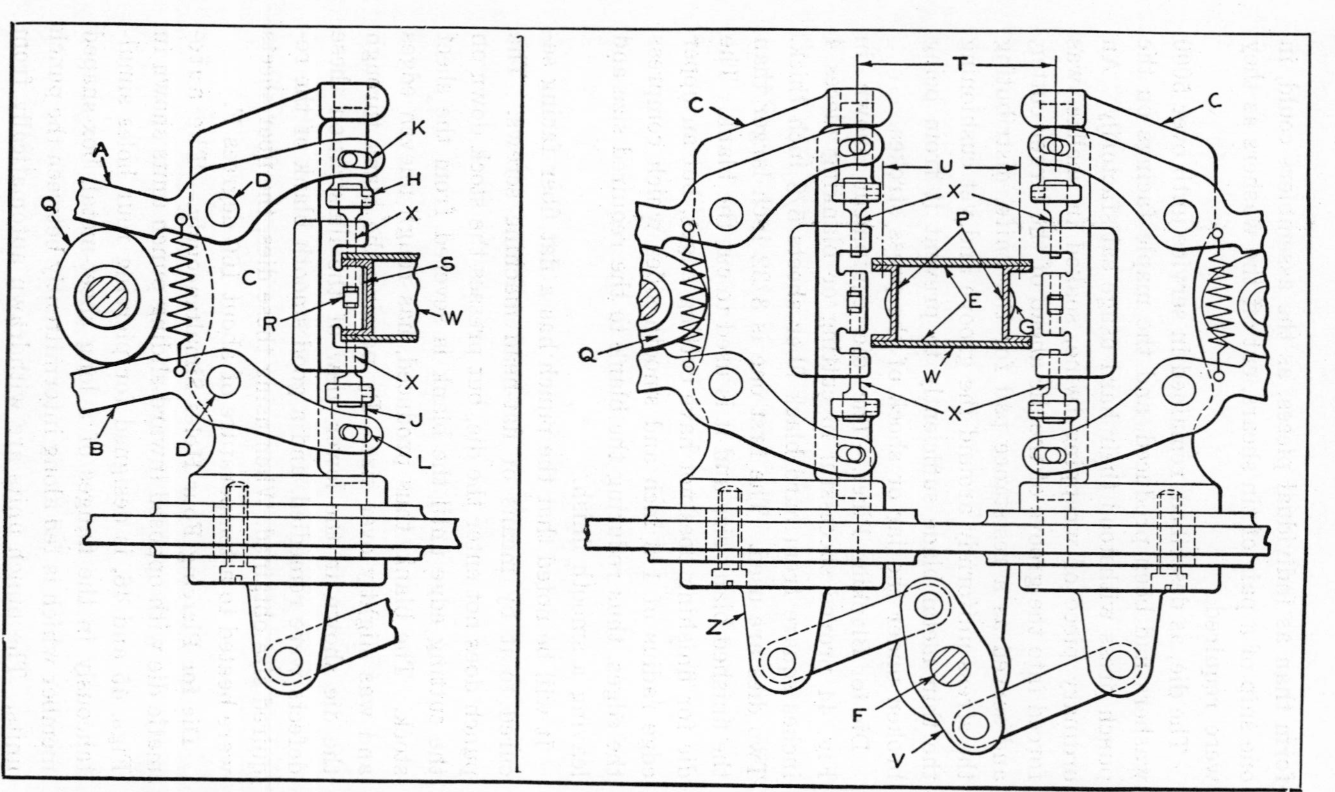

Fig. 45. Piercing Unit of Die with the Punches at the Ends of Their Strokes

Fig. 46. Die with Piercing Units Withdrawn to Permit Intermittent Feeding of Work to Successive Positions

the position indicated by dimension *U* to that indicated by dimension *T*, so that projections such as shown at *G* can pass the die units. The box-shaped member *W* is made up in strip form from two channel members *P* in combination with two side plates *E*.

The four piercing punches *X* are advanced from the positions shown in Fig. 46 to the positions shown in Fig. 45 for punching the flanges, and then withdrawn automatically. The view Fig. 45 shows only one of the sliding head units advanced to the piercing position, with the punches at the ends of their piercing strokes.

The mechanism for operating the punches is composed of levers *A* and *B*, fastened to a movable bracket *C* by means of bearing studs *D*. Levers *A* and *B* are actuated by opposite sides of the cam *Q*, being held in contact with the cam by a coil spring. Pins in the punch-holders *H* and *J* pass through slots *K* and *L* in the ends of levers *A* and *B*. This construction permits levers *A* and *B* to actuate the punches, causing them to pierce the work and enter the die-block *S*, which is attached by means of screws and dowels to the bracket *C*. The slot at *R* allows the piercings to pass through the die-block and out at its sides.

The heads are brought together, or into the piercing positions, by means of the plate *V* which is rotated or oscillated by the shaft *F*. Links between the plate *V* and the heads serve to bring the heads into and out of the piercing positions.

Both the operation of the piercing punches and the movement of the heads are synchronized with the mechanism that automatically advances the work during the intervals between the piercing operations. The work pierced is only a few thousandths inch thick, although from the cross-section views it would appear to be much thicker.

Hemming Dies for Folding Over Edge of Metal to Form Reinforcement.—A hemming operation is one in which the edge of a sheet-metal part is folded over on itself to obtain a double thickness of the material for reinforcement pur-

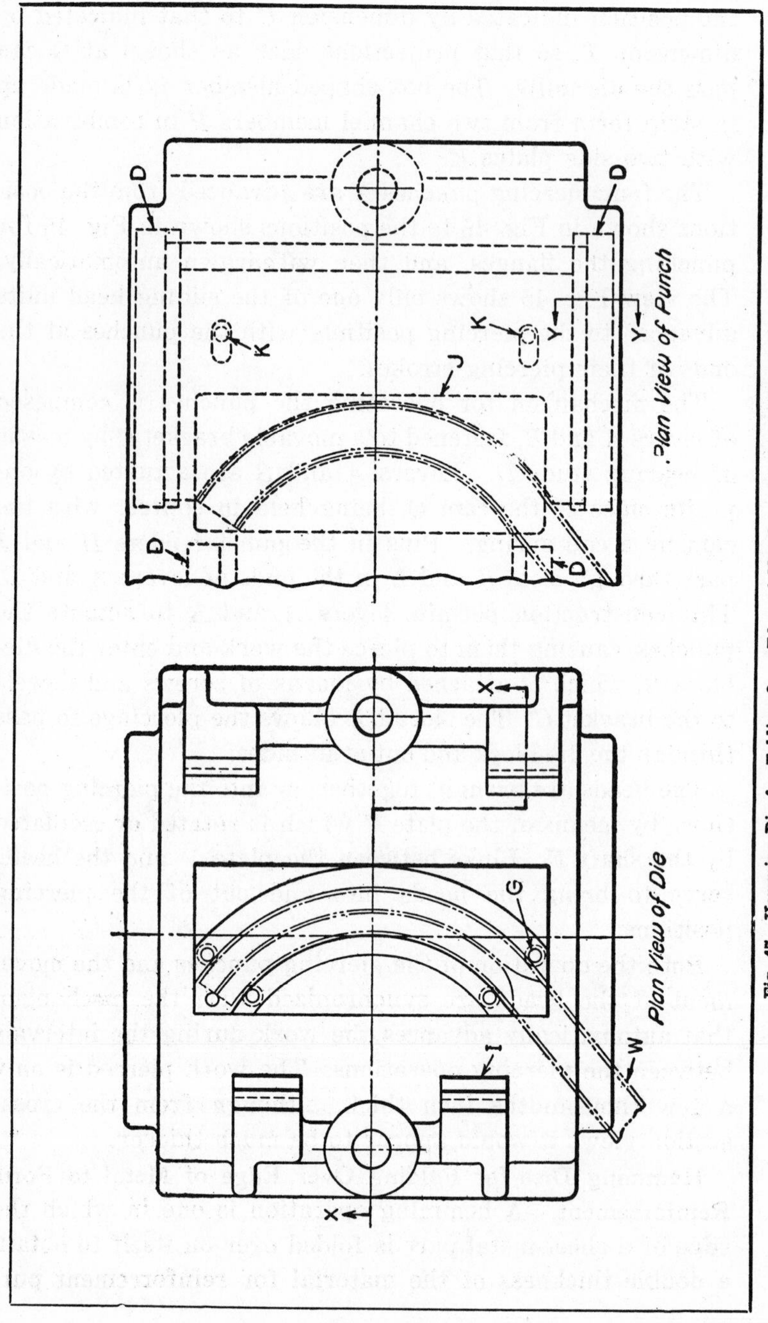

Fig. 47. Hemming Die for Folding Over Edge of Metal to Form Reinforcement

poses. Hemming is performed in one operation with the punch and die shown in Fig. 47. The part handled by this die has the hemming flanges already formed to vertical positions, as shown at *W*, Fig. 48. Cams *A* and *B* are attached to punch-shoe *C* by gibs *D*, as shown in Figs. 47 and 48. The gibs also serve as guides for the cams. The cams are in the "in" position when the die is open; they so remain until they come in contact with the beveled side surfaces of member *E*, or until space *F* has been closed up.

The beveled surfaces of the cams bend the flanges of part *W* to a 45-degree angle while the punch is traveling from the position shown in Fig. 48 at the start of the operation, to the position where gap *F* between *B* and *E* has been closed. This completes the first stage of the operation. The disappearing type gage pins *G*, which extend upward to the proper gaging height when the die is open, are pushed down by the beveled surfaces of the cams. They prevent the part from shifting or changing its position in the die until the completion of the beveling operation.

Cams *A* and *B* are held in their "in" positions by the vertical surfaces of driver plates *I* at the beginning of the operation. As soon as the beveling operation is completed, the beveled surfaces of the cams come in contact with the beveled surfaces of die *E*. The angular driving surface of the cam is then in line with angular surface *H* of the driving plate. This alignment of the members is insured by making distance *F*, measured from the beveled surface of the cam, equal to distance *Y*. This leaves the cam free to slide on the beveled surface of die-block *E* and on beveled surface *H* of driving plate *I*. As the cams are gradually forced outward, punch insert *N* (lower view, Fig. 48) comes in contact with the 45-degree flanges on the work and flattens them, as shown at *W*. The cam travel is limited by pins *K* which operate in slots in the cams.

On the up stroke of the punch, the cam is forced inward again by beveled surface *H* of the driver plate. In this design, springs are not used for returning the cams to the "in" position when the die is opened, the beveled surface of the driver plate at *L* and of the cam at *M* serving to actuate the cams. The driver plates should be beveled sufficiently so that if the cam rebounds, or if it is pushed to its outer position at any time when the die is open, the beveled surfaces will still force the cam to the "in" position on the down stroke before the first stage of the hemming operation begins.

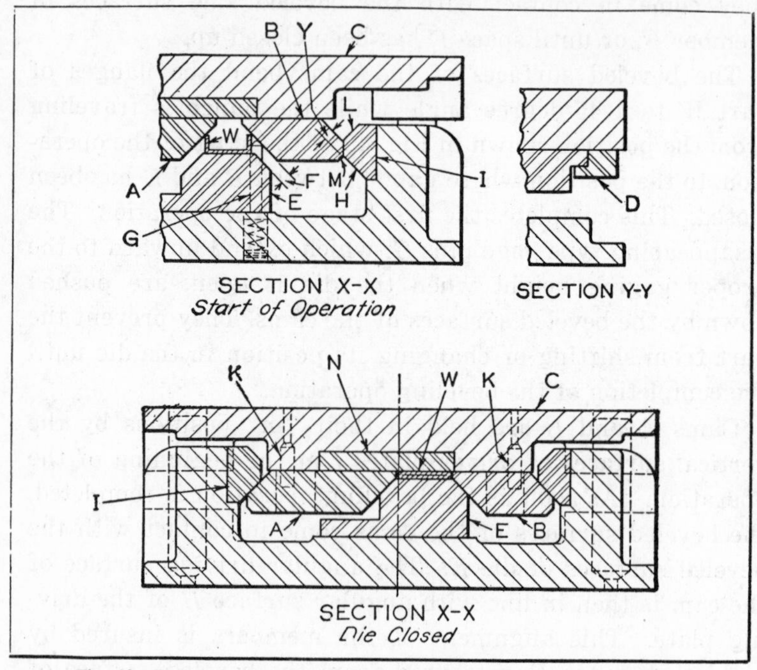

Fig. 48. Sectional Views Showing Action of Cam-operated Hemming Die

A part with a hem on a straight, rather than a curved, break line, can be formed with a much simpler type of hemming die, as shown at the start and finish of the hemming operation, respectively, Fig. 49. Pressure-pad *A* holds the part, which was flanged in a previous operation, down against *B*. Hemming die *C* has a wall *D* which prevents the part from bulging outward. Radius *E* is made as large as the part permits. As the punch continues its downward stroke, flange *F* is forced inward by radius *E* and flattened.

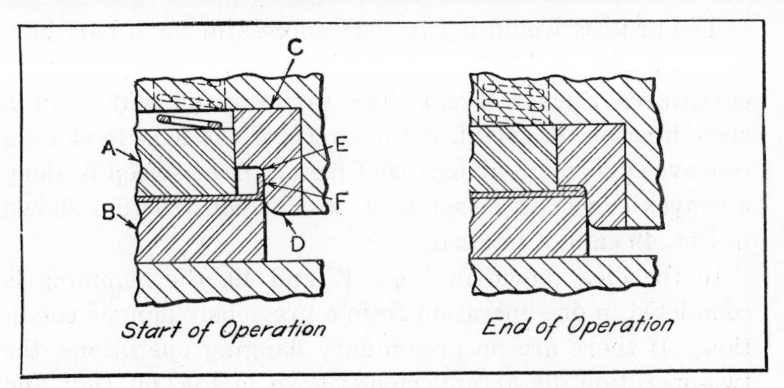

Fig. 49. Simpler Type of Die for Straight-line Hemming

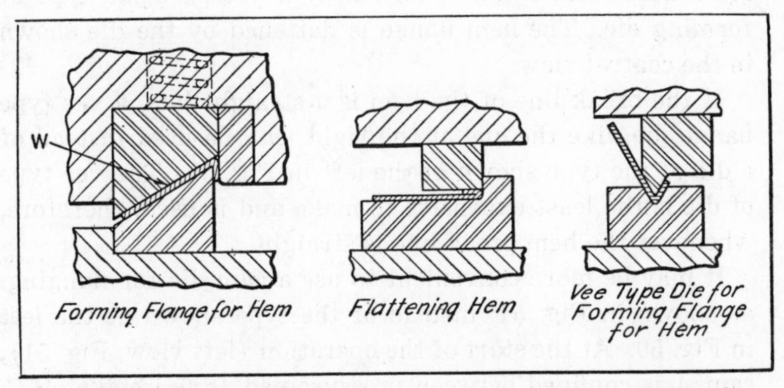

Fig. 50. (Left View) Pressure-pad Type of Die. (Central View) Die for Flattening Hem. (Right View) Vee Type of Die for Straight-line Hemming

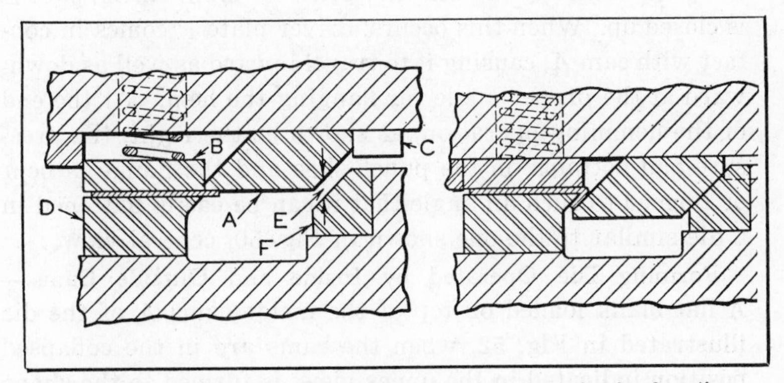

Fig. 51. Cam Type of Die at Beginning and End of Flange-forming Operation

The process would not be very successful for a part having a hem break line with a sharp sweep or small radius of curvature. Such a break line would result either in a stretching of the metal, if the sweep of the hem is along a concave edge, or in an excess of metal, if the sweep is along a convex edge. In either case, the die construction shown in Fig. 49 cannot be used.

In the dies shown in Figs. 47 and 49, the hemming is completed in one operation from a previously flanged condition. If there are no preliminary flanging operations, the two-operation die arrangement shown in Fig. 50 (left and central views) can be used. Part *W* (left view) is flanged for a hem from a flat condition by a pressure-pad type of forming die. The hem flange is flattened by the die shown in the central view.

If the break line of the hem is a straight line, a vee type flange die, like the one at the right, can be used instead of a die of the type shown at the left in Fig. 50. The vee type of die is the least expensive to make and is used, therefore, whenever the hem break line is straight.

It may be more convenient to use a cam die for flanging, as shown in Fig. 51, instead of the type shown at the left in Fig. 50. At the start of the operation (left view, Fig. 51), cam *A* is confined between pressure-pad *B* and end-stop *C*. As the punch continues to travel downward, the cam flanges the part vertically around the corner of die *D* until space *E* is closed up. When this occurs, driver plate *F* comes in contact with cam *A*, causing it to travel inward as well as downward at the proper angle for flanging the hem. At the end of the hemming operation, as shown at the right, the pressure-pad bottoms on the punch-shoe and the flange is bent or formed to such an angle that it can be easily flattened in a die similar to the one shown in Fig. 50, central view.

Forming Die Operated by Inside and Outside Cams.— A flat blank loaded on top of the inside cams *A* of the die illustrated in Fig. 52, when the cams are in the collapsed position indicated in the upper view, is formed to the shape shown at *B* in one stroke of the press. The gages for locating the blank are not shown. On the down stroke, the strong upper spring pad *C* comes in contact with the blank and pushes down cams *A*, which slide in gibs on the top surface of the weak lower spring pad *D*. As the pads move down-

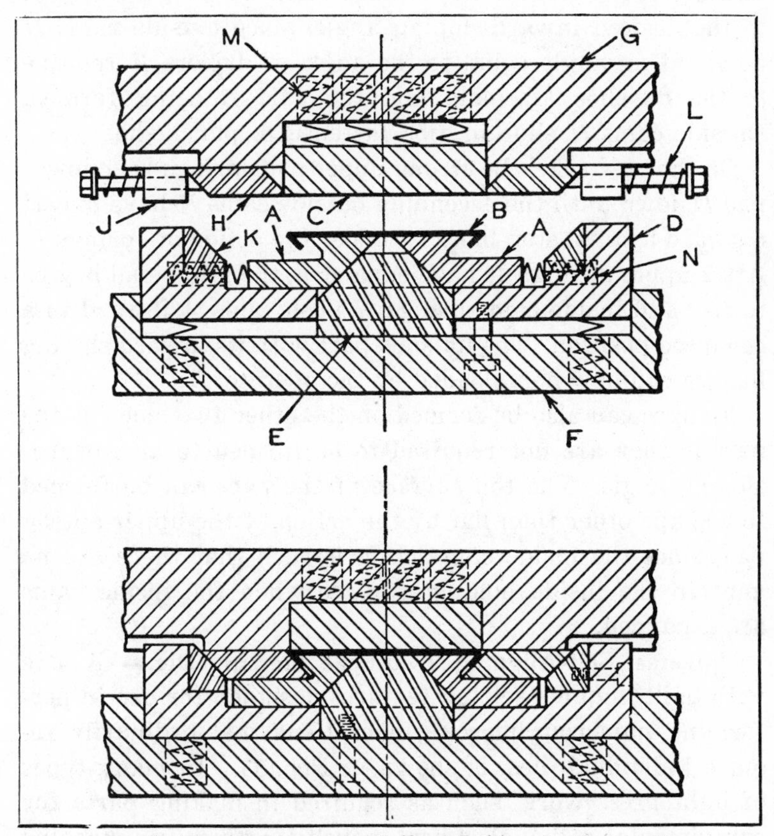

Fig 52. Views Showing Open and Closed Positions for Forming Die Operated by Inside and Outside Cams

ward, driver *E* spreads the inside cams until finally the cams and the driver form a continuous flat surface of the same size as the finished part, as indicated by the lower view, which shows the die in the closed position.

After the lower pad has bottomed on die-shoe *F*, the upper spring pad stops its downward travel, although the rest of the punch-shoe assembly, consisting of punch-shoe *G* and outside cams *H*, continues to travel downward. During this movement, the upper pad springs are compressed. Outside cams *H*, backed up by stop-blocks *J*, flange or form the part around the corners of inside cams *A*. The action of outside cam-drivers *K* causes the outside cams to flange the part to the desired inward-sloping angle, since outside cams *H* travel at an angle equal to the angle of drivers *K* relative to the die-shoe assembly and the part *B* being formed. Outside cams *H* slide in gibs fastened to punch-shoe *G*.

On the up stroke, the strong upper pad springs keep lower pad *D* down until the ascending outside cams *H* have moved outward against stop-blocks *J* under the action of springs *L*. After upper springs *M* have expanded, the lower pad begins to rise and inside cam springs *N* push cams *A* inward to a collapsed position. The finished part with its inward sloping flanges can now be unloaded by the operator.

Flanges can also be formed on the other two sides of the part if they are not required to be formed to an inward-sloping angle. The top surface of the part can be formed to a shape other than flat by the action of the upper spring pad, since the inside cam action is such that there are no gaps in the inside holding surface when the inside cams are expanded.

Universal Self-Aligning Two-Hole Piercing Die.— A die with built-in quick-setting features designed for use in performing numerous piercing operations that ordinarily require individual dies, is shown in Fig. 53. In many types of light press work, such as required in making parts for experimental radio, electrical, novelty, or vending machine products, it is necessary to pierce screw or rivet holes in pairs. It is seldom advisable to attach parts with one screw, and in many cases the use of more than two screws increases the cost unnecessarily; thus the piercing of two holes is common practice.

In the case of pieces made in lots of 100,000, the pairs of holes would be pierced by a progressive die in conjunction

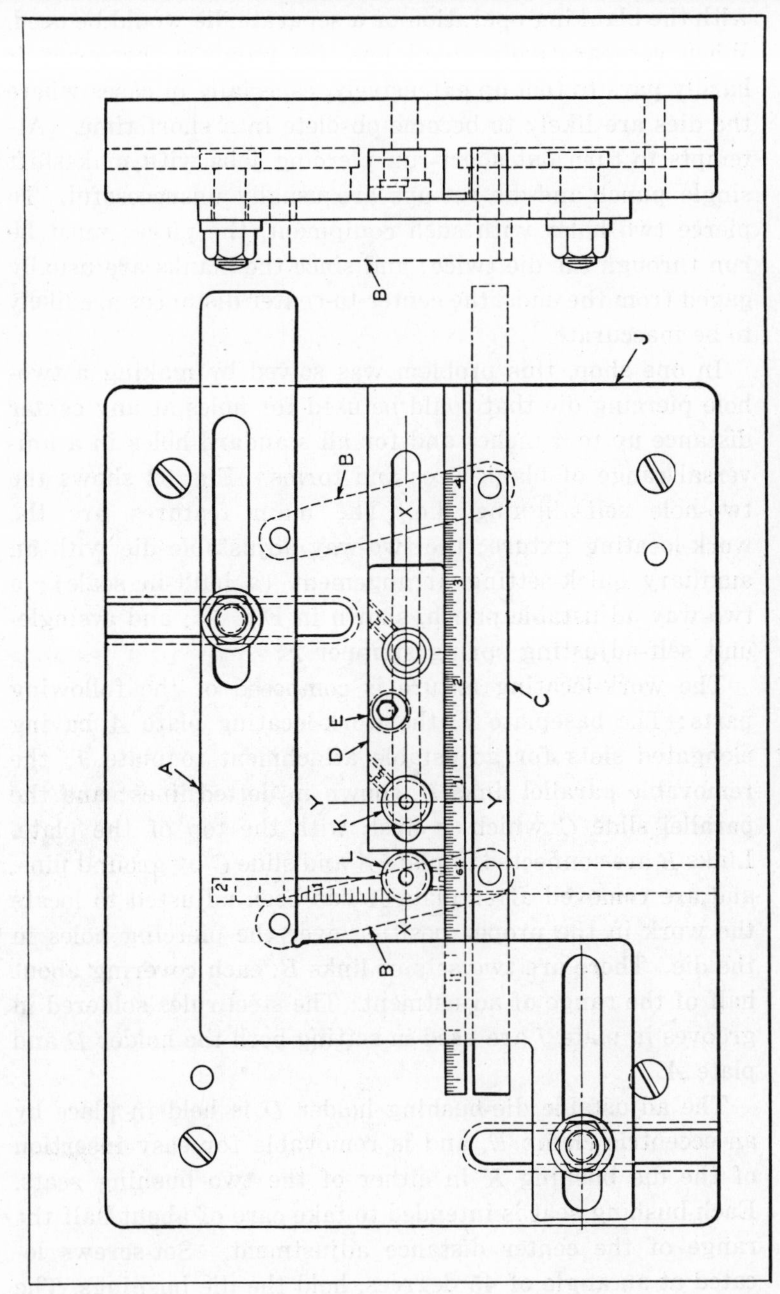

Fig. 53. Universal Self-aligning Two-hole Piercing Die.

with the blanking operation or a separate die would be used. When comparatively small lots are required, however, it hardly pays to tool up extensively, especially in cases where the dies are likely to become obsolete in a short time. Attempts to turn out short-run piercing jobs with makeshift single punch-and-die set-ups are usually unsuccessful. To pierce two holes with such equipment, the pieces must be run through the die twice; and since the blanks are usually gaged from the ends, the center-to-center distances are likely to be inaccurate.

In one shop, this problem was solved by making a two-hole piercing die that could be used for holes at any center distance up to 4 inches and for all standard holes in a universal range of blank sizes and forms. Fig. 53 shows the two-hole self-aligning die. The main features are the work-locating fixture; the two-way adjustable die with an auxiliary quick-setting arrangement (a built-in scale); a two-way adjustable punch, shown in Fig. 54; and a single-unit self-adjusting spring stripper *F*.

The work-locating fixture is composed of the following parts: The baseplate *J*; the work-locating plate *A* having elongated slots for adjustable attachment to plate *J*; the removable parallel links *B*, shown in dotted lines; and the parallel slide *C* which is flush with the top of the plate. Links *B* are connected to plate *A* and slide *C* by ground pins, and are removed after plate *A* has been adjusted to locate the work in the proper position over the piercing holes in the die. There are two sets of links *B*, each covering about half of the range of adjustment. The steel rules soldered in grooves in plate *J* are used in setting both the holder *D* and plate *A*.

The adjustable die-bushing holder *D* is held in place by an eccentric clamp *E*, and is removable for easy insertion of the die bushing *K* in either of the two bushing seats. Each bushing seat is intended to take care of about half the range of the center distance adjustment. Set-screws located at an angle of 45 degrees, hold the die bushings. The stationary die bushing L is held by a set-screw that is reached through a hole drilled from the front of the die to the slide channel.

To set up the die, locating plate A should first be adjusted to suit the work, using the two-way built-in rules and the paralleling links B for all symmetrical blanks, such as oblongs, elongated ovals, hexagons, etc. Irregular blanks

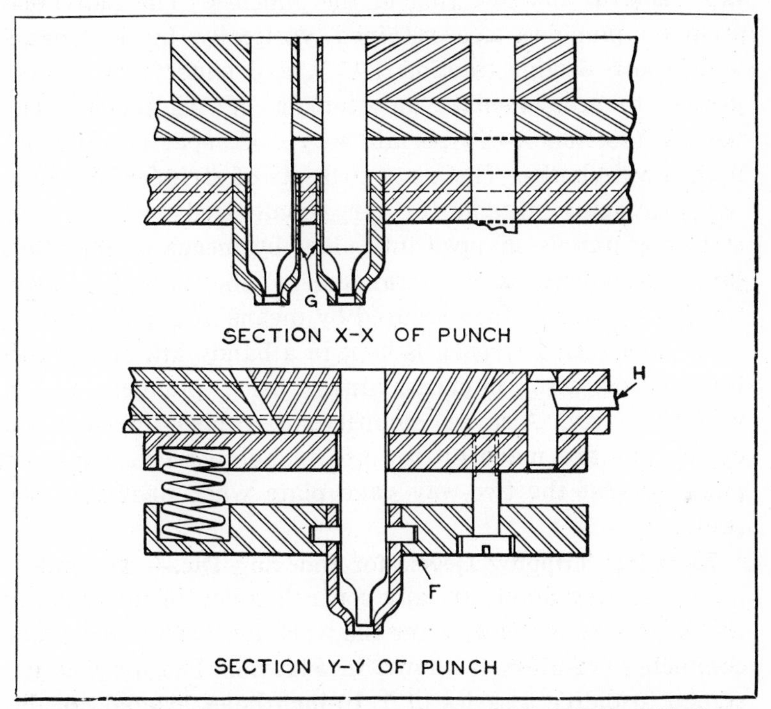

Fig. 54. Section through Punches and Construction of Adjustable Punch Member

can be held by attaching a special arm and disk to the base-plate. With the locating plate adjusted, the proper die bushings K and L are set in place, the die-holder being adjusted and set to the center-to-center distance specified for the holes by means of the scale. The punches are set last. The setting is done with the die mounted in the press, the adjustable punch being located from the die. For very close work, it is advisable to take a micrometer reading between the punches for accurately locating the center distance. The punches are made from 7/16-inch round stock, their ends being machined to the punch sizes required. The punch-holder is lined up with the die-holder and is mounted on the upper member of the set by a dovetail fit (see section *Y–Y*, Fig. 54).

The spring-actuated stripper unit is detachable to facilitate removal and resetting of the punches. The individual stripper plungers are retained vertically by a tongue-and-groove design (section *Y–Y*), and slide freely in the groove to accommodate any setting of the punch. The flats *G* (section *X–X*) permit very close spacing on minimum-sized blanks. There are two sets of stripper plungers, one pair being suitable for very small-sized punches. The stripping unit is snapped into place by means of the pilot-pin and spring latch arrangement shown at *H* (section *Y–Y*), and is then secured by means of cap-screws.

A quick-acting wrench is kept in a handy kit, along with the set of dies, punches, links, bars, plungers, Allen wrenches, etc. Also, a quantity of rubber-tipped wood dowel-rods are made up for use in holding the blanks in place against the two-way gage plate when operating the press.

Electrical Tripping Device for Indexing Die.— An indexing die having an electrically controlled device for tripping the press automatically after the work has been indexed one complete revolution is shown in Fig. 55. The die was designed to pierce a series of 1/16-inch holes around an aluminum cup 2 1/4 inches in diameter and 2 1/4 inches long. The thickness of the stock used for these cups is 0.025 inch. Thirty-two equally spaced rows of holes, with nine holes to a row, are pierced in each cup, making a total of 288 holes.

From the sectional view, the construction of the die will be readily understood. The part to be pierced is placed on the plug *A*, and clamped by turning the U-washer *B* a quarter of a revolution. Plug *A*, into which a hardened tool-steel die section *C* is inserted, is stationary and is fastened

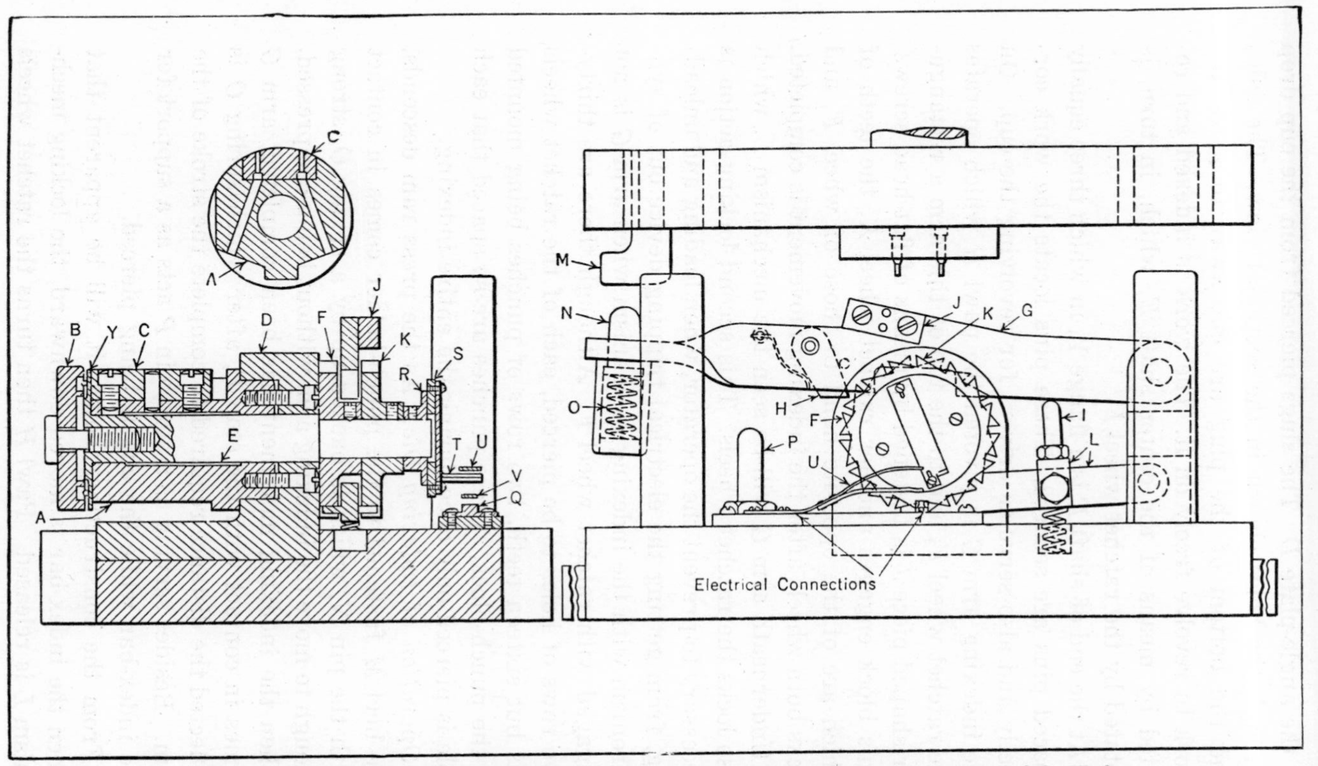

Fig. 55. Indexing Die Equipped with Electrical Device for Tripping Press after One Revolution of the Work

to the angle-plate *D*. The slugs pierced from the cup drop through the holes shown in the sectional view. The sides and the bottom of the plug are cut away to allow the work to revolve freely on it. The work is indexed and rotated by means of the center shaft *E*, which, in turn, is rotated by the ratchet wheel *F*.

At the end of shaft *E* is a flange *Y*, in which three equally spaced pins are secured. These pins locate the work correctly and also serve as drivers for revolving the cup. On the indexing arm *G* is pivoted the pawl *H* which operates the ratchet wheel *F*, and to the top of this arm a rectangular-shaped piece *J* is fastened by means of flat-head screws. This block engages another ratchet wheel *K*, the teeth of which are of the opposite hand to those of wheel *F*, and locks both wheels after the indexing movement is completed.

Underneath arm *G* will be seen the mechanism *L*, which also locks the ratchet wheels. This second locking action is necessary to prevent the operator, when loading and unloading, from getting the electrical tripping device out of synchronism with the indexing mechanism when arm *G* is not engaged with ratchet wheel *F*. Although there are thirty-two rows of holes to be pierced, each of the ratchet wheels has but sixteen teeth, two rows of punches being mounted in the punch-block. These punches are so spaced that each hole is pierced only once during the entire indexing.

Operation of Indexing Die: As the press ram descends, the heel *M* fastened to the punch-holder comes in contact with the pin *N*, which is backed up by a spring *O*, strong enough to move the indexing arm without being compressed. When the indexing movement has been completed, arm *G* comes in contact with the stop *P*, after which spring *O* is deflected the distance required to complete the stroke of the ram. Besides serving as a stop, pin *P* acts as a support for the index-bar while the cup is being pierced.

From the construction shown, it will be apparent that when the index-bar is moved downward, the locking mechanism *L* is released. Pawl *H* then turns the ratchet wheels and the piece J drops in place in the ratchet teeth, thus completing the indexing movement. At the end of the up stroke, index-arm G, being in the up position, allows the mechanism L to return to the position indicated, locking both ratchet wheels against rotation in either direction.

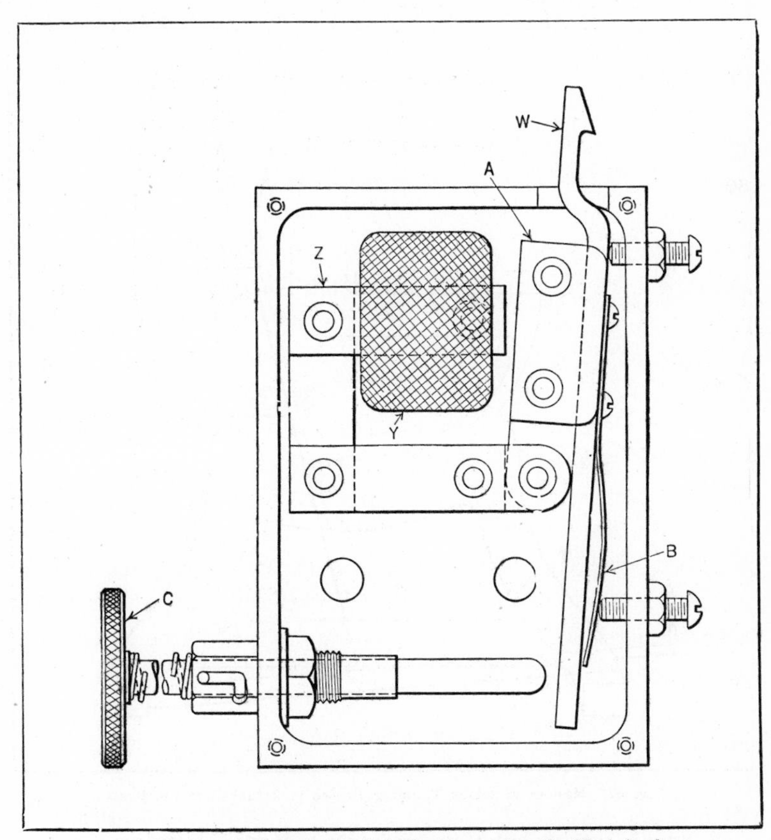

Fig. 56. Electrical Device for Tripping Press when the Work in the Die Shown in Fig. 55 Makes One Revolution

At one end of shaft E is an adjustable arm T, mounted on a Bakelite disk S which, in turn, is fastened to a steel disk R. At the end of every revolution of the cup, the spring U is depressed by arm T, making an electrical contact between the members Q and V, which disengages the arm W (Figs. 56 and 57) in the trip mechanism. The tripping device is mounted on the press as shown in Fig. 57. Here, the arm *X* replaces the standard arm on the punch press. The magnetic circuit of the tripping device is made up from laminations 0.018 inch thick, stacked to a cross-section of 3/4 by 1 inch, producing a pull on the movable

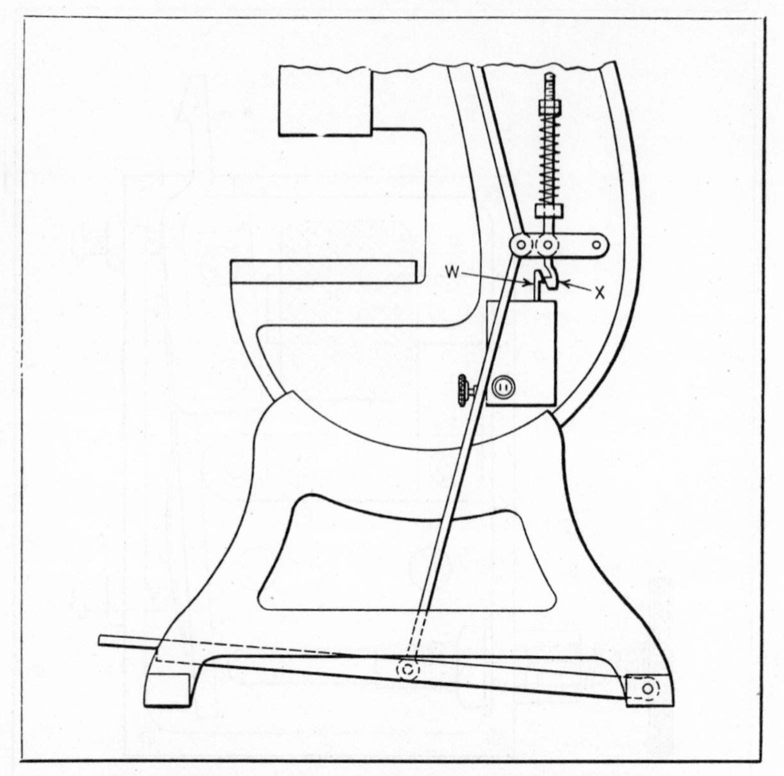

Fig. 57. Manner in which Tripping Device is Attached to the Press

arm *W* of approximately 15 pounds. The coil is made up of 650 turns of No. 24 cotton-covered wire.

Operation of Tripping Device: Referring to Fig. 56, member *W* is the tripping arm, *Y* the coil, and *Z* the laminated core. The movable part of the core to which arm *W* is fastened is shown at *A* while at *B* is shown a leaf spring, which forces arm *W* back after the circuit has been broken.

It will be apparent from Fig. 57 that when the operator

depresses the foot-pedal, arm *X* will engage the latch on arm *W* and hold the foot-pedal down until the adjustable arm *T*, Fig. 55, closes the circuit. This energizes the coil in the tripping device and causes arm *X* to be released. This device is operated on a 110-volt alternating-current line.

The plunger *C*, Fig. 56, when pushed in and held in position by means of the bayonet lock, forces arm *W* away from arm *X*, Fig. 57, thus allowing other jobs to be done without disturbing the tripping device, which is permanently fastened to the press. When the tripping device is being used, plunger *C*, Fig. 56, is released, leaving arm *W* free to operate. Another advantage of this device is that the press can be tripped at any time while the electric trip is in operation by merely pressing plunger *C*. This tripping device possibly can be used to advantage on many jobs of a similar nature.

CHAPTER XXII

DESIGNING DIES FOR INCLINABLE PRESSES

THERE are definite reasons why presses are designed and constructed so that they can be operated in an inclined position. The greatest advantage of the inclinable press is that it can be so operated that the danger element is eliminated and production greatly increased. However, the use of an inclinable press will not protect the operator or increase production unless the dies used are specifically designed for operation in that type of press. The design of dies for inclinable presses requires the application of some fundamental principles which vary from those governing conventional die design for upright presses. The information in this chapter was contributed by J. I. Karash, Plant Engineer, The Reliance Electric & Engineering Co., Cleveland, Ohio.

Safety in punch press operation generally involves the provision of auxiliary devices, such as swinging guards, roped bracelets, moving screens, two-button switches, and other equipment designed to protect the operator. The use of such equipment is desirable, but the real solution of the safety problem is to make it unnecessary for the operator to place his hands in the danger zone—between the punch-holder and the die-shoe. When this has been accomplished, through proper die design, the real objective has been achieved. The addition of protective devices is then an important, but secondary, consideration. It is generally assumed that safety devices or designs that protect the operator handicap the efficiency of the operation to some degree. The operation of correctly designed dies in an inclinable press is an outstanding exception to this.

This chapter will deal with dies for manually fed inclinable presses, stressing the safety features achieved through proper design. An incidental advantage is that production is greatly increased in most cases, though the cost of the designs suggested, in general, do not appreciably increase the tool cost.

The accompanying illustrations are greatly exaggerated to bring out fundamental principles of design. All superfluous details, such as guide posts, bushings, screws, dowels, etc., are omitted. In order that the action of the dies may be more readily understood, they are shown in both shut and open positions. The dies are drawn in an inclined position—their actual position when mounted in the press—so

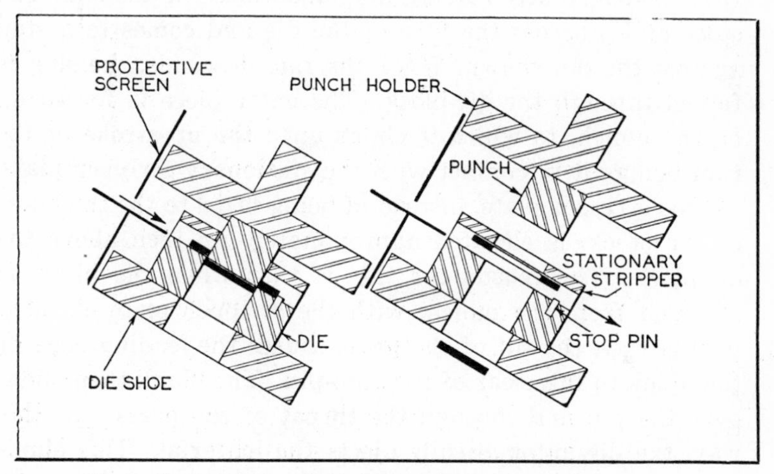

Fig. 1. Simplest Type of Self-unloading Die Used in an Inclinable Press

that the movement of the stock can be better visualized. In the designs illustrated, only the fundamental types of dies are included. It should be kept in mind that the variations and possible combinations of the elementary principles are unlimited.

In the operation of presses, the stock is in one of two forms—either unit stock or strip stock—the unit stock being punched only once, and the strip stock being fed across the die and punched several times. It will be noted that each design illustrated is intended specifically for either unit stock or for strip stock operation.

Elevated Stationary Stripper-Plate Design.—Fig. 1 shows a simple type of die designed for an inclinable press. This design is intended for piercing or blanking unit stock. In appearance, the design is similar to that of the conventional type of stationary stripper-plate dies used in upright presses for progressive operation on strip stock. However, the operation is quite different.

The stock is placed in the die by slipping it through a protective screen. This screen should have a horizontal slot which will admit the stock, but will prevent the operator from inadvertently placing his hands into the die set. The stock slides across the face of the die and comes to a stop against the pin shown. When the ram descends, the slug is forced through the die-block. The outer piece is forced up on the punch, to which it clings until the up stroke of the ram brings it in contact with the stationary stripper plate.

This stripper plate, instead of being fitted to the thickness of the stock, is elevated approximately an inch above the die-block. The reason for this is that when the blank is stripped from the punch, with the stripper plate elevated in this way, the tilt of the press causes the leading edge of the blank to fall clear of the stop-pin. The blank then slides over the pin and through the throat of the press. In this way, the die automatically ejects the material. This eliminates practically all the material-handling time, because the press can usually be loaded during the up stroke and the start of the down stroke of the ram. It should be noted that the safety screen shown could not be used if the operator had to remove the material from the die.

One stop-pin is shown to illustrate the action. Actually, two or more stop-pins may be used, so located that they will not catch in the hole, or holes, punched out. In the operation of this die, and the other dies to be described, the operator is at no time required to place his hands in the danger area in order to place or remove material.

The Use of Knock-Out Pins.—Knock-out pins, or "KO pins," as they are sometimes called, are important. Their action is shown in Fig. 2. These pins are short lengths of cold-rolled steel which are a slip fit in holes in the punch-holder. The pins rest on the stripper plate and extend approximately 2 inches above the punch-holder shank. The stripper plate itself is supported by conventional stripper bolts (not shown). The knock-out pins are actuated by a knock-out bar, which is an adjustable bar secured in a horizontal position to the ways on both sides of the ram. There is a slot through the ram which clears this bar.

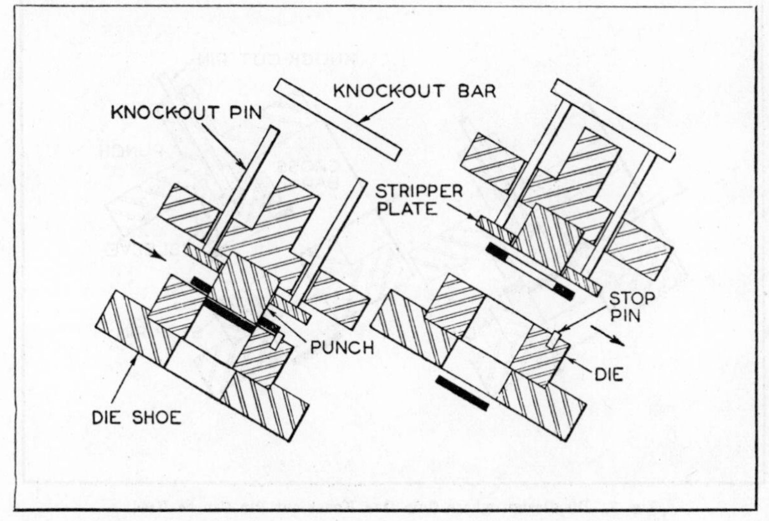

Fig. 2. Diagrammatic Illustration of the Action of Knock-out Pins

Near the top of the up stroke of the ram, the knock-out pins come in contact with the stationary knock-out bar. As the ram continues to rise, the pins force the stripper plate down, and the blank is stripped at the top of the stroke, so that the leading edge of the falling blank will clear the stop-pins, as mentioned, and the blank will slide out of the die. The type of die illustrated in Fig. 2 is used for piercing and blanking operations on unit stock.

The design shown in Fig. 3 is used for dies in which, because of space requirements, only one knock-out pin passing up through the shank can be used. In some types of presses, there is provision for this type of knock-out pin action only. This type of die is used for piercing and blanking operations on unit stock. As will be noted, a stripping sleeve is used instead of a stripper plate. The sleeve is secured to a cross-bar placed in a slot cut through the punch. At the top of the ram stroke, the knock-out pin forces down the cross-bar and the stripping sleeve. Since the material is

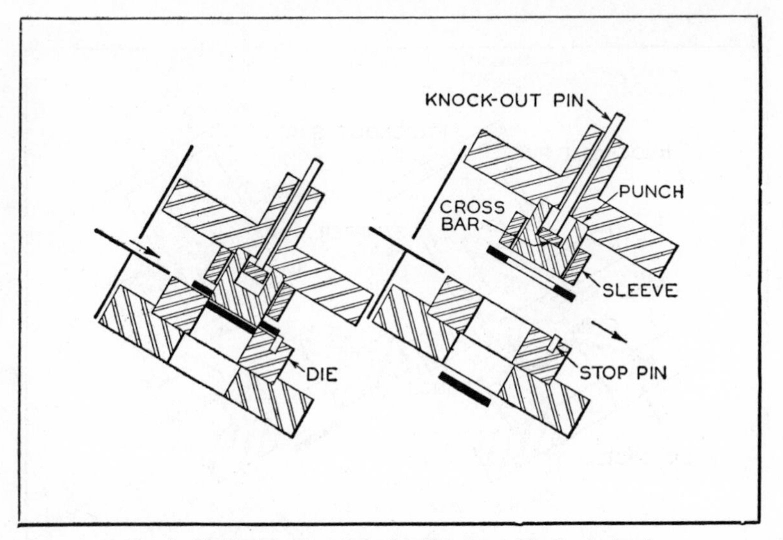

Fig. 3. Die Design where Only One Knock-out Pin Can be Used

stripped at the top of the ram stroke, the stock will automatically be removed from the press.

Inverted Type of Die.—In Fig. 4 is shown an inverted type of die, generally used for operations on strip stock. The punch is in the lower member and the die in the upper. Since the piece punched out does not pass through the die, no taper, or relief, is required on the die walls; hence, the punching produced will be the same throughout the life of the die. Ordinarily, the taper in the die causes a burr after the die has been ground down a considerable amount. The worn down die will also produce a slightly larger blank.

With this design, the stock is entered through the side of the die. Suitable protective screens should be used, so that only the stock can enter the danger area. As the ram descends, the punch forces the blank up into the die, where it remains until it is stripped at the top of the ram stroke by the pin-actuated stripper plate. From this elevation, the blank falls clear of the die set. The outer piece is forced down over the punch and depresses the spring-actuated stripper plate. As the ram starts up, the spring stripper

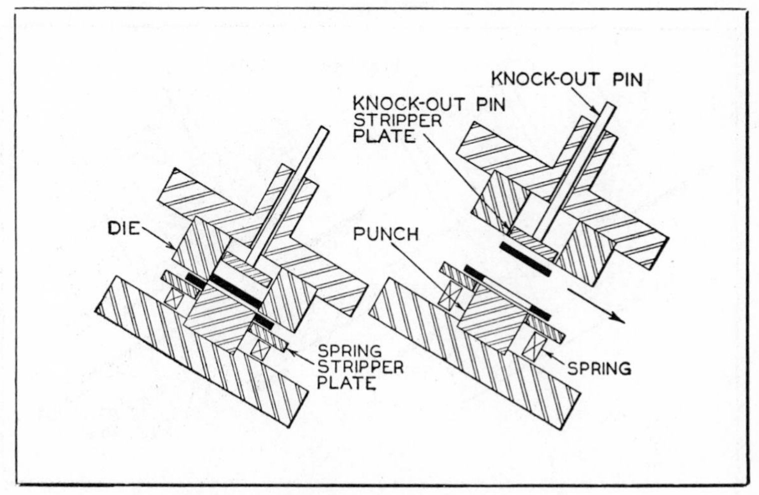

Fig. 4. Inverted Die, with the Punch below and the Die Above

plate simultaneously strips the outer piece from the punch. The strip remains on the punch, and is ready to be advanced to the new position.

It should be noted that if spring strippers were used to remove the blank from the upper member, the springs would force the blank back into the hole from which it was punched. The operator would then have to separate the blanks from the scrap after running the strip through the die. This condition is extremely awkward in that the strip cannot be positioned against a stop-pin when the previous blank has been pushed back into the stock.

Compound Die for Inclinable Press.—Fig. 5 shows the simplest form of compound die for use in an inclinable press. Variations of the design would, of course, be required, according to the conditions in each case. This type of die can be used for punching either strip stock or unit stock. When unit stock is used, the stock should be entered through a protective screen in front of the die. If possible, the outer edge of the stock should be allowed to project out through the screen when the stock is in place. In this way, the

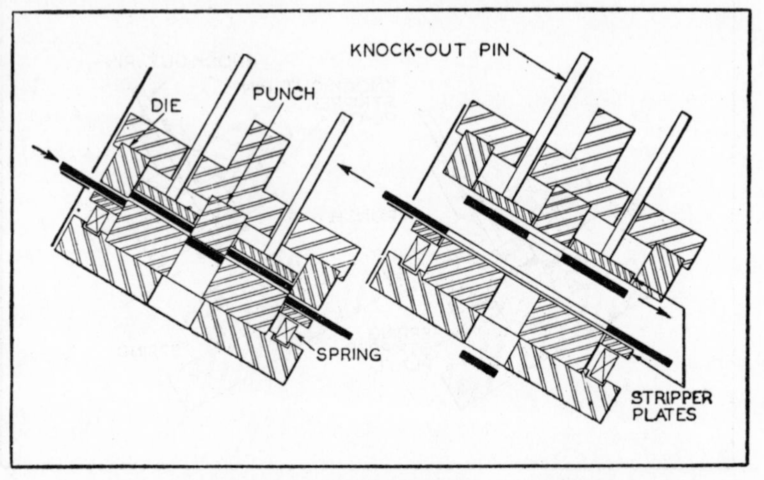

Fig. 5. Simple Form of Compound Die for Use in an Inclinable Press

operator does not have to let go of the piece during the stroke of the press. After the piece has been punched, the operator pulls the projecting part back through the screen and does not have to reach into the danger area to remove the scrap. In case the stock is in square pieces, it may be entered through the screen in a diagonal position, so that the corner will project through the screen.

When strip stock is used, the work should be fed from the side of the press through proper screen guards. The operator discards the scrap after feeding the strip across the die. The operation of this die is greatly facilitated, as none of the pieces punched out are forced back into the hole from which they were punched.

In the operation of the die, the center piece is forced down through the die-block. The middle ring is forced up into the upper member, where it remains until stripped at the top of the ram stroke. The outer piece is forced down on the blanking punch. After the punching operation, the outer ring is removed from the die manually, there being no entanglement of three pieces produced.

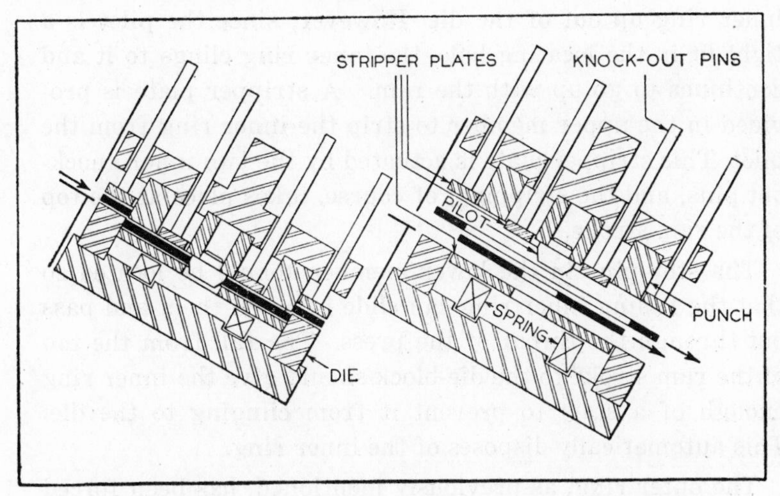

Fig. 6. A Separating Die Intended for Secondary Operations on Semi-finished Stock

Design of Separating Die.—In Fig. 6 is shown a separating die. This design is intended for secondary operations—that is, operations on a semi-finished unit stock, which must be accurately punched or blanked in relation to a hole, or holes, already in the piece. This type of operation is often met with in the electrical industry, as for example, in separating the stator and rotor laminations of an electric motor, using the shaft hole as a locating point.

The operation of this die is unusual in many respects. If possible, the semi-finished blank should be fed to the die set by a gravity chute, the stock coming to a stop slightly beyond the correct position for blanking. This is to prevent pinching the stock against the stop-pins when the locating pilot is in place. As the ram descends, the pilot enters the hole in the blank and accurately locates the piece. There is a hole in the bottom stripper plate for the pilot to pass through. As the ram continues to descend, the punch cuts the stock into two concentric rings. The inner ring is forced down into the die, and the outer ring is forced up on the punch.

As the ram starts up, the bottom stripper plate forces the inner ring up out of the die. However, since the pilot is a tight fit in the locating hole, the inner ring clings to it and continues to go up with the ram. A stripper plate is provided in the upper member to strip the inner ring from the pilot. This stripper plate is actuated by the two inner knock-out pins, and the stripping, of course, takes place at the top of the ram stroke.

The stop-pins in the lower member should be located so that the falling inner ring can slide between them and pass out through the throat of the press. The fall from the top of the ram stroke to the die-block should give the inner ring enough of a start to prevent it from clinging to the die. This automatically disposes of the inner ring.

The outer ring, as previously mentioned, has been forced up on the punch, to which it clings until stripped at the top of the ram stroke by the knock-out pin actuated stripper plate. From this elevation, the leading edge of the outer ring will clear the stop-pins. The piece will then slide over the pins and out through the throat of the press.

It is advisable to make the knock-out pins for stripping the center ring approximately 1/4 inch longer than those used for the outer ring. Thus, the inner ring is stripped first and interference of the pieces is avoided. The material-handling time has been practically eliminated, because the loading can be done during the up stroke and the start of the down stroke of the ram.

As will be noted, both pieces produced by this operation pass out through the back of the die. The two pieces can be automatically made to fall into separate boxes by using a separating chute, made of sheet metal, into which a hole is cut of such a size that the smaller ring will fall through it into a container, while the larger ring will slide over it and fall into another box. In this way, the manual sorting of the blanks can be eliminated. As previously mentioned, entanglement of the two pieces can be avoided by making

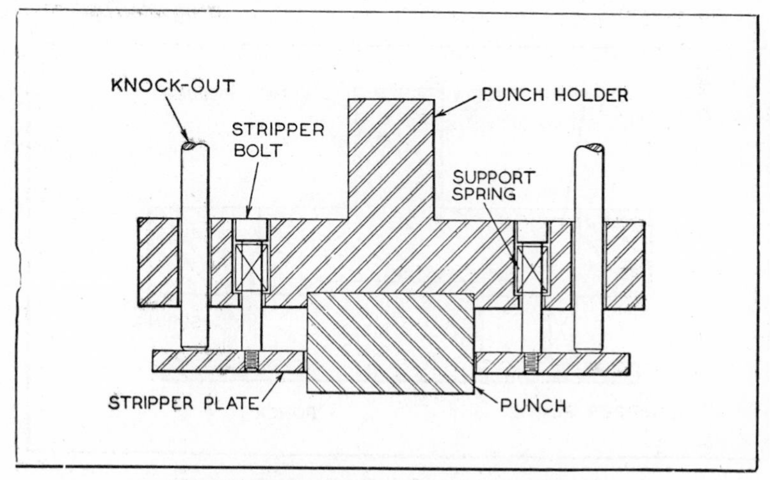

Fig. 7. Diagrammatic View Showing the Suspension of a Knock-out Pin-operated Stripper Plate

the inner knock-out pins slightly longer than the outer ones.

Stripper-Plate Suspension for Knock-Out Pins.—Fig. 7 illustrates the suspension of the knock-out pin-operated stripper plate. In some respects, this suspension is different from that of the conventional spring-operated stripper plate. The springs used with the knock-out pin operated stripper plate are comparatively light, and are used to counteract the weight of the stripper plate itself and to prevent the inertia of the plate from prematurely stripping the stock. The down and up motion of the ram produces more or less of a whip-like change of direction. Because of this, the inertia of the stripper plate would, in many cases, strip the stock. This is particularly true where the material is of light gage. The disadvantage of having the stock prematurely stripped is that the material would be left lying on the die and be unable to slide over the stop-pins. In order for the stock to go over the stop-pins, it must be stripped at the top of the ram stroke.

The suspension of the stripper plate shown in Fig. 7 has some indirect advantages over the spring-actuated type of stripper plate shown in Fig. 8. In the latter type, the

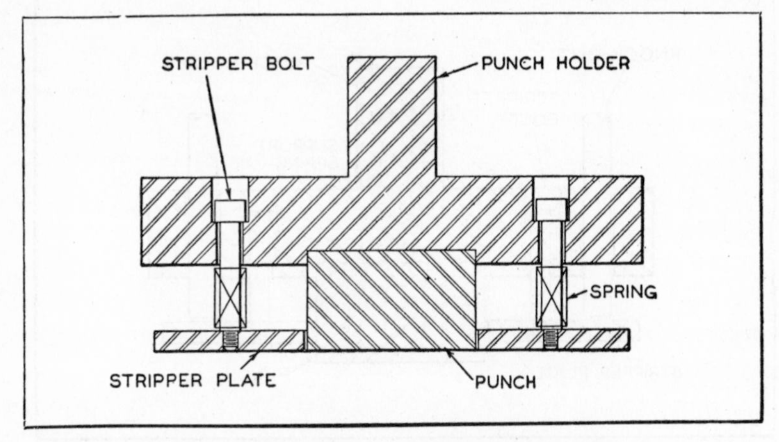

Fig. 8. Diagrammatic View Showing the Suspension of a Spring-operated Stripper Plate

stripper plate must be removed in order to grind the die. With the stripper plate suspension shown in Fig. 7, it is unnecessary to remove the stripper plate, because it is normally in the retracted position. In order to grind the die, it is only necessary to slip out the knock-out pins.

With the spring-actuated stripper plate shown in Fig. 8, it is necessary to adjust the stripper plate from time to time as the die wears. This is usually done by substituting shorter stripper bolts or by placing washers under the stripper-bolt heads. With the stripper-plate suspension shown in Fig. 7, adjustment is not necessary during the life of the die. The setting of the stripper plate is easily taken care of by the adjustable bar that actuates the knock-out pins.

In cases where no guide posts are used, a die set with the stripper plate shown in Fig. 8 is hard to set up, because the stripper plate prevents the punch from entering the die to establish alignment. With the knock-out pin type of stripper plate, the stripper plate is in a retracted position and there is no difficulty in entering the punch into the die. This greatly simplifies the set-up.

With the spring-actuated stripper plate, Fig. 8, the stripper plate acts as a pressure pad. Sometimes this is undesirable—for example, where it is necessary to have a pilot in the punch-holder. With the spring-actuated stripper plate, the plate would project beyond the holding point on the pilot; this would prevent the pilot from moving the stock into position. Operation of dies such as shown in Fig. 6 would not be possible unless the knock-out pin actuated stripper plate were used.

In the designs thus far shown, variations of each type have been avoided. Each design has shown some fundamental principle adaptable to inclinable press dies. It will be noted that, wherever possible, the blank has been punched through the die. In some cases, it is not practical to do this, because the die set is greatly weakened if a large hole is cut through it for a large blank to pass through. Another reason for not passing the blank through the die is that the die would have to be ground for taper, in order to allow the blank to pass through the die ring. As the die wears, there would be a noticeable burr and a slightly larger blank.

If a spring-actuated stripper plate such as shown in Fig. 9 is used in the die, the sides of the die can be perpendicular and will produce the same size punching throughout the life of the die without increasing the burr or size of blank. Since this will be used in an inclinable press, provision must be made to eject the material from the die ring, and the die set must also be designed so that the blank will slide out of it.

It will be noted that there is a slot cut in the stripper plate and a spring secured in the slot. When the stock is entered in the die set, the material slides over the spring and comes to position against the stop-pins. Then when the punch descends and punches the blank, the blank is forced down into the die. Upon the upward stroke of the ram, the springs behind the stripper plate force the blank up out of the die. However, there is a tendency for the blank to cling to the stripper plate, due to a very small burr around the edge of the blank. This is overcome by the action

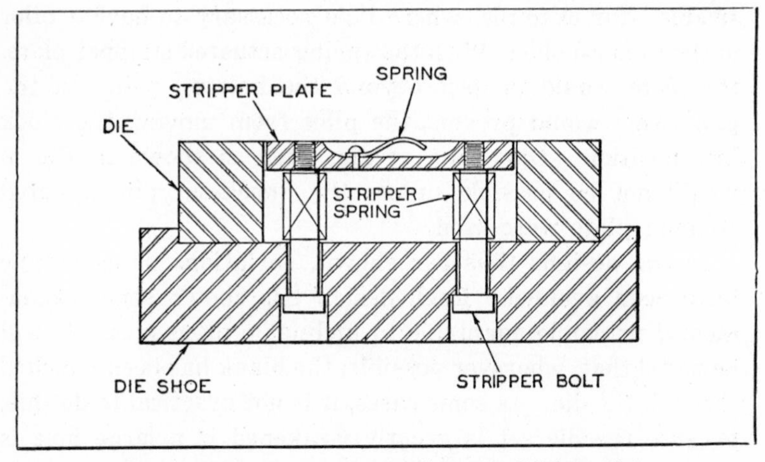

Fig. 9. Another Arrangement of Spring-operated Stripper Plate

of the spring on top of the stripper plate, which lifts the blank free, so that it can slide out of the die set.

It is important to arrange the stop-pins so that the blank can slide between them and out of the press, but they should be so arranged that the outside piece is held until punched. Any of the knock-out pin stripping schemes can dispose of the outside piece. The blank, when stripped with a spring-actuated stripper plate, must slide across the die and out of the press, and must not be held by the stop-pins.

This method of disposing of the blank, as shown in Fig. 9, should be carefully kept in mind. In all the dies shown, where the blank passes through the die ring, this type of stripper plate can be used to force the blank out of the die. In the case of compound dies such as shown in Fig. 5, the blank would slide not only over the die ring, but also over the outside stripper plate. The inside of this stripper plate should not have a sharp edge which might stop the sliding blank.

Die Design for Making Simple V-Bends.—The bending die shown in Fig. 10 is intended for simple V-bends. In opera-

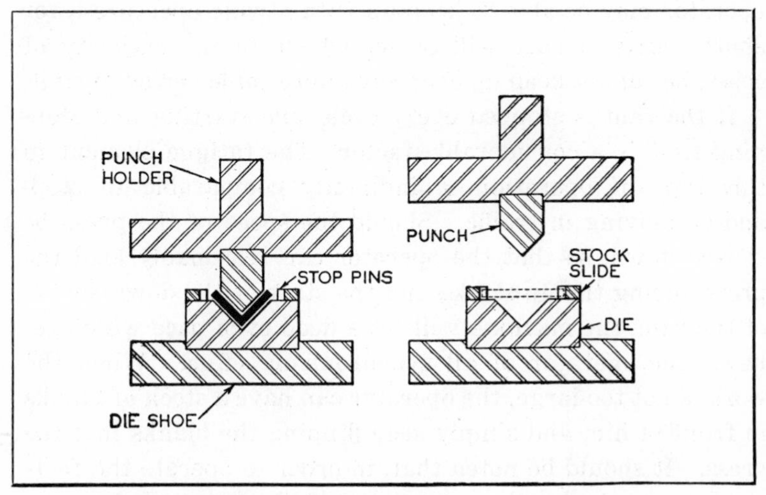

Fig. 10. Diagrammatic Views of a Bending Die for Simple V-bends

tion, the stock should be fed to the die by a gravity chute, the stock sliding between guides and coming to position against the stop-pins. When the ram descends and bends the stock, the ends of the bent piece are no longer in contact with the stop-pins. Since the die is in an inclinable press, the bent piece will slide out of the die. In some cases, it is necessary to have a simple spring-operated disappearing pin or pressure pad in the bottom of the vee to dislodge the bent piece if it sticks in the die. The main point is to so design the die that the bent piece will not be in contact with the stop-pins, but will be free to slide out of the die. In making

U-bends, it is, of course, necessary to use a pressure pad in the lower die member.

In most of the designs shown, the stock is fed to the die set by gravity, and the pieces are automatically ejected. Since the danger element has thus been entirely eliminated, the stock can be entered in the die set during the up stroke and the start of the down stroke of the ram. Theoretically, this eliminates all lost time. In many cases, it will be found that the press will be too fast to be run wide open—that is, to step on the foot-pedal and keep it down. Though the operator may be able to keep up with a wide open press for short spurts, a pace will be set which, in the majority of cases, he cannot keep up over any appreciable period of time.

If the ram is stopped every cycle, the starting and stopping time is a considerable factor. The fatigue element in this type of operation is indirectly comparable to stop-and-go driving in traffic. Should the speed of the press be slowed down, so that the operator can reasonably load the press during the up stroke and the start of the down stroke of the ram, the machine will set a dead even pace which relieves the operator of all synchronizing effort. When the work is not too large, the operator can have a stock of blanks in front of him and simply keep flipping the blanks into the press. It should be noted that, in order to operate the foot-pedal every stroke, the operator would have to stand on one foot, which would greatly increase the fatigue.

The slowing down of the press, of course, reduces the momentum of the flywheel and thus decreases the blanking capacity of the press. This scheme is not recommended for all types of work, but merely suggested as a possibility for certain types of repetitive punch-press operations. This method of increasing efficiency has been tried and found to be practical.

Gravity-Fed Piercing and Cutting-Off Die.—A quantity of parts such as shown at *A*, Fig. 11, were made from 13-gage sheet steel. The parts were approximately 1 1/2 by 2 1/2 inches with a 1-inch hole. The material used for making these parts was first sheared into long strips 1 1/2 inches wide. These strips were then fed into the piercing and cutting-off die shown in Fig. 12. This die was designed for operation in an inclined press at an angle, as shown in the illustration, so that the stock is fed to the die by gravity.

It should be noted that in the construction of the die the stock gage *B* was secured to stationary stripper plate *C*.

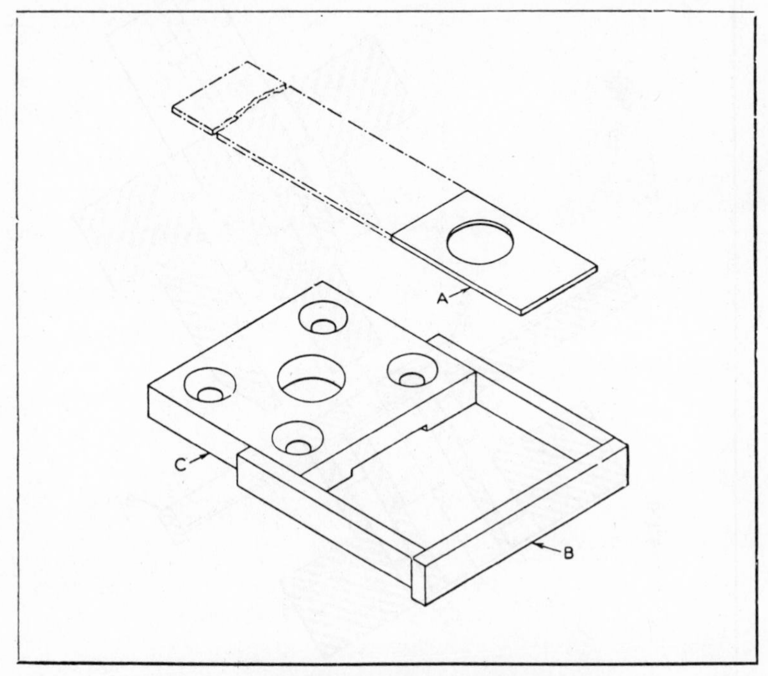

Fig. 11. Pierced and Cut-off Piece A, and Stripper Plate C with Stop B Used on Die Shown in Fig. 12.

Had the stock gage been secured to the die-shoe, it would have been necessary to use a much larger shoe. It would also have been necessary to cut a large hole through the die-shoe to allow the cut-off piece to fall through.

The specifications of the work did not call for close tolerances, and, consequently, it was permissible to have a free fit of the stripper plate slot on the strip material. If a stock support surface is provided, such as shown in the illustration, the strip stock will be free to slide through the die until it is stopped by the stock gage. Thus, if the press is run at a constant speed, the material will feed itself. On the down stroke of the ram, the material will be pierced and the cut-off piece will fall free. During the up stroke

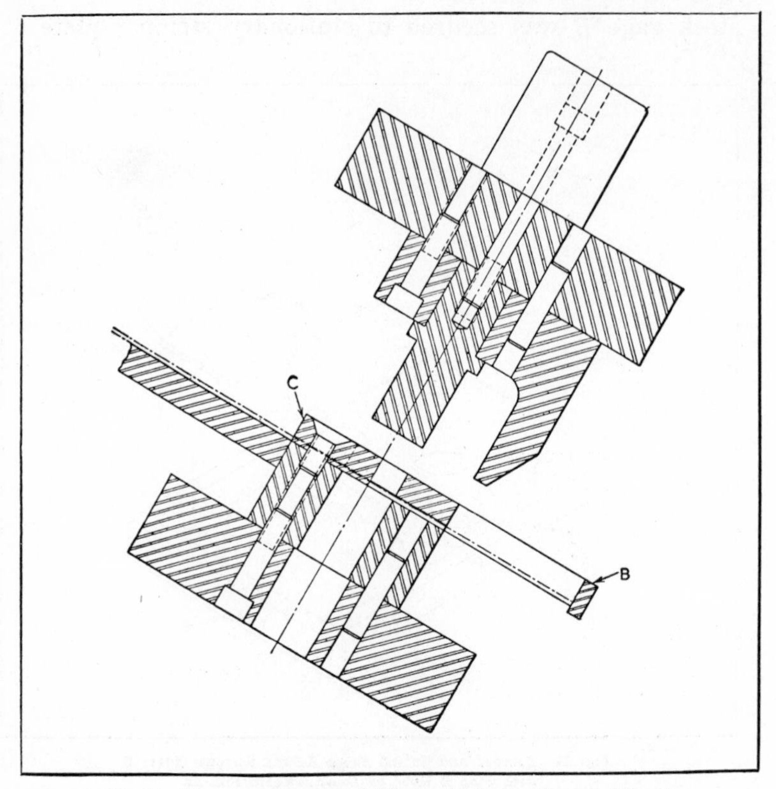

Fig. 12. Two-stage Gravity-fed Die for Producing Piece A, Fig. 11

and the start of the down stroke, the strip material will again slide into position against the stock gage.

The operation cannot be considered automatic, because of the fact that it is a two-station operation. This necessitates momentarily stopping the ram action in order to position the new strip for the first punch. In entering a new strip into the die, the operator should allow it to project slightly beyond the cut-off line, so that the end of the stock can be shaved during the first-station piercing operation. The operator can then allow the stock to feed itself, the press running at a constant speed.

The press that was used had an inclined angle of 30 degrees. An angle of 45 degrees would probably give the best results. The running speed of the press was 48 strokes per minute, and the length of the strokes 3 inches. In using gravity feed on a punch press, the speed of the press will affect the performance. Should the running speed be too fast, the material would not have time to feed itself. This would necessitate stepping on the foot-pedal every stroke. Though the die is quite conventional in appearance, it has some decided advantages from the standpoint of efficiency and safety. These advantages are realized with little increase in tool cost.

CHAPTER XXIII

POINTERS ON THE DESIGN OF STAMPINGS

LOW-CARBON steel is employed for more stampings than any other metal because of its low cost, excellent working characteristics, and high physical properties. A great number of stampings are also made from non-ferrous metals, especially brass and aluminum. Other metals used include bronze, copper, zinc, nickel alloys, magnesium alloys, silver and gold.

Among the ferrous materials used, there are several kinds of steel, such as hot- and cold-rolled steel, tin plate, and stainless steel.

Use of Hot-rolled Steel for Stampings.—Stampings used in unexposed places or as parts of some design where fine finish is not essential are usually made from hot-rolled steel. Typical stampings are those used for switch boxes, automobile-frame parts, and tractor parts. Obviously, these parts can be produced from any one of several different materials, but the purpose of a part naturally determines to a great extent the type of material to be used.

Applications of Cold-rolled Sheets.—Cold-rolled sheets are superior in finish to hot-rolled sheets. The cost is usually higher, but cold-rolled sheets are used when a superior finish is wanted and warrants the higher price. Most stampings for exposed parts used in homes, offices, and for such products as refrigerators, metal furniture, and the like, are produced from cold-rolled stock. When parts such as washing machine tubs, refrigerator inner shells, and range parts that are to be porcelain-enameled are being made, "enameled iron" sheets are specified. This is a special type of cold-rolled steel. There are, of course, many grades and several different analyses of cold-rolled steel. Certain grades are specially adapted for deep-drawing.

Tin Plate for Stampings.—Tin plate is a good grade of steel, from 38 to 15 gage, coated with tin by hot-dipping, or more recently, by an electrolytic process. It is used for such products as tin cans and containers, inexpensive toys, novelties, and a variety of other parts that are often seamed and soldered in assembly. The tin coating is very thin, but provides a bright finish, high in corrosion resistance and easily soldered.

Stainless-Steel Stampings.—Several analyses are available in both hot- and cold-rolled material. Many such sheets are furnished polished, the polishing being done after the rolling. This is an expensive and high-grade material. At first, stainless steel was used chiefly for cutlery, but it is now drawn and formed into a large variety of products. Its primary value is its high corrosion resistance. It also takes a lasting polish and presents a pleasing appearance.

Several other materials containing large percentages of nickel, such as nickel silver and Monel metal, are sometimes used for stamping products similar to those stamped from stainless steel, because these alloys, too, are high in corrosion resistance.

Copper for Stampings.—Copper is rolled into sheets and strips for fabricating into formed and drawn products, especially those requiring high corrosion resistance, great ductility, or high electrical or heat conductivity. It is available in either hard or soft grades. Copper is produced in rolls (strips) or sheets and is often tinned on one side. It does not tarnish rapidly in dry air, but corrodes in moist air, forming a poisonous compound. Stampings produced from copper include parts for electrical equipment, wash tubs, and radiator and condenser parts. Frequently, copper stampings are assembled by being folded or seamed together, or soldered where leakproof containers are essential, although deep-drawn seamless parts are readily produced.

Bronze, Brass, and Zinc Stampings.—Bronze is used for formed and drawn parts, chiefly for those which require high corrosion resistance, or in which a bronze color is wanted for ornamental purposes. Many beautiful novelties, lamp parts, artistic hardware, springs, etc., are among the parts for which bronze is effectively used.

Brass is high in corrosion resistance and is more adaptable to deep-drawing than bronze. It is available in sheets, strips, and coils for forming, drawing, and metal spinning. More types of stamped products are made from brass than from any other non-ferrous material. Parts made from brass are often polished, lacquered, enameled, or plated, and can be joined by practically all methods used for other metals.

Zinc used for forming and drawing is available chiefly in strips. It takes a high polish, but tarnishes easily, although its corrosion resistance in dry atmosphere is good. In the presence of moisture, it is subject to "white rust." Among the stampings produced from rolled zinc may be mentioned can tops and cells for dry batteries, weather stripping, embossed plates, moldings, and similar parts. Zinc is a relatively soft metal and quite ductile; hence, it is easily worked. It can be plated, lacquered, enameled, or chemically colored. It is also easily soldered. In ordering zinc sheets for stamping, it is advisable to send a sketch or drawing of the product to be made to the mill to insure the right grade of zinc for the job.

Aluminum Stampings.—Aluminum has approximately the same hardness as zinc. It is a good conductor of heat and electricity, and resists corrosion effectively in dry air; though white oxides form in moist or salt air. Aluminum sheets are available in many alloys, some of which can be heat-treated. Aluminum and aluminum-alloy stampings are used extensively in the construction of aircraft, railroad cars, bus and truck bodies, kitchen utensils, cups, thimbles, etc. These parts can be either formed or drawn in one piece, since aluminum is extremely ductile; or welding, brazing, and riveting may be used as assembly methods.

Use of Magnesium Alloys.—Magnesium alloys are used for many different applications because of the fact that they are approximately one-third lighter than aluminum. There is, however, at least one other characteristic of sheet magnesium alloys which adapts them to many applications, and that is their deep-drawing properties at elevated temperatures. Alloys of magnesium, for example, can be drawn from three to four times as deep in one operation as steel or aluminum. Magnesium alloys contain from 3 to 10 per cent aluminum and from 0.5 to 2 per cent zinc. The specific gravity of these alloys varies from 1.76 to 1.83. Steel is about four times heavier, and copper and nickel alloys five times heavier than magnesium. Although lightness is the outstanding characteristic of magnesium, it has other properties which are equally significant. Magnesium is easy to machine and can sometimes replace parts where weight saving is not important but a large amount of machining is required. Magnesium is adaptable to practically all the usual methods of metal working. It can be cast, extruded, rolled, drawn, spun, forged, blanked, coined, etc. It can be joined by gas, arc and electric resistance welding and by riveting. Other significant properties include good stability to atmospheric exposure and resistance to attack by alkalis, chromic and hydrofluoric acids, sulphur dioxide, ammonia and Freon gases, and many organic chemicals.

Importance of Using Standard Sizes of Sheets and Strips.—Stock lists should be studied, and standard sizes of strips or sheets, which are rolled without extra cost, should be chosen. The size that can be cut with minimum waste is, obviously, the most economical to use. The size and shape of blank required for each stamping must be determined in order to ascertain that it can be cut economically from a given size of sheet. The length of the sheet should also be considered to make sure that the waste at the end of the sheet, when the last pieces have been cut from it, is not excessive.

Figs. 1 and 2 show how pieces should and should not be cut from a sheet. In Fig. 1 is indicated an example of well planned "nesting"; in Fig. 2, an example where the waste is excessive. The design of the part can frequently be modified in size or contour to save material in cutting out the blanks. Often the blanks for two or more different stampings can be so arranged that they will "nest" economically, and be cut simultaneously or in a progressive die from the same sheet.

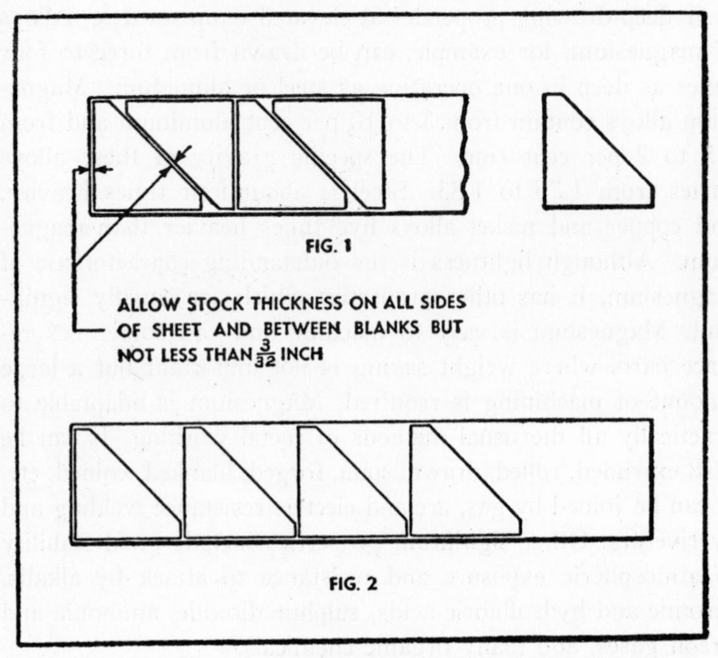

Fig. 1. Example where the Cutting of the Blanks from the Sheet has been so Planned as to Reduce the Waste Stock to a Minimum. Fig. 2. An Example where the Waste is Excessive

Thickness of Stock for Stampings.—Stock thickness should be as light as conditions permit, since the thinner stock is not only easier to work, but costs less. If it is not important that the thickness of the material be within the mill tolerance, it is well to so indicate, since this may mean a saving in the cost of the material. Furthermore, it may be possible to obtain from a mill or warehouse material on hand, ready for immediate fabrication, that can be used with little or no adjustment of tools or dies; whereas, if a definite gage is specified, it may be necessary to wait some time for delivery.

Type of Material to be Selected.—Low-carbon steel is usually the lowest cost material, and should be chosen unless specific requirements necessitate the use of some other material. Sometimes, however, it is possible that some other metal which can be worked more easily, or costs less to finish, should be chosen, because the over-all cost will be lower. It is not always the first cost of the material, but rather the total cost of the finished piece, that should be considered. Such factors as surface smoothness are often important, as they have an effect on the finishing costs, and this, in turn, affects the over-all cost. For high-grade work, it is well to specify not only the type of material, but also the analysis required. When the use of "seconds" is permissible, material of this kind is sometimes available, and can be purchased at a lower price.

Effect of Direction of Grain of Metal.—In designing a stamping, it is well to avoid bends and folds that are parallel with the grain of the metal. This is especially true in forming channel type products. The grain of the metal always runs parallel with the length of the sheet or strip. If channel type products—whether simply bent in the form of an angle or bent over on themselves—are to be made, the bends, as far as possible, should be across the grain of the metal to reduce the chances of checks and cracks. This should be considered, as well, when determining what width of sheet or strip will prove most economical.

Inside Radii of Bends.—The inside radii of bends should usually not be less than the thickness of the metal. The use of a larger radius than the thickness of the stock tends to reduce costs and is essential for all hard-tempered or otherwise nonductile materials. In general, the larger the radius, the easier the part is to produce, especially when the radius is at the bottom of a drawn product. When radii are specified that are less than the stock thickness, or when a sharp corner is required, difficulty is encountered and the cost of production is increased, because one or more additional operations or "rehitting," to sharpen the corner, are required. If a small radius is required, it can be obtained by starting with a larger radius and then decreasing it gradually; but this adds dies and operations, and consequently increases costs. A radius at least four times the stock thickness, is generally recommended at the bottom of drawn parts.

Radii for 90-degree Flanges.—Products that have flanges at the top approximately 90 degrees to the side wall, as indicated in Fig. 3, should have a radius under the flange of not less than the stock thickness. If the radius on the die is too small, regardless of what the radius on the punch may be, the material will pinch, and a ruptured stamping will be the result. It is always better to establish an inside radius at a flange to suit the draw radius necessary on the die, because if the radius specified is smaller, an additional operation for "rehitting" to the smaller radius becomes necessary, and an extra die must be made for this purpose.

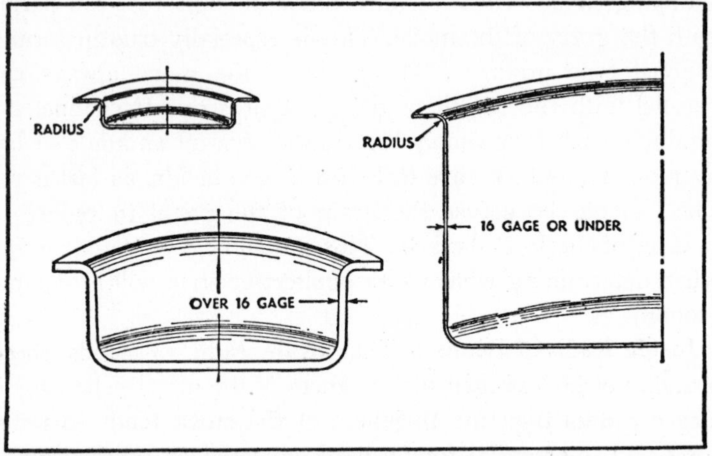

Fig. 3. The Radius under a Flange Should be as Large as Possible, but Never Less than the Stock Thickness

The following is recommended: On very light-gage metal for small shallow parts (upper diagram at left) the radius under the flange should not be less than 1/16 inch. On large parts with deep draws, using metal of 16 gage or thinner, (diagram at right), the radius at the draw edge should be between 1/8 and 5/16 inch. For materials over 16 gage, (lower diagram at left), the radius under the flange should be 1½ times the stock thickness. These figures apply to ductile metals suited for deep drawing.

Forming Panels or Depressions.—Connecting radii, as used in paneling, embossings, or depressions, preferably should not be smaller than the stock thickness—if possible, they should be larger. The metal between an upper and lower radius should be at an angle greater than 90 degrees to the sheet, as shown by the right-hand diagram, Fig. 4, and not at 90 degrees, as shown by the left-hand diagram. Considerable stretching of the metal takes place in forming a recessed or raised area, and ample radii, in addition to sloping connecting metal, tend to prevent any pinching action or tearing of the metal.

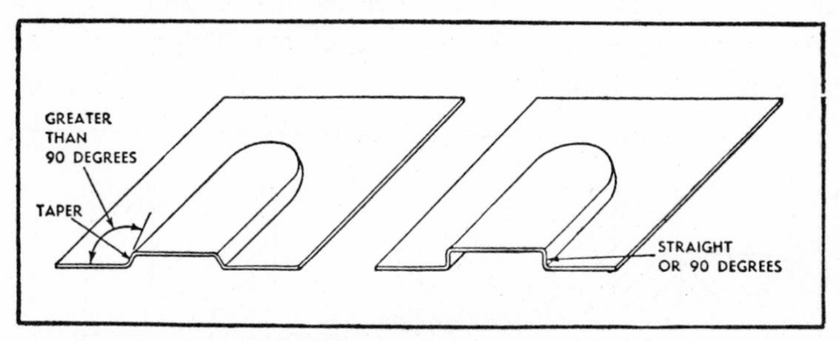

Fig. 4. The Sides of Panels for Depressions should Preferably Incline as Shown by Left-Hand Diagram

In general, it can be said that square corners or edges, where forming or drawing of metal is involved, have no place in any but exceptional stampings, unless performed by a coining operation, which is expensive; and this usually is possible on relatively small parts only. When an unusually small radius appears essential, experienced stamping producers should be consulted to determine whether the radius is feasible without prohibitive cost.

Depth of Draw.—In designing parts requiring a drawing operation, the total depth of draw should be kept as small as conditions permit, if minimum cost is desired. In general, the deeper the draw beyond that possible in a single stroke of the press, the higher will be the cost, because of the greater number of operations and the number of dies required. Drawing tends to work-harden most metals, and deep draws, therefore, often require that the metal be annealed and sometimes pickled and cleaned between draws. These operations add considerably to the cost and cannot always be performed with lighter-gage materials. Deep-drawing generally requires a highly ductile material, and this also involves greater cost. However, deep-drawing is often a highly economical method, and frequently is the only method possible for low-cost production. Draws as deep as the diameter of the punch cannot usually be produced in a single operation, but commonly require two or more operations after blanking and necessitate a corresponding number of dies. There are no fixed rules for determining the number of draws; but for ductile material to be converted into a deep cylindrical shape in a single draw, the punch area may be, say, 40 to 50 per cent of the blank area.

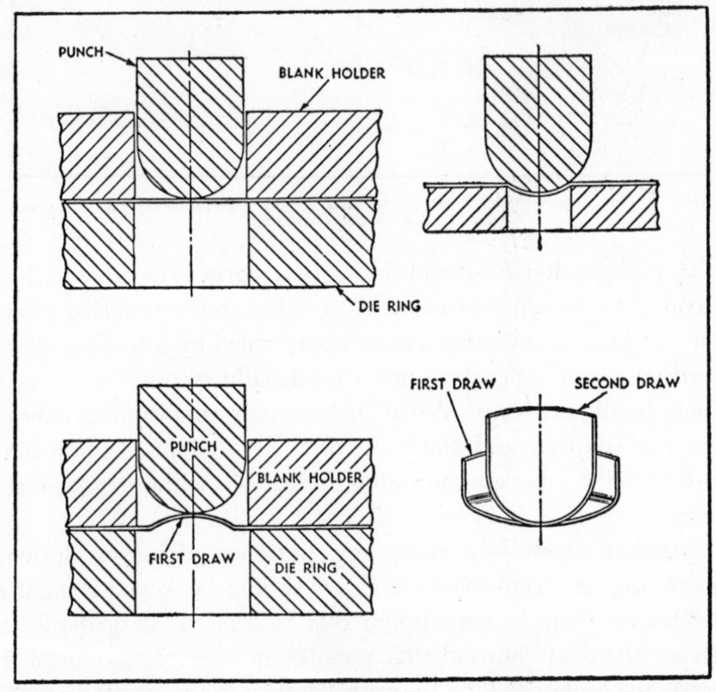

Fig. 5. Different Methods for Drawing a Cup with a Hemispherical Bottom Successfully

Drawn Parts with Curved Bottoms.—Although it is possible to draw parts having curved rather than flat bottoms, or even bottoms of hemispherical shape, a punch correspondingly shaped may tend to rupture the bottom or produce wrinkles, because as shown in Fig. 5, (upper left-hand diagram), the part of the punch that first hits the metal is too far away from the die. There are, however, expedients for meeting this difficulty. One method is illustrated by the upper right-hand diagram. A die of smaller diameter is first used to form a shallow cavity. This blank is placed in the drawing die in a reversed position as indicated by the lower left-hand diagram. The hemispherical shape can then be drawn without forming wrinkles. The lower right-hand diagram shows how the same end can be attained by a first draw of larger diameter, and a second draw of the required diameter.

Locating Holes in Designing Stampings.—In designing stampings, the following points should be considered in locating holes, determining sizes of holes, and establishing limits, especially for large quantity production, low piece-price, and low tooling cost:

The distance *A* between the outside of a hole and the outside edge of the stamping or the distance between the edges of two holes in metal of about 16-gage and heavier should be at least two times the stock thickness of the material used (see upper diagram Fig. 6). For metal under 16 gage, the distance should not be less than 1/8 inch. These rules apply whether the part is to be perforated before or after forming. If the holes are closer than noted, the wall thickness of the die between the holes may not be sufficient to stand the pressure applied to perform the piercing in one operation. To avoid excessive die maintenance, additional operations in a second die may have to be added.

When the holes are put into a stamping, the bend lines and the radii at each side of them should always be considered, whether perforating is done before or after forming. Metal flows at bends, the outside stretching and the inside being compressed; hence, holes should be kept as far away as possible from any bend if stretching or distortion of the hole while forming is to be avoided. When perforating is done after forming, it is always better to gage from the inside of the metal. If the edge of the hole is at least twice the stock thickness away from a line through the center of the radius of the bend, (see lower diagram, Fig. 6), this provides enough wall thickness between the edge of the hole and the edge of the die.

Pierced holes having a diameter less than the stock thickness should not be specified. If holes are less than the stock thickness, they usually have to be drilled, and drilling is much more expensive than perforating. Hole diameters can be held fairly accurate on the punch side. On the die side, the diameter is

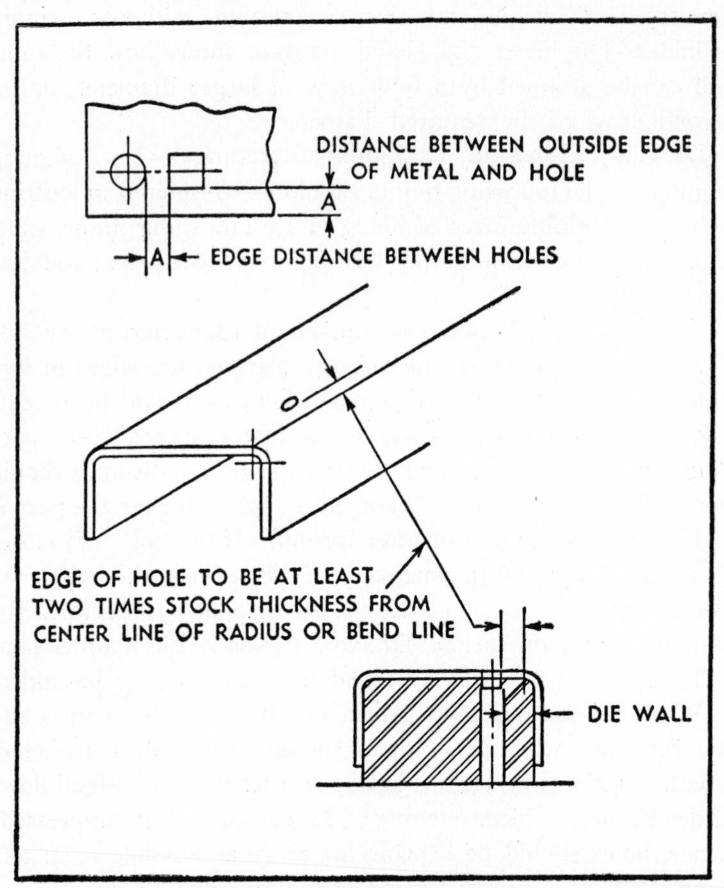

Fig. 6. Relation of Edge Distance between Holes and Distance from Edge of Hole to Outside Edge of Metal in Designing Stampings

slightly greater, because of the clearance allowed between the punch and the die. Hole diameters are determined in part by the use to which the hole is intended. If the hole is for a cold rivet, 1/64 inch clearance over the nominal rivet size is generally allowed. The clearance for a bolt is between 1/64 and

1/32 inch, as a rule, but for aircraft work the clearance is much less. A tolerance of at least 0.010 inch (plus or minus 0.005 inch) should be allowed in specifying the distance between hole centers.

When bolts are to be used in an assembly where close fits are not required and where variations in center distances are not important or are difficult to control, it is good practice to use holes in one piece and slots or larger holes in the mating stamping, provided the parts are not stressed; this facilitates assembly and decreases costs, because less care is required in holding center distances and less die maintenance is needed.

Extruded Holes in Stampings.—Extruded holes are those in which the punch does not shear away the metal, but pushes it outward, so as to form an integral flange or collar around the hole. The height of the flange of an extruded hole is considerably greater than the metal thickness, and can be made several times as great. This type of hole is used for any of the following purposes, in materials up to 5/16-inch thick:

(a) For screw threads; (b) To fit pins, bolts, studs, shafts, or bushings; (c) For countersunk screw or rivet heads, (see upper diagrams, Fig. 7); (d) For butt-welding, brazing, or soldering tubes or shafts to a part; (e) For clearance holes and lightening holes, especially where stiffening or added strength is required around the hole, (see lower left-hand diagram, Fig. 7). Such holes can be of almost any shape that does not involve sharp corners; (f) For other parts to slip into when assemblies are made, (lower right-hand diagram).

In designing such holes, the designer should consider how high a flange is necessary and where the metal to be extruded or flanged is coming from. Ordinarily, metal can come only from the area inside the hole; but if the metal required for the flange is too great to come from the center, it has to be drawn in from the area around the hole by means of one or more "pocketing" operations before punching out the center and flanging.

The operation of extruding a hole usually involves first punching out the center and then flanging. Sometimes a single operation both perforates and extrudes, depending on the gage of the material, the size of the hole, and the height of the flange. This works out satisfactorily for light-gage metal on types of holes such as those shown by the upper diagrams, Fig. 7.

The inside diameter of the extruded hole can be held close to size, but the wall at the raw edge of the flange becomes considerably thinner than the original metal, and sometimes checks or cracks. This may or may not be objectionable, depending upon the particular application. If it is essential to thicken the wall, as is sometimes necessary for tapping certain threads, this can

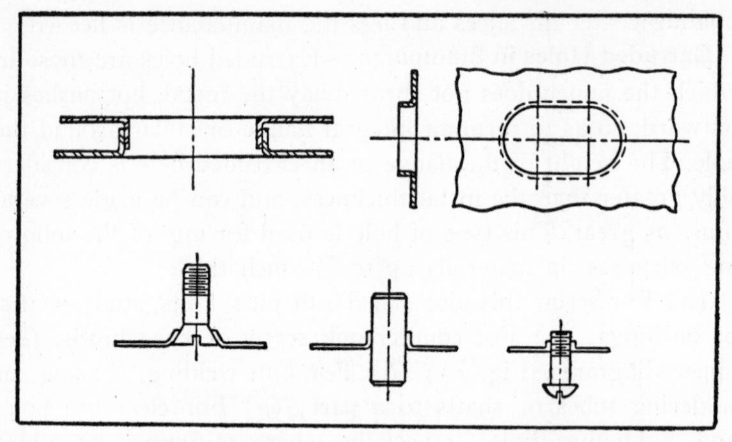

Fig. 7. Examples of Extruded Holes in Stampings

be accomplished by extruding the flange higher than required, and then "stoving" back the metal, to yield, within certain limits, the desired wall thickness. Such stoving can be done cold, if the metal is not too heavy and press equipment of proper tonnage is available. Sometimes hot operations are required. Usually, cracks or checks can be eliminated by reaming after punching, if the hole is round.

Procedure in Designing an Extruded Hole.—The procedure that should be followed in designing an extruded hole for economical manufacture and tooling is first to determine the size of the hole required, and then arrive at the minimum flange height that can be used. Next, the areas should be checked to ascertain whether the metal required will come out of the center and still allow stock thickness around the perforated hole, as shown in Fig. 8, upper diagram. If the area of the extrusion (equal to the area of a cylinder *A* and that of one-fourth of an annular ring *B*) exceeds the area of circle *E*, and the drawing of metal from the outside is necessary, much extra tooling is required and greater development expense is often involved.

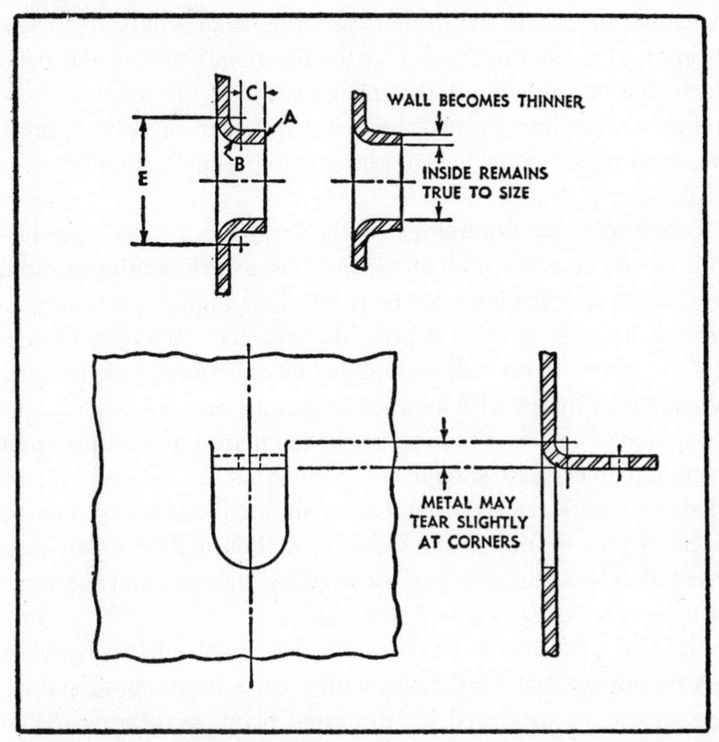

Fig. 8. (Upper Diagram) Diagrams Illustrating Procedure in Designing an Extruded Hole. (Lower Diagram) Forming Lanced Holes by Shearing and Bending

Forming Holes by Shearing and Bending.—Lanced holes are formed by shearing the metal part way around the periphery and then bending the metal adjacent to that sheared. A tab, (see lower diagram, Fig. 8), is sheared on three sides and bent outward on the fourth side, forming a projection at an angle, but integral with the original metal. Often the center of the projecting portion has a hole perforated in it for a wire, screw, or other fastening. Projections of this type are frequently used instead of attaching another small piece bent at an angle to the stamping.

Lancing and bending is much less expensive than to form a separate piece and weld or attach it by other means, but the hole may weaken the stamping and may afford a less attractive appearance than the alternative. A lanced hole and tab can be produced in one operation; in that case, the metal will have a clean sheared edge on three sides up to the points where the bend starts, but beyond, where the cutting edges of the punch and die end at the bending radius, the metal will tear slightly, because the bending is done before the cutting punch completes its stroke.

Tolerances for Stampings.—The largest tolerances permissible should be allowed on all dimensions, as this facilitates rapid production and tends to lower costs. This applies especially to over-all lengths, widths, depths, dimensions of flanges, diameters of formed or raw edges, and distances between hole centers. When a part mates with another part of an assembly, tolerances should never be closer than those for the mating part. Important fractional tolerances should be specified as $\pm \frac{1}{32}$, $\pm \frac{1}{16}$, or whatever limits are required. Closer limits, if needed, should be given to plus or minus the number of thousandths of an inch essential. The spring-back of metal being stamped and the wear on tools often greatly affect the limits.

Fits and Clearances.—When fits are involved, as between two stampings that must mate within close limits, both stampings should be produced by the same plant, as otherwise the desired fit may not be obtained. In any event, the limits that control the fits should be definitely indicated for both parts on the same drawing.

It is good practice to draw, in construction lines, at holes or notches, for example, the part or portion that must be cleared, and to put on the drawing some such note as: "Clearance hole or notch, size not important"; or if the clearances must be close, a note giving, in fractions or thousandths of an inch, the clearance desired. This tells the manufacturer how far he may go in simplifying tooling. He may be able to use an available die, thus saving on tooling costs.

Degree of Flatness Required.—When the degree of flatness of any surfaces of a stamping is important, the allowable variation from flatness should be definitely stated, as spring-back in metal and other factors affecting flatness are sometimes difficult and expensive to control. A note on the drawing should read: "This portion must be flat within, say, 0.030 inch"; or "When laid on a surface plate with this surface down, a feeler thicker than, say, 0.016 inch must not pass under the surface at any point." When no such note appears, it is general practice to assume that whatever the tools and metal normally produce is satisfactory to the purchaser.

Straightness, as applied to edges or straight bends, for example—in which camber, spring in the metal, or some other variation from a straight line is objectionable—should be designated, when it is essential, by indicating, in thousandths of an inch, the maximum deviation from a true straight line that is permissible. In some cases, it is better for the user to do his own straightening, as parts straightened by the supplier sometimes warp in shipping, involving double expense for straightening.

In the case of formed or drawn stampings where the shape and location of the edges are not important, this fact should be made clear on the drawing. Otherwise, trimming operations which are not necessary may be performed, because it is not clearly understood that any considerable deviation from the contour shown on the drawing is permissible.

When holes are drilled or when material is blanked or sheared, some burrs are bound to occur. If they must be removed, the drawing should clearly indicate where. When edges must be rounded (or "broken"), this, too, should be clearly indicated, because then tumbling, filing, or some similar operation is required.

Drawings and Specifications for Stampings.—A stamping that is considered satisfactory by the manufacturer may not be so regarded by the purchaser. The price set by the estimator may be either greater or less than is necessary to produce a satisfactory stamping for the particular use involved, all because of lack of information and consequent misinterpretation of drawings presented for quotation. This results in misunderstandings between the purchaser and manufacturer. For the satisfaction of all concerned, the purchaser and the manufacturer should get together with definite information furnished by their respective engineering departments, if a fair price and a satisfactory product are to be assured.

The designer should supply as complete information as possible regarding the requirements. He should furnish reasonable specifications on (or with) the part drawing and in such form that they can be easily interpreted by others. Often the designer does not know the method of manufacture to be followed in making the particular part he is designing; but since he can design much more intelligently if he understands production methods, he can profit greatly by discussing the design with the engineers of the stamping manufacturer, and thus adapt the design to economical production.

The designer may not know, for example, whether the stock will be blanked or sheared to size, but it does make a difference in the product, as more variations occur in shearing than in blanking; and when the stamping is formed, the height or width of flanges may vary if sheared. If a channel-shaped part is involved, the web width may vary because of the method used in forming. It may be formed in a standard "V" die in two hits of the machine, which would give variations in width because of variations in gaging; or it may be formed in a die built especially for the job, in which case the width may be held reasonably close, because both flanges are formed at one time. All metal has some spring-back. This may cause dimensional variations; for example, the flanges of a channel may open out slightly, but it may or may not be necessary to hold these flanges to an exact 90-degree angle relative to the web.

As to general appearance, there are exposed and unexposed surfaces, and any marks or wrinkles may influence greatly the tooling costs involved. Exposed surfaces, in most cases, should be free from marks and wrinkles, but on unexposed surfaces they may not matter; yet the estimator has to guess at the requirements if there is no notation on the drawing. This may raise the price needlessly, in order to permit the supplier to "play safe." Flatness and straightness are sometimes essential, but if not plainly specified, may be overlooked, with resulting misunderstandings or rejections which could be avoided by precise specifications. Assembly requirements also affect such items as lengths, clearance, notches, and fits.

These are only a few of the factors that the designer should cover in specifications intended to insure satisfactory stampings. It is evident, however, that clear and complete drawings and specifications, and close cooperation with the stamping manufacturer is the logical way to get results and effect economies that may not be realized otherwise. Stampings cannot be held to such small tolerances as machining methods permit. The more flexible the specifications are, the less costly the stamping will be as a general rule.

CHAPTER XXIV

HEAT-TREATMENT OF DIE STEELS

To PREVENT, as far as possible, the spoilage of dies during heat-treatment, it is necessary to understand the changes that take place in the steel when it is heated, quenched and tempered. That part of this chapter which deals with the heating cycles for typical tool and die steels, the quenching or cooling procedure, and the effects of single and double tempering operations on the structure and properties of the steel, is by Peter Payson, Assistant Director of Research, Crucible Steel Company of America.

In most cases, the life of tools and dies is proportional to their hardness or toughness. The chief objective of heat-treatment is, therefore, to develop the maximum hardness in the material consistent with the degree of toughness required.

Elements which Increase Hardenability of Steel.—A high degree of hardness can be developed in a plain carbon steel by heat-treatment if the steel contains over about 0.50 per cent carbon, provided the section is not very large. But when tools are made in large sections, a plain carbon steel cannot be hardened adequately, and it is necessary to add alloying elements in order to increase the hardenability. The elements usually used for this purpose are manganese, chromium, and molybdenum.

Steel becomes hard during heat-treatment because of the formation of a microstructure called martensite. For some tool applications, the wear resistance provided by the martensitic structure alone is not sufficient, and therefore, tungsten and vanadium, as well as chromium and molybdenum, are introduced into tool steel. These elements combine with some of the carbon in the steel to form very hard particles of carbides, and thus give the heat-treated steel much better abrasion resistance than can be developed without the presence of alloy carbides.

When the tool operates at high speed or under high pressures, or is in contact with hot metal, as in forging, piercing, extruding, and die-casting operations, special tool steel compositions must be used that are resistant to the high temperatures encountered. Vanadium, chromium, and cobalt combined with tungsten or molybdenum give the steel the necessary resistance to softening at high temperatures.

Finally, in some applications, the life of the tool or die is more dependent on toughness than on hardness. In such cases, by decreasing the carbon content of the steel or by heat-treating the steel to a lower hardness than the maximum which it can attain, a satisfactory compromise can be established between hardness and toughness. However, if a low percentage of carbon is depended on to provide the desired toughness, the alloying elements chromium and molybdenum must be added to get satisfactory hardenability.

Typical Tool and Die Steels.—The compositions of tool and die steels that correspond to the foregoing conditions are given in Table 1. While these are only five of the very large group of tool and die steels on the market, they are fairly representative of the essential types. One of these five could be used satisfactorily for practically any application that might be encountered. The many varieties of steels available for tools and dies are justified because each one does some job more efficiently than any of the others.

Steel of the first analysis listed is usually referred to as a plain carbon tool steel, and is also frequently termed a water-hardening or shallow-hardening tool steel. Many modifications of this type of steel are produced to provide small but controlled differences in hardenability. There are also several steels of this type containing small amounts of tungsten, which gives the steel better wear resistance.

The next analysis is characteristic of steels referred to as oil-hardening steels, and differs from the first type primarily in hardenability. Because of its greater hardenability, relatively large tools made of this steel can be hardened by an oil quench rather than a water quench, which is required for a plain carbon steel; consequently, tools made from oil-hardening steels do not undergo as much size change and distortion during hardening as those made from plain carbon tool steel.

Table 1. Composition of Five Typical Tool and Die Steels

Plain Carbon Tool Steel: Carbon, 1.14; manganese, 0.22; silicon, 0.16 per cent.

Oil-Hardening Tool Steel: Carbon, 0.85; manganese, 1.18; silicon, 0.26; chromium, 0.50; tungsten, 0.44 per cent.

High-Carbon High-Chromium Tool Steel: Carbon, 1.55; manganese, 0.27; silicon, 0.45; chromium, 11.34; vanadium, 0.24; molybdenum, 0.53 per cent.

Molybdenum High-Speed Steel: Carbon, 0.80; manganese, 0.24; silicon, 0.29; chromium, 4.15; vanadium, 1.89; tungsten, 6.64; molybdenum, 4.94 per cent.

Chromium-Molybdenum Hot-Work Steel: Carbon, 0.38; manganese, 0.50; silicon, 1.08; chromium, 5.00; vanadium, 0.40; molybdenum, 1.35; nickel, 0.30 per cent.

Steel of the third analysis is referred to as a high-carbon, high-chromium steel or as an air-hardening die steel. It differs from the first two not only in having a much higher degree of hardenability, but also in containing many hard chromium carbides that give it better wear resistance at a given hardness than the first two steels. There are several carbon and chromium variations of this type.

The fourth steel is a high-speed steel; that is, it holds a sharp edge even when the tool is cutting fast enough to cause it to get red-hot. The first three steels, although they could be treated to the same hardness, would fail very rapidly under such high-speed cutting conditions because they would become soft when heated to a dull red color. There are many varieties of high-speed steels: Some contain more tungsten and less molybdenum than given in the table; others contain more vanadium; and still others have up to 12 per cent cobalt. The type listed in the table was selected because it is an economical general-purpose steel.

The last steel generally is referred to as a hot-work steel or a chromium-molybdenum hot-work steel. It is used where the tool is in intimate contact with hot metal, as in forging, extruding, or die-casting operations. Even though it has a relatively low carbon content compared with the other alloy steels, it has a higher hardness than the first two steels when heated to about 1100 degrees F., and therefore will wear better on hot-work jobs. The high-carbon, high-chromium steel and the high-speed steel will also be wear-resistant at 1100 degrees F., but they will not be as tough, under the same conditions of high temperature, as the hot-work steel would be.

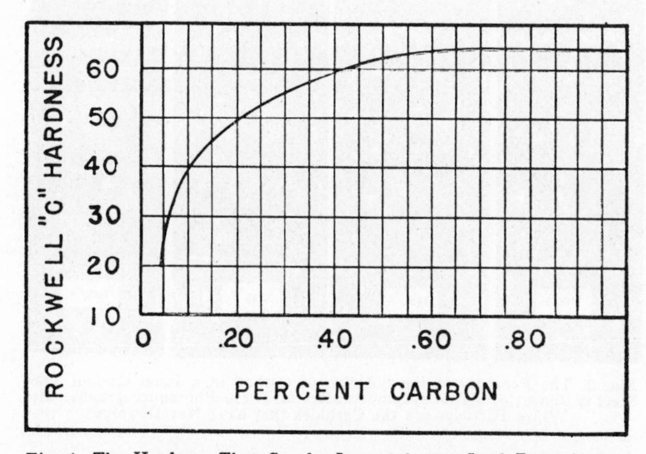

Fig. 1. The Hardness That Can be Imparted to a Steel Depends to a Large Extent on the Amount of Carbon Present. The Attainable Hardness Remains Practically Constant as the Carbon Content Increases beyond 0.70 Per Cent. (Courtesy American Society for Metals)

How Heating Changes the Structure of Tool Steel.—The first step in the heat-treatment of steel is the heating. The purpose of the heating is to form austenite and to dissolve carbon in the austenite. The solution of the carbon is necessary so that in the second step of heat-treatment, when the transformation of austenite takes place, the steel will develop the desired hardness. It is important to remember that even though a large amount of carbon is in the steel, it is not effective in developing hardness unless it is first dissolved in the austenite.

Fig. 1 shows the relationship between the attainable hardness and the carbon content. The hardness increases rapidly up to 60 Rockwell C as the carbon increases to 0.40 per cent. From this point on, the hardness increases gradually to 65 Rockwell C as the carbon increases from 0.40 to 0.70 per cent. Above about 0.70 per cent carbon, the hardness remains practically constant. For maximum hardness in the steel, therefore, approximately 0.70 per cent of carbon must be dissolved in the austenite. All of the steels being discussed except the chromium-molybdenum hot-work steel have sufficient carbon in the analysis to attain a hardness of 65 Rockwell C.

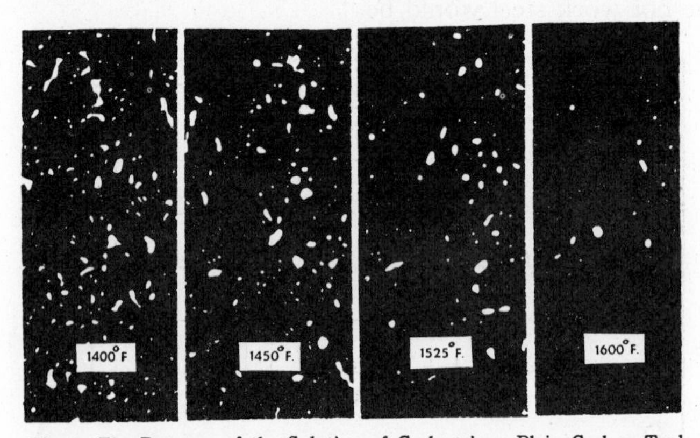

Fig. 2. The Progress of the Solution of Carbon in a Plain Carbon Tool Steel is Shown at Various Temperatures in These Photomicrographs. The White Particles are the Carbides that have Not Dissolved

Even though the carbon is in the steel, it is not necessarily all dissolved in the austenite. This is probably best explained by Figs. 2 and 3. In Fig. 2 are shown photomicrographs of the 1.14 per cent carbon tool steel after being heated to 1400, 1450, 1525, and 1600 degrees F.; quenched to preserve the condition of the carbides at the heating temperature; and tempered at a low temperature. The white particles in the photomicrographs are undissolved carbides. At 1450 degrees F. there are fewer carbides than at 1400 degrees F. At 1525 degrees F. and at 1600 degrees F. there are still fewer undissolved carbides. The amount of carbon dissolved in the austenite is therefore greater at 1450 degrees F. than at 1400 degrees F., and still greater at 1600 degrees F. But even at 1600 degrees F. all of the carbon in the steel is not dissolved in the austenite.

The solubility of carbides is not the same in all steels. The explanation for this is in the composition of the austenite and of the carbides. For example, in carbon steel, the austenite is practically all iron, and the carbide is a compound of iron and carbon. In high-speed steel, the austenite contains chromium,

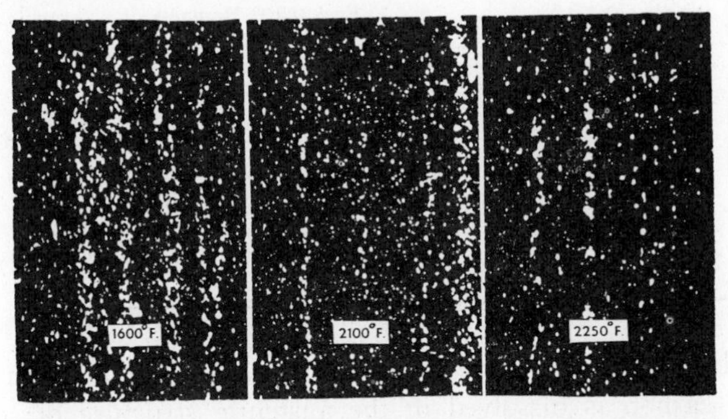

Fig. 3. The Amount of Carbon that is Dissolved in Austentite Varies with the Composition of the Steel. Molybdenum High-speed Steel Must be Heated to Approximately 2250 Degrees F. before a Sufficient Amount of Carbon Goes into Solution

tungsten, molybdenum, vanadium, and iron; and the carbides are compounds of carbon, vanadium, tungsten, molybdenum, chromium, and iron. The solution of carbides in high-speed steel increases with increasing temperatures, as in carbon steel, but a considerable amount is still present at 2100 degrees F., as illustrated in Fig. 3, which shows photomicrographs of a high-speed tool steel of the composition given in Table 1. Even after this steel is heated to 2250 degrees F., many carbides remain undissolved in the austenite.

The effect of the solution of carbides on the hardness of the high-speed steel, as quenched, is shown in Table 2. This steel hardens appreciably when quenched at 1600 degrees F., but it does not reach maximum hardness until it is quenched at about 2100 degrees F. The recommended temperature to which this steel should be heated before quenching however, is 2250 degrees F. The reason for this will be made clear later in a discussion on the effects of tempering. At least it is apparent that this steel must be heated well above its critical temperature (1530 degrees F.) before enough carbides are dissolved to obtain full hardening.

Table 2. Effect of Heating Temperature on Hardness of Tool Steel

Austenitizing Temperature, Degrees F.	Rockwell C Hardness	
	Molybdenum High-speed Steel	High-carbon High-chromium Steel
1600	53	50
1800	60	64
1950	64	59
2100	66	36
2250	65.5	..

Table 2 also illustrates another point, which is that when too much carbon is dissolved in the austenite structure of some steels, the steel is softer rather than harder. The high-carbon, high-chromium tool steel is capable of attaining its maximum hardness of 64 Rockwell C when it is heated to 1800 degrees F. At higher temperatures, more carbides dissolve, and the resultant hardness of the steel when it cools is less, owing to the fact that the high-carbon austenite does not transform to martensite when the steel is cooled, but remains as austenite at room temperature. Since austenite is much softer than martensite, the steel is softer.

Grain Size and Toughness.—Two other factors are involved in the heating of tool steels besides the formation of austenite and the solution of carbides. These are grain coarsening and melting of the steel. In tool steels, the grain size should be as small as possible, because a fine-grained hardened steel is inherently tougher than a coarse-grained steel. Usually there is little concern about coarse grain in a tool steel because coarsening of the grain does not occur until the temperature is well above the usual austenitizing temperatures.

The first two steels listed in Table 1 coarsen appreciably at temperatures as low as 1600 degrees F., but the high-speed steel still has a fine grain at 2250 degrees F. However, a startling grain coarsening occurs in high-speed steel when it is reheated to the high temperature for a second time, as shown in Fig. 4. The tremendous grains in the structure at the right produced by "double hardening" cause the fracture of the steel to have a fishscale appearance, and tools are generally very brittle

Fig. 4. Double Hardening of a High-speed Steel Results in Coarsening of the Grain, as Shown. If Reheating after Hardening is Necessary, the Steel Should be Annealed to Prevent the Formation of Large Grains

when treated in this manner. If, for some reason, a high-speed tool has to be hardened a second time, it should be annealed fully before the second hardening. This annealing between hardenings prevents the formation of large grains.

There is very little risk of melting steel during heat-treating, except in the case of high-speed steel. The molybdenum high-speed steel begins to melt at about 2275 degrees F., and there is definite evidence of melting at 2300 degrees F. This is indicated by the formation of a massive carbide network at grain boundaries. Such a structure decreases the toughness of high-speed steels.

Melting temperatures vary with the compositions of high-speed steel, and the well-known high-tungsten high-speed steels do not begin to melt until they are heated to about 2400 degrees F. or higher. Any increase of carbon at the surface of the steel brought about by contact of the steel with carbonaceous materials at the high austenitizing temperatures used for hardening lowers the melting temperature of the steel.

It is apparent from the foregoing that the changes occurring in heating control, to a large extent, the ultimate hardness of a tool or die steel. During heating, austenite forms and carbides

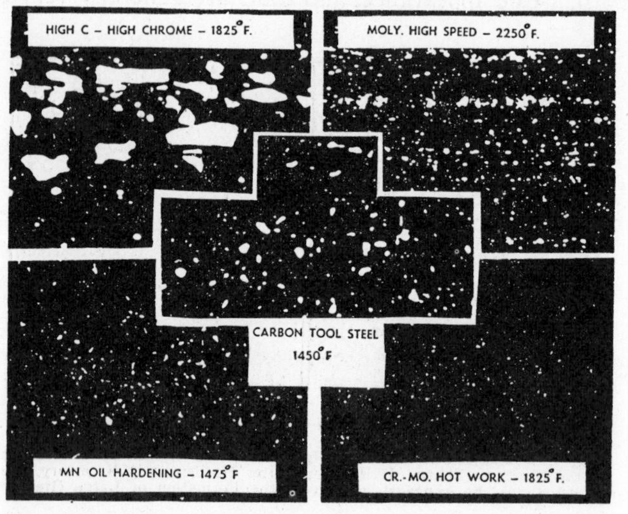

Fig. 5. The Condition, after Usual Heating, of the Five Steels Listed in Table 1 is Shown in these Photomicrographs. The Residual Carbides Indicated by the White Spots Contribute to the Wear Resistance of the Hardened Steel

go into solution, the degree of solution being dependent on the composition of the steel and on the heating temperature. Heating should be at a high enough temperature so that a sufficient amount of carbon is dissolved to give the steel a high attainable hardness. However, in practically all tool steels, there are many undissolved carbides at the usual heating temperatures.

The conditions of the five steels listed in Table 1 when heated ready for hardening are shown in Fig. 5. These photomicrographs represent longitudinal sections of relatively small sized bars at an original magnification of 1000 X. The residual carbides shown contribute appreciably to the wear resistance of the hardened steel, the massive carbides in the high-carbon, high-chromium steel accounting for the advantage of this steel over the plain carbon and manganese oil-hardening steels for such applications as blanking dies.

Overheating may cause tool failure. In the case of an oil-hardening or a plain carbon tool steel, overheating causes the grain to coarsen and the steel to become brittle; with a high-carbon, high-chromium type steel, too high a heating temperature causes an excessive amount of austenite to be retained on cooling; and in the case of high-speed steels, melting may occur.

The length of time that the steel is held at the required temperature determines the amount of carbon that goes into solution. The longer the heating time, the more complete the solution. Naturally, the larger the piece of steel, the longer is the time necessary to heat it. Usually, a quarter of an hour per inch of thickness is sufficient, although some recommend as much as an hour per inch of thickness. At very high temperatures, such as those used for high-speed steel, the time for heating is usually shorter, being about two to five minutes per inch of cross-section.

Cooling Tool and Die Steels.—There are two temperature levels that are important during the cooling of tool and die steels from the austenitizing temperature. One of these is from about 1350 degrees F. to 900 degrees F., and the other is from approximately 700 degrees F. down to room temperature. If the time taken in cooling from 1350 degrees F. to 900 degrees F. is long, the steel generally will be soft when it has cooled to room temperature; if this period of time is short, the steel generally will be hardened. Some steels must be cooled through this temperature level in as short a time as possible in order to be hardened. Others will harden even if the cooling time is not so short.

The cooling time can be regulated by the choice of the quenching medium. If the tool is cooled in air, the rate of cooling is fairly slow. For faster cooling, the part can be quenched in liquid salt at a temperature between 1100 and 400 degrees F. and then cooled to room temperature in air; or, it can be cooled in oil all the way down to room temperature. The fastest cooling is obtained by quenching in circulating water or brine held at 40 to 70 degrees F.

The time required for 1-, 2-, and 3-inch rounds to cool from 1350 to 900 degrees F. in air, in oil, and circulating water is given in the accompanying Table 3. It will be seen that the time needed to cool the bar in air is much longer than to cool it in oil or water; that the oil quench takes a much longer time to cool the steel than the water quench; and that the center of the bar in the water quench takes a much longer time to cool than the outside.

Table 3. Time Required to Cool Round Bars from 1350 Degrees F. to 900 Degrees F.

Bar Size, Inches	Section of Bar	Cooling Medium		
		Air	Oil	Water
1	Surface	4 min.	3 sec.	1 sec.
	Center		10 sec.	4 sec.
2	Surface	10 min.	10 sec.	1 1/2 sec.
	Center		30 sec.	15 sec.
3	Surface	17 min.	20 sec.	3 sec.
	Center		60 sec.	35 sec.

When steel is cooling from 1350 to 900 degrees F., the austenite has a tendency to transform to soft mixtures of ferrite and carbide, and it will transform if allowed enough time. The time necessary for transformation depends on the composition of the steel; usually, the more complex the steel—the more it contains of the alloying elements manganese, molybdenum, chromium, and nickel—the longer the time required for transformation.

Carbon tool steel of the composition given in Table 1 and indicated in the upper right-hand corner of Fig. 7, transforms very rapidly at this temperature level; the oil-hardening tool steel (Fig. 6) less rapidly; and the complex high-carbon high-chromium steel (Fig. 8), the high-speed steel (Fig. 9), and the chromium hot-work steel (Fig. 10) require even more time. The important fact to remember is that if transfomation does not take place in this temperature range, the steel will harden while it cools to room temperature, whereas if transformation does take place, the steel will be either soft or only partially hardened after it has become cooled.

Charts Indicating Behavior of Austenite in Steel.—Transformation of the austenite of any steel may take place over the entire range of temperature, from critical down to room temperature, but at some temperatures, the tendency to transform is much greater than at others. These tendencies are shown on charts called transformation-temperature-time curves, which are maps indicating the behavior of the austenite in steel. Charts for the five typical tool steels listed in Table 1 are shown in Figs. 6 to 10.

Chart for Oil-hardening Steel.—The chart for the oil-hardening tool steel is shown in Fig. 6. The curved line at the left in the diagram is marked "beginning of transformation." Austenite will remain untransformed at any temperature if the steel is held at that temperature for less than the time indicated by the line marked "beginning of transformation." For example, the austenite in this steel will remain untransformed at 1300 degrees F. for about five minutes, but if the steel is held at that temperature for a longer time, transformation will start. If the steel is held at 1100 degrees F. for more than ten seconds, transformation of the austenite will start; whereas if it is cooled quickly to 500 degrees F. and held at that temperature, transformation will not start for nearly ten minutes.

If the steel is cooled so that transformation of the austenite does not take place by the time the temperature drops to 400 degrees F., the hard martensitic structure will begin to form and will continue to form as the steel cools below 400 degrees F. This is a very important hardening operation in steel. While a certain period is required for austenite to transform to ferrite and carbide at high temperatures, the transformation to martensite does not depend on time, but takes place at once as the temperature drops below the line marked "beginning of martensite."

If only martensite forms in the steel by the time it cools to room temperature, the steel is fully hardened. But since the outside of a bar can cool more rapidly than the center, depending on the size of the bar and on the quenching medium employed, it is possible for a bar to be only partially hardened

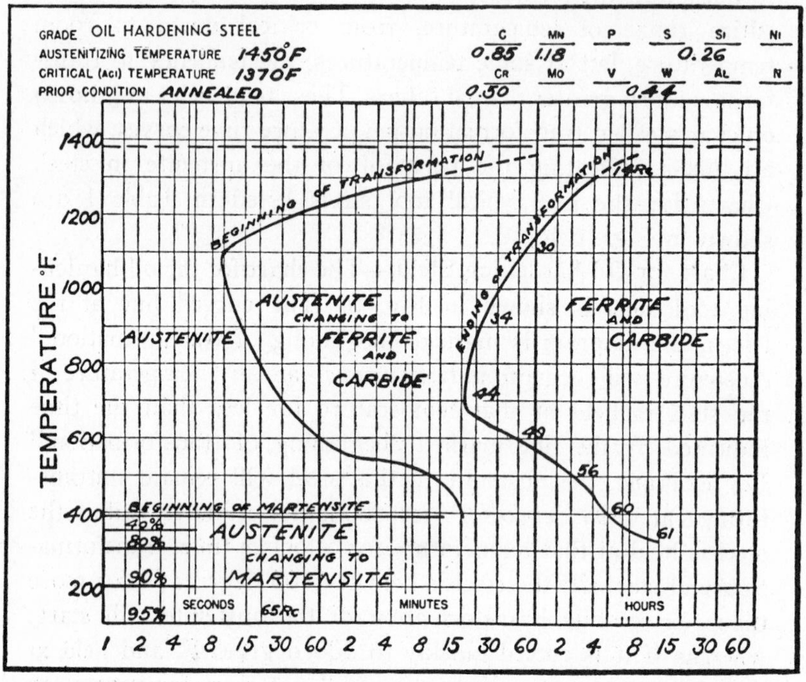

Fig. 6. Transformation Curves for a Typical Oil-hardening Steel of the Analysis Shown at Upper Right-hand Corner of Diagram

at the center while the outside is fully hardened. This is the case with carbon tool steel treated in fairly large sections.

When austenite transforms to martensite during the cooling of a steel, a definite and permanent expansion takes place in the steel due to the fact that martensite is not as dense as austenite, or as the annealed structure of the steel. If this expansion is not permitted to take place freely, stresses may develop in the steel to such a degree as to cause the part to crack or distort. To keep cracking and distortion at a minimum, it is desirable to allow the martensite to form slowly, so that the steel can gradually accommodate itself to the expansion stresses. This is the basis of the heat-treatment called "martempering," which consists of cooling the steel rapidly in hot salt, oil, or water to the martensite temperature and finish cooling in air down to room temperature.

Another modified form of hardening, introduced by Davenport and Bain about ten years ago, is called "austempering." This consists of quenching the steel in salt to a temperature below the region of rapid transformation but above the martensite temperature, and holding it at this temperature for a long enough time for the austenite to be completely transformed at this temperature. The transformation product formed in this manner is called "bainite." This product also is a hard structure, but not so hard as martensite. For example, in the oil-hardening steel referred to, martensite has a hardness of about 65 Rockwell C, whereas bainite has a hardness off about 45 to 60 Rockwell C, depending on the temperature at which the bainite is formed. This is indicated in the transformation diagram, Fig. 6, by the Rockwell hardness numbers along the curved line at the right of the chart, which represents the time required for transformation to be completed at any point below the critical temperature.

Complete transformation of the austenite to ferrite and carbide occurs when the time that the steel is held at any temperature is greater than that marked off by the line labelled "ending of transformation." For example, if the steel is cooled from 1450 to 1300 degrees F., and held at that temperature for four hours or longer, the austenite will be completely transformed to ferrite and carbide. If it is cooled to 700 degrees F. and maintained at that temperature, it will be completely transformed in about twenty minutes. Finally, if it is quenched to 400 degrees F. and held at that temperature, it will be completely transformed after about four hours.

The section between the two curved lines on the chart

shows a gradual transformation of austenite to ferrite and carbide. At 1100 degrees F., the transformation starts in about ten seconds, but it proceeds slowly and does not reach completion until the steel has been at this temperature for about thirty minutes. If the steel is cooled in such a way that it is allowed to remain at 1100 degrees F. for not longer than one minute, only a portion of the austenite transforms. The remainder of the austenite would behave like the original austenite, and could be made to transform to martensite or bainite by selected cooling or holding procedures. Once the transformation of the austenite is complete, however, no further change can be produced in the steel by cooling. The ferrite and carbide are not affected by cooling rates, and since all the austenite has been used up, there is nothing in the steel to change during cooling.

The position of the end of the transformation line indicates how long the steel has to be held at temperature to complete the transformation. For example, it has been found that knock-out pins made from the steel represented by this chart give more satisfactory service when they are "austempered" than when they are hardened to form martensite. The pins are quenched in a bath at about 450 degrees F., held at that temperature for about four hours, and then cooled in air.

The numbers beside the line marked "ending of transformation" show the Rockell C hardness of the mixtures of ferrite and carbide formed at the temperature at which the number appears. For example, the transformation product formed at 1300 degrees F. has a hardness of 14 Rockwell C, while that formed at 700 degrees F. has a hardness of 44 Rockwell C. The lower the temperature at which the transformation takes place, the higher is the hardness. Martensite has a higher hardness than any of the other transformation products.

The reverse of this rule is the basis for softening, or annealing, steel; that is, the higher the transformation temperature, the softer is the steel. It happens also that the higher the transformation temperature, the longer it takes to complete the transformation, so that when a steel is to be annealed to get a soft product, sufficient time must be allowed for the austenite to transform completely at high temperatures before the steel is cooled to room temperature.

Chart for Carbon Steel.—Steels of various compositions behave quite differently when they are cooled from an austenitizing temperature, just as they do when they are heated.

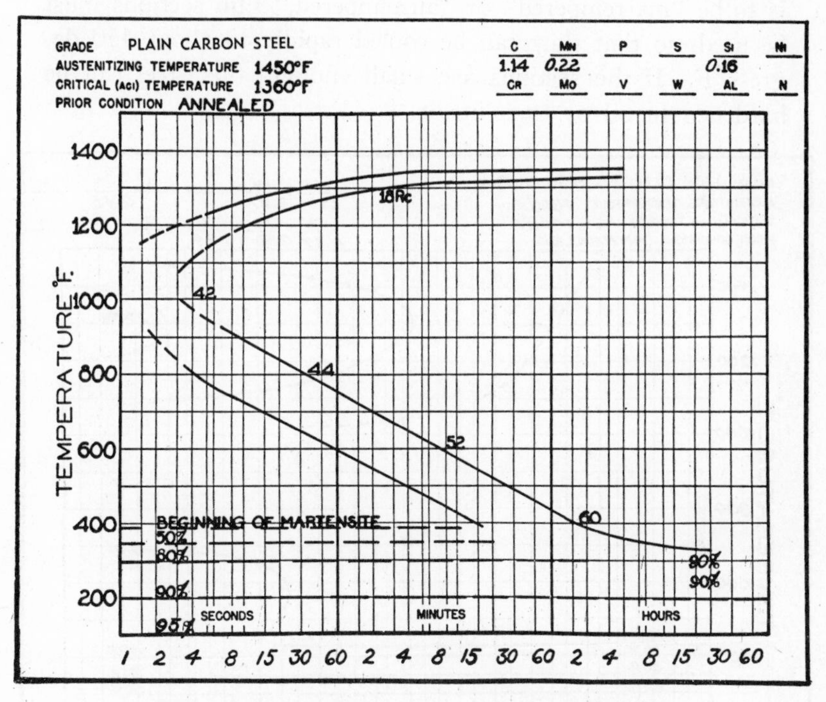

Fig. 7. Transformation Curves for a Plain Carbon Tool Steel

Fig. 7 shows the transformation curves for the carbon tool steel. The time required to complete the transformation of austenite in this steel at about 1000 degrees F. is a matter of seconds. If martensite is to be formed in this steel, it must be cooled very rapidly to a temperature below about 800 degrees F. A circulating water or brine quench is commonly used, and even then, martensite is formed only at the outside of the part. If service conditions require the center of a large part to be hard, this shallow hardening steel should not be used. Also, if a sizeable section of this steel is to be hardened, it must be quenched in water or brine; therefore there will be drastic temperature gradients from the outside to the center of the piece and it will be subject to distortion and cracking.

Finally, if a steel having these transformation characteristics is to be "martempered" or "austempered," thin sections must be used, so that they can be cooled rapidly to about 450 degress F. If the sections are small enough, this steel can be hardened in oil or even in air.

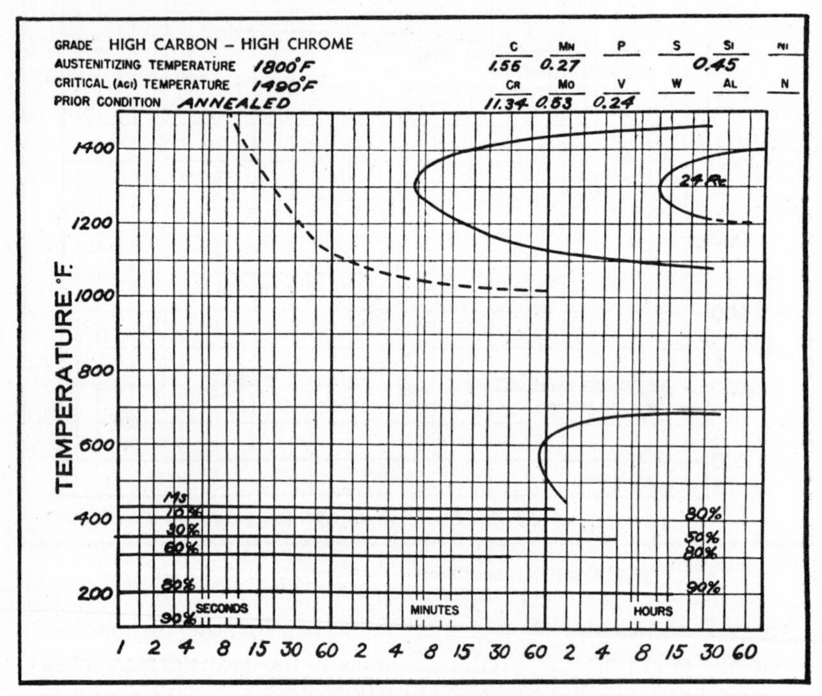

Fig. 8. Transformation Curves for a High-carbon High-chromium Steel. The Dotted Line at Left Indicates Carbide Precipitation

Chart for High-carbon, High-chromium Steel.—The transformation curves of the high-carbon, high-chromium steel are shown in Fig. 8. A new line is seen in this chart—the broken line at the upper left—which designates the time required for excess carbides to precipitate from the austenite. In many other steels of high-alloy, high-carbon content, the tendency for carbides to precipitate is appreciable, and this has considerable significance in the heat-treatment of the steel.

This line, which is known as the carbide line, indicates that carbides will precipitate quite rapidly at approximately 1600 to 1700 degrees F. The precipitation invariably occurs first at grain boundaries. Although it is not known directly what the effect of this grain boundary precipitation is, it is reasonable to expect that this condition decreases the toughness of the steel. It is known that such a condition lowers the cutting efficiency of high-speed steel.

This condition can be avoided by controlling the cooling of the steel through the temperature range in which the precipitation occurs. Obviously, the precipitation will not occur unless sufficient time is allowed at these temperatures. The cooling is usually sufficiently rapid in fairly large sections if they are quenched in oil, or in salt baths at about 1100 degrees F. or lower. Once the steel has been cooled below the carbide precipitation level, it may be cooled at the rate most suitable to the steel part being treated.

In the case of the high-carbon, high-chromium steel and the molybdenum high-speed steel (the transformation curves for which are shown in Fig. 9), treatment of the steel may be finished by an air cool, as the reactions at the lower temperatures are slow and the only change that can occur during the final cooling to room temperature is the desired formation of martensite. During the cooling below the Ms temperature, martensite forms in these air-hardening steels, as in the steels mentioned earlier. Because the cooling is relatively slow in air, the steel can accommodate itself to the expansion that takes place when martensite forms, and therefore hardens with a minimum of distortion.

The transformation to martensite progresses only as the temperature of the steel drops. If the cooling is not allowed to continue to room temperature, or close to room temperature, before tempering, the desired hard structure, martensite, will not form, and the austenite will remain in the steel, which may cause trouble at a later time in the life of the tool.

Even when the high-speed steel and the high-carbon, high-chromium steel are cooled to room temperature, all the austenite does not transform. This is also true of the plain carbon, oil-hardening, and hot-work steels, but the amount of austenite retained is about 5 to 10 per cent, whereas up to approximately 20 per cent is retained in the high-speed steel

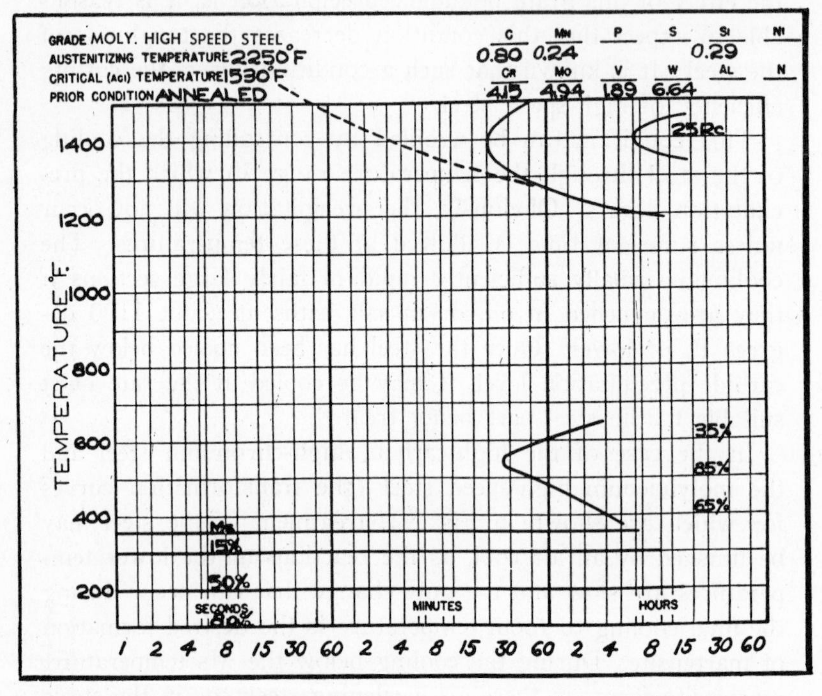

Fig. 9. Transformation Curves for Molybdenum High-speed Steel

as ordinarily treated. The amount in the high-carbon, high-chromium steel may vary from 10 to 20 per cent when the steel is austenitized at 1800 degrees F. to as much as 100 per cent if the steel is quenched from about 2100 degrees F.

As there is no advantage in retaining austenite in these steels, the heat-treated steel should be permitted to cool to at least 100 to 125 degrees F. before it is tempered. It is true that some parts have cracked because they were not tempered soon enough after they were hardened, but it is equally true that many tools have been spoiled because they were transferred to the tempering furnace too soon.

Chart for Chromium-molybdenum Hot-work Steel.—The transformation curves of the chromium-molybdenum, hot-work steel, Fig. 10, show the same sluggish, high-temperature reac-

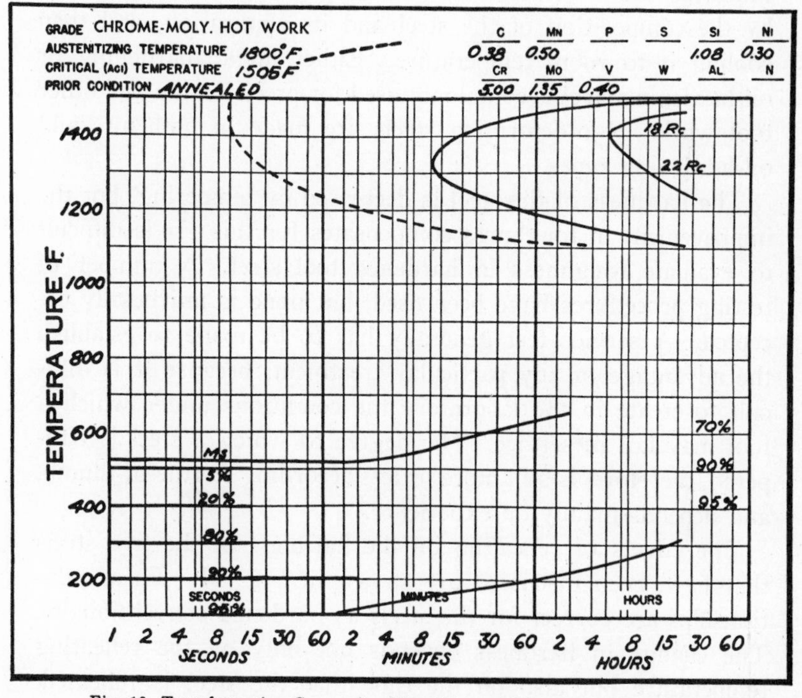

Fig. 10. Transformation Curves for Chromium-molybdenum Hot-work Steel

tions as were indicated in the case of the high-carbon, high-chromium steel and the high-speed steel, but the lower temperature transformation to bainite, from about 600 degrees F. down, is more rapid. Even here, however, a long time is required for the transformation to be completed above 300 degrees F. Nevertheless, in the ordinary heat-treatment of fairly large sections of this steel by an air cool or by an interrupted quench, the final product is a mixture of bainite and martensite rather than all martensite. Evidently there is not much difference in the properties of the hot-work steel heat-treated completely to martensite and that heat-treated to a mixture of martensite and bainite.

Tempering Tool Steels.—The final step in the heat-treatment of tool steels is tempering, the primary purpose of which is to toughen the steel. The tempering treatment consists of reheating the hardened steel to a temperature that is governed by the composition of the steel and its application, and then cooling it to room temperature. Either an air-hardening or oil-hardening steel is commonly used for precision die and other tool work. Non-deforming steels are made in both air- and oil-hardening types.

The hardness of the steel is decreased by tempering, but the improvement in toughness compensates for this. It is difficult to evaluate toughness in hardened tool steel. A number of testing procedures have been used, but none is universally accepted. A service test generally has to be made to establish the advantage of any particular treatment, because it is difficult to create in the laboratory the conditions under which a tool may fail in service. The degree to which a steel is tempered, therefore, is still more or less according to rule-of-thumb, and depends mainly on experience.

The effects of reheating on the hardness of the five steels that have been discussed are shown in Fig. 11. These relationships are correct for the steels as hardened conventionally. The change in hardness depends not only on the reheating temperature but also on the time that the steel is reheated. It is possible to develop the same hardness with a fairly wide range of temperature if the reheating time is varied. The results obtained at a high temperature in a relatively short time can generally be reproduced at a lower temperature if a long enough time is used.

The relationships shown in Fig. 11 would hold only for a uniform time—say one hour—at each temperature. Ordinarily, heating the steel at the required temperature for two to four hours is considered preferable to a shorter time, par-

applications not to relieve these internal stresses by tempering.

The high-carbon, high-chromium steel is generally tempered at between 450 and 550 degrees F. to a hardness of about 58 to 60 Rockwell C. The high-speed steel can be tempered twice at 1050 degrees F. to a hardness of 63 to 65 Rockwell C when used for cutting purposes; and it can be tempered at temperatures as high as 1100 to 1150 degrees F. to a hardness of 58 to 60 Rockwell C when employed for other than high-speed cutting purposes.

The hot-work steel is usually tempered at between 1100 and 1150 degrees F. to a hardness of about 42 to 48 Rockwell C. Although wear resistance is sacrified at this relatively low hardness, it has been found that hot-work tools tend to split if they are used at a higher hardness. Furthermore, in many severe hot-work jobs, the surface of the tool attains a temperature at least as high as 1150 degrees F., and would automatically become tempered to the lower hardness even though it was put into service at a higher hardness. On the other hand, it is desirable to keep the hardness of the hot-work steel as high as possible, in order to minimize heat checking, which is the ultimate cause of failure of practically all hot-work tools.

The Effect of Double Tempering.—Double tempering is used in the treatment of high-speed steel tools to stress-relieve the martensite, and to convert the austenite that is retained in the steel to martensite. After the steel is hardened by being cooled from the austenitizing temperature (2250 degrees F.) to room temperature, it is reheated to 1050 degrees F. and held at that temperature for two hours; cooled to room temperature; reheated to 1050 degrees F. and held at that temperature for an additional two hours; and then cooled to room temperature.

The sequence of changes that take place during this treatment of high-speed steel is illustrated schematically in Fig. 12. In the hardening operation (indicated in the column at the left) the steel is all austenite, designated by the unshaded areas, as it starts to cool from 2250 degrees F., and it remains

ticularly for large sections, as the longer heating
zation of temperature throughout the section.

It is apparent that reheating at about 300 t
F. has little effect on the hardness of any of the
carbon tool steel and the manganese oil-harde
used with a temper as low as this, in order to
wear resistance as possible. Since they both ha

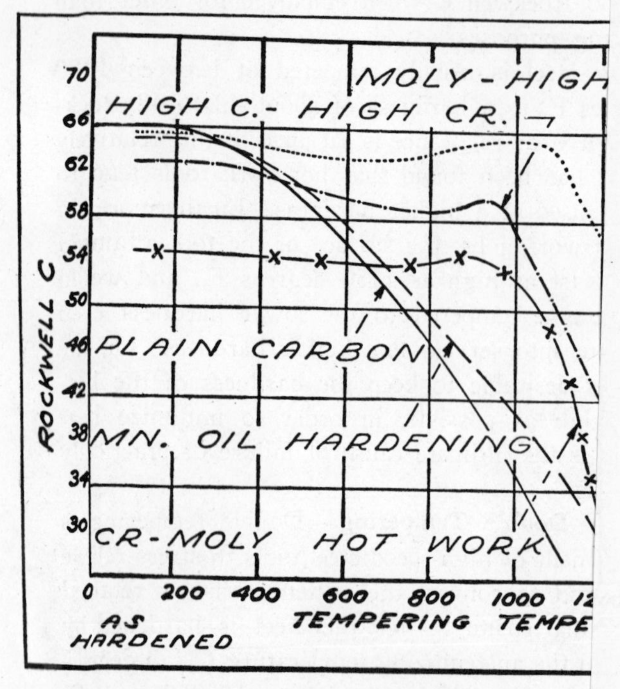

Fig. 11. Hardness versus Tempering Temperature for Five I
Carbon and Oil-hardening Tool Steels are Usually Tempered at 3
High-carbon, High-chromium Steel at 450 to 550 Degrees F.; H
to 1150 Degrees F.; and High-speed Steel Twice at 10

amount of residual carbides, their wear re
mainly on the hardness of the tempered mar
are used widely at a hardness of 62 to 64 Rc

In the shallow-hardening carbon tool st
internal stresses near the surface of the ha
in compression, and therefore are effective
applied tensile stresses. For this reason, it is

all austenite as it cools past 1050 degrees F. down to the martensite temperature. As the steel cools below the martensite temperature, martensite (designated by the sectioned area) begins to form, and continues to form until about 80 per cent of the structure is transformed to martensite at room temperature. The unshaded area represents the austenite retained at room temperature.

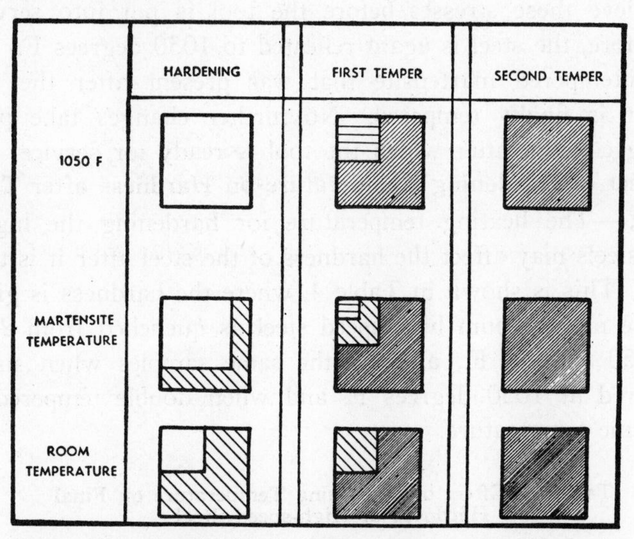

Fig. 12. Diagrams Showing the Effect of Double Tempering on the Structure of High-speed Steel. White Indicates Austenite; Horizontal Sectioning, "Conditioned" Austenite with Carbides Precipitated; Cross-sectioning, Untempered Martensite; and Dark Shaded Areas, Tempered Martensite

The middle column shows the changes that occur in the first tempering operation. When the hardened steel is reheated to 1050 degrees F., the martensite becomes tempered, as indicated by the dark shaded area. At the same time, the retained austenite is not transformed to martensite, but it does undergo a change. This change consists of a precipitation of alloy carbides from the austenite, and the precipitation, which has become known as the "conditioning" of the austenite, lowers the alloy content of the austenite, but does not change its structure. This is designated by the section with horizontal lines. When the steel is cooled below the martensite temperature, the conditioned austenite begins to transform to martensite.

The martensite that was tempered during heating remains tempered martensite when the steel is at room temperature. There is, then, a mixture of tempered and untempered martensite in the steel at the end of the first temper. The untempered martensite is internally stressed, and it is desirable to relieve these stresses before the tool is put into service. Therefore, the steel is again reheated to 1050 degrees F., and the untempered martensite that was present after the first temper is finally tempered. No further changes take place during cooling, after which the tool is ready for service.

Effect of Hardening Temperature on Hardness after Tempering.—The heating temperature for hardening the higher alloy steels may affect the hardness of the steel after it is tempered. This is shown in Table 4, where the hardness is given for the molybdenum high-speed steel as quenched from 2100 to 2250 degrees F., and for the same samples when single tempered at 1050 degrees F. and when double tempered at the same temperature.

Table 4. Effect of Hardening Temperature on Final Hardness of High-speed Steel

Austenitizing Temperature, Degrees F.	Rockwell C Hardness		
	As Quenched	Single Tempered at 1050 Degrees F.	Double Tempered at 1050 Degrees F.
2100	66.0	61.5	61.0
2150	66.0	63.0	62.5
2200	66.0	64.0	63.5
2250	65.5	65.0	64.5

It is clear that although the hardness of the samples as quenched is practically the same for all, the hardness after tempering is lower. The reason for this is that the hardness after tempering is dependent upon the precipitation of alloy carbides from the martensite and from the retained austenite during the tempering operation; and the amount of alloy that can be precipitated depends on the amount dissolved in the austenite during the heating for hardening. The amount of alloy carbides which dissolves in the austenite increases with increasing heating temperature, particularly above 2100 degrees F. and therefore, the higher the original heating temperature the greater is the amount available for precipitation during tempering. Since the minimum hardness for good cutting efficiency in a high-speed steel is about 63 Rockwell C, it is clear that poor cutting efficiency may be expected from molybdenum high-speed steel tools that are hardened at temperatures under about 2200 degrees F.

Size Changes During Heat-treatment.—Any chapter on heat-treatment would not be complete without some mention of the changes in size that occur in parts during the process. While this subject would require a series of chapters to cover it completely, the major factors can, at least, be listed here.

In the first place, steel, like all metals, expands when it is heated and contracts when it cools. In the second place, austenite is denser than any of its transformation products, all of which have different densities. The lower the temperature at which the transformation product forms, the lower is its density, martensite having the lowest density of all. In other words, when austenite is cooled so that it eventually transforms into martensite, the steel first contracts because of the drop in temperature, but as soon as martensite begins to form, the steel expands because of the difference in density between the austenite and martensite. In the third place, when martensite is tempered, the density of the steel increases; that is, the tempering of martensite causes the steel to shink in size.

The successive changes during the heat-treatment of steel, therefore, are first a contraction while the austenite cools, then an expansion when the martensite forms, and finally a contraction when the martensite is tempered. This is further complicated if, during the hardening treatment, all of the austenite does not transform, but is partially retained at room temperature, together with martensite. When this mixture of austenite and martensite is tempered, the steel shinks at first, and then expands if, during the tempering, some of the retained austenite is transformed.

On top of this, there are size changes brought about by the fact that in water quenching, and also in oil quenching of some sections, there are sizeable temperatures gradients from outside to center which may set up sufficient stresses to introduce shrinkage in some directions and expansions in others. However, in spite of all these sources of error, tools and dies are heat-treated satisfactorily, in most cases, without cracking and within reasonable size tolerances. For this, a great deal of credit is due to the skill of the heat-treater and to the quality of the tool steel.

Hardening Punches.—If punches are to be hardened—and this is generally considered best—they should be very carefully heated. It must be borne in mind that punches are subjected to a great strain; consequently, they should be heated uniformly, and to as low a temperature as will give desired results, thus making them as strong as possible. Heat slowly to avoid *overheating* the corners, as these are subjected to the greatest strain. The distance a punch should be hardened depends on the shape and size, and the use to which it is to be put. If it is a piercing punch that is long and slender, it should be hardened the entire length to avoid any tendency to bend or upset when in use. If it is of a form that insures sufficient strength to resist any tendency to upset when in use, then it need not be hardened its entire length. A simple method of hardening a punch to prevent warping, which is recommended by an expert diemaker, is as follows: The face of the punch for about 3/4 inch up is held in molten lead until it is an even red color all over. It is then quenched. This hardens the face of the punch for about 3/4 inch up and leaves the back soft. This method has very little tendency to warp the punch, the large part of it, which is cold, or comparatively so, counteracting it. Experience has shown that if properly done, the punch comes out straight and parallel and not warped at all.

Pack-hardening is an admirable method of hardening

punches for most work, but for piercing punches, it is not recommended, as the whole structure of the steel should be as nearly alike as possible. Such punches should be heated in a muffle furnace, or in a tube in the open fire, turning the work occasionally to insure uniform results, for not only can we heat a piece more uniformly if it is turned several times while heating, but a fact not generally known is that a cylindrical piece of steel heated in an ordinary fire without turning while heating will many times show softness on the side that was uppermost in the fire, no matter what care was taken when heating and dipping. If it is reheated with the opposite side uppermost, *that* will be found soft if tested after hardening, while the side that was soft before will be *hard*. In quenching, work the punch up and down and around in a luke-warm bath.

Tempering Punches.—Comparatively long slim piercing punches should have a uniform hardness throughout the entire length of the slender portion. This will insure uniform springiness, and the liability of bending, especially when punching stiff or heavy stock, is reduced to a minimum. It is generally considered good practice to temper the punch so that it is somewhat softer than the die; then, if from any accident the two come in contact, the die will in all probability cut the punch without much injury to itself. There are exceptions to this practice, however. In many shops it is customary to have the one which is the more difficult to make the harder, so it will cut the other if they come in contact with each other.

Punches should be carefully examined after hardening and tempering, and those which have been bent or sprung in the hardening should be carefully straightened. Piercing punches in compound dies are steadied by the knockout while operating on the stock. The punch is made a sliding fit in the knockout, and the knockout is also made a sliding fit in the die. When perforating thick metal where the strain on the press is great due to the action of a number of punches, a good method to reduce the pressure is to make every other punch shorter than the preceding one by an amount equal to from one-fourth to one-third the thickness of the stock. This, as can be seen, will reduce the pressure, as half the punches have practically completed their work before the remaining half operate. When heavy stock is being blanked or pierced, punches are not required to fit as snugly as when the metal is thin.

It is generally found after hardening small piercing punches, that although the holes in the punch-holder are true with the die, the punches do not line up. This is because they have bent slightly in hardening. They can usually be brought into alignment by giving those that do not enter part of a turn; if this does not align them, they should be removed and straightened.

When Punch and Die should be Hardened.—There are various opinions among practical men as to the advisability of hardening punches. For most jobs it is the custom to do so, though there are some mechanics who consider it advisable to harden them, and others who do not. There are instances where punches work well either way, and in such cases it is, of course, a matter of opinion. The blanking or cutting dies used on comparatively thin stock, such as tin, brass, aluminum, iron, steel, copper, zinc, etc., are ordinarily hardened and tempered to suit the work, and the punch is left quite soft, so that it can be "hammered up" to fit the die when worn. This practice is followed in some plants for all metals less than 1/16 inch thick which are not harder than very mild steel. After the end of the punch has been upset by hammering, the punch and the die are oiled and forced together, which causes the hard die to shave the punch to a close fit. If the die is dull, it should be sharpened prior to this shearing operation. For some classes of work, the punch is made hard and the die soft. Both the punch and die should be hardened when they are to be used for blanking thick steel, brass, or other heavy metals.

Additional information on this subject will be found in Chapter X under "Wear Resistance of Cutting Edges of Blanking Dies."

Value of Annealing.—Many diemakers overlook the importance of first roughing a die nearly to size and then carefully annealing it. There are internal strains set up in the bar of steel during its manufacture which are sure to cause distortion of the die or tool unless these strains are removed before the work is brought to its finished size. Some steel may be free from strains, but there is no way of determining beforehand whether the steel has "settled" or not; therefore, to guard against distortion, it is advisable to anneal the piece after it has been roughed out, because annealing relieves these internal strains.

The following test illustrates the value of annealing before finishing: Four pieces of tool steel were cut from the same bar and the same amount of stock was removed from each piece, finishing them all over to exactly the same dimensions. They were then marked *A*, *B*, *C*, and *D*. Pieces *A* and *B* were annealed after roughing, but pieces *C* and *D* were machined to size. The pyrometer was used to insure heating all the pieces to the same temperature of 1400 degrees F. The bath was clean water with a temperature of 68 degrees F. The pieces were heated separately in a muffle furnace and were allowed to remain in the bath exactly one minute, in each case. The result of this comparative test was as follows: The pieces *A* and *B* were slightly distorted, but the pieces *C* and *D* were distorted to such an extent that they were useless.

CHAPTER XXV

DESIGNING DIES FOR POWDERED-METAL PARTS

Economical die maintenance, high production, and minimum rejection of pressed powdered-metal parts are die design objectives which require accurate data concerning the powdered material to be worked. Such data should include:

1. Type of material (bronze, brass, iron, or other powder).
2. Pressure required (in pounds per square inch).
3. Die fill ratio (volume of loose powder to volume of pressed part).
4. "Spring-back" of part after pressing (expansion after leaving die).
5. Sintering shrinkage or growth.
6. Allowances for sizing, if required, to increase physical properties or to maintain close dimensional tolerances.

Since numerous variables affect items 2 through 6, data applicable to specific powdered-metal parts are not available in handbooks or other reference works. Therefore, in preparing for a particular job, experimental dies of relatively simple form (a round cylindrical die and punch for example) are commonly employed in tests to obtain these data. The results of such tests may be accumulated, so that at some future time, new, but similar, parts can be designed, based on this past experience.

Determining the Die Dimensions.—A drawing of the part to be molded showing its dimensions as a "green" or unsintered briquette, as a "fired" or sintered briquette and in finished form is needed as a basis for the design of the die. Such a drawing is shown in Fig. 1. Dimensions of the sintered and unsintered briquette are determined by applying the information obtained in the experimental die tests to the required dimensions of the finished part and working backwards to the "green" stage of the briquette. Thus, in Fig. 1 the finished outside diameter of the flange on this part is to be 0.500 inch plus 0.000 minus 0.004 inch.

If the mean dimension, 0.498 inch, is taken for the part after it is sintered as shown in Fig. 1, and the shrinkage factor is 1.004 (indicating a shrinkage of 0.004 inch per inch), then the dimension of the part in the unsintered stage is $0.498 \times 1.004 = 0.500$ inch. If the allowance for expansion of the briquetted part after ejection from the die is 0.0002 inch then the die cavity should be made $0.500 - 0.0002 = 0.4998$ inch, so that the ejected part can expand to the required unsintered dimension of 0.500 inch.

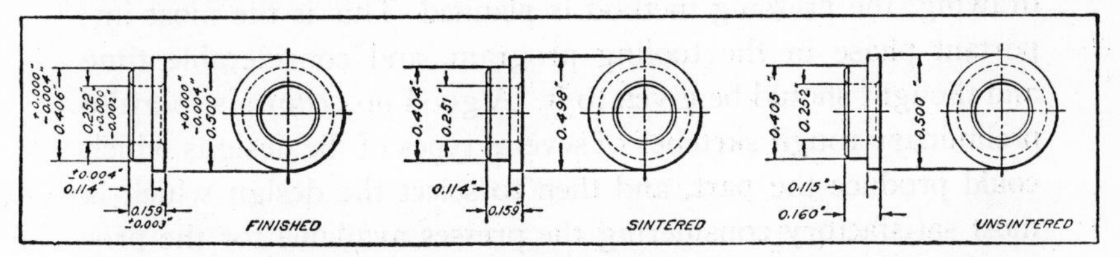

Fig. 1. Typical Specification Drawing which shows the Dimensions of the Finished Part and the Corresponding Dimensions of the Sintered and Unsintered Briquette

For parts which have relatively wide dimensional tolerances as in the example given, the "spring-back" (expansion of the briquette) is not usually considered in arriving at the die dimensions, since any dimensional variation due to a small spring-back would fall within the dimensional tolerance of the part.

These part drawings are useful for inspection purposes; at the presses, for instance, a check of the "green" briquette in comparison with the dimensions of the unsintered part on the specifications drawing shows whether or not tool changes or pressure adjustments are necessary. Parts that are not in accordance with the drawing at any particular stage can be diverted from further processing. This saves time and eliminates waste since the physical characteristics of a part after any operation depend to a considerable extent upon those resulting from a previous operation.

The dimensions of the die are based on those of the unsintered parts, since these determine the size of part required in the green state to obtain the desired final dimensions after sintering. If the physical properties of the part or the tolerances on the finished dimensions were such that a sizing operation were needed after sintering, allowances would have to be made for this too.

Die diameters should always be made to produce parts on the low side and core-pins should be made on the high side of these tolerances to allow for wear, thereby increasing the life of the die and pins. An example of this procedure is given on page 999.

Planning the Pressing Method.—After preparing the work drawing, the pressing method is planned. This is the most important phase in the tooling program, and considerable time and thought should be given to it. A good procedure is to make preliminary rough sketches of several types of die designs which could produce the part, and then to select the design which is most satisfactory considering the presses available for the production run. This procedure helps to minimize changes after the tools have been made. This is particularly true in the case of segment dies that may be made in split sections to facilitate the pressing operation and to reduce tooling costs.

It is essential to design the die so as to maintain a given die fill ratio over varying sections of a part in order to insure an even distribution of density in the pressed and sintered briquette. This is because the loose powder will not flow from one part of the cavity to another as freely as plastic or ceramic materials. Because non-uniform density causes uneven shrinkage or growth in sintering, filling the die properly is an important consideration in designing these dies.

An example of a design in which provision was made for filling the die properly is shown in Fig. 2. The top inner punch, which can move independently of the outer punch is shown at *A*, the top outer punch at *B*, the die at *C*, the lower inner core sleeve at *D*, the lower punch at *E*, and the stationary core-pin at *F*.

It can be seen that a die fill ratio of approximately 2 to 1 is maintained throughout all sections of the part by raising the inner core sleeve *D* during the filling operation. This prevents the deposit of more powder than is needed over the thin section of the part.

In pressing relatively long parts it is often found that the center section of the part lacks the proper density, compared with the ends. This condition, referred to as "bridging over" of the powder, may pass undetected at the presses unless samples are broken open and inspected. It is possible for the samples to be of the correct weight and yet not have been properly pressed, the ends being overpressed, and the center not pressed enough. It is therefore essential to use top and bottom pressure when briquetting relatively long parts, and it is good practice to design the dies to provide for proper distribution of powder where a part of irregular cross-section is to be made. In view of the fact that non-uniform density causes uneven shrinkage or growth in sintering, it is apparent that proper distribution of the powder is an important consideration in designing these dies.

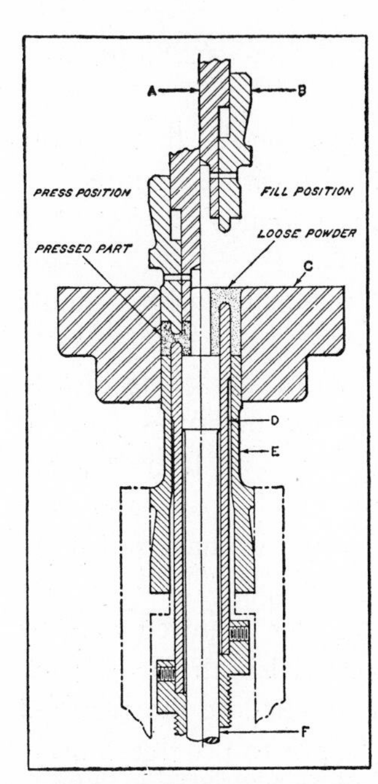

Fig. 2. Cross-section of Die Designed to Provide Uniform Density in a Powdered-metal Part Having a Thin Center Section

Selection of the Proper Press.—In selecting the press, first determine the projected cross-sectional area of the part, and then multiply this figure by the pressure in pounds per square inch required to obtain the proper density. This will be the total pressure required. Based on this figure, a press of the proper capacity can be selected.

For example, find the total pressure to briquette a 3-inch diameter bushing with a 1-inch diameter hole through the center, using a briquetting pressure of 40,000 pounds per square inch. Subtracting the area of the hole from the area of the 3-inch diameter bushing to get the actual projected area:

Area of 3-inch diameter section	7.068 sq. in.
Area of 1-inch diameter hole	0.785 sq. in.
Actual projected area	6.283 sq. in.

Then, multiplying the actual projected area by the pressure in pounds per square inch gives the total pressure required:

$$6.283 \times 40{,}000 = 251{,}320 \text{ pounds}$$
$$(\text{or } 125.66 \text{ tons})$$

The press to be used for a part of these dimensions should have a capacity greater than 125½ tons.

This data may also be used as a guide in designing dies to withstand repeated loads at relatively high pressures without springing. A very small amount of vertical and lateral spring has an immediate effect on the density of the part, and may cause the material to "bridge over." Many dies have failed because they have not been made sturdy enough.

Inasmuch as the volume of loose powder required may be two or three times as great as the pressed length of the part, the die length must be sufficient to accommodate the required amount of powder plus an additional length to provide a bearing surface for the lower punch. This requires a press with a lower ram having a stroke long enough to move the punch from the fill position to the top of the die for ejecting the part. It is also necessary to decide whether a press with auxiliary rams is needed. Many presses have inside rams that act independently of the upper and lower pressure rams. They are useful for applying pressure to sections such as the center of the part shown in Fig. 2. Often this inner action is built into the tools when such presses are not available, although this is an expensive procedure.

Actual Design of the Press Tools.—With the work drawing on hand, the rough sketch of the die made, and the proper press selected, the die design may be begun. This should start with a scale lay-out of the press table and the upper and lower punch-holders. A cross-sectional assembly drawing should be made, showing one half of the die assembly at the finish of the pressure stroke and the other half at the top of the stroke. This enables the designer to readily determine the length of punches necessary (which should be kept as short as possible consistent with stroke requirements); the clearance between the upper punch and the powder filler shoe can also easily be seen, as well as the relative positions of the punches and other mechanisms.

For mechanical, cam-operated presses, a cam and work cycle should be laid out to aid in the design of the punches and their proper location at the fill, press, and ejection positions.

After the die has been completely designed, a dimensioned assembly drawing should be made, including all views and any special cross-section views that may be required, as in Fig. 3. In this illustration, the tools for the part in Fig. 1 are shown. This method of dimensioning shows the toolmaker which mating parts must be held to a close fit.

The separate views of the details give the allowable tolerances and other data needed. It will be noted that the die diameters have been made to produce parts on the low side of the allowable tolerance while the pin diameters have been made on the high side to allow for wear. In figuring these dimensions, shrinkage of the briquette as previously discussed was allowed for but "spring-back" (expansion of the briquette after ejection) was disregarded as being too small to consider. Punches and dies must fit closely in order to prevent flash around the edges of the pressed part and to prevent small particles of powder from getting between the sides of the punches and die causing wear.

The same close fits must be used for the mating surfaces of core-pins and punches. It will be noted in Fig. 3 that the punches and core-pins are relieved wherever possible to avoid high toolmaking expense in holding close tolerances for long lengths. This illustration also shows a die sleeve assembled with the die for forming a shoulder on the part shown in Fig. 1. A close fit must be maintained between the sleeve and the die, lest powder be pressed into the clearance space, causing the part to tear at ejection. If powder builds up in such an opening, the strain on the sleeve may cause it to crack.

It is good design to use split dies for irregular-shaped parts wherever practical, as this reduces initial die costs and allows

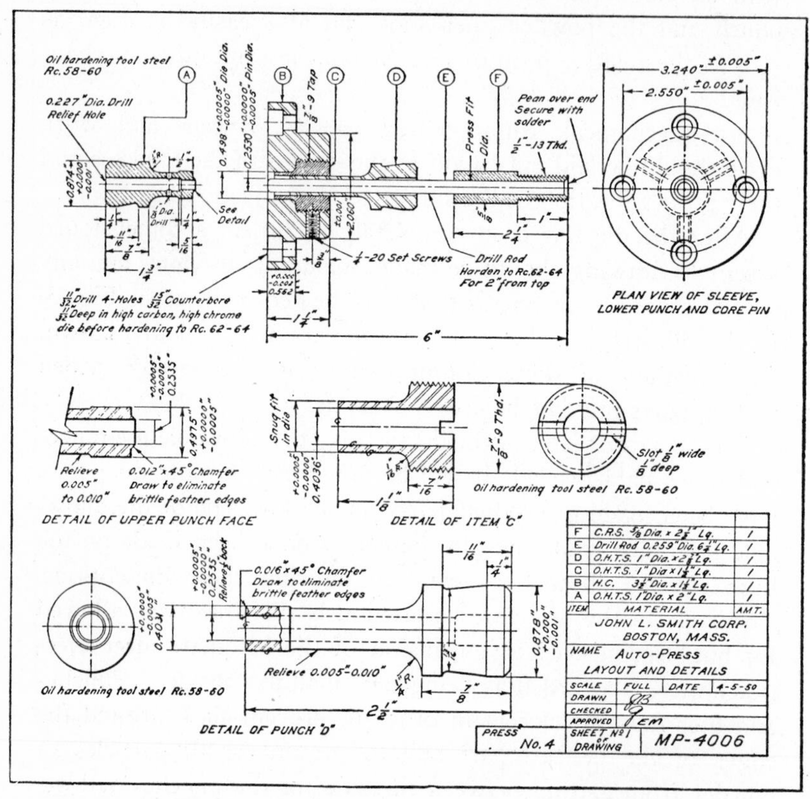

Fig. 3. A Typical Tool Lay-out Comprising an Assembly View of the Entire Set of Tools, Together with Details and Cross-section Views, which Facilitates Making Mating Parts

grinding on the split surfaces, in many cases, to correct the size of a worn die by making it smaller.

Design of Sizing Dies.—The dimensions of many powdered-metal parts must be held to such close tolerances that ordinary control of dimensional changes in sintering cannot be relied upon. Parts of this type must be sized in a separate operation, after sintering, as must parts that require physical properties not ordinarily achieved by briquetting and sintering alone.

A sizing die for an ordinary bronze bushing, the inside and outside diameters of which must be held to close tolerances, is

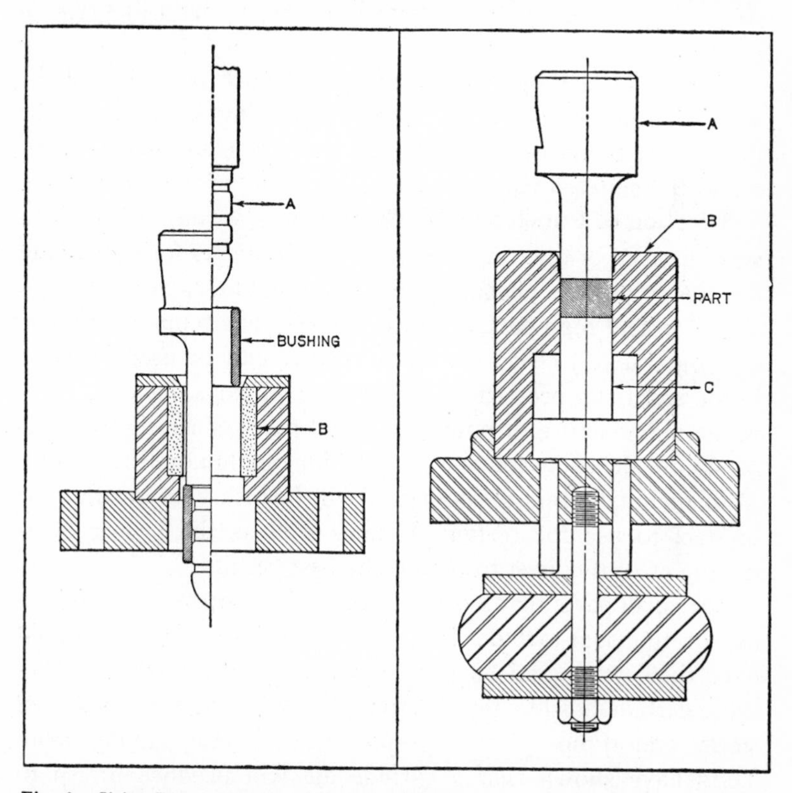

Fig. 4. Sizing Dies for Maintaining High Dimensional Accuracy in Sintered Powdered-metal Parts are Often Used. The Die at the Left Sizes the Bore and Periphery of a Sintered Bushing. Parts Requiring Increased Density and Strength are Sized by Dies of the Type Shown at the Right

shown at the left in Fig. 4. The sizing punch *A* is held in the upper ram of an ordinary punch press, while the die *B* is encased in a machine-steel adapter on the press table. The sintered bushing is placed in a nest on the die and forced through the die ring, which sizes the bore and outer periphery with little or no change in density. Parts of this type are usually impregnated with oil for use as "oilless" bearings.

A die for sizing a part to increase its density and strength is shown at the right. The cavity of this die is made to the finished dimensions of the part. The top punch *A* forces the piece into die *B*, after which it is ejected by lower punch *C*. A high degree of surface finish is obtained on the part with this type of sizing die.

Sizing dies are operated in ordinary punch presses, and the same load factors can be used as in producing stampings. The dies should be well lubricated, the usual procedure being to immerse the sintered parts in oil and kerosene prior to sizing.

Selection of Punch and Die Materials.—Because of the pressures used in briquetting, the main requirements for punch and die materials are physical strength, toughness, resistance to abrasion, and high surface finish. Inexpensive temporary tools, or comparatively cheap materials, such as may be used for tools in the short-run production of other metal parts, have no place in the manufacture of powdered-metal parts, since the requirements are the same for one piece as for one hundred thousand. Most manufacturers of tool steels will furnish data on the type of steel to use for certain jobs, as well as the proper heat-treatment of the steel to obtain the best results.

For small parts that must be produced in large quantities, the use of tungsten-carbide dies is recommended. These should have thick walls and be well supported in the die-holder, because carbide has low tensile strength, compared with most tool steels, and if not properly supported will crack under load. Tests have shown that a carbide die will produce fifteen to twenty times the number of parts that could be obtained from a tool-steel die. Inasmuch as most shops purchase their carbide dies, a complete drawing of the die is necessary, specifying the finish required in the bore, as well as the grade of tungsten carbide desired.

INDEX